Student Solutions Manual for Elementary and Intermediate Algebra

Jay Lehmann

Taken from:
Student Solutions Manual for Elementary and Intermediate Algebra
by Jay Lehmann

Learning Solutions

New York   Boston   San Francisco
London   Toronto   Sydney   Tokyo   Singapore   Madrid
Mexico City   Munich   Paris   Cape Town   Hong Kong   Montreal

Cover Art: Cover Art: Courtesy of PhotoDisc/Getty Images

Taken from:

Student Solutions Manual for Elementary & Intermediate Algebra
by Jay Lehmann
Copyright © 2011 by Pearson Education, Inc.
Published by Prentice Hall
Upper Saddle River, New Jersey 07458

This special edition published in cooperation with Pearson Learning Solutions.

Pearson Learning Solutions, 501 Boylston Street, Suite 900, Boston, MA 02116
A Pearson Education Company
www.pearsoned.com

Printed in the United States of America

1 2 3 4 5 6 7 8 9 10 V3DZ 14 13 12 11 10 09

000200010270571444

LB

ISBN 10: 0-558-64818-5
ISBN 13: 978-0-558-64818-3

Table of Contents

Chapter 1
Introduction to Modeling

Homework 1.1

1. 25 thousand fans attended the Coldplay rock concert.

3. 256 million Americans used cell phones in 2008.

5. 51.6 million iPods® were sold in 2007.

7. The U.S. Postal Service lost $2.8 billion that year.

9. The statement $t = 9$ represents the year 2009 (9 years after 2000).

11. The statement $t = -3$ represents the year 2002 (3 years before 2005)

13. Answers may vary. One possibility is:
    Let h be the height (in inches) of a person. Then h can represent the numbers 67 and 72, but h cannot represent the numbers -5 and 0.

15. Answers may vary. One possibility is:
    Let p be the price (in dollars) of an audio CD. Then p can represent the numbers 9.99 and 12.99, but p cannot represent the numbers -2 and -8.

17. Answers may vary. One possibility is:
    Let T be the total time (in hours) that a person works in a week. Then T can represent the numbers 15 and 40, but T cannot represent the numbers 240 and -10.

19. Answers may vary. One possibility is:
    Let s be the annual salary (in thousands of dollars) of a person. Then s can represent the numbers 25 and 32, but s cannot represent the numbers -15 and -9.

21. **a.** Answers may vary. Possibilities follow:

    4 inches

    6 inches

    3 inches

    8 inches

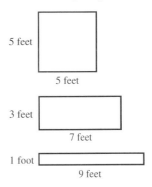

1 inch

24 inches

b. In the described situation, the symbols W and L are variables. Their values can change.

c. In the described situation, the symbol A is a constant. Its value is fixed at 24 square inches.

23. **a.** Answers may vary. Possibilities follow:

    5 feet

    5 feet

    3 feet

    7 feet

    1 foot

    9 feet

b. In the described situation, the symbols W and L are variables. Their values can change.

c. In the described situation, the symbol P is a constant. Its value is fixed at 20 feet.

25. **a.** Answers may vary. Possibilities follow:

    1 inch

    4 inches

    2 inches

    5 inches

    3 inches

    6 inches

b. In the described situation, the symbols W, L, and A are all variables. All of their values can change.

c. In the described situation, none of the symbols are constants. All of their values can change.

27. a. Answers may vary. Possibilities follow:

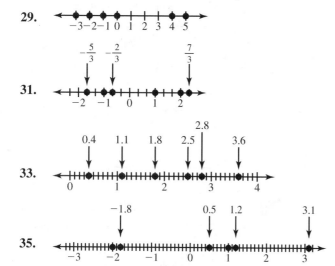

b. In the described situation, the symbols L and P are variables. Their values can change.

c. In the described situation, the symbol W is a constant. Its value is fixed at 2 yards.

29.

31.

33.

35.

37. The counting numbers between 3 and 8 are 4, 5, 6, and 7.

39. The integers between -2 and 2, inclusive, are $-2, -1, 0, 1,$ and 2.

41. The integers between -1 and 4, inclusive, are $-1, 0, 1, 2, 3,$ and 4.

43. The negative integers between -4 and 4 are $-3, -2,$ and -1.

45. The counting numbers in the list are 3 and 356.

47. The only negative integer in the list is -4.

49. The irrational numbers in the list are $\sqrt{7}$ and π.

51. Answers may vary. Three examples of negative integers are: $-2, -5,$ and -7.

53. Answers may vary. Three examples of negative integers less than -7 are: $-8, -9,$ and -27.

55. Answers may vary. Three examples of integers that are not counting numbers are: $-2, -5,$ and -40.

57. Answers may vary. Three examples of rational numbers between 1 and 2 are: $\dfrac{5}{4}, \dfrac{3}{2},$ and $\dfrac{7}{4}$.

59. Answers may vary. Three examples of real numbers between -3 and -2 are: $-2.1, -2.3,$ and -2.8.

61. $\dfrac{10+12+6+9+15+14}{6} = \dfrac{66}{6} = 11$

The average number of units taken per semester is 11 units.

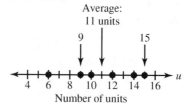

63. $\dfrac{16+14+13+11+10}{5} = \dfrac{64}{5} = 12.8$

The average percentage of disposable personal annual income spent on food is 12.8%.

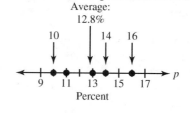

65.

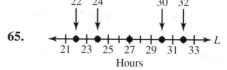

67.

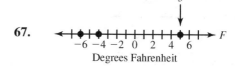

69. a. $\dfrac{0.04+0.1+0.6+1.2+2.5}{5} = \dfrac{4.44}{5} = 0.888$

The average is 0.888 billion dollars per year.

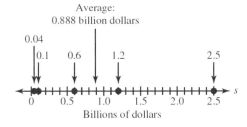

b. American annual spending on Afghan police training increased between 2003 and 2007. The amount spent increased each year.

c. The annual *increases* in American annual spending on Afghan police training increased between 2003 and 2007. The annual increases were:

Years	Increase
2003 to 2004	$0.1 - 0.04 = 0.06$
2004 to 2005	$0.6 - 0.1 = 0.5$
2005 to 2006	$1.2 - 0.6 = 0.6$
2006 to 2007	$2.5 - 1.2 = 1.3$

71. a. $\dfrac{155 + 208 + 240 + 249}{4} = \dfrac{852}{4} = 213$

The average is 213 thousand complaints of identity theft per year.

Average: 213 thousand complaints

b. The number of complaints increased between 2002 and 2005. The number of complaints went up each year.

c. The *increases* in the number of complaints per year decreased between 2002 and 2005. The annual changes were:

Years	Increase
2002 to 2003	$208 - 155 = 53$
2003 to 2004	$240 - 208 = 32$
2004 to 2005	$249 - 240 = 9$

73. a. -5

b. No. Explanations may vary. One possibility follows: The words "below zero" make the temperature negative, so T represents negative and positive numbers.

75. a. i. $\dfrac{7+9}{2} = \dfrac{16}{2} = 8$

ii. $\dfrac{1+5}{2} = \dfrac{6}{2} = 3$

iii. $\dfrac{2+8}{2} = \dfrac{10}{2} = 5$

b. Answers may vary. One possibility follows: The average value is perfectly centered between the two values being averaged.

c. There are infinitely many numbers between 0 and 1.

Answers may vary. One possibility follows: Any two numbers may be averaged, so that another value always lies between them. This process can be performed indefinitely.

77. The types of numbers discussed in this section are: real numbers, rational number, irrational numbers, integers, and counting numbers (or natural numbers). Descriptions may vary.

Homework 1.2

1–15 odds.

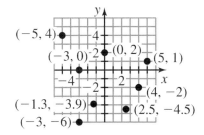

17. The *x*-coordinate is 2.

19. Presumably, the longer a student studies, the better his or her score will be on the quiz. So, the score *s* depends on the number of hours studying *n*. Thus, *n* is the independent variable and *s* is the dependent variable.

21. As a girl gets older, she will grow taller (at least for a while). So, the height h depends on the age a. Thus, a is the independent variable and h is the dependent variable.

23. As the number of credits in which a student enrolls increases, so will the tuition. So, the tuition T depends on the number of credits c. Thus, c is the independent variable and T is the dependent variable.

25. As the floor area of a classroom increases, the more students can comfortably fit into the classroom. So, the number of students n who fit comfortably into a classroom depends on the floor area A. Thus, A is the independent variable and n is the dependent variable.

27. The height of the baseball changes as time passes, going up at first and then coming back down. So, the height of the baseball h depends on the number of seconds t after it is hit. Thus, t is the independent variable and h is the dependent variable.

29. The average number of magazine subscriptions sold per week depends on the number of hours worked per week. So, t is the independent variable and n is the dependent variable. The ordered pair (32, 43) means that $t = 32$ and $n = 43$. A telemarketer who works 32 hours per week will sell an average of 43 magazine subscriptions per week.

31. The percentage of volunteers depends on age. So, A is the independent variable and p is the dependent variable. The ordered pair (21, 38) means that $t = 21$ and $n = 38$. This means that 38% of Americans at age 21 years say that they volunteer.

33. The number of threats and inappropriate communications depends on the year with respect to 2005. So, t is the independent variable and n is the dependent variable. The ordered pair (2, 1) means that $t = 2$ and $n = 1$. One thousand threats or other inappropriate communications were made toward federal judges and prosecutors in $2005 + 2 = 2007$.

35. The percentage of satisfied workers depends on the year with respect to 2010. So, t is the independent variable and p is the dependent variable. The ordered pair (-4, 47) means that that $t = -4$ and $p = 47$. This means that 47% of

workers were satisfied with their jobs in $2010 + (-4) = 2006$.

37.

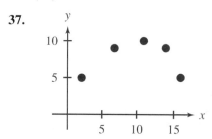

39. Point A is 4 units to the left of the origin and 3 units down. Thus, its coordinates are $(-4, -3)$.

Point B is 5 units to the left of the origin on the x-axis. Thus, its coordinates are $(-5, 0)$.

Point C is 2 units to the left of the origin and 4 units up. Thus, its coordinates are $(-2, 4)$.

Point D is 1 unit to the right of the origin and 3 units up. Thus, its coordinates are $(1, 3)$.

Point E is 2 units below the origin on the y-axis. Thus, its coordinates are $(0, -2)$.

Point F is 5 units to the right of the origin and 4 units down. Thus, its coordinates are $(5, -4)$.

41. a.

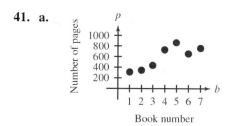

b. The fifth book has the greatest number of pages (870 pages).

c.

Books	Increase in pages
1 to 2	$341 - 309 = 32$
2 to 3	$435 - 341 = 94$
3 to 4	$734 - 435 = 299$
4 to 5	$870 - 734 = 136$
5 to 6	$652 - 870 = -218$
6 to 7	$759 - 652 = 107$

The greatest increase in the number of pages occurs from the third to the fourth book. This can be seen in the graph because there is a larger vertical change between the third and fourth points.

43. a.

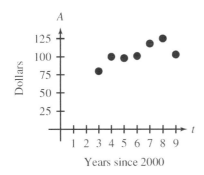

Years since 2000

b. The average amount that consumers intended to spend was greatest in 2008. The average amount was $125.

c. The average amount that consumers intended to spend was least in 2003. The average amount was $80.

45. a.

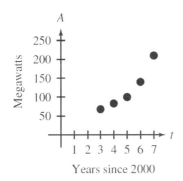

Years since 2000

b. The number of installed solar panels increased from 2003 to 2007. The number of panels, in terms of energy output, is larger for each successive year.

c. The annual *increases* in the number of installed solar panels increased between 2003 and 2007. The annual increases were:

Years	Increase in solar panels
2003 to 2004	$83 - 68 = 15$
2004 to 2005	$100 - 83 = 17$
2005 to 2006	$140 - 100 = 40$
2006 to 2007	$210 - 140 = 70$

47. a.

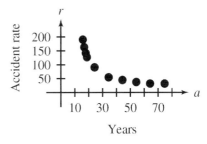

Years

b. The 60–69-year-old age group has the lowest accident rate (31.3).

c. The 16-year-old age group has the highest accident rate (190.3).

d. The greatest change in accident rates occurs between ages 16 and 17 years. The changes were:

Years	Change in accident rates
16 to 17	$163.2 - 190.3 = -27.1$
17 to 18	$142.9 - 163.2 = -20.3$
18 to 19	$127.8 - 142.9 = -15.1$
19 to 24.5	$91.4 - 127.8 = -36.4$
24.5 to 34.5	$54.7 - 91.4 = -36.7$
34.5 to 44.5	$43.9 - 54.7 = -10.8$
44.5 to 54.5	$36.4 - 43.9 = -7.5$
54.5 to 64.5	$31.3 - 36.4 = -5.1$
64.5 to 75	$32.1 - 31.3 = 0.8$

We cannot be sure of this statement from the data provided because after age 19, the rates cover a larger range of ages.

e. Answers will vary. One possibility follows: Because accident rates are highest for 16-year-old drivers, the extra precautionary measures were adopted in the hopes of reducing accidents for this group.

49. a.

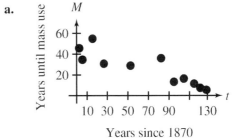

Years since 1870

b. It has taken less time for recent inventions to reach mass use. Explanations may vary.

c. No. It took longer for the microwave to reach mass use than it did for several other earlier inventions.

d. Answers will vary.

e. It took longer for the automobile to reach mass use that it did for earlier inventions of electricity and the telephone. Explanations may vary.

51. a. The average starting salary is highest for the field of computer science. That salary is approximately $53 thousand.

b. The average starting salary is lowest for the field of social science. That salary is approximately $32 thousand.

c. The average beginning salary for employees with a mathematics degree is approximately $44 thousand.

53. The ordered pairs selected and scattergrams will vary. The points will lie on the same vertical line ($x = 3$). Explanations will vary.

55. There are three possibilities for the position of the other two vertices.

(1) If the two provided vertices $(2, 1)$ and $(2, 5)$ are on the left side of the square, then the length of each side of the square is $5 - 1 = 4$. The coordinates of the other two vertices are: $(2 + 4, 1) = (6, 1)$ and $(2 + 4, 5) = (6, 5)$.

(2) If the two provided vertices $(2, 1)$ and $(2, 5)$ are on the right side of the square, then the length of each side of the square is $5 - 1 = 4$. The coordinates of the other two vertices are: $(2 - 4, 1) = (-2, 1)$ and $(2 - 4, 5) = (-2, 5)$.

(3) If the two provided vertices $(2, 1)$ and $(2, 5)$ are on opposite corners of the square (that is, if they are the ends of a diagonal), then this given diagonal is vertical with length $5 - 1 = 4$. The other diagonal will be horizontal with length 4. Since the diagonals of squares bisect each other, the coordinates of the other vertices are:

$$\left(2 - 2, \frac{1 + 5}{2}\right) = (0, 3) \text{ and}$$

$$\left(2 + 2, \frac{1 + 5}{2}\right) = (4, 3).$$

57. a. For points that lie in quadrant I, the x-coordinate is positive and the y-coordinate is positive.

b. For points that lie in quadrant II, the x-coordinate is negative and the y-coordinate is positive.

c. For points that lie in quadrant III, the x-coordinate is negative and the y-coordinate is negative.

d. For points that lie in quadrant IV, the x-coordinate is positive and the y-coordinate is negative.

59. Answers will vary. One possibility follows: An *independent* variable can be changed freely, while a *dependent* variable changes in some related way to the change in the independent variable.

Homework 1.3

1. The line contains the point $(-2, 2)$, so $y = 2$ when $x = -2$.

3. The line contains the point $(6, -2)$, so $x = 6$ when $y = -2$.

5. The line and the x-axis intersect at $(2, 0)$, so the x-intercept is $(2, 0)$.

7. The line contains the point $(-3, -2)$, so $y = -2$ when $x = -3$.

9. The line contains the point $(-6, -3)$, so $x = -6$ when $y = -3$.

11. The line and the y-axis intersect at $(0, -1)$, so the y-intercept is $(0, -1)$.

13. a–b.

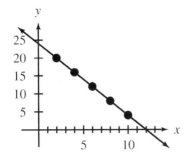

c. The line contains the point $(3, 18)$, so $y = 18$ when $x = 3$.

d. The line contains the point $(9, 6)$, so $x = 9$ when $y = 6$.

e. The line and the y-axis intersect at $(0, 24)$, so the y-intercept is $(0, 24)$.

f. The line and the x-axis intersect at $(12, 0)$, so the x-intercept is $(12, 0)$.

15. a. The line contains the point $(2, 18)$, so $v = 18$ when $t = 2$. This means that, after 2 hours of pumping, 18 thousand gallons of water will be in the basement.

b. The line contains the point $(4.2, 5)$, so $t = 4.2$ when $v = 5$. This means that 5 thousand gallons will remain in the basement after 4.2 hours of pumping.

c. The line and the v-axis intersect at $(0, 30)$, so $v = 30$ when $t = 0$. This means that 30 thousand gallons of water were in the basement before any water was pumped out.

d. The line and the t-axis intersect at $(5, 0)$, so $t = 5$ when $v = 0$. This means that all of the water will pumped out of the basement after 5 hours.

17. No, a line is not a reasonable model. The data points do not lie close to one line.

19. a.

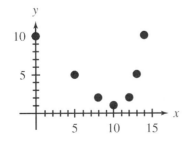

b. No, there is not a linear relationship between x and y. The data points do not lie close to one line.

21. a.

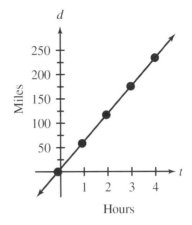

b. The line contains the point (2.5, 150), so $d = 150$ when $t = 2.5$. This means the student has traveled 150 miles in 2.5 hours.

c. The line contains the point (3.5, 210), so $t = 3.5$ when $d = 210$. This means that it took the student 3.5 hours to travel 210 miles.

23. a.

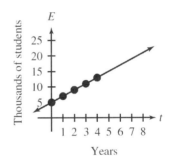

b. The line contains the point (6, 17), so $E = 17$ when $t = 6$. We predict that the college's enrollment will be 17 thousand students when it has been open for 6 years.

c. The line contains the point (7, 19), so $t = 7$ when $E = 19$. We predict that the college will have been open for 7 years when its enrollment will reach 19 thousand.

25. a.

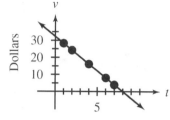

Years since 2000

b. The line contains the point (5, 12), so $t = 5$ when $v = 12$. This means the value of the stock was $12 in 2000 + 5 = 2005.

c. The line and the t-axis intersect at (8, 0), so $t = 8$ when $v = 0$. This means that the stock had no value in 2000 + 8 = 2008.

d. The line and the v-axis intersect at (0, 32), so $v = 32$ when $t = 0$. This means that the value of the stock was $32 in 2000 + 0 = 2000.

27. a.

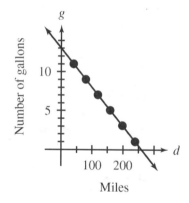

Miles

b. The line contains the point (140, 6), so $g = 6$ when $d = 140$. This means that there will still be 6 gallons of gasoline in the tank after the driver has gone 140 miles.

c. The line contains the point (220, 2), so $d = 220$ when $g = 2$. The driver has gone 220 miles when 2 gallons of gasoline remain in the tank.

d. The line and the d-axis intersect at (260, 0), so $d = 260$ when $g = 0$. This means that the gasoline tank will be empty after 260 miles of driving (if no refueling takes place).

e. The line and the g-axis intersect at (0, 13), so $g = 13$ when $d = 0$. This means that the car has a 13-gallon gasoline tank.

29. a.

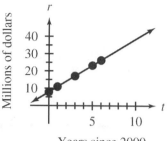

Years since 2000

b. The year 2010 corresponds to $t = 10$. The line contains the point (10, 38), so $r = 38$ when $t = 10$. We predict that the revenue of the company will be $38 million in 2010.

c. The line contains the point (2, 14), so $t = 2$ when $r = 14$. This means the revenue was $14 million in 2000 + 2 = 2002.

d. The line and the r-axis intersect at (0, 8), so $r = 8$ when $t = 0$. This means that the revenue of the company was $8 million in the year 2000.

31. a.

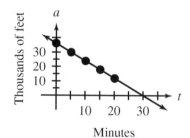

Minutes

b. The line contains the point (12, 22), so $a = 22$ when $t = 12$. This means the altitude of the plane is 22 thousand feet 12 minutes after it began its decent.

c. The line contains the point (30, 0), so $t = 30$ when $d = 0$. This means that it will take 30 minutes for the plane to reach the ground.

d. The prediction in part (c) will be an underestimate. A slower decent the last 2000 feet means it will take longer to reach the ground than predicted.

33. a.

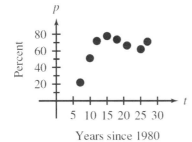

Years since 1980

b. No, there is not a linear relationship between *t* and *p*. The data points do not lie close to one line.

35. No. The 5 is the *y*-coordinate of ordered pair (2, 5), not the *y*-intercept.

37. No. The *y*-coordinate of an *x*-intercept must be 0. The *x*-intercept might be (2, 0), but not (0, 2).

39. No. An *x*-intercept is a point that corresponds to an ordered pair with two coordinates, not a single number. The *x*-intercept might be (5, 0), but not just 5.

41. Answers will vary. One possibility follows:

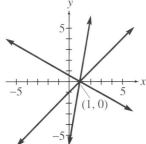

43.a. Answers will vary. One possibility follows:

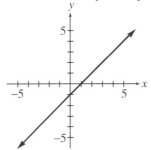

i. The line shown contains the point (2, 1), so the output is 1 when the input is 2. There is only one output.

ii. The line shown contains the point (4, 3), so the output is 3 when the input is 4. There is only one output.

iii. The line shown contains the point (−3, −4), so the output is −4 when the input is −3. There is only one output.

b. For the line shown, a single input leads to a single output. The line passes through any given point only once, so each input has a single output.

c. For *any* nonvertical line, a single input leads to a single output. In general, a line passes uniquely through each point, so each input has only one output.

45. Answers will vary. One possibility follows: Plot dependent quantities and their independent variables on a coordinate system. If they fall along or near a straight line, they can be described by a linear model. From this line, any given value for either the independent or dependent variable will allow the corresponding variable to be estimated or predicted.

Homework 1.4

Throughout this section, answers may vary.

1. a. and c.

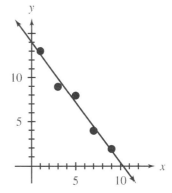

b. The variables are approximately linearly related.

d. (8, 3.2)

e. (5.9, 6)

f. (0, 14)

g. (10.3, 0)

3. a–b.

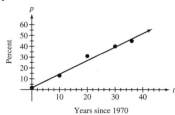

Years since 1970

c. In 2014, 57% of dentistry degrees will be earned by women.

d. In 1984, about 20% of dentistry degrees were earned by women.

5. a. and c. First, we list the values of t and n in the table below. For example, $t = 5$ represents 1985 because 1985 is 5 years after 1980.

Years since 1980	Number of Species
t	n
0	281
5	384
10	596
15	962
20	1244
25	1264

We then create the scatter plot and linear model.

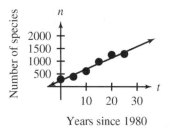

Years since 1980

b. The variables are approximately linearly related because they lie close to a straight line.

d. We estimate that the line contains the point (17, 1000), so $t = 17$ when $n = 1000$. We predict that there were 1000 species listed as endangered in $1980 + 17 = 1997$. We performed interpolation because we used a part of the model whose t-coordinates are between the t-coordinates of two data points.

e. The year 2011 is represented by $t = 31$. We estimate that the line contains the point (31, 1620), so $n = 1620$ when $t = 31$. We predict that there will be 1620 species listed as endangered or threatened in 2011. We performed extrapolation because we used a part of the model whose t-coordinates are not between the t-coordinates of two data points.

7. a–b. First, we list the values of t and n in the table below. For example, $t = 1$ represents 2001 because 2001 is 1 year after 2000.

Years since 2000	Bumping Rate
t	r
0	21
1	19
2	18
3	16
4	14
5	12
6	12

We then create the scatter plot and linear model.

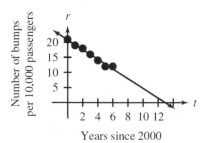

Years since 2000

c. We estimate that the line and the r-axis intersect at (0, 21), so $r = 21$ when $t = 0$. We predict that the voluntary bumping rate in 2000 was 21 bumps per 10,000 passengers.

d. We estimate that the line contains the point (10, 4), so $t = 10$ when $r = 4$. We predict that the bump rate will be 4 bumps per 10,000 passengers in $2000 + 10 = 2010$.

e. We estimate that the line and the t-axis intersect at (13, 0), so $t = 13$ when $r = 0$. We predict that there will be no voluntary bumping in 2013. Note: It is highly likely that model breakdown has occurred.

10

9. a–b.

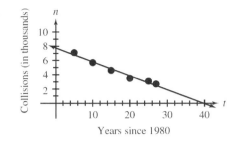

c. In 1997, there were about 4.5 thousand collisions. We performed interpolation because we used a part of the model whose *t*-coordinates are between the *t*-coordinates of two data points.

d. If the graph is extended, there will be 1.0 thousand collisions in 2015. We performed extrapolation because we used a part of the model whose *t*-coordinates are not between the *t*-coordinates of two data points.

e. The *n*-intercept of the model is when *n* = 7.8. This means that in 1980, there were 7.8 thousand collisions.

f. If the graph is extended, the *t*-intercept of the model occurs when *t* = 40. This means that there will be no collisions in 2020.

11. a–b.

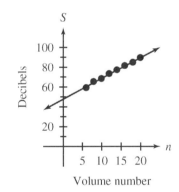

c. We estimate that the line contains the point (19,88), so *S* = 88 when *n* = 19. We predict that the sound level will be 88 decibels when the volume number is 19.

d. Note that the sound level of a noisy office is 75 decibels. We estimate that the line contains the point (13, 75), so *n* = 13 when *S* = 75. We predict that the volume number 13 is comparable to a noisy office.

13. a–b.

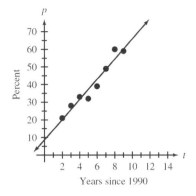

c. If the graph is extended, about 90% of Americans would be satisfied in 2004.

d.

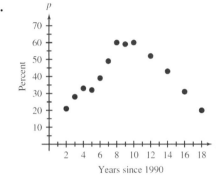

e. The estimated value from part (c) was 90%. The actual value for 2004 was 43%. The error in prediction is 90% – 43% = 47%. Up to 2000, the percent of Americans who were satisfied was steadily increasing. After 2000 the percent of Americans who were satisfied was steadily decreasing.

15. a–b.

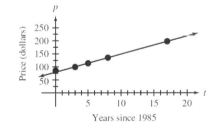

c. In 1999 the model predicts that the price will be about $178. The model overestimated by $28.

d. In 2001 the model predicts that the price will be about $192. The model overestimated by $32.

e. The graph is based on prices of Air Jordans while Michael Jordan was not retired. When he was retired, the Air Jordans were most likely less popular and less expensive. Therefore, the graph overestimates the price of Air Jordans for the years that Jordan was retired.

f.

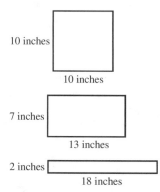

Years since 1985

17. a. The year 2001 is represented by $t = 6$. We estimate that the linear model contains the point $(6, 99)$. This means that the infection rate in 2001 was 99 infections per 1000 PCs a month.

b. From the table, the actual rate in 2001 was 113 infections per 1000 PCs a month.

c. Since the predicted rate is lower than the actual rate, the prediction is an underestimate. We can tell this from the graph since the line is under the data point.
The error in the estimate is $99 - 113 = -14$ infections per 1000 PCs a month.

19. If the data point (c, p) is below the linear model, then the model will overestimate the value of p when $t = c$.

21. Answers will vary.

23. Answers may vary. One possibility follows:
Linearly related indicates that the data follow a perfect straight line. *Approximately linearly related* indicates that the data do not follow a perfect straight line, but are close to being in a straight line.

25. Not necessarily. Model breakdown may occur for some points on the line.

Chapter 1 Review Exercises

1. The revenue was $37.8 billion in 2008.

2. $t = 8$ represents the year $2005 + 8 = 2013$.

3. Answers may vary. One possibility is:
Let p be the percentage of students who are full-

time students. Then p can represent the numbers 60 and 70, but p cannot represent the numbers -12 and 107.

4. a. Answers may vary. Possibilities follow:

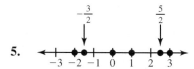

b. In the described situation, the symbols W and L are variables. Their values can change.

c. In the described situation, the symbol P is a constant. Its value is fixed at 40 inches.

5.

6. The negative integers between -5 and 5 are $-4, -3, -2,$ and -1.

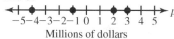

7. The numbers listed (in millions) are: $2, -4, -1$, and 3.

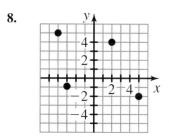

Millions of dollars

8.

9. The y-coordinate is -6.

10. The x-coordinate is -4.

11. The percentage p of home owners depends on age a. Thus, a is the independent variable and p is the dependent variable.

12. Presumably, the more education a person has, the higher his or her salary will be. So, the average salary *a* depends on the years of education *t*. Thus, *t* is the independent variable and *a* is the dependent variable.

13. The number of billionaires depends on the year. So, *t* is the independent variable and *n* is the dependent variable. The ordered pair (3, 449) means that *t* = 3 and *n* = 449. This means that there were 449 U.S. billionaires in the year 2005 + 3 = 2008.

14. The number of injuries depends on the year. So, *t* is the independent variable and *n* is the dependent variable. The ordered pair (6, 8.8) means that *t* = 6 and *n* = 8.8. This means that there were 8.8 thousand injuries on amusement park rides in the year 2000 + 6 = 2006.

15.

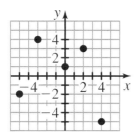

16. a.

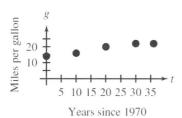

Years since 1970

b. The average gas mileage was highest in the years 2000 and 2006.

c. The average gas mileage was lowest in the year 1970.

17. a. France generates the largest percentage of its electricity by nuclear power. This percentage is about 78%.

b. The United States generates the smallest percentage of it electricity by nuclear power. This percentage is about 20%.

c. Sweden generates about 50% of its electricity by nuclear power.

18. The line contains the point $(-2, -1)$, so $y = -1$ when $x = -2$.

19. The line contains the point $(6, -5)$, so $y = -5$ when $x = 6$.

20. The line contains the point $(4, -4)$, so $x = 4$ when $y = -4$.

21. The line contains the point $(-6, 1)$, so $x = -6$ when $y = 1$.

22. The line and the *y*-axis intersect at $(0, -2)$, so the *y*-intercept is $(0, -2)$.

23. The line and the *x*-axis intersect at $(-4, 0)$, so the *x*-intercept is $(-4, 0)$.

24. a–b.

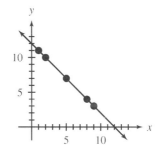

c. The line contains the point (11, 1), so *y* = 1 when *x* = 11.

d. The line contains the point (7, 5), so *x* = 7 when *y* = 5.

e. The line and the *x*-axis intersect at (12, 0), so the *x*-intercept is (12, 0).

f. The line and the *y*-axis intersect at (0, 12), so the *y*-intercept is (0, 12).

25. a.

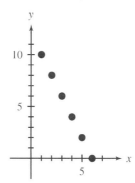

b. The variables *x* and *y* are linearly related.

26. a.

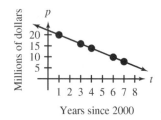

Years since 2000

b. The year 2010 is represented by $t = 10$. The line contains the point (10, 2), so $p = 2$ when $t = 10$. We predict the profit will be $2 million in 2010.

c. The line contains the point (2, 18), so $t = 2$ when $p = 18$. We predict that profit was $18 million in the year $2000 + 2 = 2002$.

d. The line and the *p*-axis intersect at (0, 22), so $p = 22$ when $t = 0$. This means that the profit was $22 million in the year 2000.

e. The line and the *t*-axis intersect at (11, 0), so $t = 11$ when $p = 0$. This means that the profit will be $0 in the year 2011.

27. The *y*-coordinate of an *x*-intercept of a line is 0.

28. a. and c.

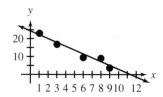

b. The variables are approximately linearly related.

d. (5, 13.5)

e. (2, 20)

f. (0, 24.3)

g. (11.2, 0)

29. a–b. First, we list the values of *t* and *p* in the table below. For example, $t = 4$ represents 2004 because 2004 is 4 years after 2000.

Years since 2000	Percent
t	*p*
4	4.6
5	6.0
6	7.9
7	11.2
8	13.0

We then create the scatter plot and linear model.

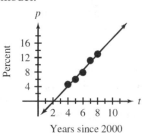

Years since 2000

c. The line contains the point (11, 20), so $t = 11$ when $p = 20$. We predict that 20% of U.S. Army recruits will need conduct waivers in the year $2000 + 11 = 2011$.

d. We estimate that the line contains the point (13, 24), so $p = 24$ when $t = 13$. We predict that, in the year $2000 + 13 = 2013$, 24% of U.S. Army recruits will need conduct waivers.

30. a–b. First, we list the values of *t* and *n* in the table below. For example, $t = 1$ represents 1956 because 1956 is 1 year after 1955.

Years since 1955	Stolen Bases
t	*n*
1	40
2	38
3	31
4	27
5	25
6	18
7	18
8	8

We then create the scatter plot and linear model.

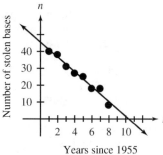

Years since 1955

c. The line and the *n*-axis intersect at (0, 45), so *n* = 45 when *t* = 0. This means that, according to the model, Mays stole about 45 bases in 1955.

d. The line and the *t*-axis intersect at (10.4, 0), so *t* = 10.4 when *v* = 0. Now 1955 + 10.4 = 1965.4. According to the model, Mays did not steal any bases in 1965.

e. Since the predicted number of stolen bases (46) is higher than the actual number of stolen bases (24), the prediction is an overestimate. Model breakdown has occurred. Explanations will vary.

f. For the year 1971, our linear model will predict a negative number of stolen bases, which is an underestimate. Model breakdown has occurred. Explanations will vary.

Chapter 1 Test

1. a. Answers may vary. Possibilities follow:

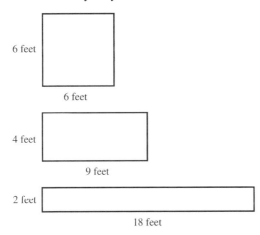

b. In the described situation, the symbols *W* and *L* are variables. Their values can change.

c. In the described situation, the symbol *A* is a constant. Its value is fixed at 36 square feet.

2. The integers between −4 and 2, inclusive, are −4, −3, −2, −1, 0, 1, and 2.

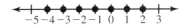

3. The numbers listed are: −5, 7, 2, and −3.

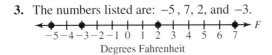

4.
$$\frac{4.5+5.2+7.0+8.7+10.4}{5} = \frac{35.8}{5} = 7.16$$
The average number of electric cars in use per year is 7.16 thousand cars.

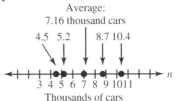

5. As the number of tickets increases, the cost will decrease. So, the cost *c* depends on the number of tickets *n*. Thus, *n* is the independent variable and *c* is the dependent variable.

6. The amount of revenue, in billions of dollars, depends on the number of years since 2005. So, *t* is the independent variable and *r* is the dependent variable. The ordered pair (2, 1) means that *t* = 2 and *r* = 1. This means that, in the year 2005 + 2 = 2007, 1 billion dollars in revenue from digital music downloads was earned.

7. a.

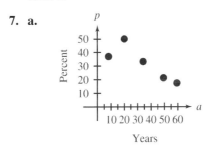

b. The point (21, 50) is the highest point. This means that Americans in the age group 18–24 are the most likely to have been without health insurance.

c. The point (59.5, 17) is the lowest point. This means that Americans in the age group 55–64 are the least likely to have been without health insurance.

8. The line contains the point (−4, −3), so *y* = −3 when *x* = −4.

9. The line contains the point (4, 1), so *x* = 4 when *y* = 1.

10. The line and the *y*-axis intersect at (0, −1), so the *y*-intercept is (0, −1).

15

11. The line and the *x*-axis intersect at $(2, 0)$, so the *x*-intercept is $(2, 0)$.

12. a.

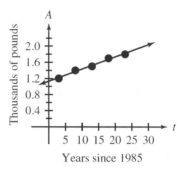

b. The line contains the point $(4, 29)$, so $s = 29$ when $t = 4$. We predict the person's salary will be $29 thousand after she has worked 4 years at the company.

c. The line contains the point $(7, 35)$, so $t = 7$ when $s = 35$. We predict that person's salary will be $35 thousand after she has worked 7 years at the company.

d. The line and the *s*-axis intersect at $(0, 21)$, so $s = 21$ when $t = 0$. This means that, when the person was initially hired, her salary was $21 thousand.

13. Answers may vary. One possibility follows: A *linear model* indicates that the independent and dependent variables of data follow a straight-line relation.

14. a–b. First, we list the values of *t* and *A* in the table below. For example, $t = 3$ represents 1988 because 1988 is 3 years after 1985

Years since 1985	Average amount of milk (thousands of pounds)
t	*A*
3	1.2
8	1.4
13	1.5
18	1.7
23	1.8

We then create the scatter plot and linear model.

c. The line and the *A*-axis intersect at $(0, 1.1)$, so $A = 1.1$ when $t = 0$. This means that, according to the model, a dairy cow in the United States produced an average of 1.1 thousand pounds of milk in March of 1985.

d. We estimate that the line contains the point $(28, 2.0)$, so $A = 2.0$ when $t = 28$. We predict that, in March of $1985 + 28 = 2013$, a U.S. dairy cow will produce an average of 2.0 thousand pounds of milk.

e. We estimate that the line contains the point $(26, 1.9)$, so $t = 26$ when $n = 1.9$. We predict that a U.S. dairy cow will produce an average of 1.9 thousand pounds of milk in March of the year $1985 + 26 = 2011$.

15. If the data point (c, p) is below the linear model, then the model will overestimate the value of *p* when $t = c$. Explanations will vary.

Chapter 2
Operations and Expressions

Homework 2.1

1. Substitute 6 for x in $x + 2$:
$(6) + 2 = 8$

3. Substitute 6 for x in $9 - x$:
$9 - (6) = 3$

5. Substitute 6 for x in $7x$:
$7(6) = 42$

7. Substitute 6 for x in $x \div 2$:
$(6) \div 2 = 3$

9. Substitute 6 for x in $x + x$:
$(6) + (6) = 12$

11. Substitute 6 for x in $x \cdot x$:
$(6) \cdot (6) = 36$

13. Substitute 4 for n in $13n$:
$13(4) = 52$
So, the person spends $52 on audio CDs.

15. Substitute 440 for T in $T \div 5$:
$440 \div 5 = 88$
The student's average test score was 88.

17. **a.**

Number of Shares	Total Value (dollars)
1	$5 \cdot 1$
2	$5 \cdot 2$
3	$5 \cdot 3$
4	$5 \cdot 4$
n	$5n$

The expression $5n$ represents the total value of the shares.

b. Substitute 7 for n in $5n$:
$5(7) = 35$
So, the total value of 7 shares is $35.

19. **a.**

Tuition (dollars)	Total Cost (dollars)
400	$400 + 12$
401	$401 + 12$
402	$402 + 12$
403	$403 + 12$
t	$t + 12$

The expression $t + 12$ represents the total cost for a student.

b. Substitute 417 for t in $t + 12$:
$417 + 12 = 429$
So, if tuition is $417, the total cost will be $429.

21. **a.**

Number of Hours of Courses	Total Cost (dollars)
1	$87 \cdot 1$
2	$87 \cdot 2$
3	$87 \cdot 3$
4	$87 \cdot 4$
n	$87n$

The expression $87n$ represents the total cost (in dollars) of enrolling in n hours of classes.

b. Substitute 15 for n in $87n$:
$87(15) = 1305$
So, the total cost of enrolling in 15 hours of classes is $1305.

23. $x + 4$
Substitute 8 for x in $x + 4$:
$(8) + 4 = 12$

25. $x \div 2$
Substitute 8 for x in $x \div 2$:
$(8) \div 2 = 4$

27. $x - 5$
Substitute 8 for x in $x - 5$:
$(8) - 5 = 3$

29. $7x$

Substitute 8 for x in $7x$:

$7(8) = 56$

31. $16 \div x$

Substitute 8 for x in $16 \div x$:

$16 \div (8) = 2$

33. The quotient of the number and 2.

35. 7 minus the number.

37. 5 more than the number.

39. The product of 9 and the number.

41. Subtract 7 from the number.

43. The product of the number and 2.

45. Substitute 6 for x and 3 for y in the expression $x + y$:

$(6) + (3) = 9$

47. Substitute 6 for x and 3 for y in the expression $x - y$:

$(6) - (3) = 3$

49. Substitute 6 for x and 3 for y in the expression yx:

$(3)(6) = 18$

51. xy

Substitute 9 for x and 3 for y in the expression xy:

$(9)(3) = 27$

53. $x - y$

Substitute 9 for x and 3 for y in the expression $x - y$:

$(9) - (3) = 6$

55. Substitute 62 for r and 3 for t in the expression rt:

$(62)(3) = 186$

So, after 3 hours the car will have traveled 186 miles.

57. Substitute 240 for m and 12 for g in the expression $m \div g$:

$240 \div 12 = 20$

So, on a trip of 240 miles, the car averages 20 miles per gallon.

59. Substitute 315 for C and 485 for R in the expression $R - C$.

$485 - 315 = 170$

So, if the total revenue is \$485 thousand and the total cost is \$315 thousand, the company will have a profit of \$170 thousand (\$170,000).

61. a.

t	$5t$
1	$5 \cdot 1 = 5$
2	$5 \cdot 2 = 10$
3	$5 \cdot 3 = 15$
4	$5 \cdot 4 = 20$

So, the person earns \$5, \$10, \$15, and \$20 for working 1, 2, 3, and 4 hours, respectively.

b. The person makes \$5 per hour. The hourly rate is a constant while the number of hours worked is a variable. In the expression, $5t$, the constant is 5 and the variable is t.

c. Answers may vary. For each additional hour worked, the total earned increases by \$5.

63. a.

t	$50t$
1	$50 \cdot 1 = 50$
2	$50 \cdot 2 = 100$
3	$50 \cdot 3 = 150$
4	$50 \cdot 4 = 200$

So, the person drives 50, 100, 150, and 200 miles after driving 1, 2, 3, and 4 hours, respectively.

b. The person is traveling at a speed of 50 miles per hour. The speed is a constant while the number of hours driving is a variable. In the expression, $50t$, the constant is 50 and the variable is t.

c. Answers may vary. For each additional hour of driving, the total distance driven increases by 50 miles.

65. Answers may vary.

67. Answers may vary. For example, the variable t can represent the amount of time for an event.

Homework 2.2

1. The denominator of $\dfrac{3}{7}$ is 7.

3. $\begin{aligned}20 &= 4 \cdot 5 \\ &= (2 \cdot 2) \cdot 5 \\ &= 2 \cdot 2 \cdot 5\end{aligned}$

5. $\begin{aligned}36 &= 4 \cdot 9 \\ &= (2 \cdot 2) \cdot (3 \cdot 3) \\ &= 2 \cdot 2 \cdot 3 \cdot 3\end{aligned}$

7. $\begin{aligned}45 &= 9 \cdot 5 \\ &= (3 \cdot 3) \cdot 5 \\ &= 3 \cdot 3 \cdot 5\end{aligned}$

9. $\begin{aligned}78 &= 3 \cdot 26 \\ &= 3 \cdot (2 \cdot 13) \\ &= 2 \cdot 3 \cdot 13\end{aligned}$

11. $\dfrac{6}{8} = \dfrac{2 \cdot 3}{2 \cdot 2 \cdot 2} = \dfrac{2}{2} \cdot \dfrac{3}{2 \cdot 2} = \dfrac{3}{2 \cdot 2} = \dfrac{3}{4}$

13. $\dfrac{3}{12} = \dfrac{3 \cdot 1}{3 \cdot 2 \cdot 2} = \dfrac{3}{3} \cdot \dfrac{1}{2 \cdot 2} = \dfrac{1}{2 \cdot 2} = \dfrac{1}{4}$

15. $\dfrac{18}{30} = \dfrac{2 \cdot 3 \cdot 3}{2 \cdot 3 \cdot 5} = \dfrac{2 \cdot 3}{2 \cdot 3} \cdot \dfrac{3}{5} = \dfrac{3}{5}$

17. $\dfrac{20}{50} = \dfrac{2 \cdot 2 \cdot 5}{2 \cdot 5 \cdot 5} = \dfrac{2 \cdot 2}{2 \cdot 2} \cdot \dfrac{2}{5} = \dfrac{2}{5}$

19. $\dfrac{5}{25} = \dfrac{5 \cdot 1}{5 \cdot 5} = \dfrac{5}{5} \cdot \dfrac{1}{5} = \dfrac{1}{5}$

21. $\dfrac{20}{24} = \dfrac{2 \cdot 2 \cdot 5}{2 \cdot 2 \cdot 2 \cdot 3} = \dfrac{2 \cdot 2}{2 \cdot 2} \cdot \dfrac{5}{2 \cdot 3} = \dfrac{5}{2 \cdot 3} = \dfrac{5}{6}$

23. $\dfrac{1}{3} \cdot \dfrac{2}{5} = \dfrac{1 \cdot 2}{3 \cdot 5} = \dfrac{2}{15}$

25. $\dfrac{4}{5} \cdot \dfrac{3}{8} = \dfrac{4 \cdot 3}{5 \cdot 8} = \dfrac{2 \cdot 2 \cdot 3}{5 \cdot 2 \cdot 2 \cdot 2} = \dfrac{3}{5 \cdot 2} = \dfrac{3}{10}$

27. $\dfrac{5}{21} \cdot 7 = \dfrac{5}{21} \cdot \dfrac{7}{1} = \dfrac{5 \cdot 7}{21 \cdot 1} = \dfrac{5 \cdot 7}{3 \cdot 7} = \dfrac{5}{3}$

29. $\dfrac{5}{8} \div \dfrac{3}{4} = \dfrac{5}{8} \cdot \dfrac{4}{3} = \dfrac{5 \cdot 4}{8 \cdot 3} = \dfrac{5 \cdot 2 \cdot 2}{2 \cdot 2 \cdot 2 \cdot 3} = \dfrac{5}{2 \cdot 3} = \dfrac{5}{6}$

31. $\dfrac{8}{9} \div \dfrac{4}{3} = \dfrac{8}{9} \cdot \dfrac{3}{4} = \dfrac{8 \cdot 3}{9 \cdot 4} = \dfrac{2 \cdot 2 \cdot 2 \cdot 3}{3 \cdot 3 \cdot 2 \cdot 2} = \dfrac{2}{3}$

33. $\dfrac{2}{3} \div 5 = \dfrac{2}{3} \cdot \dfrac{1}{5} = \dfrac{2 \cdot 1}{3 \cdot 5} = \dfrac{2}{15}$

35. $\dfrac{2}{7} + \dfrac{3}{7} = \dfrac{2 + 3}{7} = \dfrac{5}{7}$

37. $\dfrac{5}{8} + \dfrac{1}{8} = \dfrac{5 + 1}{8} = \dfrac{6}{8} = \dfrac{3}{4}$

39. $\dfrac{4}{5} - \dfrac{3}{5} = \dfrac{4 - 3}{5} = \dfrac{1}{5}$

41. $\dfrac{11}{12} - \dfrac{7}{12} = \dfrac{11 - 7}{12} = \dfrac{4}{12} = \dfrac{1}{3}$

43. The LCD is 4:

$\dfrac{1}{4} + \dfrac{1}{2} = \dfrac{1}{4} + \dfrac{1}{2} \cdot \dfrac{2}{2} = \dfrac{1}{4} + \dfrac{2}{4} = \dfrac{3}{4}$

45. The LCD is 12:

$\dfrac{5}{6} + \dfrac{3}{4} = \dfrac{5}{6} \cdot \dfrac{2}{2} + \dfrac{3}{4} \cdot \dfrac{3}{3} = \dfrac{10}{12} + \dfrac{9}{12} = \dfrac{19}{12}$

47. The LCD is 3:

$4 + \dfrac{2}{3} = \dfrac{4}{1} \cdot \dfrac{3}{3} + \dfrac{2}{3} = \dfrac{12}{3} + \dfrac{2}{3} = \dfrac{14}{3}$

49. The LCD is 9:

$\dfrac{7}{9} - \dfrac{2}{3} = \dfrac{7}{9} - \dfrac{2}{3} \cdot \dfrac{3}{3} = \dfrac{7}{9} - \dfrac{6}{9} = \dfrac{1}{9}$

51. The LCD is 63:

$\dfrac{5}{9} - \dfrac{2}{7} = \dfrac{5}{9} \cdot \dfrac{7}{7} - \dfrac{2}{7} \cdot \dfrac{9}{9} = \dfrac{35}{63} - \dfrac{18}{63} = \dfrac{17}{63}$

53. The LCD is 5:

$3 - \dfrac{4}{5} = \dfrac{3}{1} \cdot \dfrac{5}{5} - \dfrac{4}{5} = \dfrac{15}{5} - \dfrac{4}{5} = \dfrac{11}{5}$

55. $\dfrac{3172}{3172} = 1$

57. $\dfrac{599}{1} = 599$

59. $\dfrac{842}{0}$ is undefined since division by 0 is not defined.

61. $\dfrac{0}{621} = 0$

63. $\dfrac{824}{631} \cdot \dfrac{631}{824} = \dfrac{824 \cdot 631}{824 \cdot 631} = 1$

65. $\dfrac{544}{293} - \dfrac{544}{293} = \dfrac{0}{293} = 0$

67. Substitute 4 for w and 12 for z in the expression $\dfrac{w}{z}$:

$$\dfrac{4}{12} = \dfrac{2 \cdot 2 \cdot 1}{2 \cdot 2 \cdot 3} = \dfrac{1}{3}$$

69. Substitute 4 for w, 3 for x, 5 for y, and 12 for z in the expression $\dfrac{x}{w} \div \dfrac{y}{z}$:

$$\dfrac{3}{4} \div \dfrac{5}{12} = \dfrac{3}{4} \cdot \dfrac{12}{5} = \dfrac{3 \cdot 3 \cdot 2 \cdot 2}{2 \cdot 2 \cdot 5} = \dfrac{3 \cdot 3}{5} = \dfrac{9}{5}$$

71. Substitute 4 for w, 3 for x, 5 for y, and 12 for z in the expression $\dfrac{x}{w} - \dfrac{y}{z}$: $\dfrac{3}{4} - \dfrac{5}{12}$

The LCD is 12:

$$\dfrac{3}{4} - \dfrac{5}{12} = \dfrac{3}{4} \cdot \dfrac{3}{3} - \dfrac{5}{12} = \dfrac{9}{12} - \dfrac{5}{12} = \dfrac{4}{12} = \dfrac{1}{3}$$

73. $\dfrac{19}{97} \cdot \dfrac{65}{74} \approx 0.17$

```
(19/97)(65/74)
    .1720534968
```

75. $\dfrac{684}{795} \div \dfrac{24}{37} \approx 1.33$

```
(684/795)/(24/37
)
        1.326415094
■
```

77. $\dfrac{89}{102} - \dfrac{59}{133} \approx 0.43$

```
(89/102)-(59/133
)
        .4289399971
■
```

79. Answers may vary.

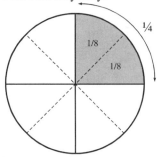

81. The area of a rectangle is given by the expression LW. Substitute $\frac{2}{5}$ for L and $\frac{1}{4}$ for W in the expression.

$$\dfrac{2}{5} \cdot \dfrac{1}{4} = \dfrac{2}{20} = \dfrac{1}{10}$$

The area of the plot is $\frac{1}{10}$ square mile.

83. Let t = the fraction of points from tests and f = the fraction of points from the final exam. The fraction of points from homework and quizzes is given by the expression $1 - t - f$. Substitute $\frac{1}{2}$ for t and $\frac{1}{4}$ for f in the expression.

$$1 - t - f = 1 - \dfrac{1}{2} - \dfrac{1}{4}$$
$$= \dfrac{1}{1} \cdot \dfrac{4}{4} - \dfrac{1}{2} \cdot \dfrac{2}{2} - \dfrac{1}{4}$$
$$= \dfrac{4}{4} - \dfrac{2}{4} - \dfrac{1}{4}$$
$$= \dfrac{4 - 2 - 1}{4}$$
$$= \dfrac{1}{4}$$

So, $\frac{1}{4}$ of the total points are from homework assignments and quizzes.

85. The quotient of the number and 3.

87.

Number of People	Cost per Person (dollars per person)
2	$\frac{19}{2}$
3	$\frac{19}{3}$
4	$\frac{19}{4}$
5	$\frac{19}{5}$
n	$\frac{19}{n}$

So, if n friends share the pizza, each will pay $\frac{19}{n}$ dollars.

89. a. i. $\dfrac{5}{6} \cdot \dfrac{2}{3} = \dfrac{5 \cdot 2}{6 \cdot 3} = \dfrac{10}{18} = \dfrac{5}{9}$

ii. $\dfrac{5}{6} \div \dfrac{2}{3} = \dfrac{5}{6} \cdot \dfrac{3}{2} = \dfrac{5 \cdot 3}{6 \cdot 2} = \dfrac{15}{12} = \dfrac{5}{4}$

iii. The LCD is 6:

$\dfrac{5}{6} + \dfrac{2}{3} = \dfrac{5}{6} + \dfrac{2}{3} \cdot \dfrac{2}{2} = \dfrac{5}{6} + \dfrac{4}{6} = \dfrac{9}{6} = \dfrac{3}{2}$

iv. The LCD is 6:

$\dfrac{5}{6} - \dfrac{2}{3} = \dfrac{5}{6} - \dfrac{2}{3} \cdot \dfrac{2}{2} = \dfrac{5}{6} - \dfrac{4}{6} = \dfrac{1}{6}$

b. Answers may vary.

91. Answers may vary. For multiplication, the student did not need to get a common denominator. The problem could be worked by simply multiplying across.

$\dfrac{1}{2} \cdot \dfrac{1}{3} = \dfrac{1 \cdot 1}{2 \cdot 3} = \dfrac{1}{6}$

93. Answers may vary. The student should have only multiplied the numerator by 2. Rewrite 2 as $\frac{2}{1}$ and then multiply across.

$2 \cdot \dfrac{3}{5} = \dfrac{2}{1} \cdot \dfrac{3}{5} = \dfrac{2 \cdot 3}{1 \cdot 5} = \dfrac{6}{5}$

95. a., b. $\dfrac{1}{4} = \dfrac{8}{32},\ \dfrac{3}{16} = \dfrac{6}{32},\ \dfrac{1}{8} = \dfrac{4}{32}$

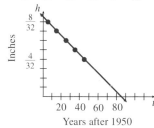

Years after 1950

c. 2005 corresponds to $t = 55$. From the graph, the height when $t = 55$ is $h = \frac{3}{32}$ inch.

d. From the graph, the height will be $\frac{1}{16}$ inch when $t = 65$. That is, in 2015.

e. The t-intercept is the point where the graph crosses the t-axis. From the graph, the t-intercept is $(85, 0)$. There will be no grass on the putting greens in 2035 (when $t = 85$). This prediction is very unlikely.

97. a. i. $-1 + (-5) = -6$

ii. $-6 + (-2) = -8$

iii. $-3 + (-4) = -7$

```
-1+( -5)
                        -6
-6+( -2)
                        -8
-3+( -4)
                        -7
```

b. The results are the same as if the absolute values of the numbers were added, and the final answer multiplied by a minus sign.

c. $-4 + (-5) = -9$

d. Answers may vary. To add two negative numbers, add the numbers without the negatives, then make the resulting value is negative.

Homework 2.3

1. $-(-4) = 4$

3. $-\bigl(-(-7)\bigr) = -(7) = -7$

5. $|3| = 3$ because 3 is a distance of 3 units from 0 on a number line.

7. $|-8| = 8$ because -8 is a distance of 8 units from 0 on a number line.

9. $-|4| = -(4) = -4$

11. $-|-7| = -(7) = -7$

13. The numbers have different signs so subtract the smaller absolute value from the larger.

$|-7| - |2| = 7 - 2 = 5$

Since $|-7|$ is greater than $|2|$, the sum is negative.

$2 + (-7) = -5$

15. The numbers have the same sign so add the absolute values.
$$|-1|+|-4|=1+4=5$$
The numbers are negative, so the sum is negative.
$$-1+(-4)=-5$$

17. The numbers have different signs so subtract the smaller absolute value from the larger.
$$|7|-|-5|=7-5=2$$
Since $|7|$ is greater than $|-5|$, the sum is positive.
$$7+(-5)=2$$

19. The numbers have different signs so subtract the smaller absolute value from the larger.
$$|-8|-|5|=8-5=3$$
Since $|-8|$ is greater than $|5|$, the sum is negative.
$$-8+5=-3$$

21. The numbers have the same sign so add the absolute values.
$$|-7|+|-3|=7+3=10$$
The numbers are negative, so the sum is negative.
$$-7+(-3)=-10$$

23. The numbers have different signs so subtract the smaller absolute value from the larger.
$$|-7|-|4|=7-4=3$$
Since $|-7|$ is greater than $|4|$, the sum is negative.
$$4+(-7)=-3$$

25. $1+(-1)=0$ because the numbers are opposites and the sum of opposites is 0.

27. $-4+4=0$ because the numbers are opposites and the sum of opposites is 0.

29. The numbers have different signs so subtract the smaller absolute value from the larger.
$$|-25|-|12|=25-12=13$$
Since $|-25|$ is greater than $|12|$, the sum is negative.
$$12+(-25)=-13$$

31. The numbers have different signs so subtract the smaller absolute value from the larger.
$$|-39|-|17|=39-17=22$$
Since $|-39|$ is greater than $|17|$, the sum is negative.
$$-39+17=-22$$

33. The numbers have the same sign so add the absolute values.
$$|-246|+|-899|=246+899=1145$$
The numbers are negative, so the sum is negative.
$$-246+(-899)=-1145$$

35. $25,371+(-25,371)=0$ because the numbers are opposites and the sum of opposites is 0.

37. The numbers have the same sign so add the absolute values.
$$|-4.1|+|-2.6|=4.1+2.6=6.7$$
The numbers are negative, so the sum is negative.
$$-4.1+(-2.6)=-6.7$$

39. The numbers have different signs so subtract the smaller absolute value from the larger.
$$|-5|-|0.2|=5-0.2=4.8$$
Since $|-5|$ is greater than $|0.2|$, the sum is negative.
$$-5+0.2=-4.8$$

41. The numbers have different signs so subtract the smaller absolute value from the larger.
$$|-99.9|-|2.6|=99.9-2.6=97.3$$
Since $|-99.9|$ is greater than $|2.6|$, the sum is negative.
$$2.6+(-99.9)=-97.3$$

43. The numbers have different signs so subtract the smaller absolute value from the larger.
$$\left|\frac{5}{7}\right|-\left|-\frac{3}{7}\right|=\frac{5}{7}-\frac{3}{7}=\frac{2}{7}$$
Since $\left|\frac{5}{7}\right|$ is greater than $\left|-\frac{3}{7}\right|$, the sum is positive.
$$\frac{5}{7}+\left(-\frac{3}{7}\right)=\frac{2}{7}$$

45. The numbers have different signs so subtract the smaller absolute value from the larger.

$$\left|-\frac{5}{8}\right|-\left|\frac{3}{8}\right|=\frac{5}{8}-\frac{3}{8}=\frac{2}{8}=\frac{1}{4}$$

Since $\left|-\frac{5}{8}\right|$ is greater than $\left|\frac{3}{8}\right|$, the sum is negative.

$$-\frac{5}{8}+\frac{3}{8}=-\frac{1}{4}$$

47. The numbers have the same sign so add the absolute values.

$$\left|-\frac{1}{4}\right|+\left|-\frac{1}{2}\right|=\frac{1}{4}+\frac{1}{2}=\frac{1}{4}+\frac{1}{2}\cdot\frac{2}{2}=\frac{1}{4}+\frac{2}{4}=\frac{3}{4}$$

The numbers are negative, so the sum is negative.

$$-\frac{1}{4}+\left(-\frac{1}{2}\right)=-\frac{3}{4}$$

49. The numbers have different signs so subtract the smaller absolute value from the larger.

$$\left|\frac{5}{6}\right|-\left|-\frac{1}{4}\right|=\frac{5}{6}-\frac{1}{4}=\frac{5}{6}\cdot\frac{2}{2}-\frac{1}{4}\cdot\frac{3}{3}=\frac{10}{12}-\frac{3}{12}=\frac{7}{12}$$

Since $\left|\frac{5}{6}\right|$ is greater than $\left|-\frac{1}{4}\right|$, the sum is positive.

$$\frac{5}{6}+\left(-\frac{1}{4}\right)=\frac{7}{12}$$

51. $-325.89+6547.29=6221.4$

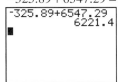

53. $-17,835.69+\left(-79,735.45\right)=-97,571.14$

55. $-\frac{34}{983}+\left(-\frac{19}{251}\right)\approx-0.11$

57. Substitute -4 for a and 3 for b in the expression $a+b$ and then find the sum:
$$\left(-4\right)+\left(3\right)=-4+3=-1$$

59. Substitute -4 for a and -2 for c in the expression $a+c$ and then find the sum:
$$\left(-4\right)+\left(-2\right)=-6$$

61. $x+2$
Substitute -6 for x in the expression and then find the sum:
$$\left(-6\right)+2=-4$$

63. $-2+x$
Substitute -6 for x in the expression and then find the sum:
$$-2+\left(-6\right)=-8$$

65. The balance is $-75+250$ dollars.
The numbers have different signs so subtract the smaller absolute value from the larger.
$$\left|250\right|-\left|-75\right|=250-75=175$$
Since $\left|250\right|$ is greater than $\left|-75\right|$, the sum is positive.
$-75+250=175$
So, the balance is $175.

67. We can find the final balance be finding the balance after each transaction.

Transaction	Balance
Transfer	$-89.00+300.00=211.00$
State Farm	$211.00-91.22=119.78$
MCI	$119.78-44.26=75.52$
Paycheck	$75.52+870=945.52$

So, the final balance is $945.52.

69. The new balance is $-5471+2600$.
The numbers have different signs so subtract the smaller absolute value from the larger.
$$\left|-5471\right|-\left|2600\right|=5471-2600=2871$$
Since $\left|-5471\right|$ is greater than $\left|2600\right|$, the sum is negative.
$-5471+2600=-2871$
So, the new balance is -2871 dollars.

71. The balance after sending the check is
$-3496 + 2500 = -996$.

The balance after buying the camera is
$-996 + (-629) = -1625$.

The balance after buying the film is
$-1625 + (-8) = -1633$.
So, the final balance is -1633 dollars.

73. The current temperature is $-5 + 9$.
The numbers have different signs so subtract the smaller absolute value from the larger.
$|9| - |-5| = 9 - 5 = 4$

Since $|9|$ is greater than $|-5|$, the sum is positive.
$-5 + 9 = 4$
So, the current temperature is $4°$ F.

75. a.

Weight before Diet (pounds)	Weight after Diet (pounds)
160	$160 + (-20)$
165	$165 + (-20)$
170	$170 + (-20)$
175	$175 + (-20)$
B	$B + (-20)$

From the last row of the table, we see that the expression $B + (-20)$ represents the person's current weight (in pounds).

b. Evaluate $B + (-20)$ for $B = 169$.
$169 + (-20) = 149$
The person's current weight is 149 pounds.

77. a.

Deposit (dollars)	New Balance (dollars)
50	$-80 + 50$
100	$-80 + 100$
150	$-80 + 150$
200	$-80 + 200$
d	$-80 + d$

From the last row of the table, we see that the expression $-80 + d$ represents the new balance (in dollars).

b. Evaluate $-80 + d$ for $d = 125$.
$-80 + 125 = 45$
The new balance is $45.

79. If a is negative and b is negative, the sum $a + b$ will also be negative.

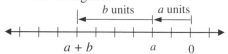

81. If $a + b = 0$ then the numbers are opposites, or the numbers are both 0.

83. a. Substitute -3 for a in $-a$:
$-(-3) = 3$

b. Substitute -4 for a in $-a$:
$-(-4) = 4$

c. Substitute -6 for a in $-a$:
$-(-6) = 6$

d. The student is not correct. The expression $-a$ represents the opposite of a. If a is positive, the result will be negative. However, if a is negative, the result will be positive, and if a is 0, the result is 0.

Homework 2.4

1. $6 - 8 = 6 + (-8) = -2$

3. $-1 - 5 = -1 + (-5) = -6$

5. $2 - (-7) = 2 + 7 = 9$

7. $-3 - (-2) = -3 + 2 = -1$

9. $4 - 7 = 4 + (-7) = -3$

11. $4 - (-7) = 4 + 7 = 11$

13. $-3 - 3 = -3 + (-3) = -6$

15. $-54 - 25 = -54 + (-25) = -79$

17. $381 - (-39) = 381 + 39 = 420$

19. $2.5 - 7.9 = 2.5 + (-7.9) = -5.4$

21. $-6.5 - 4.8 = -6.5 + (-4.8) = -11.3$

23. $3.8 - (-1.9) = 3.8 + 1.9 = 5.7$

25. $13.6 - (-2.38) = 13.6 + 2.38 = 15.98$

27. $-\dfrac{1}{3} - \dfrac{2}{3} = -\dfrac{1}{3} + \left(-\dfrac{2}{3}\right) = -\dfrac{3}{3} = -1$

29. $-\dfrac{1}{8} - \left(-\dfrac{5}{8}\right) = -\dfrac{1}{8} + \dfrac{5}{8} = \dfrac{4}{8} = \dfrac{1}{2}$

31. $\dfrac{1}{2} - \left(-\dfrac{1}{4}\right) = \dfrac{1}{2} + \dfrac{1}{4} = \dfrac{1}{2} \cdot \dfrac{2}{2} + \dfrac{1}{4} = \dfrac{2}{4} + \dfrac{1}{4} = \dfrac{3}{4}$

33. $-\dfrac{1}{6} - \dfrac{3}{8} = -\dfrac{1}{6} + \left(-\dfrac{3}{8}\right)$

$\qquad = -\dfrac{1}{6} \cdot \dfrac{4}{4} + \left(-\dfrac{3}{8} \cdot \dfrac{3}{3}\right)$

$\qquad = -\dfrac{4}{24} + \left(-\dfrac{9}{24}\right)$

$\qquad = -\dfrac{13}{24}$

35. $-5 + 7 = 2$

37. $-6 - (-4) = -6 + 4 = -2$

39. $\dfrac{3}{8} - \dfrac{5}{8} = \dfrac{3}{8} + \left(-\dfrac{5}{8}\right) = -\dfrac{2}{8} = -\dfrac{1}{4}$

41. $-4.9 - (-2.2) = -4.9 + 2.2 = -2.7$

43. $-2 + (-5) = -7$

45. $10 - 12 = 10 + (-12) = -2$

47. $-234.913 - 2893.26 \approx -3128.17$

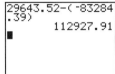

49. $29{,}643.52 - (-83{,}284.39) = 112{,}927.91$

51. $-\dfrac{17}{89} - \dfrac{51}{67} \approx -0.95$

53. $7 - 19 = 7 + (-19) = -12$

So, the current temperature is $-12°\mathrm{F}$.

55. $7 - (-4) = 7 + 4 = 11$

The change in temperature is $11°\mathrm{F}$.

57. a. $-4 - (8) = -4 + (-8) = -12$

The change in temperature is $-12°\mathrm{F}$.

b. To estimate the change in temperature over the past hour, we divide the change over two hours by 2.

$\dfrac{-12}{2} = -6$

The estimated change in temperature over the past hour is $-6°\mathrm{F}$.

c. Answers may vary. The change in temperature is affected by the time of day in addition to the weather conditions. Thus, temperature change need not be uniform.

59. $20{,}320 - (-282) = 20{,}320 + 282 = 20{,}602$

The change in elevation is 20,602 feet.

61. a.

Year	Percent who voted	Change in percentage points
1980	59.2	–
1984	59.9	$59.9 - 59.2 = 0.7$
1988	57.4	$57.4 - 59.9 = -2.5$
1992	61.9	$61.9 - 57.4 = 4.5$
1996	54.2	$54.2 - 61.9 = -7.7$
2000	54.7	$54.7 - 54.2 = 0.5$
2004	60.7	$60.7 - 54.7 = 6.0$

b. The greatest increase in percent turnout was 6.0% between 2000 and 2004.

c. The absolute value of the change in percent turnout between 1992 and 1996 is larger than the others. The large decrease in percent turnout suggests that not many of those 11 million people voted.

63. a. In 2004, Prius sales, in thousands, were $20 + 5 + 29 = 54$. So, there were 54 thousand cars sold in 2004.

b. Increasing sales are indicated by positive changes. Thus, sales were increasing during the periods 2002 – 2003, 2003 – 2004, 2004 – 2005, and 2006 – 2007.

c. Decreasing sales are indicated by negative changes. Thus, sales were decreasing during the periods 2005 – 2006 and 2007 – 2008.

65. a.

Score on the Second Exam (points)	Change in Score (points)
80	$80 - 87$
85	$85 - 87$
90	$90 - 87$
95	$95 - 87$
p	$p - 87$

From the last row of the table, we see that the expression $p - 87$ represents the change in score (in points) from the first exam to the second exam.

b. Evaluate $p - 87$ for $p = 81$:
$$81 - 87 = 81 + (-87) = -6$$
So, if a student has a score of 81 on the second exam, their score decreased 6 points from their first exam.

67. a.

Change in Enrollment	Current Enrollment
100	$100 + 24,500$
200	$200 + 24,500$
300	$300 + 24,500$
400	$400 + 24,500$
c	$c + 24,500$

From the last row of the table, we see that the expression $c + 24,500$ represents the current enrollment.

b. Evaluate $c + 24,500$ for $c = -700$:
$$-700 + 24,500 = 23,800$$
So, if the change in enrollment is -700, the current enrollment would be 23,800 due to the decrease in enrollment of 700 students in the past year.

69. The student should have changed the subtraction to adding the opposite instead of subtracting the opposite.
$$7 - (-5) = 7 + 5 = 12$$

71. a. i. $b - a = 5 - 3 = 5 + (-3) = 2$

ii. $9 - 1 = 9 + (-1) = 8$

iii. $7 - 2 = 7 + (-2) = 5$

b. Answers may vary. Since the quantity increased, the final number is larger than the beginning number. When finding the change in quantity, we subtract the beginning number from the final number. Since the final number is bigger, the result will be positive.

73. Evaluate $a + b$ for $a = -5$ and $b = 2$:
$$(-5) + (2) = -5 + 2 = -3$$

75. Evaluate $a - b$ for $a = -5$ and $b = 2$:
$$(-5) - (2) = -5 + (-2) = -7$$

77. Evaluate $b - c$ for $b = 2$ and $c = -7$:
$$(2) - (-7) = 2 + 7 = 9$$

79. $-3 - x$
Evaluate the expression for $x = -5$:
$$-3 - (-5) = -3 + 5 = 2$$

81. $x - 8$
Evaluate the expression for $x = -5$:
$$(-5) - 8 = -5 + (-8) = -13$$

83. $x - (-2)$
Evaluate the expression for $x = -5$:
$$(-5) - (-2) = -5 + 2 = -3$$

85. a. i. $-2(5) = -10$

ii. $-4(6) = -24$

iii. $-7(9) = -63$

b. Answers may vary. The results are all negative.

c. $-3(7) = -21$

d. Answers may vary. To multiply two numbers with different signs, multiply their absolute values and make the result negative.

87. a. $(8) - (5) = 8 + (-5) = 3$

b. $(5) - (8) = 5 + (-8) = -3$

c. The results have the same absolute value, but different signs.

d. $a - b$ for $a = -2$ and $b = 4$:
$(-2) - (4) = -2 + (-4) = -6$

$b - a$ for $a = -2$ and $b = 4$:
$(4) - (-2) = 4 + 2 = 6$
The results have the same absolute value, but different signs.

e. Answers may vary. The results should have the same absolute value, but different signs.

f. The results for $a - b$ and $b - a$ will have the same absolute value, but different signs. The sign of the final answer will be the same as that of the first number in the expression.

Homework 2.5

1. $63\% = 63.0\% = 0.63$

3. $9\% = 9.0\% = 0.09$

5. $0.08 = 8\%$

7. $7.3\% = 0.073$

9. $0.052 - 5.2\%$

11. $0.35(8) = 2.8$; so, 35% of \$8 is \$2.80.

13. $0.05(2500) = 125$; so, 5% of 2500 students is 125 students.

15. $0.025(7000) = 175$; so, 2.5% of 7000 cars is 175 cars.

17. Since the numbers have different signs, the product is negative: $-2(6) = -12$

19. Since the numbers have the same sign, the product is positive: $-3(-6) = 18$

21. Since the numbers have different signs, the product is negative: $1(-1) = -1$

23. Since the numbers have different signs, the quotient is negative: $-40 \div 5 = -8$

25. Since the numbers have different signs, the quotient is negative: $25 \div (-5) = -5$

27. Since the numbers have the same sign, the quotient is positive: $-56 \div (-7) = 8$

29. Since the numbers have the same sign, the product is positive: $-15(-37) = 555$

31. Since the numbers have different signs, the quotient is negative: $936 \div (-24) = -39$

33. Since the numbers have the same sign, the product is positive: $-0.2(-0.4) = 0.08$

35. Since the numbers have different signs, the product is negative: $2.5(-0.39) = -0.975$

37. Since the numbers have different signs, the quotient is negative: $-0.06 \div 0.2 = -0.3$

39. Since the numbers have different signs, the quotient is negative: $\dfrac{36}{-4} = 36 \div (-4) = -9$

41. Since the numbers have the same sign, the quotient is positive: $\dfrac{-32}{-8} = -32 \div (-8) = 4$

43. Since the numbers have different signs, the product is negative: $\dfrac{1}{2}\left(-\dfrac{1}{5}\right) = -\dfrac{1}{10}$

45. Since the numbers have the same sign, the product is positive: $\left(-\dfrac{4}{9}\right)\left(-\dfrac{3}{20}\right) = \dfrac{12}{180} = \dfrac{1}{15}$

47. Since the numbers have different signs, the quotient is negative:
$-\dfrac{3}{4} \div \dfrac{7}{6} = -\dfrac{3}{4} \cdot \dfrac{6}{7} = -\dfrac{18}{28} = -\dfrac{9}{14}$

49. Since the numbers have the same sign, the quotient is positive:
$-\dfrac{24}{35} \div \left(-\dfrac{16}{25}\right) = \dfrac{24}{35} \cdot \dfrac{25}{16} = \dfrac{600}{560} = \dfrac{15}{14}$

51. $6 + (-9) = -3$

53. $-39 \div (-3) = 13$

55. $4 - (-2) = 4 + 2 = 6$

57. $10(-10) = -100$

59. $-\dfrac{3}{4} + \dfrac{1}{2} = -\dfrac{3}{4} + \dfrac{1}{2} \cdot \dfrac{2}{2}$

$\qquad = -\dfrac{3}{4} + \dfrac{2}{4}$

$\qquad = \dfrac{-3 + 2}{4}$

$\qquad = -\dfrac{1}{4}$

61. $\left(-\dfrac{10}{7}\right)\left(-\dfrac{14}{15}\right) = \dfrac{140}{105} = \dfrac{4}{3}$

63. $\dfrac{3}{4} - \dfrac{5}{3} = \dfrac{3}{4} \cdot \dfrac{3}{3} - \dfrac{5}{3} \cdot \dfrac{4}{4}$

$\qquad = \dfrac{9}{12} - \dfrac{20}{12}$

$\qquad = \dfrac{9 - 20}{12}$

$\qquad = \dfrac{-11}{12}$

$\qquad = -\dfrac{11}{12}$

65. $-\dfrac{3}{8} \div \dfrac{5}{6} = -\dfrac{3}{8} \cdot \dfrac{6}{5} = -\dfrac{18}{40} = -\dfrac{9}{20}$

67. $\dfrac{-16}{20} = -\dfrac{2 \cdot 2 \cdot 2 \cdot 2}{2 \cdot 2 \cdot 5} = -\dfrac{2 \cdot 2}{5} = -\dfrac{4}{5}$

69. $\dfrac{-18}{-24} = \dfrac{2 \cdot 3 \cdot 3}{2 \cdot 2 \cdot 2 \cdot 3} = \dfrac{3}{2 \cdot 2} = \dfrac{3}{4}$

71. $\dfrac{3}{-4} + \dfrac{1}{4} = \dfrac{-3}{4} + \dfrac{1}{4} = \dfrac{-3 + 1}{4} = \dfrac{-2}{4} = -\dfrac{1}{2}$

73. $\dfrac{4}{7} - \left(\dfrac{3}{-7}\right) = \dfrac{4}{7} + \dfrac{3}{7} = \dfrac{4 + 3}{7} = \dfrac{7}{7} = 1$

75. $\dfrac{5}{6} + \dfrac{7}{-8} = \dfrac{5}{6} + \dfrac{-7}{8}$

$\qquad = \dfrac{5}{6} \cdot \dfrac{4}{4} + \dfrac{-7}{8} \cdot \dfrac{3}{3}$

$\qquad = \dfrac{20}{24} + \dfrac{-21}{24}$

$\qquad = \dfrac{20 + (-21)}{24}$

$\qquad = -\dfrac{1}{24}$

77. $-26.87(-381.572) \approx 10,252.84$

```
-26.87(-381.572)
       10252.83964
▪
```

79. $222.045 \div (-32.76) \approx -6.78$

```
222.045/(-32.76)
      -6.777930403
▪
```

81. $-\dfrac{11}{18}\left(-\dfrac{15}{19}\right) \approx 0.48$

```
(-11/18)(-15/19)
      .4824561404
```

83. $-\dfrac{59}{13} \div \dfrac{27}{48} \approx -8.07$

```
(-59/13)/(27/48)
      -8.068376068
```

85. Evaluate ab for $a = -6$ and $b = 4$:
$\quad (-6)(4) = -24$

87. Evaluate $\dfrac{a}{b}$ for $a = -6$ and $b = 4$:

$\quad \dfrac{-6}{4} = -\dfrac{3}{2}$

89. Evaluate $-ac$ for $a = -6$ and $c = -8$:
$\quad -(-6)(-8) = -(48) = -48$

91. Evaluate $-\dfrac{b}{c}$ for $b = 4$ and $c = -8$:

$$-\dfrac{4}{(-8)} = \dfrac{4}{8} = \dfrac{1}{2}$$

93. $\dfrac{w}{2}$

Evaluate the expression for $w = -8$:

$$\dfrac{(-8)}{2} = -4$$

95. $w(-5)$

Evaluate the expression for $w = -8$:

$$(-8)(-5) = 40$$

97. $\dfrac{6}{8} = \dfrac{3}{4}$

99. $\dfrac{1776 \text{ ft}}{790 \text{ ft}} = \dfrac{888}{395} \approx \dfrac{2.25}{1}$

So, the Freedom Tower would be 2.25 times as tall as the John Hancock Tower.

101. $\dfrac{469 \text{ billionaires}}{228 \text{ billionaires}} \approx \dfrac{2.06}{1}$

So, there were 2.06 times as many billionaires in the U.S. in 2008 as in 2002.

103. a. $\dfrac{4 \text{ red bell peppers}}{5 \text{ black olives}} = \dfrac{0.8 \text{ red bell pepper}}{1 \text{ black olive}}$

For each black olive used, 0.8 red bell pepper is required.

b. $\dfrac{5 \text{ black olives}}{4 \text{ red bell peppers}} = \dfrac{1.25 \text{ black olives}}{1 \text{ red bell pepper}}$

For each red bell pepper used, 1.25 black olives would be required.

105. a. $\dfrac{14,344}{2106} \approx \dfrac{6.81}{1}$

The FTE enrollment at Missouri State University is 6.81 times as large as that at Lincoln University of Missouri.

b. $\dfrac{353}{178} \approx \dfrac{1.98}{1}$

The FTE faculty at the Truman State University is 1.98 times as large as that at Missouri Western State University.

c. Harris-Stowe: $\dfrac{1413}{52} \approx \dfrac{27.17}{1}$

Lincoln: $\dfrac{2106}{142} \approx \dfrac{14.83}{1}$

Missouri State: $\dfrac{14344}{698} \approx \dfrac{20.55}{1}$

Missouri Western: $\dfrac{3845}{178} \approx \dfrac{21.60}{1}$

Truman: $\dfrac{5649}{353} \approx \dfrac{16.00}{1}$

d. Harris-Stowe State University has the largest FTE-enrollment to FTE-faculty ratio, while Lincoln University of Missouri has the smallest.

e. Answers may vary. The individual is not correct. Although Harris-Stowe State University has the smallest FTE enrollment, it also has the smallest FTE faculty, which serves to raise its FTE-enrollment to FTE-faculty ratio.

107. a. $\dfrac{-4360 \text{ dollars}}{-1825 \text{ dollars}} = \dfrac{872}{365} \approx \dfrac{2.39}{1}$

b. For each \$1 she pays towards her MasterCard account, she should pay about \$2.39 towards her Discover account.

109. $0.15(3720) = 558$

$-3720 + 558 = -3162$

The new balance would be -3162 dollars.

111. $12.3(2.40) = 29.52$

$0 - 29.52 = -29.52$

The new balance is -29.52 dollars.

113. a. $-2 + (-4) = -6$

b. $-2(-4) = 8$

c. The second statement is clearer because it indicates an operation as well. From parts (a) and (b), we see that just having two negative numbers is not enough to guarantee that the result is positive.

d. Answers may vary.

115. $\dfrac{a}{b} = \dfrac{-a}{-b}$; $\dfrac{-a}{b} = \dfrac{a}{-b} = -\dfrac{a}{b} = -\dfrac{-a}{-b}$

117. Answers may vary.
$$4(-5) = (-5)+(-5)+(-5)+(-5)$$

119. If ab is negative, we can say that the two numbers have different signs. We cannot say which is positive and which is negative, but we do know they have different signs.

121. If $ab = 0$ then at least one of the numbers must be 0. That is, either $a = 0$, $b = 0$, or $a = b = 0$.

123. a. $(8 \div 2) \cdot 4 = 4 \cdot 4 = 16$

b. $8 \div (2 \cdot 4) = 8 \div 8 = 1$

c. The results are different, so the order of the operations makes a difference.

Homework 2.6

1. $4^3 = 4 \cdot 4 \cdot 4 = 16 \cdot 4 = 64$

3. $2^5 = 2 \cdot 2 \cdot 2 \cdot 2 \cdot 2$
$$= 4 \cdot 2 \cdot 2 \cdot 2$$
$$= 8 \cdot 2 \cdot 2$$
$$= 16 \cdot 2$$
$$= 32$$

5. $-8^2 = -(8 \cdot 8) = -64$

7. $(-8)^2 = (-8)(-8) = 64$

9. $\left(\dfrac{6}{7}\right)^2 = \left(\dfrac{6}{7}\right)\left(\dfrac{6}{7}\right) = \dfrac{36}{49}$

11. $3 \cdot (5-1) = 3 \cdot 4 = 12$

13. $(2-5)(9-3) = (-3)(6) = -18$

15. $4-(3-8)+1 = 4-(-5)+1$
$$= 4+5+1$$
$$= 9+1$$
$$= 10$$

17. $\dfrac{1-10}{1+2} = \dfrac{-9}{3} = -3$

19. $\dfrac{2-(-3)}{5-7} = \dfrac{2+3}{5-7} = \dfrac{5}{-2} = -\dfrac{5}{2}$

21. $\dfrac{2-6}{-1-(-7)} = \dfrac{-4}{-1+7} = \dfrac{-4}{6} = -\dfrac{2}{3}$

23. $6+8 \div 2 = 6+4 = 10$

25. $-5-4 \cdot 3 = -5-12 = -17$

27. $20 \div (-2) \cdot 5 = -10 \cdot 5 = -50$

29. $-9-4+3 = -13+3 = -10$

31. $3(5-1)-4(-2) = 3(4)-4(-2)$
$$= 12-(-8)$$
$$= 12+8$$
$$= 20$$

33. $15 \div 3-(2-7)(2) = 15 \div 3-(-5)(2)$
$$= 5-(-10)$$
$$= 5+10$$
$$= 15$$

35. $\dfrac{7}{8}-\dfrac{3}{4} \cdot \dfrac{1}{2} = \dfrac{7}{8}-\dfrac{3}{8} = \dfrac{7-3}{8} = \dfrac{4}{8} = \dfrac{1}{2}$

37. $2+5^2 = 2+(5 \cdot 5) = 2+25 = 27$

39. $-3(4)^2 = -3(4 \cdot 4) = -3(16) = -48$

41. $\dfrac{2^4}{4^2} = \dfrac{2 \cdot 2 \cdot 2 \cdot 2}{4 \cdot 4} = \dfrac{16}{16} = 1$

43. $4^3-3^4 = (4 \cdot 4 \cdot 4)-(3 \cdot 3 \cdot 3 \cdot 3)$
$$= 64-81$$
$$= -17$$

45. $45 \div 3^2 = 45 \div (3 \cdot 3)$
$$= 45 \div 9$$
$$= 5$$

47. $(-1)^2-(-1)^3 = (-1)(-1)-(-1)(-1)(-1)$
$$= 1-(-1)$$
$$= 1+1$$
$$= 2$$

49. $-5(3)^2 + 4 = -5(3 \cdot 3) + 4$

$\qquad = -5(9) + 4$

$\qquad = -45 + 4$

$\qquad = -41$

51. $-4(-1)^2 - 2(-1) + 5 = -4\left[(-1)(-1)\right] - 2(-1) + 5$

$\qquad = -4(1) - 2(-1) + 5$

$\qquad = -4 - (-2) + 5$

$\qquad = -4 + 2 + 5$

$\qquad = -2 + 5$

$\qquad = 3$

53. $\dfrac{9 - 6^2}{12 + 3^2} = \dfrac{9 - (6 \cdot 6)}{12 + (3 \cdot 3)} = \dfrac{9 - 36}{12 + 9} = \dfrac{-27}{21} = -\dfrac{9}{7}$

55. $8 - (9 - 5)^2 - 1 = 8 - (4)^2 - 1$

$\qquad = 8 - (4 \cdot 4) - 1$

$\qquad = 8 - 16 - 1$

$\qquad = -8 - 1$

$\qquad = -9$

57. $8^2 + 2(4 - 8)^2 \div (-2) = 8^2 + 2(-4)^2 \div (-2)$

$\qquad = (8 \cdot 8) + 2\left[(-4)(-4)\right] \div (-2)$

$\qquad = 64 + 2(16) \div (-2)$

$\qquad = 64 + 32 \div (-2)$

$\qquad = 64 + (-16)$

$\qquad = 48$

59. $13.28 - 35.2(17.9) + 9.43 \div 2.75 \approx -613.37$

```
13.28-35.2(17.9)
+9.43/2.75
        -613.3709091
■
```

61. $5.82 - 3.16^3 \div 4.29 \approx -1.54$

```
5.82-3.16^3/4.29
    -1.535360373
```

63. $\dfrac{(25.36)(-3.42) - 17.89}{33.26 + 45.32} \approx -1.33$

```
((25.36)(-3.42)-
17.89)/(33.26+45
.32)
        -1.331397302
■
```

65. Evaluate $a + bc$ for $a = -2$, $b = -4$, and $c = 3$:

$(-2) + (-4)(3) = (-2) + (-12) = -14$

67. Evaluate $ac - b \div a$ for $a = -2$, $b = -4$, and $c = 3$:

$(-2)(3) - (-4) \div (-2) = (-6) - (2)$

$\qquad = -8$

69. Evaluate $a^2 - c^2$ for $a = -2$ and $c = 3$:

$(-2)^2 - (3)^2 = (-2)(-2) - (3)(3)$

$\qquad = 4 - 9$

$\qquad = -5$

71. Evaluate $b^2 - 4ac$ for $a = -2$, $b = -4$, and $c = 3$:

$(-4)^2 - 4(-2)(3) = (-4)(-4) - 4(-2)(3)$

$\qquad = 16 - (-24)$

$\qquad = 16 + 24$

$\qquad = 40$

73. Evaluate $\dfrac{-b - c^2}{2a}$ for $a = -2$, $b = -4$, and $c = 3$:

$\dfrac{-(-4) - (3)^2}{2(-2)} = \dfrac{-(-4) - (3)(3)}{2(-2)}$

$\qquad = \dfrac{4 - 9}{-4}$

$\qquad = \dfrac{-5}{-4}$

$\qquad = \dfrac{5}{4}$

75. Substitute $a = 3$, $b = -10$, $c = -6$, and $d = 1$ in the expression $\dfrac{a - b}{c - d}$:

$\dfrac{(3) - (-10)}{(-6) - (1)} = \dfrac{3 + 10}{(-6) + (-1)} = \dfrac{13}{-7} = -\dfrac{13}{7}$

77. Substitute $a = -3$, $b = 7$, $c = 1$, and $d = -3$ in the expression $\dfrac{a-b}{c-d}$:

$$\frac{(-3)-(7)}{(1)-(-3)} = \frac{-3+(-7)}{1+3} = \frac{-10}{4} = -\frac{5}{2}$$

79. Substitute $a = -8$, $b = -2$, $c = -15$, and $d = -5$ in the expression $\dfrac{a-b}{c-d}$:

$$\frac{(-8)-(-2)}{(-15)-(-5)} = \frac{-8+2}{-15+5} = \frac{-6}{-10} = \frac{3}{5}$$

81. Evaluate $-3x^2$ for $x = -3$:

$$-3(-3)^2 = -3(-3)(-3) = -27$$

83. Evaluate $-x^2 + x$ for $x = -3$:

$$-(-3)^2 + (-3) = -(-3)(-3) + (-3)$$
$$= -9 + (-3)$$
$$= -12$$

85. Evaluate $2x^2 - 3x + 5$ for $x = -3$:

$$2(-3)^2 - 3(-3) + 5 = 2(-3)(-3) - 3(-3) + 5$$
$$= 18 - (-9) + 5$$
$$= 18 + 9 + 5$$
$$= 27 + 5$$
$$= 32$$

87. a.

Years Since 2008	Congressional pay (thousands of dollars)
0	$4 \cdot 0 + 169.3$
1	$4 \cdot 1 + 169.3$
2	$4 \cdot 2 + 169.3$
3	$4 \cdot 3 + 169.3$
4	$4 \cdot 4 + 169.3$
t	$4t + 169.3$

From the last row of the table, we see that the expression $4t + 169.3$ represents the congressional pay (in thousands of dollars) t years after 2008.

b. Substitute 6 for t in $4t + 169.3$:

$$4(6) + 169.3 = 24 + 169.3 = 193.3$$

So, in 2014 (6 years after 2008) the congressional pay will be about \$193.3 thousand.

89. a.

Years Since 2005	Population (thousands)
0	$-1.8 \cdot 0 + 99.2$
1	$-1.8 \cdot 1 + 99.2$
2	$-1.8 \cdot 2 + 99.2$
3	$-1.8 \cdot 3 + 99.2$
4	$-1.8 \cdot 4 + 99.2$
t	$-1.8t + 99.2$

From the last row of the table, we see that the expression $-1.8t + 99.2$ represents the population of Gary (in thousands) t years after 2005.

b. Substitute 8 for t in $-1.8t + 99.2$:

$$-1.8(8) + 99.2 = -14.4 + 99.2 = 84.8$$

So, the population of Gary will be about 85 thousand in 2013 (8 years after 2005).

91. $5 + (-6)x$

Evaluate the expression for $x = -4$:

$$5 + (-6)(-4) = 5 + 24 = 29$$

93. $\dfrac{x}{-2} - 3$

Evaluate the expression for $x = -4$:

$$\frac{-4}{-2} - 3 = 2 - 3 = -1$$

95. Substitute 2 for s in the expression s^3:

$$(2)^3 = 2 \cdot 2 \cdot 2 = 8$$

So, the volume is 8 cubic feet.

97. In the first line, the student multiplied the 2 and 3 in the first term before doing the exponentiation. The solution should be:

$$2(3)^2 + 2(3) + 1 = 2(9) + 2(3) + 1 = 18 + 6 + 1 = 25$$

99. The student is incorrect. In the expression -4^2, only the 4 is being squared. That is,

$$-4^2 = -(4^2) = -(4 \cdot 4) = -16.$$

101. a. $(11 - 3) \div (1 - 5) = (8) \div (-4) = -2$

b. $11 - 3 \div 1 - 5 = 11 - 3 - 5$
$$= 8 - 5$$
$$= 3$$

c. The student did not group the numerator and denominator together as required. He or she should enter the expression in the manner displayed in part (a).

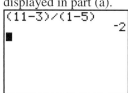

103. a. $((2)(3))(4) = (6)(4) = 24$

b. $(2)((3)(4)) = (2)(12) = 24$

c. The results are the same.

d. $((4)(-2))(5) = (-8)(5) = -40$
$(4)((-2)(5)) = (4)(-10) = -40$
The results are the same.

e. Answers may vary. In each case, the results should be the same.

f. Yes; this is the Associative Property of Multiplication.

g. Answers may vary. For a series of multiplications, the way in which the multiplications are grouped does not matter.

105. a.

x	x^2
-2	$(-2)^2 = (-2)(-2) = 4$
-1	$(-1)^2 = (-1)(-1) = 1$
0	$(0)^2 = (0)(0) = 0$
1	$(1)^2 = (1)(1) = 1$
2	$(2)^2 = (2)(2) = 4$

b. nonnegative (note that 0 is neither positive nor negative)

c. For any real number x, the value of x^2 is always nonnegative.

Chapter 2 Review Exercises

1. $8 + (-2) = 6$

2. $(-5) + (-7) = -12$

3. $6 - 9 = 6 + (-9) = -3$

4. $8 - (-2) = 8 + 2 = 10$

5. Since the numbers have different signs, the product will be negative: $8(-2) = -16$

6. Since the numbers have different signs, the quotient will be negative: $8 \div (-2) = -4$

7. $-24 \div (10 - 2) = -24 \div (8) = -3$

8. $(2 - 6)(5 - 8) = (-4)(-3) = 12$

9. $\dfrac{7 - 2}{2 - 7} = \dfrac{5}{-5} = -\dfrac{5}{5} = -1$

10. $\dfrac{2 - 8}{3 - (-1)} = \dfrac{2 - 8}{3 + 1} = \dfrac{-6}{4} = -\dfrac{6}{4} = -\dfrac{3}{2}$

11. $\dfrac{3 - 5(-6)}{-2 - 1} = \dfrac{3 - (-30)}{-2 - 1}$
$= \dfrac{3 + 30}{-2 + (-1)}$
$= \dfrac{33}{-3}$
$= -\dfrac{33}{3}$
$= -11$

12. $3(-5) + 2 = -15 + 2 = -13$

13. $-4 + 2(-6) = -4 + (-12) = -16$

14. $2 - 12 \div 2 = 2 - 6 = -4$

15. $4(-6) \div (-3) = -24 \div (-3) = 8$

16. $8 \div (-2) \cdot 5 = (-4) \cdot 5 = -20$

17. $2(4 - 7) - (8 - 2) = 2(-3) - (6)$
$= (-6) - (6)$
$= (-6) + (-6)$
$= -12$

18. $-2(3 - 6) + 18 \div (-9) = -2(-3) + 18 \div (-9)$
$= 6 + 18 \div (-9)$
$= 6 + (-2)$
$= 4$

33

19. $-14 \div (-7) - 3(1-5) = -14 \div (-7) - 3(-4)$
$$= 2 - 3(-4)$$
$$= 2 - (-12)$$
$$= 2 + 12$$
$$= 14$$

20. Since the number have the same sign, the product will be positive: $-0.3(-0.2) = 0.06$

21. $4.2 - (-6.7) = 4.2 + 6.7 = 10.9$

22. $\dfrac{4}{9}\left(-\dfrac{3}{10}\right) = -\dfrac{12}{90} = -\dfrac{2}{15}$

23. $\left(-\dfrac{8}{15}\right) \div \left(-\dfrac{16}{25}\right) = \left(-\dfrac{8}{15}\right)\left(-\dfrac{25}{16}\right)$
$$= \dfrac{8}{15} \cdot \dfrac{25}{16}$$
$$= \dfrac{200}{240}$$
$$= \dfrac{5}{6}$$

24. $\dfrac{5}{9} - \left(-\dfrac{2}{9}\right) = \dfrac{5}{9} + \dfrac{2}{9} = \dfrac{5+2}{9} = \dfrac{7}{9}$

25. $-\dfrac{5}{6} + \dfrac{7}{8} = -\dfrac{5}{6} \cdot \dfrac{4}{4} + \dfrac{7}{8} \cdot \dfrac{3}{3}$
$$= \dfrac{-20}{24} + \dfrac{21}{24}$$
$$= \dfrac{-20+21}{24}$$
$$= \dfrac{1}{24}$$

26. $\dfrac{-5}{2} - \dfrac{7}{-3} = \dfrac{-5}{2} + \dfrac{7}{3}$
$$= \dfrac{-5}{2} \cdot \dfrac{3}{3} + \dfrac{7}{3} \cdot \dfrac{2}{2}$$
$$= \dfrac{-15}{6} + \dfrac{14}{6}$$
$$= \dfrac{-15+14}{6}$$
$$= -\dfrac{1}{6}$$

27. $(-8)^2 = (-8)(-8) = 64$

28. $-8^2 = -(8 \cdot 8) = -64$

29. $2^4 = 2 \cdot 2 \cdot 2 \cdot 2 = 16$

30. $\left(\dfrac{3}{4}\right)^3 = \dfrac{3}{4} \cdot \dfrac{3}{4} \cdot \dfrac{3}{4} = \dfrac{9 \cdot 3}{16 \cdot 4} = \dfrac{27}{64}$

31. $-6(3)^2 = -6(3 \cdot 3) = -6(9) = -54$

32. $24 \div 2^3 = 24 \div (2 \cdot 2 \cdot 2)$
$$= 24 \div 8$$
$$= 3$$

33. $(-2)^3 - 4(-2) = (-2)(-2)(-2) - 4(-2)$
$$= -8 - 4(-2)$$
$$= -8 - (-8)$$
$$= -8 + 8$$
$$= 0$$

34. $\dfrac{2^3}{3+3^2} = \dfrac{2 \cdot 2 \cdot 2}{3+(3 \cdot 3)} = \dfrac{8}{3+9} = \dfrac{8}{12} = \dfrac{2}{3}$

35. $\dfrac{17 - (-3)^2}{5 - 4^2} = \dfrac{17 - (-3)(-3)}{5 - (4 \cdot 4)}$
$$= \dfrac{17 - 9}{5 - 16}$$
$$= \dfrac{8}{-11}$$
$$= -\dfrac{8}{11}$$

36. $-3(2)^2 - 4(2) + 1 = -3(2 \cdot 2) - 4(2) + 1$
$$= -3(4) - 4(2) + 1$$
$$= -12 - 8 + 1$$
$$= -20 + 1$$
$$= -19$$

37. $24 \div (3-5)^3 = 24 \div (-2)^3$
$$= 24 \div \left[(-2)(-2)(-2)\right]$$
$$= 24 \div (-8)$$
$$= -3$$

38. $7^2 - 3(2-5)^2 \div (-3)$

$= 7^2 - 3(-3)^2 \div (-3)$

$= (7 \cdot 7) - 3[(-3)(-3)] \div (-3)$

$= 49 - 27 \div (-3)$

$= 49 - (-9)$

$= 49 + 9$

$= 58$

39. $\dfrac{-18}{-24} = \dfrac{18}{24} = \dfrac{2 \cdot 3 \cdot 3}{2 \cdot 2 \cdot 2 \cdot 3} = \dfrac{3}{2 \cdot 2} = \dfrac{3}{4}$

40. $\dfrac{-28}{35} = -\dfrac{28}{35} = -\dfrac{2 \cdot 2 \cdot 7}{5 \cdot 7} = -\dfrac{2 \cdot 2}{5} = -\dfrac{4}{5}$

41. $-5.7 + 2.3^4 \div (-9.4) \approx -8.68$

```
-5.7+2.3^4/(-9.4
)
          -8.677031915
■
```

42. $\dfrac{3.5(17.4) - 97.6}{54.2 \div 8.4 - 65.3} \approx 0.62$

```
(3.5(17.4)-97.6)
/(54.2/8.4-65.3)
          .6236446027
```

43. Substitute $\dfrac{1}{4}$ for W and $\dfrac{5}{6}$ for L in the expression $2L + 2W$:

$2\left(\dfrac{5}{6}\right) + 2\left(\dfrac{1}{4}\right) = \dfrac{2}{1} \cdot \dfrac{5}{6} + \dfrac{2}{1} \cdot \dfrac{1}{4}$

$\qquad = \dfrac{10}{6} + \dfrac{2}{4}$

$\qquad = \dfrac{10}{6} + \dfrac{1}{2}$

$\qquad = \dfrac{10}{6} + \dfrac{1}{2} \cdot \dfrac{3}{3}$

$\qquad = \dfrac{10}{6} + \dfrac{3}{6}$

$\qquad = \dfrac{13}{6}$

So, the perimeter of the rectangle is $\dfrac{13}{6} = 2\dfrac{1}{6}$ yards.

44. $-4789 + 800 - (102.99 + 3.50)$

$= -4789 + 800 - 106.49$

$= -3989 - 106.49$

$= -4095.49$

The student now owes the credit card company $4095.49.

45. $27,800 - 32,500 = -4700$

The plane had a change in altitude of -4700 feet.

46. a. $-8 - 4 = -12$

The change in temperature is $-12°\text{F}$.

b. Divide the change for the past three hours by 3 to estimate the change over 1 hour.

$\dfrac{-12}{3} = -4$

The estimated change of the past hour is $-4°\text{F}$.

c. Answers may vary. Temperature need not change uniformly.

47. a. $50 - 24 = 26$

The change in private contributions to Democratic conventions from 1996 to 2000 was $26 million.

b. $3 - 8 = -5$

The change in the private contributions to Republican conventions from 1984 to 1988 was -5 million dollars.

c. The greatest change in private contributions to Democratic conventions occurred between 1996 and 2000. The change was $26 million [from part (a)].

d. $64 - 22 = 42$

The greatest change in private contributions to Republican conventions occurred between 2000 and 2004. The change was $42 million.

48. $\dfrac{220 \text{ million ringtones}}{145.5 \text{ million ringtones}} \approx \dfrac{1.51}{1}$

The number of ringtones sold in 2007 was about 1.51 times the number sold in 2004.

49. $75\% = 75.0\% = 0.75$

50. $2.9\% = 0.029$

51. $0.87(43) = 37.41$

So, 87% of \$43 is \$37.41.

52. $0.08(925) = 74$

So, 8% of 925 students is 74 students.

53. $-5493 + 0.2(5493) = -5493 + 1098.6$
$$= -4394.4$$
The new balance is -4394.4 dollars.

54. Substitute 2 for a and -4 for c in the expression
$ac + c \div a$:
$$(2)(-4) + (-4) \div (2) = -8 + (-4) \div (2)$$
$$= -8 + (-2)$$
$$= -10$$

55. Substitute 2 for a, -5 for b, and -4 for c in the expression $b^2 - 4ac$:
$$(-5)^2 - 4(2)(-4) = (-5)(-5) - 4(2)(-4)$$
$$= 25 - (-32)$$
$$= 25 + 32$$
$$= 57$$

56. Substitute 2 for a, -5 for b, and -4 for c in the expression $a(b - c)$:
$$(2)((-5) - (-4)) = 2(-5 + 4)$$
$$= 2(-1)$$
$$= -2$$

57. Substitute 2 for a, -5 for b, and -4 for c in the expression $\dfrac{-b - c^2}{2a}$:
$$\frac{-(-5) - (-4)^2}{2(2)} = \frac{-(-5) - (-4)(-4)}{2(2)}$$
$$= \frac{5 - 16}{4}$$
$$= \frac{-11}{4}$$
$$= -\frac{11}{4}$$

58. Substitute -4 for c in the expression
$2c^2 - 5c + 3$:
$$2(-4)^2 - 5(-4) + 3 = 2(-4)(-4) - 5(-4) + 3$$
$$= 32 - (-20) + 3$$
$$= 32 + 20 + 3$$
$$= 52 + 3$$
$$= 55$$

59. Substitute 2 for a, -5 for b, -4 for c, and 10 for d in the expression $\dfrac{a - b}{c - d}$:
$$\frac{(2) - (-5)}{(-4) - (10)} = \frac{2 + 5}{-4 + (-10)} = \frac{7}{-14} = -\frac{7}{14} = -\frac{1}{2}$$

60. $x + 5$

Evaluate the expression for $x = -3$:
$$(-3) + 5 = 2$$

61. $-7 - x$

Evaluate the expression for $x = -3$:
$$-7 - (-3) = -7 + 3 = -4$$

62. $2 - x(4)$

Evaluate the expression for $x = -3$:
$$2 - (-3)(4) = 2 - (-12)$$
$$= 2 + 12$$
$$= 14$$

63. $1 + \dfrac{-24}{x}$

Evaluate the expression for $x = -3$:
$$1 + \frac{-24}{-3} = 1 + 8 = 9$$

64. Substitute 650 for T and 13 for n.
$$\frac{650}{13} = 50$$

Each player must pay \$50 for the team to join the softball league.

65. a.

Time (hours)	Volume of Water (cubic feet)
0	$-50 \cdot 0 + 400$
1	$-50 \cdot 1 + 400$
2	$-50 \cdot 2 + 400$
3	$-50 \cdot 3 + 400$
4	$-50 \cdot 4 + 400$
t	$-50t + 400$

From the last row of the table, we see that the expression $-50t + 400$ represents the volume of water (in cubic feet) remaining in the basement after water has been pumped out for t hours.

b. Substitute 7 for t in $-50t + 400$:
$$-50(7) + 400 = -350 + 400 = 50$$

After 7 hours of pumping, there will be 50 cubic feet of water remaining in the basement.

Chapter 2 Test

1. $-8 - 5 = -8 + (-5) = -13$

2. Since the two numbers have the same sign, the product will be positive: $-7(-9) = 63$

3. $-3 + 9 \div (-3) = -3 + (-3) = -6$

4. $(4-2)(3-7) = (2)(-4) = -8$

5. $\dfrac{4-7}{-1-5} = \dfrac{-3}{-6} = \dfrac{1}{2}$

6. $5 - (2-10) \div (-4) = 5 - (-8) \div (-4)$
$$= 5 - 2$$
$$= 3$$

7. $-20 \div 5 - (2-9)(-3) = -20 \div 5 - (-7)(-3)$
$$= -4 - 21$$
$$= -25$$

8. Since the two numbers have different signs, the product will be negative: $0.4(-0.2) = -0.08$

9. $-\dfrac{27}{10} \div \dfrac{18}{75} = -\dfrac{27}{10} \cdot \dfrac{75}{18}$
$$= -\dfrac{3 \cdot 3 \cdot 3 \cdot 3 \cdot 5 \cdot 5}{2 \cdot 5 \cdot 2 \cdot 3 \cdot 3} = -\dfrac{3 \cdot 3 \cdot 5}{2 \cdot 2} = -\dfrac{45}{4}$$

10. $-\dfrac{3}{10} + \dfrac{5}{8} = -\dfrac{3}{10} \cdot \dfrac{4}{4} + \dfrac{5}{8} \cdot \dfrac{5}{5}$
$$= \dfrac{-12}{40} + \dfrac{25}{40}$$
$$= \dfrac{-12 + 25}{40}$$
$$= \dfrac{13}{40}$$

11. $3^4 = 3 \cdot 3 \cdot 3 \cdot 3 = 81$

12. $-4^2 = -(4 \cdot 4) = -16$

13. $7 + 2^3 - 3^2 = 7 + (2 \cdot 2 \cdot 2) - (3 \cdot 3)$
$$= 7 + 8 - 9$$
$$= 15 - 9$$
$$= 6$$

14. $1 - (3-7)^2 + 10 \div (-5) = 1 - (-4)^2 + 10 \div (-5)$
$$= 1 - (-4)(-4) + 10 \div (-5)$$
$$= 1 - 16 + (-2)$$
$$= -15 + (-2)$$
$$= -17$$

15. $\dfrac{84}{-16} = -\dfrac{84}{16} = -\dfrac{2 \cdot 2 \cdot 3 \cdot 7}{2 \cdot 2 \cdot 2 \cdot 2} = -\dfrac{3 \cdot 7}{2 \cdot 2} = -\dfrac{21}{4}$

16. $5 - 9 = 5 + (-9) = -4$

The current temperature is $-4°\text{F}$.

17. a. $5.8 - 9.0 = -3.2$
The change in the tax audit rate from 1999 to 2001 was -3.2 audits per 1000 tax returns.

b. $9.3 - 6.5 = 2.8$
The change in the tax audit rate from 2003 to 2005 was 2.8 audits per 1000 tax returns.

c. Answers may vary. The table seems to indicate the IRS increases the audit rate during weaker economic times. This may occur because, during weak economic periods, taxpayers may be more inclined to file inaccurate returns.

18. $\dfrac{40 \text{ thousand deliveries}}{25 \text{ thousand deliveries}} = \dfrac{1.6}{1}$

The number of live-birth deliveries in 2006 was 1.6 times as great as the number of deliveries in 2000.

19. Substitute -6 for a, -2 for b, and 5 for c in the expression $ac - \dfrac{a}{b}$:

$$(-6)(5) - \dfrac{(-6)}{(-2)} = -30 - \dfrac{6}{2}$$
$$= -30 - 3$$
$$= -30 + (-3)$$
$$= -33$$

20. Substitute -6 for a, -2 for b, 5 for c, and -1 for d in the expression $\dfrac{a-b}{c-d}$:

$$\dfrac{(-6)-(-2)}{(5)-(-1)} = \dfrac{-6+2}{5+1} = \dfrac{-4}{6} = -\dfrac{4}{6} = -\dfrac{2}{3}$$

21. Substitute -6 for a, -2 for b, and 5 for c in the expression $a + b^3 + c^2$:

$$(-6)+(-2)^3+(5)^2 = (-6)+(-2)(-2)(-2)+(5\cdot5)$$
$$= -6+(-8)+25$$
$$= -14+25$$
$$= 11$$

22. Substitute -6 for a, -2 for b, and 5 for c in the expression $b^2 - 4ac$:

$$(-2)^2 - 4(-6)(5) = (-2)(-2) - 4(-6)(5)$$
$$= 4 - (-120)$$
$$= 4 + 120$$
$$= 124$$

23. $2x - 3x$

Evaluate the expression for $x = -5$:
$$2(-5) - 3(-5) = -10 - (-15)$$
$$= -10 + 15$$
$$= 5$$

24. $\dfrac{-10}{x} - 6$

Evaluate the expression for $x = -5$:
$$\dfrac{-10}{-5} - 6 = 2 - 6 = 2 + (-6) = -4$$

25. a.

Years since 2006	Mail Volume (billions of pieces)
0	$-5.2 \cdot 0 + 213.1$
1	$-5.2 \cdot 1 + 213.1$
2	$-5.2 \cdot 2 + 213.1$
3	$-5.2 \cdot 3 + 213.1$
4	$-5.2 \cdot 4 + 213.1$
t	$-5.2t + 213.1$

From the last row of the table, we see that the expression $-5.2t + 213.1$ represents the volume of mail in the year that is t years after 2006.

b. Substitute 8 for t in $-5.2t + 213.1$:
$$-5.2(8) + 213.1 = -41.6 + 213.1 = 171.5$$
So, in 2014 (8 years after 2006) the volume of mail handled by the U.S. Postal Service will be 171.5 billion pieces.

Cumulative Review of Chapters 1 – 2

1. a. Answers may vary. Some possibilities:

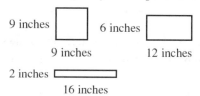

b. W and L are variables because their values are not fixed.

c. P is a constant because the perimeter is fixed at 36 inches.

2.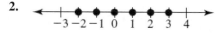

3.

Dollars

4. The x-coordinate is -5.

5. Independent variable: t
Dependent variable: V

6. a.

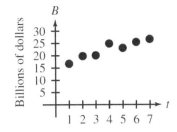

b. The box office was greatest in 2007.

c. The box office was smallest in 2001.

d. The box office increased the most between 2003 and 2004. The change in box office was $24.9 - 20.1 = 4.8$ billion dollars.

e. The box office decreased the most between 2004 and 2005. The change in box office was $23.1 - 24.9 = -1.8$ billion dollars.

7. The input $x = -4$ leads to the output $y = -3$, so $y = -3$ when $x = -4$.

8. The output $y = 1$ originates from the input $x = 4$, so $y = 1$ when $x = 4$.

9. The line and the y-axis intersect at the point $(0, -1)$ so the y-intercept is $(0, -1)$.

10. The line and the x-axis intersect at the point $(2, 0)$, so the x-intercept is $(2, 0)$.

11. a.

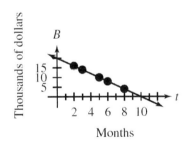

Months

b. The input $t = 4$ leads to the output $B = 12$, so the balance is $12 thousand after 4 months.

c. The output $B = 6$ originates from the input $t = 7$, so the balance will be $6 thousand after 7 months.

d. The line and the B-axis intersect at the point $(0, 20)$, so the B-intercept is $(0, 20)$. The

original balance was $20 thousand when she was laid off.

e. The line and the t-axis intersect at the point $(10, 0)$, so the t-intercept is $(10, 0)$. The checking account will be depleted after 10 months.

12. a-b.

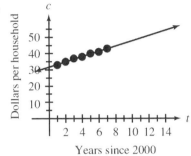

Years since 2000

c. The line and the c-axis intersect near the point $(0, 32)$, so the c-intercept is $(0, 32)$. The average monthly spending on cable TV per household in 2000 was $32.

d. The output $c = 51$ originates roughly from the input $t = 12$, so the average monthly spending will be $51 in 2000 + 12 = 2012.

e. For 2014, the input is $t = 14$. The input $t = 14$ leads roughly to the output $c = 54$, so the average monthly spending will be $54 in 2014.

13. $\dfrac{3(-8)+15}{2-7(2)} = \dfrac{-24+15}{2-14} = \dfrac{-9}{-12} = \dfrac{3}{4}$

14. $-4(3)+6-20 \div (-10) = -12+6-20 \div (-10)$
$= -12+6-(-2)$
$= -12+6+2$
$= -6+2$
$= -4$

15. $\left(-\dfrac{14}{15}\right) \div \left(-\dfrac{35}{27}\right) = \left(-\dfrac{14}{15}\right)\left(-\dfrac{27}{35}\right)$

$= \dfrac{14}{15} \cdot \dfrac{27}{35}$

$= \dfrac{2 \cdot 7 \cdot 3 \cdot 3 \cdot 3}{3 \cdot 5 \cdot 5 \cdot 7}$

$= \dfrac{2 \cdot 3 \cdot 3}{5 \cdot 5}$

$= \dfrac{18}{25}$

16. $\dfrac{3}{8} - \dfrac{5}{6} = \dfrac{3}{8} \cdot \dfrac{3}{3} - \dfrac{5}{6} \cdot \dfrac{4}{4}$

$= \dfrac{9}{24} - \dfrac{20}{24}$

$= \dfrac{9 - 20}{24}$

$= -\dfrac{11}{24}$

17. $4 - (7-9)^4 + 20 \div (-4)$

$= 4 - (-2)^4 + 20 \div (-4)$

$= 4 - (-2)(-2)(-2)(-2) + 20 \div (-4)$

$= 4 - 16 + 20 \div (-4)$

$= 4 - 16 + (-5)$

$= -12 + (-5)$

$= -17$

18. $\dfrac{5 - 3^2}{4^2 + 2} = \dfrac{5 - (3 \cdot 3)}{(4 \cdot 4) + 2} = \dfrac{5 - 9}{16 + 2} = \dfrac{-4}{18} = -\dfrac{4}{18} = -\dfrac{2}{9}$

19. $-3 - 5 = -8$

The change in temperature is $-8°\,\text{F}$.

20. $-2692 + 850 - 23 = -1842 - 23 = -1865$

The student will now owe the credit card company $1865.

21. Substitute 1 for a, -4 for b, -3 for c, and 7 for d in the expression $\dfrac{a-b}{c-d}$:

$\dfrac{(1) - (-4)}{(-3) - (7)} = \dfrac{1 + 4}{-3 + (-7)} = \dfrac{5}{-10} = -\dfrac{5}{10} = -\dfrac{1}{2}$

22. Substitute 2 for a, -3 for b, and -5 for c in the expression $b^2 - 4ac$:

$(-3)^2 - 4(2)(-5) = (-3)(-3) - 4(2)(-5)$

$= 9 - (-40)$

$= 9 + 40$

$= 49$

23. $x - \dfrac{(-12)}{x}$

Evaluate the expression for $x = -4$:

$(-4) - \dfrac{(-12)}{(-4)} = (-4) - 3$

$= (-4) + (-3)$

$= -7$

24. $-2x + 7$

Evaluate the expression for $x = -4$:

$-2(-4) + 7 = 8 + 7 = 15$

25. Evaluate $\dfrac{100(v - 42)}{42}$ for $v = 45$:

$\dfrac{100(45 - 42)}{42} = \dfrac{100(3)}{42} = \dfrac{300}{42} = \dfrac{50}{7} \approx 7.14$

A stock value today of $45 represents about a 7.14% growth of the investment.

26. a.

Years since 2005	Sales (thousands of cameras)
0	$4 \cdot 0 + 15$
1	$4 \cdot 1 + 15$
2	$4 \cdot 2 + 15$
3	$4 \cdot 3 + 15$
4	$4 \cdot 4 + 15$
t	$4t + 15$

From the last row of the table, we see that the expression $4t + 15$ represents the sales (in thousands of cameras) in the year that is t years since 2005.

b. Evaluate $4t + 15$ for $t = 9$:

$4(9) + 15 = 36 + 15 = 51$

In 2014 (9 years after 2005), the camera company will sell 51 thousand cameras.

Chapter 3
Using the Slope to Graph Linear Equations

Homework 3.1

1. Check $(-3, -10)$: $-10 \overset{?}{=} 2(-3) - 4$

$$-10 \overset{?}{=} -6 - 4$$

$$-10 \overset{?}{=} -10 \quad \text{True}$$

So, $(-3, -10)$ is a solution of $y = 2x - 4$.

Check $(1, -3)$: $-3 \overset{?}{=} 2(1) - 4$

$$-3 \overset{?}{=} 2 - 4$$

$$-3 \overset{?}{=} -2 \quad \text{False}$$

So, $(1, -3)$ is not a solution of $y = 2x - 4$.

Check $(2, 0)$: $0 \overset{?}{=} 2(2) - 4$

$$0 \overset{?}{=} 4 - 4$$

$$0 \overset{?}{=} 0 \quad \text{True}$$

So, $(2, 0)$ is a solution of $y = 2x - 4$.

3. Check $(-1, 4)$: $4 \overset{?}{=} -3(-1) + 7$

$$4 \overset{?}{=} 3 + 7$$

$$4 \overset{?}{=} 10 \quad \text{False}$$

So, $(-1, 4)$ is not a solution of $y = -3x + 7$.

Check $(0, 7)$: $7 \overset{?}{=} -3(0) + 7$

$$7 \overset{?}{=} 0 + 7$$

$$7 \overset{?}{=} 7 \quad \text{True}$$

So, $(0, 7)$ is a solution of $y = -3x + 7$.

Check $(4, -5)$: $-5 \overset{?}{=} -3(4) + 7$

$$-5 \overset{?}{=} -12 + 7$$

$$-5 \overset{?}{=} -5 \quad \text{True}$$

So, $(4, -5)$ is a solution of $y = -3x + 7$.

5. $y = x + 2$

To find the y-intercept, let $x = 0$ and solve for y. From the table that follows, we see that the y-intercept is $(0, 2)$. We also find two other solutions to the equation.

x	y
0	$(0) + 2 = 2$
1	$(1) + 2 = 3$
2	$(2) + 2 = 4$

We plot points $(0, 2)$, $(1, 3)$, and $(2, 4)$ and sketch the line through them.

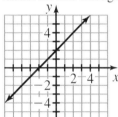

7. $y = x - 4$

To find the y-intercept, let $x = 0$ and solve for y. From the table that follows, we see that the y-intercept is $(0, -4)$. We also find two other solutions to the equation.

x	y
0	$(0) - 4 = -4$
1	$(1) - 4 = -3$
2	$(2) - 4 = -2$

We plot points $(0, -4)$, $(1, -3)$, and $(2, -2)$ and sketch the line through them.

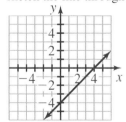

9. $y = 2x$

To find the y-intercept, let $x = 0$ and solve for y. From the table that follows, we see that the y-intercept is $(0, 0)$. We also find two other solutions to the equation.

x	y
0	$2(0) = 0$
1	$2(1) = 2$
2	$2(2) = 4$

We plot points $(0, 0)$, $(1, 2)$, and $(2, 4)$ and sketch the line through them.

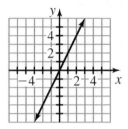

11. $y = -3x$

To find the y-intercept, let $x = 0$ and solve for y. From the table that follows, we see that the y-intercept is $(0, 0)$. We also find two other solutions to the equation.

x	y
-1	$-3(-1) = 3$
0	$-3(0) = 0$
1	$-3(1) = -3$

We plot points $(-1, 3)$, $(0, 0)$, and $(1, -3)$ and sketch the line through them.

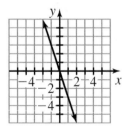

13. $y = x$

To find the y-intercept, let $x = 0$ and solve for y. From the table that follows, we see that the y-intercept is $(0, 0)$. We also find two other solutions to the equation.

x	y
0	0
1	1
2	2

We plot points $(0, 0)$, $(1, 1)$, and $(2, 2)$ and sketch the line through them.

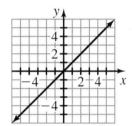

15. $y = \dfrac{1}{3}x$

To find the y-intercept, let $x = 0$ and solve for y. From the table that follows, we see that the y-intercept is $(0, 0)$. We also find two other solutions to the equation.

x	y
-3	$\dfrac{1}{3}(-3) = -1$
0	$\dfrac{1}{3}(0) = 0$
3	$\dfrac{1}{3}(3) = 1$

We plot points $(-3, -1)$, $(0, 0)$, and $(3, 1)$ and sketch the line through them.

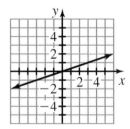

17. $y = -\dfrac{5}{3}x$

To find the y-intercept, let $x = 0$ and solve for y. From the table that follows, we see that the y-intercept is $(0, 0)$. We also find two other solutions to the equation.

x	y
-3	$-\dfrac{5}{3}(-3) = 5$
0	$-\dfrac{5}{3}(0) = 0$
3	$-\dfrac{5}{3}(3) = -5$

We plot points $(-3, 5)$, $(0, 0)$, and $(3, -5)$ and sketch the line through them.

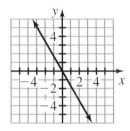

19. $y = 2x + 1$

To find the y-intercept, let $x = 0$ and solve for y. From the table that follows, we see that the y-intercept is $(0, 1)$. We also find two other solutions to the equation.

x	y
0	$2(0) + 1 = 1$
1	$2(1) + 1 = 3$
2	$2(2) + 1 = 5$

We plot points $(0, 1)$, $(1, 3)$, and $(2, 5)$ and sketch the line through them.

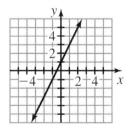

21. $y = 5x - 3$

To find the y-intercept, let $x = 0$ and solve for y. From the table that follows, we see that the y-intercept is $(0, -3)$. We also find two other solutions to the equation.

x	y
0	$5(0) - 3 = -3$
1	$5(1) - 3 = 2$
2	$5(2) - 3 = 7$

We plot points $(0, -3)$, $(1, 2)$, and $(2, 7)$ and sketch the line through them.

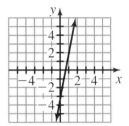

23. $y = -3x + 5$

To find the y-intercept, let $x = 0$ and solve for y. From the table that follows, we see that the y-intercept is $(0, 5)$. We also find two other solutions to the equation.

x	y
0	$-3(0) + 5 = 5$
1	$-3(1) + 5 = 2$
2	$-3(2) + 5 = -1$

We plot points $(0, 5)$, $(1, 2)$, and $(2, -1)$ and sketch the line through them.

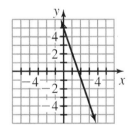

25. $y = -2x - 3$

To find the y-intercept, let $x = 0$ and solve for y. From the table that follows, we see that the y-intercept is $(0, -3)$. We also find two other solutions to the equation.

x	y
-1	$-2(-1) - 3 = -1$
0	$-2(0) - 3 = -3$
1	$-2(1) - 3 = -5$

We plot points $(-1, -1), (0, -3),$ and $(1, -5)$ and sketch the line through them.

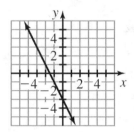

27. $y = \dfrac{1}{2}x - 3$

To find the y-intercept, let $x = 0$ and solve for y. From the table that follows, we see that the y-intercept is $(0, -3)$. We also find two other solutions to the equation.

x	y
0	$\dfrac{1}{2}(0) - 3 = -3$
2	$\dfrac{1}{2}(2) - 3 = -2$
4	$\dfrac{1}{2}(4) - 3 = -1$

We plot points $(0, -3), (2, -2),$ and $(4, -1)$ and sketch the line through them.

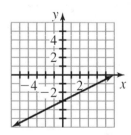

29. $y = -\dfrac{2}{3}x + 1$

To find the y-intercept, let $x = 0$ and solve for y. From the table that follows, we see that the y-intercept is $(0, 1)$. We also find two other

solutions to the equation.

x	y
-3	$-\dfrac{2}{3}(-3) + 1 = 3$
0	$-\dfrac{2}{3}(0) + 1 = 1$
3	$-\dfrac{2}{3}(3) + 1 = -1$

We plot points $(-3, 3), (0, 1),$ and $(3, -1)$ and sketch the line through them.

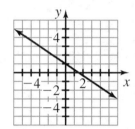

31. a. Answers may vary. One possibility follows:

x	y
0	$2(0) - 3 = -3$
1	$2(1) - 3 = -1$
2	$2(2) - 3 = 1$

b. We plot points $(0, -3), (1, -1),$ and $(2, 1)$ from the table in part (a) and sketch the line through them.

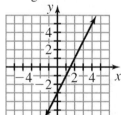

c. For each solution, the y-coordinate is 3 less than twice the x-coordinate.

33. a. $y = 3x + 1$

i. For the input $x = 2$, the output is $y = 3(2) + 1 = 7$. There is one output.

ii. For the input $x = 4$, the output is $y = 3(4) + 1 = 13$. There is one output.

iii. For the input $x = -2$, the output is $y = 3(-2) + 1 = -5$. There is one output.

b. For $y = 3x + 1$, only one output will originate from any single input. Explanations may vary. One possibility follows: This is true because the equation is a nonvertical line.

c. Answers will vary. In each case, there is one output.

d. One output will originate from any single input. Explanations may vary. One possibility follows: This is true because the equation is a nonvertical line.

e. For any equation of the form $y = mx + b$, one output will originate from any single input. Explanations may vary. One possibility follows: This is true because the equation will always be a nonvertical line.

35. a. i. $y = 3x$

We find three solutions to the equation.

x	y
-1	$3(-1) = -3$
0	$3(0) = 0$
1	$3(1) = 3$

We plot points $(-1, -3)$, $(0, 0)$, and $(1, 3)$ and sketch the line through them.

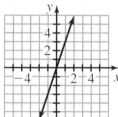

From the graph, we see that the x-intercept is $(0, 0)$ and the y-intercept is also $(0, 0)$.

ii. $y = -2x$

We find three solutions to the equation.

x	y
-1	$-2(-1) = 2$
0	$-2(0) = 0$
1	$-2(1) = -2$

We plot points $(-1, 2)$, $(0, 0)$, and $(1, -2)$ and sketch the line through them.

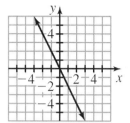

From the graph, we see that the x-intercept is $(0, 0)$ and the y-intercept is also $(0, 0)$.

iii. $y = \dfrac{2}{5}x$

We find three solutions to the equation.

x	y
-5	$\dfrac{2}{5}(-5) = -2$
0	$\dfrac{2}{5}(0) = 0$
5	$\dfrac{2}{5}(5) = 2$

We plot points $(-5, -2)$, $(0, 0)$, and $(5, 2)$ and sketch the line through them.

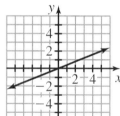

From the graph, we see that the x-intercept is $(0, 0)$ and the y-intercept is also $(0, 0)$.

b. For an equation of the form $y = mx$, $m \neq 0$, the x-intercept will be $(0, 0)$ and the y-intercept will also be $(0, 0)$.

37. Answers may vary. One possibility follows:

x	y
-4	0
-2	1
0	2
2	3
4	4

39. The line contains the point $(-4, 3)$, so $y = 3$ when $x = -4$.

41. The line contains the point $(2, 0)$, so $y = 0$ when $x = 2$.

43. The line contains the point $(4, -1)$, so $x = 4$ when $y = -1$.

45. The line contains the point $(-2, 2)$, so $x = -2$ when $y = 2$.

47. The line contains points C, D, and E, so they represent ordered pairs that satisfy the equation.

49. Answers may vary. One possibility follows: Let $x = -1$, then $y = (-1) + 2 = 1$. The point $(-1, 1)$ is a solution of $y = x + 2$ that lies in Quadrant II. There are infinitely many solutions to this equation that lie in Quadrant II.

51. Notice that in each case, we add 3 to the value of the x-coordinate and obtain the value of the y-coordinate. That is, $3 = 0 + 3$, $4 = 1 + 3$, $5 = 2 + 3$, $6 = 3 + 3$, and $7 = 4 + 3$. The equation of the line that contains the points listed is $y = x + 3$.

53. Notice that for each ordered pair, the x-coordinate and y-coordinate have the same value. The equation of the line that contains the points listed is $y = x$.

55. a. Answers may vary. One possibility follows:

x	y
-2	-6
-1	-3
0	0
1	3
2	6

b. Notice that in each case the value of the y-coordinate is three times the value of the x-coordinate. The equation of the line is $y = 3x$.

57. $x + y = 5$

Notice that the points $(0, 5)$, $(1, 4)$, and $(2, 3)$ are all solutions to this equation since each pair adds to 5 (that is, $0 + 5 = 5$, $1 + 4 = 5$, and $2 + 3 = 5$). We plot points and sketch the line through them.

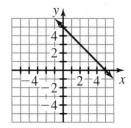

59. a. i.

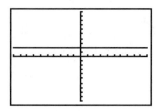

ii.

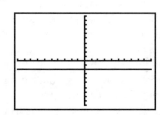

iii.

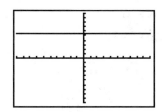

b. An equation of the form $y = b$ is a horizontal line passing through $(0, b)$.

61. Since $(7, 5)$ is a point on the graph of the equation $y = 2x + b$, $(7, 5)$ satisfies the equation. Substitute $x = 7$ and $y = 5$ into $y = 2x + b$ and solve for b.

$y = 2x + b$
$5 = 2(7) + b$
$5 = 14 + b$
$-9 = b$

Therefore, $b = -9$ in $y = 2x + b$.

63.

The ordered pair $(1, 3)$ satisfies both equations, since this point lies on the intersection of the lines.

65. Answers may vary. One possibility follows: Determine three solutions to the equation. That is, find three ordered pairs that satisfy the equation. Plot the three points and sketch a line through them.

Homework 3.2

1. a.

Drink Cost (dollars) d	Total Cost (dollars) T
2	$2 + 3$
3	$3 + 3$
4	$4 + 3$
5	$5 + 3$
d	$d + 3$

So, the equation is $T = d + 3$.

b.
$$\underset{\text{dollars}}{T} = \underset{\text{dollars}}{d} + \underset{\text{dollars}}{3}$$
So, the units on both sides of the equation are dollars, suggesting the equation is correct.

c. In the following table, we substitute values for d in the equation $T = d + 3$ to find the corresponding values for T. Then, we plot the points and sketch a line that contains the points.

d	T
2	$(2) + 3 = 5$
3	$(3) + 3 = 6$
4	$(4) + 3 = 7$
5	$(5) + 3 = 8$

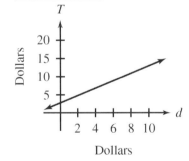

d. To find the T-intercept, let $d = 0$ and solve for T: $T = (0) + 3 = 3$. The T-intercept is $(0, 3)$. This means that, if a person does not buy any drinks, then the total cost is $3.

e. The line contains the point $(10, 13)$, so $T = 13$ when $d = 10$ as illustrated.

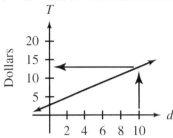

Thus, the total cost will be $13 if $10 is spent on drinks.

3. a.

Number of Credits c	Total Cost (in dollars) T
3	$67.5 \cdot 3$
6	$67.5 \cdot 6$
9	$67.5 \cdot 9$
12	$67.5 \cdot 12$
c	$67.5 \cdot c$

b.
$$\underset{\text{dollars}}{T} = \underset{\substack{\text{dollars} \\ \text{credit}}}{67.5} \cdot \underset{\text{credits}}{c}$$

We use the fact that $\dfrac{\text{credits}}{\text{credits}} = 1$ to simplify the right-hand side of the equation:
$$\dfrac{\text{dollars}}{\text{credit}} \cdot \text{credit} = \text{dollars}.$$
So, the units on both sides of the equation are dollars, suggesting the equation is correct.

c. In the following table, we substitute values for c in the equation $T = 67.5c$ to find the corresponding values for T. Then, we plot the points and sketch a line that contains the points.

c	T
3	$67.5 \cdot 3 = 202.5$
6	$67.5 \cdot 6 = 405$
9	$67.5 \cdot 9 = 607.5$
12	$67.5 \cdot 12 = 810$

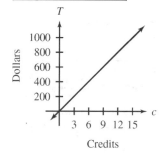

d. The line contains the point (15, 1012.5), so $T = 1012.5$ when $c = 15$ as illustrated.

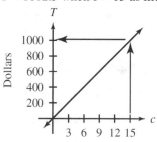

Thus, the total cost of tuition for 15 credits is $1012.50.

5. a.

Time at Company (years)	Salary (thousands of dollars)
t	s
0	$3 \cdot 0 + 24$
1	$3 \cdot 1 + 24$
2	$3 \cdot 2 + 24$
3	$3 \cdot 3 + 24$
4	$3 \cdot 4 + 24$
t	$3 \cdot t + 24$

So, the equation is $s = 3t + 24$.

b.
$$\underset{\text{thous. dollars}}{s} = \underset{\underset{\text{year}}{\text{thous. dollars}}}{3} \cdot \underset{\text{years}}{t} + \underset{\text{thous. dollars}}{24}$$

We use the fact that $\dfrac{\text{years}}{\text{years}} = 1$ to simplify the right-hand side of the equation:

$$\dfrac{\text{thousand dollars}}{\text{year}} \cdot \text{years} + \text{thousand dollars}.$$

$= \text{thousand dollars} + \text{thousand dollars}$

So, the units on both sides of the equation are thousands of dollars, suggesting the equation is correct.

c. In the following table, we substitute values for t in the equation $s = 3t + 24$ to find the corresponding values for s. Then, we plot the points and sketch a line that contains the points.

t	s
0	$3 \cdot 0 + 24 = 24$
1	$3 \cdot 1 + 24 = 27$
2	$3 \cdot 2 + 24 = 30$
3	$3 \cdot 3 + 24 = 33$
4	$3 \cdot 4 + 24 = 36$

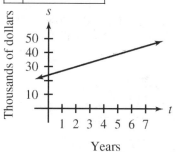

d. From the table and graph, we see the s-intercept is (0, 24). This indicates that the starting salary is $24 thousand.

e. The line contains the point (6, 42), so $s = 42$ when $t = 6$ as illustrated.

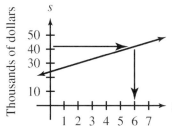

Years

Thus, the person's salary will be $42 thousand after 6 years.

7. a.

Years since 2006	Number of servicemembers
t	n
0	$600 - 70 \cdot 0$
1	$600 - 70 \cdot 1$
2	$600 - 70 \cdot 2$
3	$600 - 70 \cdot 3$
4	$600 - 70 \cdot 4$
t	$600 - 70 \cdot t$

So, the equation is $n = 600 - 70t$.

b.

$$\underset{\substack{\text{service} \\ \text{members}}}{n} = \underset{\substack{\text{service} \\ \text{members}}}{600} - \underset{\substack{\text{service members} \\ \text{year}}}{70} \cdot \underset{\text{years}}{t}$$

We use the fact that $\dfrac{\text{years}}{\text{years}} = 1$ to simplify the right-hand side of the equation:

$$\text{service members} - \frac{\text{service members}}{\text{years}} \cdot \text{years}$$

$= \text{service members} - \text{service members}$

So, the units on both sides of the equation are service members, suggesting the equation is correct.

c. In the following table, we substitute values for t in the equation $n = 600 - 70t$ to find the corresponding values for n. Then, we plot the points and sketch a line that contains the points.

t	n
0	$600 - 70 \cdot 0 = 600$
1	$600 - 70 \cdot 1 = 530$
2	$600 - 70 \cdot 2 = 460$
3	$600 - 70 \cdot 3 = 390$
4	$600 - 70 \cdot 4 = 320$

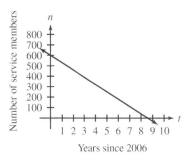

Years since 2006

d. The line contains the point (5, 250), so $n = 250$ when $t = 5$ as illustrated.

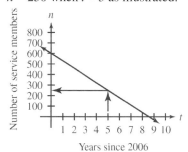

Years since 2006

Thus, in $2006 + 5 = 2011$, 250 service members will leave the military under the policy, according to the model.

e. The t-intercept is 8.6, which is how many years since 2006 that the number of service members leaving equals 0. So, this means that there will be no servicemembers leaving under the policy in $2006 + 9 = 2015$.

9. a. The actual baking time a is 5 minutes less than the suggested baking time r. So, the equation is $a = r - 5$.

b.

$$\underset{\text{minutes}}{a} = \underset{\text{minutes}}{r} - \underset{\text{minutes}}{5}$$

So, the units on both sides of the equation are minutes, suggesting the equation is correct.

c. In the following table, we substitute values for *r* in the equation $a = r - 5$ to find the corresponding values for *a*. Then, we plot the points and sketch a line that contains the points.

t	*v*
10	$10 - 5 = 5$
20	$20 - 5 = 15$
30	$30 - 5 = 25$

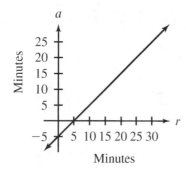

Minutes

d. The line contains the point (28, 23), so *r* = 28 when *a* = 23 as illustrated.

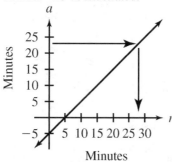

Minutes

So, if the actual baking time is 23 minutes, then the suggested baking time is 28 minutes.

11. a. The distance traveled *d* is 60 times the number of hours *t*. Thus, the equation is $d = 60t$.

b.
$$\underset{\text{miles}}{d} = \underset{\frac{\text{miles}}{\text{hour}}}{60} \cdot \underset{\text{hours}}{t}$$

We use the fact that $\dfrac{\text{hours}}{\text{hours}} = 1$ to simplify the right-hand side of the equation:

$$\frac{\text{miles}}{\text{hour}} \cdot \text{hours} = \text{miles} .$$

So, the units on both sides of the equation are miles, suggesting the equation is correct.

c. In the following table, we substitute values for *t* in the equation $d = 60t$ to find the corresponding values for *a*. Then, we plot the points and sketch a line that contains the points.

t	*d*
0	$60 \cdot 0 = 0$
1	$60 \cdot 1 = 60$
2	$60 \cdot 2 = 120$

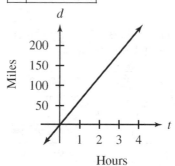

Hours

d. From the table and graph, we see the *s*-intercept is (0, 0). This indicates that the person will not travel any distance in 0 hours.

e. The line contains the point (2.5, 150), so *t* = 2.5 when *d* = 150 as illustrated.

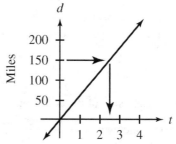

Hours

So, it will take the person 2.5 hours to travel 150 miles.

13. a. The student will pay 20*u* for tuition, plus $31 in fees ($30 for parking and $1 for student representation). Thus, the total one-semester cost *T* for *u* units of classes will be $T = 20u + 31$.

b.
$$\underset{\text{dollars}}{T} = \underset{\substack{\text{dollars} \\ \text{unit}}}{20} \cdot \underset{\text{units}}{u} + \underset{\text{dollars}}{31}$$

We use the fact that $\dfrac{\text{units}}{\text{units}} = 1$ to simplify the right-hand side of the equation:

$$\dfrac{\text{dollars}}{\text{unit}} \cdot \text{units} + \text{dollars} = \text{dollars} + \text{dollars}\,.$$

So, the units on both sides of the equation are dollars, suggesting the equation is correct.

c. If $u = 15$, then $T = 20(15) + 31 = 331$. Fifteen units of classes will cost a total of \$331.

15. a. If the person drives for t hours, then he or she will use $2t$ gallons of gasoline. Since the tank begins with 11 gallons of gas, the amount of gasoline g left in the tank is $g = 11 - 2t$.

b.
$$\underset{\text{gallons}}{g} = \underset{\text{gallons}}{11} - \underset{\substack{\text{gallons} \\ \text{hour}}}{2} \cdot \underset{\text{hours}}{t}$$

We use the fact that $\dfrac{\text{hours}}{\text{hours}} = 1$ to simplify the right-hand side of the equation:

$$\text{gallons} - \dfrac{\text{gallons}}{\text{hour}} \cdot \text{hours} = \text{gallons} - \text{gallons}\,.$$

So, the units on both sides of the equation are gallons, suggesting the equation is correct.

c. In the following table, we substitute values for t in the equation $g = 11 - 2t$ to find the corresponding values for g. Then, we plot the points and sketch a line that contains the points.

t	d
0	$11 - 2 \cdot 0 = 11$
2	$11 - 2 \cdot 2 = 7$
4	$11 - 4 \cdot 2 = 3$

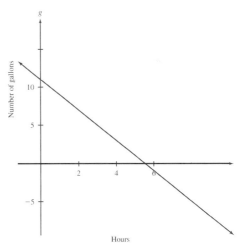

d. The line contains the point $(5, 1)$, so $t = 5$ when $g = 1$ as shown in the illustration that follows. So, the person can drive for 5 hours before refueling when 1 gallon of gasoline is left in the tank.

e. The line contains the point $(8, -5)$, so $g = -5$ when $t = 8$ as shown in the illustration that follows. This implies that -5 gallons of gasoline would be in the tank, which does not make sense. Model breakdown has occurred.

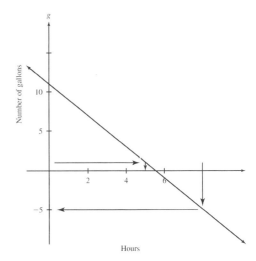

17. a. Answers may vary. One possible table follows:

Years since 2007	Daily Domestic Flights
t	n
0	$220 - 47 \cdot 0 = 220$
1	$220 - 47 \cdot 1 = 173$
2	$220 - 47 \cdot 2 = 126$
3	$220 - 47 \cdot 3 = 79$
4	$220 - 47 \cdot 4 = 32$

b. The equation is $n = 220 - 47t$.

c. We plot the points found in part (a) and sketch a line that contains the points.

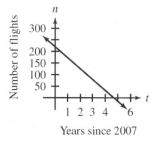

19. Since 2000, the person owned a constant 45 CDs. So, the equation of the model is $n = 45$. To graph the equation, we list some corresponding values of t and n in the following table. Then we plot the points and sketch a line that contains the points.

Years Since 2000	Number of CDs owned
t	n
0	45
1	45
2	45
3	45
4	45

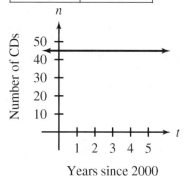

21. The graph of $x = 3$ is a vertical line. Note that x must be 3, but y can have any value. Some solutions of the equation are listed in the table that follows. We plot the corresponding points and sketch the line through them.

x	y
3	-1
3	0
3	1

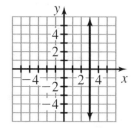

23. The graph of $y = 1$ is a horizontal line. Note that y must be 1, but x can have any value. Some solutions of the equation are listed in the table that follows. We plot the corresponding points and sketch the line through them.

x	y
-1	1
0	1
1	1

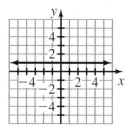

25. The graph of $y = -2$ is a horizontal line. Note that y must be -2, but x can have any value. Some solutions of the equation are listed in the table that follows. We plot the corresponding points and sketch the line through them.

x	y
-1	-2
0	-2
1	-2

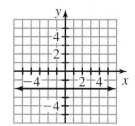

27. The graph of $x = -1$ is a vertical line. Note that x must be -1, but y can have any value. Some solutions of the equation are listed in the table that follows. We plot the corresponding points and sketch the line through them.

x	y
-1	-1
-1	0
-1	1

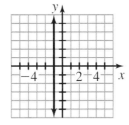

29. The graph of $x = 0$ is a vertical line. Note that x must be 0, but y can have any value. Some solutions of the equation are listed in the table that follows. We plot the corresponding points and sketch the line through them. Note the graph coincides with the y-axis.

x	y
0	-1
0	0
0	1

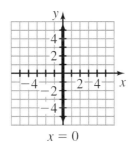

$$x = 0$$

31. To graph $y = x - 2$, we find three solutions to the equation using the table that follows. We then plot the corresponding points and sketch the line through them.

x	y
-1	$(-1) - 2 = -3$
0	$(0) - 2 = -2$
1	$(1) - 2 = -1$

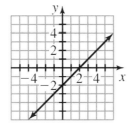

33. The graph of $y = 2$ is a horizontal line. Note that y must be 2, but x can have any value. Some solutions of the equation are listed in the table that follows. We plot the corresponding points and sketch the line through them.

x	y
-1	2
0	2
1	2

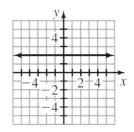

35. To graph $y = -3x + 1$, we find three solutions to the equation using the table that follows. We then plot the corresponding points and sketch the line through them.

x	y
-1	$-3(-1) + 1 = 4$
0	$-3(0) + 1 = 1$
1	$-3(1) + 1 = -2$

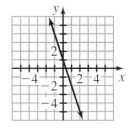

37. To graph $y = \dfrac{3}{5}x$, we find three solutions to the equation using the table that follows. We plot the corresponding points and sketch the line through them.

x	y
-5	$\dfrac{3}{5}(-5) = -3$
0	$\dfrac{3}{5}(0) = 0$
5	$\dfrac{3}{5}(5) = 3$

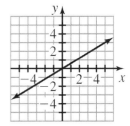

39. To graph $y = -\dfrac{5}{3}x + 1$, we find three solutions to the equation using the table that follows. We plot the corresponding points and sketch the line through them.

x	y
-3	$-\dfrac{5}{3}(-3) + 1 = 6$
0	$-\dfrac{5}{3}(0) + 1 = 1$
3	$-\dfrac{5}{3}(3) + 1 = -4$

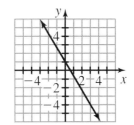

41. To graph $y = 4x - 3$, we find three solutions to the equation using the table that follows. We then plot the corresponding points and sketch the line through them.

x	y
0	$4(0) - 3 = -3$
1	$4(1) - 3 = 1$
2	$4(2) - 3 = 5$

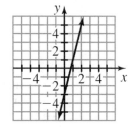

43. The graph of $x = -4$ is a vertical line. Note that x must be -4, but y can have any value. Some solutions of the equation are listed in the table that follows. We plot the corresponding points and sketch the line through them.

x	y
-4	-1
-4	0
-4	1

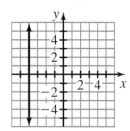

45. The graph is of a vertical line. Each point on the line has an x-coordinate -3, so the equation of the line is $x = -3$.

47. a. i. The change in the x-coordinate is $5 - 1 = 4$.

ii. The change in the y-coordinate is $2 - 2 = 0$.

b. i. The change in the x-coordinate is $1 - 5 = -4$.

ii. The change in the y-coordinate is $2 - 2 = 0$.

49. a. i. The change in the x-coordinate is $2 - (-3) = 2 + 3 = 5$.

ii. The change in the y-coordinate is $4 - 1 = 3$.

b. i. The change in the x-coordinate is $-3 - 2 = -5$.

ii. The change in the y-coordinate is $1 - 4 = -3$.

51. a. We let $Y_1 = x$, $Y_2 = 2x$, and $Y_3 = 3x$, and graph using a standard viewing window.

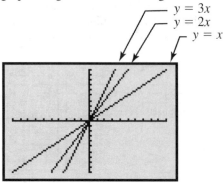

b. The order of steepness, from least to greatest steepness is: $y = x$, $y = 2x$, $y = 3x$.

c. Answers may vary. One possibility follows: For equations of the form $y = mx$, the steepness of the line increases as m increases.

d. Answers may vary. One possibility follows: The line $y = 4x$ will be steeper than $y = x$, $y = 2x$, and $y = 3x$.

53. Answers will vary.

Homework 3.3

1. Slope of road $A = \dfrac{210 \text{ feet}}{3500 \text{ feet}} = 0.06$

Slope of road $B = \dfrac{275 \text{ feet}}{5000 \text{ feet}} = 0.055$

Thus, road A is steeper since it has a larger slope.

3. Slope of ski run $A = \dfrac{80 \text{ yards}}{400 \text{ yards}} = 0.2$

Slope of ski run $B = \dfrac{90 \text{ yards}}{600 \text{ yards}} = 0.15$

Thus, ski run A is steeper since it has a larger slope.

5.

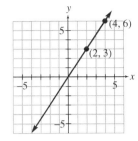

The run is $4-2=2$. The rise is $6-3=3$.

The slope is $m = \dfrac{\text{rise}}{\text{run}} = \dfrac{3}{2}$.

7.

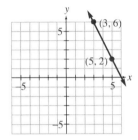

The run is $5-3=2$. The rise is $2-6=-4$.

The slope is $m = \dfrac{\text{rise}}{\text{run}} = \dfrac{-4}{2} = -2$.

9.

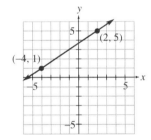

The run is $2-(-4)=2+4=6$. The rise is

$5-1=4$. The slope is $m = \dfrac{\text{rise}}{\text{run}} = \dfrac{4}{6} = \dfrac{2}{3}$.

11.

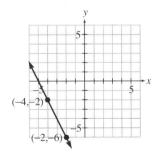

The run is $-2-(-4)=-2+4=2$.

The rise is $-6-(-2)=-6+2=-4$.

The slope is $m = \dfrac{\text{rise}}{\text{run}} = \dfrac{-4}{2} = -2$.

13. Using the slope formula with $(x_1, y_1) = (1, 5)$

and $(x_2, y_2) = (3, 9)$, the slope is

$$m = \frac{y_2 - y_1}{x_2 - x_1} = \frac{9-5}{3-1} = \frac{4}{2} = 2.$$

The slope is positive, so the line is increasing.

15. Using the slope formula with $(x_1, y_1) = (3, 10)$

and $(x_2, y_2) = (5, 2)$, the slope is

$$m = \frac{y_2 - y_1}{x_2 - x_1} = \frac{2-10}{5-3} = \frac{-8}{2} = -4.$$

The slope is negative, so the line is decreasing.

17. Using the slope formula with $(x_1, y_1) = (2, 1)$

and $(x_2, y_2) = (8, 4)$, the slope is

$$m = \frac{y_2 - y_1}{x_2 - x_1} = \frac{4-1}{8-2} = \frac{3}{6} = \frac{1}{2}.$$

The slope is positive, so the line is increasing.

19. Using the slope formula with $(x_1, y_1) = (2, 5)$

and $(x_2, y_2) = (8, 3)$, the slope is

$$m = \frac{y_2 - y_1}{x_2 - x_1} = \frac{3-5}{8-2} = \frac{-2}{6} = -\frac{1}{3}.$$

The slope is negative, so the line is decreasing.

21. Using the slope formula with $(x_1, y_1) = (-2, 4)$

and $(x_2, y_2) = (3, -1)$, the slope is

$$m = \frac{y_2 - y_1}{x_2 - x_1} = \frac{-1-4}{3-(-2)} = \frac{-1-4}{3+2} = \frac{-5}{5} = -1.$$

The slope is negative, so the line is decreasing.

23. Using the slope formula with $(x_1, y_1) = (5, -2)$

and $(x_2, y_2) = (9, -4)$, the slope is

$$m = \frac{y_2 - y_1}{x_2 - x_1} = \frac{-4-(-2)}{9-5} = \frac{-4+2}{9-5} = \frac{-2}{4} = -\frac{1}{2}.$$

The slope is negative, so the line is decreasing.

25. Using the slope formula with $(x_1, y_1) = (-7, -1)$ and $(x_2, y_2) = (-2, 9)$, the slope is

$$m = \frac{y_2 - y_1}{x_2 - x_1} = \frac{9 - (-1)}{-2 - (-7)} = \frac{9 + 1}{-2 + 7} = \frac{10}{5} = 2.$$

The slope is positive, so the line is increasing.

27. Using the slope formula with $(x_1, y_1) = (-6, -9)$ and $(x_2, y_2) = (-2, -3)$, the slope is

$$m = \frac{y_2 - y_1}{x_2 - x_1} = \frac{-3 - (-9)}{-2 - (-6)} = \frac{-3 + 9}{-2 + 6} = \frac{6}{4} = \frac{3}{2}.$$

The slope is positive, so the line is increasing.

29. Using the slope formula with $(x_1, y_1) = (6, -1)$ and $(x_2, y_2) = (-4, 7)$, the slope is

$$m = \frac{y_2 - y_1}{x_2 - x_1} = \frac{7 - (-1)}{-4 - 6} = \frac{7 + 1}{-4 - 6} = \frac{8}{-10} = -\frac{4}{5}.$$

The slope is negative, so the line is decreasing.

31. Using the slope formula with $(x_1, y_1) = (-2, -11)$ and $(x_2, y_2) = (7, -5)$, the slope is

$$m = \frac{y_2 - y_1}{x_2 - x_1} = \frac{-5 - (-11)}{7 - (-2)} = \frac{-5 + 11}{7 + 2} = \frac{6}{9} = \frac{2}{3}.$$

The slope is positive, so the line is increasing.

33. Using the slope formula with $(x_1, y_1) = (0, 0)$ and $(x_2, y_2) = (4, -2)$, the slope is

$$m = \frac{y_2 - y_1}{x_2 - x_1} = \frac{-2 - 0}{4 - 0} = \frac{-2}{4} = -\frac{1}{2}.$$

The slope is negative, so the line is decreasing.

35. Using the slope formula with $(x_1, y_1) = (3, 5)$ and $(x_2, y_2) = (7, 5)$, the slope is

$$m = \frac{y_2 - y_1}{x_2 - x_1} = \frac{5 - 5}{7 - 3} = \frac{0}{4} = 0.$$

So, the line is horizontal.

37. Using the slope formula with $(x_1, y_1) = (-3, -1)$ and $(x_2, y_2) = (-3, -2)$, the slope is

$$m = \frac{y_2 - y_1}{x_2 - x_1} = \frac{-2 - (-1)}{-3 - (-3)} = \frac{-2 + 1}{-3 + 3} = \frac{-1}{0}, \text{ which is}$$

undefined. So the line is vertical.

39. Using the slope formula with $(x_1, y_1) = (-3.2, 5.1)$ and $(x_2, y_2) = (-2.8, 1.4)$, the slope is

$$m = \frac{y_2 - y_1}{x_2 - x_1} = \frac{1.4 - 5.1}{-2.8 - (-3.2)} = \frac{-3.7}{0.4} = -9.25.$$

The slope is negative, so the line is decreasing.

41. Using the slope formula with $(x_1, y_1) = (4.9, -2.7)$ and $(x_2, y_2) = (6.3, -1.1)$, the slope is

$$m = \frac{y_2 - y_1}{x_2 - x_1} = \frac{-1.1 - (-2.7)}{6.3 - 4.9} = \frac{1.6}{1.4} \approx 1.14.$$

The slope is positive, so the line is increasing.

43. Using the slope formula with $(x_1, y_1) = (-4.97, -3.25)$ and $(x_2, y_2) = (-9.64, -2.27)$, the slope is

$$m = \frac{y_2 - y_1}{x_2 - x_1} = \frac{-2.27 - (-3.25)}{-9.64 - (-4.97)} = \frac{0.98}{-4.67} \approx -0.21.$$

The slope is negative, so the line is decreasing.

45. Using the slope formula with $(x_1, y_1) = (-2.45, -6.71)$ and $(x_2, y_2) = (4.88, -1.53)$, the slope is

$$m = \frac{y_2 - y_1}{x_2 - x_1} = \frac{-1.53 - (-6.71)}{4.88 - (-2.45)} = \frac{5.18}{7.33} \approx 0.71.$$

The slope is positive, so the line is increasing.

47. The line contains the points $(0, -1)$ and $(3, 1)$, so the slope is $m = \dfrac{1 - (-1)}{3 - 0} = \dfrac{2}{3}$.

49. The line contains the points $(1, 4)$ and $(2, 1)$, so the slope is $m = \dfrac{1 - 4}{2 - 1} = \dfrac{-3}{1} = -3$.

51. a. The line slants downward from left to right, so the slope is negative.

b. The line slants upward from left to right, so the slope is positive.

c. The line is vertical, so the slope is undefined.

d. The line is horizontal, so the slope is zero.

53 – 59. Answers will vary.

61. Descriptions of errors may vary. One possibility follows: The student has calculated with the run over the rise rather than rise over run. The correct slope is $m = \dfrac{7 - 3}{4 - 1} = \dfrac{4}{3}$.

63. Descriptions of errors may vary. One possibility follows: The student has subtracted incorrectly for both the run and the rise. The correct slope is

$$m = \frac{8-(-5)}{3-(-1)} = \frac{8+5}{3+1} = \frac{13}{4}.$$

65. Sketches may vary. One possibility follows: The graphs shown are of the lines $y = 2x$ and $y = 3x$.

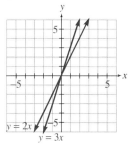

Yes, the steeper line has the greater slope.

67. a. Sketches may vary. One possibility follows: The graphs shown are of the lines $y = -2x$ and $y = -3x$.

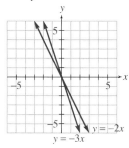

b. No. $-3 < -2$, but the line with slope -3 is steeper than the line with slope -2.

c. $|-3| = 3$; $|-2| = 2$

Yes. $|-3| > |-2|$. The steeper line has the slope with the greater absolute value.

d. Answers may vary. One possibility follows: A line having the slope with a greater absolute value will be steeper than a line with a lesser absolute value.

69. Answers may vary. One possibility follows: The slope of the line containing (2, 1) and (3, 4) is $m = \frac{4-1}{3-2} = \frac{3}{1} = 3$. From the point (3, 4), if we run 1 and rise 3, we will find another point on the line: (3 + 1, 4 + 3) = (4, 7). Now, from the point (4, 7), if we run 1 and rise 3, we will find another point on the line: (4 + 1, 7 + 3) = (5, 10).

Now, from the point (5, 10), if we run 1 and rise 3, we will find another point on the line: (5 + 1, 10 + 3) = (6, 13). In summary, the points (4, 7), (5, 10), and (6, 13) are on the line.

71. Answers may vary. One possibility follows: For a vertical line, the horizontal change (the run) is 0. So when calculating the slope, we divide by 0, which is undefined.

73. Answers may vary. One possibility follows: The slope of an increasing line is positive because the horizontal change (the run) and the vertical change (the rise) have the same sign.

75. a.   **i.** $\dfrac{\text{rise}}{\text{run}} = \dfrac{2}{1} = 2$

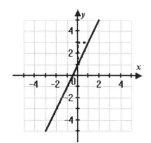

ii. $\dfrac{\text{rise}}{\text{run}} = \dfrac{3}{1} = 3$

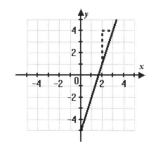

iii. $\dfrac{\text{rise}}{\text{run}} = \dfrac{2}{-1} = -2$

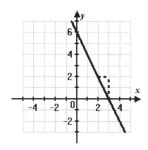

b. The slope of the line found using $\dfrac{\text{rise}}{\text{run}}$ is the same as the coefficient of x in each of the corresponding equations.

77. The line contains both points, S and Q. The slope is $-\dfrac{2}{3}$ and can be written $\dfrac{\text{rise}}{\text{run}} = \dfrac{-2}{3} = \dfrac{2}{-3}$. From point P, moving 3 units to the right and 2 units down is the equivalent of $\dfrac{\text{rise}}{\text{run}} = \dfrac{-2}{3}$. From point P, moving 3 units to the left and 2 units up is the equivalent of $\dfrac{\text{rise}}{\text{run}} = \dfrac{2}{-3}$.

79. No, Ladder A is not necessarily steeper than Ladder B. Explanations may vary. One example follows: The slope of each ladder depends not just on how high it reaches up the building (the rise), but it also depends on the length of each ladder and how far the base of each ladder is set from the wall (the run). The illustrations below show a situation where Ladder A is steeper than Ladder B, where Ladder B is steeper than Ladder A, and where Ladders A and B are equally steep. In all three cases, Ladder A reaches a higher point on the building than Ladder B.

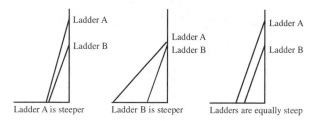

Homework 3.4

1. We first plot the y-intercept $(0, 1)$. The slope is $\dfrac{2}{3}$, so the run is 3 and the rise is 2. From $(0, 1)$, we count 3 units to the right and 2 units up, where we plot the point $(3, 3)$. We then sketch the line that contains these two points.

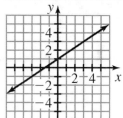

3. We first plot the y-intercept $(0, 4)$. The slope is $-\dfrac{5}{2} = \dfrac{-5}{2}$, so the run is 2 and the rise is -5. From $(0, 4)$, we count 2 units to the right and 5 units down, where we plot the point $(2, -1)$. We then sketch the line that contains these two points.

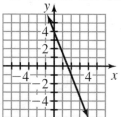

5. We first plot the y-intercept $(0, 0)$. The slope is $-\dfrac{3}{2} = \dfrac{-3}{2}$, so the run is 2 and the rise is -3. From $(0, 0)$, we count 2 units to the right and 3 units down, where we plot the point $(2, -3)$. We then sketch the line that contains these two points.

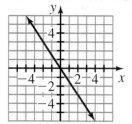

7. We first plot the y-intercept $(0, 1)$. The slope is $2 = \dfrac{2}{1}$, so the run is 1 and the rise is 2. From $(0, 1)$, we count 1 unit to the right and 2 units up, where we plot the point $(1, 3)$. We then sketch the line that contains these two points.

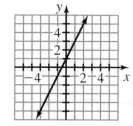

9. We first plot the *y*-intercept $(0, -2)$. The slope is $-3 = \dfrac{-3}{1}$, so the run is 1 and the rise is -3. From $(0, -2)$, we count 1 unit to the right and 3 units down, where we plot the point $(1, -5)$. We then sketch the line that contains these two points.

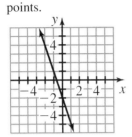

11. We first plot the *y*-intercept $(0, 3)$. The slope is $-1 = \dfrac{-1}{1}$, so the run is 1 and the rise is -1. From $(0, 3)$, we count 1 unit to the right and 1 unit down, where we plot the point $(1, 2)$. We then sketch the line that contains these two points.

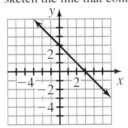

13. We first plot the point $(4, -5)$. The slope is 0, so the line is horizontal. We sketch the horizontal line that contains $(4, -5)$.

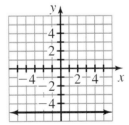

15. We first plot the point $(2, -1)$. The slope is undefined, so the line is vertical. We sketch the vertical line that contains $(2, -1)$.

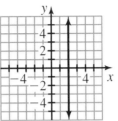

17. The equation $y = \dfrac{2}{3}x - 1$ is in slope-intercept form, so the slope is $m = \dfrac{2}{3}$ and the *y*-intercept is $(0, -1)$. We first plot $(0, -1)$. From this point we move 3 units to the right and 2 units up, where we plot the point $(3, 1)$. We then sketch the line that contains these two points.

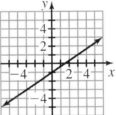

19. The equation $y = -\dfrac{1}{3}x + 4$ is in slope-intercept form, so the slope is $m = -\dfrac{1}{3}$ and the *y*-intercept is $(0, 4)$. We first plot $(0, 4)$. From this point we move 3 units to the right and 1 unit down, where we plot the point $(3, 3)$. We then sketch the line that contains these two points.

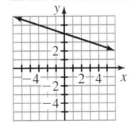

21. The equation $y = \frac{4}{3}x + 2$ is in slope-intercept form, so the slope is $m = \frac{4}{3}$ and the y-intercept is $(0, 2)$. We first plot $(0, 2)$. From this point we move 3 units to the right and 4 units up, where we plot the point $(3, 6)$. We then sketch the line that contains these two points.

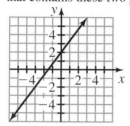

23. The equation $y = -\frac{4}{5}x - 1$ is in slope-intercept form, so the slope is $m = -\frac{4}{5}$ and the y-intercept is $(0, -1)$. We first plot $(0, -1)$. From this point we move 5 units to the right and 4 units down, where we plot the point $(5, -5)$. We then sketch the line that contains these two points.

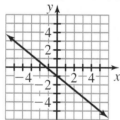

25. The equation $y = \frac{1}{2}x$ is in slope-intercept form, so the slope is $m = \frac{1}{2}$ and the y-intercept is $(0, 0)$. We first plot $(0, 0)$. From this point we move 2 units to the right and 1 unit up, where we plot the point $(2, 1)$. We then sketch the line that contains these two points.

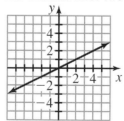

27. The equation $y = -\frac{5}{3}x$ is in slope-intercept form, so the slope is $m = -\frac{5}{3}$ and the y-intercept is $(0, 0)$. We first plot $(0, 0)$. From this point we move 3 units to the right and 5 units down, where we plot the point $(3, -5)$. We then sketch the line that contains these two points.

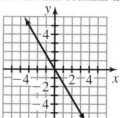

29. The equation $y = 4x - 2$ is in slope-intercept form, so the slope is $m = 4 = \frac{4}{1}$ and the y-intercept is $(0, -2)$. We first plot $(0, -2)$. From this point we move 1 unit to the right and 4 units up, where we plot the point $(1, 2)$. We then sketch the line that contains these two points.

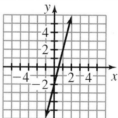

Points chosen for verification may vary.

31. The equation $y = -2x + 4$ is in slope-intercept form, so the slope is $m = -2 = \frac{-2}{1}$ and the y-intercept is $(0, 4)$. We first plot $(0, 4)$. From this point we move 1 unit to the right and 2 units down, where we plot the point $(1, 2)$. We then sketch the line that contains these two points.

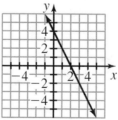

Points chosen for verification may vary.

33. The equation $y = -4x - 1$ is in slope-intercept form, so the slope is $m = -4 = \dfrac{-4}{1}$ and the y-intercept is $(0, -1)$. We first plot $(0, -1)$. From this point we move 1 unit to the right and 4 units down, where we plot the point $(1, -5)$. We then sketch the line that contains these two points.

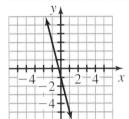

Points chosen for verification may vary.

35. The equation $y = x + 1$ is in slope-intercept form, so the slope is $m = 1 = \dfrac{1}{1}$ and the y-intercept is $(0, 1)$. We first plot $(0, 1)$. From this point we move 1 unit to the right and 1 unit up, where we plot the point $(1, 2)$. We then sketch the line that contains these two points.

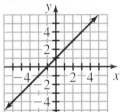

Points chosen for verification may vary.

37. The equation $y = -x + 3$ is in slope-intercept form, so the slope is $m = -1 = \dfrac{-1}{1}$ and the y-intercept is $(0, 3)$. We first plot $(0, 3)$. From this point we move 1 unit to the right and 1 unit down, where we plot the point $(1, 2)$. We then sketch the line that contains these two points.

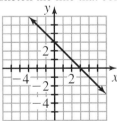

Points chosen for verification may vary.

39. The equation $y = -3x$ is in slope-intercept form, so the slope is $m = -3 = \dfrac{-3}{1}$ and the y-intercept is $(0, 0)$. We first plot $(0, 0)$. From this point we move 1 unit to the right and 3 units down, where we plot the point $(1, -3)$. We then sketch the line that contains these two points.

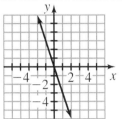

Points chosen for verification may vary.

41. The equation $y = x$ is in slope-intercept form, so the slope is $m = 1 = \dfrac{1}{1}$ and the y-intercept is $(0, 0)$. We first plot $(0, 0)$. From this point we move 1 unit to the right and 1 unit up, where we plot the point $(1, 1)$. We then sketch the line that contains these two points.

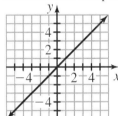

Points chosen for verification may vary.

43. The equation $y = -3$ is in slope-intercept form, so the slope is $m = 0$ and the y-intercept is $(0, -3)$. Since the slope is 0, the line is horizontal. We sketch the horizontal line with y-intercept $(0, -3)$.

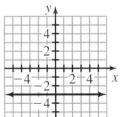

Points chosen for verification may vary.

45. The equation $y = 0$ is in slope-intercept form, so the slope is $m = 0$ and the y-intercept is $(0, 0)$. Since the slope is 0, the line is horizontal. We sketch the horizontal line with y-intercept $(0, 0)$. Note the graph coincides with the x-axis.

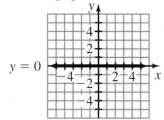

Points chosen for verification may vary.

47. a. The equation $p = 0.9t + 25.7$ is in slope-intercept form, so the slope is $m = 0.9 = \dfrac{9}{10}$ and the p-intercept is $(0, 25.7)$. We first plot $(0, 25.7)$. From this point we move 10 units to the right and 9 units up, where we plot the point $(10, 34.7)$. We then sketch the line that contains these two points.

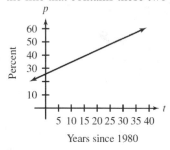

b. The line contains the point $(33.67, 56)$, so $t \approx 34$ when $p = 56$ as illustrated.

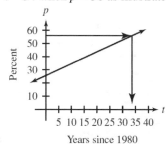

Thus, 56% of the degrees in medicine will be earned by women in the year 1980 + 34 = 2014.

49. a. The equation $n = -8.6t + 199.4$ is in slope-intercept form, so the slope is $m = -8.6 = \dfrac{-8.6}{1}$ and the n-intercept is

$(0, 199.4)$. We first plot $(0, 199.4)$. From this point we move 1 unit to the right and 8.6 units down, where we plot the point $(1, 190.8)$. We then sketch the line that contains these two points.

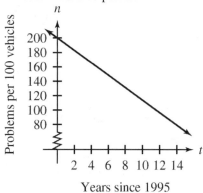

b. The line approximately contains the point $(14, 81)$, so $t = 14$ when $n = 81$ as illustrated.

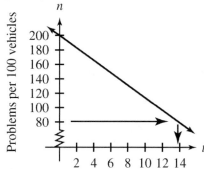

Thus, the average number of problems for all vehicles (of any brand) will reach 81 per 100 cars in the year 1995 + 14 = 2009.

51. a. The line increases from left to right, so m is positive. It crosses the y-axis below the x-axis, so b is negative.

b. The line is horizontal, so m is zero. It crosses the y-axis below the x-axis, so b is negative.

c. The line decreases from left to right, so m is negative. It crosses the y-axis above the x-axis, so b is positive.

d. The line increases from left to right, so m is positive. It crosses the y-axis above the x-axis, so b is positive.

53. Specific graphs may vary. Since m is positive, the line must increase from left to right. Since b is positive, the line must cross the y-axis above the x-axis. One possible graph follows:

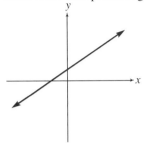

55. Specific graphs may vary. Since m is negative, the line must decrease from left to right. Since b is negative, the line must cross the y-axis below the x-axis. One possible graph follows:

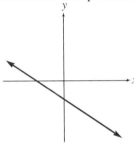

57. Specific graphs may vary. Since $m = 0$, the line must be horizontal. Since b is negative, the line must cross the y-axis below the x-axis. One possible graph follows:

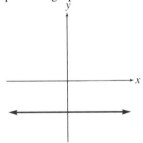

59. We substitute 3 for m and -4 for b in the equation $y = mx + b$ to obtain
$$y = 3x + (-4)$$
$$y = 3x - 4$$

61. We substitute $-\dfrac{6}{5}$ for m and 3 for b in the equation $y = mx + b$ to obtain $y = -\dfrac{6}{5}x + 3$.

63. We substitute $-\dfrac{2}{7}$ for m and 0 for b in the equation $y = mx + b$ to obtain $y = -\dfrac{2}{7}x + 0$ or $y = -\dfrac{2}{7}x$.

65. The y-intercept of the line is $(0, 3)$. The run is 1 when the rise is 2, so the slope of the line is $m = \dfrac{2}{1} = 2$. By substituting 2 for m and 3 for b in the equation $y = mx + b$, we have $y = 2x + 3$.

67. The slope of $y = \dfrac{2}{5}x + 1$ is $m_1 = \dfrac{2}{5}$. The slope of $y = -\dfrac{5}{2}x - 3$ is $m_2 = -\dfrac{5}{2}$. Since the slope $-\dfrac{5}{2}$ is the opposite of the reciprocal of the slope $\dfrac{2}{5}$, the lines are perpendicular.

69. The slope of $y = 3x - 1$ is $m_1 = 3$. The slope of $y = -3x + 2$ is $m_2 = -3$. Since the slopes are not equal, the lines are not parallel. Since the slope -3 is not the opposite of the reciprocal of the slope 3, the lines are not perpendicular. That is, the lines are neither parallel nor perpendicular.

71. The slope of $y = -4x + 2$ is $m_1 = -4$. The slope of $y = -4x + 3$ is $m_2 = -4$. Since the slopes are equal, the lines are parallel.

73. The slope of $y = \dfrac{2}{3}x - 1$ is $m_1 = \dfrac{2}{3}$. The slope of $y = \dfrac{3}{2}x + 3$ is $m_2 = \dfrac{3}{2}$. Since the slopes are not equal, the lines are not parallel. Since the slope $\dfrac{3}{2}$ is not the opposite of the reciprocal of the slope $\dfrac{2}{3}$, the lines are not perpendicular. That is, the lines are neither parallel nor perpendicular.

75. The slope of $y = 2$ is $m_1 = 0$. The slope of $y = -4$ is $m_2 = 0$. Since the slopes are equal, the lines are parallel. Note that both lines are horizontal, confirming that they are parallel.

77. The graph of the line $x = 0$ is vertical. The graph of the line $y = 0$ is horizontal. Thus, the two lines are perpendicular.

79. No, the lines sketched are not parallel. Explanations may vary. One possibility follows: The lines do not have equal slopes. The red line has slope $-\dfrac{3}{11}$, while the blue line has slope $-\dfrac{3}{10}$.

81. No. The slope is 2, not $2x$.

83. The equation $y = 2x - 1$ is in slope-intercept form, so the slope is $m = 2 = \dfrac{2}{1}$ and the y-intercept is $(0, -1)$. We first plot $(0, -1)$. From this point we move 1 unit to the right and 2 units up, where we plot the point $(1, 1)$. We then sketch the line that contains these two points.

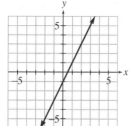

Points chosen for verification may vary. Two possible points follow:

Check $(-1, -3)$ Check $(2, 3)$

$-3 \overset{?}{=} 2(-1) - 1$ $3 \overset{?}{=} 2(2) - 1$

$-3 \overset{?}{=} -2 - 1$ $3 \overset{?}{=} 4 - 1$

$-3 = -3$ True $3 = 3$ True

85. The solutions of $y = \dfrac{1}{2}x + 2$ can be described by the equation, by a table, by a graph, or by words.

a. The equation $y = \dfrac{1}{2}x + 2$ is in slope-intercept form, so the slope is $m = \dfrac{1}{2}$ and the y-intercept is $(0, 2)$. We first plot $(0, 2)$. From this point we move 2 units to the right and 1 unit up, where we plot the point $(2, 3)$. We then sketch the line that contains these two points.

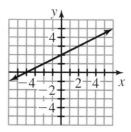

b. Answers may vary. One possibility follows:

x	y
-2	$\dfrac{1}{2}(-2) + 2 = 1$
0	$\dfrac{1}{2}(0) + 2 = 2$
2	$\dfrac{1}{2}(2) + 2 = 3$

c. Answers may vary. One possibility follows: For each solution, the y-coordinate is two more than half the x-coordinate.

87. Answers may vary. One possibility follows: The graph provided contains the points $(-1, -2)$ and $(1, 4)$. In verifying these solutions, however, we obtain the following:

Check $(-1, -2)$ Check $(1, 4)$

$-2 \overset{?}{=} -3(-1) + 1$ $4 \overset{?}{=} -3(1) + 1$

$-2 \overset{?}{=} 3 + 1$ $4 \overset{?}{=} -3 + 1$

$-2 \overset{?}{=} 4$ False $4 \overset{?}{=} -2$ False

Neither point is a solution to the equation $y = -3x - 1$, so the graph is incorrect.

To obtain the correct graph, we recognize that the equation $y = -3x + 1$ is in slope-intercept form, so the slope is $m = -3 = \dfrac{-3}{1}$ and the y-intercept is $(0, 1)$. We first plot $(0, 1)$. From this point we move 1 unit to the right and 3 units down, where we plot the point $(1, -2)$. We then sketch the line that contains these two points.

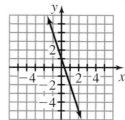

89. The line contains the point $(-3, -2)$, so $y = -2$ when $x = -3$.

91. The line contains the point $(3, 0)$, so $x = 3$ when $y = 0$.

93. The line contains the points $(-3, -2)$ and $(3, 0)$, so the slope is $m = \dfrac{0 - (-1)}{3 - 0} = \dfrac{1}{3}$.

95. a. We first plot $(-1, 1)$. From this point we move 1 unit to the right and 2 units up, where we plot the point $(0, 3)$. We then sketch the line that contains these two points.

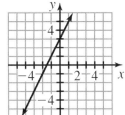

b. The slope of the line is $m = 2$ and the y-intercept is $(0, 3)$. By substituting 2 for m and 3 for b in the equation $y = mx + b$, we have $y = 2x + 3$.

97. a. All three lines are of the form $y = b$, so in each case $m = 0$. That is, the slope of each line is zero.

b. The slope of the graph of any equation of the form $y = k$, where k is a constant, is zero.

99. a. k is greater than m. We can tell because the line $y = kx + c$ is steeper than the line $y = mx + b$, so the slope of $y = kx + c$ is greater.

b. b is greater than c. We can tell because the line $y = mx + b$ crosses the y-axis above the line $y = kx + c$, so the y-coordinate of the y-intercept of $y = mx + b$ is greater.

Homework 3.5

1. $\dfrac{\text{change in salary}}{\text{change in time}} = \dfrac{\$12,400}{8 \text{ years}} = \dfrac{\$1550}{1 \text{ year}}$

The average rate of change is $1550 per year.

3. $\dfrac{\text{change in altitude}}{\text{change in time}} = \dfrac{-24,750 \text{ feet}}{15 \text{ minutes}} = \dfrac{-1650}{1 \text{ minute}}$

The average rate of change is -1650 feet per minute.

5. The average rate of change of the number of shredder models the company makes per year between 1990 and 2008 is given by dividing the change in the number of models offered by the change in years.

$$m = \dfrac{\text{change in models}}{\text{change in years}}$$
$$= \dfrac{36 - 2}{2008 - 1990}$$
$$\approx 1.89$$

This says that the average rate of change of the number of shredder models was 1.89 shredder models per year.

7. The average rate of change of the number of trips per year by Americans to Canada is given by dividing the change in trips by the change in years.

$$m = \dfrac{\text{change in trips}}{\text{change in years}}$$
$$= \dfrac{28.9 - 44.0}{2006 - 2000}$$
$$= -2.52$$

This says that the average rate of change of the number of trips per year by Americans to Canada was –2.52 million trips per year, or a decrease of 2.52 million trips per year.

9. The average rate of change of the percentage of Americans who have trust in newspapers per year is given by dividing the change in the percent of Americans who have trust in newspapers by the change in years.

$$m = \dfrac{\text{change in percentage}}{\text{change in years}}$$
$$= \dfrac{28 - 37}{2005 - 2000}$$
$$= -1.8$$

This says that the average rate of change of the percentage of Americans who have trust in newspapers per year is –1.8, or a decrease of 1.8 percent per year.

11. The average rate of change of the cost per credit hour of classes is given by dividing the change in cost by the change in credits.

$$m = \frac{\text{change in cost}}{\text{change in credits}}$$

$$= \frac{768 - 576}{12 - 9}$$

$$= 64$$

This says that the average cost of a credit hour at Triton College is $64.

13. $\dfrac{\text{change in income}}{\text{change in family size}} = \dfrac{\$44,775 - \$29,925}{7 \text{ people} - 4 \text{ people}}$

$$= \frac{\$14,850}{3 \text{ people}}$$

$$= \frac{\$4950}{1 \text{ person}}$$

The average rate of change is $4950 per person.

15. a. Yes there is a linear relationship between t and n; the rate of increase is constant. The slope of the model is 9 (million), the rate of increase of U.S. households that pay bills online per year.

b. i $n = 9t + 45$ (in millions)

b. ii

Years since 2006 t	Number of households (millions) n
0	$9(0) + 45 = 45$
1	$9(1) + 45 = 54$
2	$9(2) + 45 = 63$
3	$9(3) + 45 = 72$
4	$9(4) + 45 = 81$

b. iii

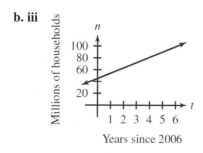

Years since 2006

17. a. The slope is -3. It means that the percentage of employers who allow casual dress every day is decreasing by about 3 percent per year.

b. Since t is the number of years since 2001, the p-intercept is $(0, 51)$. It means that, in the year 2001, 51% of employers allowed casual dress every day.

c. Substituting -3 for m and 51 for b in the equation $p = mt + b$, we obtain $p = -3t + 51$.

d. The year 2013 is $t = 12$ years after 2001.
$$p = -3(12) + 51 = 15$$
The model predicts that 15% of employers will allow casual dress every day in 2013.

19. a. The slope is -650. It means that the balance in the savings account declines by $650 per month.

b. Since t is the number of months since September 1, the B-intercept is $(0, 4700)$. It means that, on September 1, the balance in the savings account was $4700.

c. Substituting -650 for m and 4700 for b in the equation $B = mt + b$, we obtain $B = -650t + 4700$.

d. $\underbrace{B}_{\text{dollars}} = \underbrace{-650}_{\frac{\text{dollars}}{\text{month}}} \cdot \underbrace{t}_{\text{months}} + \underbrace{4700}_{\text{dollars}}$

We use the fact that $\dfrac{\text{months}}{\text{months}} = 1$ to simplify the right-hand side of the equation:
$$\frac{\text{dollars}}{\text{month}} \cdot \text{months} + \text{dollars} = \text{dollars} + \text{dollars}.$$
So, the units on both sides of the equation are dollars, suggesting the equation is correct.

e. Substituting $t = 6$ in the equation, we obtain $B = -650(6) + 4700 = 800$.

The model predicts that the savings account balance on March 1 will be $800.

21. a. The slope is 465. It means that the tuition increases by $465 per credit.

b. The tuition is $465 per credit, plus a $10 fee. Thus, the equation is $T = 465c + 10$.

c.

$$\underset{\text{dollars}}{T} = \underset{\substack{\text{dollars} \\ \text{credit}}}{465} \cdot \underset{\text{credits}}{c} + \underset{\text{dollars}}{10}$$

We use the fact that $\dfrac{\text{credits}}{\text{credits}} = 1$ to simplify the right-hand side of the equation:

$\dfrac{\text{dollars}}{\text{credit}} \cdot \text{credits} + \text{dollars} = \text{dollars} + \text{dollars}$.

So, the units on both sides of the equation are dollars, suggesting the equation is correct.

d. Substituting $c = 9$ in the equation, we obtain
$T = 465(9) + 10 = 4195$.
The tuition for 9 credits is $4195.

23. a. The slope is -0.02 . It means that the car uses 0.02 gallons of gasoline per mile.

b. Since d is the number of miles driven, the G-intercept is (0, 11.9). It means that there were 11.9 gallons of gasoline in the tank at the start of the trip (when the tank is full).

c. Substituting -0.02 for m and 11.9 for b in the equation $G = md + b$, we obtain
$G = -0.02d + 11.9$.

d.

$$\underset{\text{gallons}}{G} = \underset{\substack{\text{gallons} \\ \text{mile}}}{-0.02} \cdot \underset{\text{miles}}{d} + \underset{\text{gallons}}{10}$$

We use the fact that $\dfrac{\text{miles}}{\text{miles}} = 1$ to simplify the right-hand side of the equation:

$\dfrac{\text{gallons}}{\text{mile}} \cdot \text{miles} + \text{gallons} = \text{gallons} + \text{gallons}$.

So, the units on both sides of the equation are gallons, suggesting the equation is correct.

e. Substituting $d = 525$ in the equation, we obtain $G = -0.02(525) + 11.9 = 1.4$. This means that 1.4 gallons remain in the tank. Thus, it will take $11.9 - 1.4 = 10.5$ gallons of gasoline to fill up the tank.

25. a. The slope is -3.65 . It means that the number of refineries is decreasing by about 3.65 refineries per year.

b. Since t is the number of years since 2000, the n-intercept is (0, 157.31). It means that there were about 157 refineries in 2000.

c. The year 2011 is $t = 11$ years after 2000. Substituting $t = 11$ in the equation, we

obtain $n = -3.65(11) + 157.31 = 117.16$. The model predicts that there will be about 117 refineries in the year 2011.

27. a.

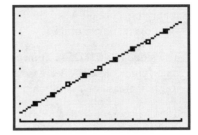

Yes, the line comes close to the data points.

b. The slope is 20.7. It means that the number of Internet users is increasing by 20.7 million users per year.

c.

Years	Rates of change
1996 to 1997	$60 - 39 = 21$
1997 to 1998	$84 - 60 = 24$
1998 to 1999	$105 - 84 = 21$
1990 to 2000	$122 - 105 = 17$
2000 to 2001	$143 - 122 = 21$
2001 to 2002	$166 - 143 = 23$
2002 to 2003	$183 - 166 = 17$
2003 to 2004	$207 - 183 = 24$

All of the rates of change are in millions of Internet users per year. Comparisons may vary.

d. The d-intercept is (0, 19.6). It means there were 19.6 million Internet users in 1995.

e. The year 2010 is represented by $t = 15$. Substituting 15 for t in the equation gives $n = 20.7(15) + 19.6 = 330.1$. The model predicts that there will be 330.1 million Internet users in 2010. This is more than the predicted U.S. population, so it appears that model breakdown has occurred.

29. a.

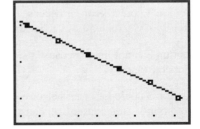

Yes, the line comes close to the data points.

b. Substituting 400 for s in the equation gives $G = -0.00254(400) + 4.58 \approx 3.56$. The model predicts that the students qualifying core GPA is 3.56. Since the actual qualifying core GPA is 3.55, the prediction is an overestimate of 0.01.

c. The slope is -0.00254. It means that the qualifying core GPA decreases by 0.00254 for an increase of 1 point on the SAT.

d. The G-intercept is (0, 4.58). It means the qualifying core GPA is 4.58 for a SAT score of 0. Since the highest GPA possible is 4.0 and the lowest possible SAT score is 400, model breakdown has occurred.

31. a. Yes, the car is traveling at a constant speed. This can be seen by the linear relationship between time and distance, showing a constant slope.

b. The line contains the points (0, 0) and (2, 120), so the slope is
$$m = \frac{120 \text{ miles} - 0 \text{ miles}}{2 \text{ hours} - 0 \text{ hours}} = \frac{120 \text{ miles}}{2 \text{ hours}} = 60$$
miles per hour.

33. a. Yes, the volume of gasoline that remains in the tank is decreasing at a constant rate. This can be seen by the linear relationship between time and volume, showing a constant slope.

b. The line contains the points (0, 12) and (3, 9), so the slope is
$$m = \frac{9 \text{ gallons} - 12 \text{ gallons}}{3 \text{ hours} - 1 \text{ hours}}$$
$$= \frac{-3 \text{ gallons}}{2 \text{ hours}}$$
$$= -1.5 \text{ gallons per hour}$$

35. Yes, t and c are linearly related. The slope is 30. It means that the total charge increases by \$30 per hour.

37. Equation 1 could be linear because, for each unit increase in x, y increases by a constant 2 units.

Equation 2 is not linear because the change in y is not constant.

Equation 3 could be linear because, for each unit increase in x, y decreases by a constant 2 units.

Equation 4 is not linear because the change in y is not constant.

39. For Equation 1, for each unit increase in x, y increases by 5 units.

x	y
0	3
1	8
2	$8+5=13$
3	$13+5=18$
4	$18+5=23$

For Equation 2, for each unit increase in x, y decreases by 7 units.

x	y
0	99
1	92
2	$92-7=85$
3	$85-7=78$
4	$78-7=71$

For Equation 3, $m = \dfrac{12-16}{23-21} = \dfrac{-4}{2} = -2$. For each unit increase in x, y decreases by 2 units.

x	y
21	16
22	$16-2=14$
23	12
24	$12-2=10$
25	$10-2=8$

For Equation 4, $m = \dfrac{29-23}{47-45} = \dfrac{6}{2} = 3$. For each unit increase in x, y increases by 3 units.

x	y
43	$20-3=17$
44	$23-3=20$
45	23
46	$29-3=26$
47	29

41. For Set 1, the slope is $m = \dfrac{7-5}{1-0} = \dfrac{2}{1} = 2$, and the y-intercept is $(0, 5)$. Substituting 2 for m and 5 for b in the equation $y = mx + b$, we obtain $y = 2x + 5$.

For Set 2, the slope is $m = \dfrac{17-20}{1-0} = \dfrac{-3}{1} = -3$, and the y-intercept is $(0, 20)$. Substituting -3 for m and 20 for b in the equation $y = mx + b$, we obtain $y = -3x + 20$.

For Set 3, the slope is $m = \dfrac{29-21}{1-0} = \dfrac{8}{1} = 8$, and the y-intercept is $(0, 21)$. Substituting 8 for m and 21 for b in the equation $y = mx + b$, we obtain $y = 8x + 21$.

For Set 4, the slope is $m = \dfrac{4-9}{1-0} = \dfrac{-5}{1} = -5$, and the y-intercept is $(0, 9)$. Substituting -5 for m and 9 for b in the equation $y = mx + b$, we obtain $y = -5x + 9$.

43. Since the slope is 7, if x is increased by 1, y will increase by 7.

45. Answers may vary. One possible table follows:

x	y
0	$-6(0) + 40 = 40$
1	$-6(1) + 40 = 34$
2	$-6(2) + 40 = 28$
3	$-6(3) + 40 = 22$
4	$-6(4) + 40 = 16$

Note $40 - 6 = 34$, $34 - 6 = 28$, $28 - 6 = 22$, and $22 - 6 = 16$. This shows that, if x is increased by 1, then y decreases by 6.

47. a. The slope 3 is the number multiplied times x.

    b. If the run is 1, then the rise is 3.

    c. As the value of x increases by 1, the value of y increases by 3.

    d. Answers will vary.

49. Answers may vary.

Chapter 3 Review Exercises

1. Check $(-3, 9)$: $9 \overset{?}{=} -2(-3) + 3$

$$9 \overset{?}{=} 6 + 3$$
$$9 \overset{?}{=} 9 \quad \text{True}$$

So, $(-3, 9)$ is a solution of $y = -2x + 3$.

Check $(1, 2)$: $2 \overset{?}{=} -2(1) + 3$
$$2 \overset{?}{=} -2 + 3$$
$$2 \overset{?}{=} 1 \quad \text{False}$$

So, $(1, 2)$ is not a solution of $y = -2x + 3$.

Check $(4, -5)$: $-5 \overset{?}{=} -2(4) + 3$
$$-5 \overset{?}{=} -8 + 3$$
$$-5 \overset{?}{=} -5 \quad \text{True}$$

So, $(4, -5)$ is a solution of $y = -2x + 3$.

2. The line contains the point $(2, -1)$, so $y = -1$ when $x = 2$.

3. The line contains the point $(-2, -3)$, so $y = -3$ when $x = -2$.

4. The line contains the point $(0, -2)$, so $y = -2$ when $x = 0$.

5. The line contains the point $(-2, -3)$, so $x = -2$ when $y = -3$.

6. The line contains the point $(-4, -4)$, so $x = -4$ when $y = -4$.

7. The line contains the point $(4, 0)$, so $x = 4$ when $y = 0$.

8. Slope of plane $A = \dfrac{6500 \text{ feet}}{12,700 \text{ feet}} \approx 0.512$

Slope of plane $B = \dfrac{7400 \text{ feet}}{15,600 \text{ feet}} \approx 0.474$

Thus, plane A is climbing at a greater incline since it has a larger slope.

9. Using the slope formula with $\left(x_1, y_1\right) = \left(-3, 1\right)$ and $\left(x_2, y_2\right) = \left(2, 11\right)$, the slope is

$m = \dfrac{y_2 - y_1}{x_2 - x_1} = \dfrac{11-1}{2-(-3)} = \dfrac{11-1}{2+3} = \dfrac{10}{5} = 2$.

The slope is positive, so the line is increasing.

10. Using the slope formula with $(x_1, y_1) = (-2, -4)$ and $(x_2, y_2) = (1, -7)$, the slope is

$m = \dfrac{y_2 - y_1}{x_2 - x_1} = \dfrac{-7-(-4)}{1-(-2)} = \dfrac{-7+4}{1+2} = \dfrac{-3}{3} = -1$.

The slope is negative, so the line is decreasing.

11. Using the slope formula with $(x_1, y_1) = (4, -3)$ and $(x_2, y_2) = (8, -1)$, the slope is

$m = \dfrac{y_2 - y_1}{x_2 - x_1} = \dfrac{-1-(-3)}{8-4} = \dfrac{-1+3}{8-4} = \dfrac{2}{4} = \dfrac{1}{2}$.

The slope is positive, so the line is increasing.

12. Using the slope formula with $(x_1, y_1) = (-6, 0)$ and $(x_2, y_2) = (0, -3)$, the slope is

$m = \dfrac{y_2 - y_1}{x_2 - x_1} = \dfrac{-3-0}{0-(-6)} = \dfrac{-3-0}{0+6} = \dfrac{-3}{6} = -\dfrac{1}{2}$.

The slope is negative, so the line is decreasing.

13. Using the slope formula with $(x_1, y_1) = (-5, 5)$ and $(x_2, y_2) = (2, -2)$, the slope is

$m = \dfrac{y_2 - y_1}{x_2 - x_1} = \dfrac{-2-5}{2-(-5)} = \dfrac{-2-5}{2+5} = \dfrac{-7}{7} = -1$.

The slope is negative, so the line is decreasing.

14. Using the slope formula with $(x_1, y_1) = (-10, -3)$ and $(x_2, y_2) = (-4, -5)$, the slope is

$m = \dfrac{y_2 - y_1}{x_2 - x_1} = \dfrac{-5-(-3)}{-4-(-10)} = \dfrac{-5+3}{-4+10} = \dfrac{-2}{6} = -\dfrac{1}{3}$.

The slope is negative, so the line is decreasing.

15. Using the slope formula with $(x_1, y_1) = (-5, 2)$ and $(x_2, y_2) = (3, -7)$, the slope is

$m = \dfrac{y_2 - y_1}{x_2 - x_1} = \dfrac{-7-2}{3-(-5)} = \dfrac{-7-2}{3+5} = \dfrac{-9}{8} = -\dfrac{9}{8}$.

The slope is negative, so the line is decreasing.

16. Using the slope formula with $(x_1, y_1) = (-4, -1)$ and $(x_2, y_2) = (2, -5)$, the slope is

$m = \dfrac{y_2 - y_1}{x_2 - x_1} = \dfrac{-5-(-1)}{2-(-4)} = \dfrac{-5+1}{2+4} = \dfrac{-4}{6} = -\dfrac{2}{3}$.

The slope is negative, so the line is decreasing.

17. Using the slope formula with $(x_1, y_1) = (-4, 7)$ and $(x_2, y_2) = (-4, -3)$, the slope is

$m = \dfrac{y_2 - y_1}{x_2 - x_1} = \dfrac{-3-7}{-4-(-4)} = \dfrac{-3-7}{-4+4} = \dfrac{-10}{0}$, which

is undefined. So the line is vertical.

18. Using the slope formula with $(x_1, y_1) = (-5, 2)$ and $(x_2, y_2) = (-1, 2)$, the slope is

$m = \dfrac{y_2 - y_1}{x_2 - x_1} = \dfrac{2-2}{-1-(-5)} = \dfrac{2-2}{-1+5} = \dfrac{0}{4} = 0$.

So, the line is horizontal.

19. Using the slope formula with $(x_1, y_1) = (5.4, 7.9)$ and $(x_2, y_2) = (8.3, -2.6)$, the slope is

$m = \dfrac{y_2 - y_1}{x_2 - x_1} = \dfrac{-2.6-7.9}{8.3-5.4} = \dfrac{-10.5}{2.9} \approx -3.62$.

The slope is negative, so the line is decreasing.

20. Using the slope formula with $(x_1, y_1) =$ $(-8.74, -2.38)$ and $(x_2, y_2) = (-1.16, 4.77)$, the slope is

$m = \dfrac{y_2 - y_1}{x_2 - x_1} = \dfrac{4.77-(-2.38)}{-1.16-(-8.74)} = \dfrac{7.15}{7.58} \approx 0.94$.

The slope is positive, so the line is increasing.

21. Answers may vary. One possible solution follows:

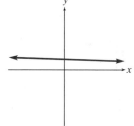

22. We first plot the y-intercept $(0, -4)$. The slope is $3 = \dfrac{3}{1}$, so the run is 1 and the rise is 3. From $(0, -4)$, we count 1 unit to the right and 3 units up, where we plot the point $(1, -1)$. We then sketch the line that contains these two points.

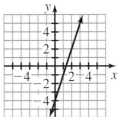

23. We first plot the y-intercept $(0, 1)$. The slope is $\dfrac{4}{3}$, so the run is 3 and the rise is 4. From $(0, 1)$, we count 3 units to the right and 4 units up, where we plot the point $(3, 5)$. We then sketch the line that contains these two points.

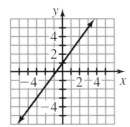

24. We first plot the point $(2, -3)$. The slope is 0, so the line is horizontal. We sketch the horizontal line that contains $(2, -3)$.

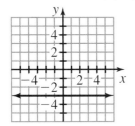

25. The equation $y = \dfrac{3}{4}x - 1$ is in slope-intercept form, so the slope is $m = \dfrac{3}{4}$ and the y-intercept is $(0, -1)$. We first plot $(0, -1)$. From this point we move 4 units to the right and 3 units up, where we plot the point $(4, 2)$. We then sketch the line that contains these two points.

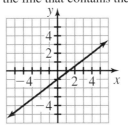

26. The equation $y = -\dfrac{1}{2}x + 3$ is in slope-intercept form, so the slope is $m = -\dfrac{1}{2}$ and the y-intercept is $(0, 3)$. We first plot $(0, 3)$. From this point we move 2 units to the right and 1 unit down, where we plot the point $(2, 2)$. We then sketch the line that contains these two points.

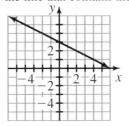

27. The equation $y = -\dfrac{2}{5}x - 1$ is in slope-intercept form, so the slope is $m = -\dfrac{2}{5}$ and the y-intercept is $(0, -1)$. We first plot $(0, -1)$. From this point we move 5 units to the right and 2 units down, where we plot the point $(5, -3)$. We then sketch the line that contains these two points.

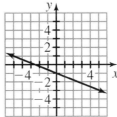

28. The equation $y = \dfrac{2}{3}x$ is in slope-intercept form, so the slope is $m = \dfrac{2}{3}$ and the *y*-intercept is $(0, 0)$. We first plot $(0, 0)$. From this point we move 3 units to the right and 2 units up, where we plot the point $(3, 2)$. We then sketch the line that contains these two points.

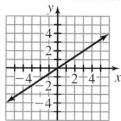

29. The equation $y = -4x$ is in slope-intercept form, so the slope is $m = -4 = \dfrac{-4}{1}$ and the *y*-intercept is $(0, 0)$. We first plot $(0, 0)$. From this point we move 1 unit to the right and 4 units down, where we plot the point $(1, -4)$. We then sketch the line that contains these two points.

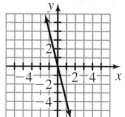

30. The equation $y = 2x - 4$ is in slope-intercept form, so the slope is $m = 2 = \dfrac{2}{1}$ and the *y*-intercept is $(0, -4)$. We first plot $(0, -4)$. From this point we move 1 unit to the right and 2 units up, where we plot the point $(1, -2)$. We then sketch the line that contains these two points.

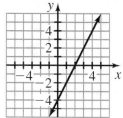

31. The equation $y = -3x + 1$ is in slope-intercept form, so the slope is $m = -3 = \dfrac{-3}{1}$ and the *y*-intercept is $(0, 1)$. We first plot $(0, 1)$. From this point we move 1 unit to the right and 3 units down, where we plot the point $(1, -2)$. We then sketch the line that contains these two points.

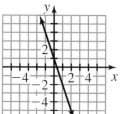

32. The equation $y = x + 2$ is in slope-intercept form, so the slope is $m = 1 = \dfrac{1}{1}$ and the *y*-intercept is $(0, 2)$. We first plot $(0, 2)$. From this point we move 1 unit to the right and 1 unit up, where we plot the point $(1, 3)$. We then sketch the line that contains these two points.

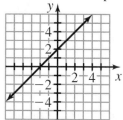

33. The equation $y = -5$ is in slope-intercept form, so the slope is $m = 0$ and the *y*-intercept is $(0, -5)$. Since the slope is 0, the line is horizontal. We sketch the horizontal line with *y*-intercept $(0, -5)$.

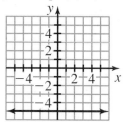

34. The graph of $x = -3$ is a vertical line. Note that x must be -3, but y can have any value. Some solutions of the equation are listed in the table that follows. We plot the corresponding points and sketch the line through them.

x	y
-3	-1
-3	0
-3	1

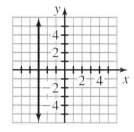

35. The equation $y = 2$ is in slope-intercept form, so the slope is $m = 0$ and the y-intercept is $(0, 2)$. Since the slope is 0, the line is horizontal. We sketch the horizontal line with y-intercept $(0, 2)$.

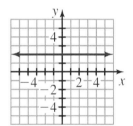

36. The solutions of $y = -2x + 1$ can be described by the equation, by a table, by a graph, or by words.

   a. Answers may vary. One possibility follows:

x	y
-1	$-2(-1)+1 = 3$
0	$-2(0)+1 = 1$
1	$-2(1)+1 = -1$

   b. The equation $y = -2x + 1$ is in slope-intercept form, so the slope is $m = -2$ and the y-intercept is $(0, 1)$. We first plot $(0, 1)$. From this point we move 1 unit to the right and 2 units down, where we plot the point $(1, -1)$. We then sketch the line that contains these two points.

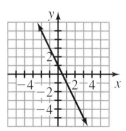

   c. Answers may vary. One possibility follows: For each solution, the y-coordinate is one more than -2 times the x-coordinate.

37. **a.**

Time (months) t	Balance (thousands of dollars) B
0	$19 - 3 \cdot 0$
1	$19 - 3 \cdot 1$
2	$19 - 3 \cdot 2$
3	$19 - 3 \cdot 3$
t	$19 - 3 \cdot t$

So, the equation is $B = 19 - 3t$.

   b. In the following table, we substitute values for t in the equation $B = 19 - 3t$ to find the corresponding values for B. Then, we plot the points and sketch a line that contains the points.

t	B
0	$19 - 3 \cdot 0 = 19$
1	$19 - 3 \cdot 1 = 16$
2	$19 - 3 \cdot 2 = 13$
3	$19 - 3 \cdot 3 = 10$

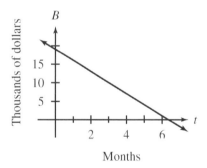

   c. From the table and graph, we see the B-intercept is $(0, 19)$. This indicates that, when the person first lost his job, the balance was $19 thousand.

d. The line contains the point $(5, 4)$, so $B = 4$ when $t = 5$ as illustrated.

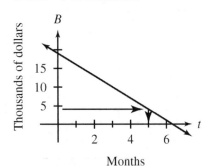

Months

Thus, if the balance is $4 thousand, then the person has been unemployed for 5 months.

38 The graph is of a vertical line. Since each point on the line has an x-coordinate of 5, the equation of the line is $x = 5$.

39. The y-intercept of the line is $(0, 4)$. The run is 3 when the rise is -2, so the slope of the line is $m = -\dfrac{2}{3}$. By substituting $-\dfrac{2}{3}$ for m and 4 for b in the equation $y = mx + b$, we have $y = -\dfrac{2}{3}x + 4$.

40. The slope of $y = 3x - 2$ is $m_1 = 3$. The slope of $y = \dfrac{1}{3}x + 6$ is $m_2 = \dfrac{1}{3}$. Since the slopes are not equal, the lines are not parallel. Since the slope $\dfrac{1}{3}$ is not the opposite of the reciprocal of the slope 3, the lines are not perpendicular. Thus, the lines are neither parallel nor perpendicular.

41. The slope of $y = \dfrac{4}{7}x + 1$ is $m_1 = \dfrac{4}{7}$. The slope of $y = -\dfrac{7}{4}x - 5$ is $m_2 = -\dfrac{7}{4}$. Since the slope $-\dfrac{7}{4}$ is the opposite of the reciprocal of the slope $\dfrac{4}{7}$, the lines are perpendicular.

42. The graph of the line $x = -2$ is vertical. The graph of the line $y = 5$ is horizontal. Thus, the two lines are perpendicular.

43. The graphs of the lines $x = -4$ and $x = 1$ are both vertical. Thus, the two lines are parallel.

44. $\dfrac{\text{change in temperature}}{\text{change in time}} = \dfrac{-6°F}{4 \text{ hours}} = \dfrac{-1.5°F}{1 \text{ hour}}$

The average rate of change is $-1.5°F$ per hour.

45. $\dfrac{\text{change in sales}}{\text{change in time}} = \dfrac{\$34 \text{ billion} - \$2.0 \text{ billion}}{\text{year } 2007 - \text{ year } 1980}$

$= \dfrac{\$32 \text{ billion}}{27 \text{ years}}$

$= \dfrac{\$1.185 \text{ billion}}{1 \text{ year}}$

The average rate of change is $1.19 billion per year.

46. a. The total charge is $2 per mile, plus a $2.50 flat fee. Thus, the equation is $c = 2d + 2.5$.

b. $\underset{\text{dollars}}{c} = \underset{\substack{\text{dollars} \\ \text{mile}}}{2} \cdot \underset{\text{miles}}{d} + \underset{\text{dollars}}{2.5}$

We use the fact that $\dfrac{\text{miles}}{\text{miles}} = 1$ to simplify the right-hand side of the equation:

$\dfrac{\text{dollars}}{\text{mile}} \cdot \text{miles} + \text{dollars} = \text{dollars} + \text{dollars}$.

So, the units on both sides of the equation are dollars, suggesting the equation is correct.

c. Substituting $d = 17$ in the equation, we obtain $c = 2(17) + 2.5 = 36.5$.

The total cost of a 17-mile trip will be $36.50.

47. a. The slope is -4. It means that the person loses 4 pounds per month.

b. Since t is the number of months since the person began the weight-loss program, the w-intercept is $(0, 195)$. Substituting -4 for m and 195 for b in the equation $w = mt + b$, we obtain $w = -4t + 195$.

c. Substituting $t = 6$ in the equation, we obtain $w = -4(6) + 195 = 171$. The person's goal was 171 pounds.

48. a. The slope of the graph is 1891. This means that the average U.S. personal income increases by $1891 per year.

b. The *A*-intercept is (0, 38,611). This means that, in 2007, the average U.S. personal income was $38,611.

c. In 2007, *t* = 0 and the average U.S. personal income was $38,611. Therefore,

$b = 38,611$. Since the slope is 1891, the equation is $A(t) = 1891t + 38,611$.

d. To find $A(7)$, substitute 7 for *t*.

$$A(7) = 1891(7) + 38,611$$
$$= 13,237 + 38,611$$
$$= 51,848$$

The average U.S. personal income in 2014 will be about $51,848, according to the model.

49. Yes, *C* and *n* are linearly related. The slope is 130. It means that the cost is $130 per calculator.

50. Equation 1 could be linear because, for each unit increase in *x*, *y* decreases by a constant 3 units.

Equation 2 is not linear because the change in *y* is not constant.

Equation 3 could be linear because, *y* is constant at 4.

Equation 4 could be linear because, for each unit increase in *x*, *y* increases by a constant 5 units.

51. For Equation 1, for each unit increase in *x*, *y* decreases by 9 units.

x	y
0	50
1	41
2	41 − 9 = 32
3	32 − 9 = 23
4	23 − 9 = 14

For Equation 2, for each unit increase in *x*, *y* increases by 4 units.

x	y
0	12
1	16
2	16 + 4 = 20
3	20 + 4 = 24
4	24 + 4 = 28

For Equation 3, $m = \dfrac{19 - 25}{64 - 61} = \dfrac{-6}{3} = -2$. For each unit increase in *x*, *y* decreases by 2 units.

x	y
61	25
62	25 − 2 = 23
63	23 − 2 = 21
64	19
65	19 − 2 = 17

For Equation 4, $m = \dfrac{8 - (-4)}{30 - 26} = \dfrac{12}{4} = 3$. For each unit increase in *x*, *y* increases by 3 units.

x	y
26	−4
27	−4 + 3 = −1
28	−1 + 3 = 2
29	2 + 3 = 5
30	8

52. The slope of $y = -6x + 39$ is -6. This means that, when the value of *x* increases by 1, the value of *y* decreases by 6.

Chapter 3 Test

1. The line contains the point $(-3, 3)$, so $y = 3$ when $x = -3$.

2. The line contains the point $(3, -1)$, so $x = 3$ when $y = -1$.

3. The line intersects the *y*-axis at the point (0, 1), so the *y*-intercept is (0, 1).

4. The line intersects the *x*-axis at approximately the point (1.5, 0), so the *x*-intercept is (1.5, 0).

5. Slope of ski run $A = \dfrac{115 \text{ yards}}{580 \text{ yards}} \approx 0.198$

Slope of ski run $B = \dfrac{150 \text{ yards}}{675 \text{ yards}} \approx 0.222$

Thus, ski run B is steeper since it has a larger slope.

6. Using the slope formula with $(x_1, y_1) = (3, -8)$ and $(x_2, y_2) = (5, -2)$, the slope is

$$m = \frac{y_2 - y_1}{x_2 - x_1} = \frac{-2 - (-8)}{5 - 3} = \frac{-2 + 8}{5 - 3} = \frac{6}{2} = 3.$$

The slope is positive, so the line is increasing.

7. Using the slope formula with $(x_1, y_1) = (-4, -1)$ and $(x_2, y_2) = (2, -4)$, the slope is

$$m = \frac{y_2 - y_1}{x_2 - x_1} = \frac{-4 - (-1)}{2 - (-4)} = \frac{-4 + 1}{2 + 4} = \frac{-3}{6} = -\frac{1}{2}.$$

The slope is negative, so the line is decreasing.

8. Using the slope formula with $(x_1, y_1) = (-5, 4)$ and $(x_2, y_2) = (1, 4)$, the slope is

$$m = \frac{y_2 - y_1}{x_2 - x_1} = \frac{4 - 4}{-1 - (-5)} = \frac{4 - 4}{-1 + 5} = \frac{0}{4} = 0.$$

So, the line is horizontal.

9. Using the slope formula with $(x_1, y_1) = (-2, -7)$ and $(x_2, y_2) = (-2, 3)$, the slope is

$$m = \frac{y_2 - y_1}{x_2 - x_1} = \frac{3 - (-7)}{-2 - (-2)} = \frac{3 + 7}{-2 + 2} = \frac{10}{0}, \text{ which is}$$

undefined. So the line is vertical.

10. Using the slope formula with $(x_1, y_1) = (-5.99, -3.27)$ and $(x_2, y_2) = (2.83, 8.12)$, the slope is

$$m = \frac{y_2 - y_1}{x_2 - x_1} = \frac{8.12 - (-3.27)}{2.83 - (-5.99)} = \frac{11.39}{8.82} \approx 1.29.$$

The slope is positive, so the line is increasing.

11. We first plot the y-intercept $(0, -3)$. The slope is $\dfrac{2}{5}$, so the run is 5 and the rise is 2. From $(0, -3)$, we count 5 units to the right and 2 units up, where we plot the point $(5, -1)$. We then sketch the line that contains these two points.

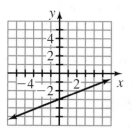

12. The equation $y = -\dfrac{3}{2}x + 2$ is in slope-intercept form, so the slope is $m = -\dfrac{3}{2}$ and the y-intercept is $(0, 2)$. We first plot $(0, 2)$. From this point we move 2 units to the right and 3 units down, where we plot the point $(2, -1)$. We then sketch the line that contains these two points.

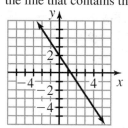

13. The equation $y = \dfrac{5}{6}x$ is in slope-intercept form, so the slope is $m = \dfrac{5}{6}$ and the y-intercept is $(0, 0)$. We first plot $(0, 0)$. From this point we move 6 units to the right and 5 units up, where we plot the point $(6, 5)$. We then sketch the line that contains these two points.

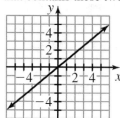

14. The equation $y = 3x - 4$ is in slope-intercept form, so the slope is $m = 3 = \dfrac{3}{1}$ and the y-intercept is $(0, -4)$. We first plot $(0, -4)$. From this point we move 1 unit to the right and 3 units up, where we plot the point $(1, -1)$. We then sketch the line that contains these two points.

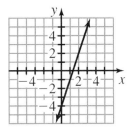

15. The equation $y = 2$ is in slope-intercept form, so the slope is $m = 0$ and the y-intercept is $(0, 2)$. Since the slope is 0, the line is horizontal. We sketch the horizontal line with y-intercept $(0, 2)$.

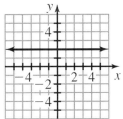

16. The equation $y = -2x + 3$ is in slope-intercept form, so the slope is $m = -2 = \dfrac{-2}{1}$ and the y-intercept is $(0, 3)$. We first plot $(0, 3)$. From this point we move 1 unit to the right and 2 units down, where we plot the point $(1, 1)$. We then sketch the line that contains these two points.

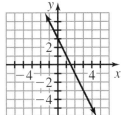

17. The y-intercept of the line is $(0, 1)$. The run is 2 when the rise is 1, so the slope of the line is $m = \dfrac{1}{2}$. By substituting $\dfrac{1}{2}$ for m and 1 for b in the equation $y = mx + b$, we have $y = \dfrac{1}{2}x + 1$.

18. a.

Time (years) t	Car's value (thousands of dollars) v
0	$17 - 2 \cdot 0$
1	$17 - 2 \cdot 1$
2	$17 - 2 \cdot 2$
3	$17 - 2 \cdot 3$
t	$17 - 2 \cdot t$

So, the equation is $v = 17 - 2t$, or $v = -2t + 17$.

b. In the following table, we substitute values for t in the equation $v = -2t + 17$ to find the corresponding values for v. Then, we plot the points and sketch a line that contains the points.

t	v
0	$17 - 2 \cdot 0 = 17$
1	$17 - 2 \cdot 1 = 15$
2	$17 - 2 \cdot 2 = 13$
3	$17 - 2 \cdot 3 = 11$

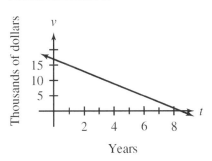

c. From the table and graph, we see the v-intercept is $(0, 17)$. This indicates that, the used car is currently worth \$17 thousand.

d. The line contains the point $(6, 5)$, so $v = 5$ when $t = 6$ as illustrated.

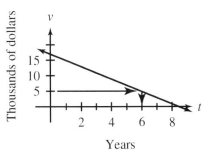

Thus, the value of the car will be \$5 thousand 6 years from now.

19. a. The line increases from left to right, so the m is positive. It crosses the y-axis above the x-axis, so b is positive.

b. The line is horizontal, so the m is zero. It crosses the y-axis below the x-axis, so b is negative.

c. The line decreases from left to right, so the m is negative. It crosses the y-axis above the x-axis, so b is positive.

d. The line decreases from left to right, so the m is negative. It crosses the y-axis below the x-axis, so b is negative.

20. The slope of $y = \dfrac{2}{5}x + 3$ is $m_1 = \dfrac{2}{5}$. The slope of $y = \dfrac{5}{2}x - 7$ is $m_2 = \dfrac{5}{2}$. Since the slopes are not equal, the lines are not parallel. Since the slope $\dfrac{5}{2}$ is not the opposite of the reciprocal of the slope $\dfrac{2}{5}$, the lines are not perpendicular. Thus, the lines are neither parallel nor perpendicular.

21. The slope of $y = -3x + 8$ is $m_1 = -3$. The slope of $y = -3x - 1$ is $m_2 = -3$. Since the slopes are equal, the lines are parallel.

22. $\dfrac{\text{change in spending}}{\text{change in time}} = \dfrac{519.6 - 239.1}{2007 - 1998}$
$= \dfrac{280.5}{9}$
$= 31.17$

The average rate of change is about \$31.2 million per year.

23. $\dfrac{\text{change in new-car dealerships}}{\text{change in time}}$
$= \dfrac{21,000 \text{ dealerships} - 31,000 \text{ dealerships}}{\text{year } 2008 - \text{ year } 1970}$
$= \dfrac{-10,000 \text{ new-car dealerships}}{38 \text{ years}}$
$\approx -\dfrac{263 \text{ new-car dealerships}}{1 \text{ year}}$

The average rate of change is –263 new-car dealerships per year.

24. a. The slope is 2. It means that the number of states with ethanol plants is increasing by 2 per year.

b. Since t is the number of years since 2007, the n-intercept is $(0, 22)$. This means that, in 2007, 22 states had ethanol plants.

c. Since t is the number of years since 2007, the n-intercept is $(0, 22)$. Substituting 2 for m and 22 for b in the equation $n = mt + b$, we obtain $n = 2t + 22$.

d. $\underset{\text{states}}{n} = \underset{\substack{\text{states} \\ \text{year}}}{2} \cdot \underset{\text{years}}{t} + \underset{\text{states}}{22}$

We use the fact that $\dfrac{\text{years}}{\text{years}} = 1$ to simplify the right-hand side of the equation:
$\dfrac{\text{states}}{\text{year}} \cdot \text{years} + \text{states} = \text{states} + \text{states}$.
So, the units on both sides of the equation are states, suggesting the equation is correct.

e. The year 2013 is represented by $t = 6$ since 2013 is 6 years after 2007. Substituting $t = 6$ in the equation, we obtain $n = 2(6) + 22 = 34$. We predict that there will be 34 states with ethanol plants in 2013.

25. a.

Yes, the line comes close to the data points.

b. The slope is 0.24. It means that the cooking time for a turkey increases by 0.24 hour per pound (or 14.4 minutes per pound).

c. The T-intercept is $(0, 1.64)$. It means the cooking time for a 0-pound turkey is 1.64 hours. Model breakdown has occurred.

d. Substituting 19 for w in the equation gives $T = 0.24(19) + 1.64 = 6.2$. The model predicts that the cooking time for a 19-pound turkey will be 6.2 hours.

26. a. Yes, the person is running at a constant speed. This can be seen by the linear relationship between minutes and miles, showing a constant slope.

b. The line contains the points $(0, 0)$ and $(30, 4)$, so the slope is

$$m = \frac{4 \text{ miles} - 0 \text{ miles}}{30 \text{ minutes} - 0 \text{ minutes}}$$

$$= \frac{4 \text{ miles}}{30 \text{ minutes}}$$

$$= \frac{4 \text{ miles}}{0.5 \text{ hour}}$$

$$= \frac{8 \text{ miles}}{1 \text{ hour}}$$

The person is running at a speed of 8 miles per hour.

27. For Set 1, the slope is $m = \dfrac{22 - 25}{1 - 0} = \dfrac{-3}{1} = -3$, and the y-intercept is $(0, 25)$. Substituting -3 for m and 25 for b in the equation $y = mx + b$, we obtain $y = -3x + 25$.

For Set 2, the slope is $m = \dfrac{6 - 2}{1 - 0} = \dfrac{4}{1} = 4$, and the y-intercept is $(0, 2)$. Substituting 4 for m and 2 for b in the equation $y = mx + b$, we obtain $y = 4x + 2$.

For Set 3, the slope is $m = \dfrac{7 - 12}{1 - 0} = \dfrac{-5}{1} = -5$, and the y-intercept is $(0, 12)$. Substituting -5 for m and 12 for b in the equation $y = mx + b$, we obtain $y = -5x + 12$.

For Set 4, the slope is $m = \dfrac{53 - 47}{1 - 0} = \dfrac{6}{1} = 6$, and the y-intercept is $(0, 47)$. Substituting 6 for m and 47 for b in the equation $y = mx + b$, we obtain $y = 6x + 47$.

28. The slope of $y = 3x - 8$ is 3. This means that, when the value of x increases by 1, the value of y increases by 3.

Chapter 4
Simplifying Expressions and Solving Equations

Homework 4.1

1. $2(5x) = (2 \cdot 5)x = 10x$

3. $-4(-9x) = -(4(-9))x = -(-36)x = 36x$

5. $\dfrac{1}{2}(-8x) = \left(\dfrac{1}{2} \cdot (-8)\right)x = -4x$

7. $7\left(\dfrac{x}{4}\right) = \left(7 \cdot \dfrac{1}{4}\right)x = \dfrac{7}{4}x = \dfrac{7x}{4}$

9. $3(x+9) = 3 \cdot x + 3 \cdot 9$
$\qquad = 3x + 27$

11. $(x-5)2 = x \cdot 2 - 5 \cdot 2$
$\qquad = 2x - 10$

13. $-2(t+5) = -2 \cdot t + (-2) \cdot 5$
$\qquad = -2t - 10$

15. $-5(6-2x) = -5 \cdot 6 - (-5)(2x)$
$\qquad = -30 + 10x$

17. $(4x+7)(-6) = 4x(-6) + 7(-6)$
$\qquad = -24x - 42$

19. $2(3x-5y) = 2 \cdot 3x - 2 \cdot 5y$
$\qquad = 6x - 10y$

21. $-5(4x+3y-8) = -5(4x) + (-5)(3y) - (-5)(8)$
$\qquad = -20x - 15y + 40$

23. $3 + 2(x+1) = 3 + 2 \cdot x + 2 \cdot 1$
$\qquad = 3 + 2x + 2$
$\qquad = 2x + 3 + 2$
$\qquad = 2x + 5$

25. $-0.3(x+0.2) = (-0.3)x + (-0.3)(0.2)$
$\qquad = -0.3x - 0.06$

27. $4(a+3) + 7 = 4 \cdot a + 4 \cdot 3 + 7$
$\qquad = 4a + 12 + 7$
$\qquad = 4a + 19$

29. $-3(4x-2) + 3 = -3(4x) - (-3)(2) + 3$
$\qquad = -12x + 6 + 3$
$\qquad = -12x + 9$

31. $4 - 3(3a-5) = 4 - 3(3a) - (-3)(5)$
$\qquad = 4 - 9a + 15$
$\qquad = -9a + 4 + 15$
$\qquad = -9a + 19$

33. $-3.7 + 4.2(2.5x-8.3)$
$\qquad = -3.7 + 4.2(2.5x) - 4.2(8.3)$
$\qquad = -3.7 + 10.5x - 34.86$
$\qquad = 10.5x - 3.7 - 34.86$
$\qquad = 10.5x - 38.56$

35. $-(t+2) = -1(t+2)$
$\qquad = -t + (-1)(2)$
$\qquad = -t - 2$

37. $-(8x-9y) = -1(8x-9y)$
$\qquad = -1(8x) - (-1)(9y)$
$\qquad = -8x + 9y$

39. $-(5x+8y-1) = -1(5x+8y-1)$
$\qquad = -1(5x) + (-1)(8y) - (-1)(1)$
$\qquad = -5x - 8y + 1$

41. $-(3x+2) + 5 = -1(3x+2) + 5$
$\qquad = -1(3x) + (-1)(2) + 5$
$\qquad = -3x - 2 + 5$
$\qquad = -3x + 3$

43. $8-(x+3)=8-1(x+3)$
$$=8-1x+(-1)(3)$$
$$=8-x-3$$
$$=-x+8-3$$
$$=-x+5$$

45. $-2-(2t-5)=-2-1(2t-5)$
$$=-2-1(2t)-(-1)(5)$$
$$=-2-2t+5$$
$$=-2t-2+5$$
$$=-2t+3$$

47. $\dfrac{1}{2}(4x+8)=\dfrac{1}{2}(4x)+\dfrac{1}{2}(8)$
$$=2x+4$$

49. $2(4x)=(2\cdot4)x=8x$

Evaluate $2(4x)$ for $x=2$:
$$2(4(2))=2(8)=16$$

Evaluate $8x$ for $x=2$:
$$8(2)=16$$
The results are the same. Additional choices of x will vary.

51. $5(x-7)=5x-5(7)$
$$=5x-35$$
Evaluate $5(x-7)$ for $x=2$:
$$5(2-7)=5(-5)=-25$$

Evaluate $5x-35$ for $x=2$:
$$5(2)-35=10-35=-25$$
The results are the same. Additional choices of x will vary.

53. $5-3(x+4)=5-3x+(-3)(4)$
$$=5-3x-12$$
$$=-3x+5-12$$
$$=-3x-7$$
Evaluate $5-3(x+4)$ for $x=2$:
$$5-3(2+4)=5-3(6)=5-18=-13$$

Evaluate $-3x-7$ for $x=2$:
$$-3(2)-7=-6-7=-13$$
The results are the same. Additional choices of x will vary.

55. $3(x+2)=3x+3(2)$
$$=3x+6$$

57. $-4(2x-5)=-4(2x)-(-4)(5)$
$$=-8x+20$$

59. $5-2(x-4)=5-2x-(-2)(4)$
$$=5-2x+8$$
$$=-2x+5+8$$
$$=-2x+13$$

61. $-2+7(2x+1)=-2+7(2x)+7(1)$
$$=-2+14x+7$$
$$=14x-2+7$$
$$=14x+5$$

63. a. $2(x-3)+4=2x-2(3)+4$
$$=2x-6+4$$
$$=2x-2$$

b. Evaluate $2(x-3)+4$ for $x=5$:
$$2(5-3)+4=2(2)+4=4+4=8$$

c. Evaluate $2x-2$ for $x=5$:
$$2(5)-2=10-2=8$$

d. The results are the same. The simplification might be correct.

65. Evaluate $3(x+4)$ for $x=2$:
$$3(2+4)=3(6)=18$$

Evaluate $3x+4$ for $x=2$:
$$3(2)+4=6+4=10$$
The results are not the same; the simplification is incorrect.

67. a. Evaluate $a(bc)$ for $a=2$, $b=3$, and $c=4$:
$$2(3\cdot4)=2(12)=24$$

Evaluate $(ab)(ac)$ for $a=2$, $b=3$, and $c=4$:
$$(2\cdot3)(2\cdot4)=(6)(8)=48$$

b. The results are not the same, so the expressions are not equivalent. The simplification is incorrect.

c. $a(bc) = (ab)c$

69. $y = 2(x - 3)$

$= 2x - 2(3)$

$= 2x - 6$

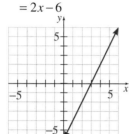

71. $y = -3(x + 1)$

$= -3x + (-3)(1)$

$= -3x - 3$

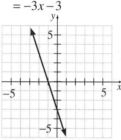

73. $y = -2(3x)$

$= (-2 \cdot 3)x$

$= -6x$

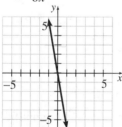

75. Answers may vary.

77. Answers may vary. Some possibilities:
$2(x - 3)$, $2(x - 2) - 2$, $2(x + 1) - 8$

79. Evaluate $a - (b - c) = (a - b) - c$ for $a = 7$,
$b = 5$, and $c = 1$:

$7 - (5 - 1) = (7 - 5) - 1$

$7 - 4 = 2 - 1$

$3 = 1$ false

The result is a contradiction, so the statement

$a - (b - c) = (a - b) - c$ is false. There is no associative law for subtraction because the order in which a series of subtraction operations are performed affects the signs of different terms.

81. Step 1: commutative law for addition
Step 2: associative law for addition
Step 3: commutative law for addition
Step 4: associative law for addition

83. Step 1: commutative law for multiplication
Step 2: distributive law
Step 3: commutative law for multiplication

85. Step 1: $-a = -1 \cdot a$

Step 2: associative law for multiplication

Step 3: the product of two real numbers with different signs is negative.

Step 4: $-1 \cdot a = -a$

Step 5: $-(-a) = a$

Homework 4.2

1. $2x + 5x = (2 + 5)x$

$= 7x$

3. $9x - 4x = (9 - 4)x$

$= 5x$

5. $-8w - 5w = (-8 - 5)w$

$= -13w$

7. $-t + 5t = -1t + 5t$

$= (-1 + 5)t$

$= 4t$

9. $6.6x - 7.1x = (6.6 - 7.1)x$

$= -0.5x$

11. $\dfrac{2}{3}x + \dfrac{5}{3}x = \left(\dfrac{2}{3} + \dfrac{5}{3}\right)x$

$= \left(\dfrac{2 + 5}{3}\right)x$

$= \dfrac{7}{3}x$

13. $2 + 4x - 5 - 7x = 4x - 7x + 2 - 5$

$= -3x - 3$

15. $-3p + 2 + p - 9 = -3p + p + 2 - 9$
$$= -2p - 7$$

17. $3y + 5x - 2y - 2x + 1 = 5x - 2x + 3y - 2y + 1$
$$= 3x + y + 1$$

19. $-4.6x + 3.9y + 2.1 - 5.3x - 2.8y$
$$= -4.6x - 5.3x + 3.9y - 2.8y + 2.1$$
$$= -9.9x + 1.1y + 2.1$$

21. $-3(a - 5) + 2a = -3a + 15 + 2a$
$$= -3a + 2a + 15$$
$$= -a + 15$$

23. $5.2(8.3x + 4.9) - 2.4 = 43.16x + 25.48 - 2.4$
$$= 43.16x + 23.08$$

25. $4(3a - 2b) - 5a = 12a - 8b - 5a$
$$= 12a - 5a - 8b$$
$$= 7a - 8b$$

27. $8 - 2(x + 3) + x = 8 - 2x - 6 + x$
$$= -2x + x + 8 - 6$$
$$= -x + 2$$

29. $6x - (4x - 3y) - 5y = 6x - 4x + 3y - 5y$
$$= 2x - 2y$$

31. $2t - 3(5t + 2) + 1 = 2t - 15t - 6 + 1$
$$= -13t - 5$$

33. $6 - 2(x + 3y) + 2y = 6 - 2x - 6y + 2y$
$$= -2x - 6y + 2y + 6$$
$$= -2x - 4y + 6$$

35. $-3(x - 2) - 5(x + 4) = -3x + 6 - 5x - 20$
$$= -3x - 5x + 6 - 20$$
$$= -8x - 14$$

37. $6(2x - 3y) - 4(9x + 5y) = 12x - 18y - 36x - 20y$
$$= 12x - 36x - 18y - 20y$$
$$= -24x - 38y$$

39. $-(x - 1) - (1 - x) = -1x + 1 - 1 + x$
$$= -x + x + 1 - 1$$
$$= 0x + 0$$
$$= 0$$

41. $2x - 5y - 3(2x - 4y + 7) = 2x - 5y - 6x + 12y - 21$
$$= 2x - 6x - 5y + 12y - 21$$
$$= -4x + 7y - 21$$

43. $5(2x - 4y) - (3x - 7y + 2)$
$$= 10x - 20y - 3x + 7y - 2$$
$$= 10x - 3x - 20y + 7y - 2$$
$$= 7x - 13y - 2$$

45. $\dfrac{2}{7}(a + 1) - \dfrac{4}{7}(a - 1) = \dfrac{2}{7}a + \dfrac{2}{7} - \dfrac{4}{7}a + \dfrac{4}{7}$
$$= \dfrac{2}{7}a - \dfrac{4}{7}a + \dfrac{2}{7} + \dfrac{4}{7}$$
$$= -\dfrac{2}{7}a + \dfrac{6}{7}$$

47. $5x - \dfrac{1}{2}(4x + 6) = 5x - \dfrac{1}{2}(4x) - \dfrac{1}{2}(6)$
$$= 5x - 2x - 3$$
$$= 3x - 3$$

49. $x + 5x = 1x + 5x$
$$= (1 + 5)x$$
$$= 6x$$

51. $4(x - 2) = 4x - 4(2)$
$$= 4x - 8$$

53. $x + 3(x - 7) = x + 3x - 21$
$$= 4x - 21$$

55. $2x - 4(x + 6) = 2x - 4x - 24$
$$= -2x - 24$$

57. Twice the number plus 6 times the number. (answers may vary)
$$2x + 6x = (2 + 6)x$$
$$= 8x$$

59. 7 times the difference of the number and 5. (answers may vary)
$$7(x - 5) = 7x - 7(5)$$
$$= 7x - 35$$

61. The number, plus 5 times the sum of the number and 1. (answers may vary)

$$x + 5(x+1) = x + 5x + 5$$
$$= 1x + 5x + 5$$
$$= 6x + 5$$

63. Twice the number, minus 3 times the difference of the number and 9. (answers may vary)

$$2x - 3(x-9) = 2x - 3x + 27$$
$$= -x + 27$$

65. $(3x-7) + (5x+2) = 3x - 7 + 5x + 2$
$$= 3x + 5x - 7 + 2$$
$$= 8x - 5$$

67. $(4x+8) - (7x-1) = 4x + 8 - 7x + 1$
$$= 4x - 7x + 8 + 1$$
$$= -3x + 9$$

69. $-2x + 5 - 3 + 7x = -2x + 7x + 5 - 3$
$$= 5x + 2$$

Evaluate for $x = 4$:

$$-2(4) + 5 - 3 + 7(4) = 5(4) + 2$$
$$-8 + 5 - 3 + 28 = 20 + 2$$
$$-3 - 3 + 28 = 22$$
$$-6 + 28 = 22$$
$$22 = 22$$

The results are the same. Similar results will be obtained using other values for x.

71. $4(x+2) - (x-3) = 4x + 8 - 1x + 3$
$$= 4x - 1x + 8 + 3$$
$$= 3x + 11$$

Evaluate for $x = 4$:

$$4(4+2) - (4-3) = 3(4) + 11$$
$$4(6) - 1 = 12 + 11$$
$$24 - 1 = 12 + 11$$
$$23 = 23$$

The results are the same. Similar results will be obtained using other values for x.

73. a. $3(x+4) + 5x = 3x + 12 + 5x$
$$= 3x + 5x + 12$$
$$= 8x + 12$$

b. Evaluate $3(x+4) + 5x$ for $x = 2$:

$$3(2+4) + 5(2) = 3(6) + 5(2)$$
$$= 18 + 10$$
$$= 28$$

c. Evaluate $8x + 12$ for $x = 2$:

$$8(2) + 12 = 16 + 12 = 28$$

d. The results are the same. The simplification may be correct.

75. $-2(x-3) = -2x + 6 = 2(3-x) = -3(x-2) + x$

77.

Expression	Evaluate for $x = 2$
$4(x-3) + 5x - 1$	$4(2-3) + 5(2) - 1 = 4(-1) + 5(2) - 1$
	$= -4 + 10 - 1$
	$= 5$
$4x - 3 + 5x - 1$	$4(2) - 3 + 5(2) - 1 = 8 - 3 + 10 - 1$
	$= 14$
$4x + 5x - 3 - 1$	$4(2) + 5(2) - 3 - 1 = 8 + 10 - 3 - 1$
	$= 14$
$9x - 4$	$9(2) - 4 = 18 - 4$
	$= 14$

The mistake occurred in the second step.

Correct simplification:

$$4(x-3) + 5x - 1 = 4x - 12 + 5x - 1$$
$$= 4x + 5x - 12 - 1$$
$$= 9x - 13$$

79. Answers may vary. Some possibilities:
$7(x-1)-2x$, $4(x-2)+(x+1)$,
$3(2x-2)-(x+1)$

81. $y = 3x - 5x$
$\quad = (3-5)x$
$\quad = -2x$

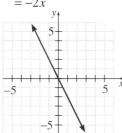

83. $y = 9x - 4 - 7x$
$\quad = 9x - 7x - 4$
$\quad = 2x - 4$

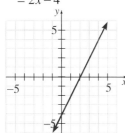

85. $y = 4(2x-1) - 5x$
$\quad = 8x - 4 - 5x$
$\quad = 8x - 5x - 4$
$\quad = 3x - 4$

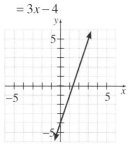

87. Answers may vary.

Homework 4.3

1. $3x + 1 = 7$

$3(2) + 1 \overset{?}{=} 7$

$6 + 1 \overset{?}{=} 7$

$7 \overset{?}{=} 7$ true

So, 2 is a solution to the equation.

3. $5(2x - 1) = 0$

$5(2(2) - 1) \overset{?}{=} 0$

$5(4 - 1) \overset{?}{=} 0$

$5(3) \overset{?}{=} 0$

$15 \overset{?}{=} 0$ false

So, 2 is not a solution to the equation.

5. $12 - x = 2(4x - 3)$

$12 - (2) \overset{?}{=} 2(4(2) - 3)$

$10 \overset{?}{=} 2(8 - 3)$

$10 \overset{?}{=} 2(5)$

$10 \overset{?}{=} 10$ true

So, 2 is a solution to the equation.

7. $x - 3 = 2$

$x - 3 + 3 = 2 + 3$

$x = 5$

Check: $x - 3 = 2$

$5 - 3 \overset{?}{=} 2$

$2 \overset{?}{=} 2$ true

So, the solution is 5.

9. $x + 6 = -8$

$x + 6 - 6 = -8 - 6$

$x = -14$

Check: $x + 6 = -8$

$-14 + 6 \overset{?}{=} -8$

$-8 \overset{?}{=} -8$ true

So, the solution is -14.

11.
$$t - 9 = 15$$
$$t - 9 + 9 = 15 + 9$$
$$t = 24$$

Check: $t - 9 = 15$
$$24 - 9 \overset{?}{=} 15$$
$$15 \overset{?}{=} 15 \text{ true}$$
So, the solution is 24.

13.
$$x + 11 = -17$$
$$x + 11 - 11 = -17 - 11$$
$$x = -28$$

Check: $x + 11 = -17$
$$-28 + 11 \overset{?}{=} -17$$
$$-17 \overset{?}{=} -17 \text{ true}$$
So, the solution is -28.

15.
$$-5 = x - 2$$
$$-5 + 2 = x - 2 + 2$$
$$-3 = x$$

Check: $-5 = x - 2$
$$-5 \overset{?}{=} -3 - 2$$
$$-5 \overset{?}{=} -5 \text{ true}$$
So, the solution is -3.

17.
$$x - 3 = 0$$
$$x - 3 + 3 = 0 + 3$$
$$x = 3$$

Check: $x - 3 = 0$
$$3 - 3 \overset{?}{=} 0$$
$$0 \overset{?}{=} 0 \text{ true}$$
So, the solution is 3.

19.
$$6r = 18$$
$$\frac{6r}{6} = \frac{18}{6}$$
$$r = 3$$

Check: $6r = 18$
$$6(3) \overset{?}{=} 18$$
$$18 \overset{?}{=} 18 \text{ true}$$
So, the solution is 3.

21.
$$-3x = 12$$
$$\frac{-3x}{-3} = \frac{12}{-3}$$
$$x = -4$$

Check: $-3x = 12$
$$-3(-4) \overset{?}{=} 12$$
$$12 \overset{?}{=} 12 \text{ true}$$
So, the solution is -4.

23.
$$15 = 3x$$
$$\frac{15}{3} = \frac{3x}{3}$$
$$5 = x$$

Check: $15 = 3x$
$$15 \overset{?}{=} 3(5)$$
$$15 \overset{?}{=} 15 \text{ true}$$
So, the solution is 5.

25.
$$6x = 8$$
$$\frac{6x}{6} = \frac{8}{6}$$
$$x = \frac{8}{6}$$
$$x = \frac{4}{3}$$

Check: $6x = 8$
$$6\left(\frac{4}{3}\right) \overset{?}{=} 8$$
$$\frac{24}{3} \overset{?}{=} 8$$
$$8 \overset{?}{=} 8 \text{ true}$$
So, the solution is $\frac{4}{3}$.

27. $-10x = -12$

$$\frac{-10x}{-10} = \frac{-12}{-10}$$

$$x = \frac{12}{10}$$

$$x = \frac{6}{5}$$

Check: $-10x = -12$

$$-10\left(\frac{6}{5}\right) \overset{?}{=} -12$$

$$\frac{-60}{5} \overset{?}{=} -12$$

$$-12 \overset{?}{=} -12 \text{ true}$$

So, the solution is $\frac{6}{5}$.

29. $-2x = 0$

$$\frac{-2x}{-2} = \frac{0}{-2}$$

$$x = 0$$

Check: $-2x = 0$

$$-2(0) \overset{?}{=} 0$$

$$0 \overset{?}{=} 0 \text{ true}$$

So, the solution is 0.

31. $\frac{1}{3}t = 5$

$$3\left(\frac{1}{3}t\right) = 3(5)$$

$$t = 15$$

Check: $\frac{1}{3}t = 5$

$$\frac{1}{3}(15) \overset{?}{=} 5$$

$$5 \overset{?}{=} 5 \text{ true}$$

So, the solution is 15.

33. $-\frac{2}{7}x = -3$

$$\left(-\frac{7}{2}\right)\left(-\frac{2}{7}x\right) = \left(-\frac{7}{2}\right)(-3)$$

$$x = \frac{21}{2}$$

Check: $-\frac{2}{7}x = -3$

$$-\frac{2}{7}\left(\frac{21}{2}\right) \overset{?}{=} -3$$

$$-\frac{42}{14} \overset{?}{=} -3$$

$$-3 \overset{?}{=} -3 \text{ true}$$

So, the solution is $\frac{21}{2}$.

35. $-9 = \frac{3x}{4}$

$$\left(\frac{4}{3}\right)(-9) = \left(\frac{4}{3}\right)\left(\frac{3x}{4}\right)$$

$$\frac{-36}{3} = x$$

$$-12 = x$$

Check: $-9 = \frac{3x}{4}$

$$-9 \overset{?}{=} \frac{3(-12)}{4}$$

$$-9 \overset{?}{=} \frac{-36}{4}$$

$$-9 \overset{?}{=} -9 \text{ true}$$

So, the solution is -12.

37. $\frac{2}{5}p = -\frac{4}{3}$

$$\frac{5}{2} \cdot \frac{2}{5}p = \frac{5}{2}\left(-\frac{4}{3}\right)$$

$$p = -\frac{20}{6}$$

$$p = -\frac{10}{3}$$

Check: $\dfrac{2}{5}p = -\dfrac{4}{3}$

$\dfrac{2}{5}\left(-\dfrac{10}{3}\right) \overset{?}{=} -\dfrac{4}{3}$

$-\dfrac{20}{15} \overset{?}{=} -\dfrac{4}{3}$

$-\dfrac{4}{3} \overset{?}{=} -\dfrac{4}{3}$ true

So, the solution is $-\dfrac{10}{3}$.

39. $-\dfrac{3x}{8} = -\dfrac{9}{4}$

$\left(-\dfrac{8}{3}\right)\left(-\dfrac{3x}{8}\right) = \left(-\dfrac{8}{3}\right)\left(-\dfrac{9}{4}\right)$

$x = \dfrac{72}{12}$

$x = 6$

Check: $-\dfrac{3x}{8} = -\dfrac{9}{4}$

$-\dfrac{3(6)}{8} \overset{?}{=} -\dfrac{9}{4}$

$-\dfrac{18}{8} \overset{?}{=} -\dfrac{9}{4}$

$-\dfrac{9}{4} \overset{?}{=} -\dfrac{9}{4}$ true

So, the solution is 6.

41. $-x = 3$

$-1(-x) = -1(3)$

$x = -3$

Check: $-x = 3$

$-(-3) \overset{?}{=} 3$

$3 = 3$ true

So, the solution is -3.

43. $-\dfrac{1}{2} = -x$

$(-1)\left(-\dfrac{1}{2}\right) = (-1)(-x)$

$\dfrac{1}{2} = x$

Check: $-\dfrac{1}{2} = -x$

$-\dfrac{1}{2} \overset{?}{=} -\left(\dfrac{1}{2}\right)$

$-\dfrac{1}{2} \overset{?}{=} -\dfrac{1}{2}$ true

So, the solution is $\dfrac{1}{2}$.

45. $x + 4.3 = -6.8$

$x + 4.3 - 4.3 = -6.8 - 4.3$

$x = -11.1$

Check: $x + 4.3 = -6.8$

$-11.1 + 4.3 \overset{?}{=} -6.8$

$-6.8 \overset{?}{=} -6.8$ true

So, the solution is -11.1.

47. $25.17 = x - 16.59$

$25.17 + 16.59 = x - 16.59 + 16.59$

$41.76 = x$

Check: $25.17 = x - 16.59$

$25.17 \overset{?}{=} 41.76 - 16.59$

$25.17 \overset{?}{=} 25.17$ true

So, the solution is 41.76.

49. $-3.7r = -8.51$

$\dfrac{-3.7r}{-3.7} = \dfrac{-8.51}{-3.7}$

$r = 2.3$

Check: $-3.7r = -8.51$

$-3.7(2.3) \overset{?}{=} -8.51$

$-8.51 \overset{?}{=} -8.51$ true

So, the solution is 2.3.

51. The line $y = -\dfrac{1}{2}x + 1$ intersects the line $y = 3$ only at the point $(-4, 3)$. The intersection point, $(-4, 3)$, has x-coordinate -4. So, -4 is the solution of $-\dfrac{1}{2}x + 1 = 3$.

53. The line $y = -\dfrac{1}{2}x + 1$ intersects the line $y = -1$ only at the point $(4, -1)$. The intersection point, $(4, -1)$, has x-coordinate 4. So, 4 is the solution of $-\dfrac{1}{2}x + 1 = -1$.

55. $x + 2 = 7$

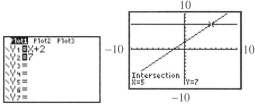

The intersection point, $(5, 7)$, has x-coordinate 5. So, 5 is the solution of $x + 2 = 7$.

57. $2x - 3 = 5$

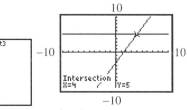

The intersection point, $(4, 5)$, has x-coordinate 4. So, 4 is the solution of $2x - 3 = 5$.

59. $-4(x - 1) = -8$

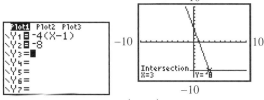

The intersection point, $(3, -8)$, has x-coordinate 3. So, 3 is the solution of $-4(x - 1) = -8$.

61. $\dfrac{2}{3}t - \dfrac{3}{2} = -\dfrac{7}{2}$

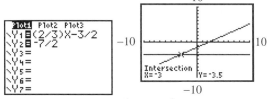

The intersection point $(-3, -3.5)$, has x-coordinate -3. So, -3 is the solution of $\dfrac{2}{3}t - \dfrac{3}{2} = -\dfrac{7}{2}$.

63. If we substitute 12 for y in the equation $y = 5x - 3$, the result is the equation $5x - 3 = 12$, which is what we are trying to solve. From the table, we see that the output $y = 12$ originates from the input $x = 3$. This means that 3 is a solution of the equation $5x - 3 = 12$.

65. If we substitute -13 for y in the equation $y = 5x - 3$, the result is the equation $5x - 3 = -13$, which is what we are trying to solve. From the table, we see that the output $y = -13$ originates from the input $x = -2$. This means that -2 is a solution of the equation $5x - 3 = -13$.

67.
$$2x + 5x = 14$$
$$(2 + 5)x = 14$$
$$7x = 14$$
$$\frac{7x}{7} = \frac{14}{7}$$
$$x = 2$$
The solution is 2.

69.
$$4x - 5x = -2$$
$$(4 - 5)x = -2$$
$$-1x = -2$$
$$\frac{-1x}{-1} = \frac{-2}{-1}$$
$$x = 2$$
The solution is 2.

71. The student subtracted two from both sides instead of dividing both sides by 2, and the subtraction itself was done incorrectly.
$$2x = 10$$
$$\frac{2x}{2} = \frac{10}{2}$$
$$x = 5$$
The solution is 5.

73.
$$4x = 12 \qquad \frac{4x}{4} = \frac{12}{4} \qquad x = 3$$
$$4(3) \overset{?}{=} 12 \qquad \frac{4(3)}{4} \overset{?}{=} \frac{12}{4} \qquad 3 \overset{?}{=} 3 \text{ true}$$
$$12 \overset{?}{=} 12 \text{ true} \qquad \frac{12}{4} \overset{?}{=} \frac{12}{4} \text{ true}$$

75. Yes, the work is correct but the equation can be solved in fewer steps.
$$x + 2 = 7$$
$$x + 2 - 2 = 7 - 2$$
$$x = 5$$
The solution is 5.

77. Answers may vary. One possibility:
$$x - 7 = 2$$
$$x - 7 + 7 = 2 + 7$$
$$x = 9$$

79. Answers may vary. One possibility:
$$\frac{x}{7} = 4$$
$$7 \cdot \frac{x}{7} = 7 \cdot 4$$
$$x = 28$$

81.
$$\frac{x}{3} = 2 \qquad x - 1 = 4$$
$$\qquad\qquad x - 1 + 1 = 4 + 1$$
$$3 \cdot \frac{x}{3} = 3 \cdot 2 \qquad x = 5$$
$$x = 6$$
The equations do not have the same solution set so they are ***not*** equivalent.

83. Answers may vary. Some examples:
$$x + 12 = 16$$
$$7x = 28$$
$$\frac{x}{2} = 2$$

85. Answers may vary. One example: $2x + 3 = 5$, $2x + 4 = 6$, and $\frac{x}{2} - \frac{3}{4} = -\frac{1}{4}$

87. Yes, the equations are equivalent. The second equation is obtained from the first by adding 6 to both sides. From the Addition Property of Equality, the two equations are equivalent.

89. a.
$$x + 2 = 7$$
$$x + 2 - 2 = 7 - 2$$
$$x = 5$$
The solution is 5.

b.
$$x + 5 = 9$$
$$x + 5 - 5 = 9 - 5$$
$$x = 4$$
The solution is 4.

c.
$$x + b = k$$
$$x + b - b = k - b$$
$$x = k - b$$
The solution is $k - b$.

91. Answers may vary.

Homework 4.4

1.
$$3x - 2 = 13$$
$$3x - 2 + 2 = 13 + 2$$
$$3x = 15$$
$$\frac{3x}{3} = \frac{15}{3}$$
$$x = 5$$
The solution is 5.

3.
$$-4x + 6 = 26$$
$$-4x + 6 - 6 = 26 - 6$$
$$-4x = 20$$
$$\frac{-4x}{-4} = \frac{20}{-4}$$
$$x = -5$$
The solution is -5.

5.
$$-5 = 6x + 3$$
$$-5 - 3 = 6x + 3 - 3$$
$$-8 = 6x$$
$$\frac{-8}{6} = \frac{6x}{6}$$
$$-\frac{4}{3} = x$$
The solution is $-\frac{4}{3}$.

7.
$$8 - x = -4$$
$$8 - x - 8 = -4 - 8$$
$$-x = -12$$
$$\frac{-x}{-1} = \frac{-12}{-1}$$
$$x = 12$$
The solution is 12.

9.
$$2x + 6 - 7x = -4$$
$$-5x + 6 = -4$$
$$-5x + 6 - 6 = -4 - 6$$
$$-5x = -10$$
$$\frac{-5x}{-5} = \frac{-10}{-5}$$
$$x = 2$$
The solution is 2.

11.
$$5x + 4 = 3x + 16$$
$$5x + 4 - 3x = 3x + 16 - 3x$$
$$2x + 4 = 16$$
$$2x + 4 - 4 = 16 - 4$$
$$2x = 12$$
$$\frac{2x}{2} = \frac{12}{2}$$
$$x = 6$$
The solution is 6.

13.
$$-3r - 1 = 2r + 24$$
$$-3r - 1 - 2r = 2r + 24 - 2r$$
$$-5r - 1 = 24$$
$$-5r - 1 + 1 = 24 + 1$$
$$-5r = 25$$
$$\frac{-5r}{-5} = \frac{25}{-5}$$
$$r = -5$$
The solution is -5.

15.
$$9 - x - 5 = 2x - x$$
$$4 - x = x$$
$$4 - x + x = x + x$$
$$4 = 2x$$
$$\frac{4}{2} = \frac{2x}{2}$$
$$2 = x$$
The solution is 2.

17.
$$2(x + 3) = 5x - 3$$
$$2x + 6 = 5x - 3$$
$$2x + 6 - 2x = 5x - 3 - 2x$$
$$6 = 3x - 3$$
$$6 + 3 = 3x - 3 + 3$$
$$9 = 3x$$
$$\frac{9}{3} = \frac{3x}{3}$$
$$3 = x$$
The solution is 3.

19.
$$1 - 3(5b - 2) = 4 - (7b + 3)$$
$$1 - 15b + 6 = 4 - 7b - 3$$
$$-15b + 7 = 1 - 7b$$
$$-15b + 7 + 15b = 1 - 7b + 15b$$
$$7 = 1 + 8b$$
$$7 - 1 = 1 + 8b - 1$$
$$6 = 8b$$
$$\frac{6}{8} = \frac{8b}{8}$$
$$\frac{3}{4} = b$$
The solution is $\frac{3}{4}$.

21.
$$4x = 3(2x - 1) + 5$$
$$4x = 6x - 3 + 5$$
$$4x = 6x + 2$$
$$4x - 6x = 6x + 2 - 6x$$
$$-2x = 2$$
$$\frac{-2x}{-2} = \frac{2}{-2}$$
$$x = -1$$
The solution is -1.

23. $3(4x-5)-(2x+3)=2(x-4)$

$12x-15-2x-3=2x-8$

$10x-18=2x-8$

$10x-18-2x=2x-8-2x$

$8x-18=-8$

$8x-18+18=-8+18$

$8x=10$

$\dfrac{8x}{8}=\dfrac{10}{8}$

$x=\dfrac{5}{4}$

The solution is $\dfrac{5}{4}$.

25. $\dfrac{x}{2}-\dfrac{3}{4}=\dfrac{1}{2}$

The LCD is 4, so multiply both sides of the equation by 4 to clear the fractions.

$4\cdot\left(\dfrac{x}{2}-\dfrac{3}{4}\right)=4\cdot\dfrac{1}{2}$

$2x-3=2$

$2x-3+3=2+3$

$2x=5$

$\dfrac{2x}{2}=\dfrac{5}{2}$

$x=\dfrac{5}{2}$

The solution is $\dfrac{5}{2}$.

27. $\dfrac{5x}{6}+\dfrac{2}{3}=2$

The LCD is 6, so multiply both sides of the equation by 6 to clear the fractions.

$6\cdot\left(\dfrac{5x}{6}+\dfrac{2}{3}\right)=6\cdot 2$

$5x+4=12$

$5x+4-4=12-4$

$5x=8$

$\dfrac{5x}{5}=\dfrac{8}{5}$

$x=\dfrac{8}{5}$

The solution is $\dfrac{8}{5}$.

29. $\dfrac{5}{6}k=\dfrac{3}{4}k+\dfrac{1}{2}$

The LCD is 12, so multiply both sides of the equation by 12 to clear the fractions.

$12\cdot\dfrac{5}{6}k=12\cdot\left(\dfrac{3}{4}k+\dfrac{1}{2}\right)$

$10k=9k+6$

$10k-9k=9k+6-9k$

$k=6$

The solution is 6.

31. $\dfrac{7}{12}x-\dfrac{5}{3}=\dfrac{7}{4}+\dfrac{5}{6}x$

The LCD is 12, so multiply both sides of the equation by 12 to clear the fractions.

$12\cdot\left(\dfrac{7}{12}x-\dfrac{5}{3}\right)=12\cdot\left(\dfrac{7}{4}+\dfrac{5}{6}x\right)$

$7x-20=21+10x$

$7x-20-10x=21+10x-10x$

$-3x-20=21$

$-3x-20+20=21+20$

$-3x=41$

$\dfrac{-3x}{-3}=\dfrac{41}{-3}$

$x=-\dfrac{41}{3}$

The solution is $-\dfrac{41}{3}$.

33. $\dfrac{4}{3}x-2=3x+\dfrac{5}{2}$

The LCD is 6, so multiply both sides of the equation by 6 to clear the fractions.

$6\cdot\left(\dfrac{4}{3}x-2\right)=6\cdot\left(3x+\dfrac{5}{2}\right)$

$8x-12=18x+15$

$8x-12-18x=18x+15-18x$

$-10x-12=15$

$-10x-12+12=15+12$

$-10x=27$

$\dfrac{-10x}{-10}=\dfrac{27}{-10}$

$x=-\dfrac{27}{10}$

The solution is $-\dfrac{27}{10}$.

35. $\dfrac{3(x-4)}{5} = -2x$

The LCD is 5, so multiply both sides of the equation by 5 to clear the fractions.

$$5 \cdot \dfrac{3(x-4)}{5} = 5(-2x)$$

$$3(x-4) = 5(-2x)$$

$$3x - 12 = -10x$$

$$3x - 12 - 3x = -10x - 3x$$

$$-12 = -13x$$

$$\dfrac{-12}{-13} = \dfrac{-13x}{-13}$$

$$\dfrac{12}{13} = x$$

The solution is $\dfrac{12}{13}$.

37. $\dfrac{4x+3}{5} = \dfrac{2x-1}{3}$

The LCD is 15, so multiply both sides of the equation by 15 to clear the fractions.

$$15 \cdot \dfrac{4x+3}{5} = 15 \cdot \dfrac{2x-1}{3}$$

$$3(4x+3) = 5(2x-1)$$

$$12x + 9 = 10x - 5$$

$$12x + 9 - 10x = 10x - 5 - 10x$$

$$2x + 9 = -5$$

$$2x + 9 - 9 = -5 - 9$$

$$2x = -14$$

$$\dfrac{2x}{2} = \dfrac{-14}{2}$$

$$x = -7$$

The solution is -7.

39. $\dfrac{4m-5}{2} - \dfrac{3m+1}{3} = \dfrac{5}{6}$

The LCD is 6, so multiply both sides of the equation by 6 to clear the fractions.

$$6 \cdot \left(\dfrac{4m-5}{2} - \dfrac{3m+1}{3} \right) = 6 \cdot \dfrac{5}{6}$$

$$3(4m-5) - 2(3m+1) = 5$$

$$12m - 15 - 6m - 2 = 5$$

$$6m - 17 = 5$$

$$6m - 17 + 17 = 5 + 17$$

$$6m = 22$$

$$\dfrac{6m}{6} = \dfrac{22}{6}$$

$$m = \dfrac{11}{3}$$

The solution is $\dfrac{11}{3}$.

41.

$$0.3x + 0.2 = 0.7$$

$$0.3x + 0.2 - 0.2 = 0.7 - 0.2$$

$$0.3x = 0.5$$

$$\dfrac{0.3x}{0.3} = \dfrac{0.5}{0.3}$$

$$x = \dfrac{5}{3}$$

$$x \approx 1.67$$

The solution is $\dfrac{5}{3}$ or 1.67.

43.

$$5.27x - 6.35 = 2.71x + 9.89$$

$$5.27x - 6.35 - 2.71x = 2.71x + 9.89 - 2.71x$$

$$2.56x - 6.35 = 9.89$$

$$2.56x - 6.35 + 6.35 = 9.89 + 6.35$$

$$2.56x = 16.24$$

$$\dfrac{2.56x}{2.56} = \dfrac{16.24}{2.56}$$

$$x \approx 6.34$$

The solution is approximately 6.34.

45. $0.4x - 1.6(2.5 - x) = 3.1(x - 5.4) - 11.3$

$0.4x - 4 + 1.6x = 3.1x - 16.74 - 11.3$

$2x - 4 = 3.1x - 28.04$

$2x - 4 - 3.1x = 3.1x - 28.04 - 3.1x$

$-1.1x - 4 = -28.04$

$-1.1x - 4 + 4 = -28.04 + 4$

$-1.1x = -24.04$

$\dfrac{-1.1x}{-1.1} = \dfrac{-24.04}{-1.1}$

$x \approx 21.85$

The solution is approximately 21.85.

47. a. An equation of the linear model can be written in slope-intercept form, $y = mx + b$.

Using t and a, we have $a = mt + b$. Since the slope (rate of change) is –27.2 and the a-intercept is (0, 315), we have $a = -27.2t + 315$.

b. Substitute $2014 - 2008 = 6$ for t in the equation from part (a).

$a = -27.2(6) + 315$

$= 151.8$

So, in 2014 there will be an average of 151.8 students per counselor.

c. Substitute 100 for a in the equation from part (a).

$100 = -27.2t + 315$

$100 - 315 = -27.2t + 315 - 315$

$-215 = -27.2t$

$\dfrac{-215}{-27.2} = \dfrac{-27.2t}{-27.2}$

$7.9 \approx t$

So, the ratio of students per counselor will be 100 in the year 2008 + 8 = 2016.

49. a. An equation of the linear model can be written in slope-intercept form, $y = mx + b$.

Using t and v, we have $v = mt + b$. Since the slope (rate of change) is 3.36 and the v-intercept is $(0, 8.16)$, we have $v = 3.36t + 8.16$.

b. Substitute 3 for t in the equation from part (a).

$v = 3.36(3) + 8.16$

$= 18.24$

So, the stock value was $18.24 per share 3 months after her sentencing.

c. Substitute 28.32 for v in the equation from part (a).

$28.32 = 3.36t + 8.16$

$28.32 - 8.16 = 3.36t + 8.16 - 8.16$

$20.16 = 3.36t$

$\dfrac{20.16}{3.36} = \dfrac{3.36t}{3.36}$

$6 = t$

So, 6 months after her sentencing, the value of a share of the stock was $28.32.

51. a. $p = 0.76t + 18.09$

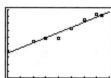

The line comes reasonably close to the data points.

b. The slope is 0.76; this means that the percent of college freshmen whose average grade in high school was an 'A' is increasing 0.76 percentage points each year.

c. Substitute 50 for p in the equation and solve for t.

$50 = 0.76t + 18.09$

$50 - 18.09 = 0.76t + 18.09 - 18.09$

$31.91 = 0.76t$

$\dfrac{31.91}{0.76} = \dfrac{0.76t}{0.76}$

$41.99 \approx t$

So, half of all college freshmen in $\backslash 1970 + 42 = 2012$ earned an average grade of 'A' in high school.

d. Substitute $2014 - 1970 = 44$ for t in the equation.

$$p = 0.76(44) + 18.09$$
$$= 33.44 + 18.09$$
$$= 51.53$$

So, in 2014 the percentage of college freshmen with an average grade of 'A' in high school will be approximately 51.5%.

e. Answers may vary.

53. Let x be the number.
$$3 + 5x = 18$$
$$3 + 5x - 3 = 18 - 3$$
$$5x = 15$$
$$\frac{5x}{5} = \frac{15}{5}$$
$$x = 3$$
The number is 3.

55. Let x be the number.
$$3(x - 2) = -18$$
$$3x - 6 = -18$$
$$3x - 6 + 6 = -18 + 6$$
$$3x = -12$$
$$\frac{3x}{3} = \frac{-12}{3}$$
$$x = -4$$
The number is -4.

57. Let x be the number.
$$x - 3 = 2x + 1$$
$$x - 3 - 2x = 2x + 1 - 2x$$
$$-x - 3 = 1$$
$$-x - 3 + 3 = 1 + 3$$
$$-x = 4$$
$$-1(-x) = -1(4)$$
$$x = -4$$
The number is -4.

59. Let x be the number.
$$1 - 4(x + 5) = 9$$
$$1 - 4x - 20 = 9$$
$$-4x - 19 = 9$$
$$-4x - 19 + 19 = 9 + 19$$
$$-4x = 28$$
$$\frac{-4x}{-4} = \frac{28}{-4}$$
$$x = -7$$
The number is -7.

61. Three less than two times a number is 7 (answers may vary).
$$2x - 3 = 7$$
$$2x - 3 + 3 = 7 + 3$$
$$2x = 10$$
$$\frac{2x}{2} = \frac{10}{2}$$
$$x = 5$$
The number is 5.

63. Three less than six times a number is equal to four less than eight times the number (answers may vary).
$$6x - 3 = 8x - 4$$
$$6x - 3 - 8x = 8x - 4 - 8x$$
$$-2x - 3 = -4$$
$$-2x - 3 + 3 = -4 + 3$$
$$-2x = -1$$
$$\frac{-2x}{-2} = \frac{-1}{-2}$$
$$x = \frac{1}{2}$$
The number is $\frac{1}{2}$.

65. Twice the difference of a number and 4 is 10 (answers may vary).
$$2(x - 4) = 10$$
$$2x - 8 = 10$$
$$2x - 8 + 8 = 10 + 8$$
$$2x = 18$$
$$\frac{2x}{2} = \frac{18}{2}$$
$$x = 9$$
The number is 9.

67. Four, minus 7 times the sum of a number and 1, is 2 (answers may vary).

$$4 - 7(x + 1) = 2$$
$$4 - 7x - 7 = 2$$
$$-7x - 3 = 2$$
$$-7x - 3 + 3 = 2 + 3$$
$$-7x = 5$$
$$\frac{-7x}{-7} = \frac{5}{-7}$$
$$x = -\frac{5}{7}$$

The number is $-\dfrac{5}{7}$.

69. $-3x + 7 = 5x + 15$

From tables 8 and 9, we see that for both of the equations $y = -3x + 7$ and $y = 5x + 15$, the input -1 leads to the output 10. Therefore, -1 is a solution of the equation $-3x + 7 = 5x + 15$.

71. $5x + 15 = 5$

Looking at table 9, we see that for the equation $y = 5x + 15$ the input -2 leads to the output 5. Therefore, -2 is a solution to the equation $5x + 15 = 5$.

73. $-4x + 8 = 2x - 9$

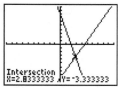

The approximate intersection point $(2.83, -3.33)$ has x-coordinate 2.83. So, the approximate solution of the original equation is 2.83.

75. $2.5x - 6.4 = -1.7x + 8.1$

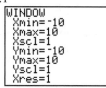

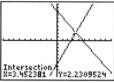

The approximate intersection point $(3.45, 2.23)$ has x-coordinate 3.45. So, the approximate solution of the original equation is 3.45.

77. $\dfrac{23}{75}x - \dfrac{99}{38} = -\dfrac{52}{89}x - \dfrac{67}{9}$

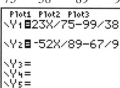

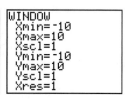

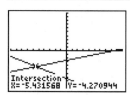

The approximate intersection point $(-5.43, -4.27)$ has x-coordinate -5.43. So, the approximate solution of the original equation is -5.43.

79. The two lines $y = -\dfrac{3}{2}x + 2$ and $y = \dfrac{1}{2}x - 2$ intersect only at $(2, -1)$, whose x-coordinate is 2. So, 2 is the solution of the equation $-\dfrac{3}{2}x + 2 = \dfrac{1}{2}x - 2$.

81. The two lines $y = -\dfrac{3}{2}x + 2$ and $y = 5$ intersect only at $(-2, 5)$, whose x-coordinate is -2. So, -2 is the solution of the equation $-\dfrac{3}{2}x + 2 = 5$.

83. The two lines $y = \dfrac{1}{2}x - 2$ and $y = 0$ intersect only at $(4, 0)$, whose x-coordinate is 4. So, 4 is the solution of the equation $\dfrac{1}{2}x - 2 = 0$.

85. The two lines $y = -\dfrac{1}{3}x + \dfrac{5}{3}$ and $y = \dfrac{3}{2}x + \dfrac{7}{2}$ intersect only at $(-1, 2)$, whose x-coordinate is -1. So, -1 is the solution of the equation $-\dfrac{1}{3}x + \dfrac{5}{3} = \dfrac{3}{2}x + \dfrac{7}{2}$.

87. The two lines $y = -\dfrac{1}{3}x + \dfrac{5}{3}$ and $y = 1$ intersect only at $(2, 1)$, whose x-coordinate is 2. So, 2 is the solution of the equation $-\dfrac{1}{3}x + \dfrac{5}{3} = 1$.

89. The two lines $y = \dfrac{3}{2}x + \dfrac{7}{2}$ and $y = -1$ intersect only at $(-3, -1)$, whose x-coordinate is -3. So, -3 is the solution of the equation $\dfrac{3}{2}x + \dfrac{7}{2} = -1$.

91.
$$3x + 4x = 7x$$
$$7x = 7x$$
$$7x - 7x = 7x - 7x$$
$$0 = 0 \text{ true}$$
Since $0 = 0$ is a true statement (of the form $a = a$), we conclude that the original equation is an identity and its solution set is the set of all real numbers.

93.
$$4x - 5 - 2x = 2x - 1$$
$$2x - 5 = 2x - 1$$
$$2x - 5 - 2x = 2x - 1 - 2x$$
$$-5 = -1 \text{ false}$$
Since $-5 = -1$ is a false statement, we conclude that the original equation is inconsistent and its solution set is the empty set.

95.
$$3k + 10 - 5k = 4k - 2$$
$$-2k + 10 = 4k - 2$$
$$-2k + 10 - 4k = 4k - 2 - 4k$$
$$-6k + 10 = -2$$
$$-6k + 10 - 10 = -2 - 10$$
$$-6k = -12$$
$$\frac{-6k}{-6} = \frac{-12}{-6}$$
$$k = 2$$
The number 2 is the only solution, so the equation is conditional.

97.
$$2(x + 3) - 2 = 2x + 4$$
$$2x + 6 - 2 = 2x + 4$$
$$2x + 4 = 2x + 4$$
$$2x + 4 - 2x = 2x + 4 - 2x$$
$$4 = 4 \text{ true}$$
Since $4 = 4$ is a true statement (of the form $a = a$), we conclude that the original equation is an identity and its solution set is the set of all real numbers.

99.
$$5(2x - 3) - 4x = 3(2x - 1) + 6$$
$$10x - 15 - 4x = 6x - 3 + 6$$
$$6x - 15 = 6x + 3$$
$$6x - 15 - 6x = 6x + 3 - 6x$$
$$-15 = 3 \text{ false}$$
Since $-15 = 3$ is a false statement, we conclude that the original equation is inconsistent and its solution set is the empty set.

101.
$$3(1 - 3) \overset{?}{=} 12 \text{ false}$$
$$3(1) - 9 \overset{?}{=} 12 \text{ false}$$
$$3(1) - 9 - 9 \overset{?}{=} 12 - 9 \text{ false}$$
$$3(1) \overset{?}{=} 3 \text{ true}$$
$$\frac{3(1)}{3} \overset{?}{=} \frac{3}{3} \text{ true}$$
$$1 \overset{?}{=} 1 \text{ true}$$
In going from the third line to the fourth, we went from a false statement to a true statement. This indicates that the mistake was made in the fourth line. In this step, the student subtracted 9 from both sides (and got the wrong result) when they should have added.
$$3(x - 3) = 12$$
$$3x - 9 = 12$$
$$3x - 9 + 9 = 12 + 9$$
$$3x = 21$$
$$\frac{3x}{3} = \frac{21}{3}$$
$$x = 7$$
The solution is 7.

103. The student has not isolated the variable on one side of the equation.

$$2(x-5)=x-3$$
$$2x-10=x-3$$
$$2x-10-x=x-3-x$$
$$x-10=-3$$
$$x-10+10=-3+10$$
$$x=7$$

The solution is 7.

105. Answers may vary.

107.
$$5(x-2)=2x-1$$
$$5x-10=2x-1$$
$$5x-10-2x=2x-1-2x$$
$$3x-10=-1$$
$$3x-10+10=-1+10$$
$$3x=9$$
$$\frac{3x}{3}=\frac{9}{3}$$
$$x=3$$

$$5(3-2)\overset{?}{=}2(3)-1 \ \text{true}$$
$$5(3)-10\overset{?}{=}2(3)-1 \ \text{true}$$
$$5(3)-10-2(3)\overset{?}{=}2(3)-1-2(3) \ \text{true}$$
$$3(3)-10\overset{?}{=}-1 \ \text{true}$$
$$3(3)-10+10\overset{?}{=}-1+10 \ \text{true}$$
$$3(3)\overset{?}{=}9 \ \text{true}$$
$$\frac{3(3)}{3}\overset{?}{=}\frac{9}{3} \ \text{true}$$
$$3=3 \ \text{true}$$

109.
$$3(x+2)+1=16$$
$$3x+6+1=16$$
$$3x+7=16$$
$$3x+7-7=16-7$$
$$3x=9$$
$$\frac{3x}{3}=\frac{9}{3}$$
$$x=3$$

The solution is 3.

$$3(x+2)=15$$
$$3x+6=15$$
$$3x+6-6=15-6$$
$$3x=9$$
$$\frac{3x}{3}=\frac{9}{3}$$
$$x=3$$

The solution is 3.

Answers may vary. All of the equations shown are equivalent, so the solution to one ($x=3$) is the solution to each of them.

Homework 4.5

1. $3x+7x=8$ is a linear equation because the statement contains an equal sign.

3. $3x+7x$ is a linear expression because the statement does not contain an equal sign.

5. $4-2(x-9)$ is a linear expression because the statement does not contain an equal sign.

7. $4-2(x-9)=5$ is a linear equation because the statement contains an equal sign.

9.
$$3x+4x=14$$
$$7x=14$$
$$\frac{7x}{7}=\frac{14}{7}$$
$$x=2$$

The solution is 2.

11. $3x+4x=(3+4)x=7x$

The simplified expression is $7x$.

13.
$$b-5(b-1)=b-5b+5$$
$$=-4b+5$$

The simplified expression is $-4b+5$.

15. $b - 5(b - 1) = 0$

$b - 5b + 5 = 0$

$-4b + 5 = 0$

$-4b + 5 - 5 = 0 - 5$

$-4b = -5$

$\dfrac{-4b}{-4} = \dfrac{-5}{-4}$

$b = \dfrac{5}{4}$

The solution is $\dfrac{5}{4}$.

17. $3(3x - 5) + 2(5x + 4) = 0$

$9x - 15 + 10x + 8 = 0$

$19x - 7 = 0$

$19x - 7 + 7 = 0 + 7$

$19x = 7$

$\dfrac{19x}{19} = \dfrac{7}{19}$

$x = \dfrac{7}{19}$

The solution is $\dfrac{7}{19}$.

19. $3(3x - 5) + 2(5x + 4) = 9x - 15 + 10x + 8$

$= 19x - 7$

The simplified expression is $19x - 7$.

21. $3(x - 2) - (7x + 2) = 4(3x + 1)$

$3x - 6 - 7x - 2 = 12x + 4$

$-4x - 8 = 12x + 4$

$-4x - 8 - 12x = 12x + 4 - 12x$

$-16x - 8 = 4$

$-16x - 8 + 8 = 4 + 8$

$-16x = 12$

$\dfrac{-16x}{-16} = \dfrac{12}{-16}$

$x = -\dfrac{3}{4}$

The solution is $-\dfrac{3}{4}$.

23. $3(x - 2) - (7x + 2) - 4(3x + 1)$

$= 3x - 6 - 7x - 2 - 12x - 4$

$= 3x - 7x - 12x - 6 - 2 - 4$

$= -16x - 12$

The simplified expression is $-16x - 12$.

25. $7.2p - 4.5 - 1.3p = 7.2p - 1.3p - 4.5$

$= 5.9p - 4.5$

The simplified expression is $5.9p - 4.5$.

27. $7.2k - 4.5 - 1.3k = 20.5 - 6.6k$

$5.9k - 4.5 = 20.5 - 6.6k$

$5.9k - 4.5 + 6.6k = 20.5 - 6.6k + 6.6k$

$12.5k - 4.5 = 20.5$

$12.5k - 4.5 + 4.5 = 20.5 + 4.5$

$12.5k = 25$

$\dfrac{12.5k}{12.5} = \dfrac{25}{12.5}$

$k = 2$

The solution is 2.

29. $-3.5(x - 8) - 2.6(x - 2.8) = 13.93$

$-3.5x + 28 - 2.6x + 7.28 = 13.93$

$-6.1x + 35.28 = 13.93$

$-6.1x + 35.28 - 35.28 = 13.93 - 35.28$

$-6.1x = -21.35$

$\dfrac{-6.1x}{-6.1} = \dfrac{-21.35}{-6.1}$

$x = 3.5$

The solution is 3.5.

31. $3.5(x \ 8) - 2.6(x - 2.8)$

$= -3.5x + 28 - 2.6x + 7.28$

$= -6.1x + 35.28$

The simplified expression is $-6.1x + 35.28$.

33. $-\dfrac{6w}{8} = -\dfrac{2 \cdot 3w}{2 \cdot 4} = -\dfrac{3w}{4}$

The simplified expression is $-\dfrac{3w}{4}$.

35.
$$-\frac{6w}{8} = \frac{3}{2}$$

$$-\frac{8}{6} \cdot \left(-\frac{6w}{8}\right) = -\frac{8}{6} \cdot \frac{3}{2}$$

$$w = -\frac{24}{12}$$

$$w = -2$$

The solution is -2.

37.
$$\frac{5x}{6} + \frac{1}{2} - \frac{3x}{4} = \frac{5x}{6} \cdot \frac{2}{2} - \frac{3x}{4} \cdot \frac{3}{3} + \frac{1}{2}$$

$$= \frac{10x}{12} - \frac{9x}{12} + \frac{1}{2}$$

$$= \frac{x}{12} + \frac{1}{2}$$

The simplified expression is $\frac{x}{12} + \frac{1}{2}$.

39.
$$\frac{5x}{6} + \frac{1}{2} - \frac{3x}{4} = 0$$

$$12\left(\frac{5x}{6} + \frac{1}{2} - \frac{3x}{4}\right) = 12 \cdot 0$$

$$10x + 6 - 9x = 0$$

$$x + 6 = 0$$

$$x + 6 - 6 = 0 - 6$$

$$x = -6$$

The solution is -6.

41.
$$\frac{7}{2}x - \frac{5}{6} = \frac{1}{3} + \frac{3}{4}x$$

$$12 \cdot \left(\frac{7}{2}x - \frac{5}{6}\right) = 12 \cdot \left(\frac{1}{3} + \frac{3}{4}x\right)$$

$$42x - 10 = 4 + 9x$$

$$42x - 10 - 9x = 4 + 9x - 9x$$

$$33x - 10 = 4$$

$$33x - 10 + 10 = 4 + 10$$

$$33x = 14$$

$$\frac{33x}{33} = \frac{14}{33}$$

$$x = \frac{14}{33}$$

The solution is $\frac{14}{33}$.

43.
$$\frac{7}{2}x - \frac{5}{6} - \frac{1}{3} + \frac{3}{4}x = \frac{7}{2}x + \frac{3}{4}x - \frac{5}{6} - \frac{1}{3}$$

$$= \frac{2}{2} \cdot \frac{7}{2}x + \frac{3}{4}x - \frac{5}{6} - \frac{1}{3} \cdot \frac{2}{2}$$

$$= \frac{14}{4}x + \frac{3}{4}x - \frac{5}{6} - \frac{2}{6}$$

$$= \frac{17}{4}x - \frac{7}{6}$$

The simplified expression is $\frac{17}{4}x - \frac{7}{6}$.

45. Answers may vary. One example:
$$(5x + 3) - (2x + 2)$$
$$5x + 3 - 2x - 2$$
$$5x - 2x + 3 - 2$$
$$3x + 1$$

47. Answers may vary. Clearing fractions first is often less messy and requires fewer steps, but either method will work.

49. No, the student is not correct. A solution is a numeric value that satisfies the equation. While it is possible to represent a solution set using variables, a solution itself will not contain any variables.

51. When simplifying an expression, we cannot multiply through by the LCD. Instead, we rewrite the fractions so they contain the LCD but are equivalent to their original forms. The student should have multiplied the first term by $\frac{3}{3}$ and the second term by $\frac{4}{4}$ in order to have both terms with the LCD of 12.

$$\frac{1}{4}x + \frac{1}{3}x = \frac{3}{3} \cdot \frac{1}{4}x + \frac{4}{4} \cdot \frac{1}{3}x$$

$$= \frac{3}{12}x + \frac{4}{12}x$$

$$= \frac{7}{12}x$$

53. This means that the linear expressions $7 + 2(x + 3)$ and $2x + 13$ are equivalent. It also means that every real number is a solution of the equation $7 + 2(x + 3) = 2x + 13$.

55. When checking a simplification, it is not sufficient to check a single value, unless that value yields a contradiction (which indicates the simplification is incorrect). Since the simplification should be true for all real numbers, the student should try several values to be more confident that the simplification is correct.

57. Answers may vary. Some possibilities:
$$4x + 5 = 25$$
$$3x - 10 = 5$$
$$10x - (7x - 15) = 30$$

59.
$$3 + 2x = -10$$
$$3 + 2x - 3 = -10 - 3$$
$$2x = -13$$
$$\frac{2x}{2} = \frac{-13}{2}$$
$$x = -\frac{13}{2}$$
The solution is $-\dfrac{13}{2}$.

61.
$$4 - 6(x - 2) = 4 - 6x + 12$$
$$= -6x + 16$$
The simplified expression is $-6x + 16$.

63.
$$-9x = x - 5$$
$$-9x - x = x - 5 - x$$
$$-10x = -5$$
$$\frac{-10x}{-10} = \frac{-5}{-10}$$
$$x = \frac{1}{2}$$
The solution is $\dfrac{1}{2}$.

65.
$$\frac{x}{2} = 3(x - 5)$$
$$2 \cdot \frac{x}{2} = 2 \cdot 3(x - 5)$$
$$x = 6(x - 5)$$
$$x = 6x - 30$$
$$x - 6x = 6x - 30 - 6x$$
$$-5x = -30$$
$$\frac{-5x}{-5} = \frac{-30}{-5}$$
$$x = 6$$
The solution is 6.

67.
$$x + x \cdot 6 = x + 6x$$
$$= 7x$$
The simplified expression is $7x$.

69.
$$x + \frac{x}{2} = \frac{x}{1} + \frac{x}{2}$$
$$= \frac{x}{1} \cdot \frac{2}{2} + \frac{x}{2}$$
$$= \frac{2x}{2} + \frac{x}{2}$$
$$= \frac{2x + x}{2}$$
$$= \frac{3x}{2}$$
The simplified expression is $\dfrac{3x}{2}$.

71. Answers may vary.

Homework 4.6

1. The polygon is a square. That is, a rectangle with equal length and width.
$$P = 2L + 2W$$
$$= 2(S) + 2(S)$$
$$= 2S + 2S$$
$$= 4S$$
The formula for the perimeter is $P = 4S$.

3. The perimeter is the sum of the lengths of all the sides of the polygon.
$$P = H + S + S + H + B$$
$$= 2H + 2S + B$$
The formula for the perimeter is
$$P = 2H + 2S + B.$$

5. The perimeter is the sum of the lengths of all the sides of the polygon. Note that the base of the polygon has length $A + C$ and the left side has length $B + D$ (see diagram).

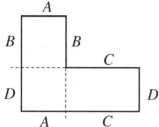

Therefore, the perimeter is given by
$$P = A + B + C + D + (A + C) + (B + D)$$
$$= A + B + C + D + A + C + B + D$$
$$= 2A + 2B + 2C + 2D$$
The formula for the perimeter is
$P = 2A + 2B + 2C + 2D$.

7.
$$P = VI$$
$$20 = V(4)$$
$$\frac{20}{4} = \frac{4V}{4}$$
$$5 = V \text{ or } V = 5$$

9.
$$A = \frac{1}{2}BH$$
$$6 = \frac{1}{2}B(3)$$
$$6 = \frac{3}{2}B$$
$$\frac{2}{3} \cdot 6 = \frac{2}{3} \cdot \frac{3}{2}B$$
$$4 = B \text{ or } B = 4$$

11.
$$v = gt + v_0$$
$$80 = (32.2)t + 20$$
$$80 - 20 = 32.2t + 20 - 20$$
$$60 = 32.2t$$
$$\frac{60}{32.2} = \frac{32.2t}{32.2}$$
$$1.86 \approx t \text{ or } t \approx 1.86$$

13.
$$S = 2WL + 2WH + 2LH$$
$$52 = 2(2)L + 2(2)(4) + 2L(4)$$
$$52 = 4L + 16 + 8L$$
$$52 = 12L + 16$$
$$52 - 16 = 12L + 16 - 16$$
$$36 = 12L$$
$$\frac{36}{12} = \frac{12L}{12}$$
$$3 = L \text{ or } L = 3$$

15.
$$A = \frac{a + b + c}{3}$$
$$5 = \frac{2 + b + 6}{3}$$
$$5 = \frac{8 + b}{3}$$
$$3 \cdot 5 = 3 \cdot \frac{8 + b}{3}$$
$$15 = 8 + b$$
$$15 - 8 = 8 + b - 8$$
$$7 = b \text{ or } b = 7$$

17.
$$A = LW$$
$$116 = L(8)$$
$$\frac{116}{8} = \frac{8L}{8}$$
$$14.5 = L$$
The length of the carpet is 14.5 feet.

19.
$$P = 2L + 2W$$
$$52 = 2L + 2(10)$$
$$52 = 2L + 20$$
$$52 - 20 = 2L + 20 - 20$$
$$32 = 2L$$
$$\frac{32}{2} = \frac{2L}{2}$$
$$16 = L$$
The rectangle has a length of 16 inches.

21.
$$P = 2L + 2W$$
$$177 = 2L + 2(29.5)$$
$$177 = 2L + 59$$
$$177 - 59 = 2L + 59 - 59$$
$$118 = 2L$$
$$\frac{118}{2} = \frac{2L}{2}$$
$$59 = L$$
The official length of the court is 59 feet.

23. a.
$$A = LW$$
$$A = x(3)$$
$$A = 3x$$

b.
$$P = 2L + 2W$$
$$P = 2x + 2(3)$$
$$P = 2x + 6$$

c.
$$\underset{\text{inches}}{P} = \underset{\text{inches}}{2x} + \underset{\text{inches}}{6}$$
The units for both of the expressions P and $2x + 6$ are inches.

25. a. Answers may vary. Some possibilities follows:

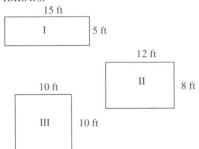

I: Length 15 feet; width 5 feet
II: Length 12 feet; width 8 feet
III: Length 10 feet; width 10 feet

b. I: $A = LW$
$$= (15)(5)$$
$$= 75$$
The area is 75 square feet.

II: $A = LW$
$$= (12)(8)$$
$$= 96$$
The area is 96 square feet.

III: $A = LW$
$$= (10)(10)$$
$$= 100$$
The area is 100 square feet.

c. Garden III would hold more flowers because it has a larger area.

27. a. $3 \text{ dimes} \cdot \dfrac{10 \text{ cents}}{1 \text{ dime}} = 30 \text{ cents}$

b. $4 \text{ dimes} \cdot \dfrac{10 \text{ cents}}{1 \text{ dime}} = 40 \text{ cents}$

c.
$$T = d(10)$$
$$T = 10d$$
The formula for the total value of d dimes is $T = 10d$.

d.
$$\underset{\text{cents}}{T} = \underset{\text{cents}}{10} \cdot \underset{\text{dimes}}{d}$$
$$\underset{\text{dime}}{}$$
The units for both of the expressions T and $10d$ are cents as required.

29. $\text{Total sales} = \left(\dfrac{\text{price}}{\text{skateboard}} \right) \cdot (\text{no. of skateboards})$
$$T = 125 \cdot n$$
$$T = 125n$$
The formula for the total price, in dollars, of n skateboards is $T = 125n$.

31. a. $\text{Total sales} = (\text{price per ticket}) \cdot (\text{num. of people})$
$$T = 195 \cdot x$$
$$T = 195x$$

The formula for the total sales, in dollars, if x people bought tickets is $T = 195x$.

b.
$$T = 195x$$
$$3,611,790 = 195x$$
$$\frac{3,611,790}{195} = \frac{195x}{195}$$
$$18,522 = x$$
If the total sales are \$3,611,790, then 18,522 people bought tickets.

33. a. Total cost = (ticket price) · (num. of tickets)

$$C = 12 \cdot k$$

$$C = 12k$$

The formula for total cost, in dollars, if k tickets are sold for \$12 per ticket is $C = 12k$.

b. Total cost = (ticket price) · (num. of tickets)

$$E = 325 \cdot n$$

$$E = 325n$$

The formula for total cost, in dollars, if n tickets are sold for \$325 per ticket is $E = 325n$.

c. $\dfrac{\text{total}}{\text{cost}} = \dfrac{\text{cost of}}{\$12 \text{ tickets}} + \dfrac{\text{cost of}}{\$325 \text{ tickets}}$

$$T = C + E$$

$$T = 12k + 325n$$

The total cost of k tickets at \$12 per ticket and n tickets at \$325 per ticket is $T = 12k + 325n$.

d.
$$T = 12k + 325n$$
$$19{,}850 = 12(300) + 325n$$
$$19{,}850 = 3600 + 325n$$
$$19{,}850 - 3600 = 3600 + 325n - 3600$$
$$16{,}250 = 325n$$
$$\frac{16{,}250}{325} = \frac{325n}{325}$$
$$50 = n$$

There were 50 tickets sold at \$325 per ticket.

35. a. $V = LWH$

b.
$$V = LWH$$
$$48 = (3)(2)H$$
$$48 = 6H$$
$$\frac{48}{6} = \frac{6H}{6}$$
$$8 = H$$

The height of the box is 8 feet.

37. a. $I = P \cdot r \cdot t$

$$I = Prt$$

b. $I = (5000)(0.04)(3)$

$$= 600$$

\$600 in interest was earned.

c. $B = P + I$

$$= P + Prt$$

The formula for the balance is $B = P + Prt$.

d. $B = 2000 + (2000)(0.05)(4)$

$$= 2000 + 400$$

$$= 2400$$

The balance after 4 years is \$2400.

39.
$$A = \frac{t_1 + t_2 + t_3 + t_4 + t_5}{5}$$
$$80 = \frac{74 + 81 + 79 + 84 + t_5}{5}$$
$$80 = \frac{318 + t_5}{5}$$
$$5 \cdot 80 = 5 \cdot \frac{318 + t_5}{5}$$
$$400 = 318 + t_5$$
$$400 - 318 = 318 + t_5 - 318$$
$$82 = t_5$$

The student needs to score an 82 on the fifth exam to have her five-test average be an 80.

41. $A = LW$

$$\frac{A}{L} = \frac{LW}{L}$$

$$\frac{A}{L} = W \text{ or } W = \frac{A}{L}$$

43. $PV = nRT$

$$\frac{PV}{nR} = \frac{nRT}{nR}$$

$$\frac{PV}{nR} = T \text{ or } T = \frac{PV}{nR}$$

45.
$$U = -\frac{GmM}{r}$$
$$-\frac{r}{Gm} \cdot U = -\frac{r}{Gm}\left(-\frac{GmM}{r}\right)$$
$$-\frac{rU}{Gm} = M \text{ or } M = -\frac{rU}{Gm}$$

47. $A = \frac{1}{2}BH$

$2 \cdot A = 2 \cdot \frac{1}{2}BH$

$2A = BH$

$\frac{2A}{H} = \frac{BH}{H}$

$\frac{2A}{H} = B$ or $B = \frac{2A}{H}$

49. $v = gt + v_0$

$v - v_0 = gt + v_0 - v_0$

$v - v_0 = gt$

$\frac{v - v_0}{g} = \frac{gt}{g}$

$\frac{v - v_0}{g} = t$ or $t = \frac{v - v_0}{g}$

51. $A = P + Prt$

$A - P = P + Prt - P$

$A - P = Prt$

$\frac{A - P}{Pt} = \frac{Prt}{Pt}$

$\frac{A - P}{Pt} = r$ or $r = \frac{A - P}{Pt}$

53. $A = \frac{a + b + c}{3}$

$3 \cdot A = 3 \cdot \frac{a + b + c}{3}$

$3A = a + b + c$

$3A - a - c = a + b + c - a - c$

$3A - a - c = b$ or $b = 3A - a - c$

55. $y - k = m(x - h)$

$y - k = mx - mh$

$y - k + mh = mx - mh + mh$

$y - k + mh = mx$

$\frac{y - k + mh}{m} = \frac{mx}{m}$

$\frac{y - k + mh}{m} = x$ or $x = \frac{y - k + mh}{m}$

57. $\frac{x}{a} + \frac{y}{a} = 1$

$a \cdot \left(\frac{x}{a} + \frac{y}{a} \right) = a \cdot 1$

$x + y = a$

$x + y - x = a - x$

$y = a - x$

59. $3x + 4y = 16$

$3x + 4y - 3x = 16 - 3x$

$4y = -3x + 16$

$\frac{4y}{4} = \frac{-3x + 16}{4}$

$y = \frac{-3x}{4} + \frac{16}{4}$

$y = -\frac{3}{4}x + 4$

61. $2x + 4y - 8 = 0$

$2x + 4y - 8 - 2x + 8 = 0 - 2x + 8$

$4y = -2x + 8$

$\frac{4y}{4} = \frac{-2x + 8}{4}$

$y = \frac{-2x}{4} + \frac{8}{4}$

$y = -\frac{1}{2}x + 2$

63. $5x - 2y = 6$

$5x - 2y - 5x = 6 - 5x$

$-2y = -5x + 6$

$\frac{-2y}{-2} = \frac{-5x + 6}{-2}$

$y = \frac{-5x}{-2} + \frac{6}{-2}$

$y = \frac{5}{2}x - 3$

65. $-3x - 7y = 5$

$-3x - 7y + 3x = 5 + 3x$

$-7y = 3x + 5$

$\dfrac{-7y}{-7} = \dfrac{3x + 5}{-7}$

$y = \dfrac{3x}{-7} + \dfrac{5}{-7}$

$y = -\dfrac{3}{7}x - \dfrac{5}{7}$

67. a. $p = 2.5t + 54.2$

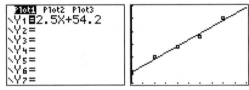

Yes, the line comes very close to the data.

b. $p = 2.5t + 54.2$

$p - 54.2 = 2.5t + 54.2 - 54.2$

$p - 54.2 = 2.5t$

$\dfrac{p - 54.2}{2.5} = \dfrac{2.5t}{2.5}$

$\dfrac{p - 54.2}{2.5} = t$ or $t = \dfrac{p - 54.2}{2.5}$

c. Substitute 72 for p in the equation from part (b).

$t = \dfrac{72 - 54.2}{2.5} = \dfrac{17.8}{2.5} = 7.12$

72% of new-vehicle buyers used the Internet during the shopping process in 2000 + 7 = 2007.

d. Use $t = \dfrac{p - 54.2}{2.5}$.

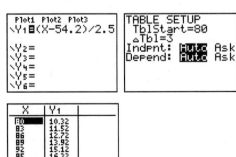

The years in which the percentage of new-vehicle buyers who use the Internet during the shopping process will be:

83% in 2000 + (11.52 ≈ 12) = 2012,
86% in 2000 + (12.72 ≈ 13) = 2013,
89% in 2000 + (13.92 ≈ 14) = 2014,
92% in 2000 + (15.12 ≈ 15) = 2015, and
95% in 2000 + (16.32 ≈ 16) = 2016.

69. a. $s = 21.4t + 305$

b. $s = 21.4t + 305$

$s - 305 = 21.4t + 305 - 305$

$s - 305 = 21.4t$

$\dfrac{s - 305}{21.4} = \dfrac{21.4t}{21.4}$

$\dfrac{s - 305}{21.4} = t$ or $t = \dfrac{s - 305}{21.4}$

c. Substitute 500 for s in the equation from part (b).

$t = \dfrac{500 - 305}{21.4} = \dfrac{195}{21.4} \approx 9.11$

Kia will not reach their goal in 2010. They will reach their goal of selling 500,000 automobiles in 2007 + 9 = 2016.

d. Use $t = \dfrac{s - 305}{21.4}$.

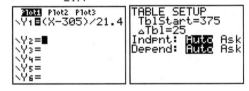

From the table, Kia's sales (in thousands) will be 375, 400, 425, 450, and 475 in the years $2007 + 3 = 2010$, $2007 + 4 = 2011$, $2007 + 6 = 2013$, $2007 + 7 = 2014$, and $2007 + 8 = 2015$, respectively.

71. a. $s = 15.4t + 460.2$

b.
$$s = 15.4t + 460.2$$
$$550 = 15.4t + 460.2$$
$$550 - 460.2 = 15.4t + 460.2 - 460.2$$
$$89.8 = 15.4t$$
$$\frac{89.8}{15.4} = \frac{15.4t}{15.4}$$
$$5.83 \approx t$$

In 2007 + 6 = 2013, holiday retail sales will be $550 billion.

c.
$$s = 15.4t + 460.2$$
$$s - 460.2 = 15.4t + 460.2 - 460.2$$
$$s - 460.2 = 15.4t$$
$$\frac{s - 460.2}{15.4} = \frac{15.4t}{15.4}$$
$$\frac{s - 460.2}{15.4} = t \quad or \quad t = \frac{s - 460.2}{15.4}$$

d.
$$t = \frac{550 - 460.2}{15.4} = \frac{89.8}{15.4} \approx 5.83$$

In 2007 + 6 = 2013, holiday retail sales will be $550 billion

e. The results are the same. The equation $t = \dfrac{s - 460.2}{15.4}$ is easier to use because it is already solved for *t*.

f. The formula $s = 15.4t + 460.2$ is easier to use in this case because it is already solved for *s*. For $t = 2014 - 2007 = 7$,
$$s = 15.4(7) + 460.2$$
$$= 107.8 + 460.2$$
$$- 568$$

In 2014, holiday retail sales will be $568 billion.

73. a.

Speed, *s* (miles per hour)	Time, *t* (hours)	Distance, *d* (miles)
50	4	50·4
70	3	70·3
65	2	65·2
55	5	55·5
s	*t*	*s·t*

From the last row of the table, we see that the formula relating *s*, *t*, and *d* is $d = st$.

b.
$$\underset{\text{miles}}{d} = \underset{\substack{\text{miles} \\ \overline{\text{hour}}}}{s} \cdot \underset{\text{hours}}{t}$$

The units for both of the expressions *d* and *st* are miles, as required.

c.
$$d = st$$
$$\frac{d}{s} = \frac{st}{s}$$
$$\frac{d}{s} = t \quad or \quad t = \frac{d}{s}$$

d.
$$t = \frac{315}{70} = 4.5$$

It will take 4.5 hours to travel 315 miles at a speed of 70 miles per hour.

e. The New Mexico portion will take
$$t = \frac{229.9}{75} \approx 3.07 \text{ hours.}$$

The Colorado portion will take
$$t = \frac{219.2}{65} \approx 3.37 \text{ hours.}$$

So, the total trip will take about $3.07 + 3.37 = 6.44$ hours (that is, 6 hours 26 minutes).

75.
$$\underset{\substack{\text{miles} \\ \overline{\text{hour}}}}{s} = \underset{\text{miles}}{d} \cdot \underset{\text{hours}}{t}$$

The unit analysis show the units on the left to be $\dfrac{\text{miles}}{\text{hour}}$ while the units on the right are $(\text{miles}) \cdot (\text{hours})$. Since the units are not the same, the formula is incorrect.

77. a. $P = 2L + 2W$

Doubling the length and width, we get:
$$2(2L) + 2(2W) = 2(2L + 2W) = 2P$$

Therefore, doubling the length and width will double the perimeter.

b. $A = LW$

Doubling the length and width, we get:
$$(2L)(2W) = 4LW = 4A$$

Therefore, doubling the length and width will multiply the area by 4.

79. Answers may vary.

Chapter 4 Review Exercises

1. $-5(4x) = (-5 \cdot 4)x = -20x$

2. $-3(8x+4) = -3(8x)+(-3)(4)$
$$= -24x+(-12)$$
$$= -24x-12$$

3. $\dfrac{4}{5}(15y-35) = \dfrac{4}{5} \cdot 15y - \dfrac{4}{5} \cdot 35$
$$= 12y-28$$

4. $-(3x-6y-8) = -1(3x-6y-8)$
$$= -1 \cdot 3x - (-1)(6y) - (-1)(8)$$
$$= -3x - (-6y) - (-8)$$
$$= -3x + 6y + 8$$

5. $\dfrac{2}{9}x + \dfrac{5}{9}x = \left(\dfrac{2}{9} + \dfrac{5}{9}\right)x = \left(\dfrac{2+5}{9}\right)x = \dfrac{7}{9}x$

6. $5a+2-13b-a+4b-9$
$$= 5a-a-13b+4b+2-9$$
$$= 4a-9b-7$$

7. $-5y-3(4x+y)-6x$
$$= -5y-12x-3y-6x$$
$$= -12x-6x-5y-3y$$
$$= -18x-8y$$

8. $-2.6(3.1x+4.5)-8.5 = -8.06x-11.7-8.5$
$$= -8.06x-20.2$$

9. $-(2m-4)-(3m+8) = -2m+4-3m-8$
$$= -2m-3m+4-8$$
$$= -5m-4$$

10. $4(3a-7b)-3(5a+4b) = 12a-28b-15a-12b$
$$= 12a-15a-28b-12b$$
$$= -3a-40b$$

11. $-4(x-7) = -4x-(-4)(7)$
$$= -4x-(-28)$$
$$= -4x+28$$

12. $-7+2(x+8) = -7+2x+16$
$$= 2x+9$$

13. Answers may vary. Some possibilities:
Let $a=4$, $b=3$, and $c=2$.
$$a(b+c) \overset{?}{=} ab+c$$
$$4(3+2) \overset{?}{=} 4(3)+2$$
$$4(5) \overset{?}{=} 12+2$$
$$20 \overset{?}{=} 14 \text{ false}$$

Let $a=-2$, $b=3$, and $c=-5$.
$$a(b+c) \overset{?}{=} ab+c$$
$$-2(3+(-5)) \overset{?}{=} (-2)(3)+(-5)$$
$$-2(-2) \overset{?}{=} -6+(-5)$$
$$4 \overset{?}{=} -11 \text{ false}$$

$$a(b+c) = a \cdot b + a \cdot c$$
$$= ab+ac$$

14. Answers may vary. Some examples:
$3(x-3)$, $2(x-2)+(x-5)$, $4x-(x+9)$

15. $-5x+20 = -5(x-4)$
$$= 5(4-x)$$
$$= -2(x-10)-3x$$

16. $y = 2x+3-4x$
$$= -2x+3$$
Since this is in the form $y = mx+b$, the graph is a line. The slope of the line is $m=-2$ and the y-intercept is $(0,3)$. We plot the y-intercept and use the slope to obtain a second point, $(1,1)$, and (to check) a third point, $(-1,5)$.

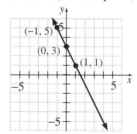

17. $y = -3(x-2)$
$$= -3x + 6$$
Since this is in the form $y = mx + b$, the graph is a line. The slope of the line is $m = -3$ and the y-intercept is $(0,6)$. We plot the y-intercept and use the slope to obtain a second point, $(1,3)$, and (to check) a third point, $(2,0)$.

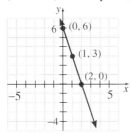

18. $2 - 5x = -3(4x-7)$
$$2 - 5(3) \stackrel{?}{=} -(4(3)-7)$$
$$2 - 5(3) \stackrel{?}{=} -(12-7)$$
$$2 - 15 \stackrel{?}{=} -(5)$$
$$-13 \stackrel{?}{=} -5 \quad \text{false}$$
Since the result is a false statement, 3 is not a solution of the equation.

19. $a + 5 = 12$
$$a + 5 - 5 = 12 - 5$$
$$a = 7$$
The solution is 7.

20. $-4x = 20$
$$\frac{-4x}{-4} = \frac{20}{-4}$$
$$x = -5$$
The solution is -5.

21. $-p = -3$
$$\frac{-p}{-1} = \frac{-3}{-1}$$
$$p = 3$$
The solution is 3.

22. $-\dfrac{7}{3}a = 14$
$$-\frac{3}{7}\left(-\frac{7}{3}a\right) = -\frac{3}{7} \cdot 14$$
$$a = -6$$
The solution is -6.

23. $4.5x - 17.2 = -5.05$
$$4.5x - 17.2 + 17.2 = -5.05 + 17.2$$
$$4.5x = 12.15$$
$$\frac{4.5x}{4.5} = \frac{12.15}{4.5}$$
$$x = 2.7$$
The solution is 2.7.

24. $5x - 9x + 3 = 17$
$$-4x + 3 = 17$$
$$-4x + 3 - 3 = 17 - 3$$
$$-4x = 14$$
$$\frac{-4x}{-4} = \frac{14}{-4}$$
$$x = -\frac{7}{2}$$
The solution is $-\dfrac{7}{2}$.

25. $8m - 3 - m = 2 - 4m$
$$7m - 3 = 2 - 4m$$
$$7m - 3 + 4m = 2 - 4m + 4m$$
$$11m - 3 = 2$$
$$11m - 3 + 3 = 2 + 3$$
$$11m = 5$$
$$\frac{11m}{11} = \frac{5}{11}$$
$$m = \frac{5}{11}$$
The solution is $\dfrac{5}{11}$.

26.
$$8x = -7(2x - 3) + x$$
$$8x = -14x + 21 + x$$
$$8x = -13x + 21$$
$$8x + 13x = -13x + 21 + 13x$$
$$21x = 21$$
$$\frac{21x}{21} = \frac{21}{21}$$
$$x = 1$$
The solution is 1.

27.
$$6(4x - 1) - 3(2x + 5) = 2(5x - 3)$$
$$24x - 6 - 6x - 15 = 10x - 6$$
$$18x - 21 = 10x - 6$$
$$18x - 21 - 10x = 10x - 6 - 10x$$
$$8x - 21 = -6$$
$$8x - 21 + 21 = -6 + 21$$
$$8x = 15$$
$$\frac{8x}{8} = \frac{15}{8}$$
$$x = \frac{15}{8}$$
The solution is $\frac{15}{8}$.

28.
$$\frac{w}{8} - \frac{3}{4} = \frac{5}{6}$$
$$24\left(\frac{w}{8} - \frac{3}{4}\right) = 24\left(\frac{5}{6}\right)$$
$$3w - 18 = 20$$
$$3w - 18 + 18 = 20 + 18$$
$$3w = 38$$
$$\frac{3w}{3} = \frac{38}{3}$$
$$w = \frac{38}{3}$$
The solution is $\frac{38}{3}$.

29.
$$\frac{3p - 4}{2} = \frac{5p + 2}{4} + \frac{7}{6}$$
$$12\left(\frac{3p - 4}{2}\right) = 12\left(\frac{5p + 2}{4} + \frac{7}{6}\right)$$
$$6(3p - 4) = 3(5p + 2) + 2(7)$$
$$18p - 24 = 15p + 6 + 14$$
$$18p - 24 = 15p + 20$$
$$18p - 24 - 15p = 15p + 20 - 15p$$
$$3p - 24 = 20$$
$$3p - 24 + 24 = 20 + 24$$
$$3p = 44$$
$$\frac{3p}{3} = \frac{44}{3}$$
$$p = \frac{44}{3}$$
The solution is $\frac{44}{3}$.

30. In the second line, the student only added 5 to one side of the equation instead of both as required.
$$x - 5 = 2$$
$$x - 5 + 5 = 2 + 5$$
$$x = 7$$
The solution is 7.

31. Answers will vary. One example:
$$3x - 5 = -23$$

32.
$$-2.5(3.8x - 1.9) = 83.7$$
$$-9.5x + 4.75 = 83.7$$
$$-9.5x + 4.75 - 4.75 = 83.7 - 4.75$$
$$-9.5x = 78.95$$
$$\frac{-9.5x}{-9.5} = \frac{78.95}{-9.5}$$
$$x = -\frac{78.95}{9.5}$$
$$x \approx -8.31$$

33. a. The rate of increase is constant, so we have a linear model. The linear model has the form $n = mt + b$, where n is the number of prisoners (in millions) and t is the number of years since 2000. The rate of change is the slope, so we have $m = 0.06$. The y-intercept is (0, 2.3), so we have $b = 2.3$. Therefore, the model is $n = 0.06t + 2.3$.

b. For 2015, we let $t = 2015 - 2007 = 8$.

$$n = 0.06(8) + 2.3$$
$$= 0.48 + 2.3$$
$$= 2.78$$

In 2015, there will be about 2.78 million prisoners in the United States.

c. Substitute 2.7 for n and solve for t

$$2.7 = 0.06t + 2.3$$
$$2.7 - 2.3 = 0.06t + 2.3 - 2.3$$
$$0.4 = 0.06t$$
$$\frac{0.4}{0.06} = \frac{0.06t}{0.06}$$
$$6.67 \approx t$$

There will be about 2.7 million prisoners in $2007 + 7 = 2014$.

34. Let x be the number.

$$4(x - 6) = 15$$
$$4x - 24 = 15$$
$$4x - 24 + 24 = 15 + 24$$
$$4x = 39$$
$$\frac{4x}{4} = \frac{39}{4}$$
$$x = \frac{39}{4}$$

The number is $\frac{39}{4}$.

35. Let x be the number.

$$2 - 3(x + 8) = 95$$
$$2 - 3x - 24 = 95$$
$$-3x - 22 = 95$$
$$-3x - 22 + 22 = 95 + 22$$
$$-3x = 117$$
$$\frac{-3x}{-3} = \frac{117}{-3}$$
$$x = -39$$

The number is -39.

36. $\dfrac{42}{89}x + \dfrac{93}{35} = -\dfrac{43}{69}x - \dfrac{17}{78}$

```
Plot1 Plot2 Plot3     WINDOW
\Y1■42X/89+93/35      Xmin=-10
                      Xmax=10
\Y2■-43X/69-17/7      Xscl=1
8                     Ymin=-10
\Y3=                  Ymax=10
\Y4=                  Yscl=1
\Y5=                  Xres=1
```

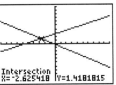

```
Intersection
X=-2.625418  Y=1.4181815
```

The approximate intersection point, $(-2.63, 1.42)$, has x-coordinate -2.63, so the approximate solution to the equation is -2.63.

37. $-2x + 17 = 5x - 4$

From tables 13 and 14, we see that for both of the equations $y = -2x + 17$ and $y = 5x - 4$, the input 3 leads to the output 11. Therefore, 3 is a solution of the equation $-2x + 17 = 5x - 4$.

38. $-2x + 17 = 15$

Looking at table 13, we see that for the equation $y = -2x + 17$ the input 1 leads to the output 15. Therefore, 1 is a solution to the equation $-2x + 17 = 15$.

39. $5x - 4 = 6$

Looking at table 14, we see that for the equation $y = 5x - 4$ the input 2 leads to the output 6. Therefore, 2 is a solution to the equation $5x - 4 = 6$.

40. $5x - 4 = -4$

Looking at table 14, we see that for the equation $y = 5x - 4$ the input 0 leads to the output -4. Therefore, 0 is a solution to the equation $5x - 4 = -4$.

41.
$$7x - 4 + 3x = 2 + 10x - 6$$
$$10x - 4 = 10x - 4$$
$$10x - 4 - 10x = 10x - 4 - 10x$$
$$-4 = -4 \quad \text{true}$$

Since $-4 = -4$ is a true statement (of the form $a = a$), we conclude that the original equation is an identity and its solution set is the set of all real numbers.

42. $6(2x-3)-(5x+2)=-2(4x-1)$

$12x-18-5x-2=-8x+2$

$7x-20=-8x+2$

$7x-20+8x=-8x+2+8x$

$15x-20=2$

$15x-20+20=2+20$

$15x=22$

$\dfrac{15x}{15}=\dfrac{22}{15}$

$x=\dfrac{22}{15}$

The number $\dfrac{22}{15}$ is the only solution, so the equation is conditional.

43. $2(x-5)+3=2x-4$

$2x-10+3=2x-4$

$2x-7=2x-4$

$2x-7-2x=2x-4-2x$

$-7=-4$ false

Since $-7=-4$ is a false statement, we conclude that the original equation is inconsistent and its solution set is the empty set.

44. $4(x-5)=28$

$4(2-5)\overset{?}{=}28$ false

$4(2)-20\overset{?}{=}28$ false

$4(2)-20-20\overset{?}{=}28-20$ false

$4(2)\overset{?}{=}8$ true

$\dfrac{4(2)}{4}\overset{?}{=}\dfrac{8}{4}$ true

$2\overset{?}{=}2$ true

In going from the fourth line to the fifth, we went from a false statement to a true statement. This indicates that the mistake was made in going from the fourth line to the fifth. In the fourth step, the subtracted 20 from both sides when they should have added (and incorrectly simplified $-20-20$).

$4(x-5)=28$

$4x-20=28$

$4x-20+20=28+20$

$4x=48$

$\dfrac{4x}{4}=\dfrac{48}{4}$

$x=12$

The solution is 12.

45. $8-3(x+5)$ is a linear expression because the statement does not contain an equal sign.

46. $8-3(x+5)=4x$ is a linear equation because the statement contains an equal sign.

47. $6t-8t=(6-8)t$

$=-2t$

The simplified expression is $-2t$.

48. $0.1+0.5a-0.3a=0.7$

$0.1+0.2a=0.7$

$0.1+0.2a-0.1=0.7-0.1$

$0.2a=0.6$

$\dfrac{0.2a}{0.2}=\dfrac{0.6}{0.2}$

$a=3$

The solution is 3.

49. $6t-8t=10$

$-2t=10$

$\dfrac{-2t}{-2}=\dfrac{10}{-2}$

$t=-5$

The solution is -5.

50. $0.1+0.5a-0.3a=0.1+(0.5-0.3)a$

$=0.1+0.2a$

$=0.2a+0.1$

The simplified expression is $0.2a+0.1$.

51. $9(2p-5)-3(7p+3)=18p-45-21p-9$

$=18p-21p-45-9$

$=-3p-54$

The simplified expression is $-3p-54$.

52.
$$\frac{5}{6}r - \frac{3}{4} = \frac{1}{6} + \frac{7}{2}r$$
$$12\left(\frac{5}{6}r - \frac{3}{4}\right) = 12\left(\frac{1}{6} + \frac{7}{2}r\right)$$
$$10r - 9 = 2 + 42r$$
$$10r - 9 - 42r = 2 + 42r - 42r$$
$$-32r - 9 = 2$$
$$-32r - 9 + 9 = 2 + 9$$
$$-32r = 11$$
$$\frac{-32r}{-32} = \frac{11}{-32}$$
$$r = -\frac{11}{32}$$

The solution is $-\dfrac{11}{32}$.

53.
$$9(2p - 5) - 3(7p + 3) = 0$$
$$18p - 45 - 21p - 9 = 0$$
$$-3p - 54 = 0$$
$$-3p - 54 + 54 = 0 + 54$$
$$-3p = 54$$
$$\frac{-3p}{-3} = \frac{54}{-3}$$
$$p = -18$$

The solution is -18.

54.
$$\frac{5}{6}r - \frac{3}{4} - \frac{1}{6} + \frac{7}{2}r = \frac{5}{6}r + \frac{7}{2}r - \frac{3}{4} - \frac{1}{6}$$
$$= \frac{5}{6}r + \frac{3}{3}\cdot\frac{7}{2}r - \frac{3}{3}\cdot\frac{3}{4} - \frac{2}{2}\cdot\frac{1}{6}$$
$$= \frac{5}{6}r + \frac{21}{6}r - \frac{9}{12} - \frac{2}{12}$$
$$= \frac{26}{6}r - \frac{11}{12}$$
$$= \frac{13}{3}r - \frac{11}{12}$$

The simplified expression is $\dfrac{13}{3}r - \dfrac{11}{12}$, or
$$\frac{4}{4}\cdot\frac{13}{3}r - \frac{11}{12} = \frac{52r - 11}{12}.$$

55. No, the student is incorrect. Expressions do not have solutions. We solve equations and simplify expressions.

56. When simplifying an expression, we cannot multiply through by the LCD. Instead, we rewrite the fractions so they contain the LCD but are equivalent to their original forms.

The expression $\dfrac{2}{3}x + \dfrac{7}{5}$ is already simplified as much as possible.

57.
$$4(6 - x) = 17$$
$$24 - 4x = 17$$
$$24 - 4x - 24 = 17 - 24$$
$$-4x = -7$$
$$\frac{-4x}{-4} = \frac{-7}{-4}$$
$$x = \frac{7}{4}$$

The solution is $\dfrac{7}{4}$.

58.
$$x - \frac{x}{2} = \frac{x}{1} - \frac{x}{2}$$
$$= \frac{2}{2}\cdot\frac{x}{1} - \frac{x}{2}$$
$$= \frac{2x}{2} - \frac{x}{2}$$
$$= \frac{x}{2}$$

The simplified expression is $\dfrac{x}{2}$, or $\dfrac{1}{2}x$.

59. We can start by labeling the remaining sides, but remember that the final answer must be in terms of A, B, C, D, and E.

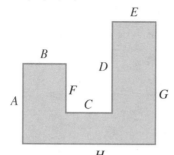

Now, note the following:

$$H = B + C + E$$
$$G = A + D - F$$

The perimeter is the sum of all the sides, so we get:

$$P = A + B + C + D + E + F + G + H$$
$$= A + B + C + D + E + F$$
$$\quad + (A + D - F) + (B + C + E)$$
$$= 2A + 2B + 2C + 2D + 2E$$

60. a. $T = 15n + 25w$

b.
$$T = 15n + 25w$$
$$11{,}050 = 15(370) + 25w$$
$$11{,}050 = 5550 + 25w$$
$$11{,}050 - 5550 = 5550 + 25w - 5550$$
$$5500 = 25w$$
$$\frac{5500}{25} = \frac{25w}{25}$$
$$220 = w$$

There were 220 tickets sold at $25 per ticket.

61. $C = 2\pi r$
$$\frac{C}{2\pi} = \frac{2\pi r}{2\pi}$$
$$\frac{C}{2\pi} = r \text{ or } r = \frac{C}{2\pi}$$

62.
$$P = a + b + c$$
$$P - a - b = a + b + c - a - b$$
$$P - a - b = c \text{ or } c = P - a - b$$

63.
$$3x - 6y = 18$$
$$3x - 6y - 3x = 18 - 3x$$
$$-6y = -3x + 18$$
$$\frac{-6y}{-6} = \frac{-3x + 18}{-6}$$
$$y = \frac{-3x}{-6} + \frac{18}{-6}$$
$$y = \frac{1}{2}x - 3$$

64.
$$A = \frac{1}{2}H(B+T)$$
$$2 \cdot A = 2 \cdot \frac{1}{2}H(B+T)$$
$$2A = H(B+T)$$
$$2A = HB + HT$$
$$2A - HB = HB + HT - HB$$
$$2A - HB = HT$$
$$\frac{2A - HB}{H} = \frac{HT}{H}$$
$$\frac{2A - HB}{H} = T \text{ or } T = \frac{2A - HB}{H}$$

65. a. A linear model has the form $y = mx + b$ where m is the slope, or average rate of change, and $(0, b)$ is the y-intercept. Using E and t, our model has the form $E = mt + b$ where E is the number of employees (in thousands) and t is the number of years since 2005. The slope is $m = 0.4$ and the y-intercept is $(0, 20)$. Therefore, our model is $E = 0.4t + 20$.

b.
$$E = 0.4t + 20$$
$$23.2 = 0.4t + 20$$
$$23.2 - 20 = 0.4t + 20 - 20$$
$$3.2 = 0.4t$$
$$\frac{3.2}{0.4} = \frac{0.4t}{0.4}$$
$$8 = t$$

There will be 23.2 thousand employees in $2005 + 8 = 2013$.

c.
$$E = 0.4t + 20$$
$$E - 20 = 0.4t + 20 - 20$$
$$E - 20 = 0.4t$$
$$\frac{E - 20}{0.4} = \frac{0.4t}{0.4}$$
$$\frac{E - 20}{0.4} = t \quad \text{or} \quad t = \frac{E - 20}{0.4}$$

d. Substitute 23.2 for E and solve for t.
$$t = \frac{E - 20}{0.4} = \frac{23.2 - 20}{0.4} = \frac{3.2}{0.4} = 8$$
There will be 23.2 thousand employees in 2005 + 8 = 2013.

e. The results are the same. The equation $t = \frac{E - 20}{0.4}$ was easier to use because it was already solved for t.

f. The equation $E = 0.4t + 20$ is easier to use when predicting the number of visits because it is already solved for E. Substitute 2015 − 2005 = 10 for t in the equation:
$$E = 0.4(10) + 20$$
$$= 4 + 20$$
$$= 24$$
In 2015, there will be 24 thousand employees.

Chapter 4 Test

1.
$$-\frac{2}{3}(6x - 9) = -\frac{2}{3} \cdot 6x - \left(-\frac{2}{3}\right)(9)$$
$$= -4x - (-6)$$
$$= -4x + 6$$

2.
$$9.36 - 2.4(1.7x + 3.5) = 9.36 - 4.08x - 8.4$$
$$= -4.08x + 9.36 - 8.4$$
$$= -4.08x + 0.96$$

3.
$$-5(2w - 7) - 3(4w - 6) = -10w + 35 - 12w + 18$$
$$= -10w - 12w + 35 + 18$$
$$= -22w + 53$$

4.
$$-(3a + 7b) - (8a - 4b + 2) = -3a - 7b - 8a + 4b - 2$$
$$= -3a - 8a - 7b + 4b - 2$$
$$= -11a - 3b - 2$$

5.
$$3(3 - 2) - (5(3) + 4) = 3(1) - (15 + 4) = 3 - 19 = -16$$
$$3(3) - 6 - 5(3) + 4 = 9 - 6 - 15 + 4 = -8$$
$$3(3) - 5(3) - 6 + 4 = 9 - 15 - 6 + 4 = -8$$
$$-2(3) - 2 = -6 - 2 = -8$$

The mistake occurred in going from the first line to the second. The negative was incorrectly distributed.
$$3(x - 2) - (5x + 4) = 3x - 6 - 5x - 4$$
$$= 3x - 5x - 6 - 4$$
$$= -2x - 10$$

6.
$$y = -2(x + 1)$$
$$= -2x - 2$$
Since this is in the form $y = mx + b$, the graph is a line. The slope of the line is $m = -2$ and the y-intercept is $(0, -2)$. We plot the y-intercept and use the slope to obtain a second point, $(1, -4)$, and (to check) a third point, $(-1, 0)$.

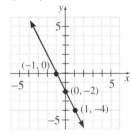

7.
$$6x - 3 = 19$$
$$6x - 3 + 3 = 19 + 3$$
$$6x = 22$$
$$\frac{6x}{6} = \frac{22}{6}$$
$$x = \frac{11}{3}$$
The solution is $\frac{11}{3}$.

8.
$$\frac{3}{5}x = 6$$
$$\frac{5}{3} \cdot \frac{3}{5}x = \frac{5}{3} \cdot 6$$
$$x = \frac{30}{3}$$
$$x = 10$$
The solution is 10.

9.
$$9a - 5 = 8a + 2$$
$$9a - 5 - 8a = 8a + 2 - 8a$$
$$a - 5 = 2$$
$$a - 5 + 5 = 2 + 5$$
$$a = 7$$
The solution is 7.

10.
$$8 - 2(3t - 1) = 7t$$
$$8 - 6t + 2 = 7t$$
$$10 - 6t = 7t$$
$$10 - 6t + 6t = 7t + 6t$$
$$10 = 13t$$
$$\frac{10}{13} = \frac{13t}{13}$$
$$\frac{10}{13} = t$$

The solution is $\frac{10}{13}$.

11.
$$3(2x - 5) - 2(7x + 9) = 49$$
$$6x - 15 - 14x - 18 = 49$$
$$-8x - 33 = 49$$
$$-8x - 33 + 33 = 49 + 33$$
$$-8x = 82$$
$$\frac{-8x}{-8} = \frac{82}{-8}$$
$$x = -\frac{41}{4}$$

The solution is $-\frac{41}{4}$.

12.
$$\frac{7}{8}x + \frac{3}{10} = \frac{1}{4}x - \frac{1}{2}$$
$$40\left(\frac{7}{8}x + \frac{3}{10}\right) = 40\left(\frac{1}{4}x - \frac{1}{2}\right)$$
$$35x + 12 = 10x - 20$$
$$35x + 12 - 10x = 10x - 20 - 10x$$
$$25x + 12 = -20$$
$$25x + 12 - 12 = -20 - 12$$
$$25x = -32$$
$$\frac{25x}{25} = \frac{-32}{25}$$
$$x = -\frac{32}{25}$$

The solution is $-\frac{32}{25}$.

13.
$$8.21x = 3.9(4.4x - 2.7)$$
$$8.21x = 17.16x - 10.53$$
$$8.21x - 17.16x = 17.16x - 10.53 - 17.16x$$
$$-8.95x = -10.53$$
$$\frac{-8.95x}{-8.95} = \frac{-10.53}{-8.95}$$
$$x \approx 1.18$$

The solution is approximately 1.18.

14. Let x be the number.
$$4 - 2(x + 7) = 54$$
$$4 - 2x - 14 = 54$$
$$-2x - 10 = 54$$
$$-2x - 10 + 10 = 54 + 10$$
$$-2x = 64$$
$$\frac{-2x}{-2} = \frac{64}{-2}$$
$$x = -32$$

The number is -32.

15.
$$9(3x + 2) - (4x - 6) = 27x + 18 - 4x + 6$$
$$= 27x - 4x + 18 + 6$$
$$= 23x + 24$$

The simplified expression is $23x + 24$.

16. $9(3x+2)-(4x-6)=x$

$27x+18-4x+6=x$

$23x+24=x$

$23x+24-23x=x-23x$

$24=-22x$

$$\frac{24}{-22}=\frac{-22x}{-22}$$

$$-\frac{12}{11}=x$$

The solution is $-\dfrac{12}{11}$.

17. No, the student is not correct. A solution is a numeric value that satisfies the equation. While it is possible to represent a solution set using variables, a solution itself will not contain any variables.

18. Answers may vary. Some examples:

$4x-2(2x-2)$, $10-15\div5+(-3)$,

$3(x+3)-(5+3x)$

19. Let x be the number.

$5(x-2)=29$

$5x-10=29$

$5x-10+10=29+10$

$5x=39$

$$\frac{5x}{5}=\frac{39}{5}$$

$$x=\frac{39}{5}$$

The solution is $\dfrac{39}{5}$.

20. $2+4(3+x)=2+12+4x$

$=14+4x$

$=4x+14$

The simplified expression is $4x+14$.

21. The two lines $y=\dfrac{3}{2}x-4$ and $y=\dfrac{1}{2}x-2$ intersect only at $(2,-1)$, whose x-coordinate is 2. So, 2 is the solution of the equation $\dfrac{3}{2}x-4=\dfrac{1}{2}x-2$.

22. The two lines $y=\dfrac{3}{2}x-4$ and $y=2$ intersect only at $(4,2)$, whose x-coordinate is 4. So, 4 is the solution of the equation $\dfrac{3}{2}x-4=2$.

23. The two lines $y=\dfrac{1}{2}x-2$ and $y=-3$ intersect only at $(-2,-3)$, whose x-coordinate is -2. So, -2 is the solution of the equation $\dfrac{1}{2}x-2=-3$.

24. The two lines $y=\dfrac{1}{2}x-2$ and $y=0$ intersect only at $(4,0)$, whose x-coordinate is 4. So, 4 is the solution of the equation $\dfrac{1}{2}x-2=0$.

25. a. The rate of increase is constant, so we have a linear model. The linear model has the form $n=mt+b$, where n is the number of patent applications (in thousands) and t is the number of years since 2007. The rate of change is the slope, so we have $m=23$. The y-intercept is $(0,456)$, so we have $b=456$. Therefore, the model is $n=23t+456$.

b. For 2014, $t=2014-2007=7$.

$n=23(7)+456$

$=161+456$

$=617$

In 2014, there will be 617 thousand U.S. patent applications.

c. Substitute 640 for n and solve for t

$640=23t+456$

$640-456=23t+456-456$

$184=23t$

$$\frac{184}{23}=\frac{23t}{23}$$

$8=t$

There will be about 640 thousand U.S. patent applications in $2007+8=2015$.

26. Start with the formula for the perimeter of a rectangle, substitute in the known values, and solve for the length.

$$P = 2L + 2W$$
$$52 = 2L + 2(8)$$
$$52 = 2L + 16$$
$$52 - 16 = 2L + 16 - 16$$
$$36 = 2L$$
$$\frac{36}{2} = \frac{2L}{2}$$
$$18 = L$$

The length of the garden is 18 feet.

27. $$A = \frac{a+b}{2}$$
$$2 \cdot A = 2 \cdot \frac{a+b}{2}$$
$$2A = a + b$$
$$2A - b = a + b - b$$
$$2A - b = a \quad \text{or} \quad a = 2A - b$$

Cumulative Review of Chapters 1 – 4

1. Let n = the number of pages in a book.
Examples of possible values: 275 , 300
Examples of values not possible: 0, −150
(answers may vary)

2.

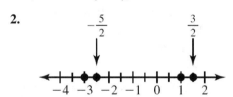

3. In 2008, there were 100 million unique visitors to the website YouTube.

4. $4 + 3(-2) = 4 + (-6) = -2$

5. $-8 \div 4 - 2(7 - 10) = -8 \div 4 - 2(-3)$
$$= -2 - (-6)$$
$$= -2 + 6$$
$$= 4$$

6. $$\frac{15}{8} \cdot \left(\frac{-4}{25}\right) = -\frac{15}{8} \cdot \frac{4}{25}$$
$$= -\frac{3 \cdot 5 \cdot 2 \cdot 2}{2 \cdot 2 \cdot 2 \cdot 5 \cdot 5}$$
$$= -\frac{2 \cdot 2 \cdot 5}{2 \cdot 2 \cdot 5} \cdot \frac{3}{2 \cdot 5}$$
$$= -\frac{3}{2 \cdot 5}$$
$$= -\frac{3}{10}$$

7. $$\left(-\frac{3}{10}\right) + \left(-\frac{7}{8}\right) = \left(-\frac{3}{10} \cdot \frac{4}{4}\right) + \left(-\frac{7}{8} \cdot \frac{5}{5}\right)$$
$$= \left(-\frac{12}{40}\right) + \left(-\frac{35}{40}\right)$$
$$= \frac{-12 + (-35)}{40}$$
$$= -\frac{47}{40}$$

8. $$\frac{27}{-45} = -\frac{27}{45} = -\frac{3 \cdot 3 \cdot 3}{3 \cdot 3 \cdot 5} = -\frac{3 \cdot 3}{3 \cdot 3} \cdot \frac{3}{5} = -\frac{3}{5}$$

9. $P = 2L + 2W$
$$= 2\left(\frac{5}{6}\right) + 2\left(\frac{3}{4}\right)$$
$$= \frac{5}{3} + \frac{3}{2}$$
$$= \frac{5}{3} \cdot \frac{2}{2} + \frac{3}{2} \cdot \frac{3}{3}$$
$$= \frac{10}{6} + \frac{9}{6}$$
$$= \frac{19}{6}$$

The rectangle has a perimeter of $\frac{19}{6}$ feet.

10. $85 - 92 = -7$
The change in the scores was −7 points.

11. $a(b - c) = (-3)(5 - (-4))$
$$= -3(5 + 4)$$
$$= -3(9)$$
$$= -27$$

12. $m = \dfrac{-4-(-2)}{-1-(-5)} = \dfrac{-4+2}{-1+5} = \dfrac{-2}{4} = -\dfrac{1}{2}$

The line is decreasing because the slope is negative.

13. $m = \dfrac{3-(-5)}{-4-(-4)} = \dfrac{8}{0}$ undefined

The slope is undefined so the line is vertical.

14. Find the average rate of change for both roads.

Road A: $\dfrac{150 \text{ ft}}{5000 \text{ ft}} = \dfrac{3}{100} = \dfrac{0.03}{1}$

Road B: $\dfrac{95 \text{ ft}}{3500 \text{ ft}} = \dfrac{19}{700} \approx \dfrac{0.027}{1}$

The rate of change for road A is larger than for road B, so road A is steeper.

15. $y = -\dfrac{2}{3}x + 4$

Since this is in the form $y = mx + b$, the graph is a non-vertical line. The slope of the line is $m = -\dfrac{2}{3}$ and the y-intercept is $(0,4)$. We plot the y-intercept and use the slope to obtain a second point, $(3,2)$, and (to check) a third point, $(-3,6)$.

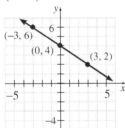

16. $y = 2x - 3$

Since this is in the form $y = mx + b$, the graph is a non-vertical line. The slope of the line is $m = 2$ and the y-intercept is $(0,-3)$. We plot the y-intercept and use the slope to obtain a second point, $(1,-1)$, and (to check) a third point,

$(-1,-5)$.

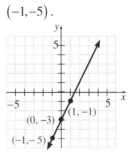

17. $x = -5$

Since this is in the form $x = a$, the graph is a vertical line (undefined slope).

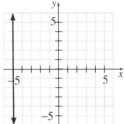

18. $y = 3$

Since this is in the form $y = b$, the graph is a horizontal line (0 slope).

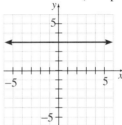

19. From the graph we see that the y-intercept is $(0,-2)$. Also, the point $(1,1)$ is clearly on the graph. Using these points, we can compute the slope.

$$\dfrac{1-(-2)}{1-0} = \dfrac{1+2}{1} = 3$$

Therefore, the slope is $m = \dfrac{3}{1} = 3$ and the equation of the line is $y = 3x - 2$.

20. $\dfrac{12.5 - 17.1}{2006 - 1975} = \dfrac{-4.6}{31} \approx -0.148$

The average rate of change of the number of hunters is about $-148{,}000$ per year.

21. $\dfrac{422-264}{2004-2000}=\dfrac{158}{4}=39.5$

The average rate of change is 39.5 thousand reports per year.

22. a. The slope is the average rate of change. In this situation, the slope is $m=10.7$. This means that sales of convertibles increase by 10.7 thousand each year.

b. A linear model has the form $y=mx+b$. Using s and t, our equation will be $s=mt+b$. We found the slope to be $m=10.7$ and are given the y-intercept as $(0,327)$, so $b=327$. Thus, our model is $s=10.7t+327$.

c. For 2014 we have $t=2014-2006=8$. Substitute 8 for t in the equation from part (b).
$$s=10.7(8)+327$$
$$=85.6+327$$
$$=412.6$$
In 2011, there will be 412.6 thousand convertibles sold in the U.S.

d. Substitute 430 for s in the equation from part (b).
$$430=10.7t+327$$
$$430-327=10.7t+327-327$$
$$103=10.7t$$
$$\dfrac{103}{10.7}=\dfrac{10.7t}{10.7}$$
$$9.63\approx t$$
The number of convertibles sold in the U.S. will be 430 thousand in 2006 + 10 = 2016.

23. Consider the average rates of change:

Equation 1: $\dfrac{13-11}{1-0}=\dfrac{2}{1}=2$

$\dfrac{16-13}{2-1}=\dfrac{3}{1}=3$

$\dfrac{20-16}{3-2}=\dfrac{4}{1}=4$

$\dfrac{25-20}{4-3}=\dfrac{5}{1}=5$

Equation 2: $\dfrac{53-56}{1-0}=\dfrac{-3}{1}=-3$

$\dfrac{50-53}{2-1}=\dfrac{-3}{1}=-3$

$\dfrac{47-50}{3-2}=\dfrac{-3}{1}=-3$

$\dfrac{44-47}{4-3}=\dfrac{-3}{1}=-3$

Equation 3: $\dfrac{44-35}{4-3}=\dfrac{9}{1}=9$

$\dfrac{53-44}{5-4}=\dfrac{9}{1}=9$

$\dfrac{62-53}{6-5}=\dfrac{9}{1}=9$

$\dfrac{71-62}{7-6}=\dfrac{9}{1}=9$

Equation 4: $\dfrac{1-1}{2-1}=\dfrac{0}{1}=0$

$\dfrac{1-1}{3-2}=\dfrac{0}{1}=0$

$\dfrac{1-1}{4-3}=\dfrac{0}{1}=0$

$\dfrac{1-1}{5-4}=\dfrac{0}{1}=0$

To be a linear equation, the average rate of change must be constant. From the data, it appears that equations 2, 3, and 4 could be linear.

24. a. $n=12.11t+21.93$

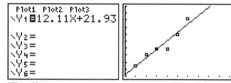

The line comes reasonably close to the data points.

b. The slope is 12.11. This means the number of colleges that offer student ID cards that double as debit cards increases by about 12 each year.

c. The n-intercept is (0, 21.93). This means that in 2000 there were about 22 colleges that offered student ID cards that double as debit cards.

d. For 2015 we have $t = 2015 - 2000 = 15$.
Substitute 15 for t in the equation
$n = 12.11t + 21.93$.

$$n = 12.11(15) + 21.93$$
$$= 181.65 + 21.93$$
$$= 203.58$$

In 2015, there will be 204 colleges that offer student ID cards that double as debit cards.

e. Substitute 180 for n in the equation
$n = 12.11t + 21.93$.

$$180 = 12.11t + 21.93$$
$$180 - 21.93 = 12.11t + 21.93 - 21.93$$
$$158.07 = 12.11t$$
$$\frac{158.07}{12.11} = \frac{12.11t}{12.11}$$
$$13.05 \approx t$$

The number of colleges that offer student ID cards that double as debit cards will be 180 in $2000 + 13 = 2013$.

25.
$$3r + 4 = 7r - 8$$
$$3r + 4 - 7r = 7r - 8 - 7r$$
$$-4r + 4 = -8$$
$$-4r + 4 - 4 = -8 - 4$$
$$-4r = -12$$
$$\frac{-4r}{-4} = \frac{-12}{-4}$$
$$r = 3$$

The solution is 3.

26.
$$2(3x - 2) = 4(3x + 5) - 3(x - 6)$$
$$6x - 4 = 12x + 20 - 3x + 18$$
$$6x - 4 = 9x + 38$$
$$6x - 4 - 9x = 9x + 38 - 9x$$
$$-3x - 4 = 38$$
$$-3x - 4 + 4 = 38 + 4$$
$$-3x = 42$$
$$\frac{-3x}{-3} = \frac{42}{-3}$$
$$x = -14$$

The solution is -14.

27. $4a - 5b + 6 - 2b - 7a = 4a - 7a - 5b - 2b + 6$
$$= -3a - 7b + 6$$
The simplified expression is $-3a - 7b + 6$.

28. $7 - 2(3p - 5) + 5(4p - 2)$
$$= 7 - 6p + 10 + 20p - 10$$
$$= -6p + 20p + 7 + 10 - 10$$
$$= 14p + 7$$
The simplified expression is $14p + 7$.

29.
$$\frac{2}{3}r - \frac{5}{6} = \frac{1}{2} + \frac{3}{4}r$$
$$\frac{2}{3}r - \frac{5}{6} - \frac{3}{4}r = \frac{1}{2} + \frac{3}{4}r - \frac{3}{4}r$$
$$\frac{2}{3}r - \frac{3}{4}r - \frac{5}{6} + \frac{5}{6} = \frac{1}{2} + \frac{5}{6}$$
$$\frac{2}{3}r - \frac{3}{4}r = \frac{1}{2} + \frac{5}{6}$$
$$12\left(\frac{2}{3}r - \frac{3}{4}r\right) = 12\left(\frac{1}{2} + \frac{5}{6}\right)$$
$$8r - 9r = 6 + 10$$
$$-r = 16$$
$$r = -16$$

The solution is -16.

30. $2(3x - 5y) - (8x + 3y - 1) = 6x - 10y - 8x - 3y + 1$
$$= 6x - 8x - 10y - 3y + 1$$
$$= -2x - 13y + 1$$
The simplified expression is $-2x - 13y + 1$.

31.
$$25.93 - 7.6(2.1x + 8.7) = 53.26$$
$$25.93 - 15.96x - 66.12 = 53.26$$
$$-15.96x - 40.19 = 53.26$$
$$-15.96x - 40.19 + 40.19 = 53.26 + 40.19$$
$$-15.96x = 93.45$$
$$\frac{-15.96x}{-15.96} = \frac{93.45}{-15.96}$$
$$x \approx -5.86$$

The solution is approximately -5.86.

32. $x + 9 \cdot \dfrac{x}{3} = x + 3x = 4x$

The simplified expression is $4x$.

33.
$$2(7-2x) = 87$$
$$14 - 4x = 87$$
$$14 - 4x - 14 = 87 - 14$$
$$-4x = 73$$
$$\frac{-4x}{-4} = \frac{73}{-4}$$
$$x = -\frac{73}{4}$$

The solution is $-\dfrac{73}{4}$.

34.
$$A = 2\pi rh$$
$$\frac{A}{2\pi r} = \frac{2\pi rh}{2\pi r}$$
$$\frac{A}{2\pi r} = h \quad \text{or} \quad h = \frac{A}{2\pi r}$$

35.
$$4x - 6y = 12$$
$$4x - 6y - 4x = 12 - 4x$$
$$-6y = 12 - 4x$$
$$\frac{-6y}{-6} = \frac{12 - 4x}{-6}$$
$$y = \frac{12}{-6} + \frac{-4x}{-6}$$
$$y = -2 + \frac{2}{3}x$$
$$y = \frac{2}{3}x - 2$$

Chapter 5
Linear Functions and Linear Inequalities
in One Variable

Homework 5.1

1. The equation $y = 2x - 3$ is in slope-intercept form, so the slope is $m = 2 = \dfrac{2}{1}$, and the y-intercept is $(0, -3)$. We first plot $(0, -3)$. From this point we move 1 unit to the right and 2 units up, where we plot the point $(1, -1)$. We then sketch the line that contains these two points.

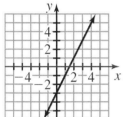

3. The equation $y = -\dfrac{3}{5}x - 2$ is in slope-intercept form, so the slope is $m = -\dfrac{3}{5}$, and the y-intercept is $(0, -2)$. We first plot $(0, -2)$. From this point we move 5 units to the right and 3 units down, where we plot the point $(5, -5)$. We then sketch the line that contains these two points.

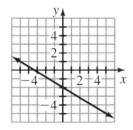

5. The equation $y = -4$ is in slope-intercept form, so the slope is $m = 0$ and the y-intercept is $(0, -4)$. The graph is a horizontal line that

passes through the point $(0, -4)$.

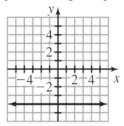

7. $y + x = 3$
$$y = -x + 3$$

The slope is $m = -1 = \dfrac{-1}{1}$, and the y-intercept is $(0, 3)$. We first plot $(0, 3)$. From this point we move 1 unit to the right and 1 unit down, where we plot the point $(1, 2)$. We then sketch the line that contains these two points.

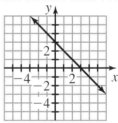

9. $y + 2x = 4$
$$y = -2x + 4$$

The slope is $m = -2 = \dfrac{-2}{1}$, and the y-intercept is $(0, 4)$. We first plot $(0, 4)$. From this point we move 1 unit to the right and 2 units down, where we plot the point $(2, 1)$. We then sketch the line that contains these two points.

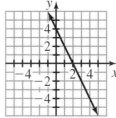

11. $y - 2x = -1$

$\qquad y = 2x - 1$

The slope is $m = 2 = \dfrac{2}{1}$, and the y-intercept is

$(0, -1)$. We first plot $(0, -1)$. From this point we move 1 unit to the right and 2 units up, where we plot the point $(1, 1)$. We then sketch the line that contains these two points.

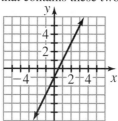

13. $3y = 2x$

$\qquad y = \dfrac{2}{3}x$

The slope is $m = \dfrac{2}{3}$, and the y-intercept is $(0, 0)$.

We first plot $(0, 0)$. From this point we move 3 units to the right and 2 units up, where we plot the point $(3, 2)$. We then sketch the line that contains these two points.

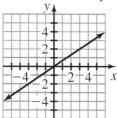

15. $2y = 5x - 6$

$\qquad \dfrac{2y}{2} = \dfrac{5x}{2} - \dfrac{6}{2}$

$\qquad y = \dfrac{5}{2}x - 3$

The slope is $m = \dfrac{5}{2}$, and the y-intercept is

$(0, -3)$. We first plot $(0, -3)$. From this point we move 2 units to the right and 5 units up, where we plot the point $(2, 2)$. We then sketch the line that contains these two points.

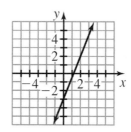

17. $5y = 4x - 15$

$\qquad \dfrac{5y}{5} = \dfrac{4x}{5} - \dfrac{15}{5}$

$\qquad y = \dfrac{4}{5}x - 3$

The slope is $m = \dfrac{4}{5}$, and the y-intercept is

$(0, -3)$. We first plot $(0, -3)$. From this point we move 5 units to the right and 4 units up, where we plot the point $(5, 1)$. We then sketch the line that contains these two points.

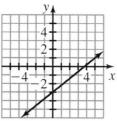

19. $3x - 4y = 8$

$\qquad -4y = -3x + 8$

$\qquad \dfrac{-4y}{-4} = \dfrac{-3x}{-4} + \dfrac{8}{-4}$

$\qquad y = \dfrac{3}{4}x - 2$

The slope is $m = \dfrac{3}{4}$, and the y-intercept is

$(0, -2)$. We first plot $(0, -2)$. From this point we move 4 units to the right and 3 units up, where we plot the point $(4, 1)$. We then sketch the line that contains these two points.

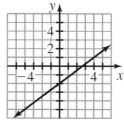

21. $6x - 15y = 30$

$$-15y = -6x + 30$$

$$\frac{-15y}{-15} = \frac{-6x}{-15} + \frac{30}{-15}$$

$$y = \frac{2}{5}x - 2$$

The slope is $m = \frac{2}{5}$, and the y-intercept is $(0, -2)$. We first plot $(0, -2)$. From this point we move 5 units to the right and 2 units up, where we plot the point $(5, 0)$. We then sketch the line that contains these two points.

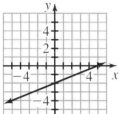

23. $x + 4y = 4$

$$4y = -x + 4$$

$$\frac{4y}{4} = \frac{-x}{4} + \frac{4}{4}$$

$$y = -\frac{1}{4}x + 1$$

The slope is $m = -\frac{1}{4}$, and the y-intercept is $(0, 1)$. We first plot $(0, 1)$. From this point we move 4 units to the right and 1 unit down, where we plot the point $(4, 0)$. We then sketch the line that contains these two points.

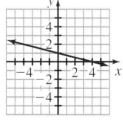

25. $-4 = x + 2y$

$$-2y = x + 4$$

$$\frac{-2y}{-2} = \frac{x}{-2} + \frac{4}{-2}$$

$$y = -\frac{1}{2}x - 2$$

The slope is $m = -\frac{1}{2}$, and the y-intercept is $(0, -2)$. We first plot $(0, -2)$. From this point we move 2 units to the right and 1 unit down, where we plot the point $(2, -3)$. We then sketch the line that contains these two points.

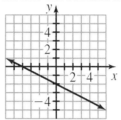

27. $4x + y + 2 = 0$

$$y = -4x - 2$$

The slope is $m = -4 = \frac{-4}{1}$, and the y-intercept is $(0, -2)$. We first plot $(0, -2)$. From this point we move 1 unit to the right and 4 units down, where we plot the point $(1, -6)$. We then sketch the line that contains these two points.

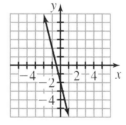

29. $6x - 4y + 8 = 0$

$$-4y = -6x - 8$$

$$\frac{-4y}{-4} = \frac{-6x}{-4} - \frac{8}{-4}$$

$$y = \frac{3}{2}x + 2$$

The slope is $m = \frac{3}{2}$, and the y-intercept is $(0, 2)$.

We first plot $(0, 2)$. From this point we move 2 units to the right and 3 units up, where we plot the point $(2, 5)$. We then sketch the line that contains these two points.

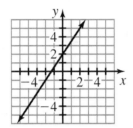

31. $0 = 5x + 3y$

$$-3y = 5x$$

$$y = -\frac{5}{3}x$$

The slope is $m = -\frac{5}{3}$, and the y-intercept is

$(0, 0)$. We first plot $(0, 0)$. From this point we move 3 units to the right and 5 units down, where we plot the point $(3, -5)$. We then sketch the line that contains these two points.

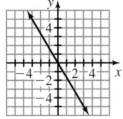

33. $y - 3 = 0$

$$y = 3$$

The slope is $m = 0$, and the y-intercept is $(0, 3)$. The graph is a horizontal line that passes through the point $(0, 3)$.

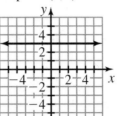

35. First, rewrite $3(x - 2y) = 9$ in slope-intercept form.

$$3(x - 2y) = 9$$

$$3x - 6y = 9$$

$$-6y = -3x + 9$$

$$y = \frac{1}{2}x - \frac{3}{2}$$

The slope is $m = \frac{1}{2}$, and the

y-intercept is $\left(0, -\frac{3}{2}\right)$. We first plot $\left(0, -\frac{3}{2}\right)$.

From this point we move 2 units to the right and 1 unit up, where we plot the point $\left(2, -\frac{1}{2}\right)$. We then sketch the line that contains these two points.

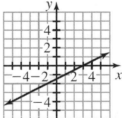

37. First, rewrite $4x - 5y + 3 = 2x - 2y - 3$ in slope-intercept form.
$$4x - 5y + 3 = 2x - 2y - 3$$
$$-3y = -2x - 6$$
$$y = \frac{2}{3}x + 2$$

The slope is $m = \frac{2}{3}$, and the y-intercept is $(0, 2)$.

We first plot $(0, 2)$. From this point we move 3 units to the right and 2 units up, where we plot the point $(3, 4)$. We then sketch the line that contains these two points.

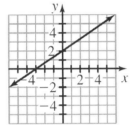

39. First, rewrite $1 - 3(y - 2x) = 7 + 3(x - 3y)$ in slope-intercept form.
$$1 - 3(y - 2x) = 7 + 3(x - 3y)$$
$$1 - 3y + 6x = 7 + 3x - 9y$$
$$6y = -3x + 6$$
$$y = -\frac{1}{2}x + 1$$

The slope is $m = -\frac{1}{2}$, and the

y-intercept is $(0, 1)$. We first plot $(0, 1)$. From this point we move 2 units to the right and 1 unit down, where we plot the point $(2, 0)$. We then sketch the line that contains these two points.

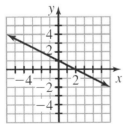

41. Solve for y.
$$ax - by = c$$
$$-by = -ax + c$$
$$y = \frac{a}{b}x - \frac{c}{b}$$

The slope is $\frac{a}{b}$ and the y-intercept is $\left(0, -\frac{c}{b}\right)$.

43. Solve for y.
$$a(y + b) = x$$
$$ay + ab = x$$
$$ay = x - ab$$
$$y = \frac{1}{a}x - b$$

The slope is $\frac{1}{a}$ and the y-intercept is $(0, -b)$.

45. Solve for y.
$$\frac{x}{a} + \frac{y}{a} = 1$$
$$x + y = a$$
$$y = -x + a$$

The slope is -1 and the y-intercept is $(0, a)$.

47. $x - 3y = 6$

To find the x-intercept, we substitute 0 for y and solve for x. To find the y-intercept, we substitute 0 for x and solve for y.

$\underline{x\text{-intercept}}$ $\underline{y\text{-intercept}}$
$x - 3(0) = 6$ $\quad 0 - 3y = 6$
$\quad\quad x = 6$ $\quad -3y = 6$
$\quad\quad\quad\quad\quad\quad\quad y = -2$

The x-intercept is $(6, 0)$; the y-intercept is $(0, -2)$.

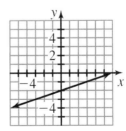

49. $15 = 3x + 5y$

To find the x-intercept, we substitute 0 for y and solve for x. To find the y-intercept, we substitute 0 for x and solve for y.

x-intercept	y-intercept
$15 = 3x + 5(0)$	$15 = 3(0) + 5y$
$15 = 3x$	$15 = 5y$
$5 = x$	$3 = y$

The x-intercept is $(5, 0)$; the y-intercept is $(0, 3)$.

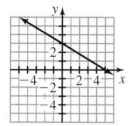

51. $2x - 3y + 12 = 0$

To find the x-intercept, we substitute 0 for y and solve for x. To find the y-intercept, we substitute 0 for x and solve for y.

x-intercept	y-intercept
$2x - 3(0) + 12 = 0$	$2(0) - 3y + 12 = 0$
$2x + 12 = 0$	$-3y + 12 = 0$
$2x = -12$	$-3y = -12$
$x = -6$	$y = 4$

The x-intercept is $(-6, 0)$; the y-intercept is $(0, 4)$.

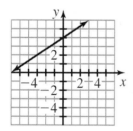

53. $y = -3x + 6$

To find the x-intercept, we substitute 0 for y and solve for x. To find the y-intercept, we substitute 0 for x and solve for y.

x-intercept	y-intercept
$0 = -3x + 6$	$y = -3(0) + 6$
$3x = 6$	$y = 6$
$x = 2$	

The x-intercept is $(2, 0)$; the y-intercept is $(0, 6)$.

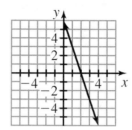

55. $\frac{1}{2}x - \frac{1}{3}y = 2$

To find the x-intercept, we substitute 0 for y and solve for x. To find the y-intercept, we substitute 0 for x and solve for y.

x-intercept	y-intercept
$\frac{1}{2}x - \frac{1}{3}(0) = 2$	$\frac{1}{2}(0) - \frac{1}{3}y = 2$
$\frac{1}{2}x = 2$	$-\frac{1}{3}y = 2$
$x = 4$	$y = -6$

The x-intercept is $(4, 0)$; the y-intercept is $(0, -6)$.

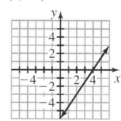

57. $\dfrac{x}{3}+\dfrac{y}{5}=1$

To find the x-intercept, we substitute 0 for y and solve for x. To find the y-intercept, we substitute 0 for x and solve for y.

x-intercept	y-intercept
$\dfrac{x}{3}+\dfrac{0}{5}=1$	$\dfrac{0}{3}+\dfrac{y}{5}=1$
$\dfrac{x}{3}=1$	$\dfrac{y}{5}=1$
$x=3$	$y=5$

The x-intercept is $(3,0)$; the y-intercept is $(0,5)$.

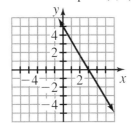

59. $6.2x+2.8y=7.5$

To find the x-intercept, we substitute 0 for y and solve for x. To find the y-intercept, we substitute 0 for x and solve for y.

x-intercept	y-intercept
$6.2x+2.8(0)=7.5$	$6.2(0)+2.8y=7.5$
$6.2x=7.5$	$2.8y=7.5$
$x\approx1.21$	$x\approx2.68$

The x-intercept is approximately $(1.21,0)$; the y-intercept is approximately $(0,2.68)$.

61. $6.62x-3.91y=-13.55$

To find the x-intercept, we substitute 0 for y and solve for x.

$$6.62x-3.91(0)=-13.55$$
$$6.62x=-13.55$$
$$x\approx-2.05$$

To find the y-intercept, we substitute 0 for x and solve for y.

$$6.62(0)-3.91y=-13.55$$
$$-3.91y=-13.55$$
$$y\approx3.47$$

The x-intercept is approximately $(-2.05,0)$; the y-intercept is approximately $(0,3.47)$.

63. $y=-4.5x+9.32$

To find the x-intercept, we substitute 0 for y and solve for x. To find the y-intercept, we substitute 0 for x and solve for y.

x-intercept	y-intercept
$0=-4.5x+9.32$	$y=-4.5(0)+9.32$
$4.5x=9.32$	$y=9.32$
$x\approx2.07$	

The x-intercept is approximately $(2.07,0)$; the y-intercept is approximately $(0,9.32)$.

65. $y=-2.49x-37.21$

To find the x-intercept, we substitute 0 for y and solve for x. To find the y-intercept, we substitute 0 for x and solve for y.

x-intercept	y-intercept
$0=-2.49x-37.21$	$y=-2.49(0)-37.21$
$2.49x=-37.21$	$y=-37.21$
$x\approx-14.94$	

The x-intercept is approximately $(-14.94,0)$; the y-intercept is approximately $(0,-37.21)$.

67. $y=mx+b$

To find the x-intercept, let $y=0$ and solve for x.
$$0=mx+b$$
$$-b=mx$$
$$-\dfrac{b}{m}=x$$

The x-intercept is $\left(-\dfrac{b}{m},0\right)$. To find the y-intercept, let $x=0$ and solve for y.
$$y=m(0)+b$$
$$y=b$$
The y-intercept is $(0,b)$.

69. $\dfrac{x}{a} + \dfrac{y}{b} = 1$

To find the x-intercept, let $y = 0$ and solve for x.

$$\dfrac{x}{a} + \dfrac{0}{b} = 1$$

$$a\left(\dfrac{x}{a}\right) = a(1)$$

$$x = a$$

The x-intercept is $(a, 0)$. To find the y-intercept, let $x = 0$ and solve for y.

$$\dfrac{0}{a} + \dfrac{y}{b} = 1$$

$$b\left(\dfrac{y}{b}\right) = b(1)$$

$$y = b$$

The y-intercept is $(0, b)$.

71. $2x - y = 5$

$$-y = -2x + 5$$

$$\dfrac{-y}{-1} = \dfrac{-2x}{-1} + \dfrac{5}{-1}$$

$$y = 2x - 5$$

The slope is $m = 2$, and the y-intercept is $(0, -5)$. We first plot $(0, -5)$. From this point we move 1 unit to the right and 2 units up, where we plot the point $(1, -3)$. We then sketch the line that contains these two points.

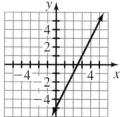

73. $3y = 4x - 3$

$$\dfrac{3y}{3} = \dfrac{4x}{3} - \dfrac{3}{3}$$

$$y = \dfrac{4}{3}x - 1$$

The slope is $m = \dfrac{4}{3}$, and the y-intercept is $(0, -1)$. We first plot $(0, -1)$. From this point we move 3 units to the right and 4 units up, where we plot the point $(3, 3)$. We then sketch

the line that contains these two points.

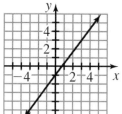

75. $4y - 3x = 0$

$$4y = 3x$$

$$\dfrac{4y}{4} = \dfrac{3x}{4}$$

$$y = \dfrac{3}{4}x$$

The slope is $m = \dfrac{3}{4}$, and the y-intercept is $(0, 0)$. We first plot $(0, 0)$. From this point we move 4 units to the right and 3 units up, where we plot the point $(4, 3)$. We then sketch the line that contains these two points.

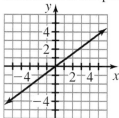

77. $2x - 3y - 12 = 0$

$$-3y = -2x + 12$$

$$\dfrac{-3y}{-3} = \dfrac{-2x}{-3} + \dfrac{12}{-3}$$

$$y = \dfrac{2}{3}x - 4$$

The slope is $m = \dfrac{2}{3}$, and the y-intercept is $(0, -4)$. We first plot $(0, -4)$. From this point we move 3 units to the right and 2 units up, where we plot the point $(3, -2)$. We then sketch the line that contains these two points.

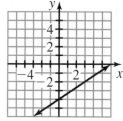

79. $6x + 5y = -13$

   a. Substitute -3 for x and solve for y:
$$6(-3) + 5y = -13$$
$$-18 + 5y = -13$$
$$5y = 5$$
$$y = 1$$

   b. Substitute -5 for y and solve for x:
$$6x + 5(-5) = -13$$
$$6x - 25 = -13$$
$$6x = 12$$
$$x = 2$$

   c. We plot the points $(-3, 1)$ and $(2, -5)$ and sketch the line that contains the two points.

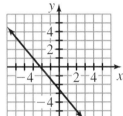

81. No, the slope is not 2 because the equation is not in slope-intercept form.
$$3y + 2x = 6$$
$$3y = -2x + 6$$
$$\frac{3y}{3} = \frac{-2x}{3} + \frac{6}{3}$$
$$y = -\frac{2}{3}x + 2$$

The slope is $m = -\dfrac{2}{3}$.

83. $3x - 5y = 10$

   a. $3x - 5y = 10$
$$-5y = -3x + 10$$
$$\frac{-5y}{-5} = \frac{-3x}{-5} + \frac{10}{-5}$$
$$y = \frac{3}{5}x - 2$$

The slope is $m = \dfrac{3}{5}$ and the y-intercept is $(0, -2)$. We first plot $(0, -2)$. From this point we move 5 units to the right and 3 units up, where we plot the point $(5, 1)$. We

then sketch the line that contains these two points.

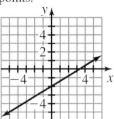

   b. Answers may vary. One possibility follows:

x	y
-5	-5
0	-2
5	1

   c. Answers may vary. One possibility follows: For each solution, the difference of three times the x-coordinate and five times the y-coordinate is equal to 10.

85. a. $\dfrac{x}{5} + \dfrac{y}{7} = 1$

x-intercept	y-intercept
Let $y = 0$:	Let $x = 0$:
$\dfrac{x}{5} + \dfrac{0}{7} = 1$	$\dfrac{0}{5} + \dfrac{y}{7} = 1$
$\dfrac{x}{5} = 1$	$\dfrac{y}{7} = 1$
$x = 5$	$y = 7$

The x-intercept is $(5, 0)$; the y-intercept is $(0, 7)$.

   b. $\dfrac{x}{4} + \dfrac{y}{6} = 1$

x-intercept	y-intercept
Let $y = 0$:	Let $x = 0$:
$\dfrac{x}{4} + \dfrac{0}{6} = 1$	$\dfrac{0}{4} + \dfrac{y}{6} = 1$
$\dfrac{x}{4} = 1$	$\dfrac{y}{6} = 1$
$x = 4$	$y = 6$

The x-intercept is $(4, 0)$; the y-intercept is $(0, 6)$.

c. $\dfrac{x}{a}+\dfrac{y}{b}=1$

<u>x-intercept</u>   <u>y-intercept</u>

Let $y=0$:   Let $x=0$:

$\dfrac{x}{a}+\dfrac{0}{b}=1$ $\dfrac{0}{a}+\dfrac{y}{b}=1$

$\dfrac{x}{a}=1$ $\dfrac{y}{b}=1$

$x=a$ $y=b$

The x-intercept is $(a,0)$; the y-intercept is $(0,b)$.

d. The x-intercept is $(2,0)$, so $a=2$ in the equation from part (c). Likewise, the y-intercept is $(0,5)$, so $b=5$ in the equation from part (c). The equation is $\dfrac{x}{2}+\dfrac{y}{5}=1$.

87. Answers may vary. One possibility follows: The y-coordinate of the x-intercept is zero because the x-intercept is a point on the x-axis, which must have a y-coordinate of zero. The x-coordinate of the y-intercept is zero because the y-intercept is a point on the y-axis, which must have an x-coordinate of zero.

89. Answers will vary.

91. The graph contains the point $(6,1)$, so $y=1$ when $x=6$.

93. The graph contains the point $(2,-1)$, so $x=2$ when $y=-1$.

95. The graph and the x-axis intersect at the point $(4,0)$, so the x-intercept is $(4,0)$.

97. The line contains the points $(4,0)$ and $(6,1)$, so the slope is $m=\dfrac{1-0}{6-4}=\dfrac{1}{2}$.

99. $5-3(2x-7)=5-6x+21$
$=-6x+26$
This is a linear expression in one variable.

101. $5-3(2x-7)=8$
$5-6x+21=8$
$-6x+26=8$
$-6x=-18$
$x=3$
This is a linear equation in one variable.

Homework 5.2

1. Relation 1 is not a function. The input $x=3$ yields *two* outputs $y=5$ and $y=7$. Relation 2 could possibly be a function since each input yields only one output. Relation 3 could possibly be a function since each input yields only one output. Relation 4 is not a function. The input $x=8$ yields *two* outputs $y=40$ and $y=50$.

3. No, the relation is not a function since an input yields more than one output.

5. Yes, it is possible that the relation is a function. Two inputs can yield the same output, but one input cannot yield two outputs.

7. This graph is a function since it passes the vertical line test.

9. This graph is not a function since a vertical line can intersect the graph at more than one point.

11. This graph is not a function since a vertical line can intersect the graph at more than one point.

13. This graph is a function since it passes the vertical line test.

15. The relation $y=5x-1$ is a function since it can be put into the form $y=mx+b$ which defines a linear function.

17. First, isolate y.
$2x-5y=10$
$-5y=-2x+10$
$y=\dfrac{2}{5}x-2$
This relation is a function since it can be put into the form $y=mx+b$ which defines a linear function.

19. $y=4$ is a horizontal line. Because every horizontal line passes the vertical line test, $y=4$ is a function.

21. $x=-3$ is a vertical line and does not pass the vertical line test. This is not a function.

23. First, isolate y.
$$7x - 2y = 21 + 3(y - 5x)$$
$$7x - 2y = 21 + 3y - 15x$$
$$-2y - 3y = -7x - 15x + 21$$
$$\frac{-5y}{-5} = \frac{22x + 21}{-5}$$
$$y = -\frac{22}{5}x - \frac{21}{5}$$

This relation is a function since it can be put into the form $y = mx + b$ which defines a linear function.

25. Yes, any nonvertical line is a function since it passes the vertical line test.

27. No, a circle is not the graph of a function since a vertical line may intersect the circle at more than one point.

29. a. Answers may vary.

x	y
0	$3(0) - 2 = -2$
1	$3(1) - 2 = 1$
2	$3(2) - 2 = 4$
3	$3(3) - 2 = 7$
4	$3(4) - 2 = 10$

b.

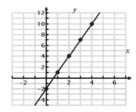

c. For each input-output pair, the output is 2 less than 3 times the input.

31. The domain is $-4 \le x \le 5$ and the range is $-2 \le y \le 3$.

33. The domain is $-5 \le x \le 4$ and the range is $-2 \le y \le 3$. The highest point on the graph appears to include a y-value of 3.

35. The domain is $-4 \le x \le 4$ and the range is $-2 \le y \le 2$. The lowest point on the graph appears to include a y-value of -2 and the highest point appears to include a y-value of 2.

37. The domain is $0 \le x \le 4$ and the range is $0 \le y \le 2$. The lowest point on the graph includes a y-value of 0.

39. The domain is all real numbers and the range is $y \le 4$. The highest point on the graph includes a y-value of 4.

41. The domain is $x \ge 0$ and the range is $y \ge 0$.

43. Answers may vary.

$y = 2^x$ is a function expressed as an equation.

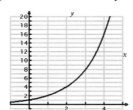

x	y
0	1
1	2
2	4
3	8
4	16

For each input-output pair, the output is 2 raised to the power of the input.

45. Answers may vary. One example follows. Suppose that when $x = 2$, $y = -1$ and $y = 4$. Then suppose when $x = 6$, $y = 0$. Sketch these points.

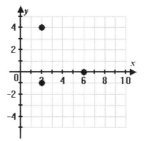

This relation is not a function since it does not pass the vertical line test.

47. Answers may vary.

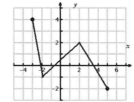

49. Answers may vary.

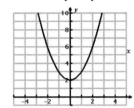

51. The relation $y = \sqrt{x}$ is a function since it passes the vertical line test.

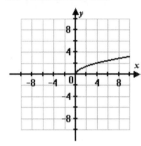

53. Consider the input $x = 16$. Substitute 16 for x and solve for y.

$y^4 = 16$

$y = \pm 2$

Since the input $x = 16$ yields *two* outputs, the relation, $y^4 = x$, is not a function.

55. No, the student's conclusion is not correct. In a function, *two* inputs can yield the same output, but one input cannot yield *two* outputs.

57. The equation of a line is $y = mx + b$, where m is the slope of the line If the slope of a line is positive, then $m > 0$ and the graph is an increasing line, and therefore a function.

59. The equation of a line is $y = mx + b$, where m is the slope of the line If the slope of a line is undefined, then m is undefined and the graph is a vertical line, and therefore not a function.

61. $2(4x-5)-4(3x+2) = 8x-10-12x-8$

$\qquad = 8x-12x-10-8$

$\qquad = -4x-18$

$-4x - 18$ is a linear expression in one variable.

63. $2(4x-5)-4(3x+2) = 0$

$\qquad 8x-10-12x-8 = 0$

$\qquad 8x-12x-10-8 = 0$

$\qquad -4x-18 = 0$

$\qquad -4x-18+18 = 0+18$

$\qquad -4x = 18$

$\qquad \dfrac{-4x}{-4} = \dfrac{18}{-4}$

$\qquad x = -\dfrac{9}{2}$

The solution to the linear equation in one variable $2(4x-5)-4(3x+2) = 0$ is $x = -\dfrac{9}{2}$.

Homework 5.3

1. Substituting 5 whenever there is an x in $f(x)$:

$f(5) = 6(5)-4$

$\qquad = 30-4$

$f(5) = 26$

3. Substituting $\dfrac{2}{3}$ wherever there is an x in $f(x)$:

$f\left(\dfrac{2}{3}\right) = 6\left(\dfrac{2}{3}\right)-4$

$\qquad = 4-4$

$f\left(\dfrac{2}{3}\right) = 0$

5. Substituting $a + 2$ wherever there is an x in $f(x)$:

$f(a+2) = 6(a+2)-4$

$\qquad = 6a+12-4$

$f(a+2) = 6a+8$

7. Substituting 2 wherever there is an x in $g(x)$:

$g(2) = 2(2)^2 -5(2)$

$\qquad = 2(4)-10$

$\qquad = 8-10$

$g(2) = -2$

9. Substituting -3 wherever there is an x in $g(x)$:

$g(-3) = 2(-3)^2 -5(-3)$

$\qquad = 2(9)+15$

$\qquad = 18+15$

$g(-3) = 33$

11. Substituting 2 wherever there is an x in $h(x)$:

$$h(2) = \frac{3(2)-4}{5(2)+2}$$

$$= \frac{6-4}{10+2}$$

$$= \frac{2}{12}$$

$$h(2) = \frac{1}{6}$$

13. Substituting $a - 3$ wherever there is an x in $h(x)$:

$$h(a-3) = \frac{3(a-3)-4}{5(a-3)+2}$$

$$= \frac{3a-9-4}{5a-15+2}$$

$$h(a-3) = \frac{3a-13}{5a-13}$$

15. Substituting -2 wherever there is an x in $g(x)$:

$$g(-2) = -3(-2)^2 + 2(-2)$$

$$= -3(4) - 4$$

$$= -12 - 4$$

$$g(-2) = -16$$

17. Substituting 5 wherever there is an x in $f(x)$:

$$f(5) = -2(5) + 7$$

$$= -10 + 7$$

$$f(5) = -3$$

19. Since $h(x) = -4$, for all x, $h(7) = -4$.

21. Substituting $5a$ wherever there is an x in $f(x)$:

$$f(5a) = -4(5a) - 7$$

$$f(5a) = -20a - 7$$

23. Substituting $\frac{a}{2}$ wherever there is an x in $f(x)$:

$$f\left(\frac{a}{2}\right) = -4\left(\frac{a}{2}\right) - 7$$

$$f\left(\frac{a}{2}\right) = -2a - 7$$

25. Substituting $a + 4$ wherever there is an x in $f(x)$:

$$f(a+4) = -4(a+4) - 7$$

$$= -4a - 16 - 7$$

$$f(a+4) = -4a - 23$$

27. Substituting $a - h$ wherever there is an x in $f(x)$:

$$f(a-h) = -4(a-h) - 7$$

$$= -4a + 4h - 7$$

29. To find x when $f(x) = 6$, substitute 6 for $f(x)$ and solve for x.

$$6 = -3x + 7$$

$$3x = 1$$

$$x = \frac{1}{3}$$

31. To find x when $f(x) = \frac{5}{2}$, substitute $\frac{5}{2}$ for $f(x)$ and solve for x.

$$\frac{5}{2} = -3x + 7$$

$$\frac{-9}{2} = -3x$$

$$\frac{3}{2} = x$$

$$x = \frac{3}{2}$$

33. To find x when $f(x) = a$, substitute a for $f(x)$ and solve for x.

$$a = -3x + 7$$

$$a - 7 = -3x$$

$$\frac{7-a}{3} = x$$

$$x = \frac{7-a}{3}$$

35. Substituting 10.91 wherever there is an x in $f(x)$:

$$f(10.91) = -5.95(10.91) + 183.22$$

$$\approx -64.91 + 183.22$$

$$\approx 118.31$$

37. To find x when $f(x) = 99.34$, substitute 99.34 for $f(x)$ and solve for x.

$$99.34 = -5.95x + 183.22$$

$$-83.88 = -5.95x$$

$$14.10 \approx x$$

$$x \approx 14.10$$

39. The student mistakenly substituted 5 for x and solved for $f(x)$. The student should have substituted 5 for $f(x)$ and solved for x.

$$5 = x + 2$$

$$3 = x$$

$$x = 3$$

41. a. To find $f(3)$, $f(5)$ and $f(8)$, substitute the correct value for x in $f(x)$:
$$f(3) = 4(3)$$
$$= 12$$
$$f(5) = 4(5)$$
$$= 20$$
$$f(8) = 4(8)$$
$$= 32$$
To check $f(3 + 5) = f(3) + f(5)$, substitute for the above values:
$$f(3+5) = f(3) + f(5)$$
$$f(8) = 12 + 20$$
$$32 = 32$$
This is a true statement, so $f(3 + 5) = f(3) + f(5)$ is a true statement.

b. To find $f(2)$, $f(3)$ and $f(5)$, substitute the correct value for x in $f(x)$:
$$f(2) = (2)^2$$
$$= 4$$
$$f(3) = (3)^2$$
$$= 9$$
$$f(5) = (5)^2$$
$$= 25$$
To check $f(2 + 3) = f(2) + f(3)$, substitute for the above values:
$$f(2+3) = f(2) + f(3)$$
$$f(5) = 4 + 9$$
$$25 = 13$$
This is not a true statement, so $f(2 + 3) = f(2) + f(3)$ is not a true statement.

c. To find $f(9)$, $f(16)$ and $f(25)$, substitute the correct value for x in $f(x)$:
$$f(9) = \sqrt{9}$$
$$= 3$$
$$f(16) = \sqrt{16}$$
$$= 4$$
$$f(25) = \sqrt{25}$$
$$= 5$$
To check $f(9 + 16) = f(9) + f(16)$, substitute for the above values:
$$f(9+16) = f(9) + f(16)$$
$$f(25) = 3 + 4$$
$$5 = 7$$
This is not a true statement, so $f(9 + 16) = f(9) + f(16)$ is not a true statement.

d. It is not true that $f(a + b) = f(a) + f(b)$ for every function f as shown by two of these three equations.

43. The third row of the chart indicates that $f(2) = 4$.

45. The second and fourth rows of the chart indicate that $f(x) = 2$ when $x = 1$ or $x = 3$.

47. Since the line includes the point $(-6, 4)$, $f(-6) = 4$.

49. Since the line includes a point at approximately $(2.5, 1.2)$, $f(2.5) \approx 1.2$.

51. Since the line includes the point $(6, 0)$, $x = 6$ when $f(x)$ or $y = 0$.

53. Since the line includes the point $(-3, 3)$, $x = -3$ when $f(x)$ or $y = 3$.

55. Since the line includes the point $(4.5, \frac{1}{2})$, $x = 4.5$ when $f(x)$ or $y = \frac{1}{2}$.

57. The domain of f is all the x-coordinates of the points in the graph. In this case f has a domain of all real numbers.

59. Here, t is the independent variable and a is the dependent variable. Since the function name is f, we can write $a = f(t)$. Then we substitute $f(t)$ for a in the equation $a = -27.2t + 315$:
$$f(t) = -27.2t + 315.$$

61. Here, E is the independent variable and B is the dependent variable. Since the function name is g, we can write $B = g(E)$. Then we substitute $g(E)$ for B in the equation $B = -5.9E + 212$:
$$g(E) = -5.9E + 212$$

63. a. Answers may vary.

x	$g(x)$
-2	10
-1	7
0	4
1	1
2	-2

b.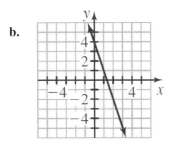

c. The output is 4 more than −3 times the input.

65. Sine the curve includes the point (−2, 1), $g(-2) = 1$.

67. The domain of g is all of the x-coordinates of the points in the graph. In this case g has a domain of $-4 \le x \le 5$.

69. Since the curve includes the point (1, −3), $h(1) = -3$.

71. The domain of h is all of the x-coordinates of the points in the graph. In this case h has a domain of $-5 \le x \le 4$.

73. $f(x)$ or $y = 5x - 8$

To find the x-intercept, set $y = 0$ and solve for x.
$$0 = 5x - 8$$
$$8 = 5x$$
$$\frac{8}{5} = x$$
$$x = \frac{8}{5}$$
x-intercept: $\left(\frac{8}{5}, 0\right)$

To find the y-intercept, set $x = 0$ and solve for y.
$$y = 5(0) - 8$$
$$y = 0 - 8$$
$$y = -8$$
y-intercept: (0, −8)

75. $f(x)$ or $y = 3x$

To find the x-intercept, set $y = 0$ and solve for x.
$$0 = 3x$$
$$0 = x$$
$$x = 0$$
x-intercept: (0, 0)

To find the y-intercept, set $x = 0$ and solve for y.
$$y = 3(0)$$
$$y = 0$$
y-intercept: (0, 0)

77. $f(x)$ or $y = 5$ is the equation of a horizontal line. The y-intercept of the line will be (0, 5). There is no x-intercept.

79. $f(x)$ or $y = \frac{1}{2}x - 3$

To find the x-intercept, set $y = 0$ and solve for x.
$$0 = \frac{1}{2}x - 3$$
$$3 = \frac{1}{2}x$$
$$6 = x$$
$$x = 6$$
x-intercept: (6, 0)

To find the y-intercept, set $x = 0$ and solve for y.
$$y = \frac{1}{2}(0) - 3$$
$$y = -3$$
y-intercept: (0, −3)

81. $f(x)$ or $y = 2.58x - 45.21$

To find the x-intercept, set $y = 0$ and solve for x.
$$0 = 2.58x - 45.21$$
$$45.21 = 2.58x$$
$$17.52 \approx x$$
$$x \approx 17.52$$
x-intercept: (17.52, 0)
To find the y-intercept, set $x = 0$ and solve for y
$$y = 2.58(0) - 45.21$$
$$y = -45.21$$
y-intercept: (0, −45.21)

83. Answers may vary. A linear model is a linear function that describes the relationship between two quantities for an authentic situation. Every linear model is a linear function. However, not every linear function is a linear model. Functions are used both to describe situations and to describe certain mathematical relationships between two variables.

85. $m = \dfrac{y_2 - y_1}{x_2 - x_1} = \dfrac{-4-2}{3-(-5)} = \dfrac{-6}{8} = -\dfrac{3}{4}$

The slope of the graph is $-\dfrac{3}{4}$.

87. The x-intercept is $(4, 0)$. The y-intercept is $(0, -3)$.

89.
$$2 = 2x - 4$$
$$2 + 4 = 2x - 4 + 4$$
$$6 = 2x$$
$$\dfrac{6}{2} = \dfrac{2x}{2}$$
$$3 = x$$
$f(x) = 2x - 4$ is a linear function.

91.
$$6 = 2x - 4$$
$$6 + 4 = 2x - 4 + 4$$
$$10 = 2x$$
$$\dfrac{10}{2} = \dfrac{2x}{2}$$
$$5 = x$$
$6 = 2x - 4$ is a linear equation in one variable.

Homework 5.4

1. We substitute $m = 2$ and $(x_1, y_1) = (3, 5)$ into the point slope form and solve for y:
$$y - y_1 = m(x - x_1)$$
$$y - 5 = 2(x - 3)$$
$$y - 5 = 2x - 6$$
$$y = 2x - 1$$

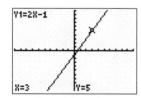

3. We substitute $m = -3$ and $(x_1, y_1) = (1, -2)$ into the point slope form and solve for y:

$$y - y_1 = m(x - x_1)$$
$$y - (-2) = -3(x - 1)$$
$$y + 2 = -3x + 3$$
$$y = -3x + 1$$

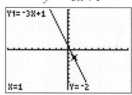

5. We substitute $m = -6$ and $(x_1, y_1) = (-2, -3)$ into the point slope form and solve for y:
$$y - y_1 = m(x - x_1)$$
$$y - (-3) = -6(x - (-2))$$
$$y + 3 = -6(x + 2)$$
$$y + 3 = -6x - 12$$
$$y = -6x - 15$$

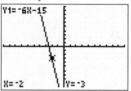

7. We substitute $m = \dfrac{2}{5}$ and $(x_1, y_1) = (3, 1)$ into the point slope form and solve for y:
$$y - y_1 = m(x - x_1)$$
$$y - 1 = \dfrac{2}{5}(x - 3)$$
$$y - 1 = \dfrac{2}{5}x - \dfrac{6}{5}$$
$$y = \dfrac{2}{5}x - \dfrac{1}{5}$$

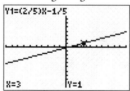

9. We substitute $m = -\dfrac{3}{4}$ and $(x_1, y_1) = (-2, -5)$ into the point slope form and solve for y:

$$y - y_1 = m(x - x_1)$$
$$y - (-5) = -\frac{3}{4}(x - (-2))$$
$$y + 5 = -\frac{3}{4}(x + 2)$$
$$y + 5 = -\frac{3}{4}x - \frac{3}{2}$$
$$y = -\frac{3}{4}x - \frac{13}{2}$$

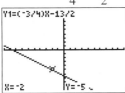

11. We substitute $m = 0$ and $(x_1, y_1) = (5, 3)$ into the point slope form and solve for y:

$$y - y_1 = m(x - x_1)$$
$$y - 3 = 0(x - 5)$$
$$y - 3 = 0$$
$$y = 3$$

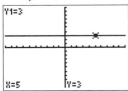

13. Since the slope of the line is undefined, the line must be vertical. Since the x-coordinate of the point on the line is -2, an equation of the line is $x = -2$.

15. We substitute $m = 2.1$ and $(x_1, y_1) = (3.7, -5.9)$ into the point slope form and solve for y:

$$y - y_1 = m(x - x_1)$$
$$y - (-5.9) = 2.1(x - 3.7)$$
$$y + 5.9 = 2.1x - 7.77$$
$$y = 2.1x - 13.67$$

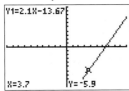

17. We substitute $m = -6.59$ and $(x_1, y_1) = (-2.48, -1.61)$ into the point slope form and solve for y:

$$y - y_1 = m(x - x_1)$$
$$y - (-1.61) = -6.59(x - (-2.48))$$
$$y + 1.61 = -6.59(x + 2.48)$$
$$y + 1.61 \approx -6.59x - 16.34$$
$$y \approx -6.59x - 17.95$$

19. We begin by finding the slope of the line:

$$m = \frac{6 - 2}{5 - 3} = \frac{4}{2} = 2$$

Then we substitute $m = 2$ and $(x_1, y_1) = (3, 2)$ into the point slope form and solve for y:

$$y - y_1 = m(x - x_1)$$
$$y - 2 = 2(x - 3)$$
$$y - 2 = 2x - 6$$
$$y = 2x - 4$$

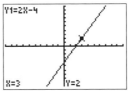 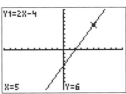

21. We begin by finding the slope of the line:

$$m = \frac{8 - (-7)}{2 - (-1)} = \frac{8 + 7}{2 + 1} = \frac{15}{3} = 5$$

Then we substitute $m = 5$ and $(x_1, y_1) = (-1, -7)$ into the point slope form and solve for y:

$$y - y_1 = m(x - x_1)$$
$$y - (-7) = 5(x - (-1))$$
$$y + 7 = 5(x + 1)$$
$$y + 7 = 5x + 5$$
$$y = 5x - 2$$

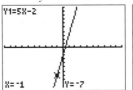 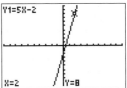

23. We begin by finding the slope of the line:

$$m = \frac{-10-(-4)}{-2-(-5)} = \frac{-10+4}{-2+5} = \frac{-6}{3} = -2$$

Then we substitute $m = 1$ and $(x_1, y_1) = (-5, -4)$
into the point slope form and solve for y:

$$y - y_1 = m(x - x_1)$$
$$y - (-4) = -2(x - (-5))$$
$$y + 4 = -2(x + 5)$$
$$y + 4 = -2x - 10$$
$$y = -2x - 14$$

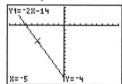 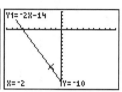

25. We begin by finding the slope of the line:

$$m = \frac{1-9}{2-0} = \frac{-8}{2} = -4$$

Then we substitute $m = -4$ and $(x_1, y_1) = (0, 9)$
into the point slope form and solve for y:

$$y - y_1 = m(x - x_1)$$
$$y - 9 = -4(x - 0)$$
$$y - 9 = -4x$$
$$y = -4x + 9$$

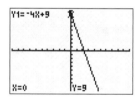 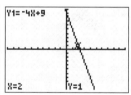

27. We begin by finding the slope of the line:

$$m = \frac{2-2}{5-3} = \frac{0}{2} = 0$$

Then we substitute $m = 0$ and $(x_1, y_1) = (3, 2)$
into the point slope form and solve for y:

$$y - y_1 = m(x - x_1)$$
$$y - 2 = 0(x - 3)$$
$$y - 2 = 0$$
$$y = 2$$

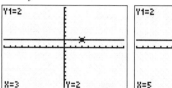 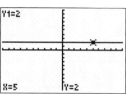

29. Since the x-coordinates of the given points are
equal (both -4), the line that contains the points
is vertical. An equation of the line is $x = -4$.

31. We begin by finding the slope of the line:

$$m = \frac{5-3}{8-4} = \frac{2}{4} = \frac{1}{2}$$

Then we substitute $m = \frac{1}{2}$ and $(x_1, y_1) = (4, 3)$
into the point slope form and solve for y:

$$y - y_1 = m(x - x_1)$$
$$y - 3 = \frac{1}{2}(x - 4)$$
$$y - 3 = \frac{1}{2}x - 2$$
$$y = \frac{1}{2}x + 1$$

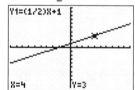 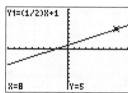

33. We begin by finding the slope of the line:

$$m = \frac{1-2}{3-(-3)} = \frac{1-2}{3+3} = \frac{-1}{6} = -\frac{1}{6}$$

Then we substitute $m = -\frac{1}{6}$ and $(x_1, y_1) = (-3, 2)$

into the point slope form and solve for y:

$$y - y_1 = m(x - x_1)$$

$$y - 2 = -\frac{1}{6}(x - (-3))$$

$$y - 2 = -\frac{1}{6}(x + 3)$$

$$y - 2 = -\frac{1}{6}x - \frac{1}{2}$$

$$y = -\frac{1}{6}x + \frac{3}{2}$$

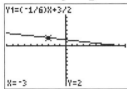 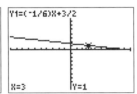

35. We begin by finding the slope of the line:

$$m = \frac{-1-1}{5-(-2)} = \frac{-1-1}{5+2} = \frac{-2}{7} = -\frac{2}{7}$$

Then we substitute $m = -\frac{2}{7}$ and $(x_1, y_1) = (-2, 1)$

into the point slope form and solve for y:

$$y - y_1 = m(x - x_1)$$

$$y - 1 = -\frac{2}{7}(x - (-2))$$

$$y - 1 = -\frac{2}{7}(x + 2)$$

$$y - 1 = -\frac{2}{7}x - \frac{4}{7}$$

$$y = -\frac{2}{7}x + \frac{3}{7}$$

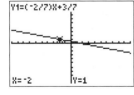 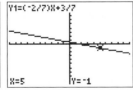

37. We begin by finding the slope of the line:

$$m = \frac{4-(-2)}{6-(-4)} = \frac{4+2}{6+4} = \frac{6}{10} = \frac{3}{5}$$

Then we substitute $m = \frac{3}{5}$ and $(x_1, y_1) = (-4, -2)$

into the point slope form and solve for y:

$$y - y_1 = m(x - x_1)$$

$$y - (-2) = \frac{3}{5}(x - (-4))$$

$$y + 2 = \frac{3}{5}(x + 4)$$

$$y + 2 = \frac{3}{5}x + \frac{12}{5}$$

$$y = \frac{3}{5}x + \frac{2}{5}$$

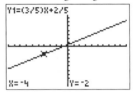 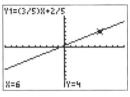

39. We begin by finding the slope of the line:

$$m = \frac{-5-(-8)}{-2-(-4)} = \frac{-5+8}{-2+4} = \frac{3}{2}$$

Then we substitute $m = \frac{3}{2}$ and $(x_1, y_1) = (-4, -8)$

into the point slope form and solve for y:

$$y - y_1 = m(x - x_1)$$

$$y - (-8) = \frac{3}{2}(x - (-4))$$

$$y + 8 = \frac{3}{2}(x + 4)$$

$$y + 8 = \frac{3}{2}x + 6$$

$$y = \frac{3}{2}x - 2$$

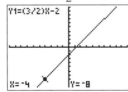 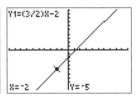

41. We begin by finding the slope of the line:
$$m = \frac{-7.5 - 2.2}{1.2 - (-4.5)} = \frac{-7.5 - 2.2}{1.2 + 4.5} = \frac{-9.7}{5.7} \approx -1.702.$$
So, the equation of the line is of the form
$y = -1.702x + b$. To find b, we substitute the
coordinates of the point $(-4.5, 2.2)$ into the
equation and solve for b:
$$y = -1.702x + b$$
$$2.2 = -1.702(-4.5) + b$$
$$2.2 = 7.659 + b$$
$$-5.459 = b$$
Rounding both m and b to two decimal places,
the approximate equation is $y = -1.70x - 5.46$.

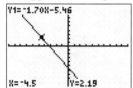 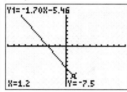

43. We begin by finding the slope of the line:
$$m = \frac{-2.69 - (-8.29)}{7.17 - (-4.57)} = \frac{5.60}{11.74} \approx 0.477.$$
So, the equation of the line is of the form
$y = 0.477x + b$. To find b, we substitute the
coordinates of the point $(-4.57, -8.29)$ into the
equation and solve for b:
$$y = 0.477x + b$$
$$-8.29 = 0.477(-4.57) + b$$
$$-8.29 = -2.17989 + b$$
$$-6.11011 = b$$
Rounding both m and b to two decimal places,
the approximate equation is $y = 0.48x - 6.11$.

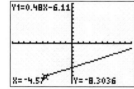 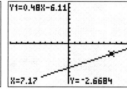

45. The slope of the given line is 3. A line parallel
to the given line also has a slope of 3 and an
equation $y = 3x + b$. Since the point (4, 5) lies
on the parallel line, substitute 4 for x and 5 for y
to solve or b.
$$5 = 3(4) + b$$
$$5 = 12 + b$$
$$-7 = b$$
The parallel line's equation is $y = 3x - 7$.

47. The slope of the given line is -2. A line parallel
to this has a slope of -2 and an equation
$y = -2x + b$. Substitute -3 for x and 8 for y to
solve for b since the parallel line contains
$(-3, 8)$.
$$8 = -2(-3) + b$$
$$8 = 6 + b$$
$$2 = b$$
The parallel line's equation is $y = -2x + 2$.

49. To find the slope, isolate y.
$$3x - 4y = 12$$
$$-4y = -3x + 12$$
$$y = \frac{3}{4}x - 3$$
The slope is $\frac{3}{4}$. A line parallel to this has the
same slope and an equation $y = \frac{3}{4}x + b$.
Substitute 3 for x and 4 for y to solve for b since
the parallel line contains (3, 4).
$$4 = \frac{3}{4}(3) + b$$
$$4 = \frac{9}{4} + b$$
$$\frac{16}{4} = \frac{9}{4} + b$$
$$\frac{7}{4} = b$$
The parallel line's equation $y = \frac{3}{4}x + \frac{7}{4}$ or
$y = 0.75x + 1.75$.

51. To find the slope, isolate y.

$$6y - x = -7$$
$$6y = x - 7$$
$$y = \frac{1}{6}x - \frac{7}{6}$$

The slope is $\frac{1}{6}$. A line parallel to this has the same slope and an equation $y = \frac{1}{6}x + b$.

Substitute -3 for x and -2 for y to solve for b since the parallel line contains $(-3, -2)$.

$$-2 = \frac{1}{6}(-3) + b$$
$$-2 = -\frac{1}{2} + b$$
$$-\frac{4}{2} = -\frac{1}{2} + b$$
$$-\frac{3}{2} = b$$

The parallel line's equation is $y = \frac{1}{6}x - \frac{3}{2}$.

53. The line $y = 6$ is horizontal and has a slope of 0. A line parallel to $y = 6$ is also horizontal. Since the parallel line contains (2, 3) and horizontal lines are of the form $y = b$, the equation of the line is $y = 3$.

55. The line $x = 2$ is vertical and has undefined slope. A line parallel to $x = 2$ is also vertical. Since vertical lines are of the form $x = a$, and the parallel line contains (−5, 4), the equation of the line is $x = -5$.

57. The slope of the given line is 2. A line perpendicular to the given line must then have a slope of $-\frac{1}{2}$ and an equation $y = -\frac{1}{2}x + b$. Substitute 3 for x and 8 for y to solve for b since the line contains (3, 8).

$$8 = -\frac{1}{2}(3) + b$$
$$8 = -\frac{3}{2} + b$$
$$\frac{16}{2} = -\frac{3}{2} + b$$
$$\frac{19}{2} = b$$

The equation of the line is $y = -\frac{1}{2}x + \frac{19}{2}$ or $y = -0.5x + 9.5$.

59. The slope of the given line is −3. A line perpendicular to the given line must then have a slope of $\frac{1}{3}$ and an equation $y = \frac{1}{3}x + b$. Substitute −1 for x and 7 for y to solve for b since the line contains (−1, 7).

$$7 = \frac{1}{3}(-1) + b$$
$$7 = -\frac{1}{3} + b$$
$$\frac{21}{3} = -\frac{1}{3} + b$$
$$\frac{22}{3} = b$$

The equation of the line is $y = \frac{1}{3}x + \frac{22}{3}$.

61. To find the slope of the given line, isolate y.

$$4x - 5y = 7$$
$$-5y = -4x + 7$$
$$y = \frac{4}{5}x - \frac{7}{5}$$

The slope of this line is $\frac{4}{5}$. A line perpendicular to this line must have a slope of $-\frac{5}{4}$ and an equation $y = -\frac{5}{4}x + b$. Substitute 10 for x and 3 for y to solve for b since the line contains $(10, 2)$.

$$3 = -\frac{5}{4}(10) + b$$
$$3 = -\frac{25}{2} + b$$
$$\frac{6}{2} = -\frac{25}{2} + b$$
$$\frac{31}{2} = b$$

The equation of the line is $y = -\frac{5}{4}x + \frac{31}{2}$ or $y = -1.25x + 15.5$.

63. To find the slope of the given line, isolate y.
$$-2x + 3y = 5$$
$$y = \frac{2}{3}x + \frac{5}{3}$$

The slope of the line is $-\frac{3}{2}$. A line perpendicular to this line must have a slope of $-\frac{3}{2}$ and an equation $y = -\frac{3}{2}x + b$. Substitute -3 for x and -1 for y to solve for b since the line contains $(-3, -1)$.

$$-1 = -\frac{3}{2}(-3) + b$$
$$-1 = \frac{9}{2} + b$$
$$-\frac{2}{2} = \frac{9}{2} + b$$
$$-\frac{11}{2} = b$$

The equation of the line is $y = -\frac{3}{2}x - \frac{11}{2}$ or $y = -1.5x - 5.5$.

65. The slope of the equation $x = 5$ is undefined. The graph of the equation is a vertical line. A line perpendicular to $x = 5$ is a horizontal line with a slope of 0. Since this perpendicular line contains $(2, 3)$ and the y-value at this point is 3, the equation of the line is $y = 3$.

67. The slope of the equation $y = -3$ is 0. The graph of the equation is a horizontal line. A line perpendicular to $y = -3$ is a vertical line with an undefined slope. Since this perpendicular line contains $(2, 8)$ and the x-value at this point is 2, the equation of the line is $x = 2$.

69. The line contains the points $(2, 5)$ and $(5, 1)$, so the slope of the line is $m = \frac{1-5}{5-2} = \frac{-4}{3} = -\frac{4}{3}$.
So, the equation of the line is of the form $y = -\frac{4}{3}x + b$. To find b, we substitute the coordinates of the point $(2, 5)$ into the equation and solve for b:

$$y = -\frac{4}{3}x + b$$
$$5 = -\frac{4}{3}(2) + b$$
$$5 = -\frac{8}{3} + b$$
$$\frac{23}{3} = b$$

So, the equation is $y = -\frac{4}{3}x + \frac{23}{3}$.

71. a. We begin by finding the slope of the line:
$$m = \frac{3 - (-6)}{4 - (-2)} = \frac{3+6}{4+2} = \frac{9}{6} = \frac{3}{2}$$

Then we substitute $m = \frac{3}{2}$ and $(x_1, y_1) = (4, 3)$ into the point slope form and solve for y:
$$y - y_1 = m(x - x_1)$$
$$y - 3 = \frac{3}{2}(x - 4)$$
$$y - 3 = \frac{3}{2}x - 6$$
$$y = \frac{3}{2}x - 3$$

b. The slope is $\frac{3}{2}$ and the y-intercept is $(0, -3)$.
We first plot $(0, -3)$. From this point we move 2 units to the right and 3 units up, where we plot the point $(2, 0)$. We then sketch the line that contains these two points.

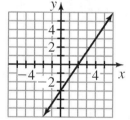

c. Answers may vary. Five possible points are included in the following table.

x	y
-4	$\frac{3}{2}(-4)-3=-9$
-2	$\frac{3}{2}(-2)-3=-6$
0	$\frac{3}{2}(0)-3=-3$
2	$\frac{3}{2}(2)-3=0$
4	$\frac{3}{2}(4)-3=3$

73. a. Yes, it is possible for a line to have no x-intercepts. Examples may vary. One possible equation is $y=2$.

b. Yes, it is possible for a line to have exactly one x-intercept. Examples may vary. One possible equation is $y=x+1$.

c. No, it is not possible for a line to have two x-intercepts. Explanations may vary. One possibility follows: Since lines are straight, they cannot intersect the x-axis in more than one place.

d. Yes, it is possible for a line to have an infinite number of x-intercepts. An equation of such a line is $y=0$.

75. We use the points (2, 9) and (4, 13) to find the equation of the line that relates t and E. We begin by finding the slope of the line:
$$m=\frac{13-9}{4-2}=\frac{4}{2}=2$$
Then we substitute $m=2$ and $(t_1,E_1)=(2,9)$ into the point slope form and solve for y:
$$E-E_1=m(t-t_1)$$
$$E-9=2(t-2)$$
$$E-9=2t-4$$
$$E=2t+5$$
Substituting the remaining points into the equation will show that all satisfy the equation.

77. a. We begin by finding the slope of the line:
$$m=\frac{7-1}{4-2}=\frac{6}{2}=3$$

(i) The equation of the line is of the form $y=3x+b$. To find b, we substitute the coordinates of the point $(2,1)$ into the equation and solve for b:
$$y=3x+b$$
$$1=3(2)+b$$
$$1=6+b$$
$$-5=b$$
So, the equation is $y=3x-5$.

(ii) We substitute $m=3$ and $(x_1,y_1)=(2,1)$ into the point slope form and solve for y:
$$y-y_1=m(x-x_1)$$
$$y-1=3(x-2)$$
$$y-1=3x-6$$
$$y=3x-5$$

b. The results from parts (ai) and (aii) are the same.

79. a. Answers may vary. Consider the following example.
Table for $y=3x-6$:

x	y
0	-6
1	-3
2	0
3	3
4	6
5	9
6	12

b. Answers may vary. Consider the following example.
Table of Points Lying Close to $y=3x-6$:

x	y
0	-5
1	-4
2	1
3	2
4	7
5	10
6	13

c. Answers may vary.

81. The student is partially correct. In the $y = mx + b$ form of a line, the slope m is 2 and the y-intercept b is the point where the line crosses the y-axis, or $(0, b)$. Thus, the given point $(3, 5)$ is not the y-intercept. You can be use $(3, 5)$ to find b by substituting it into $y = 2x + b$ and solving for b.

83. a. Answers may vary. One possible equation with slope -2 is $y = -2x + 1$.

b. Answers may vary. One possible equation with y-intercept $(0, 4)$ is $y = x + 4$.

c. Answers may vary. One possible equation that contains the point $(3, 5)$ is $y = x + 2$.

d. Such a line is not possible. Explanations may vary. One explanation follows: The equation of a line with slope -2 and y-intercept $(0, 4)$ is $y = -2x + 4$, but this line does not contain the point $(3, 5)$.

85. Set 1: We use the points $(0, 25)$ and $(1, 23)$. We begin by finding the slope of the line:
$$m = \frac{23 - 25}{1 - 0} = \frac{-2}{1} = -2$$
The y-intercept is $(0, 25)$, so $b = 25$. Thus, the equation is $y = -2x + 25$. Substituting the remaining points into the equation will show that all satisfy the equation.

Set 2: We use the points $(0, 12)$ and $(1, 16)$. We begin by finding the slope of the line:
$$m = \frac{16 - 12}{1 - 0} = \frac{4}{1} = 4$$
The y-intercept is $(0, 12)$, so $b = 12$. Thus, the equation is $y = 4x + 12$. Substituting the remaining points into the equation will show that all satisfy the equation.

Set 3: We use the points $(0, 77)$ and $(1, 72)$. We begin by finding the slope of the line:
$$m = \frac{72 - 77}{1 - 0} = \frac{-5}{1} = -5$$
The y-intercept is $(0, 77)$, so $b = 77$. Thus, the equation is $y = -5x + 77$. Substituting the remaining points into the equation will show that all satisfy the equation.

Set 4: We use the points $(0, 3)$ and $(1, 3)$. We begin by finding the slope of the line:
$$m = \frac{3 - 3}{1 - 0} = \frac{0}{1} = 0$$
The y-intercept is $(0, 3)$, so $b = 3$. Thus, the equation is $y = 0x + 3$, or simply $y = 3$. Since the y-coordinate of the remaining points are all 3, all satisfy the equation.

87. a. $y = 2x - 3$

We first plot $(0, -3)$. From this point we move 1 unit to the right and 2 units up, where we plot the point $(1, -1)$. We then sketch the line that contains these two points.

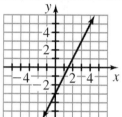

b. Points selected may vary. One possibility is to choose points $(-1, -5)$ and $(2, 1)$. The slope is $m = \frac{1 - (-5)}{2 - (-1)} = \frac{1 + 5}{2 + 1} = \frac{6}{3} = 2$. So, the equation is of the form $y = 2x + b$. We substitute $(2, 1)$ into this equation and solve for b.
$$y = 2x + b$$
$$1 = 2(2) + b$$
$$1 = 4 + b$$
$$-3 = b$$
So, the equation is $y = 2x - 3$, which is the same equation.

89. $3x + 2y = 6$

$$2y = -3x + 6$$

$$\frac{2y}{2} = \frac{-3x}{2} + \frac{6}{2}$$

$$y = -\frac{3}{2}x + 3$$

The slope is $m = -\frac{3}{2}$ and the y-intercept is $(0, 3)$. We first plot $(0, 3)$. From this point we move 2 units to the right and 3 units down, where we plot the point $(2, 0)$. We then sketch the line that contains these two points.

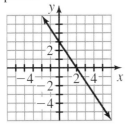

This is a linear function.

91. Substitute 4 for x and -5 for y.

$$3x + 2y = 3(4) + 2(-5)$$

$$= 12 + (-10)$$

$$= 2$$

This is an expression in two variables.

Homework 5.5

1. Since the variables t and n are approximately linearly related and n depends on t, we will find an equation of the form $n = mt + b$. The year 1999 is represented by $t = 9$ (years since 1990) and the year 2007 is represented by $t = 17$. Thus, we have the data points $(9, 30)$ and $(17, 1124)$, which can use to find m and b.

$$m = \frac{1124 - 30}{17 - 9} = \frac{1094}{8} = 136.75$$

So, the equation of the line is of the form $n = 136.75t + b$. To find b, we substitute the coordinates of the point $(9, 30)$ into the equation and solve for b:

$$n = 136.75t + b$$

$$30 = 136.75(9) + b$$

$$30 = 1230.75 + b$$

$$-1200.75 = b$$

So, the equation is $n = 136.75t - 1200.75$.

3. Since the variables t and n are approximately linearly related and n depends on t, we will find an equation of the form $n = mt + b$. The year 2001 is represented by $t = 1$ and the year 2005 is represented by $t = 5$. Thus, we have the data points $(1, 3147)$ and $(5, 2266)$, which can use to find m and b.

$$m = \frac{2266 - 3147}{5 - 1} = \frac{-881}{4} = -220.25$$

So, the equation of the line is of the form $n = -220.25t + b$. To find b, we substitute the coordinates of the point $(1, 3147)$ into the equation and solve for b:

$$n = 14.65t + b$$

$$3147 = -220.25(1) + b$$

$$3147 = -220.25 + b$$

$$3367.25 = b$$

So, the equation is $n = -220.25t + 3367.25$.

5. a. Since the variables t and r are approximately linearly related and r depends on t, we will find an equation of the form $r = mt + b$. The year 2002 is represented by $t = 2$ and the year 2007 is represented by $t = 7$. Thus, we have the data points $(2, 1853)$ and $(7, 15)$, which can use to find m and b.

$$m = \frac{15 - 1853}{7 - 2} = \frac{-1838}{5} = -367.6$$

So, the equation of the line is of the form $r = -367.6t + b$. To find b, we substitute the coordinates of the point $(2, 1853)$ into the equation and solve for b:

$$r = -367.6t + b$$

$$1853 = -367.6(2) + b$$

$$1853 = -735.2 + b$$

$$2588.2 = b$$

So, the equation is $r = -367.6t + 2588.2$.

b. The slope is -367.7. It means that the number of rushing yards by Ricky Williams is decreasing by about 368 yards per year.

c. The r-intercept is $(0, 2588.2)$. It means that Ricky Williams rushed for about 2588 yards in 2000.

7. a. Since the variables t and B are approximately linearly related and B depends on t, we will find an equation of the form $B = mt + b$. The year 2001 is represented by $t = 1$ and the year 2006 is represented by $t = 6$. Thus, we have the data points $(1, 440.00)$ and $(6, 209.72)$, which can use to find m and b.

$$m = \frac{209.72 - 440.00}{6 - 1} = \frac{-230.28}{5} \approx -46.06$$

So, the equation of the line is of the form $B = -46.06t + b$. To find b, we substitute the coordinates of the point $(1, 440.00)$ into the equation and solve for b:

$$B = -46.06t + b$$
$$440.00 = -46.06(1) + b$$
$$440.00 = -46.06 + b$$
$$486.06 = b$$

So, the equation is $B = -46.06t + 486.06$.

b. The slope is -46.06. It means that the average minimum balance for non-interest-bearing checking accounts is decreasing by about $46.06 per year.

c. The B-intercept is $(0, 486.06)$. It means that the average minimum balance for non-interest-bearing checking accounts was $486.06 in 2000.

9. Use the points $(6, 27)$ and $(20, 54.5)$ to find the equation of the line.

$$m = \frac{54.5 - 27}{20 - 6} = \frac{27.5}{14} \approx 1.96$$

So, $L = 1.96a + b$. Substitute 6 for a and 27 for L since the line contains $(6, 27)$ and then solve for b.

$$L = ma + b$$
$$27 = 1.96(6) + b$$
$$27 = 11.76 + b$$
$$15.24 = b$$

The equation of the line is $L = 1.96a + 15.24$.

11.

The value of m must increase; the value of b must decrease.

13. Answers may vary. One possibility follows: We begin by creating a scattergram of the data.

From the scattergram, we see that a line through the points $(4, 8)$ and $(8, 18)$ will come close to the rest of the data points. We use these points to find an equation of the form $y = mx + b$. We begin by finding the slope:

$$m = \frac{18 - 8}{8 - 4} = \frac{10}{4} = 2.5$$

So, the equation of the line is of the form $y = 2.5x + b$. To find b, we substitute the coordinates of the point $(4, 8)$ into the equation and solve for b:

$$y = 2.5x + b$$
$$8 = 2.5(4) + b$$
$$8 = 10 + b$$
$$-2 = b$$

So, the equation is $y = 2.5x - 2$. It comes close to the data points, as can be seen in the graph.

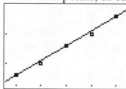

15. Answers may vary. One possibility follows: We begin by creating a scattergram of the data.

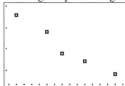

From the scattergram, we see that a line through the points $(3, 18)$ and $(16, 4)$ will come close to the rest of the data points. We use these points to find an equation of the form $y = mx + b$. We begin by finding the slope:

$$m = \frac{4 - 18}{16 - 3} = \frac{-14}{13} \approx -1.08$$

So, the equation of the line is of the form $y = -1.08x + b$. To find b, we substitute the coordinates of the point $(3, 18)$ into the equation and solve for b:

$$y = -1.08x + b$$
$$18 = -1.08(3) + b$$
$$18 = -3.24 + b$$
$$21.24 = b$$

So, the equation is $y = -1.08x + 21.24$. It comes close to the data points, as can be seen in the graph.

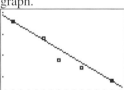

17. Student C has made the best choice. The line through the points $(6, 10.5)$ and $(9, 4.5)$ comes closer to the data points than the lines chosen by the other students.

19. a.

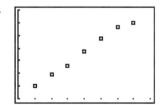

   b. Answers may vary depending on the data points selected. We use the points $(1, 70.1)$ and $(5, 77.4)$ to find an equation of the form $p = mt + b$. We begin by finding the slope:

$$m = \frac{77.4 - 70.1}{5 - 1} = \frac{7.3}{4} \approx 1.83$$

So, the equation of the line is of the form $p = 1.83t + b$. To find b, we substitute the coordinates of the point $(1, 70.1)$ into the equation and solve for b:

$$p = 1.83t + b$$
$$70.1 = 1.83(1) + b$$
$$70.1 = 1.83 + b$$
$$68.27 = b$$

So, the equation is $p = 1.83t + 68.27$.

   c. Answers may vary [depending on the data points selected for part (b)].

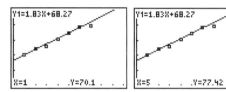

The figures show that the line passes through our selected points, $(1, 70.1)$ and $(5, 77.4)$, and comes close to all of the data points.

21. a.

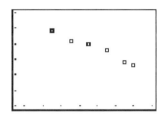

   b. Use the points $(9, 54)$ and $(18, 43)$ to find the equation of the line.

$$m = \frac{43 - 54}{18 - 9}$$
$$\approx -1.22$$

So, $p = -1.22t + b$. Substitute 9 for t and 54 for p since the line contains $(9, 54)$ and then solve for b.

$$p = mt + b$$
$$54 = -1.22(9) + b$$
$$54 = -10.98 + b$$
$$64.98 = b$$

The equation of the line is $y = -1.22t + 64.98$. (Your equation may be slightly different if you chose different points.)

149

c.

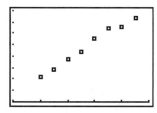

23. a.

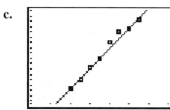

b. Use the points (70, 10.7) and (105, 36.8) to write the equation of the line. First find the slope.

$$m = \frac{36.8 - 10.7}{105 - 70}$$

$$\approx 0.75$$

So, $p = 0.75t + b$. Substitute 70 for t and 10.7 for p, since the line contains (70, 10.7) and then solve for b.

$$p = mt + b$$

$$10.7 = 0.75(70) + b$$

$$10.7 = 52.5 + b$$

$$-41.8 = b$$

The equation of the line is $p = 0.75t - 41.8$. (Your equation may be slightly different if you chose different points.)

c.

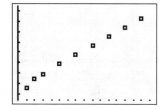

Notice that the points (70, 10.7) and (105, 36.8) are filled in, showing that the line goes through these points.

25. a.

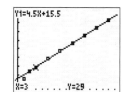

b. Answers may vary depending on the data points selected. We use the points (3, 29) and (13, 74) to find an equation of the form

$H = md + b$. We begin by finding the slope:

$$m = \frac{74 - 29}{13 - 3} = \frac{45}{10} = 4.5$$

So, the equation of the line is of the form $H = 4.5d + b$. To find b, we substitute the coordinates of the point (3, 29) into the equation and solve for b:

$$H = 4.5d + b$$

$$29 = 4.5(3) + b$$

$$29 = 13.5 + b$$

$$15.5 = b$$

So, the equation is $H = 4.5d + 15.5$.

c. Answers may vary [depending on the data points selected for part (b)]

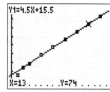

The figures show that the line passes through our selected points, (3, 29) and (13, 74), and comes close to all of the data points.

27. a.

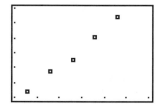

b. Use the points (23, 34) and (43, 84) to find the equation of the line.

$$m = \frac{84 - 34}{43 - 23}$$

$$= 2.5$$

So, $y = 2.5x + b$. Substitute 23 for x and 34 for y since the line contains (23, 34) and then solve for b.

$$p = mx + b$$

$$34 = 2.5(23) + b$$

$$34 = 57.5 + b$$

$$-23.5 = b$$

The equation of the line is $y = 2.5x - 23.5$. (Your equation may be slightly different if you chose different points.)

c.

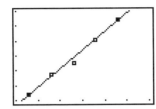

Notice that the points (23, 34) and (43, 84) are filled in, showing that the line goes through these points

29. a.

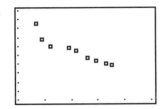

b. Use the points (69, 51.7) and (83, 47.99) to find the equation of the line.

$$m = \frac{47.99 - 51.7}{83 - 69}$$

$$\approx -0.27$$

So, $r = -0.27t + b$. Substitute 69 for t and 51.7 for r since the line contains (69, 51.7) and then solve for b.

$$r = mt + b$$

$$51.7 = -0.27(69) + b$$

$$51.7 = -18.63 + b$$

$$70.33 = b$$

The equation of the line is

$r = -0.27t + 70.33$. (Your equation may be slightly different if you chose different points.)

c.

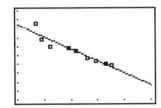

31. a.

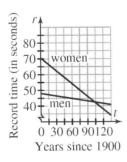

b. First, solve for t by setting both equations equal to each other.

$$-0.27t + 70.45 = -0.053t + 48.08$$

$$-0.27t + 0.27t + 70.45 = -0.053t + 0.27t + 48.08$$

$$70.45 - 48.08 = 0.217t + 48.08 - 48.08$$

$$22.37 = 0.217t$$

$$t = \frac{22.37}{0.217} \approx 103$$

This is the year 1900 + 103 = 2003. Solving for r yields

$$r = -0.053(103) + 48.08$$

$$r \approx -5.46 + 48.08$$

$$r \approx 42.62$$

Yes, the model predicts that the women's record time will equal the men's record time. This will happen in the year 2003 with a record time of approximately 42.6 seconds. Model breakdown has probably occurred.

c. Yes, the model predicts that the women's record time will be less than the men's record time in years 2004 and after. Model breakdown has probably occurred.

33. Answers may vary. One possibility follows: To find an equation of a linear model, begin by creating a scattergram of the data. Then, determine whether there is a line that comes close to the data points. If so, choose two points (not necessarily data points) that you can use to find the equation of a linear model. Next, find an equation of the line. Finally, use a graphing calculator to verify that the graph of the equation comes close to the points of the scattergram.

35. a. The value of the stock is increasing by $2 per year, so the slope of the equation is $m = 2$. Since t represents the number of years since 2005, the V-intercept is $(0, 10)$, the value of the stock in 2005. Thus, $b = 10$. An equation that describes the situation is $V = 2t + 10$.

$$\underset{\text{dollars}}{V} = \underset{\frac{\text{dollars}}{\text{year}}}{2} \cdot \underset{\text{years}}{t} + \underset{\text{dollars}}{10}$$

We use the fact that $\dfrac{\text{years}}{\text{years}} = 1$ to simplify the right-hand side of the equation:

$$\frac{\text{dollars}}{\text{year}} \cdot \text{years} + \text{dollars} = \text{dollars} + \text{dollars}.$$

So, the units on both sides of the equation are dollars, suggesting the equation is correct.

b. To graph the line, we first plot the V-intercept $(0, 10)$. The slope is $2 = \dfrac{2}{1}$, so the run is 1 and the rise is 2. From $(0, 10)$, we count 1 unit to the right and 2 units up, where we plot the point $(1, 12)$. We then sketch the line that contains these two points.

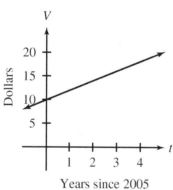

Years since 2005

c. Answers may vary. One possible table follows:

t	V
0	$2 \cdot 0 + 10 = 10$
1	$2 \cdot 1 + 10 = 12$
2	$2 \cdot 2 + 10 = 14$
3	$2 \cdot 3 + 10 = 16$
4	$2 \cdot 4 + 10 = 18$

37. a. The number of spectators is increasing by 1481 spectators per year, so the slope of the equation is $m = 1481$. Since t represents the

number of years since 2007, the n-intercept is $(0, 54078)$, the number of spectators in 2007. Thus, $b = 54{,}078$. An equation that describes the situation is $n = 1481t + 54{,}078$

b. The slope is 1481. It means that the average attendance is increasing by 1481 spectators per year.

c.
$$\underset{\text{spectators}}{n} = \underset{\frac{\text{spectators}}{\text{year}}}{1481} \cdot \underset{\text{years}}{t} + \underset{\text{spectators}}{54{,}078}$$

We use the fact that $\dfrac{\text{years}}{\text{years}} = 1$ to simplify the right-hand side of the equation:

$$\frac{\text{spectators}}{\text{year}} \cdot \text{years} + \text{spectators}$$

$$= \text{spectators} + \text{spectators}.$$

So, the units on both sides of the equation are spectators, suggesting the equation is correct.

39.
$$3 = -\frac{2}{5}x + 4$$
$$-1 = -\frac{2}{5}x$$
$$-\frac{5}{2}(-1) = -\frac{5}{2}\left(-\frac{2}{5}x\right)$$
$$\frac{5}{2} = x$$

This is a linear equation in one variable.

41. $f(x) = -\dfrac{2}{5}x + 4$

We first plot the y-intercept $(0, 4)$. The slope is $-\dfrac{2}{5} = \dfrac{-2}{5}$, so the run is 5 and the rise is -2. From $(0, 4)$, we count 5 units to the right and 2 units down, where we plot the point $(5, 2)$. We then sketch the line that contains these two points.

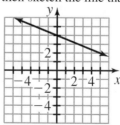

This is a linear function.

Homework 5.6

1. a. To use the name f, substitute $f(t)$ for p in the equation $p = 1.73t + 68.39$:

$$f(t) = 1.73t + 68.39$$

b. The year 2014 is represented by $t = 14$, so we substitute 14 for t in the equation $p = 1.73t + 68.39$:

$$p = 1.73(14) + 68.39$$
$$= 24.22 + 68.39$$
$$= 92.61$$

In 2014, about 92.6% of seats will be filled for the six largest airlines.

c. We substitute 100 for p and solve for t:

$$p = 1.73t + 68.39$$
$$100 = 1.73t + 68.39$$
$$31.61 = 1.73t$$
$$t = \frac{31.61}{1.73} \approx 18$$

Now, $t = 18$ represents the year 2018. Thus, the model predicts that 100% will be filled in 2018. Model breakdown has occurred.

d. Since $p = 1.73t + 68.39$ is in slope-intercept form, the p-intercept is $(0, 68.39)$. It means that about 68.4% of all seats were filled in 2000 for the six largest airlines.

e. The slope is 1.73. It means that, each year, the percentage of all seats that are filled increases by 1.73 percentage points for the six larges airlines.

3. a. To use the name f, substitute $f(t)$ for p in the equation $p = -1.19t + 64.86$:

$$f(t) = -1.19t + 64.86$$

b. $f(24) = -1.19(24) + 64.86$
$$= -28.56 + 64.86$$
$$= 36.3$$

When $t = 24$, $p = 36.3$. This means that in $1990 + 24 = 2014$, 36.3 percent of Americans will be baseball fans.

c. $24 = -1.19t + 64.86$
$$-40.86 = -1.19t$$
$$34.34 \approx t$$

This means that in $1990 + 34 \approx 2024$, 24 percent of Americans will be baseball fans.

d. To find the p-intercept of the model, we must find p when $t = 0$.
$$p = -1.19(0) + 64.86$$
$$p = 64.86$$

The p-intercept is therefore $(0, 64.86)$.

This means that in $1990 + 0 = 1990$, 64.86 percent of Americans were baseball fans.

e. To find the t-intercept of the model, we must find t when $p = 0$.
$$0 = -1.19t + 64.86$$
$$-64.86 = -1.19t$$
$$54.50 \approx t$$

The p-intercept is therefore $(54.50, 0)$. This means that in $1990 + 54.50 \approx 2045$, 0 percent of Americans will be baseball fans. Model breakdown has occurred.

5. a. To use the name f, substitute $f(t)$ for p in the equation $p = 0.77t - 43.18$:

$$f(t) = 0.77t - 43.18$$

b. $f(114) = 0.77(114) - 43.18$
$$= 87.78 - 43.18$$
$$= 44.6$$

When $t = 114$, $p = 44.6$. This means that in the year $1900 + 114 = 2014$, the percentage of births out of marriage will be 44.6%.

c. $46 = 0.77t - 43.18$
$$89.18 = 0.77t$$
$$115.82 \approx t$$

When $p = 46$, $t \approx 115.82$. This means that the percentage of out of marriage births will hit 46% in the year $1900 + 116 = 2016$.

d. $100 = 0.77t - 43.18$
$$143.18 = 0.77t$$
$$185.9 \approx t$$

In the year $1900 + 185.9 \approx 2086$, all births will be out of marriage according to this model. Model breakdown has probably occurred.

e. Find p when $t = 1997 - 1900 = 97$.

$$f(97) = 0.77(97) - 43.18$$
$$= 74.69 - 43.18 = 31.51$$

This means that in the year 1997, the percentage of births out of marriage will be about 31.5%. Since the actual percentage was 32.4%, the error was 31.5% − 32.4% = −0.9%.

7. a. To use the name g, substitute $g(d)$ for H in the equation $H = 4.5d + 15.3$:

$$g(d) = 4.5d + 15.3$$

b. We substitute 78 for H in the equation $H = 4.5d + 15.3$ and solve for d:

$$78 = 4.5d + 15.3$$
$$62.7 = 4.5d$$
$$d = \frac{62.7}{4.5} \approx 13.93$$

The model predicts that the life expectancy for dogs is about 14 years.

c. We substitute 29 for d in the equation:

$$H = 4.5d + 15.3$$
$$H = 4.5(29) + 15.3 = 145.8$$

Bluey lived to be about 146 in human years.

d. We substitute 119 for H in the equation $H = 4.5d + 15.3$ and solve for d:

$$119 = 4.5d + 15.3$$
$$103.7 = 4.5d$$
$$d = \frac{103.7}{4.5} \approx 23.04$$

Sarah Knauss lived to be about 23 in dog years.

e. Since $H = 4.5d + 15.3$ is in slope-intercept form, the slope is 4.5. It means that a dog aging 1 year is equivalent to a human aging 4.5 years.

f. If each dog year is equivalent to 7 human years, the model will be $H = 7d$.

g. The slope is 7. It means that a dog aging 1 year is equivalent to a human aging 7 years. The slope of the equation in part (f) is greater than the slope found in part (e).

9. a.

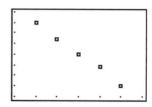

b. Answers may vary depending on the data points selected. We use the points $(3, 8.5)$ and $(7, 5.5)$ to find an equation of the form $f = mt + b$.

We begin by finding the slope:

$$m = \frac{5.5 - 8.5}{7 - 3} = \frac{-3}{4} = -0.75$$

So, the equation of the line is of the form $f = -0.75t + b$. To find b, we substitute the coordinates of the point $(3, 8.5)$ into the equation and solve for b:

$$f = -0.75t + b$$
$$8.5 = -0.75(3) + b$$
$$8.5 = -2.25 + b$$
$$10.75 = b$$

So, the equation is $f = -0.75t + 10.75$. (Your equation may be slightly different if you used different data points to form a model.) The function models the data well.

c.
$$1 = -0.75t + 10.75$$
$$-9.75 = -0.75t$$
$$13 = t$$

In 2000 + 13 = 2013, 1% of nursing home residents will be restrained daily.

d. To find the p-intercept of the model, we must find p when $t = 0$.

$$p = -0.75(0) + 10.75$$
$$p = 10.75$$

The p-intercept is (0, 10.75). This means that in 2000 + 0 = 2000, about 10.7% of nursing home residents were restrained daily.

e. To find the *t*-intercept of the model, we must find *t* when *p* = 0:
$$0 = -0.75t + 10.75$$
$$0.75t = 10.75$$
$$t = \frac{10.75}{0.75} \approx 14.33$$
The *t*-intercept is about (14.33, 0). It means that no nursing home residents will be restrained in 2000 + 14 = 2014. Model breakdown has occurred.

11. a.

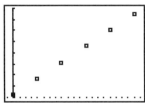

The data points lie close to the line that passes through (0, 32) and (100, 212). To find the equation for *f*, start by finding the slope using these points.
$$m = \frac{212 - 32}{100 - 0}$$
$$= \frac{180}{100}$$
$$= 1.8$$
So, *f(C)* = 1.8*C* + *b*. To solve for *b*, substitute 0 for *C* and 32 for *f(C)* since the line contains (0, 32).
$$32 = 1.8(0) + b$$
$$32 = b$$
The equation for *f* is *f(C)* = 1.8*C* + 32.

b. $f(25) = 1.8(25) + 32 = 45 + 32 = 77$
If it is 25°C, it is 77°F.

c. $40 = 1.8C + 32$
$$8 = 1.8C$$
$$\frac{8}{1.8} = C$$
$$C \approx 4.44$$
If it is 40°F, then it is 4.4°C.

d. The slope is 1.8. It means that and increase of 1°C is equivalent to an increase of 1.8°F.

13. a.

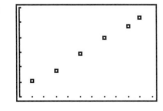

b. Use the points (1, 452) and (10, 666) to find the equation of the line.
$$m = \frac{666 - 452}{10 - 1}$$
$$= \frac{214}{9}$$
$$\approx 23.78$$
So, *y* = 23.78*x* + *b*. Substitute 1 for *x* and 452 for *y* since the line contains (1, 452) and then solve for *b*.
$$y = mx + b$$
$$452 = 23.78(1) + b$$
$$452 = 23.78 + b$$
$$428.22 = b$$
The equation of the line is *y* = 23.78*x* + 428.22. (Your equation may be slightly different if you chose different points.)

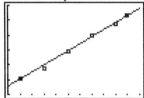

Graphing the line with the scatterplot, we see that the model fits the data very well.

c. Since 2001 − 1990 = 11, find *f*(11).
$$f(11) = 23.78(11) + 428.22$$
$$= 261.58 + 428.22 = 689.8$$
According to the model, approximately 690 million boardings were made in 2001. The actual number of boardings was 622 million. This is an error of 68 million boardings.

d. 68 million boardings is equivalent to $\frac{68}{4} = 17$ million round trips. If on average each round trip is $340, the airlines lost $17 \cdot \$340 = \$5780$ million or $5.78 billion.

15. a. $f(x) = 2.48x - 23.64$

b. $100 = 2.48x - 23.64$
$$123.64 = 2.48x$$
$$x \approx 50$$
This means that the cutoff score would have to be 50 (out of 50) to ensure that all students succeed in the intermediate algebra course.

c.
$$0 = 2.48x - 23.64$$
$$23.64 = 2.48x$$
$$x \approx 10$$

This means that for scores 10 and under, no students would succeed in the intermediate algebra course.

d. For the 16 − 20 range, we use a score of 18 to represent the group. Find the percentage for $x = 18$.
$$p = 2.48(18) - 23.64$$
$$= 44.64 - 23.64 = 21$$

This means that 21% of the students who score in the 16 − 20 range pass the intermediate algebra course. If 145 students scored in this range, we could expect 21% or $0.21 \cdot 145 \approx 30$ students to pass. It would not make sense for CSM to lower the placement score cutoff to 16. While 21% of student might pass, based on the model, the vast majority, 79%, would not pass.

e. First calculate the percentages for each of the score groups. Use the average score in each range to represent the group.

$$p = 2.48(23) - 23.64 = 33.4$$
$$p = 2.48(28) - 23.64 = 45.8$$
$$p = 2.48(33) - 23.64 = 58.2$$
$$p = 2.48(38) - 23.64 = 70.6$$
$$p = 2.48(43) - 23.64 = 83$$
$$p = 2.48(48) - 23.64 = 95.4$$

Next, multiply each of the percentages by the number of students in that category.
$$0.334 \cdot 94 = 31.4 \text{ students}$$
$$0.458 \cdot 44 = 20.2 \text{ students}$$
$$0.582 \cdot 19 = 11.1 \text{ students}$$
$$0.706 \cdot 12 = 8.5 \text{ students}$$
$$0.83 \cdot 9 = 7.5 \text{ students}$$
$$0.954 \cdot 4 = 3.8 \text{ students}$$

Add these results to obtain the total number of students, 82.5. This means that of students who scored at least 21 points on the placement test, approximately 83 students passed the class.

17. If we let t be the number of years after 1980 and let E be the public school per-student expenditures, we can make a linear model of the given information. To start, we can use the two points (1, 5.2) and (26, 9.1) to find the slope of the model:
$$m = \frac{9.1 - 5.2}{26 - 1} = \frac{3.9}{25} \approx 0.16$$
So $E = 0.16t + b$. To solve for b, substitute 1 for t and 5.2 for E, since the line contains (1, 5.2)
$$5.2 = 0.16(1) + b$$
$$5.2 = 0.16 + b$$
$$5.04 = b$$
The equation for E is $E = 0.16t + 5.04$.
To find E for 2014, or when $t = 34$, substitute 34 for t and solve for E.
$$E = 0.16(34) + 5.04$$
$$= 5.44 + 5.04$$
$$= 10.48$$
According to the model, in 2014 the public school per-student expenditures will be $10.5 thousand.

19. If we let t be the number of years after 2000, and p the percent of employers who allow casual dress every day, we can make a linear model of the given information. To start, we can use the two points (1, 51) and (6, 38) to find the slope of the model:
$$m = \frac{38 - 51}{6 - 1} = \frac{-13}{5} = -2.6$$
So $p = -2.6t + b$. To solve for b substitute 1 for t and 51 for p since the line contains (1, 51).
$$51 = -2.6(1) + b$$
$$51 = -2.6 + b$$
$$53.6 = b$$
The equation for p is $p = -2.6t + 53.6$.
To find the year when 14.5% of employers allow casual dress every day, we must substitute 14.5 for p and solve for t in the equation.
$$14.5 = -2.6t + 53.6$$
$$-39.1 = -2.6t$$
$$15.0 \approx t$$
According to the model, in 2000 + 15 = 2015, 14.5% of employers will allow casual dress every day.

21. a. If we let t be the number of years after 1990, and p the percentage of large or medium-sized companies paying 100% of their employees' health care premiums, we can make a linear model of the given information. To start, we can use the two points $(9, 33)$ and $(14, 17)$ to find the slope of the model:

$$m = \frac{17 - 33}{14 - 9} = -3.2$$

So $p = -3.2t + b$. To solve for b substitute 9 for t and 33 for p since the line contains $(9, 33)$.

$$33 = -3.2(9) + b$$
$$33 = -28.8 + b$$
$$61.8 = b$$

The equation for p is $p = -3.2t + 61.8$.
To find the year when 23 percent of large or medium-sized companies paid 100% of their employees' health care premiums, we can substitute 0 for p and solve for t.

$$23 = -3.2t + 61.8$$
$$-38.8 = -3.2t$$
$$12.13 \approx t$$

According to the model in 1990 + 12 = 2002, 23 percent of large or medium-sized companies paid 100% of their employees' health care premiums.

b. To find the percent of large or medium-sized companies who are paying 100% of their employees' health care premiums in 2006, substitute 2006 − 1990 = 16 for t and solve for p.

$$p = -3.2(16) + 61.8$$
$$= -51.2 + 61.8$$
$$= 10.6$$

According to the model in 2006, about 11 percent of large or medium-sized companies paid their employees' health care premiums.

23. If we let t be the amount of time a fourth-grader studies history a week and s be the average score a fourth-grader gets on the National Assessment of Educational Progress test in U.S. history, we can make a linear model of the given information. To start, we can use the two points $(45, 195)$ and $(150, 211)$ to find the slope of the model:

$$m = \frac{211 - 195}{150 - 45}$$
$$\approx 0.15$$

So $s = 0.15t + b$. To solve for b substitute 45 for t and 195 for s since the line contains $(45, 195)$.

$$195 = 0.15(45) + b$$
$$195 = 6.75 + b$$
$$188.25 = b$$

The equation for s is $s = 0.15t + 188.25$.
To find the average score for fourth graders who study history about 200 minutes per week, we must substitute 200 for t and solve for s in the equation.

$$s = 0.15(200) + 188.25$$
$$= 30 + 188.25$$
$$s = 218.25$$

According to the model, when a fourth grader studies history for about 200 minutes per week, they will score about 218 points.

25. a. From the information given, we have the data points $(0, 640)$ and $(4, 0)$. Use these points to find the slope of the equation for f.

$$m = \frac{640 - 0}{0 - 4} = \frac{640}{-4} = -160$$

So, $f(t) = -160t + b$. To solve for b, substitute 0 for t and 640 for $f(t)$ since the line contains $(0, 640)$.

$$640 = -160(0) + b$$
$$640 = b$$

The equation for f is $f(t) = -160t + 640$.

b.

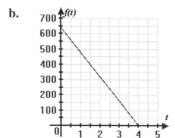

c. Since it takes 4 hours to pump out the water, the domain is $0 \le t \le 4$. Since the water level is at 640 cubic feet before starting to pump, the range is $0 \le f(t) \le 640$.

27. Answers may vary.
The four steps are: **1.** Create a scattergram of the data to determine whether there is a nonvertical line that comes close to the data points. If so, choose two points (not necessarily data points) that you can use to find the equation of a linear model. **2.** Find an equation of your model. **3.** Verify your equation by checking that the graph of your model contains the two chosen points and comes close to all of the data points. **4.** Use the equation of your model to make estimates, make predictions, and draw conclusions.

29. a. The number of Americans who live alone is increasing by 0.56 million people per year, so the slope of the equation is $m = 0.56$. Since t represents the number of years since 2007, the n-intercept is $(0, 31.1)$, the number living alone in 2007. Thus, $b = 31.1$. An equation that describes the situation is
$f(t) = 0.56t + 31.1$.

b. The n-intercept is $(0, 31.1)$. This means that there were 31.1 million Americans who lived alone in the year 2007.

c.
$$\underset{\substack{\text{million people}}}{n} = \underset{\substack{\text{million people} \\ \text{year}}}{0.56} \cdot \underset{\substack{\text{years}}}{t} + \underset{\substack{\text{million people}}}{31.1}$$

We use the fact that $\dfrac{\text{years}}{\text{years}} = 1$ to simplify the right-hand side of the equation:
$\dfrac{\text{million people}}{\text{year}} \cdot \text{years} + \text{million people} =$
million people + million people
So, the units on both sides of the equation are millions of people, suggesting the equation is correct.

d. We substitute 44.1 for n in the equation and solve for t:
$44.1 = 0.56t + 31.1$
$13.0 = 0.56t$
$t = \dfrac{13.0}{0.56} \approx 23.21$
We predict that 44.1 million people will live alone in the year $2007 + 23.2 \approx 2030$.

31. a. The sales of echinacea are decreasing by $20.67 million per year, so the slope of the equation is $m = -20.67$. Since t represents the number of years since 2004, the s-intercept is $(0, 152)$. Thus, $b = 152$. An

equation that describes the situation is
$f(t) = -20.67t + 152$.

b. The s-intercept is $(0, 152)$. This means that annual sales of echinacea were $152 million in the year 2004.

c.
$$\underset{\substack{\text{million dollars}}}{s} = \underset{\substack{\text{million dollars} \\ \text{year}}}{-20.67} \cdot \underset{\substack{\text{years}}}{t} + \underset{\substack{\text{million dollars}}}{152}$$

We use the fact that $\dfrac{\text{years}}{\text{years}} = 1$ to simplify the right-hand side of the equation:
$\dfrac{\text{million dollars}}{\text{year}} \cdot \text{years} + \text{million dollars} =$
million dollars + million dollars
So, the units on both sides of the equation are millions of dollars, suggesting the equation is correct.

d. We substitute 70 for s in the equation and solve for t:
$70 = -20.67t + 152$
$-82 = -20.67t$
$t = \dfrac{-82}{-20.67} \approx 3.97$
We predict that annual Echinacea sales were $70 million in the year $2004 + 3.97 \approx 2008$.

33. $-4(3x - 5) = 3(2x + 1)$
$-12x + 20 = 6x + 3$
$-18x + 20 = 3$
$-18x = -17$
$x = \dfrac{-17}{-18} = \dfrac{17}{18}$
This is a linear equation in one variable.

35. $-4(3x - 5) - 3(2x + 1) = -12x + 20 - 6x - 3$
$= -18x + 17$
This is a linear expression in one variable.

Homework 5.7

1. Since -3 is to the right of -5 on the number line, the statement $-3 > -5$ is true.

3. Since $4 = 4$, the statement $4 \geq 4$ is true.

5. $x < 4$

7. $x \geq -1$

9. $x \leq -2$

11. $x > 6$

13. **In words**: numbers greater than or equal to 4

Inequality: $x \geq 4$

Graph:

Interval Notation: $[4, \infty)$

In words: numbers less than or equal to -2

Inequality: $x \leq -2$

Graph:

Interval Notation: $(-\infty, 2]$

In words: numbers less than 1

Inequality: $x < 1$

Graph:

Interval Notation: $(-\infty, 1)$

In words: numbers greater than -5

Inequality: $x > -5$

Graph:

Interval Notation: $(-5, \infty)$

15. We substitute 2 for x in the inequality $3x + 5 \geq 14$:

$$3(2) + 5 \overset{?}{\geq} 14$$

$$6 + 5 \overset{?}{\geq} 14$$

$$11 \overset{?}{\geq} 14 \leftarrow \text{False}$$

So, 2 does not satisfy the inequality $3x + 5 \geq 14$.

We substitute 3 for x in the inequality $3x + 5 \geq 14$:

$$3(3) + 5 \overset{?}{\geq} 14$$

$$9 + 5 \overset{?}{\geq} 14$$

$$14 \overset{?}{\geq} 14 \leftarrow \text{True}$$

So, 3 satisfies the inequality $3x + 5 \geq 14$.

We substitute 6 for x in the inequality $3x + 5 \geq 14$:

$$3(6) + 5 \overset{?}{\geq} 14$$

$$18 + 5 \overset{?}{\geq} 14$$

$$23 \overset{?}{\geq} 14 \leftarrow \text{True}$$

So, 6 satisfies the inequality $3x + 5 \geq 14$.

17. We substitute -4 for x in the inequality $2x < x + 2$:

$$2(-4) \overset{?}{<} (-4) + 2$$

$$-8 \overset{?}{<} -2 \leftarrow \text{True}$$

So, -4 satisfies the inequality $2x < x + 2$.

We substitute 2 for x in the inequality $2x < x + 2$:

$$2(2) \overset{?}{<} (2) + 2$$

$$4 \overset{?}{<} 4 \leftarrow \text{False}$$

So, 2 does not satisfy the inequality $2x < x + 2$.

We substitute 3 for x in the inequality $2x < x + 2$:

$$2(3) \overset{?}{<} (3) + 2$$

$$6 \overset{?}{<} 5 \leftarrow \text{False}$$

So, 3 does not satisfy the inequality $2x < x + 2$.

19.

$$x + 2 > 3$$

$$x + 2 - 2 > 3 - 2$$

$$x > 1$$

We graph the solution set, $(1, \infty)$.

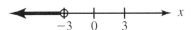

21.

$$x - 1 < -4$$

$$x - 1 + 1 < -4 + 1$$

$$x < -3$$

We graph the solution set, $(-\infty, -3)$.

23. $2x \le 6$

$$\frac{2x}{2} \le \frac{6}{2}$$

$$x \le 3$$

We graph the solution set, $(-\infty, 3]$.

25. $4x \ge -8$

$$\frac{4x}{4} \ge \frac{-8}{4}$$

$$x \ge -2$$

We graph the solution set, $[-2, \infty)$.

27. $-3t \ge 6$

$$\frac{-3t}{-3} \le \frac{6}{-3}$$

$$t \le -2$$

We graph the solution set, $(-\infty, -2]$.

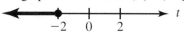

29. $-2x > 1$

$$\frac{-2x}{-2} < \frac{1}{-2}$$

$$x < -\frac{1}{2}$$

We graph the solution set, $\left(-\infty, -\frac{1}{2}\right)$.

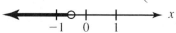

31. $5x \le 0$

$$\frac{5x}{5} \le \frac{0}{5}$$

$$x \le 0$$

We graph the solution set, $(-\infty, 0]$.

33. $-x < 2$

$$\frac{-x}{-1} > \frac{2}{-1}$$

$$x > -2$$

We graph the solution set, $(-2, \infty)$.

35. $-\frac{2}{3}x \ge 2$

$$-\frac{3}{2}\left(-\frac{2}{3}x\right) \le -\frac{3}{2}(2)$$

$$x \le -3$$

We graph the solution set, $(-\infty, -3]$.

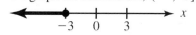

37. $3x - 1 \ge 2$

$$3x - 1 + 1 \ge 2 + 1$$

$$3x \ge 3$$

$$\frac{3x}{3} \ge \frac{3}{3}$$

$$x \ge 1$$

We graph the solution set, $[1, \infty)$.

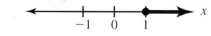

39. $5 - 3x < -7$

$$5 - 3x - 5 < -7 - 5$$

$$-3x < -12$$

$$\frac{-3x}{-3} > \frac{-12}{-3}$$

$$x > 4$$

We graph the solution set, $(4, \infty)$.

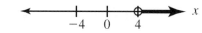

41. $3c - 6 \le 5c$

$$3c - 6 - 5c \le 5c - 5c$$

$$-2c - 6 \le 0$$

$$-2c - 6 + 6 \le 0 + 6$$

$$-2c \le 6$$

$$\frac{-2c}{-2} \ge \frac{6}{-2}$$

$$c \ge -3$$

We graph the solution set, $[-3, \infty)$.

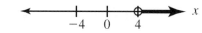

43.
$$5x \geq x - 12$$
$$5x - x \geq x - 12 - x$$
$$4x \geq -12$$
$$\frac{4x}{4} \geq \frac{-12}{4}$$
$$x \geq -3$$
We graph the solution set, $[-3, \infty)$.

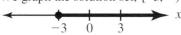

45.
$$-3.8x + 1.9 > -7.6$$
$$-3.8x + 1.9 - 1.9 > -7.6 - 1.9$$
$$-3.8x > -9.5$$
$$\frac{-3.8x}{-3.8} < \frac{-9.5}{-3.8}$$
$$x < 2.5$$
We graph the solution set, $(-\infty, 2.5)$.

47.
$$3b + 2 > 7b - 6$$
$$3b + 2 - 7b > 7b - 6 - 7b$$
$$-4b + 2 > -6$$
$$-4b + 2 - 2 > -6 - 2$$
$$-4b > -8$$
$$\frac{-4b}{-4} < \frac{-8}{-4}$$
$$b < 2$$
We graph the solution set, $(-\infty, 2)$.

49.
$$4 - 3x < 9 - 2x$$
$$4 - 3x + 2x < 9 - 2x + 2x$$
$$4 - x < 9$$
$$4 - x - 4 < 9 - 4$$
$$-x < 5$$
$$\frac{-x}{-1} > \frac{5}{-1}$$
$$x > -5$$
We graph the solution set, $(-5, \infty)$.

51.
$$2(x + 3) \leq 8$$
$$2x + 6 \leq 8$$
$$2x + 6 - 6 \leq 8 - 6$$
$$2x \leq 2$$
$$\frac{2x}{2} \leq \frac{2}{2}$$
$$x \leq 1$$
We graph the solution set, $(-\infty, 1]$.

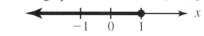

53.
$$-(a - 3) > 4$$
$$-a + 3 > 4$$
$$-a + 3 - 3 > 4 - 3$$
$$-a > 1$$
$$\frac{-a}{-1} < \frac{1}{-1}$$
$$a < -1$$
We graph the solution set, $(-\infty, -1)$.

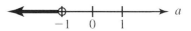

55.
$$3(2x - 1) \leq 2(2x + 1)$$
$$6x - 3 \leq 4x + 2$$
$$6x - 3 - 4x \leq 4x + 2 - 4x$$
$$2x - 3 \leq 2$$
$$2x - 3 + 3 \leq 2 + 3$$
$$2x \leq 5$$
$$\frac{2x}{2} \leq \frac{5}{2}$$
$$x \leq \frac{5}{2}$$
We graph the solution set, $\left(-\infty, \frac{5}{2}\right]$.

57. $4(2x-3)+1 \geq 3(4x-5)-x$

$8x-12+1 \geq 12x-15-x$

$8x-11 \geq 11x-15$

$8x-11-11x \geq 11x-15-11x$

$-3x-11 \geq -15$

$-3x-11+11 \geq -15+11$

$-3x \geq -4$

$\dfrac{-3x}{-3} \leq \dfrac{-4}{-3}$

$x \leq \dfrac{4}{3}$

We graph the solution set, $\left(-\infty, \dfrac{4}{3}\right]$.

59. $4.3(1.5-x) \geq 13.76$

$6.45-4.3x \geq 13.76$

$6.45-4.3x-6.45 \geq 13.76-6.45$

$-4.3x \geq 7.31$

$\dfrac{-4.3x}{-4.3} \leq \dfrac{7.31}{-4.3}$

$x \leq -1.7$

We graph the solution set, $(-\infty, -1.7]$.

61. $\dfrac{1}{2}y+\dfrac{2}{3} \geq \dfrac{3}{2}$

$6\left(\dfrac{1}{2}y+\dfrac{2}{3}\right) \geq 6\left(\dfrac{3}{2}\right)$

$3y+4 \geq 9$

$3y+4-4 \geq 9-4$

$3y \geq 5$

$\dfrac{3y}{3} \geq \dfrac{5}{3}$

$y \geq \dfrac{5}{3}$

We graph the solution set, $\left[\dfrac{5}{3}, \infty\right)$.

63. $\dfrac{5}{3}-\dfrac{1}{6}x < \dfrac{1}{2}$

$6\left(\dfrac{5}{3}-\dfrac{1}{6}x\right) < 6\left(\dfrac{1}{2}\right)$

$10-x < 3$

$10-x-10 < 3-10$

$-x < -7$

$\dfrac{-x}{-1} > \dfrac{-7}{-1}$

$x > 7$

We graph the solution set, $(7, \infty)$.

65. $-\dfrac{1}{2}x-\dfrac{5}{6} \geq \dfrac{1}{3}+\dfrac{3}{2}x$

$-\dfrac{1}{2}x-\dfrac{5}{6}+\dfrac{5}{6} \geq \dfrac{1}{3}+\dfrac{3}{2}x+\dfrac{5}{6}$

$-\dfrac{1}{2}x \geq \dfrac{3}{2}x+\dfrac{7}{6}$

$-\dfrac{1}{2}x-\dfrac{3}{2}x \geq \dfrac{3}{2}x+\dfrac{7}{6}-\dfrac{3}{2}x$

$-2x \geq \dfrac{7}{6}$

$x \leq -\dfrac{7}{12}$

Interval: $\left(-\infty, -\dfrac{7}{12}\right]$

67. $\dfrac{4c-5}{6} \leq \dfrac{3c+7}{4}$

$\left(\dfrac{4c-5}{6}\right)(12) \leq \left(\dfrac{3c+7}{4}\right)(12)$

$8c-10 \leq 9c+21$

$8c-10+10 \leq 9c+21+10$

$8c \leq 9c+31$

$8c-9c \leq 9c+31-9c$

$-c \leq 31$

$\dfrac{-c}{-1} \geq \dfrac{31}{-1}$

$c \geq -31$

Interval: $[-31, \infty)$

69.

$$\frac{3x+1}{6} - \frac{5x-2}{9} > \frac{2}{3}$$

$$\left(\frac{3x+1}{6} - \frac{5x-2}{9}\right)(18) > \left(\frac{2}{3}\right)(18)$$

$$(3x+1)(3) - (5x-2)(2) > (2)(6)$$

$$9x+3-10x+4 > 12$$

$$-x+7 > 12$$

$$-x+7-7 > 12-7$$

$$-x > 5$$

$$\frac{-x}{-1} < \frac{5}{-1}$$

$$x < -5$$

Interval: $(-\infty, -5)$

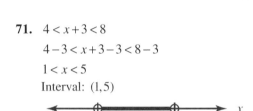

71. $4 < x+3 < 8$

$4-3 < x+3-3 < 8-3$

$1 < x < 5$

Interval: $(1,5)$

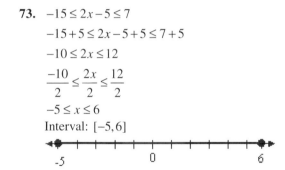

73. $-15 \le 2x-5 \le 7$

$-15+5 \le 2x-5+5 \le 7+5$

$-10 \le 2x \le 12$

$$\frac{-10}{2} \le \frac{2x}{2} \le \frac{12}{2}$$

$-5 \le x \le 6$

Interval: $[-5,6]$

75. $-17 < 3-4x \le 15$

$-17-3 < 3-4x-3 \le 15-3$

$-20 < -4x \le 12$

$$\frac{-20}{-4} > \frac{-4x}{-4} \ge \frac{12}{-4}$$

$5 > x \ge -3$

Interval: $[-3,5)$

77. $\dfrac{1}{3} \le 4 - \dfrac{2}{3}x < 2$

$$(\frac{1}{3})(3) \le (4 - \frac{2}{3}x)(3) < (2)(3)$$

$$1 \le 12 - 2x < 6$$

$$1-12 \le 12-2x-12 < 6-12$$

$$-11 \le -2x < -6$$

$$\frac{-11}{-2} \ge \frac{-2x}{-2} > \frac{-6}{-2}$$

$$5.5 \ge x > 3$$

Interval: $(3, 5.5]$

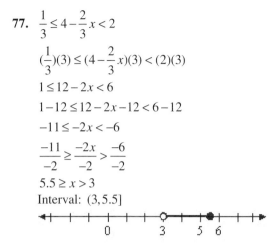

79. a. The slope is 0.87. It means that the percentage of teachers who are "very satisfied" with teaching is increasing by 0.87 percentage points per year.

b. We find where $p > 66$:

$$0.87t + 37.05 > 66$$

$$0.87t + 37.05 - 37.05 > 66 - 37.05$$

$$0.87t > 28.95$$

$$\frac{0.87t}{0.87} > \frac{28.95}{0.87}$$

$$t > 33.28 \quad \text{(rounded)}$$

Since $1980 + 33.28 \approx 2013$, more than 66% of teachers will be "very satisfied" after the year 2013.

81. a. Answers may vary depending on the data points selected to create the linear model. One possibility follows: We begin by creating a scattergram of the data.

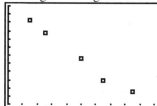

From the scattergram, we see that a line through the points $(3, 55.1)$ and $(17, 50.8)$ will come close to the rest of the data points. We use these points to find an equation of the form $f(t) = mt + b$. We begin by finding the slope:

$$m = \frac{50.8 - 55.1}{17 - 3} = \frac{-4.3}{14} \approx -0.31$$

So, the equation of the line is of the form $f(t) = -0.31t + b$. To find b, we substitute the coordinates of the point $(3, 55.1)$ into the equation and solve for b:

$$f(t) = -0.31t + b$$
$$55.1 = -0.31(3) + b$$
$$55.1 = -0.93 + b$$
$$56.03 = b$$

So, the equation is $f(t) = -0.31t + 56.03$. It comes close to the data points, as can be seen in the graph.

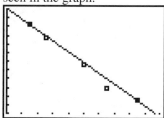

b. Answers may vary [depending on the equation found in part (a)].
We find where $f > 53.4$:

$$-0.31t + 56.03 > 53.4$$
$$-0.31t + 56.03 - 56.03 > 53.4 - 56.03$$
$$-0.31t > -2.63$$
$$\frac{-0.31t}{-0.31} < \frac{-2.63}{-0.31}$$
$$t < 8.48 \quad \text{(rounded)}$$

Before $1990 + 8.48 \approx 1998$, more than 53% of households were married-couple households.

c. Answers may vary. One possibility follows: This is possible because the number of nonmarried households is growing at a greater rate than the number of married households.

83. a. Answers may vary depending on the data points selected to create the linear model. One possibility follows: We begin by creating a scattergram of the data.

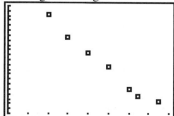

From the scattergram, we see that a line through the points $(6, 53.5)$ and $(13, 41.7)$ will come close to the rest of the data points. We use these points to find an equation of the form $f(t) = mt + b$. We begin by finding the slope:

$$m = \frac{41.7 - 53.5}{13 - 6} = \frac{-11.8}{7} \approx -1.69$$

So, the equation of the line is of the form $f(t) = -1.69t + b$. To find b, we substitute the coordinates of the point $(6, 53.5)$ into the equation and solve for b:

$$f(t) = -1.69t + b$$
$$53.5 = -1.69(6) + b$$
$$53.5 = -10.14 + b$$
$$63.64 = b$$

So, the equation is $f(t) = -1.69t + 63.64$. It comes close to the data points, as can be seen in the graph.

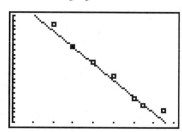

b. Answers may vary (depending on the equation found in part (a)). Since the year 2015 is represented by $t = 25$, we substitute 25 for t in the linear equation:
$f(25) = -1.69(25) + 63.64 \approx 21.4$ births per 1000 women.

The number of births to women ages 15-19 in 2015 will be:
$\dfrac{21.4}{1000} \cdot 10,365,000 \approx 221,811$ births.

c. Answers may vary [depending on the equation found in part (a)].
We find where $r < 10$:
$$-1.69t + 63.64 < 10$$
$$-1.69t + 63.64 - 63.64 < 10 - 63.64$$
$$-1.69t < -53.64$$
$$\dfrac{-1.69t}{-1.69} > \dfrac{-53.64}{-1.69}$$
$$t > 31.74 \quad \text{(rounded)}$$
Since $1990 + 31.74 \approx 2022$, we predict that the American birthrate will be less than 10 births pre 1000 women ages 15-19 after the year 2022.

85. The student failed to reverse the inequality symbol (from < to >) when he or she divided both sides of the inequality by a negative.

$$-3x < 15$$
$$\dfrac{-3x}{-3} > \dfrac{15}{-3}$$
$$x > -5$$

87. a. Answers may vary. The solution to the inequality is:
$$3x - 7 < 5$$
$$3x - 7 + 7 < 5 + 7$$
$$3x < 12$$
$$\dfrac{3x}{3} < \dfrac{12}{3}$$
$$x < 4$$
Any number less than 4 will satisfy the inequality.

b. Answers may vary. Any number greater than or equal to 4 will not satisfy the inequality.

89. Answers will vary.

91.
$$-2x + 6 = 3x - 14$$
$$-2x + 6 - 3x = 3x - 14 - 3x$$
$$-5x + 6 = -14$$
$$-5x + 6 - 6 = -14 - 6$$
$$-5x = -20$$
$$\dfrac{-5x}{-5} = \dfrac{-20}{-5}$$
$$x = 4$$

93.
$$-2x + 6 > 3x - 14$$
$$-2x + 6 - 3x > 3x - 14 - 3x$$
$$-5x + 6 > -14$$
$$-5x + 6 - 6 > -14 - 6$$
$$-5x > -20$$
$$\dfrac{-5x}{-5} < \dfrac{-20}{-5}$$
$$x < 4$$
We graph the solution set, $(-\infty, 4)$.

95.
$$x + 5 > 2$$
$$x + 5 - 5 > 2 - 5$$
$$x > -3$$
We graph the solution set, $(-3, \infty)$.

97.
$$2x \le 5x - 6$$
$$2x - 5x \le 5x - 6 - 5x$$
$$-3x \le -6$$
$$\dfrac{-3x}{-3} > \dfrac{-6}{-3}$$
$$x \ge 2$$
We graph the solution set, $[2, \infty)$.

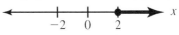

99. Answers will vary.

101. Answers will vary.

Chapter 5 Review Exercises

1. $3y = 5x$

$$\frac{3y}{3} = \frac{5x}{3}$$

$$y = \frac{5x}{3}$$

The slope is $m = \frac{5}{3}$, and the y-intercept is $(0, 0)$.

We first plot $(0, 0)$. From this point we move 3 units to the right and 5 units up, where we plot the point $(3, 5)$. We then sketch the line that contains these two points.

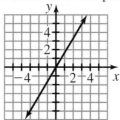

2. $3x - 2y = -6$

$$-2y = -3x - 6$$

$$\frac{-2y}{-2} = \frac{-3x}{-2} - \frac{6}{-2}$$

$$y = \frac{3}{2}x + 3$$

The slope is $m = \frac{3}{2}$, and the y-intercept is $(0, 3)$.

We first plot $(0, 3)$. From this point we move 2 units to the right and 3 units up, where we plot the point $(2, 6)$. We then sketch the line that contains these two points.

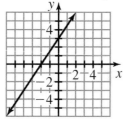

3. $x + 3y = 6$

$$3y = -x + 6$$

$$\frac{3y}{3} = \frac{-x}{3} + \frac{6}{3}$$

$$y = -\frac{1}{3}x + 2$$

The slope is $m = -\frac{1}{3}$, and the y-intercept is $(0, 2)$.

We first plot $(0, 2)$. From this point we move 3 units to the right and 1 unit down, where we plot the point $(3, 1)$. We then sketch the line that contains these two points.

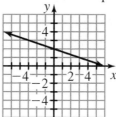

4. $2x + 5y - 20 = 0$

$$5y = -2x + 20$$

$$\frac{5y}{5} = \frac{-2x}{5} + \frac{20}{5}$$

$$y = -\frac{2}{5}x + 4$$

The slope is $m = -\frac{2}{5}$, and the y-intercept is $(0, 4)$. We first plot $(0, 4)$. From this point we move 5 units to the right and 2 units down, where we plot the point $(5, 2)$. We then sketch the line that contains these two points.

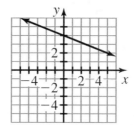

5. $y - 4 = 0$

$\quad\quad y = 4$

The slope is $m = 0$, and the y-intercept is $(0, 4)$. The graph is a horizontal line that passes through the point $(0, 4)$.

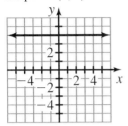

6. First, isolate y.

$\quad -3(y + 2) = 2x + 9$

$\quad\quad -3y - 6 = 2x + 9$

$\quad\quad\quad -3y = 2x + 15$

$\quad\quad\quad\quad y = -\dfrac{2}{3}x - 5$

The slope is $m = -\dfrac{2}{3}$, and the y-intercept is

$(0, -5)$. We first plot $(0, -5)$. From this point we move 3 units to the left and 2 units up, where we plot the point $(-3, -3)$. We then sketch the line that contains these two points.

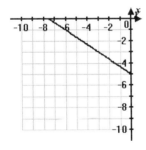

7. First, isolate y.

$\quad 3x - 2(2y - 1) = 8x - 3(x + 2)$

$\quad\quad 3x - 4y + 2 = 8x - 3x - 6$

$\quad\quad\quad \dfrac{-4y}{-4} = \dfrac{2x - 8}{-4}$

$\quad\quad\quad\quad y = -\dfrac{1}{2}x + 2$

The slope is $m = -\dfrac{1}{2}$, and the y-intercept is

$(0, 2)$. We first plot $(0, 2)$. From this point we move 2 units to the right and 1 unit down, where

we plot the point $(2, 1)$. We then sketch the line that contains these two points.

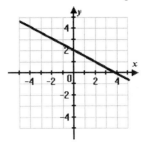

8. First, isolate y.

$\quad a(x - y) = c$

$\quad\quad x - y = \dfrac{c}{a}$

$\quad\quad -y = -x + \dfrac{c}{a}$

$\quad\quad\quad y = x - \dfrac{c}{a}$

The slope is 1 and the y-intercept is $\left(0, -\dfrac{c}{a}\right)$.

9. $4x - 5y = 20$

To find the x-intercept, we substitute 0 for y and solve for x. To find the y-intercept, we substitute 0 for x and solve for y.

x-intercept	y-intercept
$4x - 5(0) = 20$	$4(0) - 5y = 20$
$4x = 20$	$-5y = 20$
$x = 5$	$y = -4$

The x-intercept is $(5, 0)$; the y-intercept is $(0, -4)$.

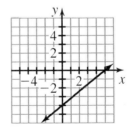

10. $3x + 4y + 12 = 0$

To find the x-intercept, we substitute 0 for y and solve for x. To find the y-intercept, we substitute 0 for x and solve for y.

x-intercept	y-intercept
$3x + 4(0) + 12 = 0$	$3(0) + 4y + 12 = 0$
$3x + 12 = 0$	$4y + 12 = 0$
$3x = -12$	$4y = -12$
$x = -4$	$y = -3$

The x-intercept is $(-4, 0)$; the y-intercept is $(0, -3)$.

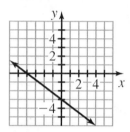

11. $y = 2x - 4$

To find the x-intercept, we substitute 0 for y and solve for x. To find the y-intercept, we substitute 0 for x and solve for y.

x-intercept	y-intercept
$0 = 2x - 4$	$y = 2(0) - 4$
$-2x = -4$	$y = -4$
$x = 2$	

The x-intercept is $(2, 0)$; the y-intercept is $(0, -4)$.

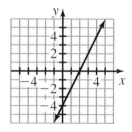

12. $\dfrac{1}{3}x - \dfrac{1}{2}y = 1$

To find the x-intercept, we substitute 0 for y and solve for x. To find the y-intercept, we substitute 0 for x and solve for y.

x-intercept	y-intercept
$\dfrac{1}{3}x - \dfrac{1}{2}(0) = 1$	$\dfrac{1}{3}(0) - \dfrac{1}{2}y = 1$
$\dfrac{1}{3}x = 1$	$-\dfrac{1}{2}y = 1$
$x = 3$	$y = -2$

The x-intercept is $(3, 0)$; the y-intercept is $(0, -2)$.

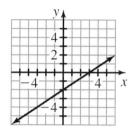

13. To find the x-intercept, substitute 0 for y.
$$ax + b = cy$$
$$ax + b = c(0)$$
$$\frac{ax}{a} = \frac{-b}{a}$$
$$x = -\frac{b}{a}$$

The x-intercept is $\left(-\dfrac{b}{a}, 0\right)$.

To find the y-intercept, substitute 0 for x.
$$ax + b = cy$$
$$a(0) + b = cy$$
$$\frac{b}{c} = y$$

The y-intercept is $\left(0, \dfrac{b}{c}\right)$.

14. $9.2x - 3.8y = 87.2$

To find the x-intercept, we substitute 0 for y and solve for x. To find the y-intercept, we substitute 0 for x and solve for y.

x-intercept	y-intercept
$9.2x - 3.8(0) = 87.2$	$9.2(0) - 3.8y = 87.2$
$9.2x = 87.2$	$-3.8y = 87.2$
$x \approx 9.48$	$x \approx -22.95$

The x-intercept is approximately $(9.48, 0)$; the y-intercept is approximately $(0, -22.95)$.

15. $y = 2.56x + 97.25$

To find the x-intercept, we substitute 0 for y and solve for x. To find the y-intercept, we substitute 0 for x and solve for y.

x-intercept	y-intercept
$0 = 2.56x + 97.25$	$y = 2.56(0) + 97.25$
$-2.56x = 97.25$	$y = 97.25$
$x \approx -37.99$	

The x-intercept is approximately $(-37.99, 0)$; the y-intercept is $(0, 97.25)$.

16. For each case, to find the x-intercept, we substitute 0 for y and solve for x. To find the y-intercept, we substitute 0 for x and solve for y.

a. $y = 3x + 7$

x-intercept	y-intercept
$0 = 3x + 7$	$y = 3(0) + 7$
$-3x = 7$	$y = 7$
$x = -\dfrac{7}{3}$	

The x-intercept is $\left(-\dfrac{7}{3}, 0\right)$; the y-intercept is $(0, 7)$.

b. $y = 2x + 9$

x-intercept	y-intercept
$0 = 2x + 9$	$y = 2(0) + 9$
$-2x = 9$	$y = 9$
$x = -\dfrac{9}{2}$	

The x-intercept is $\left(-\dfrac{9}{2}, 0\right)$; the y-intercept is $(0, 9)$.

c. $y = mx + b$

x-intercept	y-intercept
$0 = mx + b$	$y = m(0) + b$
$-mx = b$	$y = b$
$x = -\dfrac{b}{m}$	

The x-intercept is $\left(-\dfrac{b}{m}, 0\right)$; the y-intercept is $(0, b)$.

17. $2x - 4y = 8$

a.
$$-4y = -2x + 8$$
$$\frac{-4y}{-4} = \frac{-2x}{-4} + \frac{8}{-4}$$
$$y = \frac{1}{2}x - 2$$

The slope is $m = \dfrac{1}{2}$, and the y-intercept is $(0, -2)$. We first plot $(0, -2)$. From this point we move 2 units to the right and 1 unit up, where we plot the point $(2, -1)$. We then sketch the line that contains these two points.

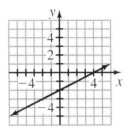

b. To find the x-intercept, we substitute 0 for y and solve for x. To find the y-intercept, we substitute 0 for x and solve for y.

x-intercept	y-intercept
$2x - 4(0) = 8$	$2(0) - 4y = 8$
$2x = 8$	$-4y = 8$
$x = 4$	$y = -2$

The x-intercept is $(4, 0)$; the y-intercept is $(0, -2)$.

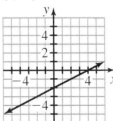

c. The graphs are the same. Preferences for graphing the equation $2x - 4y = 8$ may vary.

18. Relations 1 and 3 could possibly be functions, since there is only one output for each input. Relations 2 and 4 could not possibly be functions, since there are two or more outputs for a single input.

19. The graph is not a function because a vertical line can intersect the graph more than once.

20. First, isolate y.
$$5x - 6y = 3$$
$$\frac{-6y}{-6} = \frac{-5x + 3}{-6}$$
$$y = \frac{5}{6}x - \frac{1}{2}$$

This relation is a function since it can be put into the form $y = mx + b$ which defines a linear function.

21. $x = 9$ is a vertical line. It does not pass the vertical line test and is not a function.

22. Sketch the graph of $y^2 = x$.

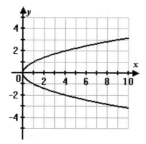

Note that this graph does not pass the vertical line test. Therefore, $y^2 = x$ is not a function.

23. The domain is all real numbers and the range is $y \leq 4$.

24. $f(-3) = 3(-3)^2 - 7$
$$= 3(9) - 7$$
$$= 27 - 7$$
$$= 20$$

25. $g(2) = \frac{2(2) + 5}{3(2) + 6}$
$$= \frac{4 + 5}{6 + 6}$$
$$= \frac{9}{12}$$
$$= \frac{3}{4}$$

26. $h(a + 3) = -10(a + 3) - 3$
$$= -10a - 30 - 3$$
$$= -10a - 33$$

27. $\frac{2}{3} = 2x + 3$

$$\frac{2}{3} - 3 = 2x + 3 - 3$$
$$\frac{-7}{3} = 2x$$
$$\frac{1}{2}\left(\frac{-7}{3}\right) = \frac{1}{2}(2x)$$
$$\frac{-7}{6} = x \quad \text{or} \quad x = -\frac{7}{6}$$

28. $a + 7 = 2x + 3$
$$a + 7 - 3 = 2x + 3 - 3$$
$$a + 4 = 2x$$
$$\frac{a + 4}{2} = \frac{2x}{2}$$
$$\frac{a}{2} + 2 = x \quad \text{or} \quad x = 2 + \frac{a}{2}$$

29. Since the graph includes the point $(0, 1)$, $f(0) = 1$.

30. Since the graph includes a point close to $(-3, 3.5)$, $f(-3) \approx 3.5$.

31. Since the graph includes the point $(2, 0)$, $x = 2$ when $f(x) = 0$.

32. Since the graph includes the point $(4, -1)$, $x = 4$ when $f(x) = -1$

33. The domain of f is $-5 \leq x \leq 6$.

34. The range of f is $-2 \leq y \leq 4$.

35. Since x is 2 when $f(x) = 4$, $f(2) = 4$.

36. When $f(x) = 2$, $x = 1$.

37. $f(x)$ or $y = -7x + 3$

To find the x-intercept, set $f(x) = y = 0$ and solve
$$0 = -7x + 3$$
for x. $-3 = -7x$
$$x = \frac{-3}{-7} = \frac{3}{7}$$
x-intercept: $\left(\frac{3}{7}, 0\right)$

To find the y-intercept, set $x = 0$ and solve for y.
$$y = -7(0) + 3$$
$$y = 0 + 3$$
$$y = 3$$
y-intercept: $(0, 3)$

38. $f(x)$ or $y = -\dfrac{4}{7}x + 2$

To find the x-intercept, set $f(x) = y = 0$ and solve for x.

$$0 = -\frac{4}{7}x + 2$$

$$-2 = -\frac{4}{7}x$$

$$-2\left(-\frac{7}{4}\right) = x$$

$$-2\left(-\frac{7}{4}\right) = x$$

$$x = \frac{7}{2}$$

x-intercept: $\left(\dfrac{7}{2}, 0\right)$

To find the y-intercept, set $x = 0$ and solve for y.

$$y = -\frac{4}{7}(0) + 2$$

$$y = 0 + 2$$

$$y = 2$$

y-intercept: $(0, 2)$

39. We substitute $m = -4$ and $(x_1, y_1) = (2, -1)$ into the point slope form and solve for y:

$$y - y_1 = m(x - x_1)$$

$$y - (-1) = -4(x - 2)$$

$$y + 1 = -4x + 8$$

$$y = -4x + 7$$

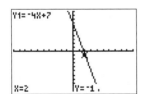

40. We substitute $m = -\dfrac{2}{3}$ and $(x_1, y_1) = (-6, -4)$ into the point slope form and solve for y:

$$y - y_1 = m(x - x_1)$$

$$y - (-4) = -\frac{2}{3}(x - (-6))$$

$$y + 4 = -\frac{2}{3}(x + 6)$$

$$y + 4 = -\frac{2}{3}x - 4$$

$$y = -\frac{2}{3}x - 8$$

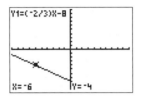

41. Since the slope of the line is undefined, the line must be vertical. Since the x-coordinate of the point on the line is 2, an equation of the line is $x = 2$.

42. We substitute $m = 0$ and $(x_1, y_1) = (-1, -4)$ into the point slope form and solve for y:

$$y - y_1 = m(x - x_1)$$

$$y - (-4) = 0(x - (-1))$$

$$y + 4 = 0(x + 1)$$

$$y + 4 = 0$$

$$y = -4$$

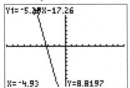

43. We substitute $m = -5.29$ and $(x_1, y_1) = (-4.93, 8.82)$ into the point slope form and solve for y:

$$y - y_1 = m(x - x_1)$$

$$y - 8.82 = -5.29(x - (-4.93))$$

$$y - 8.82 = -5.29(x + 4.93)$$

$$y - 8.82 \approx -5.29x - 26.08$$

$$y \approx -5.29x - 17.26$$

44. We substitute $m = 1.45$ and $(x_1, y_1) =$
$(-2.79, -7.13)$ into the point slope form and
solve for y:
$$y - y_1 = m(x - x_1)$$
$$y - (-7.13) = 1.45(x - (-2.79))$$
$$y + 7.13 = 1.45(x + 2.79)$$
$$y + 7.13 \approx 1.45x + 4.05$$
$$y \approx 1.45x - 3.08$$

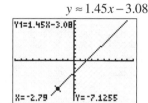

45. We begin by finding the slope of the line:
$$m = \frac{2 - (-7)}{1 - (-2)} = \frac{2 + 7}{1 + 2} = \frac{9}{3} = 3$$
Then we substitute $m = 3$ and $(x_1, y_1) = (-2, -7)$
into the point slope form and solve for y:
$$y - y_1 = m(x - x_1)$$
$$y - (-7) = 3(x - (-2))$$
$$y + 7 = 3(x + 2)$$
$$y + 7 = 3x + 6$$
$$y = 3x - 1$$

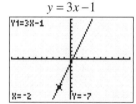 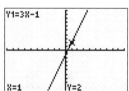

46. We begin by finding the slope of the line:
$$m = \frac{5 - (-5)}{4 - 2} = \frac{5 + 5}{4 - 2} = \frac{10}{2} = 5$$
Then we substitute $m = 1$ and $(x_1, y_1) = (2, -5)$
into the point slope form and solve for y:
$$y - y_1 = m(x - x_1)$$
$$y - (-5) = 5(x - 2)$$
$$y + 5 = 5x - 10$$
$$y = 5x - 15$$

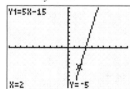 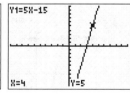

47. We begin by finding the slope of the line:
$$m = \frac{-6 - 9}{6 - (-3)} = \frac{-6 - 9}{6 + 3} = \frac{-15}{9} = -\frac{5}{3}$$
Then we substitute $m = -\frac{5}{3}$ and $(x_1, y_1) = (-3, 9)$
into the point slope form and solve for y:
$$y - y_1 = m(x - x_1)$$
$$y - 9 = -\frac{5}{3}(x - (-3))$$
$$y - 9 = -\frac{5}{3}(x + 3)$$
$$y - 9 = -\frac{5}{3}x - 5$$
$$y = -\frac{5}{3}x + 4$$

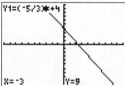 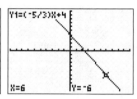

48. We begin by finding the slope of the line:
$$m = \frac{-7 - (-10)}{-2 - (-4)} = \frac{-7 + 10}{-2 + 4} = \frac{3}{2}$$
Then we substitute $m = \frac{3}{2}$ and $(x_1, y_1) = (-4, -10)$
into the point slope form and solve for y:
$$y - y_1 = m(x - x_1)$$
$$y - (-10) = \frac{3}{2}(x - (-4))$$
$$y + 10 = \frac{3}{2}(x + 4)$$
$$y + 10 = \frac{3}{2}x + 6$$
$$y = \frac{3}{2}x - 4$$

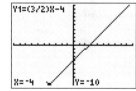 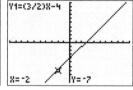

49. Since the *x*-coordinates of the given points are equal (both 5), the line that contains the points is vertical. An equation of the line is $x = 5$.

50. We begin by finding the slope of the line:
$$m = \frac{-3 - (-3)}{-1 - (-4)} = \frac{-3 + 3}{-1 + 4} = \frac{0}{3} = 0$$

Then we substitute $m = 0$ and $(x_1, y_1) = (-4, -3)$ into the point slope form and solve for *y*:
$$y - y_1 = m(x - x_1)$$
$$y - (-3) = 0(x - (-4))$$
$$y + 3 = 0(x + 4)$$
$$y + 3 = 0$$
$$y = -3$$

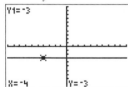 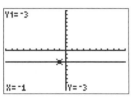

51. We begin by finding the slope of the line:
$$m = \frac{4.8 - 9.2}{8.7 - 3.5} = \frac{-4.4}{5.2} \approx -0.846 .$$

So, the equation of the line is of the form $y = -0.846x + b$. To find *b*, we substitute the coordinates of the point $(3.5, 9.2)$ into the equation and solve for *b*:
$$y = -0.846x + b$$
$$9.2 = -0.846(3.5) + b$$
$$9.2 = -2.961 + b$$

$12.161 = b$
Rounding both *m* and *b* to two decimal places, the approximate equation is $y = -0.85x + 12.16$.

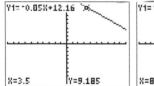 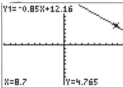

52. We begin by finding the slope of the line:
$$m = \frac{-3.99 - 2.49}{1.83 - (-5.22)} = \frac{-6.48}{7.05} \approx -0.919 .$$

So, the equation of the line is of the form $y = -0.919x + b$. To find *b*, we substitute the coordinates of the point $(-5.22, 2.49)$ into the equation and solve for *b*:

$$y = -0.919x + b$$
$$2.49 = -0.919(-5.22) + b$$
$$2.49 = 4.79718 + b$$

$-2.30718 = b$
Rounding both *m* and *b* to two decimal places, the approximate equation is $y = -0.92x - 2.31$.

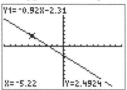 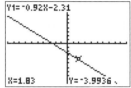

53. Since the line is parallel to the line $3x - y = 6$, or $y = 3x - 6$, it will have a slope of 3. Use the slope, 3, and the point on the line, $(-2, 5)$, to find the *y*-intercept.
$$5 = 3(-2) + b$$
$$5 = -6 + b$$
$$11 = b$$
The equation of the line is $y = 3x + 11$.

54. The line contains the points $(-2, -3)$ and $(3, -4)$, so the slope of the line is
$$m = \frac{-4 - (-3)}{3 - (-2)} = \frac{-4 + 3}{3 + 2} = \frac{-1}{5} = -\frac{1}{5} .$$

So, the equation of the line is of the form $y = -\frac{1}{5}x + b$. To find *b*, we substitute the coordinates of the point $(-2, -3)$ into the equation and solve for *b*:

$$y = -\frac{1}{5}x + b$$
$$-3 = -\frac{1}{5}(-2) + b$$
$$-3 = \frac{2}{5} + b$$
$$-\frac{17}{5} = b$$

So, the equation is $y = -\frac{1}{5}x - \frac{17}{5}$.

55. Answers may vary. One possibility follows:
We begin by creating a scattergram of the data.

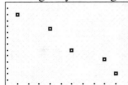

From the scattergram, we see that a line through the points $(1, 28)$ and $(10, 8)$ will come close to the rest of the data points. We use these points to find an equation of the form $y = mx + b$. We begin by finding the slope:

$$m = \frac{8 - 28}{10 - 1} = \frac{-20}{9} \approx -2.22$$

So, the equation of the line is of the form $y = -2.22x + b$. To find b, we substitute the coordinates of the point $(1, 28)$ into the equation and solve for b:

$$y = -2.22x + b$$
$$28 = -2.22(1) + b$$
$$28 = -2.21 + b$$
$$30.21 = b$$

So, the equation is $y = -2.22x + 30.21$. It comes close to the data points, as can be seen in the graph.

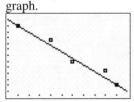

56. a. From the given information, we can select the data points $(0, 51)$ and $(7, 34)$. Use these points to find the slope of the equation for *f*.

$$m = \frac{34 - 51}{7 - 0} \approx -2.43$$

So, $f(t) = -2.43t + b$. To solve for *b*, substitute 0 for *t* and 51 for *f*(t) since the line contains $(0, 51)$.

$$51 = -2.43(0) + b$$
$$51 = b$$

The equation for *f* is $f(t) = -2.43t + 51$. Your equation may be slightly different if you chose 2 other points.

b. The slope is –2.43. This means that for every year that passes between 2000 to 2007 the percentage of Americans who thinks that the press has too much freedom decreases by 2.43%.

c. Set *f*(*t*) equal to 22 and solve for *t*.

$$22 = -2.43t + 51$$
$$-29 = -2.43t$$
$$11.9 \approx t$$

According to the model, in 2000 + 12 = 2012 22 % of Americans will think that the press has too much freedom.

d.
$$f(15) = -2.43(15) + 51$$
$$= -36.45 + 51$$
$$= 14.55$$

The model predicts that in 2000 + 15 = 2015, 14.55 % of Americans will think that the press has too much freedom.

e.
$$15 = -2.43t + 51$$
$$-36 = -2.43t$$
$$14.81 \approx t$$

The model predicts that in 2000 + 14.81 ≈ 2015, about 15% of Americans will think that the press has too much freedom.

f. To find the *t*-intercept, set *f*(*t*) equal to 0 and solve for *t*.

$$0 = -2.43t + 51$$
$$-51 = -2.43t$$
$$20.99 \approx t$$

According to the model, in 2000 + 20.99 ≈ 2021, there will be no Americans (0%) who think that the press has too much freedom. Model breakdown has likely occurred.

57. a.

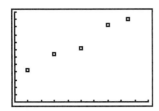

b. Answers may vary depending on the data points selected. We use the points $(2, 2.1)$ and $(17, 5.5)$ to find an equation of the form $f(t) = mt + b$. We begin by finding the slope:

$$m = \frac{5.5 - 2.1}{17 - 2} = \frac{3.4}{15} \approx 0.227$$

So, the equation of the line is of the form $f(t) = 0.227t + b$. To find b, we substitute the coordinates of the point $(2, 2.1)$ into the equation and solve for b:

$$f(t) = 0.227t + b$$
$$2.1 = 0.227(2) + b$$
$$2.1 = 0.454 + b$$
$$1.646 = b$$

So, the equation is $f(t) = 0.227t + 1.646$.

c. Answers may vary (depending on the equation found in part (b).) The slope is 0.227. It means that the revenue is increasing by $227 million per year.

d. Answers may vary (depending on the equation found in part (b).) The year 2013 is represented by $t = 23$. We substitute 23 for t in the equation:

$$f(t) = 0.227t + 1.646$$
$$f(23) = 0.227(23) + 1.646$$
$$= 5.221 + 1.646$$
$$= 6.867$$

We predict that revenue will be approximately $6.87 billion in 2013.

e. Answers may vary (depending on the equation found in part (b)). We substitute 7.4 for $f(t)$ and solve for t:

$$f(t) = 0.227t + 1.646$$
$$7.4 = 0.227t + 1.646$$
$$5.754 = 0.227t$$
$$t = \frac{5.754}{0.227} \approx 25.35$$

We predict that revenue will be $7.4 billion in the year $1990 + 25.35 \approx 2015$.

58. a. Yes, the rate of increase has remained constant, showing a linear relationship. The slope in this case is 803, or an increase of 803 Canada geese euthanized per year.

b. The n-intercept is the n value when $t = 0$, or during 2008. In 2008, $n = 14{,}041$, meaning there were 14,041 Canada geese that were euthanized in 2008.

c. Based on the first two parts, the equation of the model is $n(t) = 803t + 14{,}041$.

d. Since $2013 - 2008 = 5$, $t = 5$ corresponds to 2013.

$$n(5) = 803(5) + 14{,}041$$
$$= 4015 + 14{,}041$$
$$= 18{,}056$$

The model predicts that in 2013, 18,056 Canada geese will be enthanized in the United States.

e. To find when 20,000 Canade geese will be euthanized, substitute 20,000 for n and solve for t.

$$20{,}000 = 803t + 14{,}041$$
$$5959 = 803t$$
$$t = \frac{5959}{803} \approx 7.42$$

The model predicts that in $2008 + 7.4 \approx 2015$ 20,000 Canade geese will be euthanized,

59. Let p represent the percentage of counselors who consider admission tests as being "considerably important" at t years after 2000. Then 2002 is represented by $t = 2$ and 2006 is represented by $t = 6$. We find a linear model by using the data points (2, 57) and (6, 60). We begin by finding the slope:

$$m = \frac{60-57}{6-2} = \frac{3}{4} = 0.75$$

So, the equation of the line is of the form $p = 0.75t + b$. To find b, we substitute the coordinates of the point (2, 57) into the equation and solve for b:

$$p = 0.75t + b$$
$$57 = 0.75(2) + b$$
$$57 = 1.5 + b$$
$$55.5 = b$$

So, the equation is $p = 0.75t + 55.5$. To find when the percentage will be 67, we substitute 67 for p in the equation and solve for t:

$$67 = 0.75t + 55.5$$
$$11.5 = 0.75t$$
$$t = \frac{11.5}{0.75} = 15.33$$

We predict that 67% of counselors will consider admission tests "considerable important" in the year $2000 + 15.33 \approx 2015$.

60.
$$x - 3 \geq -4$$
$$x - 3 + 3 \geq -4 + 3$$
$$x \geq -1$$

We graph the solution set, $[-1, \infty)$.

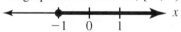

61. $-4x < 8$
$$\frac{-4x}{-4} > \frac{8}{-4}$$
$$x > -2$$

We graph the solution set, $(-2, \infty)$.

62.
$$5w - 3 > 3w - 9$$
$$5w - 3 - 3w > 3w - 9 - 3w$$
$$2w - 3 > -9$$
$$2w - 3 + 3 > -9 + 3$$
$$2w > -6$$
$$\frac{2w}{2} > \frac{-6}{2}$$
$$w > -3$$

We graph the solution set, $(-3, \infty)$.

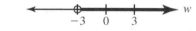

63.
$$-3(2a + 5) + 5a \geq 2(a - 3)$$
$$-6a - 15 + 5a \geq 2a - 6$$
$$-a - 15 \geq 2a - 6$$
$$-a - 15 - 2a \geq 2a - 6 - 2a$$
$$-3a - 15 \geq -6$$
$$-3a - 15 + 15 \geq -6 + 15$$
$$-3a \geq 9$$
$$\frac{-3a}{-3} \leq \frac{9}{-3}$$
$$a \leq -3$$

We graph the solution set, $(-\infty, -3]$.

64.
$$\frac{2b-4}{3} \leq \frac{3b-4}{4}$$
$$12\left(\frac{2b-4}{3}\right) \leq 12\left(\frac{3b-4}{4}\right)$$
$$4(2b - 4) \leq 3(3b - 4)$$
$$8b - 16 \leq 9b - 12$$
$$8b - 16 - 9b \leq 9b - 12 - 9b$$
$$-b - 16 \leq -12$$
$$-b - 16 + 16 \leq -12 + 16$$
$$-b \leq 4$$
$$\frac{-b}{-1} \geq \frac{4}{-1}$$
$$b \geq -4$$

We graph the solution set, $[-4, \infty)$.

65.
$$1 \le 2x+5 < 11$$
$$1-5 \le 2x+5-5 < 11-5$$
$$-4 \le 2x < 6$$
$$-2 \le x < 3$$

We graph the solution set, $[-2,3)$

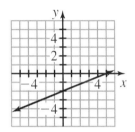

66. a. Answers may vary depending on the data points selected to create the linear model. We use the points $(9,13)$ and $(18,25)$ to find an equation of the form $f(t) = mt + b$. We begin by finding the slope:
$$m = \frac{25-13}{18-9} = \frac{12}{9} \approx 1.33$$
So, the equation of the line is of the form $f(t) = 1.33t + b$. To find b, we substitute the coordinates of the point $(9,13)$ into the equation and solve for b:
$$f(t) = 1.33t + b$$
$$13 = 1.33(9) + b$$
$$13 = 11.97 + b$$
$$1.03 = b$$
So, the equation is $f(t) = 1.33t + 1.03$.

b. Answers may vary [depending on the equation found in part (a)]. The slope is 1.33. It means that the number of entrants in the Boston Marathon is increasing by about 1333 entrants per year.

c. Answers may vary [depending on the equation found in part (a)].
We find where $f(t) < 33$:
$$1.33t + 1.03 < 33$$
$$1.33t + 1.03 - 1.03 < 33 - 1.03$$
$$1.33t < 31.97$$
$$\frac{1.33t}{1.33} < \frac{31.97}{1.33}$$
$$t < 24 \quad \text{(rounded)}$$
Since $1990 + 24 = 2014$, we predict that there will be fewer than 33,000 entrants in the Boston Marathon until the year 2014.

Chapter 5 Test

1. $2x - 5y = 10$
$$-5y = -2x + 10$$
$$\frac{-5y}{-5} = \frac{-2x}{-5} + \frac{10}{-5}$$
$$y = \frac{2}{5}x - 2$$

The slope is $m = \frac{2}{5}$, and the y-intercept is $(0,-2)$. We first plot $(0,-2)$. From this point we move 5 units to the right and 2 units up, where we plot the point $(5,0)$. We then sketch the line that contains these two points.

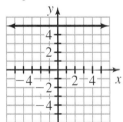

2. $y - 5 = 0$
$$y = 5$$

The slope is $m = 0$ and the y-intercept is $(0,5)$. The graph is a horizontal line that passes through the point $(0,5)$.

3. First, isolate y.

$$2(2x - y) = 2x + 9 + y$$
$$4x - 2y = 2x + 9 + y$$
$$-2y - y = 2x - 4x + 9$$
$$\frac{-3y}{-3} = \frac{-2x + 9}{-3}$$
$$y = \frac{2}{3}x - 3$$

Use the slope, $\frac{2}{3}$, and the y-intercept, $(0, -3)$, to graph the line.

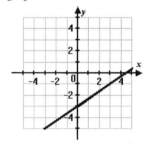

4. $6x - 3y = 18$

To find the x-intercept, we substitute 0 for y and solve for x. To find the y-intercept, we substitute 0 for x and solve for y.

x-intercept	y-intercept
$6x - 3(0) = 18$	$6(0) - 3y = 18$
$6x = 18$	$-3y = 18$
$x = 3$	$y = -6$

The x-intercept is $(3, 0)$; the y-intercept is $(0, -6)$.

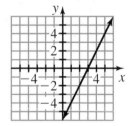

5. $\frac{x}{2} + \frac{y}{7} = 1$

To find the x-intercept, we substitute 0 for y and solve for x. To find the y-intercept, we substitute 0 for x and solve for y.

x-intercept	y-intercept
$\frac{x}{2} + \frac{0}{7} = 1$	$\frac{0}{2} + \frac{y}{7} = 1$
$\frac{x}{2} = 1$	$\frac{y}{7} = 1$
$x = 2$	$y = 7$

The x-intercept is $(2, 0)$; the y-intercept is $(0, 7)$.

6. Sketch the graph of $y = \pm x$.

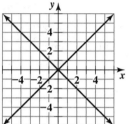

Note that this graph does not pass the vertical line test. Therefore, $y = \pm x$ is not a function.

7. The graph of $y = -2x + 5$ is a nonvertical line. Any nonvertical line is a function since it passes the vertical line test.

8. The domain is $-3 \le x \le 5$ and the range is $-3 \le y \le 4$. The relation is a function since the graph can be intersected by any vertical line only once.

9. Since the line includes the point $(-3, -2)$, $f(-3) = -2$.

10. Since the line includes the point $(3, 0)$, $x = 3$ when $f(x) = 0$.

11. The domain of f is all the x-coordinates of the points in the graph. In this case f has a domain of $-6 \le x \le 6$.

12. The range of f is all the y-coordinates of the points in the graph. In this case f has a range of $-3 \le y \le 1$.

13. To find $f(-3)$, substitute -3 for x.

$$f(-3) = -4(-3) + 7$$
$$= 12 + 7$$
$$= 19$$

14. To find $f(a-5)$, substitute $a-5$ for x.

$$f(a-5) = -4(a-5)+7$$
$$= -4a+20+7$$
$$= -4a+27$$

15. To find x when $f(x)=2$, substitute 2 for $f(x)$.

$$2 = -4x+7$$
$$-5 = -4x$$
$$\frac{-5}{-4} = x$$
$$x = \frac{5}{4}$$

16. To find x when $f(x)=a$, substitute a for $f(x)$.

$$a = -4x+7$$
$$a-7 = -4x$$
$$\frac{a-7}{-4} = x \quad \text{or} \quad x = \frac{-a+7}{4}$$

17. To find the x-intercept, let $f(x)=0$ and solve for x.

$$0 = 3x-7$$
$$7 = 3x$$
$$\frac{7}{3} = x$$
$$x = \frac{7}{3}$$

The x-intercept is $\left(\frac{7}{3}, 0\right)$.

To find the y-intercept, let $x=0$ and solve for y or $f(x)$ since $y=f(x)$.
$$y = 3(0)-7$$
$$y = -7$$
The y-intercept is $(0, -7)$.

18. To find the x-intercept, let $k(x)=0$ and solve for x.

$$0 = \frac{1}{3}x-8$$
$$8 = \frac{1}{3}x$$
$$24 = x$$
$$x = 24$$
The x-intercept is $(24, 0)$.
To find the y-intercept, let $x=0$ and solve for y or $k(x)$ since $y=k(x)$.
$$y = \frac{1}{3}(0)-8$$
$$y = -8$$
The y-intercept is $(0, -8)$.

19. We substitute $m=7$ and $(x_1, y_1) = (-2, -4)$ into the point slope form and solve for y:

$$y - y_1 = m(x - x_1)$$
$$y-(-4) = 7(x-(-2))$$
$$y+4 = 7(x+2)$$
$$y+4 = 7x+14$$
$$y = 7x+10$$

20. We substitute $m=-\frac{2}{3}$ and $(x_1, y_1) = (6, -1)$ into the point slope form and solve for y:

$$y - y_1 = m(x - x_1)$$
$$y-(-1) = -\frac{2}{3}(x-6)$$
$$y+1 = -\frac{2}{3}x+4$$
$$y = -\frac{2}{3}x+3$$

21. We begin by finding the slope of the line:

$$m = \frac{3-6}{2-(-4)} = \frac{3-6}{2+4} = \frac{-3}{6} = -\frac{1}{2}$$

Then we substitute $m=-\frac{1}{2}$ and $(x_1, y_1) = (-4, 6)$ into the point slope form and solve for y:

$$y - y_1 = m(x - x_1)$$
$$y-6 = -\frac{1}{2}(x-(-4))$$
$$y-6 = -\frac{1}{2}(x+4)$$
$$y-6 = -\frac{1}{2}x-2$$
$$y = -\frac{1}{2}x+4$$

22. We begin by finding the slope of the line:
$$m = \frac{-7.1-2.9}{1.8-(-3.4)} = \frac{-7.1-2.9}{1.8+3.4} = \frac{-10.0}{5.2} \approx -1.923.$$
So, the equation of the line is of the form
$y = -1.923x + b$. To find b, we substitute the
coordinates of the point $(-3.4, 2.9)$ into the
equation and solve for b:
$$y = -1.923x + b$$
$$2.9 = -1.923(-3.4) + b$$
$$2.9 = 6.5382 + b$$
$$-3.6382 = b$$
Rounding both m and b to two decimal places,
the approximate equation is $y = -1.92x - 3.64$.

23. First, find the slope of the line by isolating y.
$$3x - 5y = 20$$
$$-5y = -3x + 20$$
$$y = \frac{3}{5}x - 4$$

The slope of the line is $\frac{3}{5}$. The slope of a line

perpendicular to this line is $-\frac{5}{3}$. Use the slope,

$-\frac{5}{3}$, and a point on the line, $(4, -1)$, to find the

y-intercept.
$$y = mx + b$$
$$-1 = -\frac{5}{3}(4) + b$$
$$-1 = -\frac{20}{3} + b$$
$$-\frac{3}{3} = -\frac{20}{3} + b$$
$$\frac{17}{3} = b$$

The equation of the line is $y = -\frac{5}{3}x + \frac{17}{3}$.

24. The line contains the points $(2, -3)$ and $(5, -4)$, so
the slope of the line is
$$m = \frac{-4-(-3)}{5-2} = \frac{-4+3}{5-2} = \frac{-1}{3} = -\frac{1}{3}.$$
So, the equation of the line is of the form

$y = -\frac{1}{3}x + b$. To find b, we substitute the

coordinates of the point $(2, -3)$ into the equation
and solve for b:
$$y = -\frac{1}{3}x + b$$
$$-3 = -\frac{1}{3}(2) + b$$
$$-3 = -\frac{2}{3} + b$$
$$-\frac{7}{3} = b$$

So, the equation is $y = -\frac{1}{3}x - \frac{7}{3}$.

25.

The value of m must decrease; the value of b
must increase.

26. Answers may vary. One possibility follows:
We begin by creating a scattergram of the data.

From the scattergram, we see that a line through the points $(3, 11)$ and $(14, 23)$ will come close to the rest of the data points. We use these points to find an equation of the form $y = mx + b$. We begin by finding the slope:

$$m = \frac{23 - 11}{14 - 3} = \frac{12}{11} \approx 1.09$$

So, the equation of the line is of the form $y = 1.09x + b$. To find b, we substitute the coordinates of the point $(3, 11)$ into the equation and solve for b:

$$y = 1.09x + b$$
$$11 = 1.09(3) + b$$
$$11 = 3.27 + b$$
$$7.73 = b$$

So, the equation is $y = 1.09x + 7.73$. It comes close to the data points, as can be seen in the graph.

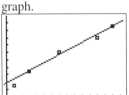

27. a.

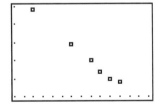

b. Answers may vary depending on the data points selected. We use the points $(8, 68)$ and $(17, 28)$ to find an equation of the form $p = mt + b$. We begin by finding the slope:

$$m = \frac{28 - 68}{17 - 8} = \frac{-40}{9} = -4.44$$

So, the equation of the line is of the form $p = -4.44t + b$. To find b, we substitute the coordinates of the point $(8, 68)$ into the

equation and solve for b:

$$p = -4.44t + b$$
$$68 = -4.44(8) + b$$
$$68 = -35.52 + b$$
$$103.52 = b$$

So, the equation is $f(t) = -4.44t + 103.52$.

c. Answers may vary (depending on the equation found in part (b).) For our linear model, the slope is –4.44. It means that the percentage of Fortune 100 companies that offer pensions is decreasing by 4.44 percentage points per year.

d. Answers may vary (depending on the equation found in part (b)). For our linear model, the p-intercept is (0, 103.52). It means that 103.52% of employers offered pensions in the year 1990. The model has broken down.

e. Answers may vary (depending on the equation found in part (b)). To find the t-intercept, we substitute 0 for p and solve for t.

$$p = -4.44t + 103.52$$
$$0 = -4.44t + 103.52$$
$$4.44t = 103.52$$
$$t \approx 23.3$$

Thus, for our linear model, the t-intercept is (23.3, 0). It means that no company will offer a pension in the year $1990 + 23.3 \approx 2013$. Model breakdown has likely occurred.

f. Answers may vary (depending on the equation found in part (b)). We substitute 100 for p and solve for t:

$$p = -4.44t + 103.52$$
$$100 = -4.44t + 103.52$$
$$-3.52 = -4.44t$$
$$t = 0.793$$

Thus, the model predicts that 100% of companies offered a pension in the year $1990 + 0.79 \approx 1991$. A little research would show that this is false. Model breakdown has occurred.

g. Answers may vary (depending on the equation found in part (b)).

$$t < 0.79 \text{ and } t > 23.3$$

h. Answers may vary (depending on the equation found in part (b)). We find where $p < 12$:
$$-4.44t + 103.52 < 12$$
$$-4.44t + 103.52 - 103.52 < 12 - 103.52$$
$$-4.44t < -91.52$$
$$\frac{-4.44t}{-4.44} > \frac{-91.52}{-4.44}$$
$$t > 20.61$$
Since $1990 + 20.61 \approx 2011$, we predict that less than 12% of all employers will offer pensions after the year 2011.

28. $$3(2x + 1) \leq 4(x + 2) - 1$$
$$6x + 3 \leq 4x + 8 - 1$$
$$6x + 3 \leq 4x + 7$$
$$6x + 3 - 4x \leq 4x + 7 - 4x$$
$$2x + 3 \leq 7$$
$$2x + 3 - 3 \leq 7 - 3$$
$$2x \leq 4$$
$$\frac{2x}{2} \leq \frac{4}{2}$$
$$x \leq 2$$
We graph the solution set, $(-\infty, 2]$.

29. $$\frac{1}{2} < 3 - \frac{5}{2}x \leq 13$$
$$2\left(\frac{1}{2}\right) < 2\left(3 - \frac{5}{2}x\right) \leq 2(13)$$
$$1 < 6 - 5x \leq 26$$
$$1 - 6 < 6 - 5x - 6 \leq 26 - 6$$
$$-5 < -5x \leq 20$$
$$\frac{-5}{-5} > \frac{-5x}{-5} \geq \frac{20}{-5}$$
$$1 > x \geq -4$$

We graph the solution set, $[-4, 1)$.

Chapter 6
Systems of Linear Equations and Systems of Linear Inequalities

Homework 6.1

1. To be a solution to the system, an ordered pair must satisfy both equations in the system.

Check $(2,3)$:

$$y = 4x - 5$$
$$3 \overset{?}{=} 4(2) - 5$$
$$3 \overset{?}{=} 3 \quad \text{true}$$

$$y = -2x + 1$$
$$3 \overset{?}{=} -2(2) + 1$$
$$3 \overset{?}{=} -3 \quad \text{false}$$

Since the ordered pair $(2,3)$ did not satisfy both equations, it is not a solution to the system.

Check $(1,-1)$:

$$y = 4x - 5$$
$$-1 \overset{?}{=} 4(1) - 5$$
$$-1 \overset{?}{=} -1 \quad \text{true}$$

$$y = -2x + 1$$
$$-1 \overset{?}{=} -2(1) + 1$$
$$-1 \overset{?}{=} -1 \quad \text{true}$$

Since the ordered pair $(1,-1)$ satisfies both equations, it is a solution to the system.

Check $(-4,6)$:

$$y = 4x - 5$$
$$6 \overset{?}{=} 4(-4) - 5$$
$$6 \overset{?}{=} -21 \quad \text{false}$$

$$y = -2x + 1$$
$$6 \overset{?}{=} -2(-4) + 1$$
$$6 \overset{?}{=} 9 \quad \text{false}$$

Since the ordered pair $(-4,6)$ did not satisfy both equations, it is not a solution to the system.

3. To be a solution to the system, an ordered pair must satisfy both equations in the system.

Check $(-1,8)$:

$$5x + 2y = 11$$
$$5(-1) + 2(8) \overset{?}{=} 11$$
$$11 \overset{?}{=} 11 \quad \text{true}$$

$$3x - 4y = 17$$
$$3(-1) - 4(8) \overset{?}{=} 17$$
$$-35 \overset{?}{=} 17 \quad \text{false}$$

Since the ordered pair $(-1,8)$ did not satisfy both equations, it is not a solution to the system.

Check $(3,-2)$:

$$5x + 2y = 11$$
$$5(3) + 2(-2) \overset{?}{=} 11$$
$$11 \overset{?}{=} 11 \quad \text{true}$$

$$3x - 4y = 17$$
$$3(3) - 4(-2) \overset{?}{=} 17$$
$$17 \overset{?}{=} 17 \quad \text{true}$$

Since the ordered pair $(3,-2)$ satisfies both equations, it is a solution to the system.

Check $(7,1)$:

$$5x + 2y = 11$$
$$5(7) + 2(1) \overset{?}{=} 11$$
$$37 \overset{?}{=} 11 \quad \text{false}$$

$$3x - 4y = 17$$
$$3(7) - 4(1) \overset{?}{=} 17$$
$$17 \overset{?}{=} 17 \quad \text{true}$$

Since the ordered pair $(7,1)$ did not satisfy both equations, it is not a solution to the system.

5.

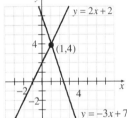

Verify that $(1,4)$ satisfies both equations.

$$y = 2x + 2$$
$$4 = 2(1) + 2$$
$$4 = 2 + 2$$
$$4 = 4 \quad \text{true}$$

$$y = -3x + 7$$
$$4 = -3(1) + 7$$
$$4 = -3 + 7$$
$$4 = 4 \quad \text{true}$$

7.

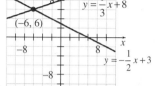

Verify that $(-6,6)$ satisfies both equations.

$$y = -\frac{1}{2}x + 3 \qquad y = \frac{1}{3}x + 8$$

$$6 = -\frac{1}{2}(-6) + 3 \qquad 6 = \frac{1}{3}(-6) + 8$$

$$6 = 3 + 3 \qquad 6 = -2 + 8$$

$$6 = 6 \text{ true} \qquad 6 = 6 \text{ true}$$

9. $y = -3x$

$y = 4x$

To begin, we graph both equations in the same coordinate system.

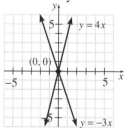

The intersection point is $(0,0)$. So, the solution is the ordered pair $(0,0)$.

Check:

$$y = -3x \qquad\qquad y = 4x$$

$$0 \overset{?}{=} -3(0) \qquad\qquad 0 \overset{?}{=} 4(0)$$

$$0 \overset{?}{=} 0 \text{ true} \qquad\qquad 0 \overset{?}{=} 0 \text{ true}$$

11. Write $y = 3(x-1)$ in slope-intercept form.

$$y = 3(x-1)$$

$$y = 3x - 3$$

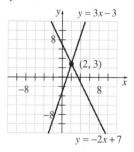

Verify that $(2,3)$ satisfies both equations.

$$y = 3(x-1) \qquad y = -2x + 7$$

$$3 = 3(2-1) \qquad 3 = -2(2) + 7$$

$$3 = 3(1) \qquad 3 = -4 + 7$$

$$3 = 3 \text{ true} \qquad 3 = 3 \text{ true}$$

13. Write $4y - 12 = -8x$ in slope-intercept form.

$$4y - 12 = -8x$$

$$4y = -8x + 12$$

$$y = -2x + 3$$

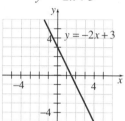

The system is dependent. The solution set is the set of numbers represented by points on the line $y = 2x + 3$.

15. Write both equations in slope-intercept form.

$$4x - 6y = 24 \qquad\qquad 6x - 9y = 18$$

$$-6y = -4x + 24 \qquad\qquad -9y = -6x + 18$$

$$y = \frac{2}{3}x - 4 \qquad\qquad y = \frac{2}{3}x - 2$$

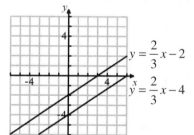

The system is inconsistent. There is no solution. The solution set is the empty set.

17. Write both equations in slope-intercept form.

$$x + 4y = 20 \qquad 2x - 4y = -8$$

$$4y = 20 - x \qquad -4y = -8 - 2x$$

$$y = 5 - \frac{1}{4}x \qquad y = 2 + \frac{1}{2}x$$

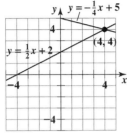

Verify that $(4, 4)$ satisfies both equations.

$$x + 4y = 20 \qquad 2x - 4y = -8$$

$$(4) + 4(4) = 20 \qquad 2(4) - 4(4) = -8$$

$$4 + 16 = 20 \qquad 8 - 16 = -8$$

$$20 = 20 \ \text{ true} \qquad -8 = -8 \ \text{ true}$$

19. $x = 3$

$\ \ \ \ y = -2$

To begin, we graph both equations in the same coordinate system.

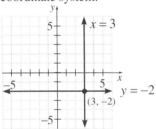

The intersection point is $(3, -2)$. So, the solution

is the ordered pair $(3, -2)$.

Check:

$x = 3 \qquad\qquad y = -2$

$\overset{?}{3 = 3} \ \text{ true} \qquad \overset{?}{-2 = -2} \ \text{ true}$

21. Write $2(2x - y) = 2$ in slope-intercept form.

$$2(2x - y) = 2$$

$$4x - 2y = 2$$

$$-2y = -4x + 2$$

$$y = 2x - 1$$

The equations are identical.

The system is dependent. The solution set

contains all ordered pairs (x, y) such that

$y = 2x - 1$.

23. Write both equations in slope-intercept form.

$$5(y - 2) = 21 - 2(x + 3) \qquad y = 3(x - 1) + 8$$

$$5y - 10 = 21 - 2x - 6 \qquad y = 3x - 3 + 8$$

$$5y = -2x + 25 \qquad\qquad y = 3x + 5$$

$$y = -\frac{2}{5}x + 5$$

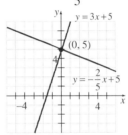

Verify that $(0, 5)$ satisfies both equations.

$$5(y - 2) = 21 - 2(x + 3) \qquad y = 3(x - 1) + 8$$

$$5(5 - 2) = 21 - 2(0 + 3) \qquad 5 = 3(0 - 1) + 8$$

$$5(3) = 21 - 2(3) \qquad\qquad 5 = 3(-1) + 8$$

$$15 = 15 \ \text{ true} \qquad\qquad 5 = 5 \ \text{ true}$$

25. Write both equations in slope-intercept form.

$$\frac{1}{2}x - \frac{1}{2}y = 1 \qquad\qquad \frac{1}{4}x + \frac{1}{2}y = 2$$

$$x - y = 2 \qquad\qquad x + 2y = 8$$

$$-y = -x + 2 \qquad\qquad 2y = -x + 8$$

$$y = x - 2 \qquad\qquad y = -\frac{1}{2}x + 4$$

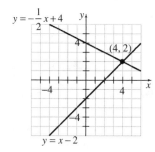

Verify that $(4, 2)$ satisfies both equations.

 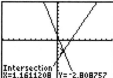

$$\frac{1}{2}x - \frac{1}{2}y = 1 \qquad\qquad \frac{1}{4}x + \frac{1}{2}y = 2$$

$$\frac{1}{2}(4) - \frac{1}{2}(2) = 1 \qquad\qquad \frac{1}{4}(4) + \frac{1}{2}(2) = 2$$

$$2 - 1 = 1 \qquad\qquad 1 + 1 = 2$$

$$1 = 1 \quad \text{true} \qquad\qquad 2 = 2 \quad \text{true}$$

27. We use "intersect" to find the approximate solution $(1.16, -2.81)$.

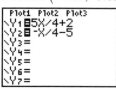 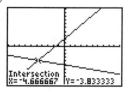

Check:

$$y = 2.18x - 5.34$$

$$-2.81 = 2.18(1.16) - 5.34$$

$$-2.81 \approx -2.8112$$

$$y = -3.53x + 1.29$$

$$-2.81 = -3.53(1.16) + 1.29$$

$$-2.81 \approx -2.8048$$

29. We use "intersect" to find the approximate solution $(-4.67, -3.83)$.

 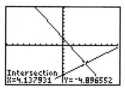

Check:

$$y = \frac{5}{4}x + 2$$

$$-3.83 = \frac{5}{4}(-4.67) + 2$$

$$-3.83 \approx -3.8375$$

$$y = -\frac{1}{4}x - 5$$

$$-3.83 = -\frac{1}{4}(-4.67) - 5$$

$$-3.83 \approx -3.8325$$

31. We first write both equations in slope-intercept form.

$$y = \frac{3}{4}x - 8 \qquad 5x + 3y = 6$$

$$\qquad\qquad 3y = -5x + 6$$

$$\qquad\qquad y = -\frac{5}{3}x + 2$$

We use "intersect" to find the approximate solution $(4.14, -4.90)$.

 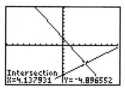

Check:

$$y = \frac{3}{4}x - 8$$

$$-4.90 = \frac{3}{4}(4.14) - 8$$

$$-4.90 \approx -4.895$$

$$5x + 3y = 6$$

$$5(4.14) + 3(-4.90) = 6$$

$$6 = 6$$

33. We first write both equations in slope-intercept form.

$$-2x + 5y = 15 \qquad 6x + 14y = -14$$
$$5y = 2x + 15 \qquad 14y = -6x - 14$$
$$y = \frac{2}{5}x + 3 \qquad y = -\frac{3}{7}x - 1$$

We use "intersect" to find the approximate solution $(-4.83, 1.07)$.

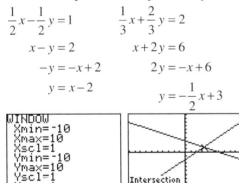

Check:
$$-2x + 5y = 15$$
$$-2(-4.83) + 5(1.07) = 15$$
$$15.01 \approx 15$$

$$6x + 14y = -14$$
$$6(-4.83) + 14(1.07) = -14$$
$$-14 = -14$$

35. Write both equations in slope-intercept form.

$$\frac{1}{2}x - \frac{1}{2}y = 1 \qquad \frac{1}{3}x + \frac{2}{3}y = 2$$
$$x - y = 2 \qquad x + 2y = 6$$
$$-y = -x + 2 \qquad 2y = -x + 6$$
$$y = x - 2 \qquad y = -\frac{1}{2}x + 3$$

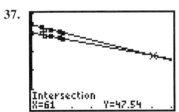

The solution is roughly $(3.33, 1.33)$.

37.

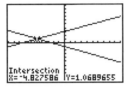

The time at which the percentages will be equal is $t = 61$, or $1990 + 61 = 2051$. The percentage will be 47.54%; not confident.

39. a. Start by plotting the data. Then find the regression lines for the data.

<u>Landline</u>

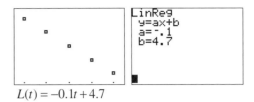

$$L(t) = -0.1t + 4.7$$

<u>Wireless</u>

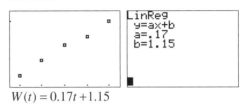

$$W(t) = 0.17t + 1.15$$

b.

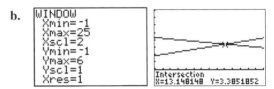

The number of land line 411 calls will be equal to the number of wireless 411 calls during 2013, at about 3.4 billion calls.

c. In 2006, $t = 6$.

$$L(6) = -0.1(6) + 4.7$$
$$= -0.6 + 4.7$$
$$= 4.1$$
$$W(6) = 0.17(6) + 1.15$$
$$= 1.02 + 1.15$$
$$= 2.17$$

The total amount of money collected from landline and wireless 411 calls in 2006 was $4.1(1.25) + 2.17(1.50) = 8.38$, or $8.38 billion.

41. a. The ordered pairs *B* and *D* are on the graph of the line $y = ax + b$, so they are solutions to the equation.

b. The ordered pairs *B* and *C* are on the graph of the line $y = cx + d$, so they are solutions to the equation.

c. The ordered pair *B* is on the graph of both lines, so it satisfies both equations.

d. The points A, E, and F, do not lie on either line, so they are not solutions to either equation.

43. The solution of the system is the ordered pair that corresponds to the intersection point of the graphs. The graphs appear to intersect at approximately $(2.8, -2.4)$, so $(2.8, -2.4)$ is the approximate solution to the system.

45. First estimate the slope of the lines.

Blue:
The line appears to pass through the points $(-2, 5)$ and $(2, 4)$. The slope is

$$m = \frac{4-5}{2-(-2)} = -\frac{1}{4}.$$

Red:
The line appears to pass through the points $(-2, -3)$ and $(2, -2)$. The slope is

$$m = \frac{-2-(-3)}{2-(-2)} = \frac{1}{4}.$$

Next, use the slopes to find additional points on each line.

Blue	Red
$(6, 3)$	$(6, -1)$
$(10, 2)$	$(10, 0)$
$(14, 1)$	$(14, 1)$
$(18, 0)$	$(18, 2)$

Since the point $(14, 1)$ lies on both lines, the ordered pair $(14, 1)$ is the solution to th system.

47. Using the tables of each line, notice that when $x = 3$, both equations are equal to –4. The intersection of these two lines is the point $(3, -4)$.

49. Using the tables of each function notice that f has a slope of –3 and g has a slope of 5. Every time x increases by one, f decreases by 3 and g increases by 5. Using the table you can see that $f(3) = 21$, $f(4) = 18$, $g(3) = 17$ and $g(4) = 22$. This shows that f and g intersect between $x = 3$ and $x = 4$, or approximately at $x = 3.5$. Since the slope of f is –3, the y-value should be $21 - 3(0.5) = 19.5$. The solution is approximately $(3.5, 19.5)$.

51. $f(-4) = 0$.

53. $f(x) = 3$ when $x = 5$.

55. $f(x) = g(x)$ when $x = -1$.

57. Graph the equations.
$$y = x + 3$$
$$y = -2x + 9$$
$$y = 3x - 1$$

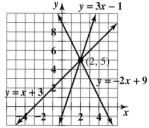

The solution of the system is $(2, 5)$.

59. a. Answers may vary. Possible answers:

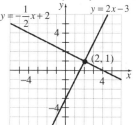

b.

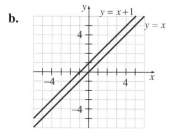

c. $y = \frac{3}{2}x$

$$y = \frac{1}{2}(3x + 2) - 1$$

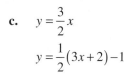

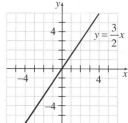

61. a. Since the system of linear equations has more than one solution, the system must be dependent. The equation of the line that contains the two given points is

$y = -\dfrac{1}{3}x + \dfrac{7}{3}$. A third solution would be any

other point that lies on the graph of this

equation. One possible answer is $\left(0, \dfrac{7}{3}\right)$.

b. There are an infinite number of solutions.

63. Written response. Answers may vary. The graph of a linear equation is a visual representation of all the ordered pairs that satisfy the equation. Therefore, any intersection of two graphs shows an ordered pair that satisfies both equations, and is therefore a solution to the system of equations.

65. a. The lines have the same slope, but different *y*-intercepts. Therefore, the lines are parallel.

b. Parallel lines do not cross so they do not have an intersection point.

c. Since the lines have the same slope, but different *y*-intercepts, the lines do not have an intersection point. The solution is the empty set.

67. The graph shows that $y = \dfrac{1}{3}x + \dfrac{5}{3}$ and $y = x - 1$

intersect at the point (4, 3). So the solution of the given equation is $x = 4$.

69. The graph shows that $y = \dfrac{1}{3}x + \dfrac{5}{2}$ and $y = 2$

intersect at the point (1, 2). So the solution to the given equation is $x = 1$.

71. The graph shows that $y = \dfrac{1}{3}x + \dfrac{5}{3}$ and

$y = -3x - 5$ intersect at the point (–2, 1). So the solution to the given system of equations is (–2, 1).

73. $y = 2x + 5$

$y = -3x - 5$

To begin, we graph both equations in the same coordinate system.

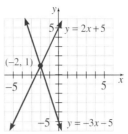

The intersection point is $(-2, 1)$. So, the solution is the ordered pair $(-2, 1)$.

Description: *system of two linear equations in two variables*

75. $2x + 5 = -3x - 5$

$\qquad 2x = -3x - 10$

$\qquad 5x = -10$

$\qquad\ \ x = -2$

The solution is -2.

Description: *linear equation in one variable*

Homework 6.2

1. $y = 2x$

$3x + y = 10$

Substitute $2x$ for *y* in the second equation and solve for *x*.

$3x + (2x) = 10$

$\qquad 5x = 10$

$\qquad\ \ x = 2$

Substitute 2 for *x* in the equation $y = 2x$ and solve for *y*.

$y = 2(2) = 4$

The solution is $(2, 4)$.

3. $x - 4y = -3$

$x = 2y - 1$

Substitute $2y - 1$ for x in the first equation and solve for y.

$(2y - 1) - 4y = -3$

$2y - 1 - 4y = -3$

$-2y - 1 = -3$

$-2y = -2$

$y = 1$

Substitute 1 for y in the equation $x = 2y - 1$ and solve for x.

$x = 2(1) - 1 = 2 - 1 = 1$

The solution is $(1, 1)$.

5. $2x + 3y = 5$

$y = x + 5$

Substitute $x + 5$ for y in the first equation and solve for x.

$2x + 3(x + 5) = 5$

$2x + 3x + 15 = 5$

$5x + 15 = 5$

$5x = -10$

$x = -2$

Substitute -2 for x in the equation $y = x + 5$ and solve for y.

$y = (-2) + 5 = 3$

The solution is $(-2, 3)$.

7. $-5x - 2y = 17$

$x = 4y + 1$

Substitute $4y + 1$ for x in the first equation and solve for y.

$-5(4y + 1) - 2y = 17$

$-20y - 5 - 2y = 17$

$-22y - 5 = 17$

$-22y = 22$

$y = -1$

Substitute -1 for y in the equation $x = 4y + 1$ and solve for x.

$x = 4(-1) + 1 = -4 + 1 = -3$

The solution is $(-3, -1)$.

9. $2x - 5y - 3 = 0$

$y = 2x - 7$

Substitute $2x - 7$ for y in the first equation and solve for x.

$2x - 5(2x - 7) - 3 = 0$

$2x - 10x + 35 - 3 = 0$

$-8x + 32 = 0$

$-8x = -32$

$x = 4$

Substitute 4 for x in the equation $y = 2x - 7$ and solve for y.

$y = 2(4) - 7 = 8 - 7 = 1$

The solution is $(4, 1)$.

11. $x = 2y + 6$

$-4x + 5y + 12 = 0$

Substitute $2y + 6$ for x in the second equation and solve for y.

$-4(2y + 6) + 5y + 12 = 0$

$-8y - 24 + 5y + 12 = 0$

$-3y - 12 = 0$

$-3y = 12$

$y = -4$

Substitute -4 for y in the equation $x = 2y + 6$ and solve for x.

$x = 2(-4) + 6 = -8 + 6 = -2$

The solution is $(-2, -4)$.

13. Substitute $\frac{1}{2}x - 5$ for y in $2x + 3y = -1$.

$2x + 3\left(\frac{1}{2}x - 5\right) = -1$

$2x + \frac{3}{2}x - 15 = -1$

$\frac{7}{2}x = 14$

$x = 4$

Let $x = 4$ in $y = \frac{1}{2}x - 5$.

$y = \frac{1}{2}(4) - 5$

$= 2 - 5$

$= -3$

The solution is $(4, -3)$.

15. $y = -2x - 1$

$y = 3x + 9$

Substitute $3x + 9$ for y in the first equation and solve for x.

$3x + 9 = -2x - 1$

$5x + 9 = -1$

$5x = -10$

$x = -2$

Substitute -2 for x in the equation $y = 3x + 9$ and solve for y.

$y = 3(-2) + 9 = -6 + 9 = 3$

The solution is $(-2, 3)$.

17. $y = 2x$

$y = 3x$

Substitute $3x$ for y in the first equation and solve for x.

$3x = 2x$

$3x - 2x = 2x - 2x$

$x = 0$

Substitute 0 for x in the equation $y = 3x$ and solve for y.

$y = 3(0) = 0$

The solution is $(0, 0)$.

19. $y = 2(x - 4)$

$y = -3(x + 1)$

Substitute $-3(x + 1)$ for y in the first equation and solve for x.

$-3(x + 1) = 2(x - 4)$

$-3x - 3 = 2x - 8$

$-5x - 3 = -8$

$-5x = -5$

$x = 1$

Substitute 1 for x in the equation $y = -3(x + 1)$ and solve for y.

$y = -3(1 + 1) = -3(2) = -6$

The solution $(1, -6)$.

21. $y = 2.57x + 7.09$

$y = -3.61x - 5.72$

Substitute $-3.61x - 5.72$ for y in the first equation and solve for x.

$-3.61x - 5.72 = 2.57x + 7.09$

$-6.18x - 5.72 = 7.09$

$-6.18x = 12.81$

$x = \dfrac{12.81}{-6.18} \approx -2.073$

Substitute -2.073 for x in the equation $y = -3.61x - 5.72$ and solve for y.

$y = -3.61(-2.073) - 5.72 \approx 1.764$

The approximate solution is $(-2.07, 1.76)$.

23. $y = -3.17x + 8.92$

$y = 1.65x - 7.24$

Substitute $1.65x - 7.24$ for y in the first equation and solve for x.

$1.65x - 7.24 = -3.17x + 8.92$

$4.82x - 7.24 = 8.92$

$4.82x = 16.16$

$x = \dfrac{16.16}{4.82} \approx 3.353$

Substitute 3.353 for x in the equation $y = 1.65x - 7.24$ and solve for y.

$y = 1.65(3.353) - 7.24 \approx -1.708$

The approximate solution is $(3.35, -1.71)$.

25. $2x + y = -9$

$5x - 3y = 5$

Solve the first equation for y.

$2x + y = -9$

$y = -2x - 9$

Substitute $-2x - 9$ for y in the second equation and solve for x.

$5x - 3(-2x - 9) = 5$

$5x + 6x + 27 = 5$

$11x + 27 = 5$

$11x = -22$

$x = -2$

Substitute -2 for x in the equation $y = -2x - 9$ and solve for y.

$y = -2(-2) - 9 = 4 - 9 = -5$

The solution is $(-2, -5)$.

27. $4x - 7y = 15$

$x - 3y = 5$

Solve the second equation for x.

$x - 3y = 5$

$\quad x = 3y + 5$

Substitute $3y + 5$ for x in the first equation and solve for y.

$4(3y + 5) - 7y = 15$

$12y + 20 - 7y = 15$

$\quad 5y + 20 = 15$

$\quad\quad 5y = -5$

$\quad\quad\quad y = -1$

Substitute -1 for y in the equation $x = 3y + 5$ and solve for x.

$x = 3(-1) + 5 = -3 + 5 = 2$

The solution is $(2, -1)$.

29. $4x + 3y = 5$

$x - 2y = -7$

Solve the second equation for x.

$x - 2y = -7$

$\quad x = 2y - 7$

Substitute $2y - 7$ for x in the first equation and solve for y.

$4(2y - 7) + 3y = 5$

$8y - 28 + 3y = 5$

$\quad 11y - 28 = 5$

$\quad\quad 11y = 33$

$\quad\quad\quad y = 3$

Substitute 3 for y in the equation $x = 2y - 7$ and solve for x.

$x = 2(3) - 7 = 6 - 7 = -1$

The solution is $(-1, 3)$.

31. $2x - y = 1$

$5x - 3y = 5$

Solve the first equation for y.

$2x - y = 1$

$\quad -y = -2x + 1$

$\quad\quad y = 2x - 1$

Substitute $2x - 1$ for y in the second equation and solve for x.

$5x - 3(2x - 1) = 5$

$5x - 6x + 3 = 5$

$\quad -x + 3 = 5$

$\quad\quad -x = 2$

$\quad\quad\quad x = -2$

Substitute -2 for x in the equation $y = 2x - 1$ and solve for y.

$y = 2(-2) - 1 = -4 - 1 = -5$

The solution is $(-2, -5)$.

33. $3x + 2y = -3$

$\quad 2x = y + 5$

Solve the second equation for y.

$\quad 2x = y + 5$

$2x - 5 = y$

Substitute $2x - 5$ for y in the first equation and solve for x.

$3x + 2(2x - 5) = -3$

$3x + 4x - 10 = -3$

$\quad 7x - 10 = -3$

$\quad\quad 7x = 7$

$\quad\quad\quad x = 1$

Substitute 1 for x in the equation $y = 2x - 5$ and solve for y.

$y = 2(1) - 5 = 2 - 5 = -3$

The solution is $(1, -3)$.

35. $\quad x = 4 - 3y$

$2x + 6y = 8$

Substitute $4 - 3y$ for x in the second equation and solve for y.

$2(4 - 3y) + 6y = 8$

$\quad 8 - 6y + 6y = 8$

$\quad\quad\quad 8 = 8 \quad$ true

The result is a true statement, so the system is dependent. The solution is the infinite set of ordered pairs that satisfy the equation $x = 4 - 3y$.

37. $5x - 2y = 18$

$\qquad y = -3x + 2$

Substitute $-3x + 2$ for y in the first equation and solve for x.

$5x - 2(-3x + 2) = 18$

$\qquad 5x + 6x - 4 = 18$

$\qquad\quad 11x - 4 = 18$

$\qquad\qquad 11x = 22$

$\qquad\qquad\quad x = 2$

Substitute 2 for x in the equation $y = -3x + 2$ and solve for y.

$y = -3(2) + 2 = -6 + 2 = -4$

The solution is $(2, -4)$.

39. $\qquad y = -5x + 3$

$15x + 3y = 6$

Substitute $-5x + 3$ for y in the second equation and solve for x.

$15x + 3(-5x + 3) = 6$

$\qquad 15x - 15x + 9 = 6$

$\qquad\qquad\qquad 9 = 6$ false

The result is a false statement, so the system is inconsistent. The solution is the empty set, $\varnothing$.

41. $-4x + 12y = 4$

$\qquad\quad x = 3y - 1$

Substitute $3y - 1$ for x in the first equation and solve for y.

$-4(3y - 1) + 12y = 4$

$\quad -12y + 4 + 12y = 4$

$\qquad\qquad\qquad 4 = 4$ true

The result is a true statement, so the system is dependent. The solution is the infinite set of ordered pairs that satisfy the equation $x = 3y - 1$.

43. $\qquad y = 3x + 2$

$12x - 4y = 9$

Substitue $3x + 2$ for y in the second equation and solve for x.

$12x - 4(3x + 2) = 9$

$\quad 12x - 12x - 8 = 9$

$\qquad\qquad\quad -8 = 9$ false

The result is a false statement, so the system is inconsistent. The solution is the empty set, $\varnothing$.

45. a. Solve the first equation for x.

$x + y = 3$

$\quad x = -y + 3$

Substitute $-y + 3$ for x in the second equation and solve for y.

$3(-y + 3) + 2y = 7$

$\quad -3y + 9 + 2y = 7$

$\qquad\quad -y + 9 = 7$

$\qquad\qquad -y = -2$

$\qquad\qquad\quad y = 2$

Substitute 2 for y in the equation $x = -y + 3$ and solve for x.

$x = -(2) + 3 = -2 + 3 = 1$

The solution is $(1, 2)$.

b. Solve the first equation for y.

$x + y = 3$

$\quad y = -x + 3$

Substitute $-x + 3$ for y in the second equation and solve for x.

$3x + 2(-x + 3) = 7$

$\quad 3x - 2x + 6 = 7$

$\qquad\quad x + 6 = 7$

$\qquad\qquad x = 1$

Substitute 1 for x in the equation $y = -x + 3$ and solve for y.

$y = -(1) + 3 = -1 + 3 = 2$

The solution is $(1, 2)$.

c. The results are the same. The solution to the system is $(1, 2)$.

47. The function *f* has a slope of 4 and an *f*-intercept of $(0,3)$. Therefore, $f(x) = 4x+3$. The function *g* has a slope of -6 and a *g*-intercept of $(0,50)$. Therefore, $g(x) = -6x+50$. Write the system that describes the functions *f* and *g*.

$y = 4x+3$

$y = -6x+50$

Solve using substitution.

Substitute $4x+3$ for *y* in $y = -6x+50$ and solve for *x*.

$4x+3 = -6x+50$

$10x = 47$

$x = 4.7$

Substitute $x = 4.7$ into $y = 4x+3$ and solve for *y*.

$y = 4(4.7)+3$

$= 18.8+3$

$= 21.8$

The solution is $(4.7, 21.8)$.

49. The student is not correct. A system is inconsistent (i.e. the solution set is the empty set) when the lines are parallel. Parallel lines must have the same slope. The slopes are different yet they are close enough that the lines look parallel around the origin. To find the correct solution, substitute $2x+3$ for *y* in $y = 2.01x+1$ and solve for *x*.

$2x+3 = 2.01x+1$

$-0.01x = -2$

$x = 200$

Substitute $x = 200$ into $y = 2x+3$ and solve for *y*.

$y = 2(200)+3$

$= 403$

The solution is $(200, 403)$.

51. *A*: This point is the origin so it has coordinates $(0,0)$.

B: This point is the *y*-intercept for line l_1. Let $x = 0$ in the equation and solve for *y*.

$y = -(0)+8 = 0+8 = 8$

The coordinates of the point are $(0,8)$.

C: This point is the intersection of the two lines. Therefore, it is the solution of the system

$y = -x+8$

$y = 2x-7$

Substitute $2x-7$ for *y* in the first equation and solve *x*.

$2x-7 = -x+8$

$3x-7 = 8$

$3x = 15$

$x = 5$

Substitute 5 for *x* in the equation $y = 2x-7$ and solve for *y*.

$y = 2(5)-7 = 10-7 = 3$

The coordinates of the point are $(5,3)$.

D: This point is the *x*-intercept of line l_2. Let $y = 0$ in the equation and solve for *x*.

$0 = 2x-7$

$7 = 2x$

$\dfrac{7}{2} = x$

The coordinates of the point are $\left(\dfrac{7}{2}, 0\right)$.

53. Answers may vary.

55. a. $y = 2x-3$

$y = -3x+7$

 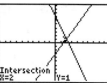

The intersection point is $(2,1)$, so the ordered pair $(2,1)$ is the solution to the system.

b. Substitute $-3x + 7$ for y in the first equation and solve for x.

$-3x + 7 = 2x - 3$

$-5x + 7 = -3$

$-5x = -10$

$x = 2$

Substitute 2 for x in the equation $y = -3x + 7$ and solve for y.

$y = -3(2) + 7 = -6 + 7 = 1$

The solution is $(2, 1)$.

c. $2x - 3 = -3x + 7$

$5x - 3 = 7$

$5x = 10$

$x = 2$

The solution is 2.

d. The solution to part (c) is the same as the x-coordinate of the solution in part (b).

e. Set each side of the equation equal to y to create a system of equations.

$y = x - 1$

$y = -2x + 8$

Use "intersect" to find the intersection point of the two lines.

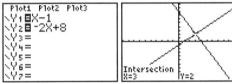

The intersection point is $(3, 2)$, so the x-coordinate is 3. The solution of the equation $x - 1 = -2x + 8$ is 3.

$x - 1 = -2x + 8$

$3x - 1 = 8$

$3x = 9$

$x = 3$

The solution is 3.

The answers are the same.

f. Answers may vary.

57.

The solution to the equation is approximately $x \approx 1.57$.

59.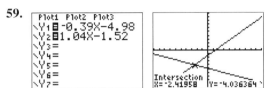

The solution to the equation is approximately $x \approx -2.42$.

61.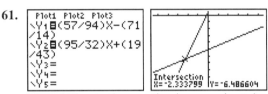

The solution to the equation is approximately $x \approx -2.33$.

63. The equation $f(x) = -3x + 5$ is in slope-intercept form, so the slope is $m = -3$ and the y-intercept is $(0, 5)$. We first plot $(0, 5)$. From this point we move 1 unit to the right and 3 units down, plotting the point $(1, 2)$. We then draw the line that connects the two points, extending in both directions.

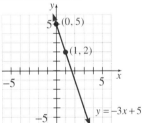

Description: *linear equation in two variables*

65. $9x + 2y = 1$

$\qquad y = -3x + 5$

Substitute $-3x + 5$ for y in the first equation and solve for x.

$9x + 2(-3x + 5) = 1$

$\qquad 9x - 6x + 10 = 1$

$\qquad\qquad 3x + 10 = 1$

$\qquad\qquad\qquad 3x = -9$

$\qquad\qquad\qquad\ x = -3$

Substitute -3 for x in the equation $y = -3x + 5$ and solve for y.

$y = -3(-3) + 5 = 9 + 5 = 14$

The solution is $(-3, 14)$. Description: *system of two linear equations in two variables*

Homework 6.3

1. $2x + 3y = 7 \quad$ Equation (1)

$-2x + 5y = 1 \quad$ Equation (2)

The coefficients of the x terms are equal in absolute value and opposite in sign. Add the left sides and the right sides of the equations and solve for y.

$\quad 2x + 3y = 7$

$\underline{-2x + 5y = 1}$

$\qquad\quad 8y = 8$

$\qquad\qquad y = 1$

Substitute 1 for y in equation (1) and solve for x.

$2x + 3(1) = 7$

$\quad 2x + 3 = 7$

$\qquad 2x = 4$

$\qquad\ x = 2$

The solution is $(2, 1)$.

3. $5x - 2y = 2 \quad$ Equation (1)

$-3x + 2y = 2 \quad$ Equation (2)

The coefficients of the y terms are equal in absolute value and opposite in sign. Add the left sides and the right sides of the equations and solve for x.

$\quad 5x - 2y = 2$

$\underline{-3x + 2y = 2}$

$\qquad\ 2x = 4$

$\qquad\ \ x = 2$

Substitute 2 for x in equation (2) and solve for y.

$-3(2) + 2y = 2$

$\quad -6 + 2y = 2$

$\qquad\quad 2y = 8$

$\qquad\qquad y = 4$

The solution is $(2, 4)$.

5. $x + 2y = -4 \quad$ Equation (1)

$3x - 4y = 18 \quad$ Equation (2)

To eliminate the y terms, we multiply both sides of equation (1) by 2, yielding the system

$2x + 4y = -8$

$3x - 4y = 18$

The coefficients of the y terms are equal in absolute value and opposite in sign. Add the left sides and the right sides of the equations and solve for x.

$\quad 2x + 4y = -8$

$\underline{\ 3x - 4y = 18}$

$\qquad\ 5x = 10$

$\qquad\ \ x = 2$

Substitute 2 for x in equation (1) and solve for y.

$(2) + 2y = -4$

$\qquad 2y = -6$

$\qquad\ y = -3$

The solution is $(2, -3)$.

7. $2x - 3y = 8$ Equation (1)

$5x + 6y = -7$ Equation (2)

To eliminate the y terms, we multiply both sides of equation (1) by 2, yielding the system

$4x - 6y = 16$

$5x + 6y = -7$

The coefficients of the y terms are equal in absolute value and opposite in sign. Add the left sides and the right sides of the equations and solve for x.

$4x - 6y = 16$

$\underline{5x + 6y = -7}$

$9x = 9$

$x = 1$

Substitute 1 for x in equation (2) and solve for y.

$5(1) + 6y = -7$

$5 + 6y = -7$

$6y = -12$

$y = -2$

The solution is $(1, -2)$.

9. $6x - 5y = 4$ Equation (1)

$2x + 3y = -8$ Equation (2)

To eliminate the x terms, we multiply both sides of equation (2) by -3, yielding the system

$6x - 5y = 4$

$-6x - 9y = 24$

The coefficients of the x terms are equal in absolute value and opposite in sign. Add the left sides and the right sides of the equations and solve for y.

$6x - 5y = 4$

$\underline{-6x - 9y = 24}$

$-14y = 28$

$y = -2$

Substitute -2 for y in equation (2) and solve for x.

$2x + 3(-2) = -8$

$2x - 6 = -8$

$2x = -2$

$x = -1$

The solution is $(-1, -2)$.

11. $5x + 7y = -16$ Equation (1)

$2x - 5y = 17$ Equation (2)

To eliminate the y terms, we multiply both sides of equation (1) by 5 and both sides of equation (2) by 7, yielding the system

$25x + 35y = -80$

$14x - 35y = 119$

The coefficients of the y terms are equal in absolute value and opposite in sign. Add the left sides and the right sides of the equations and solve for x.

$25x + 35y = -80$

$\underline{14x - 35y = 119}$

$39x = 39$

$x = 1$

Substitute 1 for x in equation (2) and solve for y.

$2(1) - 5y = 17$

$2 - 5y = 17$

$-5y = 15$

$y = -3$

The solution is $(1, -3)$.

13. $-8x + 3y = 1$ Equation (1)

$3x - 4y = 14$ Equation (2)

To eliminate the y terms, we multiply both sides of equation (1) by 4 and both sides of equation (2) by 3, yielding the system

$-32x + 12y = 4$

$9x - 12y = 42$

The coefficients of the y terms are equal in absolute value and opposite in sign. Add the left sides and the right sides of the equations and solve for x.

$-32x + 12y = 4$

$\underline{9x - 12y = 42}$

$-23x = 46$

$x = -2$

Substitute -2 for x in equation (1) and solve for y.

$-8(-2) + 3y = 1$

$16 + 3y = 1$

$3y = -15$

$y = -5$

The solution is $(-2, -5)$.

15. $y = 3x - 6 \rightarrow 3x - y = 6$ Equation (1)

$y = -4x + 1 \quad 4x + y = 1$ Equation (2)

The coefficients of the y terms are equal in absolute value and opposite in sign. Add the left sides and the right sides of the equations and solve for x.

$$3x - y = 6$$
$$\underline{4x + y = 1}$$
$$7x = 7$$
$$x = 1$$

Substitute 1 for x in equation (1) and solve for y.

$$y = 3(1) - 6$$
$$= 3 - 6$$
$$= -3$$

The solution is $(1, -3)$.

17. $3x + 6y - 18 = 0 \rightarrow 3x + 6y = 18$ Equation (1)

$17 = 7x + 9y \quad 7x + 9y = 17$ Equation (2)

To eliminate the y terms, we multiply both sides of equation (1) by 3 and both sides of equation (2) by -2, yielding the system

$$9x + 18y = 54$$
$$-14x - 18y = -34$$

The coefficients of the y terms are equal in absolute value and opposite in sign. Add the left sides and the right sides of the equations and solve for x.

$$9x + 18y = 54$$
$$\underline{-14x - 18y = -34}$$
$$-5x = 20$$
$$x = -4$$

Substitute -4 for x in equation (1) and solve for y.

$$3(-4) + 6y - 18 = 0$$
$$-12 + 6y - 18 = 0$$
$$6y - 30 = 0$$
$$6y = 30$$
$$y = 5$$

The solution is $(-4, 5)$

19. Multiply the second equation by 2 and add the equations.

$$0.9x + 0.4y = 1.9$$
$$\underline{0.6x - 0.4y = 2.6}$$
$$1.5x = 4.5$$
$$x = 3$$

Substitute $x = 3$ into $0.9x + 0.4y = 1.9$ and solve for y.

$$0.9(3) + 0.4y = 1.9$$
$$2.7 + 0.4y = 1.9$$
$$0.4y = -0.8$$
$$y = -2$$

The solution is $(3, -2)$.

21. Use the distributive property to simplify both equations.

$$3(2x - 1) + 4(y - 3) = 1$$
$$6x - 3 + 4y - 12 = 1$$
$$6x + 4y = 16$$

$$4(x + 5) - 2(4y + 1) = 18$$
$$4x + 20 - 8y - 2 = 18$$
$$4x - 8y = 0$$

The system can be rewritten as

$$6x + 4y = 16$$
$$4x - 8y = 0$$

Multiply the first equation by 2, and then add the equations.

$$12x + 8y = 32$$
$$\underline{4x - 8y = 0}$$
$$16x = 32$$
$$x = 2$$

Substitute $x = 2$ into $4x - 8y = 0$ and solve for y.

$$4(2) - 8y = 0$$
$$8 - 8y = 0$$
$$-8y = -8$$
$$y = 1$$

The solution is $(2, 1)$.

23. Multiply the first equation by 3 and the second equation by -4, then add the equations.

$$2x + \frac{3}{2}y = \frac{1}{2}$$
$$-2x - 5y = -11$$
$$\overline{\qquad -\frac{7}{2}y = -\frac{21}{2}}$$
$$y = 3$$

Substitute $y = 3$ into $\frac{2}{3}x + \frac{1}{2}y = \frac{1}{6}$ and solve for x.

$$\frac{2}{3}x + \frac{1}{2}(3) = \frac{1}{6}$$
$$\frac{2}{3}x + \frac{3}{2} = \frac{1}{6}$$
$$\frac{2}{3}x = -\frac{4}{3}$$
$$x = -2$$

The solution is $(-2, 3)$.

25. $\frac{2}{9}x + \frac{1}{3}y = 4 \quad \rightarrow 2x + 3y = 36$ Equation (1)

$\frac{1}{2}x - \frac{2}{5}y = -\frac{5}{2} \quad \rightarrow 5x - 4y = -25$ Equation (2)

To eliminate the y terms, we multiply both sides of equation (1) by 4 and both sides of equation (2) by 3, yielding the system

$$8x + 12y = 144$$
$$15x - 12y = -75$$

The coefficients of the y terms are equal in absolute value and opposite in sign. Add the left sides and the right sides of the equations and solve for x.

$$8x + 12y = 144$$
$$\underline{15x - 12y = -75}$$
$$23x = 69$$
$$x = 3$$

Substitute 3 for x in equation (1) and solve for y.

$$2(3) + 3y = 36$$
$$6 + 3y = 36$$
$$3y = 30$$
$$y = 10$$

The solution is $(3, 10)$.

27. $4x - 7y = 3$ Equation (1)

$8x - 14y = 6$ Equation (2)

To eliminate the x terms, we multiply both sides of equation (1) by -2, yielding the system

$$-8x + 14y = -6$$
$$8x - 14y = 6$$

The coefficients of the x terms are equal in absolute value and opposite in sign. Add the left sides and the right sides of the equations and solve for y.

$$-8x + 14y = -6$$
$$\underline{8x - 14y = 6}$$
$$0 = 0 \quad \text{true}$$

The result is a true statement of the form $a = a$. Therefore, the system is dependent. The solution set is the infinite set of ordered pairs that satisfy the equation $4x - 7y = 3$.

29. $8x - 6y = 4$ Equation (1)

$12x - 9y = 5$ Equation (2)

To eliminate the x terms, we multiply both sides of equation (1) by 3 and both sides of equation (2) by -2, yielding the system

$$24x - 18y = 12$$
$$-24x + 18y = -10$$

The coefficients of the x terms are equal in absolute value and opposite in sign. Add the left sides and the right sides of the equations and solve for y.

$$24x - 18y = 12$$
$$\underline{-24x + 18y = -10}$$
$$0 = 2 \quad \text{false}$$

The result is a false statement. Therefore, the system is inconsistent. The solution set is the empty set, $\varnothing$.

31. $3x - 2y = -14$ Equation (1)

$6x + 5y = -19$ Equation (2)

To eliminate the x terms, we multiply both sides of equation (1) by -2, yielding the system

$-6x + 4y = 28$

$6x + 5y = -19$

The coefficients of the x terms are equal in absolute value and opposite in sign. Add the left sides and the right sides of the equations and solve for y.

$-6x + 4y = 28$

$\underline{6x + 5y = -19}$

$9y = 9$

$y = 1$

Substitute 1 for y in equation (1) and solve for x.

$3x - 2(1) = -14$

$3x - 2 = -14$

$3x = -12$

$x = -4$

The solution is $(-4, 1)$.

33. $6x - 15y = 7$

$-4x + 10y = -5$

To eliminate the x terms, we multiply both sides of equation (1) by 2 and both sides of equation (2) by 3, yielding the system

$12x - 30y = 14$

$-12x + 30y = -15$

The coefficients of the x terms are equal in absolute value and opposite in sign. Add the left sides and the right sides of the equations and solve for y.

$12x - 30y = 14$

$\underline{-12x + 30y = -15}$

$0 = -1$ false

The result is a false statement. Therefore, the system is inconsistent. The solution set is the empty set, $\varnothing$.

35. $3x - 9y = 12$

$-4x + 12y = -16$

To eliminate the x terms, we multiply both sides of equation (1) by 4 and both sides of equation (2) by 3, yielding the system

$12x - 36y = 48$

$-12x + 36y = -48$

The coefficients of the x terms are equal in absolute value and opposite in sign. Add the left

sides and the right sides of the equations and solve for y.

$12x - 36y = 48$

$\underline{-12x + 36y = -48}$

$0 = 0$ true

The result is a true statement of the form $a = a$. Therefore, the system is dependent. The solution set is the infinite set of ordered pairs that satisfy the equation $3x - 9y = 12$.

37. $y = 4.29x - 8.91$ Equation (1)

$y = -1.26x + 9.75$ Equation (2)

$\rightarrow \ 4.29x - y = 8.91$

$1.26x + y = 9.75$

The coefficients of the y terms are equal in absolute value and opposite in sign. Add the left sides and the right sides of the equations and solve for x.

$4.29x - y = 8.91$

$\underline{1.26x + y = 9.75}$

$5.55x = 18.66$

$x = \dfrac{18.66}{5.55} \approx 3.362$

Substitute 3.362 for x in equation (1) and solve for y.

$y = 4.29(3.362) - 8.91 \approx 5.513$

The approximate solution is $(3.36, 5.51)$.

39. $y = -2.15x + 8.38$ Equation (1)

$y = 1.67x + 2.57$ Equation (2)

$\rightarrow \ 2.15x + y = 8.38$

$1.67x - y = -2.57$

The coefficients of the y terms are equal in absolute value and opposite in sign. Add the left sides and the right sides of the equations and solve for x.

$2.15x + y = 8.38$

$\underline{1.67x - y = -2.57}$

$3.82x = 5.81$

$x = \dfrac{5.81}{3.82} \approx 1.521$

Substitute 1.521 for x in equation (1) and solve for y.

$y = -2.15(1.521) + 8.38 \approx 5.110$

The approximate solution is $(1.52, 5.11)$.

41. $4x - y = -12$ Equation (1)

$3x + 5y = 14$ Equation (2)

To eliminate the y terms, we multiply both sides of equation (1) by 5, yielding the system

$20x - 5y = -60$

$3x + 5y = 14$

The coefficients of the y terms are equal in absolute value and opposite in sign. Add the left sides and the right sides of the equations and solve for x.

$20x - 5y = -60$

$\underline{3x + 5y = 14}$

$23x = -46$

$x = -2$

Substitute -2 for x in equation (1) and solve for y.

$4(-2) - y = -12$

$-8 - y = -12$

$-y = -4$

$y = 4$

The solution is $(-2, 4)$.

43. $-2x + 7y = -3$

$x = 3y + 2$

Substitute $3y + 2$ for x in the first equation and solve for y.

$-2(3y + 2) + 7y = -3$

$-6y - 4 + 7y = -3$

$y - 4 = -3$

$y = 1$

Substitute 1 for y in the equation $x = 3y + 2$ and solve for x.

$x = 3(1) + 2 = 3 + 2 = 5$

The solution is $(5, 1)$.

45. $2x + 7y = 13$ Equation (1)

$3x - 4y = -24$ Equation (2)

To eliminate the x terms, we multiply both sides of equation (1) by 3 and both sides of equation (2) by -2, yielding the system

$6x + 21y = 39$

$-6x + 8y = 48$

The coefficients of the x terms are equal in absolute value and opposite in sign. Add the left sides and the right sides of the equations and solve for y.

$6x + 21y = 39$

$\underline{-6x + 8y = 48}$

$29y = 87$

$y = 3$

Substitute 3 for y in equation (1) and solve for x.

$2x + 7(3) = 13$

$2x + 21 = 13$

$2x = -8$

$x = -4$

The solution is $(-4, 3)$.

47. $2x - 7y = -1$ Equation (1)

$-x - 3y = 7$ Equation (2)

To eliminate the x terms, we multiply both sides of equation (2) by 2, yielding the system

$2x - 7y = -1$

$-2x - 6y = 14$

The coefficients of the x terms are equal in absolute value and opposite in sign. Add the left sides and the right sides of the equations and solve for y.

$2x - 7y = -1$

$\underline{-2x - 6y = 14}$

$-13y = 13$

$y = -1$

Substitute -1 for y in equation (1) and solve for x.

$2x - 7(-1) = -1$

$2x + 7 = -1$

$2x = -8$

$x = -4$

The solution is $(-4, -1)$.

49. $y = -2x - 3$

$y = 3x + 7$

Substitute $3x + 7$ for y in the first equation and solve for x.

$3x + 7 = -2x - 3$

$5x + 7 = -3$

$5x = -10$

$x = -2$

Substitute -2 for x in the equation $y = 3x + 7$ and solve for y.

$y = 3(-2) + 7 = -6 + 7 = 1$

The solution is $(-2, 1)$.

51. $8x + 5y = 7$ Equation (1)

$\qquad 7y = -6x + 15$ Equation (2)

$\rightarrow 8x + 5y = 7$

$\qquad 6x + 7y = 15$

To eliminate the x terms, we multiply both sides of equation (1) by 3 and both sides of equation (2) by -4, yielding the system

$24x + 15y = 21$

$-24x - 28y = -60$

The coefficients of the x terms are equal in absolute value and opposite in sign. Add the left sides and the right sides of the equations and solve for y.

$24x + 15y = 21$

$\underline{-24x - 28y = -60}$

$\qquad -13y = -39$

$\qquad y = 3$

Substitute 3 for y in equation (1) and solve for x.

$8x + 5(3) = 7$

$8x + 15 = 7$

$8x = -8$

$x = -1$

The solution is $(-1, 3)$.

53. $3(2x - 5) + 4y = 11$

$5x - 2(3y + 1) = 1$

Begin by writing each equation in standard form.

$3(2x - 5) + 4y = 11 \qquad 5x - 2(3y + 1) = 1$

$6x - 15 + 4y = 11 \qquad 5x - 6y - 2 = 1$

$6x + 4y = 26 \qquad\quad 5x - 6y = 3$

This yields the system

$6x + 4y = 26$ Equation (1)

$5x - 6y = 3$ Equation (2)

To eliminate the y terms, we multiply both sides of equation (1) by 3 and both sides of equation (2) by 2, yielding the system

$18x + 12y = 78$

$10x - 12y = 6$

The coefficients of the y terms are equal in absolute value and opposite in sign. Add the left sides and the right sides of the equations and solve for x.

$18x + 12y = 78$

$\underline{10x - 12y = 6}$

$\qquad 28x = 84$

$\qquad x = 3$

Substitute 3 for x in equation (1) and solve for y.

$6(3) + 4y = 26$

$18 + 4y = 26$

$4y = 8$

$y = 2$

The solution is $(3, 2)$.

55. Substitute $\frac{1}{2}x + 3$ for y in $2y - x = 6$.

$2\left(\frac{1}{2}x + 3\right) - x = 6$

$x + 6 - x = 6$

$6 = 6$ true

This is an identity. The system is dependent. The solution set is the set of ordered pairs (x, y) such that $y = \frac{1}{2}x + 3$.

57. Multiply the first equation by 2 and the second equation by 5, then add the equations.

$$\frac{5}{3}x + \frac{1}{2}y = 6$$

$$-\frac{5}{3}x + \frac{25}{2}y = 20$$

$$\overline{\phantom{-\frac{5}{3}x+}13y = 26}$$

$$y = 2$$

Substitute $y = 2$ into $\frac{5}{6}x + \frac{1}{4}y = 3$ and solve for x.

$$\frac{5}{6}x + \frac{1}{4}(2) = 3$$

$$\frac{5}{6}x + \frac{1}{2} = 3$$

$$\frac{5}{6}x = \frac{5}{2}$$

$$x = 3$$

The solution is $(3,2)$.

59. First simplify the equations by multiplying by their LCD.

$$2(x+2y) - 3(x-y) = 13$$

$$2x + 4y - 3x + 3y = 13$$

$$-x + 7y = 13$$

$$2(x+3y) + (x+y) = 17$$

$$2x + 6y + x + y = 17$$

$$3x + 7y = 17$$

The system can be rewritten as

$$-x + 7y = 13$$

$$3x + 7y = 17$$

Multiply the first equation by -1 and add both equations.

$$x - 7y = -13$$

$$3x + 7y = 17$$

$$\overline{4x = 4}$$

$$x = 1$$

Substitute $x = 1$ into $3x + 7y = 17$ and solve for y.

$$3(1) + 7y = 17$$

$$3 + 7y = 17$$

$$7y = 14$$

$$y = 2$$

The solution is $(1, 2)$.

61. $3x + 2y = 8$

$2x - y = 3$

Graphing by hand:
Begin by writing each equation in slope-intercept form.

$3x + 2y = 8$ $\qquad$ $2x - y = 3$

$2y = -3x + 8$ $\qquad$ $-y = -2x + 3$

$y = -\frac{3}{2}x + 4$ $\qquad$ $y = 2x - 3$

Next we graph both equations in the same coordinate system.

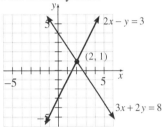

The intersection point is $(2,1)$. So, the ordered pair $(2,1)$ is the solution.

Substitution:

$3x + 2y = 8$

$2x - y = 3$

Solve the second equation for y.

$$2x - y = 3$$

$$y = 2x - 3$$

Substitute $2x - 3$ for y in the first equation and solve for x.

$$3x + 2(2x - 3) = 8$$

$$3x + 4x - 6 = 8$$

$$7x - 6 = 8$$

$$7x = 14$$

$$x = 2$$

Substitute 2 for x in the equation $y = 2x - 3$ and solve for y.

$$y = 2(2) - 3 = 4 - 3 = 1$$

The solution is $(2,1)$.

Elimination:

$3x + 2y = 8$ Equation (1)

$2x - y = 3$ Equation (2)

To eliminate the y terms, we multiply both sides of equation (2) by 2, yielding the system

$3x + 2y = 8$

$4x - 2y = 6$

The coefficients of the y terms are equal in absolute value and opposite in sign. Add the left sides and the right sides of the equations and solve for x.

$$3x + 2y = 8$$
$$\underline{4x - 2y = 6}$$
$$7x = 14$$
$$x = 2$$

Substitute 2 for x in equation (2) and solve for y.

$$2(2) - y = 3$$
$$4 - y = 3$$
$$-y = -1$$
$$y = 1$$

The solution is $(2, 1)$.

Preference may vary.

63. $5x + 3y = 11$ Equation (1)

     $2x - 4y = -6$ Equation (2)

a.   To eliminate the x terms, we multiply both sides of equation (1) by 2 and both sides of equation (2) by -5, yielding the system

$10x + 6y = 22$

$-10x + 20y = 30$

The coefficients of the x terms are equal in absolute value and opposite in sign. Add the left sides and the right sides of the equations and solve for y.

$$10x + 6y = 22$$
$$\underline{-10x + 20y = 30}$$
$$26y = 52$$
$$y = 2$$

Substitute 2 for y in equation (2) and solve for x.

$$2x - 4(2) = -6$$
$$2x - 8 = -6$$
$$2x = 2$$
$$x = 1$$

The solution is $(1, 2)$.

b.   To eliminate the y terms, we multiply both sides of equation (1) by 4 and both sides of equation (2) by 3, yielding the system

$20x + 12y = 44$

$6x - 12y = -18$

The coefficients of the y terms are equal in absolute value and opposite in sign. Add the left sides and the right sides of the equations and solve for x.

$$20x + 12y = 44$$
$$\underline{6x - 12y = -18}$$
$$26x = 26$$
$$x = 1$$

Substitute 1 for x in equation (2) and solve for y.

$$2(1) - 4y = -6$$
$$2 - 4y = -6$$
$$-4y = -8$$
$$y = 2$$

The solution is $(1, 2)$.

c.   The results are the same.

65.   The function f has a slope of -3 and an f-intercept of $(0, 93)$. Therefore, $f(x) = -3x + 93$. The function g has a slope of 2 and a g-intercept of $(0, -22)$. Therefore, $g(x) = 2x - 22$. Write the system that describes the functions f and g.

$y = -3x + 93$

$y = 2x - 22$

Solve using substitution.

Substitute $-3x + 93$ for y in $y = 2x - 22$ and solve for x.

$$-3x + 93 = 2x - 22$$
$$-5x = -115$$
$$x = 23$$

Substitute $x = 23$ into $y = -3x + 93$ and solve for y.

$$y = -3(23) + 93$$
$$= -69 + 93$$
$$= 24$$

The solution is $(23, 24)$.

67. The coordinates for A are $(0,0)$ since it lies at the origin. The coordinates for B are the same as the coordinates of the y-intercept of ℓ_1, which is $(0,3)$. The coordinates for C are the same as the point of intersection of ℓ_1 and ℓ_2. Solve the following system.

$\ell_1 : y = 2x + 3$

$\ell_2 : 3y + x = 30$

Substitute $2x + 3$ for y in the second equation.

$3(2x + 3) + x = 30$

$\qquad 6x + 9 + x = 30$

$\qquad\qquad 7x = 21$

$\qquad\qquad\quad x = 3$

Substitute $x = 3$ into the first equation and solve for y.

$y = 2(3) + 3$

$\quad = 6 + 3$

$\quad = 9$

The solution is $(3,9)$ so the coordinates of C are $(3,9)$. The coordinates for D are the same as the coordinates of the point of intersection of ℓ_2 and ℓ_3. Solve the following system.

$\ell_2 : 3y + x = 30$

$\ell_3 : y + 3x = 26$

Multiply the second equation by -3 and add the equations.

$\qquad 3y + x = 30$

$\underline{-3y - 9x = -78}$

$\qquad\quad -8x = -48$

$\qquad\qquad\ x = 6$

Substitute $x = 6$ into $3y + x = 30$ and solve for y.

$3y + (6) = 30$

$\qquad 3y = 24$

$\qquad\ y = 8$

The solution is $(6,8)$ so the coordinates of D are $(6,8)$. The coordinates for E are the same as the coordinates of the point of intersection of ℓ_3 and ℓ_4. Solve the following system.

$\ell_3 : y + 3x = 26$

$\ell_4 : y = 2x - 10$

Substitute $2x - 10$ in for y in $y + 3x = 26$.

$2x - 10 + 3x = 26$

$\qquad\quad 5x = 36$

$\qquad\quad\ x = 7.2$

Substitute $x = 7.2$ into $y = 2x - 10$ and solve for x.

$y = 2(7.2) - 10$

$\quad = 4.4$

The solution is $(7.2, 4.4)$ so the coordinates of E are $(7.2, 4.4)$. The coordinates of F are the same as the coordinates of the x-intercept of ℓ_4. Let $y = 0$ in ℓ_4 and solve for x.

$\quad y = 2x - 10$

$\quad 0 = 2x - 10$

$2x = 10$

$\quad x = 5$

The coordinates of F are $(5,0)$.

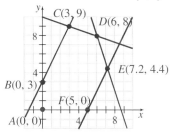

69. Answers may vary

71. a. $\qquad y = mx + b$

$\qquad\quad 5 = m(2) + b$

$\qquad 2m + b = 5$

b. $\qquad y = mx + b$

$\qquad\quad 9 = m(4) + b$

$\qquad 4m + b = 9$

c. $2m+b=5$ Equation (1)

$4m+b=9$ Equation (2)

To eliminate the b terms, we multiply both sides of equation (1) by -1, yielding the system

$-2m-b=-5$

$4m+b=9$

The coefficients of the b terms are equal in absolute value and opposite in sign. Add the left sides and the right sides of the equations and solve for m.

$-2m-b=-5$

$\underline{4m+b=9}$

$2m=4$

$m=2$

Substitute 2 for m in equation (2) and solve for b.

$4(2)+b=9$

$8+b=9$

$b=1$

The solution of the system is $(m,b)=(2,1)$.

d. The equation of the line is $y=2x+1$.

e. Graph the equation and check if the points $(2,5)$ and $(4,9)$ are on the graph.

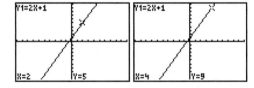

73. Notice that for $y=\dfrac{1}{2}x+\dfrac{7}{2}$ and $y=\dfrac{4}{5}x+2$ when $x=5$ they are both equal to 6. So the solution to the given equation is $x=5$.

75. Notice that for $y=\dfrac{11}{10}x+\dfrac{17}{10}$ and $y=5$ when $x=3$ they are both equal to 5. So the solution to the given equation is $x=3$.

77. Notice that for $y=\dfrac{4}{5}x+2$ and $y=\dfrac{11}{10}x+\dfrac{17}{10}$ when $x=1$ they are both equal to 2.8. So the solution to the given system of equations is $(1, 2.8)$.

79. $2(5x+4)-6(3x+2)=10x+8-18x-12$

$=10x-18x+8-12$

$=-8x-4$

Description: *linear expression in one variable*

81. $2(5x+4)-6(3x+2)=0$

$10x+8-18x-12=0$

$-8x-4=0$

$-8x=4$

$x=-\dfrac{1}{2}$

The solution is $-\dfrac{1}{2}$.

Description: *linear equation in one variable*

Homework 6.4

1. $p=-0.20t+59.74$

$p=-0.27t+64.01$

Substitute $-0.27t+64.01$ for p in the first equation and solve for t.

$-0.27t+64.01=-0.20t+59.74$

$-0.07t+64.01=59.74$

$-0.07t=-4.27$

$t=\dfrac{-4.27}{-0.07}=61$

Substitute 61 for t in the equation $p=-0.20t+59.74$ and solve for n.

$n=-0.20(61)+59.74=47.54$

The approximate solution of the system is $(61,47.54)$.

According to the models, the percentage of women who are married will equal the percentage of men who are married (47.54%) in 2051.

3. $n = -0.1t + 4.7$

$n = 0.17t + 1.15$

Substitute $1.17t + 1.15$ for n in the first equation and solve for t.

$0.17t + 1.15 = -0.1t + 4.7$

$0.27t + 1.15 = 4.7$

$0.27t = 3.55$

$t = \dfrac{3.55}{0.27} \approx 13.15$

Substitute 13.15 for t in the equation $n = -0.1t + 4.7$ and solve for n.

$n = -0.1(13.15) + 4.7 \approx 3.39$

The solution of the system is about $(13.15, 3.4)$.

According to the models, the number of landline 411 calls will equal the number of wireless 411 calls (3.4 billion) in 2013.

5. a. Milk

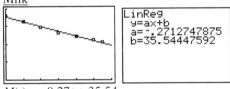

$M(t) = -0.27t + 35.54$

Soft Drinks

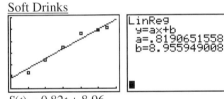

$S(t) = 0.82t + 8.96$

b. Substitute the $M(t)$ for $S(t)$ and solve for t.

$-0.27t + 35.54 = 0.82t + 8.96$

$26.58 = 1.09t$

$24.39 \approx t$

During 1974 the per-person milk and soft drink consumptions were the same.

$M(24.39) = -0.27(24.39) + 35.54$

$= -6.5853 + 35.54$

≈ 28.95

$S(24.39) = 0.82(24.39) + 8.96$

$= 19.9998 + 8.96$

≈ 28.96

The annual consumption per-person in 1974 was about 29.0 gallons.

c.

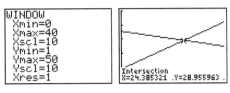

7. a. Start by plotting the data. Then find the regression lines for the data.

Knowledge

$K(a) = 0.014a - 0.747$

Memory

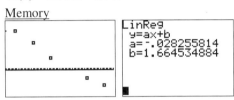

$M(a) = -0.028a + 1.66$

b. Solve the system

$K(a) = 0.014a - 0.747$

$M(a) = -0.028a + 1.66$

Substitute $0.014a - 0.747$ in for $M(a)$ in the second equation and solve for a.

$0.014a - 0.747 = -0.028a + 1.66$

$0.042a = 2.407$

$a \approx 57.31$

The scores will be roughly equal when a person is 57 years old.

c. Find the intersection point using a graphing utility.

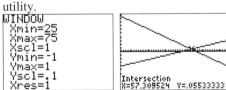

This confirms our original solution of 57 years old.

9. a. Solve the system
$$y = 13.5t + 229$$
$$y = -5t + 365$$
Substitute $13.5t + 229$ for y in the second equation and solve for t.
$$13.5t + 229 = -5t + 365$$
$$18.5t = 136$$
$$t \approx 7.35$$
Substitute this result into the first equation and solve for y.
$$y = 13.5(7.35) + 229$$
$$\approx 328.23$$
According to the models, the two newspapers had equal circulations of roughly 328 thousand in 1997.

b. Since the circulations were roughly equal in 1997, competition heated up as each newspaper tried to overtake the other.

c.
$$D(10) = 13.5(10) + 229$$
$$= 135 + 229$$
$$= 364$$
$$R(10) = -5(10) + 365$$
$$= -50 + 365$$
$$= 315$$
$$826 - (364 + 315) = 826 - 679 = 147$$
According to the models, the combined increase due to bonus copies was roughly 147 thousand bonus copies.

d.
$$D(11) = 13.5(11) + 229$$
$$= 377.5$$
$$R(11) = -5(11) + 365$$
$$= 310$$
$$377.5 + 310 = 687.5$$
According to the models, the combined circulation of the two newspapers was roughly 688 thousand copies in 2001.

e. The estimate in part d. was an overestimate. After joining revenue streams, the competition for subscribers ceased (or, at least, reduced if there were other competitors). The end of bonus copies, or just the merger in general, may have caused some subscribers to cancel subscriptions.

11. a. Since the number of students who earned a bachelor's degree in biological and biomedical sciences increases by 0.8 thousand each year, we can model the situation by a linear equation. The slope is 0.8 thousand degrees per year. Since the number of degrees earned in 2006 was 69.2 thousand, the d-intercept is $(0, 69.2)$. So, a reasonable model is
$$B(t) = 0.8t + 69.2.$$
By the same reasoning, the model for the number of bachelor's degrees in security and protective services is $S(t) = 1.5t + 35.3$.

b.
$$B(t) = 0.8t + 69.2$$
$$S(t) = 1.5t + 35.3$$
Substitute $1.5t + 35.3$ for $B(t)$ in the first equation and solve for t.
$$1.5t + 35.3 = 0.8t + 69.2$$
$$0.7t + 35.3 = 69.2$$
$$0.7t = 33.9$$
$$t = \frac{33.9}{0.7} \approx 48.43$$
Substitute 48.43 for t in the equation $B(t) = 0.8t + 69.2$ and solve.
$$B(48.43) = 0.8(48.43) + 69.2 \approx 107.94$$
The approximate solution of the system is $(48.43, 107.94)$.

According to the models, the same number of bachelor's degrees (107.9 thousand each) will be earned in 2054.

13. a. We are given that the average daily calorie consumption is approximately linear for both men and women. Let t = the number of years since 2000, and c = the average daily calorie consumption.
Men: The slope is 8.4 calories per year. Since the average daily calorie consumption is 2618, the c-intercept is $(0, 2618)$. So, a reasonable model is
$$M(t) = 8.4t + 2618.$$
Women: The slope is 17.8 calories per year. Since the average daily calorie consumption is 1877, the c-intercept is $(0, 1877)$. So, a reasonable model is
$$W(t) = 17.8t + 1877.$$

b. $M(t) = 8.4t + 2618$

$W(t) = 17.8t + 1877$

Substitute $17.8t + 1877$ for $M(t)$ in the first equation and solve for t.

$17.8t + 1877 = 8.4t + 2618$

$9.4t + 1877 = 2618$

$9.4t = 741$

$t = \dfrac{741}{9.4} \approx 78.83$

Substitute 78.83 for t in the equation $M(t) = 8.4t + 2618$ and solve.

$M(78.83) = 8.4(78.83) + 2618 \approx 3280.17$

The approximate solution of the system is $(78.83, 3280)$.

According to the models, the daily average calorie consumption by men and women (3280 calories) will be the same in 2079.

15. a. For both $T(t)$ and $E(t)$ we are given the T and E intercepts and the slope in terms of the price of the cars in 2008 and their depreciation rates, respectively.

$T(t) = -1725t + 12281$

$E(t) = -1424t + 10952$

b. Substitute $-1725t + 12281$ for E in $E(t) = -1424t + 10952$ and solve for t.

$-1725t + 12281 = -1424t + 10952$

$-301t = -1329$

$t \approx 4.42$

So both cars will have the same value around $2008 + 4.42 \approx 2012$. To find that value substitute $t = 4.42$ into $T(t)$.

$T(4.42) = -1725(4.42) + 12281$

≈ 4665

So in 2012 they will both be worth about $4665.

c. Find the intersection point using a graphing utility.

This confirms our original solution of (4.42, 4665).

17. a. Since Jenny Craig's program fees increase by a constant $72 each week, the function J is linear and its slope is 72. The J-intercept is $(0, 19)$, since the start-up fee is $19 at $t = 0$. So, an equation for $J(t)$ is

$J(t) = 72t + 19$.

Since Weight Watchers' program fees increase by a constant $77 each week ($17 fee + $60 food), the function W is linear and its slope is 77. The W-intercept is $(0, 0)$ since there is no start-up fee at $t = 0$. An equation for $W(t)$ is $W(t) = 77t$.

b.

$J(t) = 72t + 19$

$\text{dollars} = \dfrac{\text{dollars}}{\text{weeks}} \text{weeks} + \text{dollars}$

$\text{dollars} = \text{dollars} + \text{dollars}$

$\text{dollars} = \text{dollars}$

The units of $J(t)$ are correct.

$W(t) = 77t$

$\text{dollars} = \dfrac{\text{dollars}}{\text{weeks}} \text{weeks}$

$\text{dollars} = \text{dollars}$

The units of $W(t)$ are correct.

c. Solve the system

$y = 72t + 19$

$y = 77t$

Substitute $72t + 19$ for y into the second equation.

$72t + 19 = 77t$

$5t = 19$

$t = 3.8$

Substitute this result into the first equation and solve for y.

$y = 72(3.8) + 19$

$= 292.6$

The total cost at both Jenny Craig and Weight Watchers is approximately $293 in 4 weeks.

d. Find the intersection point using a graphing utility.

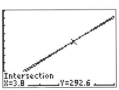

19. The percentage of households with a television tuned in to ad-supported cable $C(t)$ and the percentage of households with a television tuned in to the major networks $N(t)$ can be represented by functions in terms of t, the years after 2007.

$C(t) = 2.1t + 51.4$

$N(t) = -2.0t + 22.9$

To estimate when cable and the major networks are equal, set $C(t) = N(t)$ and solve for t.

$2.1t + 51.4 = -2.0t + 22.9$

$4.1t + 51.4 = 22.9$

$4.1t = -28.5$

$t \approx -6.95$

In $2007 - 6.95 \approx 2000$, the same percentage of households had a television tuned in to ad-supported cable and the major networks.

21. a. Due to rounding, it is not exact. In the following graph, notice that the intersection is not at an integer value of t.

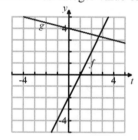

b. $f(I)$ will be larger than $g(I)$. Notice in the previous graph the slope of f is larger than the slope of g.

23. For each state we are given the personal incomes in 2003 and the personal incomes in 2007. Since the personal income in both states increased linearly we can write a linear model. To do this we first need to find the rate of increase for both states.

$m_f = \dfrac{31474 - 23941}{2007 - 2003} = \dfrac{7533}{4} \approx 1883$

$m_g = \dfrac{34874 - 29405}{2007 - 2003} = \dfrac{5469}{4} \approx 1367$

So $f(t) = 1883t + b$ and $g(t) = 1367t + b$. Since t is the years since 2000, $f(3) = 23,941$ and $g(3) = 29,405$. We can find the intercept b by using these values.

$f(t) = 1883t + +b$

$23,941 = 1883(3) + b$

$18292 = b$

$g(t) = 1367t + b$

$29405 = 1367(3) + b$

$25304 = b$

The equations are below.

$f(t) = 1883t + 18,291$

$g(t) = 1367t + 25,304$

Substitute $1883t + 18,291$ for $g(t)$ in $g(t) = 1367t + 25,304$ and solve for t.

$1883t + 18,291 = 1367t + 25,304$

$516t = 7013$

$t \approx 13.59$

So during $2000 + 13.59 \approx 2014$, personal income in New Mexico will equal the personal income in Ohio.

25. $y = -2x + 6$

$y = 3x + 1$

Substitute $3x + 1$ for y in the first equation and solve for x.

$3x + 1 = -2x + 6$

$5x + 1 = 6$

$5x = 5$

$x = 1$

Substitute 1 for x in the equation $y = 3x + 1$ and solve for y.

$y = 3(1) + 1 = 3 + 1 = 4$

The solution is $(1, 4)$.

Description: *system of two linear equations in two variables*

27. $-2x + 6 = 3x + 1$

$-5x + 6 = 1$

$-5x = -5$

$x = 1$

The solution is 1.

Description: *linear equation in one variable*

Homework 6.5

1. Let L = the length and W = the width.

$$L = 1.62W \qquad P = 2L + 2W$$
$$600 = 2L + 2W$$

To determine the dimensions of the rectangle, we solve the system

$$L = 1.62W$$
$$600 = 2L + 2W$$

Substitute $1.62W$ for L in the second equation and solve for w.

$$600 = 2(1.62W) + 2W$$
$$600 = 3.24W + 2W$$
$$600 = 5.24W$$
$$W = \frac{600}{5.24} \approx 114.504$$

Substitute 114.504 for W in the equation $L = 1.62W$ and solve for L.

$$L = 1.62(114.504) \approx 185.496$$

The width of the rectangle is approximately 114.50 feet and the length is approximately 185.50 feet.

3. L = the length and W = the width.

$$L = W + 5 \qquad P = 2L + 2W$$
$$42 = 2L + 2W$$
$$21 = L + W$$

To determine the dimensions of the garden, we solve the system

$$L = W + 5$$
$$21 = L + W$$

Substitute $W + 5$ for L in the second equation and solve for W.

$$21 - (W + 5) + W$$
$$21 = 2W + 5$$
$$16 = 2W$$
$$8 = W$$

Substitute 8 for W in the equation $L = W + 5$ and solve for L.

$$L = 8 + 5 = 13$$

The width of the garden is 8 feet and the length is 13 feet.

5. L = the length and W = the width.

$$L = 2W + 6 \qquad P = 2L + 2W$$
$$228 = 2L + 2W$$
$$114 = L + W$$

To determine the dimensions of the court, we solve the system

$$L = 2W + 6$$
$$114 = L + W$$

Substitute $2W + 6$ for L in the second equation and solve for W.

$$114 = (2W + 6) + W$$
$$114 = 3W + 6$$
$$108 = 3W$$
$$36 = W$$

Substitute 36 for W in the equation $L = 2W + 6$ and solve for L.

$$L = 2(36) + 6 = 72 + 6 = 78$$

The width of the court is 36 feet and the length is 78 feet.

7. L = the length and W = the width.

$$L = 2W - 3 \qquad P = 2L + 2W$$
$$108 = 2L + 2W$$
$$54 = L + W$$

To determine the dimensions of the rectangle, we solve the system

$$L = 2W - 3$$
$$54 = L + W$$

Substitute $2W - 3$ for L in the second equation and solve for W.

$$54 = (2W - 3) + W$$
$$54 = 3W - 3$$
$$57 = 3W$$
$$19 = W$$

Substitute 19 for W in the equation $L = 2W - 3$ and solve for L.

$$L = 2(19) - 3 = 38 - 3 = 35$$

The width of the rectangle is 19 inches and the length is 35 inches.

9. Let x = the number of \$15 tickets and y = the number of \$22 tickets.

There are a total of 2000 tickets, so our first equation is $x + y = 2000$.

The total revenue is \$33,500. The revenue for each ticket type is obtained by multiplying the ticket price by the number of tickets sold at that price. Therefore, our second equation is $15x + 22y = 33,500$

The system is

$$x + y = 2000 \qquad \text{Equation (1)}$$
$$15x + 22y = 33,500 \qquad \text{Equation (2)}$$

To eliminate the x terms, multiply both sides of equation (1) by -15, yielding the system

$$-15x - 15y = -30,000$$
$$15x + 22y = 33,500$$

Add the left sides and right sides and solve for y.

$$-15x - 15y = -30,000$$
$$\underline{15x + 22y = 33,500}$$
$$7y = 3,500$$
$$y = 500$$

Substitute 500 for y in equation (1) and solve for x.

$$x + (500) = 2000$$
$$x = 1500$$

The theater should sell 1500 of the \$15 tickets and 500 of the \$22 tickets.

11. Let x = the number sold of *Amnesiac* and y = the number sold of *Hail to the Thief*.

A total of 253 CDs were sold, so our first equation is $x + y = 253$.

The total revenue was \$4762.94. The revenue for each CD is obtained by multiplying the CD price by the number of CDs sold at that price. Therefore, our second equation is $17.98x + 18.98y = 4762.94$

The system is

$$x + y = 253$$
$$17.98x + 18.98y = 4762.94$$

Solve the first equation for y.

$$x + y = 253$$
$$y = -x + 253$$

Substitute $-x + 253$ for y in the second equation and solve for x.

$$17.98x + 18.98(-x + 253) = 4762.94$$
$$17.98x - 18.98x + 4801.94 = 4762.94$$
$$-x + 4801.94 = 4762.94$$
$$-x = -39$$
$$x = 39$$

Substitute 39 for x in the equation $y = -x + 253$ and solve for y.

$$y = -39 + 253 = 214$$

The store sold 39 *Amnesiac* CDs and 214 *Hail to the Thief* CDs.

13. Let x = the price of balcony seats and y = the price of main-level seats.

Tickets for the balcony are \$12 less than tickets for the main-level, so our first equation is $x = y - 12$.

The total revenue is \$40,600. To obtain the revenue for each seat type, we multiply the price of each seat type by the number of seats at that price. Therefore, our second equation is $300x + 1400y = 40,600$.

The system is

$$x = y - 12$$
$$300x + 1400y = 40,600$$

Substitute $y - 12$ for x in the second equation and solve for y.

$$300(y - 12) + 1400y = 40,600$$
$$300y - 3600 + 1400y = 40,600$$
$$1700y - 3600 = 40,600$$
$$1700y = 44,200$$
$$y = 26$$

Substitute 26 for y in the equation $x = y - 12$ and solve for x.

$$x = 26 - 12 = 14$$

Each balcony seat should cost \$14 and each main-level seat should cost \$26.

15. Let x = the price of general seats and y = the price of reserved seats.
Tickets for the general are $25 less than tickets for the reserved, so our first equation is
$x = y - 25$.
The total revenue is $544,000. To obtain the revenue for each seat type, we multiply the price of each seat type by the number of seats at that price. Therefore, our second equation is
$8000x + 4000y = 544,000$.

The system is
$$x = y - 25$$
$$8000x + 4000y = 544,000$$

Substitute $y - 25$ for x in the second equation and solve for y.
$$8000(y - 25) + 4000y = 544,000$$
$$8000y - 200,000 + 4000y = 544,000$$
$$12,000y - 200,000 = 544,000$$
$$12,000y = 744,000$$
$$y = 62$$

Substitute 62 for y in the equation $x = y - 25$ and solve for x.
$x = 62 - 25 = 37$
Each general seat should cost $37 and each reserved seat should cost $62.

17. a. The total revenue will be given by multiplying the number of tickets by their respective price, and adding these amounts. The total number of tickets will be 20,000 so $x + y = 20,000$. We only want R to be in terms of x so $y = 20,000 - x$.
$$f(x) = 50x + 75(20,000 - x)$$
$$f(x) = -25x + 1,500,000$$

b.

The slope of the graph is –25. This represents the fact that as more $50 tickets are sold, the revenue decreases by $25 per ticket compared to selling only $75 tickets.

c. $f(16,000)$
$$= 50(16,000) + 75(20,000 - 16,000)$$
$$= 800,000 + 75(4,000)$$
$$= 800,000 + 300,000$$
$$= 1,100,000$$
$f(16,000)$ represents the amount of revenue made when 16,000 $50 tickets are sold.

d. The total revenue must cover the $475,000 production cost and make $600,000 in profit. This means that the total revenue must be $1,075,000.
$$1,075,000 = 50x + 75(20,000 - x)$$
$$1,075,000 = 50x + 1,500,000 - 75x$$
$$1,075,000 = -25x + 1,500,000$$
$$-425,000 = -25x$$
$$17,000 = x$$
So 17,000 of the $50 tickets and 3000 of the $75 tickets must be sold.

19. a. The total revenue will be given by multiplying the number of tickets by their respective prices, and adding these amounts. The total number of tickets will be 12,000 so $x + y = 12,000$. We only want R to be in terms of x so $y = 12,000 - x$.
$$f(x) = 45x + 70(12,000 - x)$$
$$= 45x + 840,000 - 70x$$
$$= -25x + 840,000$$

b.

X	Y1	
0	840000	
2000	790000	
4000	740000	
6000	690000	
8000	640000	
10000	590000	
12000	540000	
X=0		

In each case $f(x)$ is the total revenue when x of the $45 tickets are sold.

c. The possible revenues from the concert range from $540,000 to $840,000.

d. $602,500 = -25x + 840,000$
$$-237,500 = -25x$$
$$9500 = x$$
So 9500 of the $45 tickets and 2500 of the $75 tickets should be sold.

21. a. Since a first-class ticket is $242 more than a coach ticket, $y = 242 + x$. To find the total revenue of a single flight, multiply the number of tickets sold by their respective prices, and then add these amounts.

$$R = 8y + 126x$$
$$f(x) = 8(242 + x) + 126x$$
$$= 1936 + 8x + 126x$$
$$= 134x + 1936$$

b. The slope of the graph of f is 134. As the price of a coach ticket increases by a dollar, the total revenue increases by $134 on a full plane.

c. $14,130 = 134x + 1936$

$$12,194 = 134x$$
$$91 = x$$

United Airlines should charge $91 for a coach ticket, and $333 for a first-class ticket.

23. a. We find 8% of 2500.
$$(0.08)(2500) = 200$$
The interest in one year would be $200.

b. We find 8% of 3500.
$$(0.08)(3500) = 280$$
The interest in one year would be $280.

c. We find 8% of d.
$$(0.08)(d) = 0.08d$$
The interest in one year would be $0.08d$ dollars.

25. a. $0.03(2000) + 0.06(7000) = 60 + 420$
$$= 480$$
The total interest would be $480.

b. $0.03(4000) + 0.06(5000) = 120 + 300$
$$= 420$$
The total interest would be $420.

c. $0.03(x) + 0.06(y) = 0.03x + 0.06y$
The total interest would be $0.03x + 0.06y$.

27. Let x = the amount invested in the First Funds TN Tax-Free I account and y = the amount invested in the W&R International Growth C account.

The total amount invested is $20,000 so our first equation is $x + y = 20,000$.

The total interest after one year is $1500. Therefore, our second equation is $0.06x + 0.11y = 1500$.

The system is
$$x + y = 20,000$$
$$0.06x + 0.11y = 1500$$

Solve the first equation for y.
$$x + y = 20,000$$
$$y = -x + 20,000$$

Substitute $-x + 20,000$ for y in the second equation and solve for x.
$$0.06x + 0.11(-x + 20,000) = 1500$$
$$0.06x - 0.11x + 2200 = 1500$$
$$-0.05x + 2200 = 1500$$
$$-0.05x = -700$$
$$x = 14,000$$

Substitute 14,000 for x in the equation $y = -x + 20,000$ and solve for y.

$$y = -(14,000) + 20,000 = 6,000$$

She should invest $14,000 in the First Funds TN Tax-Free I account and $6,000 in the W&R International Growth C account.

29. Let x = the amount invested in the Middlesex Savings Bank CD account and y = the amount invested in the First Funds Growth & Income I account.

The total amount invested is $8500, so our first equation is $x + y = 8500$.

The total interest after one year is $990, so our second equation is $0.036x + 0.15y = 990$.

The system is
$$x + y = 8500 \quad \text{Equation (1)}$$
$$0.036x + 0.15y = 990 \quad \text{Equation (2)}$$

To eliminate the y terms, multiply both sides of equation (1) by -0.15, yielding the system
$$-0.15x - 0.15y = -1275$$
$$0.036x + 0.15y = 990$$

Add the left sides and the right sides, and solve for x.
$$-0.15x - 0.15y = -1275$$
$$\underline{0.036x + 0.15y = 990}$$
$$-0.114x = -285$$
$$x = \frac{-285}{-0.114} = 2500$$

Substitute 2500 for x in equation (1) and solve for y.
$$2500 + y = 8500$$
$$y = 6000$$

He should invest $2500 in the Middlesex Savings Bank CD account and $6000 in the First Funds Growth & Income I account.

31. Let x = the amount invested in the Limited Term NY Municipal X account and y = the amount invested in the Calvert Income A account.

The amount invested in the Limited Term NY Municipal X account will be three times as much as the amount in the Calvert Income A account, so our first equation is $x = 3y$.

The total interest for one year is $625, so our second equation is $0.05x + 0.10y = 625$.

The system is
$$x = 3y$$
$$0.05x + 0.10y = 625$$

Substitute $3y$ for x in the second equation and solve for y.
$$0.05(3y) + 0.10y = 625$$
$$0.15y + 0.10y = 625$$
$$0.25y = 625$$
$$y = 2500$$

Substitute 2500 for y in the equation $x = 3y$ and solve for x.
$$x = 3(2500) = 7500$$

The person should invest $7500 in the Limited Term NY Municipal X account and $2500 in the Calvert Income A account.

33. Let x = the amount invested in the USAA Tax Exempt Short-Term account and y = the amount invested in the Putnam Global Equity B account.

The amounts invested in each account are equal, so our first equation is $x = y$.

The total interest for one year is $700, so our second equation is $0.05x + 0.09y = 700$.

The system is
$$x = y$$
$$0.05x + 0.09y = 700$$

Substitute x for y in the second equation and solve for x.
$$0.05x + 0.09x = 700$$
$$0.14x = 700$$
$$x = 5000$$

Since the amounts are equal, $y = 5000$.

The person should invest $5000 in each account.

35. a. Since the total amount of money to be invested is $10,000, the sum of x and y must be $10,000. The interest for any account is the amount deposited into the account, multiplied by its return as a decimal.
$$x + y = 10000$$
$$I = 0.0287x + 0.081y$$
$$f(x) = 0.0287x + 0.081(10,000 - x)$$
$$= 0.0287x + 810 - 0.081x$$
$$= -0.0523x + 810$$

b.

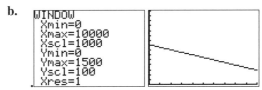

The slope is –0.0523, this is the decrease in the total amount of interest for every dollar put into the Charter One Bank CD. The more money put into the mutual fund, the higher the interest. The more money put into the CD the lower the interest.

c.
$$400 = -0.0523x + 810$$
$$-410 = -0.0523x$$
$$7839.39 \approx x$$
So about $7839.39 should go into the CD, while about $2160.61 should go into the mutual fund to earn a total of $400 in one year.

37. a. Since the total amount of money to be invested is $9000, the sum of x and y must be $9000. The interest for any account is the product of the amount deposited into the account and its interest rate in decimal form.
$$x + y = 9000$$
$$I = 0.025x + 0.0945y$$
$$f(x) = 0.025x + 0.0945(9,000 - x)$$
$$= 0.025x + 850.5 - 0.0945x$$
$$= -0.695x + 850.5$$

b. When $x = 500$, this means that $500 has been invested in the CD. $f(500)$ is the amount of interest earned per year when $500 has been invested in the CD, and the rest has been invested in the mutual fund.
$$f(500) = -0.0695(500) + 850.5$$
$$= -34.75 + 850.5$$
$$= 815.75$$

c. $f(x) = 500$ is when x amount of dollars has been invested into the CD, and both investments return $500 in interest per year.
$$500 = -0.0695x + 850.5$$
$$-350.5 = -0.0695x$$
$$5043.17 = x$$
So when about $5043.17 is invested in the CD and about $3956.83 is invested in the mutual fund, the total interest earned is $500.

d. When $x = 10,000$, this means that $10,000 has been invested in the CD. $f(10,000)$ is the amount of interest earned per year when $10,000 has been invested in the CD.
$$f(10,000) = -0.0695(10,000) + 850.5$$
$$= -695 + 850.5$$
$$= 155.5$$
Since the total amount of money available to be invested is $9000, this implies that negative $1000 has been invested in the mutual fund. This is impossible, so model breakdown has occurred.

39. a. Since the total amount of money to be invested is $8000, the sum of x and y must be $8000. The interest for any account is the product of the amount deposited into the account and its interest rate in decimal form.
$$x + y = 8000$$
$$I = 0.015x + 0.116y$$
$$f(x) = 0.015x + 0.116(8,000 - x)$$
$$= 0.015x + 928 - 0.116x$$
$$= -0.101x + 928$$

b. The minimum principal of $2500 relates to the function above by restricting the domain. Now $2,500 \leq x \leq 8,000$.
$$f(2,500) = -0.101(2,500) + 928$$
$$= -252.5 + 928$$
$$= 675.5$$
$$f(8,000) = -0.101(8,000) + 928$$
$$= -808 + 928$$
$$= 120$$
So the interest is between $675.50 and $120.

c.
$$400 = -0.101x + 928$$
$$-528 = -0.101x$$
$$5227.72 = x$$
So about $5227.72 should be invested in the CD, and $2772.28 should be invested in the mutual fund.

41. a. Since the total amount of money to be invested is $6000, the sum of x and y must be $6000. The interest for any account is the product of the amount deposited into the account and its interest rate in decimal form.
$$x + y = 6000$$
$$I = 0.0285x + 0.09y$$
$$f(x) = 0.0285x + 0.09(6,000 - x)$$
$$= 0.0285x + 540 - 0.09x$$
$$= -0.0615x + 540$$

b. The I-intercept of the model is when $x = 0$, or when no money has been invested in the CD and all of it is invested in the mutual fund.
$$I = -0.0615(0) + 540$$
$$= 540$$
This means that if no money was invested in the CD, the interest per year would be $540.

c. The *x*-intercept is when $I = 0$, or when there is no interest being earned.

$$0 = -0.0615x + 540$$

$$-540 = -0.0615x$$

$$8780.49 = x$$

The *x*-intercept is (8780.49, 0), which means that when $8780.49 is invested in the CD, no interest is earned. However, only $6000 is being invested, so model breakdown has occurred.

d. The slope is –0.0615, or a decrease of 0.0615 dollars of interest for every dollar invested in the CD.

43. a. We compute 65% of 2.

$$0.65(2) = 1.3$$

There are 1.3 ounces of oil in the solution.

b. We compute 65% of 3.

$$0.65(3) = 1.95$$

There are 1.95 ounces of oil in the solution.

c. We compute 65% of *x*.

$$0.65(x) = 0.65x$$

There are $0.65x$ ounces of oil in the solution.

45. a. $0.35(4) + 0.10(3) = 1.4 + 0.3$
$$= 1.7$$

There are 1.7 ounces of pure alcohol in the mixture.

b. Let *x* = the number of ounces of the 35% solution and *y* = the number of ounces of the 10% solution.

The total number of ounces is 15, so our first equation is $x + y = 15$.

The total amount of acid between the two solutions must be the same as the total amount of acid in the mixture, so our second equation is $0.35x + 0.10y = 0.20(15)$.

The system is
$$x + y = 15$$
$$0.35x + 0.10y = 0.20(15)$$

Solve the first equation for *y*.
$$x + y = 15$$
$$y = -x + 15$$

Substitute $-x + 15$ for *y* in the second equation and solve for *x*.

$$0.35x + 0.10(-x + 15) = 0.20(15)$$

$$0.35x - 0.10x + 1.50 = 3$$

$$0.25x + 1.50 = 3$$

$$0.25x = 1.50$$

$$x = 6$$

Substitute 6 for *x* in the equation $y = -x + 15$ and solve for *y*.

$$y = -(6) + 15 = 9$$

The mixture should contain 6 ounces of the 35% solution and 9 ounces of the 10% solution.

47. Let *x* = the number of quarts of the 20% solution and *y* = the number of quarts of the 30% solution.

The total number of quarts is 5, so our first equation is $x + y = 5$.

The total amount of acid between the two solutions must be the same as the total amount of acid in the mixture, so our second equation is $0.20x + 0.30y = 0.22(5)$.

The system is
$$x + y = 5$$
$$0.20x + 0.30y = 0.22(5)$$

Solve the first equation for *y*.
$$x + y = 5$$
$$y = -x + 5$$

Substitute $-x + 5$ for *y* in the second equation and solve for *x*.

$$0.20x + 0.30(-x + 5) = 0.22(5)$$

$$0.20x - 0.30x + 1.50 = 1.1$$

$$-0.1x + 1.50 = 1.1$$

$$-0.1x = -0.4$$

$$x = 4$$

Substitute 4 for *x* in the equation $y = -x + 5$ and solve for *y*.

$$y = -(4) + 5 = 1$$

The mixture should contain 4 quarts of the 20% solution and 1 quart of the 30% solution.

49. Let x = the number of gallons of the 10% solution and y = the number of gallons of 25% solution.

The total number of gallons is 3, so our first equation is $x + y = 3$.

The total amount of pure antifreeze between the two solutions must be the same as the total amount of pure antifreeze in the mixture, so our second equation is $0.10x + 0.25y = 0.20(3)$.

The system is
$$x + y = 3$$
$$0.10x + 0.25y = 0.20(3)$$

Solve the first equation for y.
$$x + y = 3$$
$$y = -x + 3$$

Substitute $-x + 3$ for y in the second equation and solve for x.
$$0.10x + 0.25(-x + 3) = 0.20(3)$$
$$0.10x - 0.25x + 0.75 = 0.60$$
$$-0.15x + 0.75 = 0.60$$
$$-0.15x = -0.15$$
$$x = 1$$

Substitute 1 for x in the equation $y = -x + 3$ and solve for y.
$$y = -(1) + 3 = 2$$

The mixture should contain 1 gallon of the 10% antifreeze solution and 2 gallons of the 25% antifreeze solution.

51. Let x = the number of quarts of the 15% solution and y = the number of quarts of the 35% solution.

The total number of quarts is 4, so our first equation is $x + y = 4$.

The total amount of acid between the two solutions must be the same as the total amount of acid in the mixture, so our second equation is $0.15x + 0.35y = 0.30(4)$.

The system is
$$x + y = 4$$
$$0.15x + 0.35y = 0.30(4)$$

Solve the first equation for y.
$$x + y = 4$$
$$y = -x + 4$$

Substitute $-x + 4$ for y in the second equation and solve for x.

$$0.15x + 0.35(-x + 4) = 0.30(4)$$
$$0.15x - 0.35x + 1.40 = 1.20$$
$$-0.2x + 1.40 = 1.20$$
$$-0.2x = -0.20$$
$$x = 1$$

Substitute 1 for x in the equation $y = -x + 4$ and solve for y.
$$y = -(1) + 4 = 3$$

The mixture should contain 1 quart of the 15% solution and 3 quarts of the 35% solution.

53. Let x = the number of ounces of the 20% alcohol solution and y = the number of ounces of pure water.

The total number of ounces is 5, so our first equation is $x + y = 5$.

The total amount of alcohol in the 20% solution must be the same as the total amount of alcohol in the mixture since there is no alcohol in pure water. Therefore, our second equation is $0.20x = 0.12(5)$.

The system is
$$x + y = 5$$
$$0.20x = 0.12(5)$$

Solve the second equation for x.
$$0.20x = 0.12(5)$$
$$0.20x = 0.60$$
$$x = 3$$

Substitute 3 for x in the equation $x + y = 5$ and solve for y.
$$3 + y = 5$$
$$y = 2$$

The mixture should contain 3 ounces of the 20% solution and 2 ounces of pure water.

55. a. $10(300) = 3000$

The revenue is $3000.

b. $15(300) = 4500$

The revenue is $4500.

c. i. Since all tickets cost at least $10, the minimum revenue will be $3000. Therefore, it is not possible to have revenue of $2500.

ii. Since all tickets cost at most $15, the maximum revenue will be $4500. Therefore, it is not possible to have revenue of $4875.

iii. Since $3250 is between $3000 and $4500, it is possible to achieve this revenue.

Let x = the number of $10 tickets and y = the number of $15 tickets.

The total number of tickets is 300, so our first equation is $x + y = 300$.

The total revenue is $3250, so our second equation is $10x + 15y = 3250$.

The system is

$$x + y = 300 \qquad \text{Equation (1)}$$
$$10x + 15y = 3250 \qquad \text{Equation (2)}$$

To eliminate the x terms, multiply both

57. Descriptions may vary.
$$y = x + 3$$
$$2x + 2y = 50$$

Substitute $x + 3$ for y in the second equation and solve for x.
$$2x + 2(x + 3) = 50$$
$$2x + 2x + 6 = 50$$
$$4x + 6 = 50$$
$$4x = 44$$
$$x = 11$$

Substitute 11 for x in the equation $y = x + 3$ and solve for y.
$$y = 11 + 3 = 14$$

The solution is $(11, 14)$.

59. Descriptions may vary.
$$y = 2x$$
$$0.03x + 0.07y = 340$$

Substitute $2x$ for y in the second equation and solve for x.
$$0.03x + 0.07(2x) = 340$$
$$0.03x + 0.14x = 340$$
$$0.17x = 340$$
$$x = 2000$$

Substitute 2000 for x in the equation $y = 2x$ and solve for y.
$$y = 2(2000) = 4000.$$

The solution is $(2000, 4000)$.

sides of equation (1) by -10, yielding the system
$$-10x - 10y = -3000$$
$$10x + 15y = 3250$$

Add the left sides and right sides, and solve for y.
$$\begin{array}{r} -10x - 10y = -3000 \\ \underline{10x + 15y = 3250} \\ 5y = 250 \\ y = 50 \end{array}$$

Substitute 50 for y in equation (1) and solve for x.
$$x + 50 = 300$$
$$x = 250$$

The theater should sell 250 of the $10 tickets and 50 of the $15 tickets.

61.
$$P = 2(L + W)$$
$$P = 2L + 2W$$
$$P - 2W = 2L$$
$$\frac{P - 2W}{2} = L \quad \text{or} \quad L = \frac{P - 2W}{2}$$

63.
$$A = P(1 + rt)$$
$$A = P + Prt$$
$$A - P = Prt$$
$$\frac{A - P}{Pt} = r \quad \text{or} \quad r = \frac{A - P}{Pt}$$

65.
$$-4(7x - 3) = -4(7x) - (-4)(3)$$
$$= -28x - (-12)$$
$$= -28x + 12$$

Description: *linear expression in one variable*

67.
$$-4(7x - 3) = 5x + 2$$
$$-28x + 12 = 5x + 2$$
$$-33x + 12 = 2$$
$$-33x = -10$$
$$x = \frac{10}{33}$$

The solution is $\frac{10}{33}$.

Description: *linear equation in one variable*

Homework 6.6

1. Check $(4,1)$:

$y < 2x - 3$

$1 \overset{?}{<} 2(4) - 3$

$1 \overset{?}{<} 8 - 3$

$1 \overset{?}{<} 5$ true

The ordered pair $(4,1)$ satisfies the inequality.

Check $(-2,3)$:

$y < 2x - 3$

$3 \overset{?}{<} 2(-2) - 3$

$3 \overset{?}{<} -4 - 3$

$3 \overset{?}{<} -7$ false

The ordered pair $(-2,3)$ does not satisfy the inequality.

Check $(-3,-1)$:

$y < 2x - 3$

$-1 \overset{?}{<} 2(-3) - 3$

$-1 \overset{?}{<} -6 - 3$

$-1 \overset{?}{<} -9$ false

The ordered pair $(-3,-1)$ does not satisfy the inequality.

3. Check $(-3,-1)$:

$2x - 5y \geq 10$

$2(-3) - 5(-1) \overset{?}{\geq} 10$

$-6 - (-5) \overset{?}{\geq} 10$

$-6 + 5 \overset{?}{\geq} 10$

$-1 \overset{?}{\geq} 10$ false

The ordered pair $(-3,-1)$ does not satisfy the inequality.

Check $(-1,-4)$:

$2x - 5y \geq 10$

$2(-1) - 5(-4) \overset{?}{\geq} 10$

$-2 - (-20) \overset{?}{\geq} 10$

$-2 + 20 \overset{?}{\geq} 10$

$18 \overset{?}{\geq} 10$ true

The ordered pair $(-1,-4)$ satisfies the inequality.

Check $(5,0)$:

$2x - 5y \geq 10$

$2(5) - 5(0) \overset{?}{\geq} 10$

$10 - 0 \overset{?}{\geq} 10$

$10 \overset{?}{\geq} 10$ true

The ordered pair $(5,0)$ satisfies the inequality.

5. The graph of $y > x - 3$ is the region above the line $y = x - 3$. We use a dashed line along the border to indicate that the points on the line $y = x - 3$ are not solutions of $y > x - 3$.

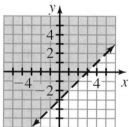

7. The graph of $y \leq -2x + 3$ is the line $y = -2x + 3$ and the region below that line. We use a solid line along the border to indicate that the points on the line $y = -2x + 3$ are solutions of $y \leq -2x + 3$.

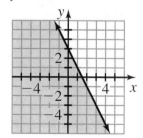

9. The graph of $y < \frac{1}{3}x + 1$ is the region below the line $y = \frac{1}{3}x + 1$. We use a dashed line along the border to indicate that the points on the line $y = \frac{1}{3}x + 1$ are not solutions of $y < \frac{1}{3}x + 1$.

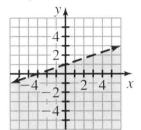

11. The graph of $y \geq -\frac{3}{5}x - 1$ is the line $y = -\frac{3}{5}x - 1$ and the region above that line. We use a solid line along the border to indicate that the points on the line $y = -\frac{3}{5}x - 1$ are solutions of $y \geq -\frac{3}{5}x - 1$.

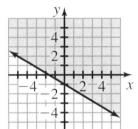

13. The graph of $y > x$ is the region above the line $y = x$. We use a dashed line along the border to indicate that the points on the line $y = x$ are not solutions of $y > x$.

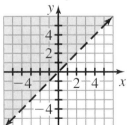

15. First, we get y alone on one side of the inequality.

$y - 2x < 0$

$\quad y < 2x$

The graph of $y < 2x$ is the region below the line $y = 2x$. We use a dashed line along the border to indicate that the points on the line $y = 2x$ are not solutions of $y - 2x < 0$.

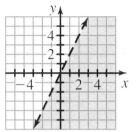

17. First, we get y alone on one side of the inequality.

$3x + y \leq 2$

$\quad y \leq -3x + 2$

The graph of $y \leq -3x + 2$ is the line $y = -3x + 2$ and the region below that line. We use a solid line along the border to indicate that the points on the line are solutions to $3x + y \leq 2$.

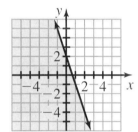

19. First, we get y alone on one side of the inequality.

$4x - y > 1$

$\quad -y > -4x + 1$

$\quad y < 4x - 1$

The graph of $y < 4x - 1$ is the region below the line $y = 4x - 1$. We use a dashed line along the border to indicate that the points on the line are not solutions to $4x - y > 1$.

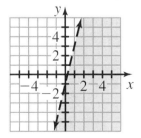

21. First, we get y alone on one side of the inequality.

$$4x - 3y \ge 0$$
$$-3y \ge -4x$$
$$y \le \frac{4}{3}x$$

The graph of $y \le \frac{4}{3}x$ is the line $y = \frac{4}{3}x$ and the region below that line. We use a solid line along the border to indicate that the points on the line are solutions to $4x - 3y \ge 0$.

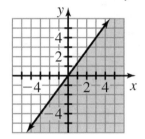

23. First, we get y alone on one side of the inequality.

$$4x + 5y \ge 10$$
$$5y \ge -4x + 10$$
$$y \ge -\frac{4}{5}x + 2$$

The graph of $y \ge -\frac{4}{5}x + 2$ is the line

$y = -\frac{4}{5}x + 2$ and the region above that line. We use a solid line along the border to indicate that the points on the line are solutions of $4x + 5y \ge 10$.

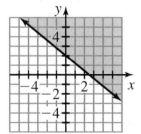

25. First, we get y alone on one side of the inequality.

$$2x - 5y < 5$$
$$-5y < -2x + 5$$
$$y > \frac{2}{5}x - 1$$

The graph of $y > \frac{2}{5}x - 1$ is the region above the

line $y = \frac{2}{5}x - 1$. We use a dashed line along the

border to indicate that the points on the line are not solutions of $2x - 5y < 5$.

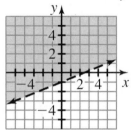

27. First, we get y alone on one side of the inequality.

$$3(x - 2) + y \le -2$$
$$3x - 6 + y \le -2$$
$$y \le -3x + 4$$

The graph of $y \le -3x + 4$ is the line

$y = -3x + 4$ and the region below that line. We use a solid line along the border to indicate tha the points on the line are solutions of $y \le -3x + 4$.

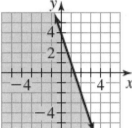

29. The graph of $y > 3$ is the region above the line $y = 3$. We use a dashed line along the border to indicate that the points on the line are not solutions to $y > 3$.

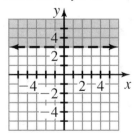

31. The graph of $x \geq -3$ is the vertical line $x = -3$ and the region to the right of that line. We use a solid line along the border to indicate that the points on the line are solutions to $x \geq -3$.

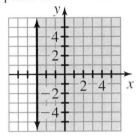

33. The graph of $x < -2$ is the region to the left of the vertical line $x = -2$. We use a dashed line along the border to indicate that the points on the line are not solutions to $x < -2$.

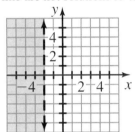

35. The graph of $y \leq 0$ is the line $y = 0$ and the region below that line. We use a solid line along the border to indicate that the points on the line are solutions to $y \leq 0$

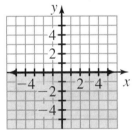

37. First we sketch the graph of $y \geq \frac{1}{3}x - 3$ and the graph of $y \leq -\frac{3}{2}x + 2$. The graph of $y \geq \frac{1}{3}x - 3$ is the line $y = \frac{1}{3}x - 3$ (graph the line with a solid line) and the region above the line. The graph of $y \leq -\frac{3}{2}x + 2$ is the line $y = -\frac{3}{2}x + 2$ (graph the line with a solid line) and the region below that line. The graph of the solution set of the system is the intersection of the graphs of the

inequalities.

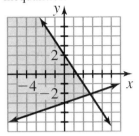

39. First we sketch the graph of $y > 2x - 3$ and the graph of $y > -\frac{3}{4}x + 1$. The graph of $y > 2x - 3$ is the region above the line $y = 2x - 3$ (graph the line with a dashed line). The graph of $y > -\frac{3}{4}x + 1$ is the region above the line $y = -\frac{3}{4}x + 1$ (graph the line with a dashed line). The graph of the solution set of the system is the intersection of the graphs of the inequalities.

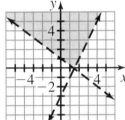

41. First we sketch the graph of $y \leq -\frac{2}{3}x - 3$ and the graph of $y > 2x + 1$. The graph of $y \leq -\frac{2}{3}x - 3$ is the line $y = -\frac{2}{3}x - 3$ (graph the line with a solid line) and the region below that line. The graph of $y > 2x + 1$ is the region above the line $y = 2x + 1$ (graph the line with a dashed line). The graph of the solution set of the system is the intersection of the graphs of the inequalities.

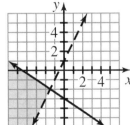

43. First we sketch the graph of $y \ge -2x - 1$ and the graph of $y > \frac{1}{3}x + 2$. The graph of $y \ge -2x - 1$ is the line $y = -2x - 1$ (graph the line with a solid line) and the region above that line. The graph of $y > \frac{1}{3}x + 2$ is the region above the line $y = \frac{1}{3}x + 2$ (graph the line with a dashed line). The graph of the solution set of the system is the intersection of the graphs of the inequalities.

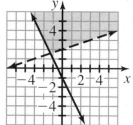

45. First we sketch the graph of $y > -3x + 4$ and the graph of $y \le 2x + 3$. The graph of $y > -3x + 4$ is the region above the line $y = -3x + 4$ (graph the line with a dashed line). The graph of $y \le 2x + 3$ is the line $y = 2x + 3$ (graph the line with a solid line) and the region below that line. The graph of the solution set of the system is the intersection of the graphs of the inequalities.

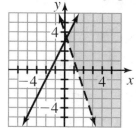

47. First we sketch the graph of $y \le \frac{2}{3}x$ and the graph of $y < -\frac{2}{5}x$. The graph of $y \le \frac{2}{3}x$ is the line $y = \frac{2}{3}x$ (graph the line with a solid line) and the region below that line. The graph of $y < -\frac{2}{5}x$ is the region below the line $y = -\frac{2}{5}x$ (graph the line with a dashed line). The graph of the solution set of the system is the intersection

of the graphs of the inequalities.

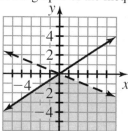

49. First we get y alone on one side of each inequality.

$$5x - 3y \le 12 \qquad\qquad -2y < x$$
$$-3y \le -5x + 12 \qquad\qquad y > -\frac{1}{2}x$$
$$\frac{-3y}{-3} \ge \frac{-5x + 12}{-3}$$
$$y \ge \frac{5}{3}x - 4$$

Next we sketch the graph of $y \ge \frac{5}{3}x - 4$ and the graph of $y > -\frac{1}{2}x$. The graph of $y \ge \frac{5}{3}x - 4$ is the line $y = \frac{5}{3}x - 4$ (graph the line with a solid line) and the region above that line. The graph of $y > -\frac{1}{2}x$ is the region above the line $y = -\frac{1}{2}x$ (graph the line with a dashed line). The graph of the solution set of the system is the intersection of the graphs of the inequalities.

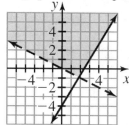

51. First we get y alone on one side of each inequality.

$$x - y \le 2 \qquad\qquad 2x + y < 1$$
$$-y \le -x + 2 \qquad\qquad y < -2x + 1$$
$$y \ge x - 2$$

Next we sketch the graph of $y \ge x - 2$ and the graph of $y < -2x + 1$. The graph of $y \ge x - 2$ is the line $y = x - 2$ (graph the line with a solid line) and the region above that line. The graph of $y < -2x + 1$ is the region below the line $y = -2x + 1$ (graph the line with a dashed line). The graph of the solution set of the system is the intersection of the graphs of the inequalities.

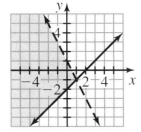

53. First we get y alone on one side of each inequality.

$$2x - 3y > 3 \qquad\qquad 3x + 5y \ge 10$$
$$-3y > -2x + 3 \qquad\qquad 5y \ge -3x + 10$$
$$y < \frac{2}{3}x - 1 \qquad\qquad y \ge -\frac{3}{5}x + 2$$

Next we sketch the graph of $y < \frac{2}{3}x - 1$ and the graph of $y \ge -\frac{3}{5}x + 2$. The graph of $y < \frac{2}{3}x - 1$ is the region below the line $y = \frac{2}{3}x - 1$ (graph the line with a dashed line). The graph of $y \ge -\frac{3}{5}x + 2$ is the line $y = -\frac{3}{5}x + 2$ (graph the line with a solid line) and the region above that line. The graph of the solution set of the system is the intersection of the graphs of the inequalities.

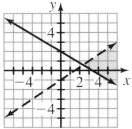

55. First we get y alone on one side of each inequality.

$$1 + y \ge \frac{1}{2}(x - 4) \qquad 3 - y > 2(x - 1)$$
$$y \ge \frac{1}{2}x - 2 - 1 \qquad -y > 2x - 2 - 3$$
$$y \ge \frac{1}{2}x - 3 \qquad -y > 2x - 5$$
$$y < -2x + 5$$

Next we sketch the graph of $y \ge \frac{1}{2}x - 3$ and the graph of $y < -2x + 5$. The graph of $y \ge \frac{1}{2}x - 3$ is the region above the line $y = \frac{1}{2}x - 3$ (graph the line with a solid line). The graph of $y < -2x + 5$ is the line $y = -2x + 5$ (graph the line with a dashed line) and the region below that line. The graph of the solution set of the system is the intersection of the graphs of the inequalities.

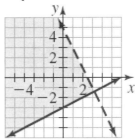

57. First we sketch the graph of $y < 3$ and the graph of $x \ge -2$. The graph of $y < 3$ is the region below the line $y = 3$ (graph the line with a dashed line). The graph of $x \ge -2$ is the vertical line $x = -2$ (graph the line with a solid line) and the rgion to the right of that line. The graph of the solution set of the system is the intersection of the graphs of the inequalities.

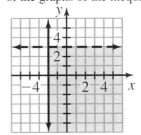

59. First we sketch the graph of $y \leq 1$, the graph of $y \geq -2$, the graph of $x \geq -3$, and the graph of $x \leq 4$. The graph of $y \leq 1$ is the horizontal line $y = 1$ (graph the line with a solid line) and the region below that line. The graph of $y \geq -2$ is the horizontal line $y = -2$ (graph the line with a solid line) and the region above that line. The graph of $x \geq -3$ is the vertical line $x = -3$ (graph the line with a solid line) and the region to the right of that line. The graph of $x \leq 4$ is the vertical line $x = 4$ (graph the line with a solid line) and the region to the left of that line. The graph of the solution set of the system is the intersection of the graphs of the inequalities.

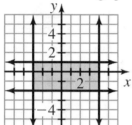

61. First we get y alone on one side of each of the first two inequalities.

$$2x - 5y \geq -5 \qquad\qquad 2x - 5y \leq 15$$
$$-5y \geq -2x - 5 \qquad\quad -5y \leq -2x + 15$$
$$y \leq \frac{2}{5}x + 1 \qquad\qquad y \geq \frac{2}{5}x - 3$$

Next, we sketch the graph of $y \leq \frac{2}{5}x + 1$, the graph of $y \geq \frac{2}{5}x - 3$, the graph of $x \geq -1$, and the graph of $x \leq 3$. The graph of $y \leq \frac{2}{5}x + 1$ is the line $y = \frac{2}{5}x + 1$ (graph the line with a solid line) and the region below that line. The graph of $y \geq \frac{2}{5}x - 3$ is the line $y = \frac{2}{5}x - 3$ (graph the line with a solid line) and the region above that line. The graph of $x \geq -1$ is the vertical line $x = -1$ (graph the line with a solid line) and the region to the right of that line. The graph of $x \leq 3$ is the vertical line $x = 3$ (graph the line with a solid line) and the region to the left of that line. The graph of the solution set of the system is the intersection of the graphs of the

inequalities.

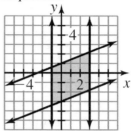

63. First we sketch the graph of $y < -x + 5$, the graph of $y \leq x + 5$, and the graph of $y > \frac{1}{2}x + 1$. The graph of $y < -x + 5$ is the line $y = -x + 5$ (graph the line with a dashed line) and the region below that line. The graph of $y \leq x + 5$ is the line $y = x + 5$ (graph the line with a solid line) and the region below the line. The graph of $y > \frac{1}{2}x + 1$ is the line $y = \frac{1}{2}x + 1$ (graph the line with a dashed line) and the region above the line. The graph of the solution set of the system is the intersection of the graphs of the inequalities.

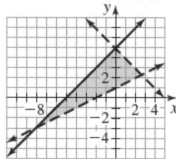

65. a. Answers may vary. By entering the sets of data into a graphing calculator, using the linear regression feature, and rounding to the second decimal place, we find the following equations.

$$B(t) = 0.20t + 69.97$$
$$T(t) = 0.17t + 51.73$$

b. The life expectancies of U.S. males from 0 years to 20 years must be less than or equal to $T(t)$ and greater than or equal to $B(t)$. Also, limiting the years to 1980 to 2015 means that t must be greater than or equal to 0 and less than or equal to 35. Therefore, the system of equations is:

$L \le 0.20t + 69.97$

$L \ge 0.17t + 51.73$

$t \ge 0$

$t \le 35$

c.

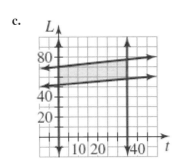

d.
$$T(34) \le L \le B(34)$$
$$0.17(34) + 51.73 \le L \le 0.20(34) + 69.97$$
$$5.78 + 51.73 \le L \le 6.8 + 69.97$$
$$57.51 \le L \le 76.77$$

67. a. Answers may vary. By entering the sets of data into a graphing calculator, using the linear regression feature, and rounding to the second decimal place, we find the following equations.

$B(w) = 0.44w + 84.21$

$I(w) = 0.44w + 89.21$

b. The ski lengths for beginning to intermediate skiers must be greater than or equal to $B(w)$ and less than or equal to $I(w)$. Also, w must be greater than or equal to 130 and less than or equal to 150. Therefore, the system of equations is:

$L \ge 0.44w + 84.21$

$L \le 0.44w + 89.21$

$w \ge 130$

$w \le 150$

c.

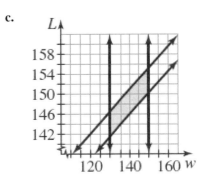

d.
$$B(140) \le L \le I(140)$$
$$0.44(140) + 84.21 \le L \le 0.44(140) + 89.21$$
$$61.6 + 84.21 \le L \le 61.6 + 89.21$$
$$145.81 \le L \le 150.81$$

69. First we find the equation of the border line. From the graph we see the y-intercept is $(0, 2)$, the x-intercept is $(4, 0)$, and so the slope is $m = \dfrac{-2}{4} = -\dfrac{1}{2}$. Therefore, the equation of the border line is $y = -\dfrac{1}{2}x + 2$. Since the border line is solid, and the region below the line is shaded, the inequality is $y \le -\dfrac{1}{2}x + 2$.

71. Start by isolating y on one side of the inequality.
$5x - 2y < 6$

$-2y < -5x + 6$

$y > \dfrac{5}{2}x - 3$

The student is incorrect. The graph of $5x - 2y < 6$ is the region above the line $5x - 2y = 6$.

73. a. The points A, B, C, and D satisfy the inequality $y > ax + b$ because the points lie above the line $y = ax + b$.

b. The points A, B, C, F, G, and H satisfy the inequality $y \le cx + d$ because the points either lie on the line $y = cx + d$ or in the region below the line.

c. Comparing the results from parts (a) and (b), we see that the points A, B, and C satisfy both $y > ax + b$ and $y \le cx + d$.

d. Combining the results from parts (a) and (b), we see that the remaining point, E, satisfies neither $y > ax + b$ nor $y \le cx + d$.

75. Answers may vary. Some examples are given below.

Solutions: $(1,3)$, $(2,5)$, $(0,0)$

Not solutions: $(4,2)$, $(4,4)$, $(5,3)$

77. Answers may vary. One possible answer:
$y > x$

$(3,4)$ is a solution but $(4,3)$ is not a solution.

79. The intersection of the solution regions of $y \ge 2x+1$ and $y \le 2x+1$ is the solid line $y = 2x+1$.

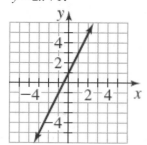

81. Answers may vary.

83. The equation $y = 2x - 1$ is in slope-intercept form, so the slope is $m = 2$ (or $m = \frac{2}{1}$) and the y-intercept is $(0,-1)$. We first plot $(0,-1)$. From this point we move 1 unit to the right and 2 units up, where we plot the point $(1,1)$. We then sketch the line that contains these two points.

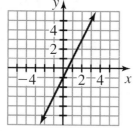

85. The graph of $y \le 2x - 1$ is the line $y = 2x - 1$ and the region below that line. We use a solid line along the border to indicate that the points on the line $y = 2x - 1$ are solutions of $y \le 2x - 1$.

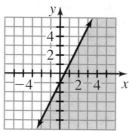

87.
$$3 \le 2x - 1$$
$$3 + 1 \le 2x - 1 + 1$$
$$4 \le 2x$$
$$\frac{4}{2} \le \frac{2x}{2}$$
$$2 \le x \quad \text{or} \quad x \ge 2$$

In interval notation, the solution set is $[2, \infty)$.

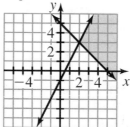

89. First we sketch the graph of $y \le 2x - 1$ and the graph of $y \ge -x + 5$. The graph of $y \le 2x - 1$ is the line $y = 2x - 1$ (graph the line with a solid line) and the region below that line. The graph of $y \ge -x + 5$ is the line $y = -x + 5$ (graph the line with a solid line) and the region above that line. The graph of the solution set of the system is the intersection of the graphs of the inequalities.

91. $y = 2x - 1$

$y = -x + 5$

Substitute $-x + 5$ for y in the first equation and solve for x.

$-x + 5 = 2x - 1$

$-3x + 5 = -1$

$-3x = -6$

$x = 2$

Substitute 2 for x in the equation $y = -x + 5$ and solve for y.

$y = -(2) + 5 = 3$

The solution is $(2, 3)$.

93. Answers may vary.

95. Answers may vary.

97. Answers may vary.

Chapter 6 Review Exercises

1. $y = 2x - 3$

$y = -3x + 7$

To begin, we graph both equations in the same coordinate system.

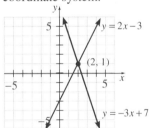

The intersection point is $(2, 1)$. So, the solution is the ordered pair $(2, 1)$.

2. $y = \frac{3}{2}x + 4$

$y = -\frac{1}{2}x - 4$

To begin, we graph both equations in the same coordinate system.

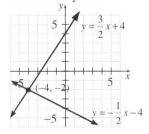

The intersection point is $(-4, -2)$. So, the solution is the ordered pair $(-4, -2)$.

3. $y = \frac{2}{5}x$

$y = -2x$

To begin, we graph both equations in the same coordinate system.

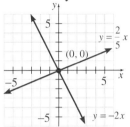

The intersection point is $(0, 0)$. So, the solution is the ordered pair $(0, 0)$.

4. $4x + y = 3$

$-3x + y = -4$

To begin, we rewrite each equation in slope-intercept form.

$4x + y = 3 \qquad\qquad -3x + y = -4$

$\quad y = -4x + 3 \qquad\qquad y = 3x - 4$

Next, we graph both equations in the same coordinate system.

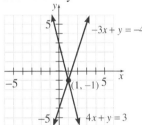

The intersection point is $(1, -1)$. So, the solution is the ordered pair $(1, -1)$.

5. $3x - 5y = -1$

$y = -2(x - 4)$

To begin, we rewrite each equation in slope-intercept form.

$3x - 5y = -1 \qquad y = -2(x - 4)$

$-5y = -3x - 1 \qquad = -2x + 8$

$y = \dfrac{3}{5}x + \dfrac{1}{5}$

Next, we graph both equations in the same coordinate system.

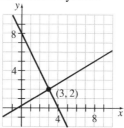

The intersection point is $(3, 2)$. So, the solution is the ordered pair $(3, 2)$.

6. $x - 3y = 3$

$2x + 3y = -12$

To begin, we rewrite each equation in slope-intercept form.

$x - 3y = 3 \qquad 2x + 3y = -12$

$-3y = -x + 3 \qquad 3y = -2x - 12$

$y = \dfrac{1}{3}x - 1 \qquad y = -\dfrac{2}{3}x - 4$

Next, we graph both equations in the same coordinate system.

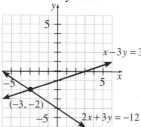

The intersection point is $(-3, -2)$. So, the solution is the ordered pair $(-3, -2)$.

7. $3x - 2y = 11$

$y = 5x - 16$

Substitute $5x - 16$ for y in the first equation and solve for x.

$3x - 2(5x - 16) = 11$

$3x - 10x + 32 = 11$

$-7x + 32 = 11$

$-7x = -21$

$x = 3$

Substitute 3 for x in the equation $y = 5x - 16$ and solve for y.

$y = 5(3) - 16 = -1$

The solution is $(3, -1)$.

8. $4x - 3y - 5 = 0$

$x = 4 - 2y$

Substitute $4 - 2y$ for x in the first equation and solve for y.

$4(4 - 2y) - 3y - 5 = 0$

$16 - 8y - 3y - 5 = 0$

$-11y + 11 = 0$

$-11y = -11$

$y = 1$

Substitute 1 for y in the equation $x = 4 - 2y$ and solve for x.

$x = 4 - 2(1) = 4 - 2 = 2$

The solution is $(2, 1)$. **9.** $y = -5x$

$y = 2x$

Substitute $2x$ for y in the first equation and solve for x.

$2x = -5x$

$7x = 0$

$x = 0$

Substitute 0 for x in the equation $y = 2x$ and solve for y.

$y = 2(0) = 0$

The solution is $(0, 0)$.

10. $y = -3(x+2)$

$y = 4(x-5)$

Substitute $4(x-5)$ for y in the first equation and solve for x.

$4(x-5) = -3(x+2)$

$4x - 20 = -3x - 6$

$7x - 20 = -6$

$7x = 14$

$x = 2$

Substitute 2 for x in the equation $y = 4(x-5)$ and solve for y.

$y = 4(2-5) = 4(-3) = -12$

The solution is $(2, -12)$.

11. $x + y = -1$

$2x - y = 4$

Solve the first equation for y.

$x + y = -1$

$y = -x - 1$

Substitute $-x-1$ for y in the second equation and solve for x.

$2x - (-x-1) = 4$

$2x + x + 1 = 4$

$3x + 1 = 4$

$3x = 3$

$x = 1$

Substitute 1 for x in the equation $y = -x-1$ and solve for y.

$y = -(1) - 1 = -2$

The solution is $(1, -2)$.

12. $x + 2y = 5$

$4x + 2y = -4$

Solve the first equation for x.

$x + 2y = 5$

$x = -2y + 5$

Substitute $-2y+5$ for x in the second equation and solve for y.

$4(-2y+5) + 2y = -4$

$-8y + 20 + 2y = -4$

$-6y + 20 = -4$

$-6y = -24$

$y = 4$

Substitute 4 for y in the equation $x = -2y+5$ and solve for x.

$x = -2(4) + 5 = -8 + 5 = -3$

The solution is $(-3, 4)$.

13. $y = -2.19x + 3.51$

$y = 1.54x - 6.22$

Substitute $1.54x - 6.22$ for y in the first equation and solve for x.

$1.54x - 6.22 = -2.19x + 3.51$

$3.73x - 6.22 = 3.51$

$3.73x = 9.73$

$x = \dfrac{9.73}{3.73} \approx 2.609$

Substitute 2.609 for x in the equation $y = 1.54x - 6.22$ and solve for y.

$y = 1.54(2.609) - 6.22 \approx -2.202$

The approximate solution is $(2.61, -2.20)$.

14. $y = -4.98x - 1.18$

$y = -0.57x + 4.08$

Substitute $-0.57x + 4.08$ for y in the first equation and solve for x.

$-0.57x + 4.08 = -4.98x - 1.18$

$4.41x + 4.08 = -1.18$

$4.41x = -5.26$

$x = \dfrac{-5.26}{4.41} \approx -1.193$

Substitute -1.193 for x in the equation $y = -0.57x + 4.08$ and solve for y.

$y = -0.57(-1.193) + 4.08 \approx 4.760$

The approximate solution is $(-1.19, 4.76)$.

15. $x - 2y = -1$ Equation (1)

$3x + 5y = 19$ Equation (2)

To eliminate the x terms, we multiply both sides of equation (1) by -3, yielding the system

$-3x + 6y = 3$

$3x + 5y = 19$

The coefficients of the x terms are equal in absolute value and opposite in sign. Add the left sides and the right sides of the equations and solve for y.

$-3x + 6y = 3$

$\underline{3x + 5y = 19}$

$11y = 22$

$y = 2$

Substitute 2 for y in equation (1) and solve for x.

$x - 2(2) = -1$

$x - 4 = -1$

$x = 3$

The solution is $(3, 2)$.

16. $2x - 5y = -3$ Equation (1)

$4x + 3y = -19$ Equation (2)

To eliminate the x terms, we multiply both sides of equation (1) by -2, yielding the system

$-4x + 10y = 6$

$4x + 3y = -19$

The coefficients of the x terms are equal in absolute value and opposite in sign. Add the left sides and the right sides of the equations and solve for y.

$-4x + 10y = 6$

$\underline{4x + 3y = -19}$

$13y = -13$

$y = -1$

Substitute -1 for y in equation (1) and solve for x.

$2x - 5(-1) = -3$

$2x + 5 = -3$

$2x = -8$

$x = -4$

The solution is $(-4, -1)$.

17. $3x + 8y = 2$ Equation (1)

$5x - 2y = -12$ Equation (2)

To eliminate the y terms, we multiply both sides of equation (2) by 4, yielding the system

$3x + 8y = 2$

$20x - 8y = -48$

The coefficients of the y terms are equal in absolute value and opposite in sign. Add the left sides and the right sides of the equations and solve for x.

$3x + 8y = 2$

$\underline{20x - 8y = -48}$

$23x = -46$

$x = -2$

Substitute -2 for x in equation (2) and solve for y.

$5(-2) - 2y = -12$

$-10 - 2y = -12$

$-2y = -2$

$y = 1$

The solution is $(-2, 1)$.

18. $4x - 3y = -6$ Equation (1)

$-7x + 5y = 11$ Equation (2)

To eliminate the y terms, we multiply both sides of equation (1) by 5 and both sides of equation (2) by 3, yielding the system

$20x - 15y = -30$

$-21x + 15y = 33$

The coefficients of the y terms are equal in absolute value and opposite in sign. Add the left sides and the right sides of the equations and solve for x.

$20x - 15y = -30$

$\underline{-21x + 15y = 33}$

$-x = 3$

$x = -3$

Substitute -3 for x in equation (1) and solve for y.

$4(-3) - 3y = -6$

$-12 - 3y = -6$

$-3y = 6$

$y = -2$

The solution is $(-3, -2)$.

19. $-2x - 5y = 2$ Equation (1)

    $3x + 6y = 0$ Equation (2)

To eliminate the x terms, we multiply both sides of equation (1) by 3 and both sides of equation (2) by 2, yielding the system

$-6x - 15y = 6$

  $6x + 12y = 0$

The coefficients of the x terms are equal in absolute value and opposite in sign. Add the left sides and the right sides of the equations and solve for y.

$-6x - 15y = 6$

$\underline{6x + 12y = 0}$

    $-3y = 6$

      $y = -2$

Substitute -2 for y in equation (2) and solve for x.

$3x + 6(-2) = 0$

  $3x - 12 = 0$

     $3x = 12$

      $x = 4$

The solution is $(4, -2)$.

20. $y = 3x - 5$ Equation (1)

    $y = -2x + 5$ Equation (2)

$\rightarrow$ $3x - y = 5$

    $2x + y = 5$

The coefficients of the y terms are equal in absolute value and opposite in sign. Add the left sides and the right sides of the equations and solve for x.

$3x - y = 5$

$\underline{2x + y = 5}$

  $5x = 10$

    $x = 2$

Substitute 2 for x in equation (2) and solve for y.

$y = -2(2) + 5 = -4 + 5 = 1$

The solution is $(2, 1)$.

21. $2(x + 3) + y = 6$

   $x - 3(y - 2) = -1$

Begin by writing each equation in standard form.

$2(x + 3) + y = 6$ $x - 3(y - 2) = -1$

   $2x + 6 + y = 6$ $x - 3y + 6 = -1$

      $2x + y = 0$ $x - 3y = -7$

This yields the system

$2x + y = 0$ Equation (1)

$x - 3y = -7$ Equation (2)

To eliminate the y terms, we multiply both sides of equation (1) by 3, yielding the system

$6x + 3y = 0$

  $x - 3y = -7$

The coefficients of the y terms are equal in absolute value and opposite in sign. Add the left sides and the right sides of the equations and solve for x.

$6x + 3y = 0$

$\underline{x - 3y = -7}$

    $7x = -7$

     $x = -1$

Substitute -1 for x in equation (1) and solve for y.

$2(-1) + y = 0$

  $-2 + y = 0$

       $y = 2$

The solution is $(-1, 2)$.

22. $\dfrac{1}{2}x - \dfrac{2}{3}y = -\dfrac{5}{3}$ Equation (1)

$\dfrac{1}{3}x - \dfrac{3}{2}y = -\dfrac{13}{6}$ Equation (2)

To eliminate the x terms (and clear fractions), we multiply both sides of equation (1) by -12 and both sides of equation (2) by 18, yielding the system

$-6x + 8y = 20$

$6x - 27y = -39$

The coefficients of the x terms are equal in absolute value and opposite in sign. Add the left sides and the right sides of the equations and solve for y.

$-6x + 8y = 20$

$\underline{6x - 27y = -39}$

$-19y = -19$

$y = 1$

Substitute 1 for y in equation (2) and solve for y.

$\dfrac{1}{3}x - \dfrac{3}{2}(1) = -\dfrac{13}{6}$

$\dfrac{1}{3}x - \dfrac{3}{2} = -\dfrac{13}{6}$

$\dfrac{1}{3}x = -\dfrac{13}{6} + \dfrac{9}{6}$

$\dfrac{1}{3}x = -\dfrac{4}{6}$

$x = -\dfrac{4}{2} = -2$

The solution is $(-2, 1)$.

23. $y = 4.59x + 1.25$ Equation (1)

$y = 0.52x + 4.39$ Equation (2)

$\rightarrow \quad 4.59x - y = -1.25$

$-0.52x + y = 4.39$

The coefficients of the y terms are equal in absolute value and opposite in sign. Add the left sides and the right sides of the equations and solve for x.

$4.59x - y = -1.25$

$\underline{-0.52x + y = 4.39}$

$4.07x = 3.14$

$x = \dfrac{3.14}{4.07} \approx 0.771$

Substitute 0.771 for x in equation (1) and solve for y.

$y = 4.59(0.771) + 1.25 \approx 4.789$

The approximate solution is $(0.77, 4.79)$.

24. $y = 0.91x - 3.57$ Equation (1)

$y = -3.58x + 6.05$ Equation (2)

$\rightarrow \quad 0.91x - y = 3.57$

$3.58x + y = 6.05$

The coefficients of the y terms are equal in absolute value and opposite in sign. Add the left sides and the right sides of the equations and solve for x.

$0.91x - y = 3.57$

$\underline{3.58x + y = 6.05}$

$4.49x = 9.62$

$x = \dfrac{9.62}{4.49} \approx 2.143$

Substitute 2.143 for x in equation (1) and solve for y.

$y = 0.91(2.143) - 3.57 \approx -1.620$

The approximate solution is $(2.14, -1.62)$.

25. $2x - 7y = -13$

$5x + 3y = -12$

To eliminate the x terms, we multiply both sides of equation (1) by 5 and both sides of equation (2) by -2, yielding the system

$10x - 35y = -65$

$-10x - 6y = 24$

The coefficients of the x terms are equal in absolute value and opposite in sign. Add the left sides and the right sides of the equations and solve for y.

$10x - 35y = -65$

$\underline{-10x - 6y = 24}$

$-41y = -41$

$y = 1$

Substitute 1 for y in equation (1) and solve for x.

$2x - 7(1) = -13$

$2x - 7 = -13$

$2x = -6$

$x = -3$

The solution is $(-3, 1)$.

26. $4x + 7y = 8$

$\qquad x = 3 - 2y$

Substitute $3 - 2y$ for x in the first equation and solve for y.

$4(3 - 2y) + 7y = 8$

$\quad 12 - 8y + 7y = 8$

$\qquad 12 - y = 8$

$\qquad\quad -y = -4$

$\qquad\quad\ y = 4$

Substitute 4 for y in the equation $x = 3 - 2y$ and solve for x.

$x = 3 - 2(4) = 3 - 8 = -5$

The solution is $(-5, 4)$.

27. $-3x + 7y = 6$

$\qquad 6x + 2y = -12$

To eliminate the x terms, we multiply both sides of equation (1) by 2, yielding the system

$-6x + 14y = 12$

$\quad 6x + 2y = -12$

The coefficients of the x terms are equal in absolute value and opposite in sign. Add the left sides and the right sides of the equations and solve for y.

$-6x + 14y = 12$

$\underline{\quad 6x + 2y = -12}$

$\qquad 16y = 0$

$\qquad\quad y = 0$

Substitute 0 for y in equation (1) and solve for x.

$-3x + 7(0) = 6$

$\qquad -3x = 6$

$\qquad\quad x = -2$

The solution is $(-2, 0)$.

28. $y = -x + 7$

$y = 2x - 5$

Substitute $2x - 5$ for y in the first equation and solve for x.

$2x - 5 = -x + 7$

$3x - 5 = 7$

$\quad 3x = 12$

$\qquad x = 4$

Substitute 4 for x in the equation $y = 2x - 5$ and solve for y.

$y = 2(4) - 5 = 8 - 5 = 3$

The solution is $(4, 3)$.

29. $4x + 5y = -6$

$\qquad 2y = -3x - 8$

Solve the second equation for y.

$2y = -3x - 8$

$y = -\dfrac{3}{2}x - 4$

Substitute $-\dfrac{3}{2}x - 4$ for y in the first equation and solve for x.

$4x + 5\left(-\dfrac{3}{2}x - 4\right) = -6$

$\quad 4x - \dfrac{15}{2}x - 20 = -6$

$\qquad -\dfrac{7}{2}x - 20 = -6$

$\qquad\quad -\dfrac{7}{2}x = 14$

$\qquad\qquad x = -4$

Substitute -4 for x in the equation $y = -\dfrac{3}{2}x - 4$ and solve for y.

$y = -\dfrac{3}{2}(-4) - 4 = 6 - 4 = 2$

The solution is $(-4, 2)$.

30. $\qquad\qquad y = x - 2$

$3x + 5y - 30 = 0$

Substitute $x - 2$ for y in the second equation and solve for x.

$3x + 5(x - 2) - 30 = 0$

$\quad 3x + 5x - 10 - 30 = 0$

$\qquad\quad 8x - 40 = 0$

$\qquad\qquad 8x = 40$

$\qquad\qquad\ x = 5$

Substitute 5 for x in the equation $y = x - 2$ and solve for y.

$y = 5 - 2 = 3$

The solution is $(5, 3)$.

31. $2x - 3y = 0$

$5x - 7y = -1$

To eliminate the x terms, we multiply both sides of equation (1) by 5 and both sides of equation (2) by -2, yielding the system

$10x - 15y = 0$

$-10x + 14y = 2$

The coefficients of the x terms are equal in absolute value and opposite in sign. Add the left sides and the right sides of the equations and solve for y.

$10x - 15y = 0$

$\underline{-10x + 14y = 2}$

$-y = 2$

$y = -2$

Substitute -2 for y in equation (1) and solve for x.

$2x - 3(-2) = 0$

$2x + 6 = 0$

$2x = -6$

$x = -3$

The solution is $(-3, -2)$.

32. $\quad\quad y = -4x + 3 \rightarrow \quad 4x + y = 3 \quad$ Equation (1)

$8x + 2y = 6 \quad\quad\quad 8x + 2y = 6 \quad$ Equation (2)

To eliminate the x terms, we multiply both sides of equation (1) by -2, yielding the system

$-8x - 2y = -6$

$8x + 2y = 6$

The coefficients of the x terms are equal in absolute value and opposite in sign. Add the left sides and the right sides of the equations and solve for y.

$-8x - 2y = -6$

$\underline{8x + 2y = 6}$

$0 = 0 \quad$ true

The result is a true statement of the form $a = a$. Therefore, the system is dependent. The solution set is the infinite set of ordered pairs that satisfy the equation $y = -4x + 3$.

33. $2x - 6y = 4 \quad$ Equation (1)

$-3x + 9y = -3 \quad$ Equation (2)

To eliminate the x terms, we multiply both sides of equation (1) by 3 and both sides of equation (2) by 2, yielding the system

$6x - 18y = 12$

$-6x + 18y = -6$

The coefficients of the x terms are equal in absolute value and opposite in sign. Add the left sides and the right sides of the equations and solve for y.

$6x - 18y = 12$

$\underline{-6x + 18y = -6}$

$0 = 6 \quad$ false

The result is a false statement. Therefore, the system is inconsistent. The solution set is the empty set, $\varnothing$.

34. $2(4x - 3) - 5y = 12$

$5(3x - 1) + 2y = 6$

Begin by writing each equation in standard form.

$2(4x - 3) - 5y = 12 \quad\quad 5(3x - 1) + 2y = 6$

$8x - 6 - 5y = 12 \quad\quad\quad 15x - 5 + 2y = 6$

$8x - 5y = 18 \quad\quad\quad\quad 15x + 2y = 11$

This yields the system

$8x - 5y = 18 \quad$ Equation (1)

$15x + 2y = 11 \quad$ Equation (2)

To eliminate the y terms, we multiply both sides of equation (1) by 2 and both sides of equation (2) by 5, yielding the system

$16x - 10y = 36$

$75x + 10y = 55$

The coefficients of the y terms are equal in absolute value and opposite in sign. Add the left sides and the right sides of the equations and solve for x.

$16x - 10y = 36$

$\underline{75x + 10y = 55}$

$91x = 91$

$x = 1$

Substitute 1 for x in equation (2) and solve for y.

$15(1) + 2y = 11$

$15 + 2y = 11$

$2y = -4$

$y = -2$

The solution is $(1, -2)$.

35. First use the distributive property to simplify each equation.

$$2(3x-4)+3(2y-1)=-5$$
$$6x-8+6y-3=-5$$
$$6x+6y-11=-5$$
$$6x+6y=6$$
$$-3(2x+1)+4(y+3)=-7$$
$$-6x-3+4y+12=-7$$
$$-6x+4y+9=-7$$
$$-6x+4y=-16$$

Solve using elimination.

$$\begin{vmatrix} 6x+6y=6 \\ -6x+4y=-16 \end{vmatrix}$$

Add the two equations together.

$$\begin{array}{r} 6x+6y=6 \\ \underline{-6x+4y=-16} \\ 10y=-10 \\ y=-1 \end{array}$$

Substitute $y=-1$ into $6x+6y=6$ and solve for x.

$$6x+6y=6$$
$$6x+6(-1)=6$$
$$6x-6=6$$
$$6x=12$$
$$x=2$$

The solution is $(2,-1)$.

36. Solve using elimination. Multiply both sides of the first equation by 2.

$$\frac{6}{5}x-\frac{4}{3}y=8$$
$$\underline{-\frac{6}{5}x+\frac{8}{3}y=-4}$$
$$\frac{4}{3}y=4$$
$$y=3$$

Substitute $y=3$ into $\frac{3}{5}x-\frac{2}{3}y=4$ and solve for x.

$$\frac{3}{5}x-\frac{2}{3}(3)=4$$
$$\frac{3}{5}x-2=4$$
$$\frac{3}{5}x=6$$
$$x=10$$

The solution is $(10,3)$.

37. a. Answers may vary. One possibility: $(1,5)$

b. Answers may vary. One possibility: $(1,0)$

c. Answers may vary. One possibility: $(1,1)$

d. A point that satisfies both equations would be a solution to the system.

$$y=-2x+7$$
$$y=3x-3$$

Substitute $3x-3$ for y in the first equation and solve for x.

$$3x-3=-2x+7$$
$$5x-3=7$$
$$5x=10$$
$$x=2$$

Substitute 2 for x in the equation $y=3x-3$ and solve for y.

$$y=3(2)-3=6-3=3$$

The solution of the system is $(2,3)$.

Therefore, an ordered pair that satisfies both equations is $(2,3)$.

38. We can start by writing equations for the two lines.

Red Line:
Examining the graph, it appears that the points $(-1,3)$ and $(4,5)$ are on the graph.

$$m = \frac{5-3}{4-(-1)} = \frac{2}{5}$$

$$y - y_1 = m(x - x_1)$$

$$y - 5 = \frac{2}{5}(x - 4)$$

$$y - 5 = \frac{2}{5}x - \frac{8}{5}$$

$$y = \frac{2}{5}x + \frac{17}{5}$$

Blue Line:
Examining the graph, it appears that the points $(-2,3)$ and $(2,2)$ are on the graph.

$$m = \frac{2-3}{2-(-2)} = \frac{-1}{4} = -\frac{1}{4}$$

$$y - y_1 = m(x - x_1)$$

$$y - 2 = -\frac{1}{4}(x - 2)$$

$$y - 2 = -\frac{1}{4}x + \frac{1}{2}$$

$$y = -\frac{1}{4}x + \frac{5}{2}$$

Using the two equations, we get the system

$$y = \frac{2}{5}x + \frac{17}{5}$$

$$y = -\frac{1}{4}x + \frac{5}{2}$$

Substitute $-\frac{1}{4}x + \frac{5}{2}$ for y in the first equation and solve for x.

$$-\frac{1}{4}x + \frac{5}{2} = \frac{2}{5}x + \frac{17}{5}$$

$$-\frac{13}{20}x + \frac{5}{2} = \frac{17}{5}$$

$$-\frac{13}{20}x = \frac{9}{10}$$

$$x = -\frac{18}{13} \approx -1.385$$

Substitute -1.385 for x in the equation $y = -\frac{1}{4}x + \frac{5}{2}$ and solve for y.

$$y = -\frac{1}{4}(-1.385) + \frac{5}{2} \approx 2.846$$

The approximate solution is $(-1.4, 2.8)$.

39. Answers will vary. Notice that the functions cross between 0 and 1, and between 2 and 3. Approximate solutions may include (0.5, 15.5) and (2.5, 21.5).

40.

$$2(5) + 3(3) = a \qquad\qquad 6(5) - 4(3) = b$$

$$10 + 9 = a \qquad\qquad 30 - 12 = b$$

$$19 = a \qquad\qquad 18 = b$$

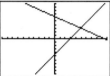

41.

$$3x + 4y = 15$$

$$2y = -5x + 11$$

Graphing by hand:
Begin by writing each equation in slope-intercept form.

$$3x + 4y = 15 \qquad\qquad 2y = -5x + 11$$

$$4y = -3x + 15 \qquad\qquad y = -\frac{5}{2}x + \frac{11}{2}$$

$$y = -\frac{3}{4}x + \frac{15}{4}$$

Next we graph both equations in the same coordinate system.

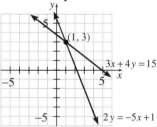

The intersection point is $(1,3)$. So, the ordered pair $(1,3)$ is the solution.

Substitution:

$$3x + 4y = 15$$

$$2y = -5x + 11$$

Solve the second equation for y.

$$2y = -5x + 11$$

$$y = -\frac{5}{2}x + \frac{11}{2}$$

Substitute $-\dfrac{5}{2}x+\dfrac{11}{2}$ for y in the first equation and solve for x.

$$3x+4\left(-\dfrac{5}{2}x+\dfrac{11}{2}\right)=15$$

$$3x-10x+22=15$$

$$-7x+22=15$$

$$-7x=-7$$

$$x=1$$

Substitute 1 for x in the equation $y=-\dfrac{5}{2}x+\dfrac{11}{2}$ and solve for y.

$$y=-\dfrac{5}{2}(1)+\dfrac{11}{2}=\dfrac{6}{2}=3$$

The solution is $(1,3)$.

Elimination:

$$3x+4y=15$$

$$2y=-5x+11$$

Start by writing both equations in standard form.

$$3x+4y=15 \qquad\qquad 2y=-5x+11$$

$$5x+2y=11$$

This yields the system

$$3x+4y=15 \quad \text{Equation (1)}$$

$$5x+2y=11 \quad \text{Equation (2)}$$

To eliminate the y terms, we multiply both sides of equation (2) by -2, yielding the system

$$3x+4y=15$$

$$-10x-4y=-22$$

The coefficients of the y terms are equal in absolute value and opposite in sign. Add the left sides and the right sides of the equations and solve for x.

$$3x+4y=15$$

$$\underline{-10x-4y=-22}$$

$$-7x=-7$$

$$x=1$$

Substitute 1 for x in equation (1) and solve for y.

$$3(1)+4y=15$$

$$3+4y=15$$

$$4y=12$$

$$y=3$$

The solution is $(1,3)$.

Preference may vary.

42. a. Start by creating a scatter diagram of the data for regional jets.

 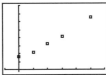

The data appear fairly linear so we use the regression feature of a graphing utility to obtain the line of best fit.

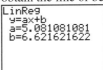 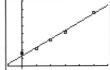

A reasonable model for the data is $R(t)=5.08t+6.62$.

Then create a scatter diagram of the data for turboprops or large jets.

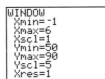 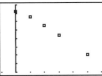

The data appear fairly linear so we use the regression feature of a graphing utility to obtain the line of best fit.

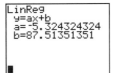 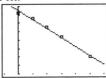

A reasonable model for the data is $L(t)=-5.32t+87.51$.

b. To estimate when the percentages will be equal, we solve the system

$$R(t)=5.08t+6.62$$

$$L(t)=-5.32t+87.51$$

Substitute $-5.32t+87.51$ for $R(t)$ in the first equation and solve for t.

$$-5.32t+87.51=5.08t+6.62$$

$$-10.4t+87.51=6.62$$

$$-10.4t=-80.89$$

$$t=\dfrac{-80.89}{-10.4}\approx7.778$$

Substitute 7.778 for t in the equation $L(t)=-5.32t+87.51$ and solve.

$$L(7.778)=-5.32(7.778)+87.51\approx46.13$$

The approximate solution of the system is $(7.78,46.13)$.

According to the models, the percentage of airplanes that are regional jets will be equal to the percentage that are turboprops or large jets (46.1%) in 2008.

43. **a.** Start by plotting each set of data, then find the regression lines for the data.
2-Year Colleges:

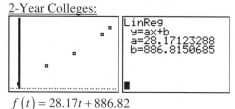

$f(t) = 28.17t + 886.82$

4-Year Colleges

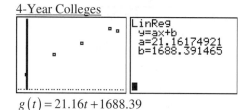

$g(t) = 21.16t + 1688.39$

b. In 2014, $t = 44$.
$$f(44) = 28.17(44) + 886.82$$
$$= 2126.3$$
$$g(44) = 21.16(44) + 1688.39$$
$$= 2619.43$$
The models predict that there will be a total of about 2126.3 + 2619.43 ≈ 4746 two-year and four-year colleges in 2014.

c.
$$f(t) = g(t)$$
$$28.17t + 886.82 = 21.16t + 1688.39$$
$$7.01t = 801.57$$
$$t \approx 114.35$$
So, during 2084 there will be as many four-year colleges as two-year colleges.
$(28.17)(114.35) + 886.82 = 4108$.
At that time there will be about 4108 educational institutions of each type.

d. In 1970 there were over 700 more four-year colleges than two year colleges. The slopes are similar so it will take many years for the number of two-year colleges to overcome the number of four-year colleges.

44. **a.** Since U-Haul's charge increases at a constant rate of $0.69 per mile, the equation is linear with slope 0.69. The U-intercept is 29.95 since U-Haul charges a flat fee of $29.95.

$U(x) = 0.69x + 29.95$.
Similar work yields an equation for Rent A Wreck's charge.
$R(x) = 0.22x + 75.00$.

b.
$$U(x) = R(x)$$
$$0.69x + 29.95 = 0.22x + 75$$
$$0.69x + 29.95 - 29.95 = 0.22x + 75 - 29.95$$
$$0.69x = 0.22x + 45.05$$
$$0.69x - 0.22x = 0.22x + 45.05 - 0.22x$$
$$0.47x = 45.05$$
$$x \approx 95.85$$
The two charges will be the same when the number of miles driven is roughly 95.85 miles, for a charge of approximately $96.09.

45. Let $P(t)$ represent the average price (in dollars) of a home in a community and $S(t)$ represent the amount of money (in dollars) a family has saved at t years since 2009.
Since the average price of a home increases at a constant $9000 per year, the function P is linear and its slope is 9000. The P-intercept is $(0, 250000)$ since the price of a home is $250,000 in year $t = 0$.
$P(t) = 9000t + 250,000$.

Similar work yields the equation for the function S.
$S(t) = 2760t + 12,000$. (The slope of S is 2760 because the family plans to save $230 each month which is $2760 each year.)
In order to predict when the family will be able to pay a 10% down payment on an average-priced house, solve the following system for t.
$$y = 0.1(P(t)) = 0.1(9000t + 250,000)$$
$$y = S(t) = 2760t + 12,000$$

Substitute $0.1(9000t + 250000)$ for y in the second equation and solve for t.
$$0.1(9000t + 250,000) = 2760t + 12,000$$
$$900t + 25,000 = 2760t + 12,000$$
$$-1860t = -13000$$
$$t \approx 6.99$$
The family will be able to pay a 10% down payment in about 7 years, or in 2009 + 7 = 2016.

46. Let L = the length of the rectangle in feet and W = the width of the rectangle in feet.

$L = 3W + 2$ $\qquad$ $P = 2L + 2W$

$\qquad\qquad\qquad 44 = 2L + 2W$

To determine the dimensions of the rectangle, we solve the system

$L = 3W + 2$

$44 = 2L + 2W$

Substitute $3W + 2$ for L in the second equation and solve for w.

$44 = 2(3W + 2) + 2W$

$44 = 8W + 4$

$40 = 8W$

$5 = W$

Substitute 5 for W in the equation $L = 3W + 2$ and solve for L.

$L = 3(5) + 2 = 17$

The width of the rectangle is 5 feet and the length is 17 feet.

47. Let x = the number of $22 tickets and y = the number of $39 tickets.

There are a total of 8000 tickets, so our first equation is $x + y = 8000$.

The total revenue is $201,500. The revenue for each ticket type is obtained by multiplying the ticket price by the number of tickets sold at that price. Therefore, our second equation is $22x + 39y = 201,500$

The system is

$\qquad x + y = 8000$ $\qquad$ Equation (1)

$22x + 39y = 201,500$ $\qquad$ Equation (2)

To eliminate the x terms, multiply both sides of equation (1) by -22, yielding the system

$-22x - 22y = -176,000$

$\quad 22x + 39y = 201,500$

Add the left sides and right sides and solve for y.

$\begin{aligned}-22x - 22y &= -176,000 \\ \underline{22x + 39y} &= \underline{201,500} \\ 17y &= 25,500 \\ y &= 1500\end{aligned}$

Substitute 1500 for y in equation (1) and solve for x.

$x + (1500) = 8000$

$\qquad x = 6500$

The theater should sell 6500 of the $22 tickets and $1500 of the $39 tickets.

48. Let x be the number of gallons of the 10% solution, and y be the number of gallons of the 20% solution.

$x + y = 10$

$x(0.10) + y(0.20) = 10(0.16)$

$(10 - y)(0.10) + 0.2y = 1.6$

$1 - 0.1y + 0.2y = 1.6$

$0.1y = 0.6$

$y = 6$

Substitute $y = 6$.

$x + 6 = 10$

$\quad x = 4$

4 gallons of a 10% antifreeze solution and 6 gallons of a 20% antifreeze solution must be mixed to make 10 gallons of a 16% antifreeze solution.

49. a. To formulate a function $f(x)$ for total interest, substitute $(8000 - x)$ for y.

$x + y = 8000$

$x + y - x = 8000 - x$

$\quad y = 8000 - x$

Write the equation for the total interest earned (in dollars) from investing $8,000 for one year.

$I = f(x) = 0.068x + 0.13y$

$f(x) = 0.068x + 0.13(8000 - x)$

$f(x) = -0.062x + 1040$

b. $f(575) = -0.062(575) + 1040$

$\qquad\quad = 1004.35$

This means that if the person invests $575 in the 6.8% interest account (and therefore $7425 in the 13.0% interest account), she will earn $1004.35 total interest.

c. $\qquad 575 = -0.062x + 1040$

$575 - 1040 = -0.062x + 1040 - 1040$

$\qquad -465 = -0.062x$

$\qquad 7500 = x$

This means that by investing $7500 in the 6.8% interest account and $2,500 in the 13.0% interest account, the person will earn $575.

50. The graph of $y \leq 3x - 5$ is the line $y = 3x - 5$ and the region below that line. We use a solid line along the border to indicate that the points on the line $y = 3x - 5$ are solutions of $y \leq 3x - 5$.

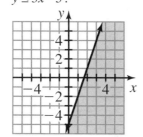

51. The graph of $y \geq -2x + 4$ is the line $y = -2x + 4$ and the region above that line. We use a solid line along the border to indicate that the points on the line $y = -2x + 4$ are solutions of $y \geq -2x + 4$.

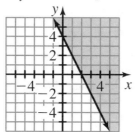

52. First, we get y alone on one side of the inequality.
$$3x - 2y > 4$$
$$-2y > -3x + 4$$
$$y < \frac{3}{2}x - 2$$

The graph of $y < \frac{3}{2}x - 2$ is the region below

that line $y = \frac{3}{2}x - 2$. We use a dashed line along

the border to indicate that the points on the line

$y = \frac{3}{2}x - 2$ are not solutions of $3x - 2y > 4$.

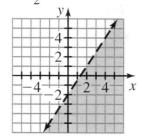

53. First, we get y alone on one side of the inequality.
$$2y - 5x < 0$$
$$2y < 5x$$
$$y < \frac{5}{2}x$$

The graph of $y < \frac{5}{2}x$ is the region below that

line $y = \frac{5}{2}x$. We use a dashed line along the

border to indicate that the points on the line

$y = \frac{5}{2}x$ are not solutions of $2y - 5x < 0$.

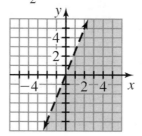

54. $x \geq 3$

The graph of $x \geq 3$ is the vertical line $x = 3$ and the region to the right of that line. We use a solid line to indicate that the points on the line $x = 3$ are solutions of $x \geq 3$.

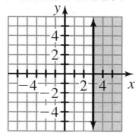

55. $y < -2$

The graph of $y < -2$ is the region below the horizontal line $y = -2$. We use a dashed line to indicate that the points on the line $y = -2$ are not solutions of $y < -2$.

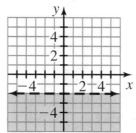

56. First, we get y alone on one side of the inequality.

$$-2(y+3)+4x \geq -8$$
$$-2y-6+4x \geq -8$$
$$-2y \geq -4x-2$$
$$y \leq 2x+1$$

The graph of $y \leq 2x+1$ is the region below that line $y = 2x+1$. We use a solid line along the border to indicate that the points on the line $y = 2x+1$ are solutions of $y \leq 2x+1$.

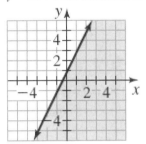

57. First we sketch the graph of $y > x+1$ and the graph of $y \leq -2x+5$. The graph of $y > x+1$ is the region above the line $y = x+1$ (graph the line with a dashed line). The graph of $y \leq -2x+5$ is the line $y = -2x+5$ (graph the line with a solid line) and the region below that line. The graph of the solution set of the system is the intersection of the graphs of the inequalities.

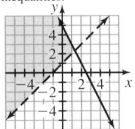

58. First we sketch the graph of $y \geq \frac{3}{5}x+1$ and the graph of $x < -1$. The graph of $y \geq \frac{3}{5}x+1$ is the line $y = \frac{3}{5}x+1$ (graph the line with a solid line) and the region above the line. The graph of $x < -1$ is the region to the left of the vertical line $x = -1$ (graph the line with a dashed line). The graph of the solution set of the system is the intersection of the graphs of the inequalities.

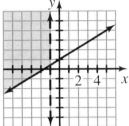

59. First we get y alone on one side of each inequality.

$$3x-4y \geq 12 \qquad\qquad 5y \leq -3x$$
$$-4y \geq -3x+12 \qquad\qquad y \leq -\frac{3}{5}x$$
$$y \leq \frac{3}{4}x-3$$

Next we sketch the graph of $y \leq \frac{3}{4}x-3$ and the graph of $y \leq -\frac{3}{5}x$. The graph of $y \leq \frac{3}{4}x-3$ is the line $y = \frac{3}{4}x-3$ (graph the line with a solid line) and the region below that line. The graph of $y \leq -\frac{3}{5}x$ is the line $y = -\frac{3}{5}x$ (graph the line with a solid line) and the region below that line. The graph of the solution set of the system is the intersection of the graphs of the inequalities.

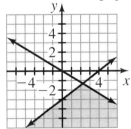

60. First we sketch the graph of $x > 2$ and the graph of $y \le -1$. The graph of $x > 2$ is the region to the right of the vertical line $x = 2$ (graph the line with a dashed line). The graph of $y \le -1$ is the line $y = -1$ (graph the line with a solid line) and the region below that line. The graph of the solution set of the system is the intersection of the graphs of the inequalities.

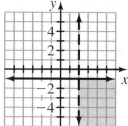

61. $x - y < 3 = y > x - 3$

$x + y < 5 = y < -x + 5$

$\quad x > 0$

$\quad y > 0$

Graph the lines $y = x - 3$, $y = -x + 5$, $x = 0$, and $y = 0$ with dashed lines. The solution region of the system is the intersection of the solution regions of $y > x - 3$, $y < -x + 5$, $x > 0$, and $y > 0$.

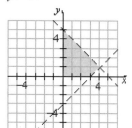

62. a. Start by plotting each set of data, then find the regression lines for the data.

Lower Limit:

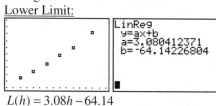

$L(h) = 3.08h - 64.14$

Upper Limit:

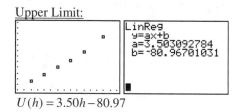

$U(h) = 3.50h - 80.97$

b. We are given equations for the upper limit $U(h)$ and lower limit $L(h)$ and we know that the height is between 63 and 78 inches, inclusive. The system is

$w \le 3.50h - 80.97$

$w \ge 3.08h - 64.14$

$h \ge 63$

$h \le 78$

c. First we sketch the graph of $w \le 3.50h - 80.97$, the graph of $w \ge 3.08h - 64.14$, the graph of $h \ge 63$, and the graph of $h \le 78$. The graph of $w \le 3.50h - 80.97$ is the line $w = 3.50h - 80.97$ (graph the line with a solid line) and the region below that line. The graph of $w \ge 3.08h - 64.14$ is the line $w = 3.08h - 64.14$ (graph the line with a solid line) and the region above that line. The graph of $h \ge 63$ is the vertical line $h = 63$ (graph the line with a solid line) and the region to the right of that line. The graph of $h \le 78$ is the vertical line $h = 78$ (graph the line with a solid line) and the region to the left of that line. The graph of the solution set of the system is the intersection of the graphs of the inequalities.

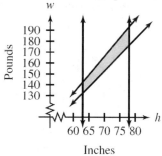

Inches

d. Lower limit:

$L(h) = 3.08(68) - 64.14$

$\quad = 209.44 - 64.14$

$\quad = 145.3$

Upper limit:

$U(h) = 3.50(68) - 80.97$

$\quad = 238 - 80.97$

$\quad = 157.03$

The ideal weights are approximately between 145 pounds and 157 pounds, inclusive.

63. Answers may vary. Some possible answers:

Solutions: $(2,-1)$, $(5,1)$, $(10,5)$

Non-solutions: $(0,0)$, $(1,2)$, $(3,2)$

Chapter 6 Test

1. $y = -\dfrac{2}{5}x - 1$

$y = -2x + 7$

To begin, we graph both equations in the same coordinate system.

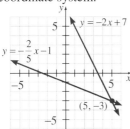

The intersection point is $(5,-3)$. So, the solution is the ordered pair $(5,-3)$.

2. $y = \dfrac{2}{3}x + 4$

$3x + 4y = -2$

To begin, write both equations in slope-intercept form.

$y = \dfrac{2}{3}x + 4$ $3x + 4y = -2$

$4y = -3x - 2$

$y = -\dfrac{3}{4}x - \dfrac{1}{2}$

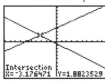

The intersection point is approximately $(-3.176, 1.882)$, so the approximate solution to the system is $(-3.18, 1.88)$.

3. $5x - 2y = 4$

$y = 3x - 1$

Substitute $3x - 1$ for y in the first equation and solve for x.

$5x - 2(3x - 1) = 4$

$5x - 6x + 2 = 4$

$-x + 2 = 4$

$-x = 2$

$x = -2$

Substitute -2 for x in the equation $y = 3x - 1$ and solve for y.

$y = 3(-2) - 1 = -6 - 1 = -7$

The solution is $(-2, -7)$.

4. $3x + 4y = 9$

$x - 2y = -7$

Solve the second equation for x.

$x - 2y = -7$

$x = 2y - 7$

Substitute $2y - 7$ for x in the first equation and solve for y.

$3(2y - 7) + 4y = 9$

$6y - 21 + 4y = 9$

$10y - 21 = 9$

$10y = 30$

$y = 3$

Substitute 3 for y in the equation $x = 2y - 7$ and solve for x.

$x = 2(3) - 7 = 6 - 7 = -1$

The solution is $(-1, 3)$.

5. $-7x - 2y = -8$ Equation (1)

$\qquad 5x + 4y = -2$ Equation (2)

To eliminate the y terms, we multiply both sides of equation (1) by 2, yielding the system

$-14x - 4y = -16$

$\quad 5x + 4y = -2$

The coefficients of the y terms are equal in absolute value and opposite in sign. Add the left sides and the right sides of the equations and solve for x.

$-14x - 4y = -16$

$\underline{\quad 5x + 4y = -2\quad}$

$\qquad -9x = -18$

$\qquad x = 2$

Substitute 2 for x in equation (2) and solve for y.

$5(2) + 4y = -2$

$\quad 10 + 4y = -2$

$\qquad 4y = -12$

$\qquad y = -3$

The solution is $(2, -3)$.

6. $2x - 5y = -18$

$\quad 3x + 4y = -4$

To eliminate the x terms, we multiply both sides of equation (1) by 3 and both sides of equation (2) by -2, yielding the system

$6x - 15y = -54$

$-6x - 8y = 8$

The coefficients of the x terms are equal in absolute value and opposite in sign. Add the left sides and the right sides of the equations and solve for y.

$6x - 15y = -54$

$\underline{-6x - 8y = 8\quad}$

$\qquad -23y = -46$

$\qquad y = 2$

Substitute 2 for y in equation (2) and solve for x.

$3x + 4(2) = -4$

$\quad 3x + 8 = -4$

$\qquad 3x = -12$

$\qquad x = -4$

The solution is $(-4, 2)$.

7. $3x - 5y = -21$

$\qquad x = 2(2 - y)$

Substitute $2(2 - y)$ for x in the first equation and solve for y.

$3(2(2 - y)) - 5y = -21$

$\quad 3(4 - 2y) - 5y = -21$

$\quad 12 - 6y - 5y = -21$

$\qquad 12 - 11y = -21$

$\qquad -11y = -33$

$\qquad y = 3$

Substitute 3 for y in the equation $x = 2(2 - y)$ and solve for x.

$x = 2(2 - 3) = 2(-1) = -2$

The solution is $(-2, 3)$.

8. $\quad 2x - 3y = 4$

$\quad -4x + 6y = -8$

To eliminate the x terms, we multiply both sides of equation (1) by 2, yielding the system

$\quad 4x - 6y = 8$

$-4x + 6y = -8$

The coefficients of the x terms are equal in absolute value and opposite in sign. Add the left sides and the right sides of the equations and solve for y.

$\quad 4x - 6y = 8$

$\underline{-4x + 6y = -8\quad}$

$\qquad 0 = 0 \quad$ true

The result is a true statement of the form $a = a$. Therefore, the system is dependent. The solution set is the infinite set of ordered pairs that satisfy the equation $2x - 3y = 4$.

9. $\qquad x = 2y - 3$

$\quad 3x - 6y = 12$

Substitute $2y - 3$ for x in the second equation and solve for y.

$3(2y - 3) - 6y = 12$

$\quad 6y - 9 - 6y = 12$

$\qquad -9 = 12 \quad$ false

The result is a false statement. Therefore, the system is inconsistent. The solution set is the empty set, $\varnothing$.

10. $4x - 7y = 6$

$-5x + 2y = -21$

To eliminate the x terms, we multiply both sides of equation (1) by 5 and both sides of equation (2) by 4, yielding the system

$20x - 35y = 30$

$-20x + 8y = -84$

The coefficients of the x terms are equal in absolute value and opposite in sign. Add the left sides and the right sides of the equations and solve for y.

$20x - 35y = 30$

$\underline{-20x + 8y = -84}$

$-27y = -54$

$y = 2$

Substitute 2 for y in equation (1) and solve for x.

$4x - 7(2) = 6$

$4x - 14 = 6$

$4x = 20$

$x = 5$

The solution is $(5, 2)$.

11. First use the distributive property to simplify each equation.

$-4(x + 2) + 3(2y - 1) = 21$

$-4x - 8 + 6y - 3 = 21$

$-4x + 6y - 11 = 21$

$-4x + 6y = 32$

$2x - 3y = -16$

$5(3x - 2) - (4y + 3) = -59$

$15x - 10 - 4y - 3 = -59$

$15x - 4y - 13 = -59$

$15x - 4y = -46$

These equations can be written as a system.

$2x - 3y = -16$

$15x - 4y = -46$

Solve using elimination.

Multiply the first equation by 4 and the second equation by -3, then add the equations.

$8x - 12y = -64$

$\underline{-45x + 12y = 138}$

$-37x = 74$

$x = -2$

Substitute $x = -2$ into $2x - 3y = -16$ and solve for y.

$2(-2) - 3y = -16$

$-4 - 3y = -16$

$-3y = -12$

$y = 4$

The solution is $(-2, 4)$.

12. Solve using elimination.

Multiply the second equation by 3 and add the equations.

$\dfrac{2}{5}x - \dfrac{3}{4}y = 8$

$\dfrac{9}{5}x + \dfrac{3}{4}y = 3$

$\dfrac{11}{5}x = 11$

$x = 5$

Substitute $x = 5$ into $\dfrac{9}{5}x + \dfrac{3}{4}y = 3$ and solve for y.

$\dfrac{3}{5}(5) + \dfrac{1}{4}y = 1$

$3 + \dfrac{1}{4}y = 1$

$\dfrac{1}{4}y = 1 - 3$

$\dfrac{1}{4}y = -2$

$y = -8$

The solution is $(5, -8)$.

13. $y = -1.94x + 8.62$

$y = 1.25x - 2.38$

$1.25x - 2.38 = -1.94x + 8.62$

$3.19x - 2.38 = 8.62$

$3.19x = 11$

$x = \dfrac{11}{3.19} \approx 3.448$

Substitute 3.448 for x in the equation $y = 1.25x - 2.38$ and solve for y.

$y = 1.25(3.448) - 2.38 = 1.93$

The approximate solution is $(3.45, 1.93)$.

14. Elimination
First rewrite the second equation so that all the variables are on the left side and the constant is on the right side.
$$4x - 3y = 9$$
$$-2x + y = -5$$
Multiply the second equation by 2 and add the equations.
$$4x - 3y = 9$$
$$\underline{-4x + 2y = -10}$$
$$-y = -1$$
$$y = 1$$
Substitute $y = 1$ into $4x - 3y = 9$ and solve for x.
$$4x - 3(1) = 9$$
$$4x - 3 = 9$$
$$4x = 12$$
$$x = 3$$
The solution is $(3, 1)$.

Substitution
Substitute $2x - 5$ for y in the first equation.
$$4x - 3y = 9$$
$$4x - 3(2x - 5) = 9$$
$$4x - 6x + 15 = 9$$
$$-2x + 15 = 9$$
$$-2x = -6$$
$$x = 3$$
Substitute $x = 3$ into $y = 2x - 5$ and solve for y.
$$y = 2(3) - 5$$
$$= 1$$
The solution is $(3, 1)$.

Graphically
$$4x - 3y = 9 \qquad\qquad y = 2x - 5$$
$$y = \frac{4}{3}x - 3$$

The solution is $(3, 1)$.

15. a. The points C and D lie on the graph of $y = ax + b$, so they are solutions to the equation $y = ax + b$.

  b. The points D and F lie on the graph of $y = cx + d$, so they are solutions to the equation $y = cx + d$.

  c. The point D lies on both graphs, so it is a solution to both equations.

  d. The points A, B, and E do not lie on either graph, so they are not solutions to either equation.

16. We can start by writing equations for the two lines.

Blue Line:
Examining the graph, the line crosses the y-axis at the point $(0, 1)$, so the y-intercept is $(0, 1)$.

The point $(6, 2)$ also appears to be on the graph, so $m = \frac{2 - 1}{6 - 0} = \frac{1}{6}$. The equation of the line is $y = \frac{1}{6}x + 1$.

Red Line:
Examining the graph, the line crosses the y-axis at the point $(0, -3)$, so the y-intercept is $(0, -3)$.

The point $(3, -2)$ also appears to be on the graph, so $m = \frac{-2 - (-3)}{3 - 0} = \frac{-2 + 3}{3} = \frac{1}{3}$. The equation of the line is $y = \frac{1}{3}x - 3$.

Using the two equations, we get the system
$$y = \frac{1}{6}x + 1$$
$$y = \frac{1}{3}x - 3$$

Substitute $\frac{1}{3}x - 3$ for y in the first equation and solve for x.

$$\frac{1}{3}x - 3 = \frac{1}{6}x + 1$$

$$6\left(\frac{1}{3}x - 3\right) = 6\left(\frac{1}{6}x + 1\right)$$

$$2x - 18 = x + 6$$

$$x - 18 = 6$$

$$x = 24$$

Substitute 24 for x in the equation $y = \frac{1}{6}x + 1$ and solve for y.

$$y = \frac{1}{6}(24) + 1 = 4 + 1 = 5$$

The solution is $(24, 5)$.

17. If the solution set is the empty set, the system consists of two parallel lines. Therefore, m in $y = mx + b$ is 5, because this is the slope in $y = 5x - 13$ and parallel lines have the same slope. The y-intercept in $y = mx + b$ is any number other than -13 since $y = 5x - 13$ and $y = mx + b$ intersect the y-axis at different points. So $b \neq -13$.

18. The coordinates of point A are the same as the coordinates of the origin, $(0, 0)$.
The coordinates of point B is the same as the y-intercept of $y = 3x + 4$, $(0, 4)$.
Use substitution to find the intersection of l_1 and l_2.

$$3(3x + 4) + 2x = 34$$

$$9x + 12 + 2x = 34$$

$$11x = 22$$

$$x = 2$$

Substitute to find the other coordinate.

$$y = 3(2) + 4$$

$$= 10$$

C is the point $(2, 10)$.
Substitute $-4x + 28$ into l_2.

$$3(-4x + 28) + 2x = 34$$

$$-12x + 84 + 2x = 34$$

$$-10x = -50$$

$$x = 5$$

Substitute to find the other coordinate.

$$y + 4(5) = 28$$

$$y + 20 = 28$$

$$y = 8$$

D is the point $(5, 8)$.
Substitute $3x - 14$ for y in l_3.

$$(3x - 14) + 4x = 28$$

$$7x - 14 = 28$$

$$7x = 42$$

$$x = 6$$

$$y = 3(6) - 14$$

$$y = 18 - 14$$

$$y = 4$$

E is the point $(6, 4)$.
Find the x-intercept of l_4.

$$0 = 3x - 14$$

$$14 = 3x$$

$$\frac{14}{3} = x$$

F is the point $\left(\frac{14}{3}, 0\right)$.

19. **a.** Start by plotting the data sets, then find the regression line for each region.

United States

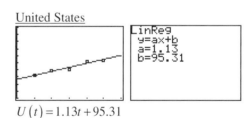

$$U(t) = 1.13t + 95.31$$

China

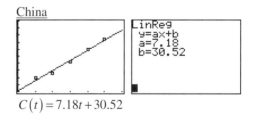

$$C(t) = 7.18t + 30.52$$

b. Both slopes are positive indicating an increase in consumption each year. The slope for China of 7.18 is much greater than the slope for the United States of 1.13. So, the energy consumption is increasing at a much faster rate in China than in the United States.

c.
$$U(t) = C(t)$$
$$1.13t + 95.31 = 7.18t + 30.52$$
$$95.31 = 6.05t + 30.52$$
$$64.79 = 6.05t$$
$$10.71 \approx t$$

Energy consumption was the same for the China and the United States in $2000 + 10.71 \approx 2011$.

$$U(10.71) = 1.13(10.71) + 95.31$$
$$\approx 12.10 + 95.31$$
$$\approx 107.41$$

The consumption amount for each country will be about 107.4 quadrillion Btu in 2011.

20. a. Since the number of guns in circulation in the U.S. has increased by about 4.9 million per year, we can model the situation by a linear equation. The slope is 4.9 million guns per year. Since the number of guns in circulation in 2007 was 270 million, the n-intercept is $(0, 270)$. So, a reasonable model is $g(t) = 4.9t + 270$.

By the same reasoning, the model for the U.S. population is $p(t) = 2.6t + 302$.

b. $g(t) = 4.9t + 270$

$p(t) = 2.6t + 302$

Substitute $2.6t + 302$ for $g(t)$ in the first equation and solve for t.
$$2.6t + 302 = 4.9t + 270$$
$$-2.3t + 302 = 270$$
$$-2.3t = -32$$
$$t \approx 13.91$$

Substitute 13.91 for t in the equation $p(t) = 2.6t + 302$ and solve for $p(t)$.

$$p(13.91) = 2.6(13.91) + 302 \approx 338.2$$

The solution of the system is $(13.9, 338.2)$.

According to the models, there will be (on average) one gun per person in the U.S. (338.2 million) in 2021. However, not everyone will own a gun in that year.

21. Let A represent the number of $55 tickets sold, and B represent the number of $70 tickets sold. There are 20,000 total tickets available, so $A + B = 20000$.

Selling A tickets at $55 and B tickets at $70, the theater wants to make $1,197,500.
$$55A + 70B = 1197500.$$

Use substitution or elimination to solve for A and B.
$$55(A + B) = 55(20000)$$
$$55A + 70B = 1197500$$

Subtract the second equation from the first.
$$55A + 55B = 1100000$$
$$-(55A + 70B = 1197500)$$
$$-15B = -97500$$
$$B = 6500$$

Now use this information to solve for A.
$$A + B = 20000$$
$$A + 6500 = 20000$$
$$A = 20000 - 6500$$
$$A = 13500$$

The theater must sell 13,500 tickets at $55 and 6500 tickets at $70 in order to generate a total revenue of $1,197,500.

22. Let x = the amount invested in the 3% account and y = the amount invested in 7% account. The total amount invested is $7,000 so our first equation is $x + y = 7,000$.

The total interest after one year is $410. Therefore, our second equation is $0.03x + 0.07y = 410$.

The system is
$$x + y = 7,000$$
$$0.03x + 0.07y = 410$$

Solve the first equation for y.
$$x + y = 7,000$$
$$y = -x + 7,000$$

Substitute $-x + 7,000$ for y in the second equation and solve for x.
$$0.03x + 0.07(-x + 7,000) = 410$$
$$0.03x - 0.07x + 490 = 410$$
$$-0.04x + 490 = 410$$
$$-0.04x = -80$$
$$x = 2000$$

Substitute 2,000 for x in the equation $y = -x + 7,000$ and solve for y.

$$y = -(2,000) + 7,000 = 5,000$$

She should invest $2,000 in the 3% acoount and $5000 in the 7% account.

23. $5x - 2y \le 6$

$$-2y \le -5x + 6$$

$$y \ge \frac{5}{2}x - 3$$

The graph of $y \ge \frac{5}{2}x - 3$ is the line $y = \frac{5}{2}x - 3$

and the region above that line. We use a solid line along the border to indicate that the points

on the line $y = \frac{5}{2}x - 3$ are solutions to

$y \ge \frac{5}{2}x - 3$.

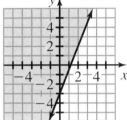

24. $y < -3$

The graph of $y < -3$ is the region below the horizontal line $y = -3$. We graph the line with a dashed line to indicate that points on the line $y = -3$ are not solutions to $y < -3$.

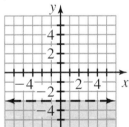

25. First we get *y* alone on one side of each inequality.

$$y \le -3x + 4 \qquad x - 3y > 6$$

$$-3y > -x + 6$$

$$y < \frac{1}{3}x - 2$$

Next we sketch the graph of $y \le -3x + 4$ and the

graph of $y < \frac{1}{3}x - 2$. The graph of $y \le -3x + 4$

is the line $y = -3x + 4$ (graph the line with a

solid line) and the region below that line. The

graph of $y < \frac{1}{3}x - 2$ is the region below the line

$y = \frac{1}{3}x - 2$ (graph the line with a dashed line).

The graph of the solution set of the system is the intersection of the graphs of the inequalities.

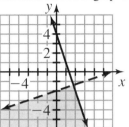

26. First we sketch the graph of $y > 2$ and the graph of $x \ge -3$. The graph of $y > 2$ is the region above the line $y = 2$ (graph the line with a dashed line). The graph of $x \ge -3$ is the vertical line $x = -3$ (graph the line with a solid line) and the region to the right of that line. The graph of the solution set of the system is the intersection of the graphs of the inequalities.

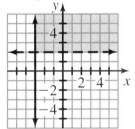

Cumulative Review of Chapters 1 – 6

1.

Fahrenheit degrees

2. When the price of the scanner is $165, the company can sell 180 thousand scanners in one year.

3.
$$-\frac{26}{27} \cdot \frac{12}{13} = -\frac{2 \cdot 13 \cdot 2 \cdot 2 \cdot 3}{3 \cdot 3 \cdot 3 \cdot 13}$$

$$= -\frac{3 \cdot 13 \cdot 2 \cdot 2 \cdot 2}{3 \cdot 13 \cdot 3 \cdot 3}$$

$$= -\frac{2 \cdot 2 \cdot 2}{3 \cdot 3}$$

$$= -\frac{8}{9}$$

4. $\dfrac{5}{7} - \left(-\dfrac{3}{5}\right) = \dfrac{5}{7} + \dfrac{3}{5}$

$$= \dfrac{5}{7} \cdot \dfrac{5}{5} + \dfrac{3}{5} \cdot \dfrac{7}{7}$$

$$= \dfrac{25}{35} + \dfrac{21}{35}$$

$$= \dfrac{46}{35}$$

5. $a^2 - bc + b^2 = (-3)^2 - (-2)(4) + (-2)^2$

$$= 9 - (-8) + 4$$

$$= 9 + 8 + 4$$

$$= 21$$

6. $m = \dfrac{-8 - (-2)}{5 - (-3)} = \dfrac{-8 + 2}{5 + 3} = \dfrac{-6}{8} = -\dfrac{3}{4}$

Since the slope is negative, the line is decreasing.

7. a. The line is decreasing, so $m < 0$. The line crosses the y-axis above the x-axis, so $b > 0$.

b. The line is increasing, so $m > 0$. The line crosses the y-axis below the x-axis, so $b < 0$.

c. The line is horizontal, so $m = 0$. The line crosses the y-axis above the x-axis, so $b > 0$.

d. The line is decreasing, so $m < 0$. The line crosses the y-axis below the x-axis, so $b < 0$.

8. Equation 1:
The input $x = 0$ yields the output $y = 49$, so the y-intercept is $(0, 49)$.

$m = \dfrac{41 - 49}{1 - 0} = \dfrac{-8}{1} = -8$, so the slope is -8. The equation of the line is $y = -8x + 49$.

Equation 2:
The input $x = 0$ yields the output $y = 11$, so the y-intercept is $(0, 11)$.

$m = \dfrac{15 - 11}{1 - 0} = \dfrac{4}{1} = 4$, so the slope is 4. The equation of the line is $y = 4x + 11$.

Equation 3:
$m = \dfrac{37 - 39}{4 - 3} = \dfrac{-2}{1} = -2$, so the slope is -2.
The input $x = 3$ yields the output $y = 39$, the the ordered pair $(3, 39)$ is a solution to the equation. Using this point and the slope, we get
$y - y_1 = m(x - x_1)$
$y - 39 = -2(x - 3)$
$y - 39 = -2x + 6$
$\quad y = -2x + 45$
The equation of the line is $y = -2x + 45$.

Equation 4:
$m = \dfrac{20 - 14}{4 - 2} = \dfrac{6}{2} = 3$, so the slope is 3.
The input $x = 2$ yields the output $y = 14$, the the ordered pair $(2, 14)$ is a solution to the equation. Using this point and the slope, we get
$y - y_1 = m(x - x_1)$
$y - 14 = 3(x - 2)$
$y - 14 = 3x - 6$
$\quad y = 3x + 8$
The equation of the line is $y = 3x + 8$.

9. $2 - 5(4x + 8) = 3(2x - 7) + 3$
$2 - 20x - 40 = 6x - 21 + 3$
$-20x - 38 = 6x - 18$
$-26x - 38 = -18$
$\quad -26x = 20$
$\quad\quad x = -\dfrac{20}{26} = -\dfrac{10}{13}$

The solution is $-\dfrac{10}{13}$.

10. $-3(2p - w) - (7p + 2w) + 5$
$= -6p + 3w - 7p - 2w + 5$
$= -13p + w + 5$

11. $\dfrac{2}{3}(6w + 9y - 15) = \dfrac{2}{3}(6w) + \dfrac{2}{3}(9y) - \dfrac{2}{3}(15)$
$\quad = 4w + 6y - 10$

12.
$$\frac{3m}{5} - \frac{2}{3} = \frac{m}{2}$$
$$30\left(\frac{3m}{5} - \frac{2}{3}\right) = 30\left(\frac{m}{2}\right)$$
$$18m - 20 = 15m$$
$$3m = 20$$
$$m = \frac{20}{3}$$

13. $ax + by = c$
$$by = -ax + c$$
$$\frac{by}{b} = \frac{-ax + c}{b}$$
$$y = \frac{-ax + c}{b} \quad \text{or} \quad y = \frac{c - ax}{b}$$

14. $6 + 3(4 + x) = 6 + 12 + 3x$
$$= 18 + 3x$$

15. $4 - \dfrac{x}{3} = 2$
$$-\frac{x}{3} = -2$$
$$x = 6$$
The solution is 6.

16. $y = 2x - 4$

The equation is in slope-intercept form, so the slope is $m = 2$ and the y-intercept is $(0, -4)$. Starting with the point $(0, -4)$ and writing the slope as $m = \dfrac{2}{1}$, we can obtain a second point on the graph by adding 2 units to the y coordinate and adding 1 unit to the x-coordinate to obtain $(1, -2)$. We plot the two points and connect them with a line, extending the line in both directions.

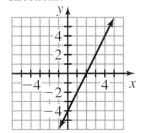

17. $x - 2y = 6$
$$-2y = -x + 6$$
$$y = \frac{1}{2}x - 3$$

The equation is now in slope-intercept form, so we see that the slope is $m = \dfrac{1}{2}$ and the y-intercept is $(0, -3)$. Starting with the point $(0, -3)$ and using the slope, we can obtain a second point on the graph by adding 1 unit to the y-coordinate and adding 2 units to the x-coordinate to obtain $(2, -2)$. We plot the two points and connect them with a line, extending the line in both directions.

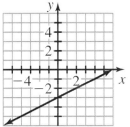

18. $5x + 2y - 12 = 0$
$$5x + 2y = 12$$
$$2y = -5x + 12$$
$$y = -\frac{5}{2}x + 6$$

The equation is now in slope-intercept form, so we see that the slope is $m = -\dfrac{5}{2}$ and the y-intercept is $(0, 6)$. Starting with the point $(0, 6)$ and writing the slope as $m = \dfrac{-5}{2}$, we can obtain a second point on the graph by subtracting 5 units from the y-coordinate and adding 2 units to the x-coordinate to obtain $(2, 1)$. We plot the two points and connect them with a line, extending the line in both directions.

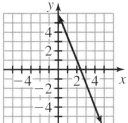

19. $y = -3$

This is the equation of a horizontal line. The y-intercept is $(0, -3)$ and the slope is $m = 0$.

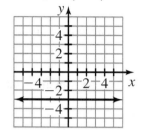

20. $2x - 5y = 10$

To find the x-intercept, we let $y = 0$ and solve for x.
$$2x - 5(0) = 10$$
$$2x = 10$$
$$x = 5$$
The x-intercept is $(5, 0)$.

To find the y-intercept, we let $x = 0$ and solve for y.
$$2(0) - 5y = 10$$
$$-5y = 10$$
$$y = -2$$
The y-intercept is $(0, -2)$.

We plot the two intercepts, connect them with a line, and extend the line in both directions.

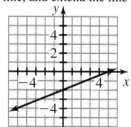

21. $y = -2x + 4$

The equation is in slope-intercept form, so the y-intercept is $(0, 4)$.

To find the x-intercept, we let $y = 0$ and solve for x.
$$0 = -2x + 4$$
$$2x = 4$$
$$x = 2$$
The x-intercept is $(2, 0)$.

We plot the two intercepts, connect them with a line, and extend the line in both directions.

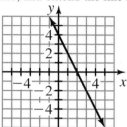

22. The graph of $x = 4$ is a vertical line passing through the point $(4, 0)$.

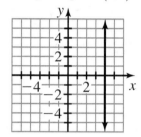

23. Write both equations in $y = mx + b$ form.

$$2x + 5y = 7 \qquad\qquad y = \frac{2}{3}x - 3$$
$$5y = -2x + 7$$
$$y = -\frac{2}{5}x + \frac{7}{5}$$

Since the slopes are different, the lines are not parallel.

24.
$$y - y_1 = m(x - x_1)$$
$$y - (-2) = -\frac{2}{5}(x - 3)$$
$$y + 2 = -\frac{2}{5}x + \frac{6}{5}$$
$$y = -\frac{2}{5}x - \frac{4}{5}$$

Check:
$$y = -\frac{2}{5}x - \frac{4}{5}$$
$$-2 \overset{?}{=} -\frac{2}{5}(3) - \frac{4}{5}$$
$$-2 \overset{?}{=} -\frac{6}{5} - \frac{4}{5}$$
$$-2 \overset{?}{=} -\frac{10}{5}$$
$$-2 \overset{?}{=} -2 \quad \text{true}$$

25. $(-5, 1)$; $(-2, -3)$

$$m = \frac{-3-1}{-2-(-5)} = \frac{-3-1}{-2+5} = \frac{-4}{3} = -\frac{4}{3}$$

$$y - 1 = -\frac{4}{3}(x - (-5))$$

$$y - 1 = -\frac{4}{3}(x + 5)$$

$$y - 1 = -\frac{4}{3}x - \frac{20}{3}$$

$$y = -\frac{4}{3}x - \frac{17}{3}$$

26. Since the x-coordinates are the same for the two points, the line is vertical and has an undefined slope. The equation is $x = -2$.

27. We locate -3 on the x-axis and move up to the graph. Then we move to the y-axis to find that $f(x) = 2$ when $x = -3$.

28. We locate -1 on the y-axis and move right until we reach the graph. Then we move up to the x-axis to find that $x = 6$ when $f(x) = -1$.

29. The graph crosses the x-axis at the point $(3, 0)$ so the x-intercept is $(3, 0)$.

30. The graph crosses the y-axis at the point $(0, 1)$, so the y-intercept is $(0, 1)$. From problem 29, the x-intercept is $(3, 0)$. Therefore,

$$m = \frac{0-1}{3-0} = -\frac{1}{3}$$

The equation of the line is $y = -\frac{1}{3}x + 1$.

31. The domain of the relation is $-5 \le x \le 5$.

32. The range of the relation is $-2 \le y \le 3$.

33. Yes, the graph is that of a function. The graph passes the vertical line test.

34. $-3(x - 5) > 18$

$$-3x + 15 > 18$$

$$-3x > 3$$

$$\frac{-3x}{-3} < \frac{3}{-3}$$

$$x < -1$$

Interval notation: $(-\infty, -1)$

35. $y = 2x - 3$

$x + y = 3$

Write both equations in slope-intercept form.

$y = 2x - 3 \qquad x + y = 3$

$\qquad\qquad\qquad y = -x + 3$

Graph both equations in the same coordinate system.

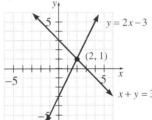

The intersection point is $(2, 1)$, so the solution to the system is $(2, 1)$.

36. $y = -2.9x + 7.8$

$y = 1.3x - 6.1$

The approximate intersection point is $(3.310, -1.798)$, so the approximate solution to the system is $(3.31, -1.80)$.

37. $3x + 5y = -1$ Equation (1)

$2x - 3y = 12$ Equation (2)

To eliminate the x terms, we multiply both sides of equation (1) by 2 and both sides of equation (2) by -3, yielding the system

$6x + 10y = -2$

$-6x + 9y = -36$

The coefficients of the x terms are equal in absolute value and opposite in sign. Add the left sides and the right sides of the equations and solve for y.

$6x + 10y = -2$

$\underline{-6x + 9y = -36}$

$19y = -38$

$y = -2$

Substitute -2 for y in equation (2) and solve for x.

$2x - 3(-2) = 12$

$2x + 6 = 12$

$2x = 6$

$x = 3$

The solution is $(3, -2)$.

38. $4x - y - 9 = 0$

$y = 5 - 3x$

Substitute $5 - 3x$ for y in the first equation and solve for x.

$4x - (5 - 3x) - 9 = 0$

$4x - 5 + 3x - 9 = 0$

$7x - 14 = 0$

$7x = 14$

$x = 2$

Substitute 2 for x in the equation $y = 5 - 3x$ and solve for y.

$y = 5 - 3(2) = 5 - 6 = -1$

The solution is $(2, -1)$.

39. $y = -2.9x + 97.8$

$y = 3.1x - 45.6$

Rewrite the system in standard form.

$2.9x + y = 97.8$ Equation (1)

$3.1x - y = 45.6$ Equation (2)

The coefficients of the y terms are equal in absolute value and opposite in sign. Add the left sides and the right sides of the equations and solve for x.

$2.9x + y = 97.8$

$\underline{3.1x - y = 45.6}$

$6x = 143.4$

$x = \dfrac{143.4}{6} = 23.9$

Substitute 23.9 for x in equation (1) and solve for y.

$2.9(23.9) + y = 97.8$

$69.31 + y = 97.8$

$y = 28.49$

The solution is $(23.9, 28.49)$.

40. Graphing:

$2x - 3y = 19$

$y = 4x - 13$

Write both equations in slope-intercept form.

$2x - 3y = 19 \qquad\qquad y = 4x - 13$

$-3y = -2x + 19$

$y = \dfrac{2}{3}x - \dfrac{19}{3}$

Graph both equations in the same coordinate system.

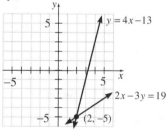

The intersection point is $(2, -5)$, so the solution of the system is $(2, -5)$.

Substitution:

$2x - 3y = 19$

$y = 4x - 13$

Substitute $4x - 13$ for y in the first equation and solve for x.

$2x - 3(4x - 13) = 19$

$2x - 12x + 39 = 19$

$-10x + 39 = 19$

$-10x = -20$

$x = 2$

Substitute 2 for x in the equation $y = 4x - 13$ and solve for y.

$$y = 4(2) - 13 = 8 - 13 = -5$$

The solution is $(2, -5)$.

Elimination:

$$2x - 3y = 19$$
$$y = 4x - 13$$

Write the equations in standard form.

$$2x - 3y = 19 \quad \text{Equation (1)}$$
$$4x - y = 13 \quad \text{Equation (2)}$$

To eliminate the y terms, we multiply both sides of equation (2) by -3, yielding the system

$$2x - 3y = 19$$
$$-12x + 3y = -39$$

The coefficients of the y terms are equal in absolute value and opposite in sign. Add the left sides and the right sides of the equations and solve for x.

$$2x - 3y = 19$$
$$\underline{-12x + 3y = -39}$$
$$-10x = -20$$
$$x = 2$$

Substitute 2 for x in equation (2) and solve for y.

$$4(2) - y = 13$$
$$8 - y = 13$$
$$-y = 5$$
$$y = -5$$

The solution is $(2, -5)$.

41. We begin by finding the equations for each table.

Table 40:
The input $x = 0$ yields the output $y = 97$, so the y-intercept is $(0, 97)$.

$$m = \frac{93 - 97}{1 - 0} = \frac{-4}{1} = -4, \text{ so the slope is } -4.$$

The first equation is $y = -4x + 97$.

Table 41:
The input $x = 0$ yields the output $y = 7$, so the y-intercept is $(0, 7)$.

$$m = \frac{9 - 7}{1 - 0} = \frac{2}{1} = 2, \text{ so the slope is } 2.$$

The second equation is $y = 2x + 7$.

Now we solve the system

$$y = -4x + 97$$
$$y = 2x + 7$$

Substitute $2x + 7$ for y in the first equation and solve for x.

$$2x + 7 = -4x + 97$$
$$6x + 7 = 97$$
$$6x = 90$$
$$x = 15$$

Substitute 15 for x in the equation $y = 2x + 7$ and solve for y.

$$y = 2(15) + 7 = 30 + 7 = 37$$

The solution is $(15, 37)$.

42. The graph of $y < -\dfrac{2}{3}x + 3$ is the region below

the line $y = -\dfrac{2}{3}x + 3$. We use a dashed line

along the border to indicate that the points on the

line $y = -\dfrac{2}{3}x + 3$ are not solutions to

$y < -\dfrac{2}{3}x + 3$.

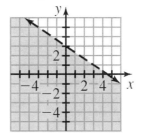

43. $3x - 5y \le 10$

$\quad\quad x > -4$

First we get y alone on one side of the first inequality.

$$3x - 5y \le 10 \quad\quad\quad\quad x > -4$$
$$-5y \le -3x + 10$$
$$y \ge \frac{3}{5}x - 2$$

Next we sketch the graph of $y \geq \frac{3}{5}x - 2$ and the

graph of $x > -4$. The graph of $y \geq \frac{3}{5}x - 2$ is the

line $y = \frac{3}{5}x - 2$ (graph the line with a solid line)

and the region above that line. The graph of $x > -4$ is the region to the right of the vertical line $x = -4$ (graph the line with a dashed line). The graph of the solution set of the system is the intersection of the graphs of the inequalities.

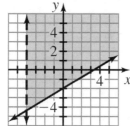

44. a. Answers may vary. If the population increases, the number of traffic deaths is likely to rise as will the number of miles traveled. If the number of miles traveled rises at a faster rate than the number of traffice deaths, then the fatality rate will be decreasing even though the number of deaths is increasing.

b.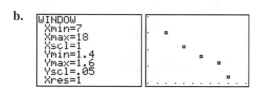

c. Using the regression capability of a graphing calculator, we get

LinReg
y=ax+b
a=-.0169512195
b=1.70097561

A reasonable model is
$f(t) = -0.0170t + 1.70$.

d. The equation in part (c) is in slope-intercept form, so the r-intercept is $(0, 1.70)$. This indicates that there were approximately 1.7 deaths per 100 million miles traveled in 1990.

e. Substitute 1.0 for $f(t)$ in the equation $f(t) = -0.0170t + 1.70$ and solve for t.

$1.0 = -0.017t + 1.7$

$-0.7 = -0.017t$

$t = \frac{-0.7}{-0.017} \approx 41.2$

The model predicts that the death rate will be 1.0 deaths per 100 million miles traveled in 2031. The Transportation Secretary's plan is ambitious.

f. For 204, we have $t = 24$.

$f(24) = -0.0170(24) + 1.70 = 1.292$

The model predicts that the fatality rate in 2014 will be about 1.29 deaths per 100 million miles traveled.

45. a. Start by creating a scatter diagram of the data for the divorce rate in Japan.

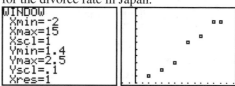

The data appear fairly linear so we use the regression feature of a graphing utility to obtain the line of best fit.

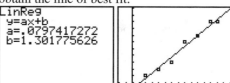

A reasonable model for the data is
$J(t) = 0.080t + 1.30$.

Then create a scatter diagram of the data for the divorce rate in the United States.

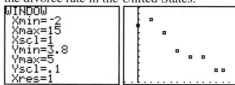

The data appear fairly linear so we use the regression feature of a graphing utility to obtain the line of best fit.

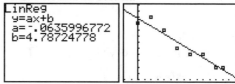

A reasonable model for the data is
$U(t) = -0.064t + 4.79$.

b. To estimate when the percentages will be equal, we solve the system

$$J(t) = 0.080t + 1.30$$

$$U(t) = -0.064t + 4.79$$

Substitute $-0.064t + 4.79$ for $J(t)$ in the first equation and solve for t.

$$-0.064t + 4.79 = 0.080t + 1.30$$

$$-0.144t + 4.79 = 1.30$$

$$-0.144t = -3.49$$

$$t = \frac{-3.49}{-0.144} \approx 24.236$$

Substitute 24.236 for t in the equation $U(t) = -0.064t + 4.79$ and solve for $U(t)$.

$$U(24.236) = -0.064(24.236) + 4.79 \approx 3.239$$

The approximate solution of the system is $(24.2, 3.2)$.

According to the models, the divorce rates in Japan and the United States will be equal (about 3.2 per 1000 people) in 2014.

46. a. The college enrollment has decreased by 375 students per year, so the slope (average rate of change) is -375 students per year.

b. Since there were 25,700 students at the college in 2005, the E-intercept is $(0, 25700)$. Using the slope from part (a) and the E-intercept, the equation of the line is $f(t) = -375t + 25,700$.

c. Substitute 21,500 for $f(t)$ and solve for t.

$$21,500 = -375t + 25,700$$

$$375t = 4200$$

$$t = \frac{4200}{375} = 11.2$$

Enrollment at the college will reach 21,500 in the year 2016.

d. Solve the following inequality:

$$-375t + 25,700 < 20,000$$

$$-375t < -5,700$$

$$t > \frac{-5,700}{-375} = 15.2$$

Enrollment will be less than 20,000 after 2020.

47. a. Since the number of lines controlled by Bell companies decreased by 6.8 million per year, we can model the situation by a linear equation. The slope is -6.8 million lines per year. Since the number of lines controlled in 2000 was 181.3 million, the n-intercept is $(0, 181.3)$. So, a reasonable model is $B(t) = -6.8t + 181.3$.

By the same reasoning, the model for the number of lines controlled by other companies is $O(t) = 6.8t + 9.4$.

b. Since a line is controlled by a Bell company or some other company, any increase in the number controlled by one group must be matched by an equal decrease in the number controlled by the other group (assuming the number of lines remains constant). Therefore, it makes sense that the slopes (average rate of change) are equal in absolute value, but opposite in sign.

c.
$$n = -6.8t + 181.3$$
$$n = 6.8t + 9.4$$

Substitute $6.8t + 9.4$ for n in the first equation and solve for t.

$$6.8t + 9.4 = -6.8t + 181.3$$

$$13.6t + 9.4 = 18113$$

$$13.6t = 171.9$$

$$t = \frac{171.9}{13.6} \approx 12.640$$

Substitute 12.640 for t in the equation $n = 6.8t + 9.4$ and solve for n.

$$n = 6.8(12.640) + 9.4 = 95.352$$

The approximate solution of the system is $(12.64, 95.35)$.

According to the models, there will be an equal number of lines (95.35 million each) controlled by Bell companies and other companies in 2013.

d. After 2013. Since Bell companies no longer have to lease lines to competing companies, it will take longer for the competing companies to gain an equal market share.

48. Let x = the number of quarts of the 16% solution and y = the number of quarts of 28% solution. The total number of quarts is 12, so our first equation is $x + y = 12$.

The total amount of pure acid between the two solutions must be the same as the total amount of pure acid in the mixture, so our second equation is $0.16x + 0.28y = 0.20(12)$.

The system is
$$x + y = 12$$
$$0.16x + 0.28y = 0.20(12)$$

Solve the first equation for y.
$$x + y = 12$$
$$y = -x + 12$$

Substitute $-x + 12$ for y in the second equation and solve for x.
$$0.16x + 0.28(-x + 12) = 0.20(12)$$
$$0.16x - 0.28x + 3.36 = 2.4$$
$$-0.12x + 3.36 = 2.4$$
$$-0.12x = -0.96$$
$$x = 8$$

Substitute 8 for x in the equation $y = -x + 12$ and solve for y.
$$y = -(8) + 12 = 4$$

The mixture should contain 8 quarts of the 16% acid solution and 4 quarts of the 28% acid solution.

Chapter 7
Polynomial Functions and Properties of Exponents

Homework 7.1

1. $3x^2 - 4x + 2$

The term $3x^2$ has degree 2, which is larger than the degrees of the other terms. So $3x^2 - 4x + 2$ is a quadratic (or second-degree) polynomial in one variable.

3. $-7x^3 - 9x - 4$

The term $-7x^3$ has degree 3, which is larger than the degrees of the other terms. So $-7x^3 - 9x - 4$ is a cubic (or third-degree) polynomial in one variable.

5. $3p^5q^2 - 5p^3q^3 + 7pq^4$

The term $3p^5q^2$ has degree $5 + 2 = 7$, which is larger than the degrees of the other terms. So $3p^5q^2 - 5p^3q^3 + 7pq^4$ is a seventh-degree polynomial in two variables.

7. $3t^2 + 5t^2 = 8t^2$

9. $-8a^4b^3 - 3a^4b^3 = -11a^4b^3$

11. $4x^2 + x^2 = 4x^2 + 1x^2 = 5x^2$

13. $7x^2 - 3x$

The terms $7x^2$ and $-3x$ are not like terms, so they cannot be combined.

15. $5b^3 - 8b^3 = -3b^3$

17. $-x^6 + 7x^6 = 6x^6$

19. $2t^3w^5 + 4t^5w^3$

The terms $2t^3w^5$ and $4t^5w^3$ are not like terms, so they cannot be combined.

21. $6x^2 - 3x - 2x^2 + 4x = 6x^2 - 2x^2 - 3x + 4x$
$= (6-2)x^2 + (-3+4)x$
$= 4x^2 + x$

23. $-5x^3 - 4x + 2x^2 - 7x^3 + 5 - x$
$= -5x^3 - 7x^3 + 2x^2 - 4x - x + 5$
$= (-5-7)x^3 + 2x^2 + (-4-1)x + 5$
$= -12x^3 + 2x^2 - 5x + 5$

25. $4a^4b^2 - 7ab^3 - 9a^4b^2 + 2ab^3$
$= 4a^4b^2 - 9a^4b^2 - 7ab^3 + 2ab^3$
$= (4-9)a^4b^2 + (-7+2)ab^3$
$= -5a^4b^2 - 5ab^3$

27. $2x^4 - 4x^3y + 2x^2y^2 + x^3y - 2x^2y^2 + xy^3$
$= 2x^4 - 4x^3y + x^3y + 2x^2y^2 - 2x^2y^2 + xy^3$
$= 2x^4 + (-4+1)x^3y + (2-2)x^2y^2 + xy^3$
$= 2x^4 - 3x^3y + xy^3$

29. $\left(3x^2 - 5x - 2\right) + \left(6x^2 + 2x - 7\right)$
$= 3x^2 + 6x^2 - 5x + 2x - 2 - 7$
$= 9x^2 - 3x - 9$

31. $\left(-2x^3 + 4x - 3\right) + \left(5x^3 - 6x^2 + 2\right)$
$= -2x^3 + 5x^3 - 6x^2 + 4x - 3 + 2$
$= 3x^3 - 6x^2 + 4x - 1$

33. $\left(8a^2 - 7ab + 2b^2\right) + \left(3a^2 + 4ab - 7b^2\right)$
$= 8a^2 + 3a^2 - 7ab + 4ab + 2b^2 - 7b^2$
$= 11a^2 - 3ab - 5b^2$

35. $\left(2m^4p + m^3p^2 - 7m^2p^3\right) + \left(m^3p^2 + 7m^2p^3 - 8mp^3\right)$
$= 2m^4p + m^3p^2 + m^3p^2 - 7m^2p^3 + 7m^2p^3 - 8mp^3$
$= 2m^4p + 2m^3p^2 - 8mp^3$

37. $\left(2x^2 + 4x - 7\right) - \left(9x^2 - 5x + 4\right)$
$= 2x^2 - 9x^2 + 4x + 5x - 7 - 4$
$= -7x^2 + 9x - 11$

39. $\left(6x^3 - 3x^2 + 4\right) - \left(-7x^3 + x - 1\right)$
$= 6x^3 + 7x^3 - 3x^2 - x + 4 + 1$
$= 13x^3 - 3x^2 - x + 5$

261

41. $\left(8m^2 + 3mp - 5p^2\right) - \left(-2m^2 - 7mp - 4p^2\right)$
$= 8m^2 + 2m^2 + 3mp + 7mp - 5p^2 + 4p^2$
$= 10m^2 + 10mp - p^2$

43. $\left(a^3b - 5a^2b^2 + ab^3\right) - \left(5a^2b^2 - 7ab^3 + b^3\right)$
$= a^3b - 5a^2b^2 - 5a^2b^2 + ab^3 + 7ab^3 - b^3$
$= a^3b - 10a^2b^2 + 8ab^3 - b^3$

45. $f(3) = -2(3)^2 - 5(3) + 3$
$\quad = -30$

47. $g(-4) = 3(-4)^2 - 8(-4) - 1$
$\quad = 79$

49. $f(0) = -2(0)^2 - 5(0) + 3$
$\quad = 3$

51. $h(3) = 2(3)^3 - 4(3)$
$\quad = 42$

53. $h(-2) = 2(-2)^3 - 4(-2)$
$\quad = -8$

55. $f(-1) = 3$
57. $a = -1$ or $a = 3$

59. $a = 1$

61. $f(4) = 3$

63. $x = 0$ or $x = 6$

65. $x = 3$

67. a. $x = 1$ or $x = 5$

b. $f(x)$ does not have an inverse function because $f(2) = f(4) = 3$. There would be two values of $f^{-1}(x)$ for one value of x, and such a relation is not a function.

69.

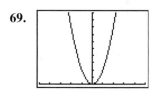

71.

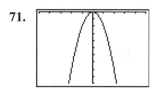

73.

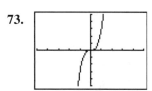

75.

77. $(f + g)(x) = \left(4x^2 - 2x + 8\right) + \left(7x^2 + 5x - 1\right)$
$= 4x^2 + 7x^2 - 2x + 5x + 8 - 1$
$= 11x^2 + 3x + 7$
$(f + g)(3) = 11(3)^2 + 3(3) + 7$
$\quad = 115$

79. $(f - h)(x) = \left(4x^2 - 2x + 8\right) - \left(-3x^2 - 4x - 9\right)$
$= 4x^2 + 3x^2 - 2x + 4x + 8 + 9$
$= 7x^2 + 2x + 17$
$(f - h)(4) = 7(4)^2 + 2(4) + 17$
$\quad = 137$

81. $(f + g)(x) = \left(2x^3 - 4x + 1\right) + \left(-3x^2 + 5x - 3\right)$
$= 2x^3 - 3x^2 - 4x + 5x + 1 - 3$
$= 2x^3 - 3x^2 + x - 2$
$(f + g)(2) = 2(2)^3 - 3(2)^2 + 2 - 2$
$\quad = 4$

83. $(f - h)(x) = \left(2x^3 - 4x + 1\right) - \left(x^3 - 3x^2 + 2x\right)$
$= 2x^3 - x^3 + 3x^2 - 4x - 2x + 1$
$= x^3 + 3x^2 - 6x + 1$
$(f - h)(-1) = (-1)^3 + 3(-1)^2 - 6(-1) + 1$
$\quad = 9$

85. a. $(M + S)(t) = (-0.27t + 35.54) + (0.82t + 8.96)$
$= -0.27t + 0.82t + 35.54 + 8.96$
$= 0.55t + 44.5$

b. For the expression $M(t) + S(t)$, we have $M(t)$ = gallons of milk per person + $S(t)$ = gallons of soft drinks per person. The units of the expression are gallons per person.

c. $(M + S)(64) = 0.55(64) + 44.5$

$= 79.7$

In 2014, the annual consumption of milk and soft drinks (combined) will be 79.7 gallons per person.

d. $(M - S)(t) = (-0.27t + 35.54) - (0.82t + 8.96)$

$= -0.27t - 0.82t + 35.54 - 8.96$

$= -1.09t + 26.58$

e. $(M - S)(64) = -1.09(64) + 26.58$

$= -43.18$

This means that in 2014, consumption of soft drinks will exceed consumption of milk by 43.18 gallons per person.

87. a. $(B + S)(t)$

$= (2.3t^2 - 12.1t + 98) + (1.57t^2 - 10.9t + 28)$

$= 2.3t^2 + 1.57t^2 - 12.1t - 10.9t + 98 + 28$

$= 3.87t^2 - 23t + 126$

b. For the expression $B(t) + S(t)$, we have $B(t)$ = base pay in thousands of dollars + $S(t)$ = signing bonus in thousands of dollars. The expression is the total compensation in thousands of dollars.

c. $(B + S)(14) = 3.87(14)^2 - 23(14) + 126$

$= 562.52$

In 2014, the total average base pay plus average signing bonus for MBA graduates will be about $562,520.

d. $(B - S)(t)$

$= (2.3t^2 - 12.1t + 98) - (1.57t^2 - 10.9t + 28)$

$= 2.3t^2 - 1.57t^2 - 12.1t + 10.9t + 98 - 28$

$= 0.73t^2 - 1.2t + 70$

e. $(B - S)(14) = 0.73(14)^2 - 1.2(14) + 70$

$= 196.28$

In 2014, average base pay will be more than the average signing bonuses by about $196,280.

89. The student did not apply the negative sign to $4x$ and 3.

$(6x^2 + 8x + 5) - (2x^2 + 4x + 3)$

$= 6x^2 + 8x + 5 - 2x^2 - 4x - 3$

$= 4x^2 + 4x + 2$

91. a. $(f - g)(x) = (3x + 7) - (5x + 2)$

$= 3x - 5x + 7 - 2$

$= -2x + 5$

$(g - f)(x) = (5x + 2) - (3x + 7)$

$= 5x - 3x + 2 - 7$

$= 2x - 5$

b. $(f - g)(2) = -2(2) + 5 = 1$

$(g - f)(2) = 2(2) - 5 = -1$

$(f - g)(2) = -(g - f)(2)$

c. $(f - g)(4) = -2(4) + 5 = -3$

$(g - f)(4) = 2(4) - 5 = 3$

$(f - g)(4) = -(g - f)(4)$

d. $(f - g)(7) = -2(7) + 5 = -9$

$(g - f)(7) = 2(7) - 5 = 9$

$(f - g)(7) = -(g - f)(7)$

e. In each case, $(f - g)(x) = -(g - f)(x)$. This makes sense because

$f - g = (-1)(g - f)$.

93. Answers will vary.
For example, to add two polynomials, combine like terms. To subtract polynomials, first distribute –1 to the second polynomial and then combine like terms.

95. a. $(C - S)(t)$

$= (-0.8t + 66.4) - (2.5t + 14.2)$

$= -0.8t - 2.5t + 66.4 - 14.2$

$= -3.3t + 52.2$

b. $(C - S)(14) = -3.3(14) + 52.2$

$= 6$

In 2014, there will be 6 million more cable TV subscriptions than satellite TV subscriptions.

c.
$$0 = -3.3t + 52.2$$
$$3.3t = 52.2$$
$$\frac{3.3t}{3.3} = \frac{52.2}{3.3}$$
$$t \approx 15.82$$

In 2016, the number of cable TV subscriptions and satellite TV subscriptions will be the same.

d.
$$-0.8t + 66.4 = 2.5t + 14.2$$
$$-0.8t + 66.4 - 66.4 = 2.5t + 14.2 - 66.4$$
$$-0.8t = 2.5t - 55.2$$
$$-0.8t - 2.5t = 2.5t - 2.5t - 55.2$$
$$-3.3t = -55.2$$
$$\frac{-3.3t}{-3.3} = \frac{-55.2}{-3.3}$$
$$t \approx 15.82$$

The result is the same.

97. $3x - 2y = -4$ Equation (1)

$4x + 5y = 33$ Equation (2)

We multiply both sides of equation (1) by 5, multiply both sides of equation (2) by 2, and add the results to eliminate the y-variable:
$$15x - 10y = -20$$
$$\underline{8x + 10y = 66}$$
$$23x + 0 = 46$$
$$23x = 46$$
$$x = 2$$

We substitute 2 for x in equation (1) and solve for y:
$$3x - 2y = -4$$
$$3(2) - 2y = -4$$
$$6 - 2y = -4$$
$$-2y = -10$$
$$y = 5$$

The solution is (2, 5). This is a system of two linear equations in two variables.

99. $3x - 2y = -4$
$$-2y = -3x - 4$$
$$\frac{-2y}{-2} = \frac{-3x}{-2} - \frac{4}{-2}$$
$$y = \frac{3}{2}x + 2$$

The slope is $m = \dfrac{3}{2}$, and the y-intercept is $(0, 2)$.

We first plot $(0, 2)$. From this point we move 2 units to the right and 3 units up, where we plot the point $(2, 5)$. We then sketch the line that contains these two points.

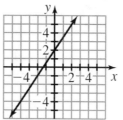

This is a linear equation in two variables.

Homework 7.2

1. $x^4 x^3 = x^{4+3} = x^7$

3. $w^8 w = w^8 w^1 = w^{8+1} = w^9$

5. $-5x^4 \left(-6x^3\right) = -5(-6)\left(x^4 x^3\right) = 30x^7$

7. $4p^2 t\left(-9p^3 t^2\right) = 4(-9)\left(p^2 p^3\right)\left(t^1 t^2\right) = -36p^5 t^3$

9. $\dfrac{4}{5}x^3\left(-\dfrac{7}{2}x^2\right) = \dfrac{4}{5}\left(-\dfrac{7}{2}\right)\left(x^3 x^2\right) = -\dfrac{14}{5}x^5$

11. $3w(w - 2) = 3w \cdot w - 3w \cdot 2$
$$= 3w^2 - 6w$$

13. $-4x(2x^2 + 3) = -4x \cdot 2x^2 + (-4x) \cdot 3$
$$= -8x^3 - 12x$$

15. $2mn^2(3m^2 + 5n) = 2mn^2 \cdot 3m^2 + 2mn^2 \cdot 5n$
$$= 6m^3 n^2 + 10mn^3$$

17. $2x(3x^2 - 2x + 7) = 2x \cdot 3x^2 + 2x \cdot (-2x) + 2x \cdot 7$
$$= 6x^3 - 4x^2 + 14x$$

19. $-3t^2\left(2t^2 + 4t - 2\right)$
$$= -3t^2 \cdot 2t^2 + \left(-3t^2\right) \cdot 4t + \left(-3t^2\right) \cdot (-2)$$
$$= -6t^4 - 12t^3 + 6t^2$$

21. $2xy^2\left(3x^2 - 4xy + 5y^2\right)$
$$= 2xy^2 \cdot 3x^2 - 2xy^2 \cdot 4xy + 2xy^2 \cdot 5y^2$$
$$= 6x^3 y^2 - 8x^2 y^3 + 10xy^4$$

23. $(x+2)(x+4) = x \cdot x + x \cdot 4 + 2 \cdot x + 2 \cdot 4$
$$= x^2 + 4x + 2x + 8$$
$$= x^2 + 6x + 8$$

25. $(x-2)(x+5) = x \cdot x + x \cdot 5 + (-2) \cdot x + (-2) \cdot 5$
$$= x^2 + 5x - 2x - 10$$
$$= x^2 + 3x - 10$$

27. $(a-3)(a-2) = a \cdot a + a(-2) + (-3)a + (-3)(-2)$
$$= a^2 - 2a - 3a + 6$$
$$= a^2 - 5a + 6$$

29. $(x+6)(x-6) = x \cdot x + x \cdot (-6) + 6 \cdot x + 6 \cdot (-6)$
$$= x^2 - 6x + 6x - 36$$
$$= x^2 - 36$$

31. $(x-5.3)(x-9.2)$
$$= x \cdot x + x(-9.2) + (-5.3)x + (-5.3)(-9.2)$$
$$= x^2 - 9.2x - 5.3x + 48.76$$
$$= x^2 - 14.5x + 48.76$$

33. $(5y-2)(3y+4)$
$$= 5y \cdot 3y + 5y \cdot 4 + (-2) \cdot 3y + (-2) \cdot 4$$
$$= 15y^2 + 20y - 6y - 8$$
$$= 15y^2 + 14y - 8$$

35. $(2x+4)(2x+4) = 2x \cdot 2x + 2x \cdot 4 + 4 \cdot 2x + 4 \cdot 4$
$$= 4x^2 + 8x + 8x + 16$$
$$= 4x^2 + 16x + 16$$

37. $(3x-1)(3x-1)$
$$= 3x \cdot 3x + 3x(-1) + (-1) \cdot 3x + (-1)(-1)$$
$$= 9x^2 - 3x - 3x + 1$$
$$= 9x^2 - 6x + 1$$

39. $(3x-5y)(4x+y)$
$$= 3x \cdot 4x + 3x \cdot y + (-5y) \cdot 4x + (-5y) \cdot y$$
$$= 12x^2 + 3xy - 20xy - 5y^2$$
$$= 12x^2 - 17xy - 5y^2$$

41. $(2a-8b)(3a-4b)$
$$= 2a \cdot 3a + 2a(-4b) + (-8b) \cdot 3a + (-8b)(-4b)$$
$$= 6a^2 - 8ab - 24ab + 32b^2$$
$$= 6a^2 - 32ab + 32b^2$$

43. $(3x-4)(3x+4) = 3x \cdot 3x + 3x \cdot 4 - 4 \cdot 3x - 4 \cdot 4$
$$= 9x^2 + 12x - 12x - 16$$
$$= 9x^2 - 16$$

45. $(9x+4y)(9x-4y)$
$$= 9x \cdot 9x + 9x(-4y) + 4y \cdot 9x + 4y(-4y)$$
$$= 81x^2 - 36xy + 36xy - 16y^2$$
$$= 81x^2 - 16y^2$$

47. $(2.5x+9.1)(4.6x-7.7)$
$$= 2.5x \cdot 4.6x + 2.5x(-7.7) + 9.1 \cdot 4.6x + 9.1(-7.7)$$
$$= 11.5x^2 - 19.25x + 41.86x - 70.07$$
$$= 11.5x^2 + 22.61x - 70.07$$

49. $(x+6)(x^2-3) = x \cdot x^2 + x \cdot (-3) + 6 \cdot x^2 + 6 \cdot (-3)$
$$= x^3 - 3x + 6x^2 - 18$$
$$= x^3 + 6x^2 - 3x - 18$$

51. $(2t^2-5)(3t-2)$
$$= 2t^2 \cdot 3t + 2t^2(-2) + (-5) \cdot 3t + (-5)(-2)$$
$$= 6t^3 - 4t^2 - 15t + 10$$

54. $(3a^2+5b^2)(2a^2-3b^2)$
$$= 3a^2 \cdot 2a^2 + 3a^2(-3b^2) + 5b^2 \cdot 2a^2 + 5b^2(-3b^2)$$
$$= 6a^4 - 9a^2b^2 + 10a^2b^2 - 15b^4$$
$$= 6a^4 + a^2b^2 - 15b^4$$

55. $3x^2(2x-5)(4x+1)$
$$= 3x^2(8x^2 + 2x - 20x - 5)$$
$$= 3x^2(8x^2 - 18x - 5)$$
$$= 24x^4 - 54x^3 - 15x^2$$

57. $5x(x^2+3)(x-4)$
$$= 5x(x^3 - 4x^2 + 3x - 12)$$
$$= 5x^4 - 20x^3 + 15x^2 - 60x$$

59. $(x+2)(x^2+3x+5)$
$= x \cdot x^2 + x \cdot 3x + x \cdot 5 + 2 \cdot x^2 + 2 \cdot 3x + 2 \cdot 5$
$= x^3 + 3x^2 + 5x + 2x^2 + 6x + 10$
$= x^3 + 3x^2 + 2x^2 + 5x + 6x + 10$
$= x^3 + 5x^2 + 11x + 10$

61. $(x+2)(x^2-2x+4)$
$= x \cdot x^2 + x(-2x) + x \cdot 4 + 2 \cdot x^2 + 2(-2x) + 2 \cdot 4$
$= x^3 - 2x^2 + 4x + 2x^2 - 4x + 8$
$= x^3 - 2x^2 + 2x^2 + 4x - 4x + 8$
$= x^3 + 8$

63. $(2b^2-3b+2)(b-4)$
$= 2b^2 \cdot b + 2b^2(-4) + (-3b) \cdot b + (-3b)(-4) + 2 \cdot b + 2(-4)$
$= 2b^3 - 8b^2 - 3b^2 + 12b + 2b - 8$
$= 2b^3 - 11b^2 + 14b - 8$

65. $(a+b)(a^2-ab+b^2)$
$= a^3 - a^2b + ab^2 + a^2b - ab^2 + b^3$
$= a^3 + b^3$

67. $(4x-3y)(2x^2-xy+5y^2)$
$= 8x^3 - 4x^2y + 20xy^2 - 6x^2y + 3xy^2 - 15y^3$
$= 8x^3 - 10x^2y + 23xy^2 - 15y^3$

69. $(2x^2+3)(3x^2-x+4)$
$= 2x^2 \cdot 3x^2 + 2x^2(-x) + 2x^2 \cdot 4 + 3 \cdot 3x^2 + 3(-x) + 3 \cdot 4$
$= 6x^4 - 2x^3 + 8x^2 + 9x^2 - 3x + 12$
$= 6x^4 - 2x^3 + 17x^2 - 3x + 12$

71. $(2x^2+4x-1)(3x^2-x+2)$
$= 2x^2 \cdot 3x^2 + 2x^2(-x) + 2x^2 \cdot 2 + 4x \cdot 3x^2 + 4x(-x) + 4x \cdot 2 + (-1) \cdot 3x^2 + (-1)(-x) + (-1) \cdot 2$
$= 6x^4 - 2x^3 + 4x^2 + 12x^3 - 4x^2 + 8x - 3x^2 + x - 2$
$= 6x^4 - 2x^3 + 12x^3 + 4x^2 - 4x^2 - 3x^2 + 8x + x - 2$
$= 6x^4 + 10x^3 - 3x^2 + 9x - 2$

73. $(2x^2+xy-3y^2)(x^2-2xy+y^2)$
$= 2x^4 - 4x^3y + 2x^2y^2 + x^3y - 2x^2y^2 + xy^3 - 3x^2y^2 + 6xy^3 - 3y^4$
$= 2x^4 - 3x^3y - 3x^2y^2 + 7xy^3 - 3y^4$

75. $(f \cdot g)(x) = (2x-3)(3x+2)$
$= 6x^2 + 4x - 9x - 6$
$= 6x^2 - 5x - 6$
$(f \cdot g)(3) = 6(3)^2 - 5(3) - 6 = 33$

77. $(f \cdot h)(x) = (2x-3)(2x^2-4x+3)$
$= 4x^3 - 8x^2 + 6x - 6x^2 + 12x - 9$
$= 4x^3 - 14x^2 + 18x - 9$
$(f \cdot h)(2) = 4(2)^3 - 14(2)^2 + 18(2) - 9 = 3$

79. $(f \cdot f)(x) = (2x-3)(2x-3)$
$= 4x^2 - 6x - 6x + 9$
$= 4x^2 - 12x + 9$
$(f \cdot f)(4) = 4(4)^2 - 12(4) + 9 = 25$

81. $(f \cdot g)(x) = (4x+1)(5x+3)$
$= 20x^2 + 12x + 5x + 3$
$= 20x^2 + 17x + 3$
$(f \cdot g)(-1) = 20(-1)^2 + 17(-1) + 3 = 6$

83. $(f \cdot h)(x) = (4x+1)(3x^2-x-2)$
$= 12x^3 - 4x^2 - 8x + 3x^2 - x - 2$
$= 12x^3 - x^2 - 9x - 2$
$(f \cdot h)(-2) = 12(-2)^3 - (-2)^2 - 9(-2) - 2$
$= -84$

85. $(h \cdot h)(x) = (3x^2-x-2)(3x^2-x-2)$
$= 9x^4 - 3x^3 - 6x^2 - 3x^3 + x^2 + 2x - 6x^2 + 2x + 4$
$= 9x^4 - 6x^3 - 11x^2 + 4x + 4$
$(h \cdot h)(1) = 9(1)^4 - 6(1)^3 - 11(1)^2 + 4(1) + 4 = 0$

87. a. $V(t) = 55t + 557$

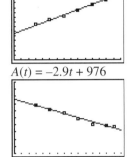

$A(t) = -2.9t + 976$

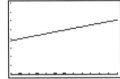

Both models fit the data well.

b. $(V \cdot A)(t) = (55t + 557)(-2.9t + 976)$
$$= -159.5t^2 + 52,064.7t + 543,632$$

c. For the expression $V(t) \cdot A(t)$, we have $V(t) =$ average value of farmland in dollars per acre $\times A(t) =$ amount of farmland in millions of acres. The units of the expression are total value of farmland in millions of dollars.

d. $(V \cdot A)(24)$
$$= -159.5(24)^2 + 52,064.7(24) + 543,632$$
$$= 1,701,312.8$$
The total value of U.S. farmland in 2014 will be $1,701,312.8 million, or about $1.70 trillion.

e.

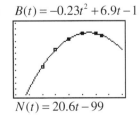

The function is increasing. This means that the total value of farmland is increasing. The average value of farmland is increasing from 1990 to 2014 at a faster rate than the amount of farmland is decreasing.

89. a. $B(t) = -0.23t^2 + 6.9t - 1$

$N(t) = 20.6t - 99$

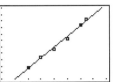

Both models fit the data well.

b. $(B \cdot N)(t)$
$$= (-0.23t^2 + 6.9t - 1)(20.6t - 99)$$
$$= -4.738t^3 + 22.77t^2 + 142.14t^2 - 683.1t$$
$$\qquad\qquad\qquad - 20.6t + 99$$
$$= -4.738t^3 + 164.91t^2 - 703.7t + 99$$

c. For the expression $B(t) \cdot N(t)$, we have $B(t) =$ average bill in dollars per month $\times N(t) =$ number of subscribers in millions of people. The units of the expression are millions of dollars per month.

d. $(B \cdot N)(24)$
$$= -4.738(24)^3 + 164.91(24)^2 - 703.7(24) + 99$$
$$= 12,700.248$$
In 2014, total monthly cell phone revenue will be about $12,700 million, or $12.7 billion.

e.

The function is increasing. This means that the total value of cell phone bills will be increasing from 1998 to 2010.

91. Answers may vary. One possibility follows: The student subtracted the rather than multiply. The correct result is:
$$6x(-4x) = 6(-4) \cdot x \cdot x = -24x^2.$$

93. a. (i) $(2x + 3)(4x + 5)$
$$= 2x \cdot 4x + 2x \cdot 5 + 3 \cdot 4x + 3 \cdot 5$$
$$= 8x^2 + 10x + 12x + 15$$
$$= 8x^2 + 22x + 15$$
This is a quadratic polynomial.

(ii) $(3x-7)(5x+2)$
$$= 3x \cdot 5x + 3x \cdot 2 + (-7) \cdot 5x + (-7) \cdot 2$$
$$= 15x^2 + 6x - 35x - 14$$
$$= 15x^2 - 29x - 14$$
This is a quadratic polynomial.

b. Examples will vary. The result will be a quadratic polynomial.

c. In general, the product of two linear polynomials will be a quadratic polynomial. Explanations will vary. One possibility follows: Each linear polynomial will be of degree one. Multiplying these will result in a polynomial that is degree two.

95. a. $(x+4)(x+7) = x \cdot x + x \cdot 7 + 4 \cdot x + 4 \cdot 7$
$$= x^2 + 7x + 4x + 28$$
$$= x^2 + 11x + 28$$

b. $(x+7)(x+4) = x \cdot x + x \cdot 4 + 7 \cdot x + 7 \cdot 4$
$$= x^2 + 4x + 7x + 28$$
$$= x^2 + 11x + 28$$

c. Answers may vary. One possibility follows: The fact that $(x+4)(x+7) = (x+7)(x+4)$ is a result of the commutative property of multiplication.

97. $(2x-5)(3x+4) = 6x^2 + 8x - 15x - 20$
$$= 6x^2 - 7x - 20$$
$$3x(2x-2) - x - 20 = 6x^2 - 6x - x - 20$$
$$= 6x^2 - 7x - 20$$
$$(3x+4)(2x-5) = 6x^2 - 15x + 8x - 20$$
$$= 6x^2 - 7x - 20$$
$$(3x-4)(2x+5) = 6x^2 + 15x - 8x - 20$$
$$= 6x^2 + 7x - 20$$

99. $(3x-5)(2x^2 - 4x + 2)$
$$= 3x \cdot 2x^2 + 3x(-4x) + 3x \cdot 2 + (-5) \cdot 2x^2 +$$
$$(-5)(-4x) + (-5) \cdot 2$$
$$= 6x^3 - 12x^2 + 6x - 10x^2 + 20x - 10$$
$$= 6x^3 - 12x^2 - 10x^2 + 6x + 20x - 10$$
$$= 6x^3 - 22x^2 + 26x - 10$$

101. $(3x-5) - (2x^2 - 4x + 2) = 3x - 5 - 2x^2 + 4x - 2$
$$= -2x^2 + 3x + 4x - 5 - 2$$
$$= -2x^2 + 7x - 7$$

103. $f(x) = 3x(x-2)$
$$f(x) = 3x \cdot x + 3x(-2)$$
$$f(x) = 3x^2 - 6x$$
The equation is quadratic. The graph will be a parabola.

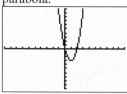

105. $f(x) = (x+2) - (3x+5)$
$$f(x) = x + 2 - 3x - 5$$
$$f(x) = x - 3x + 2 - 5$$
$$f(x) = -2x - 3$$
The equation is linear. The graph will be a line.

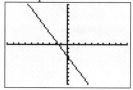

107. $f(x) = (2x+1)(5x-2)$
$$f(x) = 2x \cdot 5x + 2x(-2) + 1 \cdot 5x + 1(-2)$$
$$f(x) = 10x^2 - 4x + 5x - 2$$
$$f(x) = 10x^2 + x - 2$$
The equation is quadratic. The graph will be a parabola.

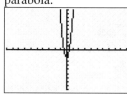

109. $2w - 5 = 7w + 5$
$$2w - 5 - 7w = 7w + 5 - 7w$$
$$-5w - 5 = 5$$
$$-5w - 5 + 5 = 5 + 5$$
$$-5w = 10$$
$$\frac{-5w}{-5} = \frac{10}{-5}$$
$$w = -2$$
This is a linear equation in one variable.

111. $(2w-5)(7w+5)$

$= 2w \cdot 7w + 2w \cdot 5 + (-5) \cdot 7w + (-5) \cdot 5$

$= 14w^2 + 10w - 35w - 25$

$= 14x^2 - 25w - 25$

This is a quadratic (or second-degree) polynomial in one variable.

Homework 7.3

1. $(xy)^8 = x^8 y^8$

3. $(6x)^2 = 6^2 x^2 = 36x^2$

5. $(4x)^3 = 4^3 x^3 = 64x^3$

7. $(-8x)^2 = (-8)^2 x^2 = 64x^2$

9. $(-3x)^3 = (-3)^3 x^3 = -27x^3$

11. $(-a)^5 = (-1a)^5 = (-1)^5 a^5 = -1a^5 = -a^5$

13. $(x+5)^2 = x^2 + 2 \cdot x \cdot 5 + 5^2$

$= x^2 + 10x + 25$

15. $(x-4)^2 = x^2 - 2 \cdot x \cdot 4 + 4^2$

$= x^2 - 8x + 16$

17. $(2x+3)^2 = (2x)^2 + 2 \cdot 2x \cdot 3 + 3^2$

$= 4x^2 + 12x + 9$

19. $(5y-2)^2 = (5y)^2 - 2 \cdot 5y \cdot 2 + 2^2$

$= 25y^2 - 20y + 4$

21. $(2a+5b)^2 = (2a)^2 + 2 \cdot 2a \cdot 5b + (5b)^2$

$= 4a^2 + 20ab + 25b^2$

23. $(8x-3y)^2 = (8x)^2 - 2 \cdot 8x \cdot 3y + (3y)^2$

$= 64x^2 - 48xy + 9y^2$

25. $\left(2x^2 - 6y^2\right)^2 = \left(2x^2 - 6y^2\right)\left(2x^2 - 6y^2\right)$

$= 4x^4 - 12x^2 y^2 - 12x^2 y^2 + 36y^4$

$= 4x^4 - 24x^2 y^2 + 36y^4$

27. $-2x(2x+5)^2 = -2x(2x+5)(2x+5)$

$= -2x\left(4x^2 + 10x + 10x + 25\right)$

$= -2x\left(4x^2 + 20x + 25\right)$

$= -8x^3 - 40x^2 - 50x$

29. $f(5b) = (5b)^2 - 3(5b) = 25b^2 - 15b$

31. $f(c+4) = (c+4)^2 - 3(c+4)$

$= c^2 + 8c + 16 - 3c - 12$

$= c^2 + 5c + 4$

33. $f(b-3) = (b-3)^2 - 3(b-3)$

$= b^2 - 6b + 9 - 3b + 9$

$= b^2 - 9b + 18$

35. $f(a+2) - f(a)$

$= \left((a+2)^2 - 3(a+2)\right) - \left((a)^2 - 3(a)\right)$

$= a^2 + 4a + 4 - 3a - 6 - a^2 + 3a$

$= 4a - 2$

37. $f(a+h) - f(a)$

$= \left((a+h)^2 - 3(a+h)\right) - \left((a)^2 - 3(a)\right)$

$= a^2 + 2ah + h^2 - 3a - 3h - a^2 + 3a$

$= h^2 + 2ah - 3h$

39. $f(x) = (x+6)^2$

$f(x) = x^2 + 2 \cdot x \cdot 6 + 6^2$

$f(x) = x^2 + 12x + 36$

41. $f(x) = (x-3)^2 + 1$

$f(x) = x^2 - 2 \cdot x \cdot 3 + 3^2 + 1$

$f(x) = x^2 - 6x + 9 + 1$

$f(x) = x^2 - 6x + 10$

43. $f(x) = 2(x+4)^2 - 3$

$f(x) = 2(x^2 + 2 \cdot x \cdot 4 + 4^2) - 3$

$f(x) = 2(x^2 + 8x + 16) - 3$

$f(x) = 2x^2 + 16x + 32 - 3$

$f(x) = 2x^2 + 16x + 29$

45. $f(x) = -3(x-1)^2 - 2$

$f(x) = -3(x^2 - 2 \cdot x \cdot 1 + 1^2) - 2$

$f(x) = -3(x^2 - 2x + 1) - 2$

$f(x) = -3x^2 + 6x - 3 - 2$

$f(x) = -3x^2 + 6x - 5$

47. $(x+4)(x-4) = x^2 - 4^2 = x^2 - 16$

49. $(t-7)(t+7) = t^2 - 7^2 = t^2 - 49$

51. $(7a+9)(7a-9) = (7a)^2 - 9^2 = 49a^2 - 81$

53. $(8t-4w)(8t+4w) = (8t)^2 - (4w)^2$

$\qquad = 64t^2 - 16w^2$

55. $(3rt - 9w)(3rt + 9w)$

$= 9r^2t^2 - 27rtw + 27rtw - 81w^2$

$= 9r^2t^2 - 81w^2$

57. $(8a^2 + 3b^2)(8a^2 - 3b^2)$

$= 64a^4 - 24a^2b^2 + 24a^2b^2 - 9b^4$

$= 64a^4 - 9b^4$

59. $(x-2)(x+2)(x^2+4)$

$= (x^2 + 2x - 2x - 4)(x^2 + 4)$

$= (x^2 - 4)(x^2 + 4)$

$= x^4 + 4x^2 - 4x^2 - 16$

$= x^4 - 16$

61. $(3a + 2b)(3a - 2b)(9a^2 + 4b^2)$

$= (9a^2 - 6ab + 6ab - 4b^2)(9a^2 + 4b^2)$

$= (9a^2 - 4b^2)(9a^2 + 4b^2)$

$= 81a^4 + 36a^2b^2 - 36a^2b^2 - 16b^4$

$= 81a^4 - 16b^4$

63. $(4x^2 - 5x) - (2x^3 - 8x) = 4x^2 - 5x - 2x^3 + 8x$

$= -2x^3 + 4x^2 - 5x + 8x$

$= -2x^3 + 4x^2 + 3x$

65. $5t(-2t^2) = 5(-2)t^1 \cdot t^2 = -10t^{1+2} = -10t^3$

67. $(3x+4)(x^2 - x + 2)$

$= 3x \cdot x^2 + 3x(-x) + 3x \cdot 2 + 4 \cdot x^2 + 4(-x) + 4 \cdot 2$

$= 3x^3 - 3x^2 + 6x + 4x^2 - 4x + 8$

$= 3x^3 - 3x^2 + 4x^2 + 6x - 4x + 8$

$= 3x^3 + x^2 + 2x + 8$

69. $(2tw - 3p)(2tw + 3p) = (2tw)^2 - (3p)^2$

$\qquad = 4t^2w^2 - 9p^2$

71. $2xy^2(4x^2 - 8x - 5)$

$= 2xy^2 \cdot 4x^2 + 2xy^2 \cdot (-8x) + 2xy^2 \cdot (-5)$

$= 8x^3y^2 - 16x^2y^2 - 10xy^2$

73. $(-6x^2 - 4x + 5) + (-2x^2 + 3x - 8)$

$= -6x^2 + (-2x^2) - 4x + 3x + 5 - 8$

$= -8x^2 - x - 3$

75. $(4w-8)^2 = (4w)^2 - 2 \cdot 4w \cdot 8 + 8^2$

$\qquad = 16w^2 - 64w + 64$

77. $(3x - 7y)(2x + 3y)$

$= 3x \cdot 2x + 3x \cdot 3y + (-7y)(2x) + (-7y)(3y)$

$= 6x^2 + 9xy - 14xy - 21y^2$

$= 6x^2 - 5xy - 21y^2$

79. $(6x-7)(6x+7) = (6x)^2 - 7^2$

$\qquad = 36x^2 - 49$

81. $(2t^2 + 5w^2)^2 = (2t^2)^2 + 2 \cdot 2t^2 \cdot 5w^2 + (5w^2)^2$

$\qquad = 4t^4 + 20t^2w^2 + 25w^4$

83. Answers may vary. One possibility follows: The student failed to raise the 4 to the second power. The correct answer is:

$(4x)^2 = 4^2 x^2 = 16x^2$

85. Answers may vary. One possibility follows: The student has left out the middle term. The correct answer is:

$(x+7)^2 = x^2 + 2 \cdot x \cdot 7 + 7^2$

$\qquad = x^2 + 14x + 49$

87. Answers may vary. One possibility follows:

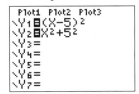

Since the y-values differ, the expression $(x-5)^2$

is not equivalent to $x^2 - 5^2$.

Since the y-values differ, the expression $(x-5)^2$

is not equivalent to $x^2 + 5^2$.

The correct simplification is:

$$(x-5)^2 = x^2 - 2 \cdot x \cdot 5 + 5^2$$
$$= x^2 - 10x + 25$$

Since the y-values are always the same, the two expressions are equivalent.

89. a. Answers may vary. One possibility follows:

Since the y-values differ, the expression $(x+4)^2$ is not equivalent to $x^2 + 4^2$.

b. $(x+4)^2 = x^2 + 2 \cdot x \cdot 4 + 4^2$
$$= x^2 + 8x + 16$$

c. Answers may vary. One possibility follows:

Since the y-values are always the same, the two expressions are equivalent.

91. If $A = 2$ and $B = 3$, then we obtain the statement

$$(A+B)^2 = A^2 + B^2$$
$$(2+3)^2 = 2^2 + 3^2$$
$$5^2 = 4 + 9$$
$$25 = 13$$

Explanations may vary. One possibility follows: Since the last line is not true, this shows that $(A+B)^2 = A^2 + B^2$ is not true for all values of A and B. In other words, $(A+B)^2 \neq A^2 + B^2$.

A true statement is $(A+B)^2 = A^2 + 2AB + B^2$.

93. The expressions $(x-2)^2$, $x(x-4)+4$, and $x^2 - 4x + 4$ are all equivalent.

95. Answers may vary. One possibility follows: Since $(x+7)^2$ is equivalent to $(x+7)(x+7)$, the $14x$ term comes from the "outer" and "inner" multiplications.

97. a. **(i)** $2^5 = 32$, $2^4 = 16$, $2^3 = 8$, $2^2 = 4$, $2^1 = 2$

   (ii) Answers may vary. One possibility follows: Each result is half of the previous result. For example, $16 = \frac{1}{2} \cdot 32$, $8 = \frac{1}{2} \cdot 16$, and so on.

   (iii) $2^0 = \frac{1}{2} \cdot 2 = 1$

b. $3^4 = 81$, $3^3 = 27$, $3^2 = 9$, $3^1 = 3$, $3^0 = 1$

c. If b is a nonzero real number, then $b^0 = 1$.

99. $f(x) = 2x(5x - 3)$
$$f(x) = 2x \cdot 5x - 2x \cdot 3$$
$$f(x) = 10x^2 - 6x$$

This is a quadratic function. The graph will be a parabola.

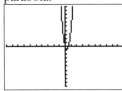

101. $f(x) = (4x-3)(6x-5)$

$f(x) = 4x \cdot 6x + 4x(-5) + (-3) \cdot 6x + (-3)(-5)$

$f(x) = 24x^2 - 20x - 18x + 15$

$f(x) = 24x^2 - 38x + 15$

This is a quadratic function. The graph will be a parabola.

103. $f(x) = x^2 - (x-3)^2$

$f(x) = x^2 - (x^2 - 2 \cdot x \cdot 3 + 3^2)$

$f(x) = x^2 - (x^2 - 6x + 9)$

$f(x) = x^2 - x^2 + 6x - 9$

$f(x) = 6x - 9$

This is a linear function. The graph will be a line.

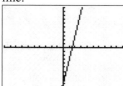

105. $2x - 5y = 15$ Equation (1)

      $y = 3x - 16$ Equation (2)

From equation (2), we substitute $3x - 16$ for y in equation (1) and solve for x:

$2x - 5y = 15$

$2x - 5(3x - 16) = 15$

$2x - 15x + 80 = 15$

$-13x + 80 = 15$

$-13x = -65$

$x = 5$

We substitute 5 for x in equation (2) to find y:

$y = 3x - 16$

$y = 3(5) - 16 = -1$

The solution is $(5, -1)$. This is a system of two linear equations in two variables.

107. $2x - 5y = 15$

$-5y = -2x + 15$

$\dfrac{-5y}{-5} = \dfrac{-2x}{-5} + \dfrac{15}{-5}$

$y = \dfrac{2}{5}x - 3$

The slope is $m = \dfrac{2}{5}$, and the y-intercept is $(0, -3)$.

We first plot $(0, -3)$. From this point we move 5 units to the right and 2 units up, where we plot the point $(5, -1)$. We then sketch the line that contains these two points.

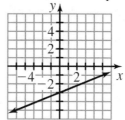

This is a linear equation in two variables.

Homework 7.4

1. $x^3 x^5 = x^{3+5} = x^8$

3. $r^5 r = r^5 r^1 = r^{5+1} = r^6$

5. $\left(5x^4\right)\left(3x^5\right) = (5 \cdot 3)\left(x^4 x^5\right) = 15x^9$

7. $\left(-4b^3\right)\left(-8b^5\right) = -4(-8)\left(b^3 b^5\right) = 32b^8$

9. $\left(6a^2 b^5\right)\left(9a^4 b^3\right) = (6 \cdot 9)\left(a^2 a^4\right)\left(b^5 b^3\right) = 54a^6 b^8$

11. $(rt)^7 = r^7 t^7$

13. $(8x)^2 = 8^2 x^2 = 64x^2$

15. $(2xy)^5 = 2^5 x^5 y^5 = 32x^5 y^5$

17. $(-2a)^4 = (-2)^4 a^4 = 16a^4$

19. $(9xy)^0 = 1$

21. $\dfrac{a^5}{a^2} = a^{5-2} = a^3$

23. $\dfrac{6x^7}{3x^3} = \dfrac{6}{3}\cdot\dfrac{x^7}{x^3} = 2\cdot x^{7-3} = 2x^4$

25. $\dfrac{15x^6 y^8}{12x^3 y} = \dfrac{15}{12}\cdot\dfrac{x^6}{x^3}\cdot\dfrac{y^8}{y^1} = \dfrac{5}{4}\cdot x^{6-3}\cdot y^{8-1} = \dfrac{5x^3 y^7}{4}$

27. $\left(\dfrac{t}{w}\right)^7 = \dfrac{t^7}{w^7}$

29. $\left(\dfrac{3}{t}\right)^3 = \dfrac{3^3}{t^3} = \dfrac{27}{t^3}$

31. $\left(\dfrac{x}{3}\right)^0 = 1$

33. $\left(r^2\right)^4 = r^{2\cdot4} = r^8$

35. $\left(x^4\right)^9 = x^{4\cdot9} = x^{36}$

37. $\left(6x^3\right)^2 = 6^2\left(x^3\right)^2 = 36x^{3\cdot2} = 36x^6$

39. $\left(-t^3\right)^4 = \left(-1\cdot t^3\right)^4 = (-1)^4\left(t^3\right)^4 = 1\cdot t^{3\cdot4} = t^{12}$

41. $\left(2a^2 a^7\right)^3 = \left(2a^{2+7}\right)^3 = \left(2a^9\right)^3 = 2^3\left(a^9\right)^3 = 8a^{27}$

43. $\left(x^2 y^3\right)^4 x^5 y^8 = \left(x^2\right)^4\left(y^3\right)^4 x^5 y^8$
$\qquad = x^8 y^{12} x^5 y^8$
$\qquad = x^{8+5} y^{12+8}$
$\qquad = x^{13} y^{20}$

45. $5x^4\left(3x^6\right)^2 = 5x^4\cdot3^2\left(x^6\right)^2$
$\qquad = 5x^4\cdot9x^{12}$
$\qquad = 5\cdot9x^{4+12}$
$\qquad = 45x^{16}$

47. $-3c^6\left(c^4\right)^5 = -3c^6\cdot c^{20} = -3c^{6+20} = -3c^{26}$

49. $\left(xy^3\right)^5 (xy)^4 = x^5\left(y^3\right)^5 x^4 y^4$
$\qquad = x^5 y^{15} x^4 y^4$
$\qquad = x^{5+4} y^{15+4}$
$\qquad = x^9 y^{19}$

51. $\dfrac{10t^5 t^7}{8t^4} = \dfrac{10t^{5+7}}{8t^4} = \dfrac{10t^{12}}{8t^4} = \dfrac{10}{8}\cdot t^{12-4} = \dfrac{5}{4}\cdot t^8 = \dfrac{5t^8}{4}$

53. $\dfrac{18x^{10}}{24x^4 x^6} = \dfrac{18}{24}\cdot\dfrac{x^{10}}{x^{4+6}} = \dfrac{3}{4}\cdot\dfrac{x^{10}}{x^{10}} = \dfrac{3}{4}\cdot x^{10-10} = \dfrac{3x^0}{4} = \dfrac{3}{4}$

55. $\left(\dfrac{y}{2x}\right)^3 = \dfrac{y^3}{(2x)^3} = \dfrac{y^3}{2^3 x^3} = \dfrac{y^3}{8x^3}$

57. $\left(\dfrac{x^2}{y^5}\right)^4 = \dfrac{\left(x^2\right)^4}{\left(y^5\right)^4} = \dfrac{x^8}{y^{20}}$

59. $\left(\dfrac{r^6}{6}\right)^2 = \dfrac{\left(r^6\right)^2}{6^2} = \dfrac{r^{12}}{36}$

61. $\left(\dfrac{2a^4}{3b^2}\right)^3 = \dfrac{\left(2a^4\right)^3}{\left(3b^2\right)^3} = \dfrac{2^3\left(a^4\right)^3}{3^3\left(b^2\right)^3} = \dfrac{8a^{12}}{27b^6}$

63. $\left(\dfrac{3x^4}{5y^7}\right)^0 = 1$

65. $\left(\dfrac{2a^6 b}{3c^5}\right)^3 = \dfrac{\left(2a^6 b\right)^3}{\left(3c^5\right)^3} = \dfrac{2^3\left(a^6\right)^3 b^3}{3^3\left(c^5\right)^3} = \dfrac{8a^{18} b^3}{27c^{15}}$

67. $\dfrac{\left(x^4 y\right)^4}{x^5} = \dfrac{\left(x^4\right)^4 y^4}{x^5} = \dfrac{x^{16} y^4}{x^5} = x^{16-5} y^4 = x^{11} y^4$

69. $\dfrac{\left(w^3\right)^4}{(2w)^5} = \dfrac{w^{12}}{2^5 w^5} = \dfrac{w^{12}}{32w^5} = \dfrac{w^{12-5}}{32} = \dfrac{w^7}{32}$

71. $\dfrac{\left(4x^5 y^8\right)^2}{8x^8 y^9} = \dfrac{4^2\left(x^5\right)^2\left(y^8\right)^2}{8x^8 y^9}$
$\qquad = \dfrac{16x^{10} y^{16}}{8x^8 y^9}$
$\qquad = \dfrac{16}{8}\cdot x^{10-8}\cdot y^{16-9}$
$\qquad = 2x^2 y^7$

273

73. We substitute 5 for t in the equation $f(t) = 16t^2$.

$$f(t) = 16(5)^2 = 400$$

The sky diver will have fallen 400 feet.

75. We substitute 0.57 for r and 12.5 for v in the equation $P = 0.8r^2v^3$.

$$P = 0.8(0.57)^2(12.5)^3 = 507.65625$$

The windmill can generate approximately 507.66 watts of power.

77. Answers may vary. One possibility follows: The student should have added the exponents instead of multiplying them. The correct simplification is: $x^3x^5 = x^{3+5} = x^8$.

79. Answers may vary. One possibility follows: When raising the product to the power, the student failed to raise both factors to the power. The correct simplification is:

$$\left(5x^3\right)^2 = 5^2\left(x^3\right)^2 = 25x^6.$$

81. Answers may vary. One possibility follows: When raising the product to the fourth power, the student should have raised the factor 2 to the 4th power instead of multiplying it by 4. The correct simplification is:

$$\left(2x^2\right)^4 = 2^4\left(x^2\right)^4 = 16x^8.$$

83. $x^3x^2 = x^{3+2} = x^5$

85. $x^3 + x^2$ can be simplified no further.

87. $2x^4 + 3x^4 = 5x^4$

89. $\left(2x^4\right)\left(3x^4\right) = (2\cdot3)x^4x^4 = 6x^{4+4} = 6x^8$

91. $(3x)^2 = 3^2x^2 = 9x^2$

93. $(3+x)^2 = 3^2 + 2\cdot3\cdot x + x^2$
$= 9 + 6x + x^2$
$= x^2 + 6x + 9$

95. Answers may vary.

97. Answers may vary.

99. Answers may vary.

Chapter 7 Review Exercises

1. $-4x^3 + 5x - 2x^2 - 8x + x^3$
$= -4x^3 + x^3 - 2x^2 + 5x - 8x$
$= -3x^3 - 2x^2 - 3x$

2. $3a^4b - 2a^3b^2 + 5a^2b^3 - 7a^3b^2 - 9a^2b^3$
$= 3a^4b - 2a^3b^2 - 7a^3b^2 + 5a^2b^3 - 9a^2b^3$
$= 3a^4b - 9a^3b^2 - 4a^2b^3$

3. $\left(-7x^3 + 5x^2 - 9\right) + \left(2x^3 - 8x^2 + 3x\right)$
$= -5x^3 - 3x^2 + 3x - 9$

4. $\left(5a^3b - 2a^2b^2 + 9ab^3\right) - \left(8a^3b + 4a^2b^2 - ab^3\right)$
$= -3a^3b - 6a^2b^2 + 10ab^3$

5. $f(-2) = 3(-2)^2 - 5(-2) + 2 = 24$

6. $f(-3) = -3$

7. There is no solution.

8. $x = 1$

9. $x = -3$ and $x = 5$

10. $f(2) = 9$

11. $x = 2$ or $x = 4$

12. $f(3) = 10$

13. There is no solution.

14. $(f+g)(x)$
$= \left(3x^3 - 7x^2 - 4x + 2\right) + \left(-2x^3 + 5x^2 - 3x + 1\right)$
$= x^3 - 2x^2 - 7x + 3$
$(f+g)(2) = (2)^3 - 2(2)^2 - 7(2) + 3 = -11$

15. $(f-g)(x)$
$= \left(3x^3 - 7x^2 - 4x + 2\right) - \left(-2x^3 + 5x^2 - 3x + 1\right)$
$= 5x^3 - 12x^2 - x + 1$
$(f-g)(-3) = 5(-3)^3 - 12(-3)^2 - (-3) + 1 = -239$

16. a. $(R+L)(t) = (5.08t+6.62)+(-5.32t+87.51)$
$$= 5.08t - 5.32t + 6.62 + 87.51$$
$$= -0.24t + 94.13$$

b. Substitute 14 for t in our expression:
$(R+L)(14) = -0.24(14)+94.13 = 90.77$

Note that $t = 14$ represents the year 2014. The above result means that about 90.8% of airplanes will be regional jets, turboprops, or large jets in the year 2014.

c. $(R-L)(t) = (5.08t+6.62)-(-5.32t+87.51)$
$$= 5.08t + 6.62 + 5.32t - 87.51$$
$$= 5.08t + 5.32t + 6.62 - 87.51$$
$$= 10.4t - 80.89$$

d. Substitute 14 for t in our expression:
$(R-L)(14) = 10.4(14)-80.89 = 64.71$

This means that, in 2014, the percentage of airplanes that are regional jets will be 64.71 percentage points more than the percentage of airplanes that are turboprops or large jets. Model breakdown has likely occurred.

17. $(x-7)(x+7) = x^2 - 49$

18. $8a^2b(-5a^3b^5) = -40a^5b^6$

19. $(4p+9t)(2p-5t) = 8p^2 - 2pt - 45t^2$

20. $(4x-3)(5x^2 - 2x + 4)$
$$= 20x^3 - 23x^2 + 22x - 12$$

21. $(3x+7y)^2 = 9x^2 + 42xy + 49y^2$

22. $(6p^2 - 9t^3)(6p^2 + 9t^3) = 36p^4 - 81t^6$

23. $-3rt^3(2r^2 - 5rt + 3t^2) = -6r^3t^3 + 15r^2t^4 - 9rt^5$

24. $-4x(3x-2)^2 = -36x^3 + 48x^2 - 16x$

25. $(3m^2 - mp + 2p^2)(2m^2 + 3mp - 4p^2)$
$$= 6m^4 + 7m^3p - 11m^2p^2 + 10mp^3 - 8p^4$$

26. $(2a^2 + 3b^2)(5a^2 - 2b^2)$
$$= 2a^2 \cdot 5a^2 + 2a^2 \cdot (-2b^2) + 3b^2 \cdot 5a^2 + 3b^2 \cdot (-2b^2)$$
$$= 10a^4 - 4a^2b^2 + 15a^2b^2 - 6b^4$$
$$= 10a^4 + 11a^2b^2 - 6b^4$$

27. $(3p-4t)(3p+4t)(9p^2 + 16t^2)$
$$= (9p^2 - 16t^2)(9p^2 + 16t^2)$$
$$= 81p^4 - 256t^4$$

28. $(x-4)^2 = x^2 - 2 \cdot x \cdot 4 + 4^2$
$$= x^2 - 8x + 16$$

29. $(4b^2 - b + 3)(2b - 7)$
$$= 4b^2 \cdot 2b + 4b^2(-7) + (-b) \cdot 2b + (-b)(-7) + 3 \cdot 2b + 3(-7)$$
$$= 8b^3 - 28b^2 - 2b^2 + 7b + 6b - 21$$
$$= 8b^3 - 30b^2 + 13b - 21$$

30. $(w-3)(w-9)$
$$= w \cdot w + w \cdot (-9) + (-3) \cdot w + (-3)(-9)$$
$$= w^2 - 9w - 3w + 27$$
$$= w^2 - 12w + 27$$

31. $-5(c+2)^2 = -5(c^2 + 2 \cdot c \cdot 2 + 2^2)$
$$= -5(c^2 + 4c + 4)$$
$$= -5c^2 - 20c - 20$$

32. $(4m-7n)(4m+7n) = (4m)^2 - (7n)^2$
$$= 16m^2 - 49n^2$$

33. $f(a-4) = (a-4)^2 - 2(a-4)$
$$= a^2 - 10a + 24$$

34. $f(a+3) - f(a)$
$$= (a+3)^2 - 2(a+3) - (a^2 - 2a)$$
$$= 6a + 3$$

35. $f(x) = -2(x-4)^2 + 3$
$$= -2x^2 + 16x - 29$$

36. $(f \cdot g)(x) = (3x - 7)(2x^2 - 4x + 3)$

$\qquad = 6x^3 - 26x^2 + 37x - 21$

$(f \cdot g)(3) = 6(3)^3 - 26(3)^2 + 37(3) - 21$

$\qquad = 18$

37. a. $(g \cdot p)(t)$

$\qquad = (0.47t - 3)(3.1t + 249)$

$\qquad = 0.47t \cdot 3.1t + 0.47t \cdot 249 - 3 \cdot 3.1t - 3 \cdot 249$

$\qquad = 1.457t^2 + 117.03t - 9.3t - 747$

$\qquad = 1.457t^2 + 107.73t - 747$

This expression represents the total annual consumption (in millions of gallons) of sports drinks in the United States at t years since 1990.

b. $\underbrace{(0.47t - 3)}_{\substack{\text{gallons} \\ \text{person}}} \underbrace{(3.1t + 249)}_{\text{millions of people}}$

We use the fact that $\dfrac{\text{people}}{\text{people}} = 1$ to simplify

the expression:

$\dfrac{\text{gallons}}{\text{person}} \cdot \text{millions of people}$

$= \text{gallons} \cdot \text{millions}$

$= \text{millions of gallons}$

Thus, the units of the expression are millions of gallons of sports drinks consumed by Americans per year.

c. Substitute 25 for t in the expression:

$(g \cdot p)(25) = 1.457(25)^2 + 107.73(25) - 747$

$\qquad = 2856.875$

In the year 2015, the total annual consumption of sports drinks in the United States will be about 2856.9 million gallons, or about 2.86 billion gallons.

d.

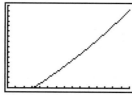

The function $g \cdot p$ is increasing for values of t between 10 and 30. This means that total annual consumption of sports drinks is increasing for the years from 2000 to 2020.

38. The product of a linear polynomial and a quadratic polynomial is a cubic polynomial. Examples may vary.

39. $\left(-x^5\right)^2 = (-1)^2 \left(x^5\right)^2 = 1x^{5 \cdot 2} = x^{10}$

40. $(2x^3)(6x^4) = 2 \cdot 6x^3 x^4 = 12x^{3+4} = 12x^7$

41. $\left(8a^2b^3\right)\left(-5a^4b^9\right) = 8 \cdot (-5)\left(a^2a^4\right)\left(b^3b^9\right)$

$\qquad = -40a^6b^{12}$

42. $\dfrac{8x^4y^8}{16x^3y^5} = \dfrac{8}{16} \cdot x^{4-3} \cdot y^{8-5} = \dfrac{1}{2}x^1y^3 = \dfrac{xy^3}{2}$

43. $\left(\dfrac{x}{2}\right)^3 = \dfrac{x^3}{2^3} = \dfrac{x^3}{8}$

44. $\left(2x^9y^3\right)^5 = 2^5\left(x^9\right)^5\left(y^3\right)^5 = 32x^{45}y^{15}$

45. $3x^6\left(5x^4\right)^2 = 3x^6 \cdot 5^2\left(x^4\right)^2$

$\qquad = 3x^6 \cdot 25x^8$

$\qquad = 3 \cdot 25x^{6+8}$

$\qquad = 75x^{14}$

46. $\dfrac{15c^2c^7}{10c^4} = \dfrac{15c^{2+7}}{10c^4} = \dfrac{15c^9}{10c^4} = \dfrac{15}{10} \cdot c^{9-4} = \dfrac{3}{2} \cdot c^5 = \dfrac{3c^5}{2}$

47. $\left(\dfrac{a^4}{9}\right)^2 = \dfrac{\left(a^4\right)^2}{9^2} = \dfrac{a^8}{81}$

48. $\left(\dfrac{-9x^5}{5y^7}\right)^0 = 1$

49. $\dfrac{\left(3x^5y^4\right)^2}{6x^7y^3} = \dfrac{3^2\left(x^5\right)^2\left(y^4\right)^2}{6x^7y^3}$

$\qquad = \dfrac{9x^{10}y^8}{6x^7y^3}$

$\qquad = \dfrac{9}{6} \cdot x^{10-7} \cdot y^{8-3}$

$\qquad = \dfrac{3}{2}x^3y^5$

$\qquad = \dfrac{3x^3y^5}{2}$

50. $\left(\dfrac{3x^5}{4x^2}\right)^3 = \left(\dfrac{3x^{5-2}}{4}\right)^3 = \left(\dfrac{3x^3}{4}\right)^3 = \dfrac{3^3\left(x^3\right)^3}{4^3} = \dfrac{27x^9}{64}$

Chapter 7 Test

1. $\left(4a^3b - 9a^2b^2 - 2ab^3\right) + \left(-5a^3b + 4a^2b^2 + 3ab^3\right)$

  $= -a^3b - 5a^2b^2 + ab^3$

2. $(2x^3 - 4x^2 + 7x) - (6x^3 - 3x^2 + 9x)$

  $= 2x^3 - 4x^2 + 7x - 6x^3 + 3x^2 - 9x$

  $= 2x^3 - 6x^3 - 4x^2 + 3x^2 + 7x - 9x$

  $= -4x^3 - x^2 - 2x$

3. The graph contains the point $(-5, 5)$, so

  $f(a) = 5$ when $a = -5$.

4. The graph contains the points $(-3, -3)$ and

  $(-1, -3)$, so $a = -3$ or $a = -1$ when $f(a) = -3$.

5. The graph contains the point $(-2, -4)$, so

  $a = -2$ when $f(a) = -4$.

6. There are no points on the graph for which *f*(*a*) is
  -5. That is, there is no value of *a* for which
  $f(a) = -5$.

7. $(f - g)(x) = \left(4x^2 + 5x - 9\right) - \left(6x^2 - 3x + 7\right)$

  $= -2x^2 + 8x - 16$

  $(f - g)(-2) = -2(-2)^2 + 8(-2) - 16 = -40$

8. a. $(E + C)(t)$

  $= \left(12.7t^2 - 35t + 235\right) + \left(8t^2 - 24.5t + 125\right)$

  $= 20.7t^2 - 59.5t + 360$

  b. For the expression *E*(*t*) + *C*(*t*), we have *E*(*t*) =
  ExxonMobil's revenue in billions of dollars +
  C(*t*) = Chevron's revenue in billions of dollars.
  The units of the expression are in billions of
  dollars.

  c. $(E + C)(14) = 20.7(14)^2 - 59.5(14) + 360$

  $= 3584.2$

  It means that in 2014 the combined revenues
  of both corporations will be \$3584 billion, or
  \$3.584 trillion.

  d. $(E - C)(t)$

  $= \left(12.7t^2 - 35t + 235\right) - \left(8t^2 - 24.5t + 125\right)$

  $= 4.7t^2 - 10.5t + 110$

  e. $(E - C)(14) = 4.7(14)^2 - 10.5(14) + 110$

  $= 884.2$

  It means that, in 2014, ExxonMobil's revenue
  will exceed Chevron's revenue by \$884.2
  billion.

9. $-2xy^2\left(7x^2 - 3xy + 6y^2\right)$

  $= -14x^3y^2 + 6x^2y^3 - 12xy^4$

10. $(4x - 7y)(3x + 5y) = 12x^2 - xy - 35y^2$

11. $(2w - 5t)\left(3w^2 - wt + 4t^2\right)$

  $= 6w^3 - 17w^2t + 13wt^2 - 20t^3$

12. $(x - 7)^2 = x^2 - 14x + 49$

13. $3x(2x + 3)^2 = 12x^3 + 36x^2 + 27x$

14. $\left(3x^2 + x - 5\right)\left(2x^2 + 4x - 1\right)$

  $= 6x^4 + 14x^3 - 9x^2 - 21x + 5$

15. $\left(4x^2 + 9y^2\right)\left(4x^2 - 9y^2\right) = 16x^4 - 81y^4$

16. $f(a - 5) = (a - 5)^2 - 3(a - 5)$

  $= a^2 - 13a + 40$

17. $(f \cdot g)(x) = \left(2x^2 - 5x + 4\right)(3x - 2)$

  $= 6x^3 - 19x^2 + 22x - 8$

  $(f \cdot g)(3) = 6(3)^3 - 19(3)^2 + 22(3) - 8$

  $= 49$

18. a. $R(t) = -7.8t + 564$

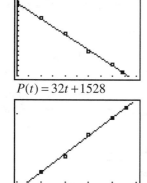

$P(t) = 32t + 1528$

The models fit the data well.

b. $(R \cdot P)(t)$

$= (-7.8t + 564)(32t + 1528)$

$= -249.6t^2 - 11,918.4t + 18,048t + 861,792$

$= -249.6t^2 + 6129.6t + 861,792$

c. For the expression $R(t) \cdot P(t)$, we have $R(t) =$ number of deaths per 100,000 people × $P(t) =$ population in hundred-thousands. The units of the expression are number of total deaths in the U.S.

d. $(R \cdot P)(54)$

$= -249.6(54)^2 + 6129.6(54) + 861,792$

$= 464,956.8$

This means that in 2014, there will be about 464,957 deaths from heart disease.

e.

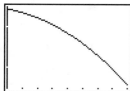

The function $(R \cdot P)$ is decreasing for values of t between 20 and 60. This means that the number of people dying from heart disease is decreasing between the years 1980 and 2020. This occurs because the number of deaths from heart disease is decreasing at a faster rate than the population is growing.

19. $f(x) = -3(x-1)^2 + 5$

$f(x) = -3(x^2 - 2 \cdot x \cdot 1 + 1^2) + 5$

$f(x) = -3(x^2 - 2x + 1) + 5$

$f(x) = -3x^2 + 6x - 3 + 5$

$f(x) = -3x^2 + 6x + 2$

20. Answers may vary. One possibility follows: The student failed to find the middle term in the simplified expression. The correct answer is:

$(x+4)^2 = x^2 + 2 \cdot x \cdot 4 + 4^2$

$= x^2 + 8x + 16$

21. $\dfrac{6x^7 y^4}{8x^3 y^9} = \dfrac{6}{8} \cdot x^{7-3} \cdot y^{4-9} = \dfrac{3}{4} x^4 y^{-5} = \dfrac{3x^4}{4y^5}$

22. $\left(4a^3 b^5\right)^3 a^6 b = 4^3 \left(a^3\right)^3 \left(b^5\right)^3 a^6 b$

$= 64 a^9 b^{15} a^6 b$

$= 64 a^{9+6} b^{15+1}$

$= 64 a^{15} b^{16}$

23. $\left(\dfrac{x^3}{y^4}\right)^6 = \dfrac{\left(x^3\right)^6}{\left(y^4\right)^6} = \dfrac{x^{18}}{y^{24}}$

24. $\left(7x^3\right)^2 = 7^2 \left(x^3\right)^2 = 49x^6$

25. $\left(\dfrac{x^2 y^6}{2w^3}\right)^4 = \dfrac{\left(x^2\right)^4 \left(y^6\right)^4}{2^4 \left(w^3\right)^4} = \dfrac{x^8 y^{24}}{16 w^{12}}$

26. $\dfrac{\left(2p^5 t^2\right)^3}{4p^2 t^3} = \dfrac{2^3}{4} \cdot p^{5 \cdot 3 - 2} \cdot t^{2 \cdot 3 - 3} = \dfrac{8}{4} \cdot p^{13} \cdot t^3 = 2p^{13} t^3$

27. $f(30) = \dfrac{58,000}{30^2} = \dfrac{58,000}{900} \approx 64.44$

The sound level at 30 feet is about 64.44 decibels.

Review of Chapters 1 – 7

1. a. The independent variable is a and the dependent variable is p.

b. The ordered pair (45, 85) means that 85% of 45-year-old Americans work.

2. $1-(-5)=6$
The change in temperature is $-6°$F.

3. $5(-2)-(-6)^2+4=-10-36+4=-42$

4. $9-(6-8)^3+4÷(-2)=9-(-2)^3-2$
$$=9+8-2$$
$$=15$$

5. $b^2-4ac=(-2)^2-4(-4)(5)$
$$=4+80$$
$$=84$$

6. $\dfrac{c+a^2}{a-b^2}=\dfrac{5+(-4)^2}{-4-(-2)^2}=\dfrac{5+16}{-4-4}=-\dfrac{21}{8}$

7.
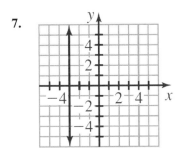

8. $m=\dfrac{y_2-y_1}{x_2-x_1}=\dfrac{3-(-1)}{5-(-3)}=\dfrac{4}{8}=\dfrac{1}{2}$

The line is increasing.

9.
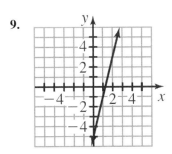

10.
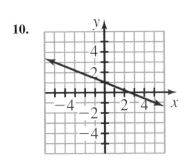

11. Solve the equation of the line $y = mx + b$.
Find the slope m of the line that passes through the points $(-2, 0)$ and $(2, 2)$.
$$m=\dfrac{y_2-y_1}{x_2-x_1}=\dfrac{2-0}{2-(-2)}=\dfrac{2}{4}=\dfrac{1}{2}$$
Then use the point $(2, 2)$ to solve for b.
$$y=\dfrac{1}{2}x+b$$
$$2=\dfrac{1}{2}(2)+b$$
$$2=1+b$$
$$1=b$$
The equation of the line is $y=\dfrac{1}{2}x+1$.

12. $m=\dfrac{1.16-0.33}{2006-1996}=\dfrac{0.83}{10}=0.083$
The average rate of change of sales is 0.083 million (or 83,000) motorcycles per year.

13. a. Yes, there is an approximate linear relationship between t and r. The slope is -7.7, which means that revenue is decreasing by $7.7 million per year.

b. The r-intercept is $(0, 59.5)$, which means that in 2006, the revenue of rap albums was $59.5 million.

c. $f(t)=-7.7t+59.5$

d. $2012-2006=6$
$f(6)=-7.7(6)+59.5=13.3$
In 2012, revenue of rap albums will be $13.3 million.

14. $7(2x-5y)-4(6x+3y)$
$$=14x-35y-24x-12y$$
$$=14x-24x-35y-12y$$
$$=-10x-47y$$

15. $7-4\left(\dfrac{x}{2}\right)=7-\dfrac{4x}{2}=7-2x$

16.
$$5t - 10 = 4 - 7t$$
$$5t - 10 + 10 = 4 - 7t + 10$$
$$5t = 14 - 7t$$
$$5t + 7t = 14 - 7t + 7t$$
$$12t = 14$$
$$\frac{12t}{12} = \frac{14}{12}$$
$$t = \frac{7}{6}$$

17.
$$3(4x - 1) - (7x + 2) = 8(x - 3)$$
$$12x - 3 - 7x - 2 = 8x - 24$$
$$5x - 5 = 8x - 24$$
$$5x - 5 + 5 = 8x - 24 + 5$$
$$5x = 8x - 19$$
$$5x - 8x = 8x - 8x - 19$$
$$-3x = -19$$
$$\frac{-3x}{-3} = \frac{-19}{-3}$$
$$x = \frac{19}{3}$$

18.
$$\frac{3}{4}x - \frac{7}{2} = \frac{3}{8}x$$
$$8\left(\frac{3}{4}x - \frac{7}{2}\right) = 8\left(\frac{3}{8}x\right)$$
$$6x - 28 = 3x$$
$$6x - 6x - 28 = 3x - 6x$$
$$-28 = -3x$$
$$\frac{-28}{-3} = \frac{-3x}{-3}$$
$$\frac{28}{3} = x$$

19.
$$3(x + 5) = 9$$
$$3x + 15 = 9$$
$$3x + 15 - 15 = 9 - 15$$
$$3x = -6$$
$$\frac{3x}{3} = \frac{-6}{3}$$
$$x = -2$$

20. $x = 6$

21. $x = -2$

22.
$$S = 2\pi r^2 + rh$$
$$S - 2\pi r^2 = rh$$
$$\frac{S - 2\pi r^2}{r} = h$$

23. First solve for y.
$$2x - 4y = 8$$
$$-4y = -2x + 8$$
$$y = \frac{1}{2}x - 2$$

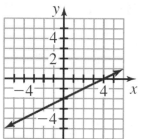

24.
$$2x - 5(0) = 20$$
$$2x = 20$$
$$x = 10$$
x-intercept: (10, 0)
$$2(0) - 5y = 20$$
$$-5y = 20$$
$$y = -4$$
y-intercept: (0, –4)

25. Domain: $-4 \leq x \leq 5$

26. Range: $-3 \leq y \leq 3$

27. Yes. Answers may vary.

28.
$$f(-2) = -3(-2)^2 + 7(-2)$$
$$= -3(4) - 14$$
$$= -12 - 14$$
$$= -26$$

29.
$$6x - 2 = -5$$
$$6x - 2 + 2 = -5 + 2$$
$$6x = -3$$
$$\frac{6x}{6} = \frac{-3}{6}$$
$$x = -\frac{1}{2}$$

30.
$$y = \frac{2}{3}x + b$$
$$-6 = \frac{2}{3}(-2) + b$$
$$-6 = -\frac{4}{3} + b$$
$$-\frac{14}{3} = b$$

The equation of the line is $y = \frac{2}{3}x - \frac{14}{3}$.

31. $m = \frac{-3-7}{2-(-4)} = \frac{-10}{6} = -\frac{5}{3}$
$$y = -\frac{5}{3}x + b$$
$$7 = -\frac{5}{3}(-4) + b$$
$$7 = \frac{20}{3} + b$$
$$\frac{1}{3} = b$$

The equation of the line is $y = -\frac{5}{3}x + \frac{1}{3}$.

32. a.

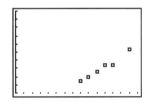

b. The linear regression is $f(t) = 0.063t + 10.13$. (Your answer may vary if you use the points of the graph.)

c. The slope is 0.063, which means that Marion Jones' best time in the 100-meter run is increasing by 0.063 seconds per year.

d. $f(13) = 0.063(13) + 10.13 = 10.95$
Marion Jones' best time for the 100-meter run in 2013 would have been about 10.95 seconds.

e. There was a change of 0.0 seconds from 2001 to 2002.

f. Answers may vary.

33. We use the points (0, 18.8) and (12, 13.6) to find an equation of the form $f(t) = mt + b$. We begin by finding the slope:
$$m = \frac{13.6 - 18.8}{12 - 0} = \frac{-5.2}{12} \approx -0.43$$

So, the equation of the line is of the form $f(t) = -0.43t + b$. To find b, we substitute the coordinates of the point (0, 18.8) into the equation and solve for b:
$$f(t) = -0.43t + b$$
$$18.8 = -0.43(0) + b$$
$$18.8 = b$$
So, the equation is $f(t) = -0.43t + 18.8$.
We then solve for t when $f(t) = 10.0$.
$$f(t) = -0.43t + 18.8$$
$$10.0 = -0.43t + 18.8$$
$$-8.8 = -0.43t$$
$$20.47 \approx t$$
The number of overnight stays will be 10 millikon in 1994 + 20 = 2014.

34. $2(x-1) + 4 < 5(x+3) - 1$
$$2x - 2 + 4 < 5x + 15 - 1$$
$$2x + 2 < 5x + 14$$
$$2x + 2 - 2 < 5x + 14 - 2$$
$$2x < 5x + 12$$
$$2x - 5x < 5x - 5x + 12$$
$$-3x < 12$$
$$\frac{-3x}{-3} > \frac{12}{-3}$$
$$x > -4$$
$(-4, \infty)$

35. $-10 \le 3x - 7 \le 2$
$$-10 + 7 \le 3x - 7 + 7 \le 2 + 7$$
$$-3 \le 3x \le 9$$
$$\frac{-3}{3} \le \frac{3x}{3} \le \frac{9}{3}$$
$$-1 \le x \le 3$$
$[-1, 3]$

36. Blue line: We use the points (0, 3) and (3, 2) to find an equation of the form $y = mx + b$. We begin by finding the slope:

$$m = \frac{2-3}{3-0} = -\frac{1}{3}$$

So, the equation of the line is of the form $y = -\frac{1}{3}x + b$. To find b, we substitute the coordinates of the point (0, 3) into the equation and solve for b:

$$y = -\frac{1}{3}x + b$$

$$3 = -\frac{1}{3}(0) + b$$

$$3 = b$$

So, the equation is $y = -\frac{1}{3}x + 3$.

Red line: We use the points (0, –3) and (3, –2) to find an equation of the form $y = mx + b$. We begin by finding the slope:

$$m = \frac{-2-(-3)}{3-0} = \frac{1}{3}$$

So, the equation of the line is of the form $y = \frac{1}{3}x + b$. To find b, we substitute the coordinates of the point (0, –3) into the equation and solve for b:

$$y = \frac{2}{3}x + b$$

$$-3 = \frac{1}{3}(0) + b$$

$$-3 = b$$

So, the equation is $y = \frac{1}{3}x - 3$.

We then solve the equations by setting them equal to each other.

$$-\frac{1}{3}x + 3 = \frac{1}{3}x - 3$$

$$-\frac{1}{3}x + 3 - 3 = \frac{1}{3}x - 3 - 3$$

$$-\frac{1}{3}x = \frac{1}{3}x - 6$$

$$-\frac{1}{3}x - \frac{1}{3}x = \frac{1}{3}x - 6 - \frac{1}{3}x$$

$$-\frac{2}{3}x = -6$$

$$x = 9$$

Solve for y.

$$y = -\frac{1}{3}(9) + 3 = -3 + 3 = 0$$

The solution is (9, 0).

37. Substitute $y = 4x - 9$ into the first equation.

$$2x - 3(4x - 9) = 7$$

$$2x - 12x + 27 = 7$$

$$-10x + 27 = 7$$

$$-10x = -20$$

$$x = 2$$

Solve for y.

$$y = 4(2) - 9 = 8 - 9 = -1$$

The solution is (2, –1).

38. To eliminate the y terms, multiply equation (1) by 5 and multiply equation (2) by 4. Then add the equations and solve for x.

$$5(3x + 4y = 4)$$

$$4(7x - 5y = 38)$$

$$15x + 20y = 20$$

$$28x - 20y = 152$$

$$43x \qquad = 172$$

$$x \qquad = 4$$

Substitute $x = 4$ into equation (1).

$$3(4) + 4y = 4$$

$$12 + 4y = 4$$

$$4y = -8$$

$$y = -2$$

The solution is (4, –2).

39. a. $D(t) = 240t + 140$

b. $P(t) = -85t + 805$

c.
$$240t + 140 = -85t + 805$$

$$240t + 140 - 140 = -85t + 805 - 140$$

$$240t = -85t + 665$$

$$240t + 85t = -85t + 665 + 85t$$

$$325t = 665$$

$$\frac{325t}{325} = \frac{665}{325}$$

$$t \approx 2.046$$

Sales of digital downloads of music are equal to sales of physical media of music in 2006. 240(2.046) + 140 = 491.04 + 140 = 631.04 Sales of both digital downloads and physical media are about $631 million.

40. Let x = the number of \$20 tickets sold and let y = the number of \$35 tickets sold. Let T = total revenue of tickets sold

$T = 20x + 35y$

Substitute 147,000 for T to find the first equation: (1) $147,000 = 20x + 35y$

Since there are 6000 tickets, the second equation is: (2) $x + y = 6000$.

Use elimination to solve the system. To eliminate the y terms, multiply both sides of equation (2) by -35 and then solve for x.

$-35(x + y = 6000)$

$$\underline{20x + 35y = 147,000}$$

$$-35x - 35y = -210,000$$
$$\underline{20x + 35y = 147,000}$$
$$-15x \qquad = -63,000$$
$$x \qquad = 4200$$

Substitute $x = 4200$ into equation (1) and solve for y.

$4200 + y = 6000$

$\qquad y = 6000 - 4200 = 1800$

There were 4200 \$20 tickets and 1800 \$35 tickets solds.

41. Solve for y.

$$4x - 5y \geq 20$$
$$4x - 4x - 5y \geq -4x + 20$$
$$-5y \geq -4x + 20$$
$$\frac{-5y}{-5} \geq \frac{-4x}{-5} + \frac{20}{-5}$$
$$y \leq \frac{4}{5}x - 4$$

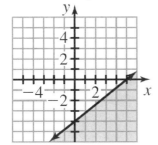

42.

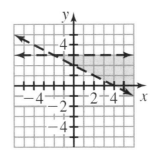

43. $(3x^2 - 5x) + (-7x^2 - 2x + 9)$

$= 3x^2 - 5x - 7x^2 - 2x + 9$

$= 3x^2 - 7x^2 - 5x - 2x + 9$

$= -4x^2 - 7x + 9$

44. $(7a^2 - ab - 4b^2) - (2a^2 - 5ab + 3b^2)$

$= 7a^2 - ab - 4b^2 - 2a^2 + 5ab - 3b^2$

$= 7a^2 - 2a^2 - ab + 5ab - 4b^2 - 3b^2$

$= 5a^2 + 4ab - 7b^2$

45. $(f - g)(x) = (4x^2 - 8x - 3) - (-2x^2 - x + 5)$

$= 4x^2 - 8x - 3 + 2x^2 + x - 5$

$= 4x^2 + 2x^2 - 8x + x - 3 - 5$

$= 6x^2 - 7x - 8$

$(f - g)(-3) = 6(-3)^2 - 7(-3) - 8$

$= 54 + 21 - 8$

$= 67$

46. $f(4) = -5$

47. $x - 1$

48. $x = 0$ and $x = 2$

49. There is no solution.

50. $(8p - 3t)(2p + 5t)$

$= 8p \cdot 2p + 8p \cdot 5t - 3t \cdot 2p - 3t \cdot 5t$

$= 16p^2 + 40pt - 6pt - 15t^2$

$= 16p^2 + 34pt - 15t^2$

51. $\left(x^2 - 2x + 4\right)\left(2x^2 + x - 3\right)$

$= x^2 \cdot 2x^2 + x^2 \cdot x + x^2 \cdot (-3) - 2x \cdot 2x^2 - 2x \cdot x$

$\quad -2x \cdot (-3) + 4 \cdot 2x^2 + 4 \cdot x + 4(-3)$

$= 2x^4 + x^3 - 3x^2 - 4x^3 - 2x^2 + 6x + 8x^2 + 4x - 12$

$= 2x^4 - 3x^3 + 3x^2 + 10x - 12$

52. $(f \cdot g)(x) = (3x - 5)\left(2x^2 - 4x + 3\right)$

$\quad\quad = 6x^3 - 12x^2 + 9x - 10x^2 + 20x - 15$

$\quad\quad = 6x^3 - 22x^2 + 29x - 15$

$(f \cdot g)(2) = 6(2)^3 - 22(2)^2 + 29(2) - 15$

$\quad\quad = 48 - 88 + 58 - 15$

$\quad\quad = 3$

53. a.

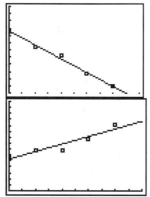

The models fit the data well.

b. $C(t) \cdot T(t) = (C \cdot T)(t)$

$\quad = (-2.4t + 103)(0.032t + 0.53)$

$\quad = -0.0768t^2 - 1.272t + 3.296t + 54.59$

$\quad = -0.0768t^2 + 2.024t + 54.59$

c. For the expression $C(t) \cdot T(t)$, we have

$\quad \underbrace{C(t)}_{\substack{\text{packs of cigarettes} \\ \text{person}}} \cdot \underbrace{T(t)}_{\substack{\text{average annual tax on cigarettes} \\ \text{pack}}}$. Since

$\dfrac{\text{packs}}{\text{packs}} = 1$, the units of the expression are

average annual tax on cigarettes in dollars per person.

d. $(C \cdot T)(24)$

$\quad = -0.0768(24)^2 + 2.024(24) + 54.59$

$\quad = -44.2368 + 48.576 + 54.59$

$\quad = 58.9292$

This means that, in 2014, the average annual

tax on cigarettes paid per person will be about $58.93.

e.

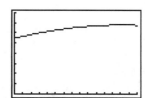

The function is increasing. This means that the average annual tax on cigarettes paid per person is increasing from 1990 to 2003. Answers may vary.

54. $(x + 6)^2 = x^2 + 2 \cdot x \cdot 6 + 6^2$

$\quad\quad = x^2 + 12x + 36$

55. $(3p - 7q)^2 = (3p)^2 + 2 \cdot 3p \cdot (-7q) + (-7q)^2$

$\quad\quad = 9p^2 - 42pq + 49q^2$

56. $f(x) = -3(x - 2)^2 + 5$

$\quad\quad = -3\left(x^2 - 4x + 4\right) + 5$

$\quad\quad = -3x^2 + 12x - 12 + 5$

$\quad\quad = -3x^2 + 12x - 7$

57. $(8b - 5c)(8b + 5c) = 64b^2 - 25c^2$

58. $3x^5 \left(2x^2\right)^3 = 3x^5 \cdot 8x^6 = 24x^{11}$

59. $\left(\dfrac{x^4 w}{2y^8}\right)^5 = \dfrac{x^{20} w^5}{32 y^{40}}$

60. $\dfrac{\left(3x^2 y^3\right)^4}{x^7 y^2} = \dfrac{81x^8 y^{12}}{x^7 y^2} = 81x^{8-7} y^{12-2} = 81xy^{10}$

Chapter 8
Factoring Polynomials and Solving Polynomial Equations

Homework 8.1

1. $x^2 + 5x + 6$

We are looking for two factors of $c = 6$ whose sum is $b = 5$. Since c is positive the two factors have the same sign, and since b is positive the factors are both positive.

Factors	1, 6	2, 3
Sum	7	5

$x^2 + 5x + 6 = (x+2)(x+3)$

3. $t^2 + 9t + 20$

We are looking for two factors of $c = 20$ whose sum is $b = 9$. Since c is positive the two factors have the same sign, and since b is positive the factors are both positive.

Factors	1, 20	2, 10	4, 5
Sum	21	12	9

$t^2 + 9t + 20 = (t+4)(t+5)$

5. $x^2 + 8x + 16$

We are looking for two factors of $c = 16$ whose sum is $b = 8$. Since c is positive the two factors have the same sign, and since b is positive the factors are both positive.

Factors	1, 16	2, 8	4, 4
Sum	17	10	8

$x^2 + 8x + 16 = (x+4)(x+4) = (x+4)^2$

7. $x^2 - 2x - 8$

We are looking for two factors of $c = -8$ whose sum is $b = -2$. Since c is negative, the two factors will have opposite signs. Since b is also negative, the factor with the larger absolute value will be negative.

Factors	-8, 1	-4, 2
Sum	-7	-2

$x^2 - 2x - 8 = (x-4)(x+2)$

9. $a^2 - 6a - 16$

We are looking for two factors of $c = -16$ whose sum is $b = -6$. Since c is negative, the two factors will have opposite signs. Since b is also negative, the factor with the larger absolute value will be negative.

Factors	-16, 1	-8, 2	-4, 4
Sum	-15	-6	0

$a^2 - 6a - 16 = (a-8)(a+2)$

11. $x^2 + 5x - 24$

We are looking for two factors of $c = -24$ whose sum is $b = 5$. Since c is negative the two factors have opposite signs, and since b is positive the factor with the larger absolute value must be positive.

Factors	-1, 24	-2, 12	-3, 8	-4, 6
Sum	23	10	5	2

$x^2 + 5x - 24 = (x-3)(x+8)$

13. $x^2 + 8x - 12$

We are looking for two factors of $c = -12$ whose sum is $b = 8$. Since c is negative the two factors have opposite signs, and since b is positive the factor with the larger absolute value must be positive.

Factors	-1, 12	-2, 6	-3, 4
Sum	11	4	1

Since none of the possibilities work, we can say that $x^2 + 8x - 12$ is prime.

15. $3t - 28 + t^2 = t^2 + 3t - 28$

We are looking for two factors of $c = -28$ whose sum is $b = 3$. Since c is negative the two factors have opposite signs, and since b is positive the factor with the larger absolute value must be positive.

Factors	-1, 28	-2, 14	-4, 7
Sum	27	12	3

$3t - 28 + t^2 = t^2 + 3t - 28$
$$= (t-4)(t+7)$$

17. $x^2 - 10x + 16$

We are looking for two factors of $c = 16$ whose sum is $b = -10$. Since c is positive the two factors have the same sign, and since b is negative the factors are both negative.

Factors	$-1, -16$	$-2, -8$	$-4, -4$
Sum	-17	-10	-8

$x^2 - 10x + 16 = (x - 8)(x - 2)$

19. $24 - 11x + x^2 = x^2 - 11x + 24$

We are looking for two factors of $c = 24$ whose sum is $b = -11$. Since c is positive the two factors have the same sign, and since b is negative the factors are both negative.

Factors	$-1, -24$	$-2, -12$	$-3, -8$	$-4, -6$
Sum	-25	-14	-11	-10

$24 - 11x + x^2 = x^2 - 11x + 24$
$= (x - 8)(x - 3)$

21. $x^2 - 3x + 10$

We are looking for two factors of $c = 10$ whose sum is $b = -3$. Since c is positive the two factors have the same sign, and since b is negative the factors are both negative.

Factors	$-1, -10$	$-2, -5$
Sum	-11	-7

Since none of the possibilities work, we can say that $x^2 - 3x + 10$ is prime.

23. $r^2 - 10r + 25$

We are looking for two factors of $c = 25$ whose sum is $b = -10$. Since c is positive the two factors have the same sign, and since b is negative the factors are both negative.

Factors	$-1, -25$	$-5, -5$
Sum	-26	-10

$r^2 - 10r + 25 = (r - 5)(r - 5) = (r - 5)^2$

25. $x^2 + 10xy + 9y^2 = x^2 + (10y)x + 9y^2$

We need two monomials whose product is $9y^2$ and whose sum is $10y$. Since $9y^2$ has a positive coefficient, the coefficients of the monomials must be the same sign. Since the coefficient of $10y$ is positive, both coefficients must be positive.

$1y \cdot 9y = 9y^2$ and $1y + 9y = 10y$

Therefore, $x^2 + 10xy + 9y^2 = (x + y)(x + 9y)$.

27. $m^2 - mn - 6n^2 = m^2 - (n)m - 6n^2$

We need two monomials whose product is $-6n^2$ and whose sum is $-n$. Since $-6n^2$ has a negative coefficient, the coefficients of the monomials must be opposite signs. Since the coefficient of $-n$ is negative, the coefficient with the larger absolute value will be negative.

$-3n \cdot 2n = -6n^2$ and $-3n + 2n = -n$

Therefore, $m^2 - mn - 6n^2 = (m - 3n)(m + 2n)$.

29. $a^2 - 7ab + 6b^2 = a^2 - (7b)a + 6b^2$

We need two monomials whose product is $6b^2$ and whose sum is $-7b$. Since $6b^2$ has a positive coefficient, the coefficients of the monomials must be the same sign. Since the coefficient of $-7b$ is negative, both coefficients must be negative.

$(-1b)(-6b) = 6b^2$ and $(-1b) + (-6b) = -7b$

Therefore, $a^2 - 7ab + 6b^2 = (a - 6b)(a - b)$.

31. $p^2 + 3pq - 28q^2 = (p + 7q)(p - 4q)$

33. $p^2 - 6pq - 16q^2 = (p - 8q)(p + 2q)$

35. $x^2 - 25 = x^2 - 5^2$
$= (x - 5)(x + 5)$

37. $x^2 - 81 = x^2 - 9^2$
$= (x - 9)(x + 9)$

39. $x^2 + 36$

We are looking for two factors of $c = 36$ whose sum is $b = 0$. Since 36 is positive, the two factors have the same sign. However, there are no factors of 36 whose sum is 0. Therefore, $x^2 + 36$ is prime.

41. $4x^2 - 25 = (2x)^2 - 5^2$
$= (2x - 5)(2x + 5)$

43. $81r^2 - 1 = (9r)^2 - 1^2$
$= (9r - 1)(9r + 1)$

45. $36x^2 + 49$

The binomial $36x^2 + 49$ is the sum of two squares. Since the sum of two squares does not factor over the integers, $36x^2 + 49$ is prime. (see #39)

47. $49p^2 - 100q^2 = (7p)^2 - (10q)^2$
$$= (7p - 10q)(7p + 10q)$$

49. $64m^2 - 9n^2 = (8m)^2 - (3n)^2$
$$= (8m - 3n)(8m + 3n)$$

51. $16x^4 - 81 = (4x^2 + 9)(4x^2 - 9)$
$$= (4x^2 + 9)(2x + 3)(2x - 3)$$

53. $t^4 - w^4 = (t^2 + w^2)(t^2 - w^2)$
$$= (t^2 + w^2)(t + w)(t - w)$$

55. $x^2 - 3x - 18$

We are looking for two factors of $c = -18$ whose sum is $b = -3$. Since c is negative, the two factors will have opposite signs. Since b is also negative, the factor with the larger absolute value will be negative.

Factors	$-18, 1$	$-9, 2$	$-6, 3$
Sum	-17	-7	-3

$x^2 - 3x - 18 = (x - 6)(x + 3)$

57. $x^2 + 14x + 49$

We are looking for two factors of $c = 49$ whose sum is $b = 14$. Since c is positive the two factors have the same sign, and since b is positive the factors are both positive.

Factors	$1, 49$	$7, 7$
Sum	50	14

$x^2 + 14x + 49 = (x + 7)(x + 7)$
$$= (x + 7)^2$$

59. $a^2 - 4 = a^2 - 2^2$
$$= (a - 2)(a + 2)$$

61. $x^2 + 4x + 12$

We are looking for two factors of $c = 12$ whose sum is $b = 4$. Since c is positive the two factors have the same sign, and since b is positive the factors are both positive.

Factors	$1, 12$	$2, 6$	$3, 4$
Sum	13	8	7

Since none of the possibilities work, we can say that $x^2 + 4x + 12$ is prime.

63. $x^2 - 8x + 12$

We are looking for two factors of $c = 12$ whose sum is $b = -8$. Since c is positive the two factors have the same sign, and since b is negative the factors are both negative.

Factors	$-1, -12$	$-2, -6$	$-3, -4$
Sum	-13	-8	-7

$x^2 - 8x + 12 = (x - 6)(x - 2)$

65. $-2w - 48 + w^2 = w^2 - 2w - 48$

We are looking for two factors of $c = -48$ whose sum is $b = -2$. Since c is negative, the two factors will have opposite signs. Since b is also negative, the factor with the larger absolute value will be negative.

Factors	$-48, 1$	$-24, 2$	$-16, 3$	$-12, 4$	$-8, 6$
Sum	-47	-22	-13	-8	-2

$-2w - 48 + w^2 = w^2 - 2w + 48$
$$= (w - 8)(w + 6)$$

67. $t^4 - 16 = t^4 - 2^4$
$$= (t^2 - 2^2)(t^2 + 2^2)$$
$$= (t - 2)(t + 2)(t^2 + 4)$$

69. $w^2 + 49$

The binomial $w^2 + 49$ is the sum of two squares. Since the sum of two squares does not factor over the integers, $w^2 + 49$ is prime. (see #39)

71. $m^2 - 6mn - 27n^2 = m^2 - (6n)m - 27n^2$

We need to monomials whose product is $-27n^2$ and whose sum is $-6n$. Since $-27n^2$ has a negative coefficient, the coefficients of the monomials must have opposite signs. Since the coefficient of $-6n$ is negative, the coefficient with the larger absolute value must be negative.

$(-9n)(3n) = -27n^2$ and $-9n + 3n = -6n$

Therefore, $m^2 - 6mn - 27n^2 = (m - 9n)(m + 3n)$.

73. $32 - 18x + x^2 = x^2 - 18x + 32$

We are looking for two factors of $c = 32$ whose sum is $b = -18$. Since c is positive the two factors have the same sign, and since b is negative the factors are both negative.

Factors	$-1, -32$	$-2, -16$	$-4, -8$
Sum	-33	-18	-12

$32 - 18x + x^2 = x^2 - 18x + 32$
$= (x - 16)(x - 2)$

75. $100p^2 - 9t^2 = (10p)^2 - (3t)^2$
$= (10p - 3t)(10p + 3t)$

77. $p^2 + 12pt + 36t^2$

We are looking for two factors of $c = 36$ whose sum is $b = 12$. Since c is positive the two factors have the same sign, and since b is positive the factors are both positive.

Factors	1, 36	2, 18	3, 12	4, 9	6, 6
Sum	37	20	15	13	12

$p^2 + 12pt + 36t^2 = (p + 6t)(p + 6t)$
$= (p + 6t)^2$

79. The student is incorrectly factoring $A^2 + B^2$ as
$A^2 + B^2 = (A + B)(A + B)$, but
$(A + B)(A + B) = A^2 + 2AB + B^2$. The binomial
$x^2 + 9$ is the sum of two squares. Since the sum of two squares does not factor over the integers, $x^2 + 9$ is prime.

81. $(x - 3)(x + 7) = x^2 + 7x - 3x - 21$
$= x^2 + 4x - 21$
$(x + 7)(x - 3) = x^2 - 3x + 7x - 21$
$= x^2 + 4x - 21$
Therefore,
$(x - 3)(x + 7) = (x + 7)(x - 3) = x^2 + 4x - 21$.

83. $x^2 - 5x - 24$

We are looking for two factors of $c = -24$ whose sum is $b = -5$. Since c is negative, the two factors will have opposite signs. Since b is also negative, the factor with the larger absolute value will be negative.

Factors	$-24, 1$	$-12, 2$	$-8, 3$	$-6, 4$
Sum	-23	-10	-5	-2

$x^2 - 5x - 24 = (x - 8)(x + 3)$

$(x - 8)(x + 3) = x^2 + 3x - 8x - 24$
$= x^2 - 5x - 24$
Multiplying the factors yields the original expression.

85. a. $x^2 - 5x + 4 = (x - 4)(x - 1)$

b.

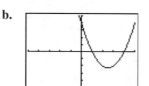

The x-intercepts are $x = 1$ and $x = 4$.

c. The factors in part (a) are equal to the x-intercept of f. This makes sense when $f(x) = 0$.

87. Answers may vary.

89. $x^2 + kx + 12$

We are looking for two factors of $c = 12$ whose sum is $b = k$. Since c is positive the two factors have the same sign.

Factors	1, 12	2, 6	3, 4	$-1, -12$	$-2, -6$	$-3, -4$
Sum, k	13	8	7	-13	-8	-7

The possible values for k are -13, -8, -7, 7, 8, and 13.

91. Answers may vary.

93. $(x-9)(x+2) = x \cdot x + 2 \cdot x + (-9) \cdot x + (-9) \cdot 2$

$$= x^2 + 2x - 9x - 18$$

$$= x^2 - 7x - 18$$

95. $x^2 - 15x + 50$

We are looking for two factors of $c = 50$ whose sum is $b = -15$. Since c is positive the two factors have the same sign, and since b is negative the factors are both negative.

Factors	$-1, -50$	$-2, -25$	$-5, -10$
Sum	-51	-27	-15

$x^2 - 15x + 50 = (x-10)(x-5)$

97. $(3x-7)(3x+7) = 3x \cdot 3x + 7 \cdot 3x + (-7) \cdot 3x + (-7) \cdot 7$

$$= 9x^2 + 21x - 21x - 49$$

$$= 9x^2 - 49$$

99. $25x^2 - 36 = (5x)^2 - 6^2$

$$= (5x - 6)(5x + 6)$$

101. $(5p + 7w) - (2p - 4w) = 5p + 7w - 2p + 4w$

$$= 5p - 2p + 7w + 4w$$

$$= 3p + 11w$$

Description: *linear (first degree) polynomial in two variables*

103. $(5p + 7w)(2p - 4w)$

$$= (5p)(2p) + (5p)(-4w) + (7w)(2p) + (7w)(-4w)$$

$$= 10p^2 - 20pw + 14pw - 28w^2$$

$$= 10p^2 - 6pw - 28w^2$$

Description: *factored quadratic (second degree) polynomial in two variables*

105. $p^2 - 11pw + 18w^2 = p^2 - (11w)p + 18w^2$

We need to monomials whose product is $18w^2$ and whose sum is $-11w$. Since $18w^2$ has a positive coefficient, the coefficients of the monomials must be the same sign. Since the coefficient of $-11w$ is negative, both coefficients must be negative.

$(-2w)(-9w) = 18w^2$ and $(-2w) + (-9w) = -11w$

Therefore, $p^2 - 11pw + 18w^2 = (p - 9w)(p - 2w)$.

Description: *quadratic (second degree) polynomial in two variables*

Homework 8.2

1. The GCF is 2, so we get

$6x + 8 = 2 \cdot 3x + 2 \cdot 4$

$$= 2(3x + 4)$$

3. The GCF is $5w$, so we get

$20w^2 + 35w = 5w \cdot 4w + 5w \cdot 7$

$$= 5w(4w + 7)$$

5. The GCF is $6x^2$, so we get

$12x^3 - 30x^2 = 6x^2 \cdot 2x - 6x^2 \cdot 5$

$$= 6x^2(2x - 5)$$

7. The GCF is $3ab$, so we get

$6a^2b - 9ab = 3ab \cdot 2a - 3ab \cdot 3$

$$= 3ab(2a - 3)$$

9. The GCF is $4x^2y^2$, so we get

$8x^3y^2 + 12x^2y^3 = 4x^2y^2 \cdot 2x + 4x^2y^2 \cdot 3y$

$$= 4x^2y^2(2x + 3y)$$

11. The GCF is 5, so we get

$15x^3 - 10x - 30 = 5 \cdot 3x^3 - 5 \cdot 2x - 5 \cdot 6$

$$= 5(3x^3 - 2x - 6)$$

13. The GCF is $4t$, so we get

$12t^4 + 8t^3 - 16t = 4t \cdot 3t^3 + 4t \cdot 2t^2 - 4t \cdot 4$

$$= 4t(3t^3 + 2t^2 - 4)$$

15. The GCF is $5ab$, so we get

$10a^4b - 15a^3b + 25ab = 5ab \cdot 2a^3 - 5ab \cdot 3a^2 + 5ab \cdot 5$

$$= 5ab(2a^3 - 3a^2 + 5)$$

17. $2x^2 - 18 = 2(x^2 - 9)$

$$= 2(x^2 - 3^2)$$

$$= 2(x - 3)(x + 3)$$

19. $3m^2 + 21m + 30 = 3(m^2 + 7m + 10)$

$$= 3(m + 2)(m + 5)$$

21. $2x^2 - 18x + 36 = 2(x^2 - 9x + 18)$
$$= 2(x-6)(x-3)$$

23. $4r^3 - 16r^2 - 20r = 4r(r^2 - 4r - 5)$
$$= 4r(r-5)(r+1)$$

25. $6x^4 - 24x^2 = 6x^2(x^2 - 4)$
$$= 6x^2(x^2 - 2^2)$$
$$= 6x^2(x-2)(x+2)$$

27. $8m^4n - 18m^2n = 2m^2n(4m^2 - 9)$
$$= 2m^2n((2m)^2 - 3^2)$$
$$= 2m^2n(2m-3)(2m+3)$$

29. $5x^4 + 10x^3 - 120x^2 = 5x^2(x^2 + 2x - 24)$
$$= 5x^2(x-4)(x+6)$$

31. $36t^2 + 32t + 4t^3 = 4t^3 + 36t^2 + 32t$
$$= 4t(t^2 + 9t + 8)$$
$$= 4t(t+1)(t+8)$$

33. $-12x^3 + 27x = -3x(4x^2 - 9)$
$$= -3x((2x)^2 - 3^2)$$
$$= -3x(2x-3)(2x+3)$$

35. $-3x^3 - 18x^2 + 48x = -3x(x^2 + 6x - 16)$
$$= -3x(x-2)(x+8)$$

37. $-x^2 + 11x - 10 = -1(x^2 - 11x + 10)$
$$= -1(x-10)(x-1)$$

39. $6a^4b + 36a^3b + 54a^2b = 6a^2b(a^2 + 6a + 9)$
$$= 6a^2b(a+3)(a+3)$$
$$= 6a^2b(a+3)^2$$

41. $4x^4y - 12x^3y^2 - 40x^2y^3 = 4x^2y(x^2 - 3xy - 10y^2)$
$$= 4x^2y(x-5y)(x+2y)$$

43. $-2x^3y^2 + 16x^2y^3 - 32xy^4 = -2xy^2(x^2 - 8xy + 16y^2)$
$$= -2xy^2(x-4y)(x-4y)$$
$$= -2xy^2(x-4y)^2$$

45. The GCF is $(x-3)$, so we get
$$5x^2(x-3) + 2(x-3) = (5x^2 + 2)(x-3)$$

47. The GCF is $(2x+5)$, so we get
$$6x^2(2x+5) - 7(2x+5) = (6x^2 - 7)(2x+5)$$

49. $2p^3 + 6p^2 + 5p + 15 = 2p^2(p+3) + 5(p+3)$
$$= (2p^2 + 5)(p+3)$$

51. $6x^3 - 2x^2 + 21x - 7 = 2x^2(3x-1) + 7(3x-1)$
$$= (2x^2 + 7)(3x-1)$$

53. $15w^3 + 5w^2 - 6w - 2 = 5w^2(3w+1) - 2(3w+1)$
$$= (5w^2 - 2)(3w+1)$$

55. $16x^3 - 12x^2 - 36x + 27 = 4x^2(4x-3) - 9(4x-3)$
$$= (4x^2 - 9)(4x-3)$$
$$= ((2x)^2 - 3^2)(4x-3)$$
$$= (2x-3)(2x+3)(4x-3)$$

57. $2b^3 - 5b^2 - 18b + 45 = b^2(2b-5) - 9(2b-5)$
$$= (b^2 - 9)(2b-5)$$
$$= (b^2 - 3^2)(2b-5)$$
$$= (b-3)(b+3)(2b-5)$$

59. $x^3 - x^2 - x + 1 = x^2(x-1) - 1(x-1)$
$$= (x^2 - 1)(x-1)$$
$$= (x^2 - 1^2)(x-1)$$
$$= (x-1)(x+1)(x-1)$$
$$= (x-1)^2(x+1)$$

61. $ax - 3ay - 2bx + 6by = (x-3y)(a-2b)$

63. $5a^2x + 2a^2y - 5bx - 2by = (a^2 - b)(5x + 2y)$

65. $81x^2 - 25 = (9x)^2 - 5^2$
$= (9x - 5)(9x + 5)$

67. $w^2 - 10w + 16$
We are looking for two factors of $c = 16$ whose sum is $b = -10$. Since c is positive, the two factors will have the same sign. Since b is negative, the factors will both be negative.
$(-8)(-2) = 16$ and $(-8) + (-2) = -10$
Therefore, $w^2 - 10w + 16 = (w - 8)(w - 2)$.

69. $24 - 10x + x^2 = x^2 - 10x + 24$
We are looking for two factors of $c = 24$ whose sum is $b = -10$. Since c is positive, the two factors will have the same sign. Since b is negative, the factors will both be negative.
$(-6)(-4) = 24$ and $(-6) + (-4) = -10$
Therefore, $x^2 - 10x + 24 = (x - 6)(x - 4)$.

71. $20a^2b - 15ab^3 = 5ab(4a) - 5ab(3b^2)$
$= 5ab(4a - 3b^2)$

73. $x^2 + xy - 30y^2 = (x + 6y)(x - 5y)$

75. $-6r^3 + 24r^2 - 24r = -6r(r^2 - 4r + 4)$
$= -6r(r - 2)(r - 2)$
$= -6r(r - 2)^2$

77. $64x^3 - 49x = x(64x^2 - 49)$
$= x((8x)^2 - 7^2)$
$= x(8x - 7)(8x + 7)$

79. $-m^2 + 6m - 9 = -1 \cdot m^2 + (-1)(-6m) + (-1)(9)$
$= -1(m^2 - 6m + 9)$
$= -1(m - 3)(m - 3)$
$= -(m - 3)^2$

81. $x^3 + 9x^2 - 4x - 36 = x^2(x + 9) - 4(x + 9)$
$= (x^2 - 4)(x + 9)$
$= (x^2 - 2^2)(x + 9)$
$= (x - 2)(x + 2)(x + 9)$

83. $2m^3n - 10m^2n^2 + 12mn^3$
$= 2mn \cdot m^2 - 2mn \cdot 5mn + 2mn \cdot 6n^2$
$= 2mn(m^2 - 5mn + 6n^2)$
$= 2mn(m - 3n)(m - 2n)$

85. The factorization is not complete.
$6x^3 + 8x^2 + 15x + 20 = 2x^2(3x + 4) + 5(3x + 4)$
$= (2x^2 + 5)(3x + 4)$

87. The factorization is not complete.
$4x^3 + 28x^2 + 40x = 4x(x^2 + 7x + 10)$
$= 4x(x + 2)(x + 5)$

89. The student should factor out the GCF first.
$4x^2 - 100 = 4(x^2 - 25)$
$= 4(x^2 - 5^2)$
$= 4(x - 5)(x + 5)$

91. Answers may vary.

93. The factorization is not complete.
$2x^2 + 10x + 12 = 2(x^2 + 5x + 6)$
$= 2(x + 2)(x + 3)$

95. $2x(x - 3)(x + 4) = 2x(x^2 + 4x - 3x - 12)$
$= 2x(x^2 + x - 12)$
$= 2x^3 + 2x^2 - 24x$

97. $5x^3 - 40x^2 + 80x = 5x(x^2 - 8x + 16)$
$= 5x(x - 4)(x - 4)$
$= 5x(x - 4)^2$

99. $6x^3 - 9x^2 - 4x + 6 = 3x^2(2x - 3) - 2(2x - 3)$
$= (3x^2 - 2)(2x - 3)$

101. $(x-3)(x^2+5) = x^3+5x-3x^2-15$

$$= x^3-3x^2+5x-15$$

103. The equation $y=-4x+1$ is in slope-intercept form, so the slope is $m=-4$ and the y-intercept is $(0,1)$. We first plot $(0,1)$. From this point we move 1 unit to the right and 4 units down, plotting the point $(1,-3)$. We then draw the line that connects the two points, extending in both directions.

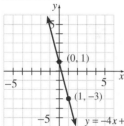

Description: *linear equation in two variables*

105. $-4x+1 = 2x-5$

$-6x+1 = -5$

$-6x = -6$

$x = 1$

The solution is 1.

Description: *linear equation in one variable*

107. $y = -4x+1$

$y = 2x-5$

Substitute $2x-5$ for y in the first equation and solve for x.

$2x-5 = -4x+1$

$6x-5 = 1$

$6x = 6$

$x = 1$

Substitute 1 for x in the equation $y = 2x-5$ and solve for y.

$y = 2(1)-5 = 2-5 = -3$

The solution is $(1,-3)$.

Description: *system of two linear equations in two variables*

Homework 8.3

1. *ac* Method:

$a \cdot c = 2 \cdot 3 = 6$

We are looking for two factors of 6 whose sum is $b=7$. Since the product is positive, the factors

will have the same sign. The sum is positive so the factors will be positive.

factor 1	factor 2	sum	
1	6	7	← okay
2	3	5	

$2x^2+7x+3 = 2x^2+x+6x+3$

$$= x(2x+1)+3(2x+1)$$

$$= (x+3)(2x+1)$$

Trial and Error Method:

First note that there are no common factors and that $a=2$, $b=7$, and $c=3$. Since c is positive the signs of our factors will be the same. Since b is positive, the signs in our factors will be positive. We will consider factorizations with this form:

$(\underline{}x+\underline{})(\underline{}x+\underline{})$

Since $a=2$ can be factored as $1 \cdot 2$, we have the following form:

$(x+\underline{})(2x+\underline{})$

$|c| = |3| = 3$ can be factored as $1 \cdot 3$. Since the original expression had no common factors, the binomials we select cannot have a common factor.

$(x+3)(2x+1) \rightarrow 2x^2+7x+3$

The correct factorization is

$2x^2+7x+3 = (x+3)(2x+1)$.

3. *ac* Method:

$a \cdot c = 5 \cdot 2 = 10$

We are looking for two factors of 10 whose sum is $b=11$. Since the product is positive, the factors will have the same sign. The sum is positive so the factors will be positive.

factor 1	factor 2	sum	
1	10	11	← okay
2	5	7	

$5x^2+11x+2 = 5x^2+1x+10x+2$

$$= x(5x+1)+2(5x+1)$$

$$= (x+2)(5x+1)$$

Trial and Error Method:

First note that there are no common factors and that $a=5$, $b=11$, and $c=2$. Since c is positive the signs of our factors will be the same. Since b is positive, the signs in our factors will be positive. We will consider factorizations with this form:

$(\underline{}x+\underline{})(\underline{}x+\underline{})$

Since $a = 5$ can be factored as $1 \cdot 5$, we have the following form:

$$\left(x + \underline{\quad}\right)\left(5x + \underline{\quad}\right)$$

$|c| = |2| = 2$ can be factored as $1 \cdot 2$.

$$\left(x + 2\right)\left(5x + 1\right) \rightarrow 5x^2 + 11x + 2$$

The correct factorization is

$$5x^2 + 11x + 2 = \left(x + 2\right)\left(5x + 1\right).$$

5. *ac* Method:

$a \cdot c = 3 \cdot 4 = 12$

We are looking for two factors of 12 whose sum is 8. Since the product is positive, the factors will have the same sign. The sum is positive so the factors will be positive.

factor 1	factor 2	sum
1	12	13
2	6	8 ← okay
3	4	7

$$3x^2 + 8x + 4 = 3x^2 + 2x + 6x + 4$$
$$= x\left(3x + 2\right) + 2\left(3x + 2\right)$$
$$= \left(x + 2\right)\left(3x + 2\right)$$

Trial and Error Method:

First note that there are no common factors and that $a = 3$, $b = 8$, and $c = 4$. Since c is positive the signs of our factors will be the same. Since b is positive, the signs in our factors will be positive. We will consider factorizations with this form:

$$\left(\underline{\quad}x + \underline{\quad}\right)\left(\underline{\quad}x + \underline{\quad}\right)$$

Since $a = 3$ can be factored as $1 \cdot 3$, we have the following form:

$$\left(x + \underline{\quad}\right)\left(3x + \underline{\quad}\right)$$

$|c| = |4| = 4$ can be factored as $1 \cdot 4$ and $2 \cdot 2$.

$$\left(x + 1\right)\left(3x + 4\right) \rightarrow 3x^2 + 7x + 4$$
$$\left(x + 4\right)\left(3x + 1\right) \rightarrow 3x^2 + 13x + 4$$
$$\left(x + 2\right)\left(3x + 2\right) \rightarrow 3x^2 + 8x + 4$$

The correct factorization is

$$3x^2 + 8x + 4 = \left(x + 2\right)\left(3x + 2\right)$$

7. *ac* Method:

$a \cdot c = 2 \cdot \left(-6\right) = -12$

We are looking for two factors of -12 whose sum is 1. Since the product is negative, the factors will have opposite signs. The sum is positive so the factor with the larger absolute value will be positive.

factor 1	factor 2	sum
−1	12	1
−2	6	4
−3	4	1 ← okay

$$2t^2 + t - 6 = 2t^2 - 3t + 4t - 6$$
$$= t\left(2t - 3\right) + 2\left(2t - 3\right)$$
$$= \left(t + 2\right)\left(2t - 3\right)$$

Trial and Error Method:

First note that there are no common factors and that $a = 2$, $b = 1$, and $c = -6$. Since c is negative, the signs in our factors will be opposites. We will consider factorizations with this form:

$$\left(\underline{\quad}t + \underline{\quad}\right)\left(\underline{\quad}t - \underline{\quad}\right)$$

If our choice results in a middle term with the wrong sign, we simply switch the signs of the factors.

Since $a = 2$ can be factored as $1 \cdot 2$, we have the following form:

$$\left(t + \underline{\quad}\right)\left(2t - \underline{\quad}\right)$$

$|c| = |-6| = 6$ can be factored as $1 \cdot 6$ and $2 \cdot 3$.

Since the original expression had no common factors, the binomials we select cannot have a common factor.

$$\left(t + 6\right)\left(2t - 1\right) \rightarrow 2t^2 + 11t - 6$$
$$\left(t + 2\right)\left(2t - 3\right) \rightarrow 2t^2 + t - 6$$

The correct factorization is

$$2t^2 + t - 6 = \left(t + 2\right)\left(2t - 3\right).$$

9. *ac* Method:

$a \cdot c = 6 \cdot 6 = 36$

We are looking for two factors of 36 whose sum is -13. Since the product is positive, the factors will have the same sign. The sum is negative so the factors will be negative.

factor 1	factor 2	sum
−1	−36	−37
−2	−18	−20
−3	−12	−15
−4	−9	−13 ← okay
−6	−6	−12

$$6x^2 - 13x + 6 = 6x^2 - 4x - 9x + 6$$
$$= 2x\left(3x - 2\right) - 3\left(3x - 2\right)$$
$$= \left(2x - 3\right)\left(3x - 2\right)$$

<u>Trial and Error Method:</u>
First note that there are no common factors and
that $a = 6$, $b = -13$, and $c = 6$. Since c is positive
the signs of our factors will be the same. Since b is
negative, the signs in our factors will be negative.
We will consider factorizations with this form:
$$(\underline{}x - \underline{})(\underline{}x - \underline{})$$
Since $a = 6$ can be factored as $1 \cdot 6$ or $2 \cdot 3$, we
have the following forms:
$$(x - \underline{})(6x - \underline{})$$
$$(2x - \underline{})(3x - \underline{})$$
$|c| = |6| = 6$ can be factored as $1 \cdot 6$ and $2 \cdot 3$. Since
the original expression had no common factors, the
binomials we select cannot have a common factor.
$$(x - 6)(6x - 1) \rightarrow 6x^2 - 37x + 6$$
$$(2x - 3)(3x - 2) \rightarrow 6x^2 - 13x + 6$$
The correct factorization is
$$6x^2 - 13x + 6 = (2x - 3)(3x - 2).$$

11. <u>*ac* Method:</u>
$a \cdot c = 4 \cdot 25 = 100$
We are looking for two factors of 100 whose sum
is 20. Since the product is positive, the factors will
have the same sign. The sum is positive so the
factors will both be positive. Since we are adding
two positive numbers to get 20, neither factor can
exceed 20.

factor 1	factor 2	sum
5	20	25
10	10	20 $\leftarrow$ okay

$$4x^2 + 20x + 25 = 4x^2 + 10x + 10x + 25$$
$$= 2x(2x + 5) + 5(2x + 5)$$
$$= (2x + 5)(2x + 5)$$
$$= (2x + 5)^2$$

<u>Trial and Error Method:</u>
First note that there are no common factors and
that $a = 4$, $b = 20$, and $c = 25$. Since c is
positive, the signs in our factors will be the same.
Since b is also positive, the signs of our factors will
be positive. We will consider factorizations with
this form:
$$(\underline{}x + \underline{})(\underline{}x + \underline{})$$
Since $a = 4$ can be factored as $1 \cdot 4$ and $2 \cdot 2$, we
have the following forms:
$$(x + \underline{})(4x + \underline{})$$
$$(2x + \underline{})(2x + \underline{})$$

$|c| = |25| = 25$ can be factored as $1 \cdot 25$ and $5 \cdot 5$.
Therefore, we have
$$(x + 1)(4x + 25) \rightarrow 4x^2 + 29x + 25$$
$$(x + 25)(4x + 1) \rightarrow 4x^2 + 101x + 25$$
$$(2x + 1)(2x + 25) \rightarrow 4x^2 + 52x + 25$$
$$(2x + 5)(2x + 5) \rightarrow 4x^2 + 20x + 25$$
The correct factorization is
$$4x^2 + 20x + 25 = (2x + 5)(2x + 5)$$
$$= (2x + 5)^2$$

13. <u>*ac* Method:</u>
$a \cdot c = 2 \cdot 4 = 8$
We need two factors of 8 whose sum is 5. Since the
product is positive, the factors will have the same
sign. The sum is positive so the factors will both be
positive. Since we are adding two positive numbers
to get 5, neither factor can exceed 5.

factor 1	factor 2	sum
2	4	6

The only remaining possibility for the factors does
not yield the correct sum so the expression is prime.

<u>Trial and Error Method:</u>
First note that there are no common factors and that
$a = 2$, $b = 5$, and $c = 4$. Since c is positive, the
signs in our factors will be the same. Since b is also
positive, the signs of our factors will be positive. We
will consider factorizations with this form:
$$(\underline{}r + \underline{})(\underline{}r + \underline{})$$
Since $a = 2$ can be factored as $1 \cdot 2$, we have the
following form:
$$(r + \underline{})(2r + \underline{})$$
$|c| = |4| = 4$ can be factored as $1 \cdot 4$ and $2 \cdot 2$. Since
the original expression had no common factors, the
binomials we select cannot have a common factor.
$$(r + 4)(2r + 1) \rightarrow 2r^2 + 9r + 4$$

The only remaining possibility does not result in the
correct middle term. Therefore, the expression is
prime.

15. _ac_ Method:

$a \cdot c = 18 \cdot -4 = -72$

We are looking for two factors of -72 whose sum is 21. Since the product is negative, the factors will have opposite signs. The sum is positive so the factor with the larger absolute value will be positive.

factor 1	factor 2	sum
-1	72	71
-2	36	34
-3	24	21 ← okay
-4	18	14
-6	12	6
-8	9	1

$$18x^2 + 21x - 4 = 18x^2 - 3x + 24x - 4$$
$$= 3x(6x-1) + 4(6x-1)$$
$$= (3x+4)(6x-1)$$

Trial and Error Method:

First note that there are no common factors and that $a = 18$, $b = 21$, and $c = -4$. Since c is negative, the signs in our factors will be opposites. We will consider factorizations with this form:

$$(\underline{\quad}x + \underline{\quad})(\underline{\quad}x - \underline{\quad})$$

If our choice results in a middle term with the wrong sign, we simply switch the signs of the factors.

Since $a = 18$ can be factored as $1 \cdot 18$, $2 \cdot 9$, and $3 \cdot 6$, we have the following forms:

$$(x + \underline{\quad})(18x - \underline{\quad})$$
$$(2x + \underline{\quad})(9x - \underline{\quad})$$
$$(3x + \underline{\quad})(6x - \underline{\quad})$$

$|c| = |-4| = 4$ can be factored as $1 \cdot 4$ and $2 \cdot 2$. Since the original expression had no common factors, the binomials we select cannot have a common factor.

$$(x+4)(18x-1) \rightarrow 18x^2 + 71x - 4$$
$$(2x+1)(9x-4) \rightarrow 18x^2 + x - 4$$
$$(3x+4)(6x-1) \rightarrow 18x^2 + 21x - 4$$

The correct factorization is
$$18x^2 + 21x - 4 = (3x+4)(6x-1)$$

17. _ac_ Method:

$a \cdot c = 3 \cdot 24 = 72$

We are looking for two factors of 72 whose sum is -22. Since the product is positive, the factors will have the same sign. The sum is negative so the factors will be negative.

factor 1	factor 2	sum
-1	-72	-73
-2	-36	-38
-3	-24	-27
-4	-18	-22 ← okay
-6	-12	-18
-8	-9	-17

$$3m^2 - 22m + 24 = 3m^2 - 4m - 18m + 24$$
$$= m(3m-4) - 6(3m-4)$$
$$= (m-6)(3m-4)$$

Trial and Error Method:

First note that there are no common factors and that $a = 3$, $b = -22$, and $c = 24$. Since c is positive the signs of our factors will be the same. Since b is negative, the signs in our factors will be negative. We will consider factorizations with this form:

$$(\underline{\quad}m - \underline{\quad})(\underline{\quad}m - \underline{\quad})$$

Since $a = 3$ can be factored as $1 \cdot 3$, we have the following form:

$$(m - \underline{\quad})(3m - \underline{\quad})$$

$|c| = |24| = 24$ can be factored as $1 \cdot 24$, $2 \cdot 12$, $3 \cdot 8$, and $4 \cdot 6$. Since the original expression had no common factors, the binomials we select cannot have a common factor.

$$(m-24)(3m-1) \rightarrow 3m^2 - 73m + 24$$
$$(m-12)(3m-2) \rightarrow 3m^2 - 38m + 24$$
$$(m-3)(3m-8) \rightarrow 3m^2 - 17m + 24$$
$$(m-6)(3m-4) \rightarrow 3m^2 - 22m + 24$$

The correct factorization is
$$3m^2 - 22m + 24 = (m-6)(3m-4).$$

19. <u>*ac* Method:</u>

$a \cdot c = 2 \cdot 40 = 80$

We are looking for two factors of 80 whose sum is -21. Since the product is positive, the factors will have the same sign. The sum is negative so the factors will be negative.

factor 1	factor 2	sum
-1	-80	-81
-2	-40	-42
-4	-20	-24
-5	-16	$-21 \leftarrow$ okay
-8	-10	-18

$$2x^2 - 21x + 40 = 2x^2 - 5x - 16x + 40$$
$$= x(2x - 5) - 8(2x - 5)$$
$$= (x - 8)(2x - 5)$$

<u>Trial and Error Method:</u>

First note that there are no common factors and that $a = 2$, $b = -21$, and $c = 40$. Since c is positive the signs of our factors will be the same. Since b is negative, the signs in our factors will be negative. We will consider factorizations with this form:

$$(\underline{\quad}x - \underline{\quad})(\underline{\quad}x - \underline{\quad})$$

Since $a = 2$ can be factored as $1 \cdot 2$, we have the following form:

$$(x - \underline{\quad})(2x - \underline{\quad})$$

$|c| = |40| = 40$ can be factored as $1 \cdot 40$, $2 \cdot 20$, $4 \cdot 10$, and $5 \cdot 8$. Since the original expression had no common factors, the binomials we select cannot have a common factor.

$$(x - 40)(2x - 1) \rightarrow 2x^2 - 81x + 40$$
$$(x - 8)(2x - 5) \rightarrow 2x^2 - 21x + 40$$

The correct factorization is
$$2x^2 - 21x + 40 = (x - 8)(2x - 5).$$

21. <u>*ac* Method:</u>

$a \cdot c = 9 \cdot 1 = 9$

We are looking for two factors of 9 whose sum is -6. Since the product is positive, the factors will have the same sign. The sum is negative so the factors will be negative.

factor 1	factor 2	sum
-1	-9	-10
-3	-3	$-6 \leftarrow$ okay

$$1 + 9w^2 - 6w = 9w^2 - 6w + 1$$
$$= 9w^2 - 3w - 3w + 1$$
$$= 3w(3w - 1) - 1(3w - 1)$$
$$= (3w - 1)(3w - 1)$$
$$= (3w - 1)^2$$

<u>Trial and Error Method:</u>

First note that there are no common factors and that $a = 9$, $b = -6$, and $c = 1$. Since c is positive the signs of our factors will be the same. Since b is negative, the signs in our factors will be negative. We will consider factorizations with this form:

$$(\underline{\quad}w - \underline{\quad})(\underline{\quad}w - \underline{\quad})$$

Since $a = 9$ can be factored as $3 \cdot 3$ and $1 \cdot 9$, we have the following forms:

$$(w - \underline{\quad})(9w - \underline{\quad})$$
$$(3w - \underline{\quad})(3w - \underline{\quad})$$

$|c| = |1| = 1$ can be factored as $1 \cdot 1$. Since the original expression had no common factors, the binomials we select cannot have a common factor.

$$(w - 1)(9w - 1) \rightarrow 9w^2 - 10w + 1$$
$$(3w - 1)(3w - 1) \rightarrow 9w^2 - 6w + 1$$

The correct factorization is
$$1 + 9w^2 - 6w = (3w - 1)(3w - 1) = (3w - 1)^2.$$

23. <u>*ac* Method:</u>

$a \cdot c = 2 \cdot 3 = 6$

We are looking for two factors of 6 whose sum is 5. Since the product is positive, the factors will have the same sign. The sum is positive so the factors will both be positive. Since we are adding two positive numbers to get 5, neither factor can exceed 5.

factor 1	factor 2	sum
2	3	$5 \leftarrow$ okay

$$2a^2 + 5ab + 3b^2 = 2a^2 + 2ab + 3ab + 3b^2$$
$$= 2a(a + b) + 3b(a + b)$$
$$= (2a + 3b)(a + b)$$

Trial and Error Method:
First note that there are no common factors and that $a = 2$, $b = 5$, and $c = 3$. Since c is positive, the signs in our factors will be the same. Since b is also positive, the signs of our factors will be positive. We will consider factorizations with this form:

$$\left(\underline{\quad} a + \underline{\quad} b\right)\left(\underline{\quad} a + \underline{\quad} b\right)$$

Since $a = 2$ can be factored as $1 \cdot 2$, we have the following form:

$$\left(a + \underline{\quad} b\right)\left(2a + \underline{\quad} b\right)$$

$|c| = |3| = 3$ can be factored as $1 \cdot 3$.

$$(a + b)(2a + 3b) \to 2a^2 + 5ab + 3b^2$$
$$(a + 3b)(2a + b) \to 2a^2 + 7ab + 3b^2$$

The correct factorization is
$$2a^2 + 5ab + 3b^2 = (a + b)(2a + 3b).$$

25. *ac* Method:

$$a \cdot c = 5 \cdot (-8) = -40$$

We are looking for two factors of -40 whose sum is 18. Since the product is negative, the factors will have opposite signs. The sum is positive so the factor with the larger absolute value will be positive.

factor 1	factor 2	sum	
-1	40	39	
-2	20	18	$\leftarrow$ okay
-4	10	6	
-5	8	3	

$$5x^2 + 18xy - 8y^2 = 5x^2 - 2xy + 20xy - 8y^2$$
$$= x(5x - 2y) + 4y(5x - 2)$$
$$= (x + 4y)(5x - 2y)$$

Trial and Error Method:
First note that there are no common factors and that $a = 5$, $b = 18$, and $c = -8$. Since c is negative, the signs in our factors will be opposites. We will consider factorizations with this form:

$$\left(\underline{\quad} x + \underline{\quad} y\right)\left(\underline{\quad} x - \underline{\quad} y\right)$$

Since $a = 5$ can be factored as $1 \cdot 5$, we have the following form:

$$\left(x + \underline{\quad} y\right)\left(5x - \underline{\quad} y\right)$$

If our choice results in a middle term with the wrong sign, we simply switch the signs of the factors.

$|c| = |-8| = 8$ can be factored as $1 \cdot 8$ and $2 \cdot 4$.

$$(x + y)(5x - 8y) \to 5x^2 - 3xy - 8y^2$$
$$(x + 8y)(5x - y) \to 5x^2 + 39xy - 8y^2$$
$$(x + 2y)(5x - 4y) \to 5x^2 + 6xy - 8y^2$$
$$(x + 4y)(5x - 2y) \to 5x^2 + 18xy - 8y^2$$

The correct factorization is
$$5x^2 + 18xy - 8y^2 = (x + 4y)(5x - 2y).$$

27. *ac* Method:
Start by factoring out the GCF, 3.
$$6b^2 - 15bc + 6c^2 = 3\left(2b^2 - 5bc + 2c^2\right)$$

Now factor the expression in parentheses.
$$a \cdot c = 2 \cdot 2 = 4$$
We are looking for two factors of 4 whose sum is -5. Since the product is positive, the factors will have the same sign. The sum is negative so the factors will be negative.

factor 1	factor 2	sum	
-1	-4	-5	$\leftarrow$ okay
-2	-2	-4	

$$2b^2 - 5bc + 2c^2 = 2b^2 - bc - 4bc + 2c^2$$
$$= b(2b - c) - 2c(2b - c)$$
$$= (b - 2c)(2b - c)$$

Therefore,
$$6b^2 - 15bc + 6c^2 = 3(b - 2c)(2b - c)$$

Trial and Error Method:
First factor out the GCF, 3.
$$6b^2 - 15bc + 6c^2 = 3\left(2b^2 - 5bc + 2c^2\right)$$

Now factor the expression in parentheses. Note that $a = 2$, $b = -5$, and $c = 2$. Since c is positive the signs of our factors will be the same. Since b is negative, the signs in our factors will be negative. We will consider factorizations with this form:

$$\left(\underline{\quad} b - \underline{\quad} c\right)\left(\underline{\quad} b - \underline{\quad} c\right)$$

Since $a = 2$ can be factored as $1 \cdot 2$, we have the following form:

$$\left(b - \underline{\quad} c\right)\left(2b - \underline{\quad} c\right)$$

$|c| = |2| = 2$ can be factored as $1 \cdot 2$. Since the parenthetical expression had no common factors, the binomials we select cannot have a common factor.

$$(b - 2c)(2b - c) \to 2b^2 - 5bc + 2c^2$$

The correct factorization is
$$6b^2 - 15bc + 6c^2 = 3(b - 2c)(2b - c).$$

29. *ac* Method:

$a \cdot c = 4 \cdot 25 = 100$

We are looking for two factors of 100 whose sum is -20. Since the product is positive, the factors will have the same sign. The sum is negative so the factors will be negative.

factor 1	factor 2	sum
-1	-100	-101
-2	-50	-52
-4	-25	-29
-5	-20	-25
-10	-10	$-20 \leftarrow$ okay

$$4r^2 - 20ry + 25y^2 = 4r^2 - 10ry - 10ry + 25y^2$$
$$= 2r(2r - 5y) - 5y(2r - 5y)$$
$$= (2r - 5y)(2r - 5y)$$
$$= (2r - 5y)^2$$

Trial and Error Method:

First note that there are no common factors and that $a = 4$, $b = -20$, and $c = 25$. Since c is positive the signs of our factors will be the same. Since b is negative, the signs in our factors will be negative. We will consider factorizations with this form:

$$(\underline{\quad} r - \underline{\quad} y)(\underline{\quad} r - \underline{\quad} y)$$

Since $a = 4$ can be factored as $4 \cdot 1$ and $2 \cdot 2$, we have the following forms:

$$(4r - \underline{\quad} y)(r - \underline{\quad} y)$$
$$(2r - \underline{\quad} y)(2r - \underline{\quad} y)$$

$|c| = |25| = 25$ can be factored as $25 \cdot 1$ and $5 \cdot 5$.

Since the original expression had no common factors, the binomials we select cannot have a common factor.

$$(4r - 25y)(r - y) \rightarrow 4r^2 - 29ry + 25y^2$$
$$(4r - y)(r - 25y) \rightarrow 4r^2 - 101ry + 25y^2$$
$$(4r - 5y)(r - 5y) \rightarrow 4r^2 - 25ry + 25y^2$$
$$(2r - 25y)(2r - y) \rightarrow 4r^2 - 52ry + 25y^2$$
$$(2r - y)(2r - 25y) \rightarrow 4r^2 - 52ry + 25y^2$$
$$(2r - 5y)(2r - 5y) \rightarrow 4r^2 - 20ry + 25y^2$$

The correct factorization is

$$4r^2 - 20ry + 25y^2 = (2r - 5y)(2r - 5y)$$
$$= (2r - 5y)^2$$

31. $4x^2 + 26x + 30$

Start by factoring out the GCF, 2.

$$4x^2 + 26x + 30 = 2(2x^2 + 13x + 15)$$

The leading coefficient of the expression inside the parentheses is not 1, so we try factoring by grouping.

$a \cdot c = 2 \cdot 15 = 30$

We need two numbers whose product is 30 and whose sum is 13. The product and sum are both positive, so the numbers are both positive. Since $10 \cdot 3 = 30$ and $10 + 3 = 13$, we get

$$4x^2 + 26x + 30 = 2(2x^2 + 13x + 15)$$
$$= 2(2x^2 + 3x + 10x + 15)$$
$$= 2(x(2x + 3) + 5(2x + 3))$$
$$= 2(x + 5)(2x + 3)$$

33. $20a^2 - 40a + 15$

Start by factoring out the GCF, 5.

$$20a^2 - 40a + 15 = 5(4a^2 - 8a + 3)$$

The leading coefficient of the expression inside the parentheses is not 1, so we try factoring by grouping.

$a \cdot c = 4 \cdot 3 = 12$

We need two numbers whose product is 12 and whose sum is -8. The product is positive but the sum is negative, so the two numbers must be negative. Since $(-2)(-6) = 12$ and

$(-2) + (-6) = -8$, we get

$$20a^2 - 40a + 15 = 5(4a^2 - 8a + 3)$$
$$= 5(4a^2 - 2a - 6a + 3)$$
$$= 5(2a(2a - 1) - 3(2a - 1))$$
$$= 5(2a - 3)(2a - 1)$$

35. $24x^2 + 15x - 9$

Start by factoring out the GCF, 3.

$$24x^2 + 15x - 9 = 3(8x^2 + 5x - 3)$$

The leading coefficient of the expression inside the parentheses is not 1, so we try factoring by grouping.

$$a \cdot c = 8 \cdot (-3) = -24$$

We need two numbers whose product is -24 and whose sum is 5. The product is negative, so the numbers have opposite signs. The sum is positive, so the number with the larger absolute value must be positive. Since $(8)(-3) = -24$ and $8 + (-3) = 5$, we get

$$24x^2 + 15x - 9 = 3(8x^2 + 5x - 3)$$
$$= 3(8x^2 + 8x - 3x - 3)$$
$$= 3(8x(x+1) - 3(x+1))$$
$$= 3(8x - 3)(x + 1)$$

37. $-20x^2 + 22x + 12$

Start by factoring out the GCF, -2.

$$-20x^2 + 22x + 12 = -2(10x^2 - 11x - 6)$$

The leading coefficient of the expression inside the parentheses is not 1, so we try factoring by grouping.

$$a \cdot c = 10(-6) = -60$$

We need two numbers whose product is -60 and whose sum is -11. The product is negative, so the numbers have opposite signs. The sum is negative, so the number with the larger absolute value must be negative. Since $-15(4) = -60$ and $-15 + 4 = -11$, we get

$$-20x^2 + 22x + 12 = -2(10x^2 - 11x - 6)$$
$$= -2(10x^2 - 15x + 4x - 6)$$
$$= -2(5x(2x - 3) + 2(2x - 3))$$
$$= -2(5x + 2)(2x - 3)$$

39. $-12x^2 + 3x + 9$

Start by factoring out the GCF, -3.

$$-12x^2 + 3x + 9 = -3(4x^2 - x - 3)$$

The leading coefficient of the expression inside the parentheses is not 1, so we try factoring by grouping.

$$a \cdot c = 4(-3) = -12$$

We need two numbers whose product is -12 and whose sum is -1. The product is negative, so the numbers have opposite signs. The sum is negative, so the number with the larger absolute value must be negative. Since $-4(3) = -12$ and $-4 + 3 = -1$, we get

$$-12x^2 + 3x + 9 = -3(4x^2 - x - 3)$$
$$= -3(4x^2 - 4x + 3x - 3)$$
$$= -3(4x(x - 1) + 3(x - 1))$$
$$= -3(4x + 3)(x - 1)$$

41. $12x^2 - 32x + 16x^3$

Start by factoring out the GCF, $4x$.

$$12x - 32x^2 + 16x^3 = 16x^3 - 32x^2 + 12x$$
$$= 4x(4x^2 - 8x + 3)$$

The leading coefficient of the expression inside the parentheses is not 1, so we try factoring by grouping.

$$a \cdot c = 4(3) = 12$$

We need two numbers whose product is 12 and whose sum is -8. The product is positive but the sum is negative, so the two numbers must be negative. Since $(-6)(-2) = 12$ and $(-2) + (-6) = -8$, we get

$$16x^3 - 32x^2 + 12x = 4x(4x^2 - 8x + 3)$$
$$= 4x(4x^2 - 2x - 6x + 3)$$
$$= 4x(2x(2x - 1) - 3(2x - 1))$$
$$= 4x(2x - 3)(2x - 1)$$

43. $4w^4 - 6w^3 - 12w^2$

Start by factoring out the GCF, $2w^2$.

$$4w^4 - 6w^3 - 12w^2 = 2w^2 \left(2w^2 - 3w - 6 \right)$$

The leading coefficient of the expression inside the parentheses is not 1, so we try factoring by grouping.

$$a \cdot c = 2(-6) = -12$$

We need two numbers whose product is -12 and whose sum is -3. The product is negative, so the numbers have opposite signs. The sum is negative, so the number with the larger absolute value must be negative.

Factors	1,–12	2,–6	3,–4
Sum	–11	–4	–1

Since none of the possibilities work, the expression inside the parentheses is prime. Therefore,

$$4w^4 - 6w^3 - 12w^2 = 2w^2 \left(2w^2 - 3w - 6 \right).$$

45. $10x^4 - 5x^3 - 50x^2$

Start by factoring out the GCF, $5x^2$.

$$10x^4 - 5x^3 - 50x^2 = 5x^2 \left(2x^2 - x - 10 \right)$$

The leading coefficient of the expression inside the parentheses is not 1, so we try factoring by grouping.

$$a \cdot c = 2(-10) = -20$$

We need two numbers whose product is -20 and whose sum is -1. The product is negative, so the numbers have opposite signs. The sum is negative, so the number with the larger absolute value must be negative.

Since $4(-5) = -20$ and $4 + (-5) = -1$, we get

$$\begin{aligned}
10x^4 - 5x^3 - 50x^2 &= 5x^2 \left(2x^2 - x - 10 \right) \\
&= 5x^2 \left(2x^2 + 4x - 5x - 10 \right) \\
&= 5x^2 \left(2x(x+2) - 5(x+2) \right) \\
&= 5x^2 (2x-5)(x+2)
\end{aligned}$$

47. $6a^2 - 34ab - 12b^2$

Start by factoring out the GCF, 2.

$$6a^2 - 34ab - 12b^2 = 2 \left(3a^2 - 17ab - 6b^2 \right)$$

The leading coefficient of the expression inside the parentheses is not 1, so we try factoring by grouping.

$$a \cdot c = 3(-6) = -18$$

We need two numbers whose product is -18 and whose sum is -17. The product is negative, so the numbers have opposite signs. The sum is negative, so the number with the larger absolute value must be negative.

Since $-18(1) = -18$ and $-18 + 1 = -17$, we get

$$\begin{aligned}
6a^2 - 34ab - 12b^2 &= 2 \left(3a^2 - 17ab - 6b^2 \right) \\
&= 2 \left(3a^2 - 18ab + 1ab - 6b^2 \right) \\
&= 2 \left(3a(a-6b) + b(a-6b) \right) \\
&= 2(3a+b)(a-6b)
\end{aligned}$$

49. $12r^3 + 40r^2w + 32rw^2$

Start by factoring out the GCF, $4r$.

$$12r^3 + 40r^2w + 32rw^2 = 4r \left(3r^2 + 10rw + 8w^2 \right)$$

The leading coefficient of the expression inside the parentheses is not 1, so we try factoring by grouping.

$$a \cdot c = 3 \cdot 8 = 24$$

We need two numbers whose product is 24 and whose sum is 10. The product and sum are positive, so the numbers are both positive.

Since $4 \cdot 6 = 24$ and $4 + 6 = 10$, we get

$$\begin{aligned}
12r^3 &+ 40r^2w + 32rw^2 \\
&= 4r \left(3r^2 + 10rw + 8w^2 \right) \\
&= 4r \left(3r^2 + 4rw + 6rw + 8w^2 \right) \\
&= 4r \left(r(3r+4w) + 2w(3r+4w) \right) \\
&= 4r(r+2w)(3r+4w)
\end{aligned}$$

51. $20a^3b^2 + 30a^2b^3 - 140ab^4$

Start by factoring out the GCF, $10ab^2$.

$20a^3b^2 + 30a^2b^3 - 140ab^4$
$= 10ab^2\left(2a^2 + 3ab - 14b^2\right)$

The leading coefficient of the expression inside the parentheses is not 1, so we try factoring by grouping.

$a \cdot c = 2 \cdot (-14) = -28$

We need two numbers whose product is -28 and whose sum is 3. Since c is negative, the two factors will have opposite signs. Since b is positive, the factor with the larger absolute value will be positive.

Since $7 \cdot (-4) = -28$ and $7 + (-4) = 3$, we get

$20a^3b^2 + 30a^2b^3 - 140ab^4$
$= 10ab^2\left(2a^2 + 3ab - 14b^2\right)$
$= 10ab^2\left(2a^2 - 4ab + 7ab - 14b^2\right)$
$= 10ab^2\left(2a(a - 2b) + 7b(a - 2b)\right)$
$= 10ab^2(2a + 7b)(a - 2b)$

53. $x^2 - 6x - 27$

We are looking for two factors of $c = -27$ whose sum is $b = -6$. Since c is negative, the two factors will have opposite signs. Since b is negative, the factor with the larger absolute value will be negative.

$(3)(-9) = -27$ and $3 + (-9) = -6$

Therefore, $x^2 - 6x - 27 = (x - 9)(x + 3)$.

55. $48x^2 + 40x = -8x \cdot 6x + (-8x) \cdot (-5)$
$\qquad\qquad\quad = -8x(6x - 5)$

57. $x^2 + 9$

Since the sum of two squares is prime over the integers, $x^2 + 9$ is prime.

59. $4x^2 - 12x + 9$

The leading coefficient is not 1, so we try factoring by grouping.

$a \cdot c = 4 \cdot 9 = 36$

We need two numbers whose product is 36 and whose sum is -12. The product is positive, so the numbers have the same sign. The sum is negative, so the numbers are both negative.

Since $(-6)(-6) = 36$ and $-6 + (-6) = -12$, we get

$4x^2 - 12x + 9 = 4x^2 - 6x - 6x + 9$
$\qquad\qquad\quad = 2x(2x - 3) - 3(2x - 3)$
$\qquad\qquad\quad = (2x - 3)(2x - 3)$
$\qquad\qquad\quad = (2x - 3)^2$

61. $-17p^2 + 17 = -17\left(p^2 - 1\right)$
$\qquad\qquad\quad = -17\left(p^2 - 1^2\right)$
$\qquad\qquad\quad = -17(p - 1)(p + 1)$

63. $24 + 10x + x^2 = x^2 + 10x + 24$

We are looking for two factors of $c = 24$ whose sum is $b = 10$. Since c is positive the two factors will have the same sign. Since b is positive, the factors will both be positive.

$4 \cdot 6 = 24$ and $4 + 6 = 10$

Therefore, $24 + 10x + x^2 = x^2 + 10x + 24$
$\qquad\qquad\qquad\qquad = (x + 6)(x + 4)$.

65. $b^2 - 3bc - 28c^2$

We are looking for two factors of $c = -28$ whose sum is $b = -3$. Since c is negative, the two factors will have opposite signs. Since b is negative, the factor with the larger absolute value will be negative.

$(-7)(4) = -28$ and $-7 + 4 = -3$

Therefore, $b^2 - 3bc - 28c^2 = (b + 4c)(b - 7c)$.

67. $8t^2 - 10t + 3$

The leading coefficient is not 1, so we try factoring by grouping.

$a \cdot c = 8 \cdot 3 = 24$

We need two numbers whose product is 24 and whose sum is -10. The product is positive, so the numbers have the same sign. The sum is negative, so the numbers are both negative.

Since $(-6)(-4) = 24$ and $-6 + (-4) = -10$, we get

$8t^2 - 10t + 3 = 8t^2 - 4t - 6t + 3$
$\qquad\qquad\quad = 4t(2t - 1) - 3(2t - 1)$
$\qquad\qquad\quad = (4t - 3)(2t - 1)$

69. $7x^4 - 28x^2 = 7x^2 \left(x^2 - 4 \right)$

$$= 7x^2 \left(x^2 - 2^2 \right)$$

$$= 7x^2 \left(x - 2 \right) \left(x + 2 \right)$$

71. $3x^4 - 21x^3 y - 54x^2 y^2$

$= 3x^2 \left(x^2 - 7xy - 18y^2 \right)$

$= 3x^2 \left(x + 2y \right) \left(x - 9y \right)$

73. $12p^3 - 4p^2 - 27p + 9 = 4p^2 \left(3p - 1 \right) - 9 \left(3p - 1 \right)$

$$= \left(4p^2 - 9 \right) \left(3p - 1 \right)$$

$$= \left(\left(2p \right)^2 - 3^2 \right) \left(3p - 1 \right)$$

$$= \left(2p - 3 \right) \left(2p + 3 \right) \left(3p - 1 \right)$$

75. $x^2 - 6x + 12$

We are looking for two factors of $c = 12$ whose sum is $b = -6$. Since c is positive, the two factors will have the same sign. Since b is negative, the factors will both be negative.

Factors	$-1, -12$	$-2, -6$	$-3, -4$
Sum	-13	-8	-7

Since none of the possibilities work, we can say that $x^2 - 6x + 12$ is prime.

77. $3x^4 - 21x^3 + 30x^2 = 3x^2 \left(x^2 - 7x + 10 \right)$

To factor the expression in parentheses, we are looking for two factors of $c = 10$ whose sum is $b = -7$. Since c is positive, the two factors will have the same sign. Since b is negative, the factors will both be negative.

$\left(-2 \right) \left(-5 \right) = 10$ and $\left(-2 \right) + \left(-5 \right) = -7$

Therefore, $3x^4 - 21x^3 + 30x^2 = 3x^2 \left(x^2 - 7x + 10 \right)$

$$= 3x^2 \left(x - 2 \right) \left(x - 5 \right).$$

79. $20x^2 + 16x^4 - 42x^3 = 16x^4 - 42x^3 + 20x^2$

$$= 2x^2 \left(8x^2 - 21x + 10 \right)$$

The leading coefficient of the expression inside the parentheses is not 1, so we try factoring by grouping.

$a \cdot c = 8 \cdot 10 = 80$

We need two numbers whose product is 80 and whose sum is -21. The product is positive but the sum is negative, so the two numbers must be

negative. Since $\left(-5 \right) \left(-16 \right) = 80$ and $\left(-5 \right) + \left(-16 \right) = -21$, we get

$20x^2 + 16x^4 - 42x^3 = 16x^4 - 42x^3 + 20x^2$

$$= 2x^2 \left(8x^2 - 21x + 10 \right)$$

$$= 2x^2 \left(8x^2 - 16x - 5x + 10 \right)$$

$$= 2x^2 \left(8x \left(x - 2 \right) - 5 \left(x - 2 \right) \right)$$

$$= 2x^2 \left(8x - 5 \right) \left(x - 2 \right)$$

81. $36a^2 - 49b^2 = \left(6a \right)^2 - \left(7b \right)^2$

$$= \left(6a - 7b \right) \left(6a + 7b \right)$$

83. $-2x^2 y + 8xy + 24y = -2y \left(x^2 - 4x - 12 \right)$

To factor the expression in parentheses, we are looking for two factors of $c = -12$ whose sum is $b = -4$. Since c is negative, the two factors will have opposite signs. Since b is negative, the factor with the larger absolute value will be negative.

$\left(2 \right) \left(-6 \right) = -12$ and $2 + \left(-6 \right) = -4$

Therefore,

$-2x^2 y + 8xy + 24y = -2y \left(x^2 - 4x - 12 \right)$

$$= -2y \left(x - 6 \right) \left(x + 2 \right).$$

85. $10p^3 t^2 + 22p^2 t^3 - 24pt^4$

$= 2pt^2 \left(5p^2 + 11pt - 12t^2 \right)$

The leading coefficient of the expression inside the parentheses is not 1, so we try factoring by grouping.

$a \cdot c = 5 \cdot -12 = -60$

We need two numbers whose product is -60 and whose sum is 11. Since c is negative, the two factors will have opposite signs. Since b is positive, the factor with the larger absolute value will be positive. Since $\left(15 \right) \left(-4 \right) = -60$ and $15 + \left(-4 \right) = 11$, we get

$10p^3 t^2 + 22p^2 t^3 - 24pt^4$

$= 2pt^2 \left(5p^2 + 11pt - 12t^2 \right)$

$= 2pt^2 \left(5p^2 + 15pt - 4pt - 12t^2 \right)$

$= 2pt^2 \left(5p \left(p + 3t \right) - 4t \left(p + 3t \right) \right)$

$= 2pt^2 \left(5p - 4t \right) \left(p + 3t \right)$

87. The student's work is incorrect because they have not completely factored. In each factor of the student's answer, there is a common factor that can be pulled out.

$$8x^2 + 28x + 12 = 4\left(2x^2 + 7x + 3\right)$$
$$= 4(x+3)(2x+1)$$

89. The student is not correct. If we multiply the right side of the equation, we see that the middle term is not correct. The student disregarded the coefficient of x^2

$$2x^2 + 7x + 10 = (2x+5)(x+1)$$

91. Answers may vary.

93.
$$2(x-2)(x-6) = 2x^2 - 16x + 24$$
$$2\left(x^2 - 8x + 12\right) = 2x^2 - 16x + 24$$
$$(x-2)(2x-12) = 2x^2 - 16x + 24$$
$$2(x-4)^2 - 8 = 2x^2 - 16x + 24$$
$$(2x-4)(x-6) = 2x^2 - 16x + 24$$

95. $3x^2 + 16x - 12$
The leading coefficient is not 1, so we try factoring by grouping.
$$a \cdot c = 3(-12) = -36$$
We need two numbers whose product is -36 and whose sum is 16. The product is negative, so the two numbers will have opposite signs. The sum is positive, so the number with the larger absolute value will be positive
Since $(-2)(18) = -36$ and $-2 + (18) = 16$, we get
$$3x^2 + 16x - 12 = 3x^2 - 2x + 18x - 12$$
$$= x(3x-2) + 6(3x-2)$$
$$= (x+6)(3x-2)$$

97. $(4x-7)(3x-1) = 12x^2 - 4x - 21x + 7$
$$= 12x^2 - 25x + 7$$

99. $(x-3)\left(2x^2 + 3x - 5\right)$
$$= x\left(2x^2 + 3x - 5\right) - 3\left(2x^2 + 3x - 5\right)$$
$$= 2x^3 + 3x^2 - 5x - 6x^2 - 9x + 15$$
$$= 2x^3 - 3x^2 - 14x + 15$$

101. $6x^3 + 10x^2 - 4x = 2x\left(3x^2 + 5x - 2\right)$

The leading coefficient of the expression inside the parentheses is not 1, so we try factoring by grouping.
$$a \cdot c = 3(-2) = -6$$
We need two numbers whose product is -6 and whose sum is 5. The product is negative, so the two numbers will have opposite signs. The sum is positive, so the number with the larger absolute value must be positive.
Since $(-1)(6) = -6$ and $-1 + 6 = 5$, we get
$$6x^3 + 10x^2 - 4x = 2x\left(3x^2 + 5x - 2\right)$$
$$= 2x\left(3x^2 - 1x + 6x - 2\right)$$
$$= 2x\left(x(3x-1) + 2(3x-1)\right)$$
$$= 2x(x+2)(3x-1)$$

103. $y = 2x^2$

First we list some solutions of $y = 2x^2$. Then, we sketch a curve that contains the points corresponding to the solutions.

x	y	(x, y)
-2	$2(-2)^2 = 8$	$(-2, 8)$
-1	$2(-1)^2 = 2$	$(-1, 2)$
0	$2(0)^2 = 0$	$(0, 0)$
1	$2(1)^2 = 2$	$(1, 2)$
2	$2(2)^2 = 8$	$(2, 8)$

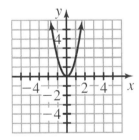

Description: *quadratic equation in two variables*

105. $x^2 - 2x - 3$

We are looking for two factors of $c = -3$ whose sum is $b = -2$. Since c is negative, the two factors will have opposite signs. Since b is negative, the factor with the larger absolute value will be negative.

$(1)(-3) = -3$ and $1 + (-3) = -2$

Therefore, $x^2 - 2x - 3 = (x-3)(x+1)$.

Description: *quadratic (or second degree) polynomial in one variable*

107. $f(-5) = x^2 - 2x - 3$

$$= (-5)^2 - 2(-5) - 3$$
$$= 25 - 2(-5) - 3$$
$$= 25 + 10 - 3$$
$$= 32$$

Description: *quadratic (or second degree) function in one variable*

Homework 8.4

1. $x^3 + 27 = x^3 + 3^3$

$$= (x+3)(x^2 - 3x + 3^2)$$
$$= (x+3)(x^2 - 3x + 9)$$

3. $x^3 + 125 = x^3 + 5^3$

$$= (x+5)(x^2 - 5x + 5^2)$$
$$= (x+5)(x^2 - 5x + 25)$$

5. $x^3 - 8 = x^3 - 2^3$

$$= (x-2)(x^2 + 2x + 2^2)$$
$$= (x-2)(x^2 + 2x + 4)$$

7. $x^3 - 1 = x^3 - 1^3$

$$= (x-1)(x^2 + 1x + 1^2)$$
$$= (x-1)(x^2 + x + 1)$$

9. $8t^3 + 27 = (2t)^3 + 3^3$

$$= (2t+3)((2t)^2 - 3(2t) + 3^2)$$
$$= (2t+3)(4t^2 - 6t + 9)$$

11. $27x^3 - 8 = (3x)^3 - 2^3$

$$= (3x-2)((3x)^2 + 2(3x) + 2^2)$$
$$= (3x-2)(9x^2 + 6x + 4)$$

13. $5x^3 + 40 = 5(x^3 + 8)$

$$= 5(x^3 + 2^3)$$
$$= 5(x+2)(x^2 - 2x + 2^2)$$
$$= 5(x+2)(x^2 - 2x + 4)$$

15. $2x^3 - 54 = 2(x^3 - 27)$

$$= 2(x^3 - 3^3)$$
$$= 2(x-3)(x^2 + 3x + 3^2)$$
$$= 2(x-3)(x^2 + 3x + 9)$$

17. $8x^3 + 27y^3 = (2x)^3 + (3y)^3$

$$= (2x+3y)((2x)^2 - (2x)(3y) + (3y)^2)$$
$$= (2x+3y)(4x^2 - 6xy + 9y^2)$$

19. $64a^3 - 27b^3 = (4a)^3 - (3b)^3$

$$= (4a-3b)((4a)^2 + (4a)(3b) + (3b)^2)$$
$$= (4a-3b)(16a^2 + 12ab + 9b^2)$$

21. $2x^4 - 54xy^3 = 2x(x^3 - 27y^3)$

$$= 2x(x-3y)(x^2 + 3xy + 9y^2)$$

23. $k^6 - 1 = (k^3 - 1)(k^3 + 1)$

$$= (k-1)(k^2 + k + 1)(k+1)(k^2 - k + 1)$$

25. $64x^6 - y^6$

$$= (8x^3 - y^3)(8x^3 + y^3)$$
$$= (2x-y)(4x^2 + 2xy + y^2)(2x+y)(4x^2 - 2xy + y^2)$$

27. $x^2 - 64 = x^2 - 8^2$

$$= (x-8)(x+8)$$

29. $2t^2 + 2t - 24 = 2(t^2 + t - 12)$

The leading coefficient inside the parentheses is 1 so we need two integers whose product is $c = -12$ and whose sum is $b = 1$. Since $4 \cdot (-3) = -12$ and $4 + (-3) = 1$, we get

$2t^2 + 2t - 24 = 2(t - 3)(t + 4)$.

31. $x^2 + 49$

Since the sum of two squares is prime over the integers, $x^2 + 49$ is prime.

33. $-3x^2 + 24x - 45 = -3(x^2 - 8x + 15)$

The leading coefficient inside the parentheses is 1 so we need two integers whose product is $c = 15$ and whose sum is $b = -8$. Since $(-5) \cdot (-3) = 15$ and $(-5) + (-3) = -8$, we get

$-3x^2 + 24x - 45 = -3(x - 5)(x - 3)$.

35. $1 + 15p^2 - 8p = 15p^2 - 8p + 1$

The leading coefficient is not 1, so we try factoring by grouping. $a \cdot c = 15 \cdot 1 = 15$, so we need two numbers whose product is 15 and whose sum is $b = -8$. Since $(-5)(-3) = 15$ and $(-5) + (-3) = -8$, we get

$$15p^2 - 8p + 1 = 15p^2 - 5p - 3p + 1$$
$$= 5p(3p - 1) - 1(3p - 1)$$
$$= (5p - 1)(3p - 1)$$

37. $x^2 - 2x + 1$

The leading coefficient is 1 so we need two integers whose product is $c = 1$ and whose sum is $b = -2$. Since $(-1)(-1) = 1$ and $(-1) + (-1) = -2$, we get

$$x^2 - 2x + 1 = (x - 1)(x - 1)$$
$$= (x - 1)^2$$

39. $24r^2 + 4r - 4 = 4(6r^2 + r - 1)$

The leading coefficient inside the parentheses is not 1, so we try factoring by grouping. $a \cdot c = 6(-1) = -6$, so we need two numbers whose product is -6 and whose sum is $b = 1$. Since $(3)(-2) = -6$ and $3 + (-2) = 1$, we get

$$24r^2 + 4r - 4 = 4(6r^2 + r - 1)$$
$$= 4(6r^2 + 3r - 2r - 1)$$
$$= 4(3r(2r + 1) - 1(2r + 1))$$
$$= 4(3r - 1)(2r + 1)$$

41. $-4ab^3 + 6a^2b^2 = (-2ab^2) \cdot 2b + (-2ab^2)(-3a)$
$$= -2ab^2(2b - 3a)$$

43. $a^2 - ab - 20b^2$

We need two monomials whose product is $-20b^2$ and whose sum is $-b$. Since $-20b^2$ has a negative coefficient, the coefficients of the monomials must have opposite signs. Since the coefficient of $-b$ is negative, the coefficient with the larger absolute value must be negative.

$(-5b)(4b) = -20b^2$ and $(-5b) + (4b) = -b$

Therefore, $a^2 - ab - 20b^2 = (a - 5b)(a + 4b)$.

45. $64a^3 + 27 = (4a)^3 + 3^3$
$$= (4a + 3)((4a)^2 - 3(4a) + 3^2)$$
$$= (4a + 3)(16a^2 - 12a + 9)$$

47. $8x^3 - 20x^2 - 2x + 5 = 4x^2(2x - 5) - 1(2x - 5)$
$$= (4x^2 - 1)(2x - 5)$$
$$= ((2x)^2 - 1^2)(2x - 5)$$
$$= (2x - 1)(2x + 1)(2x - 5)$$

49. $-12x^4 - 4x^3 = -4x^3 \cdot 3x + (-4x^3) \cdot 1$
$$= -4x^3(3x + 1)$$

51. $15a^4 + 25a^3 + 10a^2 = 5a^2(3a^2 + 5a + 2)$

The leading coefficient inside the parentheses is not 1, so we try factoring by grouping. $a \cdot c = 3 \cdot 2 = 6$, so we need two numbers whose product is 6 and whose sum is $b = 5$. Since $(3)(2) = 6$ and $3 + 2 = 5$, we get

$15a^4 + 25a^3 + 10a^2 = 5a^2(3a^2 + 5a + 2)$
$= 5a^2(3a^2 + 3a + 2a + 2)$
$= 5a^2(3a(a+1) + 2(a+1))$
$= 5a^2(3a+2)(a+1)$

53. $24 - 14x + x^2 = x^2 - 14x + 24$

The leading coefficient is 1 so we need two integers whose product is $c = 24$ and whose sum is $b = -14$. Since $-12 \cdot (-2) = 24$ and $-12 + (-2) = -14$, we get

$24 - 14x + x^2 = x^2 - 14x + 24$
$= (x - 12)(x - 2)$

55. $2w^4 + 4w^3 - 8w^2 = 2w^2(w^2 + 2w - 4)$

The leading coefficient inside the parentheses is 1 so we need two integers whose product is $c = -4$ and whose sum is $b = 2$. Since the product is negative, the integers have opposite signs. Since the sum is positive, the integer with the larger absolute value must be positive.

Factors	$-1, 4$	$-2, 2$
Sum	3	0

Since none of the possibilities work, the expression inside the parentheses is prime.
$2w^4 + 4w^3 - 8w^2 = 2w^2(w^2 + 2w - 4)$

57. $12x^4 - 27x^2 = 3x^2(4x^2 - 9)$
$= 3x^2((2x)^2 - 3^2)$
$= 3x^2(2x - 3)(2x + 3)$

59. $x^2 + 10x + 25$

The leading coefficient is 1 so we need two integers whose product is $c = 25$ and whose sum is $b = 10$. Since $5 \cdot 5 = 25$ and $5 + 5 = 10$, we get
$x^2 + 10x + 25 = (x + 5)(x + 5)$
$= (x + 5)^2$

61. $2x^2 + x - 21$

The leading coefficient is not 1, so we try factoring by grouping. $a \cdot c = 2(-21) = -42$, so we need two numbers whose product is -42 and whose sum is $b = 1$. Since $7(-6) = -42$ and $7 + (-6) = 1$, we get
$2x^2 + x - 21 = 2x^2 + 7x - 6x - 21$
$= x(2x + 7) - 3(2x + 7)$
$= (x - 3)(2x + 7)$

63. $81p^4 - 16q^4$
$= (9p^2 + 4q^2)(9p^2 - 4q^2)$
$= (9p^2 + 4q^2)(3p + 2q)(3p - 2q)$

65. $3x^3 + 24 = 3(x^3 + 8)$
$= 3(x + 2)(x^2 - 2x + 4)$

67. $m^3 - 13m^2n + 36mn^2 = m(m^2 - 13mn + 36n^2)$

For the expression in parentheses, we need two monomials whose product is $36n^2$ and whose sum is $-13n$. Since $36n^2$ has a positive coefficient, the coefficients of the monomials must have the same sign. Since the coefficient of $-13n$ is negative, the coefficients must both be negative. $(-9n)(-4n) = 36n^2$ and $-9n + (-4n) = -13n$
Therefore,
$m^3 - 13m^2n + 36mn^2 = m(m^2 - 13mn + 36n^2)$
$= m(m - 9n)(m - 4n)$

69. $4x - 5 + 2x^2 = 2x^2 + 4x - 5$

The leading coefficient is not 1, so we try factoring by grouping. $a \cdot c = 2(-5) = -10$, so we need two integers whose product is -10 and whose sum is $b = 4$. Since the product is negative, the integers will have opposite signs. Since the sum is positive, the integer with the larger absolute value will be positive.

Factors	$-1, 10$	$-2, 5$
Sum	9	3

Since none of the possibilities work, the expression is prime.

71. $100x^2 - 9y^2 = (10x)^2 - (3y)^2$
$= (10x - 3y)(10x + 3y)$

73. $4x^2 + 12x + 9$

The leading coefficient is not 1, so we try factoring by grouping. $a \cdot c = 4 \cdot 9 = 36$, so we need two numbers whose product is 36 and whose sum is $b = 12$. Since $6 \cdot 6 = 36$ and $6 + 6 = 12$, we get

$4x^2 + 12x + 9 = 4x^2 + 6x + 6x + 9$

$\qquad = 2x(2x+3) + 3(2x+3)$

$\qquad = (2x+3)(2x+3)$

$\qquad = (2x+3)^2$

75. $18x^3 + 27x^2 - 8x - 12 = 9x^2(2x+3) - 4(2x+3)$

$\qquad = (9x^2 - 4)(2x+3)$

$\qquad = ((3x)^2 - 2^2)(2x+3)$

$\qquad = (3x-2)(3x+2)(2x+3)$

77. $3a^3 - 10a^2b + 8ab^2 = a(3a^2 - 10ab + 8b^2)$

$\qquad = a(3a^2 - 6ab - 4ab + 8b^2)$

$\qquad = a(3a(a-2b) - 4b(a-2b))$

$\qquad = a(3a-4b)(a-2b)$

79. $x^2 - 9x - 20$

The leading coefficient is 1 so we need two integers whose product is $c = -20$ and whose sum is $b = -9$. Since the product is negative, the integers will have opposite signs. Since the sum is also negative, the integer with the larger absolute value will be negative.

Factors	1, −20	2, −10	4, −5
Sum	−19	−8	−1

Since none of the possibilities work, the expression is prime.

81. $x^3 - 1000 = x^3 - 10^3$

$\qquad = (x-10)(x^2 + 10x + 10^2)$

$\qquad = (x-10)(x^2 + 10x + 100)$

83. $12x^2 y - 26xy^2 - 10y^3$

$= 2y(6x^2 - 13xy - 5y^2)$

$= 2y(3x+y)(2x-5y)$

85. Answers may vary.

87. Answers may vary.

89. The coefficient on x in the second factor is incorrect.

$x^3 - 27 = x^3 - 3^3$

$\qquad = (x-3)(x^2 + 3x + 3^2)$

$\qquad = (x-3)(x^2 + 3x + 9)$

91. No; the middle term in the second factor should be AB.

93. In terms of correctness, it does not matter if the GCF is factored out in the first step or the last step. However, factoring it out in the first step often makes the coefficients easier to work with in the resulting expression.

95. $(5x-7)(5x+7) = 5x \cdot 5x + 5x \cdot 7 - 7 \cdot 5x - 7 \cdot 7$

$\qquad = 25x^2 + 35x - 35x - 49$

$\qquad = 25x^2 - 49$

97. $81x^2 - 16 = (9x)^2 - 4^2$

$\qquad = (9x-4)(9x+4)$

99. $3x^3 + 9x^2 - 12x = 3x(x^2 + 3x - 4)$

$\qquad = 3x(x-1)(x+4)$

101. $-2x(7x^2 - 5x + 1) = -2x(7x^2) - 2x(-5x) - 2x(1)$

$\qquad = -14x^3 + 10x^2 - 2x$

103. The function $f(x) = 4x - 5$ is in slope-intercept form, so the slope is $m = 4$ and the y-intercept is $(0, -5)$. We first plot $(0, -5)$. From this point we move 1 unit to the right and 4 units up, plotting the point $(1, -1)$. We then draw the line that connects the two points, extending in both directions.

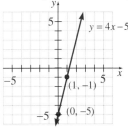

Description: *linear function in two variables*

105. $4x - 5 = 3x + 2$

$x - 5 = 2$

$x = 7$

The solution is 7.

Description: *linear equation in one variable*

107. $(4x - 5)(3x + 2) = 4x \cdot 3x + 4x \cdot 2 - 5 \cdot 3x - 5 \cdot 2$

$= 12x^2 + 8x - 15x - 10$

$= 12x^2 - 7x - 10$

Description: *quadratic (or second degree) polynomial in one variable*

Homework 8.5

1. $(x + 4)(x - 7) = 0$

$x = -4$ or $x = 7$

3. $x^2 + 7x + 10 = 0$

$(x + 2)(x + 5) = 0$

$x = -2$ or $x = -5$

5. $w^2 + w - 12 = 0$

$(w + 4)(w - 3) = 0$

$w = -4$ or $w = 3$

7. $x^2 - 8x + 15 = 0$

$(x - 5)(x - 3) = 0$

$x = 5$ or $x = 3$

9. $14x + 49 + x^2 = 0$

$(x + 7)(x + 7) = 0$

$x = -7$

11. $-24 - 2t + t^2 = 0$

$(t - 6)(t + 4) = 0$

$t = 6$ or $t = -4$

13. $25x^2 - 49 = 0$

$(5x + 7)(5x - 7) = 0$

$x = -\dfrac{7}{5}$ or $x = \dfrac{7}{5}$

15. $6m^2 - 11m + 3 = 0$

$(3m - 1)(2m - 3) = 0$

$m = \dfrac{1}{3}$ or $m = \dfrac{3}{2}$

17. $3x^2 + 3x - 90 = 0$

$3(x^2 + x - 30) = 0$

$3(x + 6)(x - 5) = 0$

$x = -6$ or $x = 5$

19. $8x^3 - 12x^2 - 20x = 0$

$4x(2x^2 - 3x - 5) = 0$

$4x(2x - 5)(x + 1) = 0$

$x = 0$, $x = \dfrac{5}{2}$ or $x = -1$

21. $x^2 = 5x + 14$

$x^2 - 5x - 14 = 0$

$(x - 7)(x + 2) = 0$

$x = 7$ or $x = -2$

23. $4x^2 - 8x = 32$

$4x^2 - 8x - 32 = 0$

$4(x^2 - 2x - 8) = 0$

$4(x - 4)(x + 2) = 0$

$x = 4$ or $x = -2$

25. $12t - 36 = t^2$

$t^2 - 12t + 36 = 0$

$(t - 6)(t - 6) = 0$

$t = 6$

27. $x^2 = 49$

$x^2 - 49 = 0$

$(x - 7)(x + 7) = 0$

$x = 7$ or $x = -7$

29. $16x^2 = 25$

$16x^2 - 25 = 0$

$(4x + 5)(4x - 5) = 0$

$x = -\dfrac{5}{4}$ or $x = \dfrac{5}{4}$

31.
$$6x^3 - 24x = 0$$
$$6x(x^2 - 4) = 0$$
$$6x(x-2)(x+2) = 0$$
$$x = 0, \ x = 2 \text{ or } x = -2$$

33.
$$3r^2 = 6r$$
$$3r^2 - 6r = 0$$
$$3r(r-2) = 0$$
$$r = 0 \text{ or } r = 2$$

35.
$$9x = -2x^2 + 5$$
$$2x^2 + 9x - 5 = 0$$
$$(2x-1)(x+5) = 0$$
$$x = \frac{1}{2} \text{ or } x = -5$$

37.
$$2x^3 = 6x^2 + 36x$$
$$2x^3 - 6x^2 - 36x = 0$$
$$2x(x^2 - 3x - 18) = 0$$
$$2x(x-6)(x+3) = 0$$
$$x = 0, \ x = 6 \text{ or } x = -3$$

39.
$$18y^3 + 3y^2 = 6y$$
$$18y^3 + 3y^2 - 6y = 0$$
$$3y(6y^2 + y - 2) = 0$$
$$3y(3y+2)(2y-1) = 0$$
$$y = 0, \ y = -\frac{2}{3} \text{ or } y = \frac{1}{2}$$

41.
$$\frac{a^2}{2} - \frac{a}{6} = \frac{1}{3}$$
$$\frac{a^2}{2} - \frac{a}{6} - \frac{1}{3} = 0$$
$$\frac{1}{6}(3a^2 - a - 2) = 0$$
$$\frac{1}{6}(3a+2)(a-1) = 0$$
$$a = -\frac{2}{3} \text{ or } a = 1$$

43.
$$-\frac{1}{3}x^2 + \frac{1}{3}x + 10 = 6$$
$$-3\left(-\frac{1}{3}x^2 + \frac{1}{3}x + 10\right) = -3(6)$$
$$x^2 - x - 30 = -18$$
$$x^2 - x - 12 = 0$$
$$(x-4)(x+3) = 0$$
$$x = 4 \text{ or } x = -3$$

45.
$$x^2 - \frac{1}{25} = 0$$
$$\left(x - \frac{1}{5}\right)\left(x + \frac{1}{5}\right) = 0$$
$$x = \frac{1}{5} \text{ or } x = -\frac{1}{5}$$

47.
$$(x+2)(x+5) = 40$$
$$x^2 + 7x + 10 - 40 = 0$$
$$x^2 + 7x - 30 = 0$$
$$(x-3)(x+10) = 0$$
$$x = 3 \text{ or } x = -10$$

49.
$$4r^3 - 2r^2 - 36r + 18 = 0$$
$$(2r^2 - 18)(2r - 1) = 0$$
$$2(r^2 - 9)(2r - 1) = 0$$
$$2(r+3)(r-3)(2r-1) = 0$$
$$r = -3, \ r = 3 \text{ or } r = \frac{1}{2}$$

51.
$$9x^3 - 12 = 4x - 27x^2$$
$$9x^3 + 27x^2 - 4x - 12 = 0$$
$$(9x^2 - 4)(x+3) = 0$$
$$(3x+2)(3x-2)(x+3) = 0$$
$$x = -\frac{2}{3}, \ x = \frac{2}{3} \text{ or } x = -3$$

53.
$$2x(x+1) = 5x(x-7)$$
$$5x^2 - 35x - 2x^2 - 2x = 0$$
$$3x^2 - 37x = 0$$
$$x(3x - 37) = 0$$
$$x = 0 \text{ or } x = \frac{37}{3}$$

55.
$$4p(p-1)-24=3p(p-2)$$
$$4p^2-4p-24-3p^2+6p=0$$
$$p^2+2p-24=0$$
$$(p+6)(p-4)=0$$
$$p=-6 \text{ or } p=4$$

57. $(x^2+5x+6)(x^2-5x-24)=0$
$$(x+3)(x+2)(x-8)(x+3)=0$$
$$x=-3,\ x=-2 \text{ or } x=8$$

59. $f(x)=x^2-9x+20$
$$=(x-5)(x-4)$$

The x-intercepts are $(5,0)$ and $(4,0)$.

61. $f(x)=36x^2-25$
$$=(6x-5)(6x+5)$$

The x-intercepts are $\left(-\dfrac{5}{6},0\right)$ and $\left(\dfrac{5}{6},0\right)$.

63. $f(x)=24x^3-14x^2-20x$
$$=2x(12x^2-7x-10)$$
$$=2x(4x-5)(3x+2)$$

The x-intercepts are $(0,0), \left(\dfrac{5}{4},0\right),$ and $\left(-\dfrac{2}{3},0\right)$.

65. $f(x)=x^3+2x^2-x-2$
$$=(x^2-1)(x+2)$$
$$=(x-1)(x+1)(x+2)$$

The x-intercepts are $(1,0),\ (-1,0),$ and $(-2,0)$.

67. $f(3)=(3)^2-(3)-6=0$

69. $x^2-x-6=14$
$$x^2-x-20=0$$
$$(x-5)(x+4)=0$$
$$x=5 \text{ or } x=-4$$

71. $x=-5$ or $x=3$

73. $x=-1$

75. $x=-1$ or $x=2$

77. $x=-1,\ x=1$ or $x=3$

79.

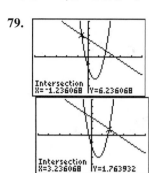

$x\approx-1.24$ or $x\approx 3.24$

81.

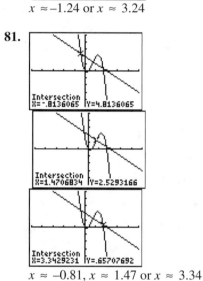

$x\approx-0.81,\ x\approx 1.47$ or $x\approx 3.34$

83. $x=-2$ or $x=4$

85. There is no solution.

87. You cannot divide out solutions, as this eliminates possible answers.
$$x^2=x$$
$$x^2-x=0$$
$$x(x-1)=0$$
$$x=0 \text{ or } x=1$$

89. The equation $x = 2$ is incorrect. The student should have written $2 = 0$ which has no real solution.

$$2x^2 - 26x + 80 = 0$$

$$2\left(x^2 - 13x + 40\right) = 0$$

$$2(x - 8)(x - 5) = 0$$

$2 = 0$ or $x - 8 = 0$ or $x - 5 = 0$
false $x = 8$ $x = 5$

The solutions are 5 and 8.

91. Answers may vary.

93. Answers may vary.

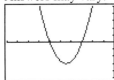

The quadratic function $h(x) = \dfrac{4}{3}x^2 + 12x + 24$ is a possible match for the graph.

95. Answers may vary.

97. $x^2 + 5x + 6 = (x + 3)(x + 2)$

99. $x^2 + 5x + 6 = 0$

$(x + 3)(x + 2) = 0$

$x = -3$ or $x = -2$

101. $3p^3 + 8p^2 + 4p = 0$

$p\left(3p^2 + 8p + 4\right) = 0$

$p(3p + 2)(p + 2) = 0$

$p = 0$, $p = -\dfrac{2}{3}$ or $p = -2$

103. $3p^3 + 8p^2 + 4p$

$= p\left(3p^2 + 8p + 4\right)$

$= p(3p + 2)(p + 2)$

105. $A = P + PRT$

$A = P(1 + RT)$

$\dfrac{A}{1 + RT} = \dfrac{P(1 + RT)}{(1 + RT)}$

$P = \dfrac{A}{1 + RT}$

107. $-2x(3x - 5)^2 = -2x(3x - 5)(3x - 5)$

$= -2x\left(9x^2 - 30x + 25\right)$

$= -18x^3 + 60x^2 - 50x$

Description: *cubic polynomial in one variable*

109. $8x^3 - 40x^2 + 50x$

$= 2x\left(4x^2 - 20x + 25\right)$

$= 2x(2x - 5)(2x - 5)$

$= 2x(2x - 5)^2$

Description: *cubic polynomial in one variable*

111. $f(-2) = 8(-2)^3 - 40(-2)^2 + 50(-2)$

$= -64 - 160 - 100$

$= -324$

Description: *cubic function*

Homework 8.6

1. a.

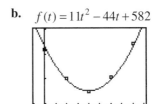

The curvature in the graph suggests that the data would be better fit by a quadratic model. The average rate of change is not constant.

b. $f(t) = 11t^2 - 44t + 582$

The model appears to fit the data well.

c. $f(13) = 11(13)^2 - 44(13) + 582$

$= 1859 - 572 + 582$

$= 1869$

The model predicts that in 2013 total spending by travelers in the U.S. will be \$1869 billion.

d. $637 = 11t^2 - 44t + 582$

$0 = 11t^2 - 44t - 55$

$0 = (11t - 55)(t + 1)$

$11t - 55 = 0$ or $t + 1 = 0$

       $11t = 55$ $t = -1$

          $t = 5$

The model predicts that total spending by travelers in the U.S. was \$637 billion in 1999 and 2005.

3. a.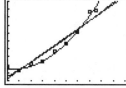

The quadratic model $Q(t)$ describes the situation better.

b.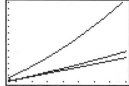

The quadratic model $Q(t)$ predicts the greater participation between 2005 and 2020.

c. For $L(t)$, the n-intercept is $(0, 1314)$. For $E(t)$, the n-intercept is $(0, 1324)$. For $Q(t)$, the n-intercept is $(0, 1374)$. The quadratic model $Q(t)$ describes the situation better.

d. $2t^2 - 4t + 1374 = 1390$

$2t^2 - 4t - 16 = 0$

$2(t^2 - 2t - 8) = 0$

$2(t - 4)(t + 2) = 0$

$t = 4$ or $t = -2$

Assuming that the competition took place before 1990, there would have been 1390 participants in $1900 + 4 = 1994$, and in $1990 - 2 = 1988$.

5. a.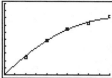

The model fits the data well.

b. $f(7) = -\dfrac{1}{3}(7)^2 + \dfrac{22}{3}(7) = 35$

This means that, 7 years after being rated B2, 35% of companies defaulted on their bonds.

c. $7 = -\dfrac{1}{3}t^2 + \dfrac{22}{3}t$

$\dfrac{1}{3}t^2 - \dfrac{22}{3}t + 7 = 0$

$\dfrac{1}{3}(t^2 - 22t + 21) = 0$ $t = 1$ or $t = 21$

$\dfrac{1}{3}(t - 21)(t - 1) = 0$

This means that, 1 year and 21 years after begin rated B2, 7% of companies defaulted on their bonds. Model breakdown has occurred for the estimate of 21 years.

d. $0 = -\dfrac{1}{3}t^2 + \dfrac{22}{3}t$

$ = -\dfrac{1}{3}t(t - 22)$

$t = 0$ or $t = 22$

It means that, at the time of the B2 rating and 22 years after receiving a B2 rating, no companies defaulted on their bonds. Model breakdown has occurred for the estimate of 22 years.

7. a.

The model fits the data well.

b. $f(7) = 0.64(7)^2 - 6.32(7) + 17 = 4.12$

In 2005, the model shows there were about 4 fatalities per 100 tornadoes.

c. $0.64t^2 - 6.32t + 17 = 17$

$0.64t^2 - 6.32t = 0$

$t(0.64t - 6.32) = 0$

$t = 0$ or $t \approx 9.9$

The model shows 17 fatalities per 100 tornadoes in 1998 and 2008.

9. a.

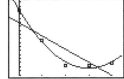

The quadratic model appears to be a better fit to the data.

b. Since economists felt that sales of Firestone tires would continue to decline, the linear model (with its constant negative average rate of change) better fits this viewpoint. The economists would likely feel the linear model would best describe future sales.

c. After an initial decline in tire sales, Firestone experienced an increase in sales. This would indicate that the graph of sales should initial be decreasing, then 'turn around' so that it is increasing. Firestone would likely feel the quadratic model better predicts future sales.

d.
$$\frac{4}{5}t^2 - \frac{24}{5}t + 23 = 19$$
$$\frac{4}{5}t^2 - \frac{24}{5}t + 4 = 0$$
$$\frac{5}{4}\left(\frac{4}{5}t^2 - \frac{24}{5}t + 4\right) = \frac{5}{4} \cdot 0$$
$$t^2 - 6 + 5 = 0$$
$$(t - 5)(t - 1) = 0$$
$$t - 5 = 0 \quad \text{or} \quad t - 1 = 0$$
$$t = 5 \qquad t = 1$$

$Q(t)$ predicts that sales of Firestone tires were 19 million tires in 2000 and 2004.

11.
$$t^2 - 3t + 5 = 23$$
$$t^2 - 3t - 18 = 0$$
$$(t - 6)(t + 3) = 0$$
$$t - 6 = 0 \quad \text{or} \quad t + 3 = 0$$
$$t = 6 \qquad t = -3$$

The model estimates that the company's profit was $23 thousand in 2004 and predicts that it will be again in 2013.

13.
$$2t^2 - 13t + 25 = 10$$
$$2t^2 - 13t + 15 = 0$$
$$(2t - 3)(t - 5) = 0$$
$$2t - 3 = 0 \quad \text{or} \quad t - 5 = 0$$
$$2t = 3 \qquad t = 5$$
$$t = \frac{3}{2}$$

The model predicts that the company's revenue was $10 million in 2009 and will be $10 million again in 2012.

15. a.
$$-16t^2 + 64t + 3 = 3$$
$$-16t^2 + 64t = 0$$
$$t^2 - 4t = 0$$
$$t(t - 4) = 0$$
$$t = 0 \quad \text{or} \quad t - 4 = 0$$
$$t = 4$$

The ball will be at a height of 3 feet after 0 seconds and again after 4 seconds.

There are two such times because the ball is at a height of 3 feet when it is hit and again on its way back down to the ground.

b.
$$-16t^2 + 64t + 3 = 51$$
$$-16t^2 + 64t - 48 = 0$$
$$t^2 - 4t + 3 = 0$$
$$(t - 3)(t - 1) = 0$$
$$t - 3 = 0 \quad \text{or} \quad t - 1 = 0$$
$$t = 3 \qquad t = 1$$

One second after the ball is hit, and again 3 seconds after it is hit, the ball is at a height of 51 feet. It makes sense that there are two times, because the ball reaches 51 feet both on its way up and on its way down.

c.
$$-16t^2 + 64t + 3 = 67$$
$$-16t^2 + 64t - 64 = 0$$
$$t^2 - 4t + 4 = 0$$
$$(t - 2)(t - 2) = 0$$
$$t - 2 = 0$$
$$t = 2$$

Two seconds after the ball is hit, the ball is at a height of 67 feet. It makes sense that there is only one time if the ball reaches a height of 67 feet only at the top of its climb.

17. Let L = the length of the table (in feet) and W = the width (in feet).

Since the length is 7 feet more than the width, our first equation is $L = 7 + W$. Because the area is

$A = LW$

$60 = LW$

we get the following system:

$L = 7 + W$

$60 = LW$

Substitute $7 + W$ for L in the second equation and solve for W.

$60 = (7 + W)W$

$60 = 7W + W^2$

$0 = W^2 + 7W - 60$

$0 = (W - 5)(W + 12)$

$W - 5 = 0$ or $W + 12 = 0$

$\quad W = 5 \qquad\qquad W = -12$

The width must be positive, so discard the negative solution. Substitute 5 for W in the equation $L = 7 + W$ and solve for L.

$L = 7 + 5 = 12$

The table has a length of 12 feet and a width of 5 feet.

19. $A = l \times w = 60$

$l = 2w + 2$

$\quad (2w + 2)w = 60$

$\quad 2w^2 + 2w - 60 = 0$

$\quad 2(w^2 + w - 30) = 0$

$\quad 2(w + 6)(w - 5) = 0$

$\quad w = -6 \text{ or } w = 5$

$\quad l = 2(5) + 2 = 12$

The rug is 12 feet long by 5 feet wide.

21. $l = w + 4$

$2l \times 2w = 48$

$2(w + 4)(2w) - 48 = 0$

$\quad 2(2w^2 + 8w) - 48 = 0$

$\quad\quad 4w^2 + 16w - 48 = 0$

$\quad\quad 4(w^2 + 4w - 12) = 0$

$\quad\quad 4(w + 6)(w - 2) = 0$

$\quad w = -6 \text{ or } w = 2$

$\quad l = 2 + 4 = 6$

The original rectangle is 6 centimeters long and 2 centimeters wide.

23. $A = 6 \times 10 = 60$

$(6 + 2x)(10 + 2x) - 60 = 80$

$\quad 4x^2 + 32x - 80 = 0$

$\quad 4(x^2 + 8x - 20) = 0$

$\quad 4(x + 10)(x - 2) = 0$

$\quad x = -10 \text{ or } x = 2$

The border is 2 feet wide.

25. $A = (14 \times 10) + 52 = 140 + 52 = 192$

$(14 + 2x)(10 + 2x) = A$

$(14 + 2x)(10 + 2x) = 192$

$\quad 140 + 48x + 4x^2 - 192 = 0$

$\quad\quad 4x^2 + 48x - 52 = 0$

$\quad\quad 4(x^2 + 12x - 13) = 0$

$\quad\quad 4(x + 13)(x - 1) = 0$

$\quad x = -13 \text{ or } x = 1$

The frame has a border width of 1 inch. The actual width of the frame is 12 inches.

27. Answers may vary. A linear model is appropriate if the average rate of change is roughly constant. A quadratic model may be appropriate if the rate of change switches from increasing to decreasing, or from decreasing to increasing. In either case, a scatter diagram can be helpful in determining which model is appropriate.

29. a.

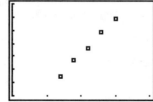

The graph appears to be more linear than parabolic in shape. Therefore, a linear model would better fit the data.

b.

Using the regression feature of a graphing calculator, an equation of a model is

$f(t) = 109.15t + 538.35$.

c. Substitute 3300 for $f(t)$ in the equation from part (b) and solve for t.

$$109.15t + 538.35 = 3300$$
$$109.15t = 2761.65$$
$$t = \frac{2761.65}{109.15} \approx 25.30$$

The model predicts that the average tax refund will be \$3300 in 2015.

31. a. Since farmed shrimp production has decreased by about 1.8 million pounds per year, a linear model is appropriate. The slope is -1.8 million pounds per year. Since the number of pounds produced per year was 6.0 million pounds in 2007, the g-intercept is (0, 6.0). So, a reasonable model is $g(t) = -1.8t + 6.0$.

b. Substitute 1.0 for $g(t)$ in our model and solve for t.

$$-1.8t + 6.0 = 1.0$$
$$-1.8t = -5.0$$
$$t = \frac{-5.0}{-1.8} \approx 2.78$$

The model predicts that U.S. farmed shrimp production will be 1 million pounds in 2010.

33. Let c = average cost of campus housing and t = the number of years after 1999. The average cost has increased linearly with slope

$$m = \frac{5475 - 4340}{2004 - 1999} = \frac{1135}{5} = 227.$$

Since the average cost was \$4340 in 1999, the c-intercept is $(0, 4340)$. So, a reasonable model is

$c = 227t + 4340$.

For 2014, we have $t = 15$.

$c = 227(15) + 4340 = 7745$

The model predicts that the average cost of campus housing will be \$7745 for the school year ending in 2014.

35. – 41. Answers may vary.

Chapter 8 Review Exercises

1. $x^2 + 9x + 20$
The leading coefficient is 1 so we need two integers whose product is $c = 20$ and whose sum is $b = 9$. Since $4 \cdot 5 = 20$ and $4 + 5 = 9$, we get

$$x^2 + 9x + 20 = (x + 4)(x + 5)$$

2. $6x^2 - 2x - 8 = 2(3x^2 - x - 4)$
The leading coefficient of the expression inside the parentheses is not 1, so we try factoring by grouping. $a \cdot c = 3(-4) = -12$, so we need two numbers whose product is -12 and whose sum is -1. Since $3(-4) = -12$ and $3 + (-4) = -1$, we get

$$6x^2 - 2x - 8 = 2(3x^2 - x - 4)$$
$$= 2(3x^2 + 3x - 4x - 4)$$
$$= 2(3x(x+1) - 4(x+1))$$
$$= 2(3x - 4)(x + 1)$$

3. $x^2 + 14x + 49$
The leading coefficient is 1 so we need two integers whose product is $c = 49$ and whose sum is $b = 14$. Since $7 \cdot 7 = 49$ and $7 + 7 = 14$, we get

$$x^2 + 14x + 49 = (x + 7)(x + 7)$$
$$= (x + 7)^2$$

4. $-18t^4 - 33t^3 + 30t^2 = -3t^2(6t^2 + 11t - 10)$
The leading coefficient of the expression inside the parentheses is not 1, so we try factoring by grouping. $a \cdot c = 6(-10) = -60$, so we need two numbers whose product is -60 and whose sum is 11. Since $15(-4) = -60$ and $15 + (-4) = 11$, we get

$$-18t^4 - 33t^3 + 30t^2 = -3t^2(6t^2 + 11t - 10)$$
$$= -3t^2(6t^2 + 15t - 4t - 10)$$
$$= -3t^2(3t(2t + 5) - 2(2t + 5))$$
$$= -3t^2(3t - 2)(2t + 5)$$

5. $p^2 - 3pq - 54q^2$
The leading coefficient is 1, so we need two monomials whose product is $-54q^2$ and whose sum is $-3q$. Since $(6q)(-9q) = -54q^2$ and $6q + (-9q) = -3q$, we get

$$p^2 - 3pq - 54q^2 = (p - 9q)(p + 6q).$$

6. $32 - 12x + x^2 = x^2 - 12x + 32$

The leading coefficient is 1 so we need two integers whose product is $c = 32$ and whose sum is $b = -12$. Since $-8 \cdot (-4) = 32$ and

$-4 + (-8) = -12$, we get

$32 - 12x + x^2 = x^2 - 12x + 32$
$$= (x - 8)(x - 4)$$

7. $-9x^2 + 4 = -1(9x^2 - 4)$
$$= -1\left((3x)^2 - 2^2\right)$$
$$= -(3x - 2)(3x + 2)$$

8. $4w^2 + 25 = (2w)^2 + 5^2$

Since the sum of two squares is prime over the integers, the expression $4w^2 + 25$ is prime.

9. $20m^2n - 45mn^3 = 5mn \cdot 4m - 5mn \cdot 9n^2$
$$= 5mn\left(4m - 9n^2\right)$$

10. $16x^2 + 14x + 2x^3 = 2x^3 + 16x^2 + 14x$
$$= 2x\left(x^2 + 8x + 7\right)$$

The leading coefficient of the expression in parentheses is 1, so we need two integers whose product is $c = 7$ and whose sum is $b = 8$. Since $7 \cdot 1 = 7$ and $7 + 1 = 8$, we get

$16x^2 + 14x + 2x^3 = 2x^3 + 16x^2 + 14x$
$$= 2x\left(x^2 + 8x + 7\right)$$
$$= 2x(x + 1)(x + 7).$$

11. $16x^3 - 32x^2 + 16x = 16x\left(x^2 - 2x + 1\right)$

The leading coefficient of the expression in parentheses is 1, so we need two integers whose product is $c = 1$ and whose sum is $b = -2$. Since $(-1)(-1) = 1$ and $(-1) + (-1) = -2$, we get

$16x^3 - 32x^2 + 16x = 16x\left(x^2 - 2x + 1\right)$
$$= 16x(x - 1)(x - 1)$$
$$= 16x(x - 1)^2.$$

12. $24x^3 - 32x^2 = 8x^2 \cdot 3x - 8x^2 \cdot 4$
$$= 8x^2(3x - 4)$$

13. $5x^4y - 35x^3y + 60x^2y = 5x^2y\left(x^2 - 7x + 12\right)$

The leading coefficient of the expression in parentheses is 1, so we need two integers whose product is $c = 12$ and whose sum is $b = -7$. Since $(-3)(-4) = 12$ and $(-3) + (-4) = -7$, we get

$5x^4y - 35x^3y + 60x^2y = 5x^2y\left(x^2 - 7x + 12\right)$
$$= 5x^2y(x - 3)(x - 4).$$

14. $-m^2 - 2m + 35 = -1\left(m^2 + 2m - 35\right)$

The leading coefficient of the expression in parentheses is 1, so we need two integers whose product is $c = -35$ and whose sum is $b = 2$. Since $7(-5) = -35$ and $7 + (-5) = 2$, we get

$-m^2 - 2m + 35 = -1\left(m^2 + 2m - 35\right)$
$$= -(m - 5)(m + 7).$$

15. $4r^3 - 10r^2 + 6r - 15 = 2r^2(2r - 5) + 3(2r - 5)$
$$= (2r^2 + 3)(2r - 5)$$

16. $81t^4 - 16w^4 = \left(9t^2 + 4w^2\right)\left(9t^2 - 4w^2\right)$
$$= \left(9t^2 + 4w^2\right)(3t + 2w)(3t - 2w)$$

17. $2y^3 - 54 = 2\left(y^3 - 27\right)$
$$= 2(y - 3)\left(y^2 + 3y + 9\right)$$

18. $x^2 - 9x + 20$
The leading coefficient is 1 so we need two integers whose product is $c = 20$ and whose sum is $b = -9$. Since $-5 \cdot (-4) = 20$ and $-5 + (-4) = -9$, we get
$x^2 - 9x + 20 = (x - 5)(x - 4).$

19. $6t^2 + 11ty - 10y^2$

The leading coefficient is not 1, so we try factoring by grouping. $a \cdot c = 6(-10y^2) = -60y^2$, so we need two monomials whose product is $-60y^2$ and whose sum is $11y$. Since $-4y(15y) = -60y^2$ and $-4y + 15y = 11y$, we get

$$6t^2 + 11ty - 10y^2 = 6t^2 - 4ty + 15ty - 10y^2$$
$$= 2t(3t - 2y) + 5y(3t - 2y)$$
$$= (2t + 5y)(3t - 2y)$$

20. $2x^3 - 50x = 2x \cdot x^2 - 2x \cdot 25$

$$= 2x(x^2 - 25)$$
$$= 2x(x^2 - 5^2)$$
$$= 2x(x - 5)(x + 5)$$

21. $x^2 - 10x + 25$

The leading coefficient is 1 so we need two integers whose product is $c = 25$ and whose sum is $b = -10$. Since $-5 \cdot (-5) = 25$ and $-5 + (-5) = -10$, we get

$$x^2 - 10x + 25 = (x - 5)(x - 5)$$
$$= (x - 5)^2$$

22. $p^2 - 81 = p^2 - 9^2$

$$= (p - 9)(p + 9)$$

23. $8w^2 - 12w + 3$

The leading coefficient is not 1, so we try factoring by grouping. $a \cdot c = 8(3) = 24$, so we need two numbers whose product is 24 and whose sum is -12. Since the product is positive and the sum is negative, the two numbers must be negative.

factor 1	factor 2	sum
-1	-24	-25
-2	-12	-14
-3	-8	-11
-4	-6	-10

Since none of the possibilities work, we can say that the expression is prime.

24. $4x^2 + 20x + 25$

The leading coefficient is not 1, so we try factoring by grouping. $a \cdot c = 4(25) = 100$, so we need two

numbers whose product is 100 and whose sum is 20. Since $10 \cdot 10 = 100$ and $10 + 10 = 20$, we get

$$4x^2 + 10x + 10x + 25 = 2x(2x + 5) + 5(2x + 5)$$
$$= (2x + 5)(2x + 5)$$
$$= (2x + 5)^2$$

25. $12w^3 - 50w^2 + 8w = 2w(6w^2 - 25w + 4)$

The leading coefficient of the expression inside the parentheses is not 1, so we try factoring by grouping. $a \cdot c = 6 \cdot 4 = 24$, so we need two numbers whose product is 24 and whose sum is -25. Since $(-1)(-24) = 24$ and $(-1) + (-24) = -25$, we get

$$12w^3 - 50w^2 + 8w = 2w(6w^2 - 25w + 4)$$
$$= 2w(6w^2 - w - 24w + 4)$$
$$= 2w(w(6w - 1) - 4(6w - 1))$$
$$= 2w(w - 4)(6w - 1)$$

26. $49a^2 - 9b^2 = (7a)^2 - (3b)^2$

$$= (7a - 3b)(7a + 3b)$$

27. $x^2 - 7x - 12$

The leading coefficient is 1 so we need two integers whose product is $c = -12$ and whose sum is $b = -7$. Since the product is negative, the integers will have opposite signs. Since the sum is also negative, the factor with the larger absolute value will be negative.

Factors	$1, -12$	$2, -6$	$3, -4$
Sum	-11	-4	-1

Since none of the possibilities work, the expression $x^2 - 7x - 12$ is prime.

28. $x^3 + 3x^2 - 4x - 12 = x^2(x + 3) - 4(x + 3)$

$$= (x^2 - 4)(x + 3)$$
$$= (x - 2)(x + 2)(x + 3)$$

29. $r^3 + 8 = r^3 + 2^3$

$$= (r + 2)(r^2 - 2 \cdot r + 2^2)$$
$$= (r + 2)(r^2 - 2r + 4)$$

30. $2ax - 10ay - 3bx + 15by$

$= 2a(x - 5y) - 3b(x - 5y)$

$= (2a - 3b)(x - 5y)$

31. $x^2 + 25 = x^2 + 5^2$

The student tried to factor the sum of two squares as $a^2 + b^2 = (a + b)(a + b)$. However, the sum of two squares is not factorable over the integers, so the expression is prime.

Note: $(a + b)(a + b) = a^2 + 2ab + b^2$ not $a^2 + b^2$

32. The student factored out the GCF, but did not factor completely since the expression inside parentheses can be factored further.

$5x^3 + 35x^2 + 60x = 5x(x^2 + 7x + 12)$

$= 5x(x + 3)(x + 4)$

33. For $x^2 + kx + 24$ to be factorable, we need two integers whose product is 24 and whose sum is k. Since 24 is positive, the two integers must have the same sign.

Factors	Sum $= k$
$-1, -24$	-25
$-2, -12$	-14
$-3, -8$	-11
$-4, -6$	-10
$4, 6$	10
$3, 8$	11
$2, 12$	14
$1, 24$	25

34. $2x^3 + 16x^2 = -24x$

$2x^3 + 16x^2 + 24x = 0$

$2x(x^2 + 8x + 12) = 0$

$2x(x + 2)(x + 6) = 0$

$2x = 0$ or $x + 2 = 0$ or $x + 6 = 0$

$x = 0$ $\qquad x = -2$ $\qquad x = -6$

The solutions are -6, -2, and 0.

35. $(m - 3)(m + 2) = -4$

$m^2 - m - 6 = -4$

$m^2 - m - 2 = 0$

$(m - 2)(m + 1) = 0$

$m - 2 = 0$ or $m + 1 = 0$

$m = 2$ $\qquad m = -1$

The solutions are -1 and 2.

36. $t^2 - 6t + 9 = 0$

$(t - 3)(t - 3) = 0$

$t - 3 = 0$

$t = 3$

The solution is 3.

37. $x^2 - 3x = 5x - 15$

$x^2 - 8x + 15 = 0$

$(x - 5)(x - 3) = 0$

$x - 5 = 0$ or $x - 3 = 0$

$x = 5$ $\qquad x = 3$

The solutions are 3 and 5.

38. $25x^2 - 81 = 0$

$(5x)^2 - 9^2 = 0$

$(5x - 9)(5x + 9) = 0$

$5x - 9 = 0$ or $5x + 9 = 0$

$5x = 9$ $\qquad 5x = -9$

$x = \dfrac{9}{5}$ $\qquad x = -\dfrac{9}{5}$

The solutions are $-\dfrac{9}{5}$ and $\dfrac{9}{5}$.

39. $2x^3 - 7x^2 - 2x + 7 = 0$

$x^2(2x - 7) - 1(2x - 7) = 0$

$(x^2 - 1)(2x - 7) = 0$

$(x - 1)(x + 1)(2x - 7) = 0$

$x - 1 = 0$ or $x + 1 = 0$ or $2x - 7 = 0$

$x = 1$ $\qquad x = -1$ $\qquad 2x = 7$

$x = \dfrac{7}{2}$

The solutions are -1, 1, and $\dfrac{7}{2}$.

40. $6x^2 + x - 2 = 0$

$(3x + 2)(2x - 1) = 0$

$3x + 2 = 0$ or $2x - 1 = 0$

$3x = -2$ $\qquad 2x = 1$

$x = -\dfrac{2}{3}$ $\qquad x = \dfrac{1}{2}$

The solutions are $-\dfrac{2}{3}$ and $\dfrac{1}{2}$.

41.
$$3x^2 = 15x$$
$$3x^2 - 15x = 0$$
$$3x(x-5) = 0$$
$$3x = 0 \quad \text{or} \quad x - 5 = 0$$
$$x = 0 \qquad\qquad x = 5$$
The solutions are 0 and 5.

42.
$$8r^2 - 18r + 9 = 0$$
$$(4r - 3)(2r - 3) = 0$$
$$4r - 3 = 0 \quad \text{or} \quad 2r - 3 = 0$$
$$4r = 3 \qquad\qquad 2r = 3$$
$$r = \frac{3}{4} \qquad\qquad r = \frac{3}{2}$$
The solutions are $\frac{3}{4}$ and $\frac{3}{2}$.

43.
$$a^2 = 2a + 35$$
$$a^2 - 2a - 35 = 0$$
$$(a - 7)(a + 5) = 0$$
$$a - 7 = 0 \quad \text{or} \quad a + 5 = 0$$
$$a = 7 \qquad\qquad a = -5$$
The solutions are -5 and 7.

44.
$$\frac{1}{3}x^2 - \frac{1}{3}x - 4 = 6$$
$$3\left(\frac{1}{3}x^2 - \frac{1}{3}x - 4\right) = 3(6)$$
$$x^2 - x - 12 = 18$$
$$x^2 - x - 30 = 0$$
$$(x - 6)(x + 5) = 0$$
$$x - 6 = 0 \quad \text{or} \quad x + 5 = 0$$
$$x = 6 \qquad\qquad x = -5$$
The solutions are -5 and 6.

45.
$$3x^3 - 2x^2 = 27x - 18$$
$$3x^3 - 2x^2 - 27x + 18 = 0$$
$$x^2(3x - 2) - 9(3x - 2) = 0$$
$$(x^2 - 9)(3x - 2) = 0$$
$$(x - 3)(x + 3)(3x - 2) = 0$$
$$x - 3 = 0 \quad \text{or} \quad x + 3 = 0 \quad \text{or} \quad 3x - 2 = 0$$
$$x = 3 \qquad\qquad x = -3 \qquad\qquad 3x = 2$$
$$x = \frac{2}{3}$$
The solutions are -3, $\frac{2}{3}$, and 3.

46.
$$a^2 = 4$$
$$a^2 - 4 = 0$$
$$a^2 - 2^2 = 0$$
$$(a - 2)(a + 2) = 0$$
$$a - 2 = 0 \quad \text{or} \quad a + 2 = 0$$
$$a = 2 \qquad\qquad a = -2$$
The solutions are -2 and 2.

47.
$$5p^2 + 20p - 60 = 0$$
$$\tfrac{1}{5}\left(5p^2 + 20p - 60\right) = \tfrac{1}{5}(0)$$
$$p^2 + 4p - 12 = 0$$
$$(p - 2)(p + 6) = 0$$
$$p - 2 = 0 \quad \text{or} \quad p + 6 = 0$$
$$p = 2 \qquad\qquad p = -6$$
The solutions are -6 and 2.

48.
$$\frac{m^2}{2} - \frac{7m}{6} + \frac{1}{3} = 0$$
$$3m^2 - 7m + 2 = 0$$
$$(3m - 1)(m - 2) = 0$$
$$m = \frac{1}{3} \text{ or } m = 2$$

49.
$$4p(5p - 6) = (2p + 3)(2p - 3)$$
$$20p^2 - 24p = 4p^2 - 9$$
$$16p^2 - 24p + 9 = 0$$
$$(4p - 3)(4p - 3) = 0$$
$$p = \frac{3}{4}$$

50. $f(x) = 3x^3 + 3x^2 - 18x$

$\qquad = 3x(x^2 - x - 6)$

$\qquad = 3x(x+3)(x-2)$

The *x*-intercepts are $(0,0),(-3,0),$ or $(2,0)$

51. $2x^2 + 4x - 5 = 2x + 3$

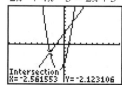 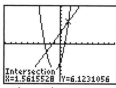

The approximate intersection points are $(-2.56, -2.12)$ and $(1.56, 6.12)$, which have *x*-coordinates of -2.56 and 1.56, respectively. Therefore, the approximate solutions to the equation are -2.56 and 1.56.

52. $y = -3x^2 + 6x + 20$

From the table, the input $x = 1$ yields the output $y = 23$. Therefore, 1 is the solution to the equation $-3x^2 + 6x + 20 = 23$.

53. $y = -3x^2 + 6x + 20$

From the table, the inputs $x = -2$ and $x = 4$ yield the output $y = -4$. Therefore, -2 and 4 are solutions to the equation $-3x^2 + 6x + 20 = -4$.

54. From the table we see the maximum value for $y = -3x^2 + 6x + 20$ is $y = 23$. There are no input values such that the output is 27. Therefore, the equation $-3x^2 + 6x + 20 = 27$ has no real solutions.

55. $y = -3x^2 + 6x + 20$

From the table, the inputs $x = 0$ and $x = 2$ yield the output $y = 20$. Therefore, 0 and 2 are solutions to the equation $-3x^2 + 6x + 20 = 20$.

56. $f(x) = x^2 - 49$

$\qquad 0 = x^2 - 49$

$\qquad 0 = (x-7)(x+7)$

$x - 7 = 0 \quad$ or $\quad x + 7 = 0$

$\quad x = 7 \qquad\qquad x = -7$

The solutions are -7 and 7, so the *x*-intercepts are $(-7, 0)$ and $(7, 0)$.

57. $f(x) = 8x^2 - 14x - 15$

$\qquad 0 = 8x^2 - 14x - 15$

$\qquad 0 = (4x+3)(2x-5)$

$4x + 3 = 0 \quad$ or $\quad 2x - 5 = 0$

$\quad 4x = -3 \qquad\qquad 2x = 5$

$\quad x = -\dfrac{3}{4} \qquad\qquad x = \dfrac{5}{2}$

The solutions are $-\dfrac{3}{4}$ and $\dfrac{5}{2}$, so the *x*-intercepts are $\left(-\dfrac{3}{4}, 0\right)$ and $\left(\dfrac{5}{2}, 0\right)$.

58. Answers may vary. One example:

$(x-3)(x+6) = 0$

$x^2 + 3x - 18 = 0$

59. Answers may vary. One example:

$x(x+2)(x-1) = 0$

$x^3 + x^2 - 2x = 0$

60. a.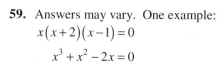

The curvature in the graph suggests that the data would be better fit by a quadratic model since the average rate of change is not constant.

b.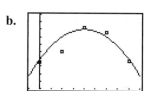

The model appears to fit the data reasonably well.

c. For 2004, we have $t = 5$.

$f(5) = -(5)^2 + 4(5) + 39 = 34$

The model predicts that the number of asthma episodes per 1000 people was 34 in 2004.

d. $27 = -t^2 + 4t + 39$

$0 = t^2 - 4t - 12$

$0 = (t - 6)(t + 2)$

$t - 6 = 0$ or $t + 2 = 0$

$t = 6 \qquad t = -2$

The annual asthma episode rate was 27 per 1000 people in 1997 and 2005.

61. $68 = -16t^2 + 80t + 4$

$0 = -16t^2 + 80t - 64$

$0 = -16(t^2 - 5t + 4)$

$0 = -16(t - 4)(t - 1)$

$t = 4$ or $t = 1$

The baseball is at a height of 68 feet 1 second after the ball is hit and 4 seconds after the ball is hit.

62. Let L = the length of the banner (in feet) and W = the width (in feet).
Since the length is 4 feet more than twice the width, our first equation is $L = 4 + 2W$. Because the area is

$A = LW$

$30 = LW$

we get the following system:

$L = 4 + 2W$

$30 = LW$

Substitute $4 + 2W$ for L in the second equation and solve for W.

$30 = (4 + 2W)W$

$30 = 4W + 2W^2$

$0 = 2W^2 + 4W - 30$

$0 = W^2 + 2W - 15$

$0 = (W - 3)(W + 5)$

$W - 3 = 0$ or $W + 5 = 0$

$W = 3 \qquad W = -5$

The width must be positive, so discard the negative solution. Substitute 3 for W in the equation $L = 4 + 2W$ and solve for L.

$L = 4 + 2(3) = 10$

The banner has a length of 10 feet and a width of 3 feet.

Chapter 8 Test

1. $x^2 - 3x - 40$
The leading coefficient is 1 so we need two integers whose product is $c = -40$ and whose sum is $b = -3$. Since $-8 \cdot (5) = -40$ and $-8 + 5 = -3$, we get $x^2 - 3x - 40 = (x - 8)(x + 5)$.

2. $24 + x^2 - 10x = x^2 - 10x + 24$
The leading coefficient is 1 so we need two integers whose product is $c = 24$ and whose sum is $b = -10$. Since $-6(-4) = 24$ and

$-6 + (-4) = -10$, we get

$24 + x^2 - 10x = x^2 - 10x + 24$

$\qquad = (x - 6)(x - 4)$.

3. $8m^2n^3 - 10m^3n = 2m^2n \cdot 4n^2 - 2m^2n \cdot 5m$

$\qquad = 2m^2n(4n^2 - 5m)$

4. $p^2 - 14pq + 40q^2$
The leading coefficient is 1, so we need two monomials whose product is $40q^2$ and whose sum is $-14q$. Since $(-10q)(-4q) = 40q^2$ and $-10q + (-4q) = -14q$, we get

$p^2 - 14pq + 40q^2 = (p - 10q)(p - 4q)$

5. $25p^2 - 36y^2 = (5p)^2 - (6y)^2$

$\qquad = (5p - 6y)(5p + 6y)$

6. $3x^4y - 21x^3y + 36x^2y = 3x^2y(x^2 - 7x + 12)$

The leading coefficient of the expression in parentheses is 1, so we need two integers whose product is $c = 12$ and whose sum is $b = -7$. Since $(-3)(-4) = 12$ and $(-3) + (-4) = -7$, we get

$3x^4y - 21x^3y + 36x^2y = 3x^2y(x^2 - 7x + 12)$

$\qquad = 3x^2y(x - 4)(x - 3)$.

7. $8x^3 + 20x^2 - 18x - 45 = 4x^2(2x + 5) - 9(2x + 5)$

$\qquad = (4x^2 - 9)(2x + 5)$

$\qquad = (2x - 3)(2x + 3)(2x + 5)$

8. $8x^2 - 26x + 15$

The leading coefficient is not 1, so we try factoring by grouping. $a \cdot c = 8(15) = 120$, so we need two numbers whose product is 120 and whose sum is -26. Since the product is positive and the sum is negative, the two numbers must be negative. Since $-6(-20) = 120$ and $-6 + (-20) = -26$, we get

$$8x^2 - 26x + 15 = 8x^2 - 6x - 20x + 15$$
$$= 2x(4x - 3) - 5(4x - 3)$$
$$= (2x - 5)(4x - 3)$$

9. $-16x^2 - 26x + 12 = -2(8x - 3)(x + 2)$

10. $16a^4b - 36a^3b^2 + 18a^2b^3$
$$= 2a^2b(4a - 3b)(2a - 3b)$$

11. $54m^3 + 128p^3$
$$= 2(3m + 4p)(9m^2 - 12mp + 16p^2)$$

12. $(x - 5)(x + 2) = x^2 - 3x - 10$
$$= (x + 2)(x - 5)$$

13. The student did not factor completely.
$$5x^3 + 3x^2 - 20x - 12 = x^2(5x + 3) - 4(5x + 3)$$
$$= (x^2 - 4)(5x + 3)$$
$$= (x - 2)(x + 2)(5x + 3)$$

14. $x^2 - 13x + 36 = 0$
$$(x - 4)(x - 9) = 0$$
$$x - 4 = 0 \quad \text{or} \quad x - 9 = 0$$
$$x = 4 \qquad\qquad x = 9$$
The solutions are 4 and 9.

15. $49x^2 - 9 = 0$
$$(7x)^2 - 3^2 = 0$$
$$(7x - 3)(7x + 3) = 0$$
$$7x - 3 = 0 \quad \text{or} \quad 7x + 3 = 0$$
$$7x = 3 \qquad\qquad 7x = -3$$
$$x = \frac{3}{7} \qquad\qquad x = -\frac{3}{7}$$
The solutions are $-\frac{3}{7}$ and $\frac{3}{7}$.

16. $(2x - 7)(x - 3) = 10$
$$2x^2 - 13x + 11 = 0$$
$$(2x - 11)(x - 1) = 0$$
$$x = \frac{11}{2} \quad \text{or} \quad x = 1$$

17. $\frac{1}{4}p^2 - \frac{1}{2}p - 6 = 0$
$$4\left(\frac{1}{4}p^2 - \frac{1}{2}p - 6\right) = \frac{1}{4}(0)$$
$$p^2 - 2p - 24 = 0$$
$$(p - 6)(p + 4) = 0$$
$$p - 6 = 0 \quad \text{or} \quad p + 4 = 0$$
$$p = 6 \qquad\qquad p = -4$$
The solutions are -4 and 6.

18. $3x^3 - 12x = 8 - 2x^2$
$$3x^3 + 2x^2 - 12x - 8 = 0$$
$$x^2(3x + 2) - 4(3x + 2) = 0$$
$$(x^2 - 4)(3x + 2) = 0$$
$$(x - 2)(x + 2)(3x + 2) = 0$$
$$x - 2 = 0 \quad \text{or} \quad x + 2 = 0 \quad \text{or} \quad 3x + 2 = 0$$
$$x = 2 \qquad\qquad x = -2 \qquad\qquad 3x = -2$$
$$x = -\frac{2}{3}$$
The solutions are -2, $-\frac{2}{3}$, and 2.

19. $2x^3 = 8x^2 + 10x$
$$2x^3 - 8x^2 - 10x = 0$$
$$2x(x^2 - 4x - 5) = 0$$
$$2x(x - 5)(x + 1) = 0$$
$$2x = 0 \quad \text{or} \quad x - 5 = 0 \quad \text{or} \quad x + 1 = 0$$
$$x = 0 \qquad\qquad x = 5 \qquad\qquad x = -1$$
The solutions are -1, 0, and 5.

20. $3x(2x - 5) + 4x = 2(x - 3)$
$$6x^2 - 13x + 6 = 0$$
$$(3x - 2)(2x - 3) = 0$$
$$x = \frac{2}{3} \quad \text{or} \quad x = \frac{3}{2}$$

21. $f(x) = 10x^2 - 19x + 6$
$$= (5x - 2)(2x - 3)$$
The *x*-intercepts are $\left(\dfrac{2}{5}, 0\right)$ and $\left(\dfrac{3}{2}, 0\right)$.

22. $x^2 + 6x + 7 = 2$

The graphs of $y = x^2 + 6x + 7$ and $y = 2$ intersect only at the points $(-5, 2)$ and $(-1, 2)$, which have *x*-coordinates -5 and -1. So, -5 and -1 are the solutions of $x^2 + 6x + 7 = 2$.

23. $x^2 + 6x + 7 = -1$

The graphs of $y = x^2 + 6x + 7$ and $y = -1$ intersect only at the points $(-4, -1)$ and $(-2, -1)$, which have *x*-coordinates -4 and -2. So, -4 and -2 are the solutions of $x^2 + 6x + 7 = -1$.

24. $x^2 + 6x + 7 = -2$

The graphs of $y = x^2 + 6x + 7$ and $y = -2$ intersect only at the point $(-3, -2)$, which has *x*-coordinate -3. So, -3 is the solution of $x^2 + 6x + 7 = -2$.

25. $x^2 + 6x + 7 = -4$

The graphs of $y = x^2 + 6x + 7$ and $y = -4$ do not intersect. So, there are no real solutions to the equation $x^2 + 6x + 7 = -4$.

26. $f(x) = 10x^2 - 11x - 6$
$$0 = 10x^2 - 11x - 6$$
$$0 = (5x + 2)(2x - 3)$$
$$5x + 2 = 0 \quad \text{or} \quad 2x - 3 = 0$$
$$5x = -2 \qquad\qquad 2x = 3$$
$$x = -\frac{2}{5} \qquad\qquad x = \frac{3}{2}$$
The solutions are $-\dfrac{2}{5}$ and $\dfrac{3}{2}$.

27. Answers may vary. One example:
$$(x + 3)(x - 8) = 0$$
$$x^2 - 5x - 24 = 0$$

28. a.

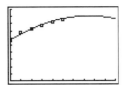

The model fits the data well.

b. $f(13) = -\dfrac{3}{5}(13)^2 + 9(13) + 57 = 72.6$

In 2013, there will be 73 million available nights for extended-stay hotel rooms.

c.
$$-\frac{3}{5}t^2 + 9t + 57 = 87$$
$$-\frac{3}{5}t^2 + 9t - 30 = 0$$
$$t^2 - 15t + 50 = 0$$
$$(t - 5)(t - 10) = 0$$
$$t = 5 \text{ or } t = 10$$

In 2005 and 2010 there will be 87 million available nights for extended-stay hotel rooms.

29. $(11 + 2x)(15 + 2x) - 120 = 165$
$$4x^2 + 52x - 120 = 0$$
$$4(x + 15)(x - 2) = 0$$
$$x = -15 \text{ or } x = 2$$
The width of the border is 2 inches. The actual width of the frame is 15 inches.

Review of Chapters 1 – 8

1. a. The independent variable is age *a* in years. The dependent variable is the percentage *p* who own a home .

b. The ordered pair (50, 75) means that 75% of 50-year-old Americans own a home.

2.
$$-65 + x = 145$$
$$-65 + 65 + x = 145 + 65$$
$$x = 210$$
The change in balance is $210.

3. $\dfrac{a - b}{c - a} = \dfrac{3 - (-4)}{-2 - 3} = \dfrac{7}{-5} = -\dfrac{7}{5}$

4. $b^2 - 4ac = (-4)^2 - 4(3)(-2) = 16 + 24 = 40$

5.

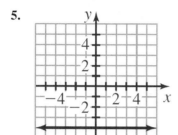

6. $m = \dfrac{y_2 - y_1}{x_2 - x_1} = \dfrac{-3 - 5}{4 - (-2)} = \dfrac{-8}{6} = -\dfrac{4}{3}$, decreasing

7.

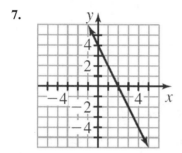

8.

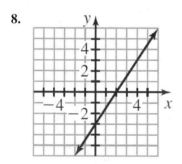

9. From the graph we see that the y-intercept is $(0, 2)$ and the x-intercept is $(3, 0)$. The slope is then

$$m = \frac{0 - 2}{3 - 0} = \frac{-2}{3} = -\frac{2}{3}$$

The equation of the line is $y = -\dfrac{2}{3}x + 2$.

10. $m = \dfrac{0.27 - 5.84}{2007 - 2003} = \dfrac{-5.57}{4} = -1.3925$

The average rate of change of revenue is –$1.3925 billion per year.

11. a. At $t = 0$ (2007), the number of bicyclists younger than 16 who were hit and killed by motor vehicles was 106. The slope is –8. These values can be substituted into an equation of the form $y = mx + b$.

$f(t) = -8t + 106$.

b. The slope, –8, means that 8 fewer bicyclists younger than 16 are hit and killed by motor vehicles each year.

c. The n-intercept is 106, which is how many bicyclists younger than 16 were hit and killed by motor vehicles in the year 2007 ($t = 0$).

d. $0 = -8t + 106$

$8t = 106$

$t = 13.25$

This means that in the year 2007 + 13.25 ≈ 2020, it is expected that no bicyclists younger than 16 will be hit and killed by motor vehicles.

e. According to this model, every year after 2020 (2021 and beyond), there will be less than 0 bicyclists younger than 16 hit and killed by motor vehicles, which is impossible.

12. $2(6x + 3y) - (4x - 5y + 9)$

$= 12x + 6y - 4x + 5y - 9$

$= 12x - 4x + 6y + 5y - 9$

$= 8x + 11y - 9$

13. $5 - 3(x - 4) = 5 - 3x + 12 = -3x + 17$

14.
$$3t - 14 = 6 - 8t$$
$$3t - 14 + 14 = 6 - 8t + 14$$
$$3t = 20 - 8t$$
$$3t + 8t = 20 - 8t + 8t$$
$$11t = 20$$
$$\frac{11t}{11} = \frac{20}{11}$$
$$t = \frac{20}{11}$$

15. $2 - 5(4t - 3) = 9 - (6t - 2)$

$2 - 20t + 15 = 9 - 6t + 2$

$-20t + 17 = -6t + 11$

$-20t + 17 - 17 = -6t + 11 - 17$

$-20t = -6t - 6$

$-20t + 6t = -6t - 6 + 6t$

$-14t = -6$

$\dfrac{-14t}{-14} = \dfrac{-6}{-14}$

$t = \dfrac{3}{7}$

16. $\dfrac{2x - 1}{5} = \dfrac{3x + 4}{2}$

$10\left(\dfrac{2x - 1}{5}\right) = 10\left(\dfrac{3x + 4}{2}\right)$

$4x - 2 = 15x + 20$

$4x - 2 + 2 = 15x + 20 + 2$

$4x = 15x + 22$

$4x - 15x = 15x + 22 - 15x$

$-11x = 22$

$\dfrac{-11x}{-11} = \dfrac{22}{-11}$

$x = -2$

17. $4(x - 7) = 25$

$4x - 28 = 25$

$4x - 28 + 28 = 25 + 28$

$4x = 53$

$\dfrac{4x}{4} = \dfrac{53}{4}$

$x = \dfrac{53}{4} = 13.25$

18. $x = -5$

19. $x = 1$

20. $y - y_1 = m(x - x_1)$

$\dfrac{y - y_1}{m} = x - x_1$

$\dfrac{y - y_1}{m} + x_1 = x$

21. First solve for y.

$3x - 2y + 4 = 0$

$-2y = -3x - 4$

$\dfrac{-2y}{-2} = \dfrac{-3x - 4}{-2}$

$y = \dfrac{3}{2}x + 2$

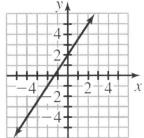

22. $3x - 7(0) = 28$

$3x = 28$

$x = \dfrac{28}{3}$

The *x*-intercept is $\left(\dfrac{28}{3}, 0\right)$.

$3(0) - 7y = 28$

$-7y = 28$

$y = \dfrac{28}{-7} = -4$

The *y*-intercept is (0, –4).

23. The domain is $-5 \le x \le 4$.

24. The range is $-3 \le y \le 3$.

25. The relation is a function because the graph passes the vertical line test.

26. $f(-3) = 2(-3)^2 - 5(-3) = 18 + 15 = 33$

27. $-4 = \dfrac{2}{3}x + 5$

$-9 = \dfrac{2}{3}x$

$-\dfrac{27}{2} = x$

28. The equation of the line is $y = -\dfrac{3}{5}x + b$.

Substitute the point $(4, -2)$ into the equation.

$-2 = -\dfrac{3}{5}(4) + b$

$-2 = -\dfrac{12}{5} + b$

$\dfrac{2}{5} = b$

The equation of the line is $y = -\dfrac{3}{5}x + \dfrac{2}{5}$.

29. First find the slope of the line.

$m = \dfrac{-6 - (-3)}{1 - (-5)} = \dfrac{-3}{6} = -\dfrac{1}{2}$

The equation of the line is $y = -\dfrac{1}{2}x + b$.

Substitute the point $(-5, -3)$ into the equation and solve for b.

$-3 = -\dfrac{1}{2}(-5) + b$

$-3 = \dfrac{5}{2} + b$

$-\dfrac{11}{2} = b$

The equation of the line is $y = -\dfrac{1}{2}x - \dfrac{11}{2}$.

30. a. Start by plotting the data set, and then find the regression line for the data.

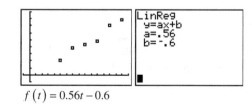

$f(t) = 0.56t - 0.6$

b. $f(12) = 0.56(12) - 0.6$

$\qquad = 6.72 - 0.6$

$\qquad = 6.12$

This means that about 6.12 thousand Chinese children were adopted by American families in $1990 + 12 = 2002$.

c. $f(t) = 0.56t - 0.6$

$\qquad 12 = 0.56t - 0.6$

$\qquad 12.6 = 0.56t$

$\qquad 22.5 = t$

This means that about 12 thousand Chinese children will be adopted by American families in the year $1990 + 22.5 \approx 2013$.

d. The equation $f(t) = 0.56t - 0.6$ is of the form $y = mx + b$. The slope is 0.56. This means that the increase in expected number of Chinese children adopted by American families is 0.56 thousand per year, or 560.

e. $f(1) = 0.56(1) - 0.6$

$\qquad = -0.04$

Because the model predicts the expected number of Chinese children adopted by American families in 1991 to be a negative value, model breakdown has occurred.

31. $m = \dfrac{28.5 - 17}{2006 - 2001} = \dfrac{11.5}{5} = 2.3$

The function is $f(t) = 2.3t + 17$.

$\qquad 49 = 2.3t + 17$

$\qquad 32 = 2.3t$

$\qquad 13.9 \approx t$

The model predicts that there will be 49 million Ambien prescriptions in $2001 + 13.9 \approx 2015$.

32. $5 - 4(3x - 3) \le -19$

$\qquad 5 - 12x + 12 \le -19$

$\qquad -12x + 17 \le -19$

$-12x + 17 - 17 \le -19 - 17$

$\qquad -12x \le -36$

$\qquad \dfrac{-12x}{-12} \ge \dfrac{-36}{-12}$

$\qquad x \ge 3$

Interval: $[3, \infty)$

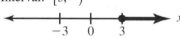

33.
$$-1 < 2x + 7 < 11$$
$$-1 - 7 \le 2x + 7 - 7 < 11 - 7$$
$$-8 < 2x < 4$$
$$\frac{-8}{2} < \frac{2x}{2} < \frac{4}{2}$$
$$-4 < x < 2$$
Interval: $(-4, 2)$

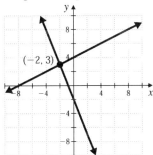

34. Solve for y in the first equation.
$$x - 2y = -8$$
$$-2y = -x - 8$$
$$\frac{-2y}{-2} = \frac{-x - 8}{-2}$$
$$y = \frac{1}{2}x + 4$$

Graph both equations on the same graph.

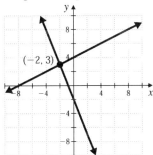

The solution is $(-2, 3)$.

35.
$$3x + 7y = 11$$
$$3(2y - 5) + 7y = 11$$
$$6y - 15 + 7y = 11$$
$$13y - 15 = 11$$
$$13y - 15 + 15 = 11 + 15$$
$$13y = 26$$
$$\frac{13y}{13} = \frac{26}{13}$$
$$y = 2$$
$$x = 2(2) - 5 = 4 - 5 = -1$$

The solution is $(-1, 2)$.

36.
$$2x - 5y = 16$$
$$\underline{4x + 3y = 6}$$
$$2(2x - 5y = 16)$$
$$\underline{4x + 3y = 6}$$
$$4x - 10y = 32$$
$$\underline{4x + 3y = 6}$$
$$-13y = 26$$
$$\frac{-13y}{-13} = \frac{26}{-13}$$
$$y = -2$$
$$2x - 5(-2) = 16$$
$$2x + 10 = 16$$
$$2x = 6$$
$$x = 3$$

The solution is $(3, -2)$.

37. a. Start by creating a scatter diagram of the data $f(t)$.

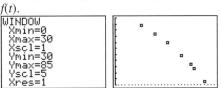

The data appear fairly linear so we use the regression feature of a graphing utility to obtain the line of best fit.

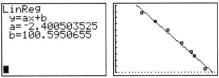

A reasonable model for the data is
$$f(t) = -2.4t + 100.6.$$

Create a scatter diagram of the data for $g(t)$.

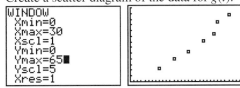

The data appear fairly linear so we use the regression feature of a graphing utility to obtain the line of best fit.

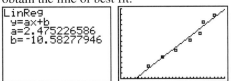

A reasonable model for the data is
$$g(t) = 2.48t - 10.58.$$

b. To estimate when the viewing shares will be equal, we solve the system

$$f(t) = -2.4t + 100.6$$

$$g(t) = 2.48t - 10.58$$

Substitute $2.48t - 10.58$ for $f(t)$ in the first equation and solve for t.

$$2.48t - 10.58 = -2.4t + 100.6$$

$$4.88t - 10.58 = 100.6$$

$$4.88t = 111.18$$

$$t = \frac{111.18}{4.88} \approx 22.783$$

Substitute 22.783 for t in the equation $g(t) = 2.48t - 10.58$ and solve for $g(t)$.

$$g(22.783) = 2.48(22.783) - 10.58 \approx 45.922$$

The approximate solution of the system is $(22.78, 45.9)$.

According to the models, the primetime household viewing shares for all broadcast stations and all ad-supported cable stations were equal (45.9%) in 2003.

c. We use our models to predict the viewing shares of broadcast stations and ad-supported cable stations in 2014 ($t = 34$). Broadcast stations:

$$f(34) = -2.4(34) + 100.6 = 19.0$$

Ad-supported stations:

$$g(34) = 2.48(34) - 10.58 = 73.74$$

The combined viewing share of broadcast stations and ad-supported stations is predicted to be $19.0 + 73.74 = 92.74$ percent. Therefore, the viewing share for PBS, pay cable, and other types of cable stations is predicted to be $100 - 92.74 = 7.26$ %.

38. a. Since a one-year-old Acura CL coupe depreciates about $1903 per year, we can model the situation by a linear equation. The slope is -1903 dollars per year. Since a one-year-old Acura CL coupe was worth $18,249 in 2007, the V-intercept is $(0,18249)$. So, a reasonable model is

$$f(t) = -1903t + 18,249.$$

By the same reasoning, the model for a Subura Legacy is $g(t) = -1225t + 14,564$.

b. $f(t) = -1903t + 18,249$

$g(t) = -1225t + 14,564$

Substitute $-1225t + 14,564$ for $f(t)$ in the first

equation and solve for t.

$$-1225t + 14,564 = -1903t + 18,249$$

$$678t + 14,564 = 18,249$$

$$678t = 3685$$

$$t = \frac{3685}{678} \approx 5.435$$

Substitute 5.435 for t in the equation $g(t) = -1225t + 14,564$ and solve for $g(t)$.

$g(5.435) = -1225(5.435) + 14,564 \approx 7906.13$.

The approximate solution to the system is $(5.44, 7906.13)$.

According to the models, the two cars will have the same value ($7906) in 2012.

39. $2x(0.072) + x(0.094) = 595$

$$0.144x + 0.094x = 595$$

$$0.238x = 595$$

$$x = 2500$$

The person will have to invest $5000 in a UBS Global Equity Y account and $2500 in a Fidelity Worldwide account.

40. $\quad x - 2y > 4 \qquad$ **s/b − 2**

$\quad x - 2y - x > 4 - x$

$\qquad -2y > 4 - x$

$\qquad \dfrac{-2y}{-2} < \dfrac{4 - x}{-2}$

$\qquad y < \dfrac{1}{2}x - 2$

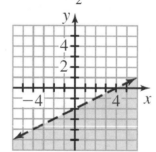

41. $y \geq \dfrac{1}{3}x - 2$

$y \leq -\dfrac{3}{4}x + 1$

First we sketch the graph of $y \geq \dfrac{1}{3}x - 2$ and the

graph of $y \leq -\dfrac{3}{4}x + 1$. The graph of $y \geq \dfrac{1}{3}x - 2$ is

the region above the line $y = \dfrac{1}{3}x - 2$ (graph the

line with a dashed line). The graph of $y \leq -\dfrac{3}{4}x + 1$

is the region below the line $y = -\dfrac{3}{4}x + 1$. The

graph of the solution set of the system is the
intersection of the graphs of the inequalities.

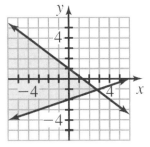

42. $3x - 7x^3 + 5x^2 - 9x + x^3$

$= -7x^3 + x^3 + 5x^2 + 3x - 9x$

$= -6x^3 + 5x^2 - 6x$

43. $\left(2a^2 + 3ab - 7b^2\right) - \left(5a^2 - 6ab + 3b^2\right)$

$= 2a^2 + 3ab - 7b^2 - 5a^2 + 6ab - 3b^2$

$= 2a^2 - 5a^2 + 3ab + 6ab - 7b^2 - 3b^2$

$= -3a^2 + 9ab - 10b^2$

44. $\left(f - g\right) = \left(3x^2 + 5x - 2\right) - \left(5x^2 - 2x - 3\right)$

$= 3x^2 + 5x - 2 - 5x^2 + 2x + 3$

$= 3x^2 - 5x^2 + 5x + 2x - 2 + 3$

$= -2x^2 + 7x + 1$

$\left(f - g\right)\left(-2\right) = -2\left(-2\right)^2 + 7\left(-2\right) + 1$

$= -8 - 14 + 1$

-21

45. $f(-3) = -2$

46. $x = -3$ and $x = -1$

47. $x = -2$

48. There is no solution.

49. $y = -3x^2$

First we list some solutions of $y = -3x^2$. Then, we
sketch a curve that contains the points
corresponding to the solutions.

x	y	(x, y)
-2	$-3(-2)^2 = -12$	$(-2, -12)$
-1	$-3(-1)^2 = -3$	$(-1, -3)$
0	$-3(0)^2 = 0$	$(0, 0)$
1	$-3(1)^2 = -3$	$(1, -3)$
2	$-3(2)^2 = -12$	$(2, -12)$

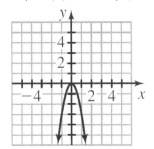

50. $\left(5r - 6t\right)\left(3r - 2t\right)$

$= 5r \cdot 3r + 5r \cdot \left(-2t\right) - 6t \cdot 3r - 6t \cdot \left(-2t\right)$

$= 15r^2 - 10rt - 18rt + 12t^2$

$= 15r^2 - 28rt + 12t^2$

51. $\left(2x^2 - x + 3\right)\left(4x^2 + 3x - 2\right)$

$= 2x^2 \cdot 4x^2 + 2x^2 \cdot 3x + 2x^2 \cdot -2 - x \cdot 4x^2 - x \cdot 3x$

$-x \cdot \left(-2\right) + 3 \cdot 4x^2 + 3 \cdot 3x + 3 \cdot \left(-2\right)$

$= 8x^4 + 6x^3 - 4x^2 - 4x^3 - 3x^2 + 2x + 12x^2 + 9x - 6$

$= 8x^4 + 2x^3 + 5x^2 + 11x - 6$

52.
$$(f \cdot g) = (4x+2)(3x^2 - 5x - 1)$$
$$= 4x \cdot 3x^2 + 4x \cdot (-5x) + 4x \cdot (-1)$$
$$+2 \cdot 3x^2 + 2 \cdot (-5x) + 2 \cdot -1$$
$$= 12x^3 - 20x^2 - 4x + 6x^2 - 10x - 2$$
$$= 12x^3 - 14x^2 - 14x - 2$$
$$(f \cdot g)(-1) = 12(-1)^3 - 14(-1)^2 - 14(-1) - 2$$
$$= -12 - 14 + 14 - 2$$
$$= -14$$

53.
$$(2x-5)^2 = (2x)^2 + 2 \cdot 2x \cdot (-5) + (-5)^2$$
$$= 4x^2 - 20x + 25$$

54.
$$(4a+3b)^2 = (4a)^2 + 2 \cdot 4a \cdot 3b + (3b)^2$$
$$= 16a^2 + 24ab + 9b^2$$

55.
$$f(x) = 2(x-3)^2 - 2$$
$$= 2(x^2 - 6x + 9) - 2$$
$$= 2x^2 - 12x + 18 - 2$$
$$= 2x^2 - 12x + 16$$

56.
$$(3x^2 - 8)(3x^2 + 8) = (3x^2)^2 - (8)^2$$
$$= 9x^4 - 64$$

57. $2x^4 (3x^3)^4 = 2x^4 \cdot 81x^{12} = 162x^{16}$

58. $\left(\dfrac{3x^3}{y^7 w^4}\right)^3 = \dfrac{27x^9}{y^{21} w^{12}}$

59. $\dfrac{(2x^4 y^2)^4}{x^9 y^5} = \dfrac{16x^{16} y^8}{x^9 y^5} = 16x^{16-9} y^{8-5} = 16x^7 y^3$

60. $w^2 + 5w - 14 = (w+7)(w-2)$

61.
$$4m^2 - 49n^2 = (2m)^2 - (7n)^2$$
$$= (2m+7n)(2m-7n)$$

62. $a^2 - 3ab - 40b^2 = (a-8b)(a+5b)$

63.
$$3x^4 - 33x^3 y + 54x^2 y^2$$
$$= 3x^2 (x^2 - 11xy + 18y^2)$$
$$= 3x^2 (x-9y)(x-2y)$$

64.
$$8x^3 - 27 = (2x)^3 - (3)^3$$
$$= (2x-3)\left((2x)^2 + 2x \cdot 3 + (3)^2\right)$$
$$= (2x-3)(4x^2 + 6x + 9)$$

65.
$$x^2 = 2x + 35$$
$$x^2 - 2x - 35 = 0$$
$$(x-7)(x+5) = 0$$
$$x = 7 \text{ or } x = -5$$

66.
$$5x^2 + 18x - 8 = 0$$
$$(5x-2)(x+4) = 0$$
$$x = \frac{2}{5} \text{ or } x = -4$$

67.
$$4r^3 - 9r = 18 - 8r^2$$
$$4r^3 + 8r^2 - 9r - 18 = 0$$
$$4r^2(r+2) - 9(r+2) = 0$$
$$(4r^2 - 9)(r+2) = 0$$
$$(2r-3)(2r+3)(r+2) = 0$$
$$r = \frac{3}{2}, r = -\frac{3}{2} \text{ or } r = -2$$

68.
$$x^2 + 4x - 21 = 0$$
$$(x+7)(x-3) = 0$$
$$x = -7 \text{ or } x = 3$$
The *x*-intercepts are (–7, 0) and (3, 0).

69.
$$t^2 - 2t + 8 = 32$$
$$t^2 - 2t - 24 = 0$$
$$(t-6)(t+4) = 0$$
$$t = 6 \text{ or } t = -4$$
The model predicts that the company's profit was $32 million in 2001 and will be again in 2011.

70. Let L = the length of the rug (in feet) and
W = the width (in feet).

Since the length is 8 feet more than the width, our
first equation is $L = 8 + W$. Because the area is

$A = LW$

$84 = LW$

we get the following system:

$L = 8 + W$

$84 = LW$

Substitute $8 + W$ for L in the second equation and
solve for W.

$84 = (8 + W)W$

$84 = 8W + W^2$

$0 = W^2 + 8W - 84$

$0 = (W - 6)(W + 14)$

$W - 6 = 0$ or $W + 14 = 0$

$W = 6$ $W = -14$

The width must be positive, so discard the negative
solution. Substitute 6 for W in the equation
$L = 8 + W$ and solve for L.

$L = 8 + 6 = 14$

The rug has a length of 14 feet and a width of 6
feet.

71. a.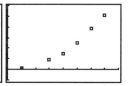

The curvature in the graph suggests that the
data would be better fit by a quadratic model
since the average rate of change is not constant.

b.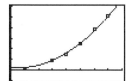

The model appears to fit the data well.

c. For 2015, we have $t = 20$.

$$n = \frac{7}{4}(20)^2 - 2(20) + 4 = 664$$

The model predicts that there will be 664
thousand Edison students in 2015.

d.

$$7 = \frac{7}{4}t^2 - 2t + 4$$

$$0 = \frac{7}{4}t^2 - 2t - 3$$

$$4 \cdot 0 = 4\left(\frac{7}{4}t^2 - 2t - 3\right)$$

$$0 = 7t^2 - 8t - 12$$

$$0 = (7t + 6)(t - 2)$$

$$t - 2 = 0 \quad \text{or} \quad 7t + 6 = 0$$

$$t = 2 \qquad\qquad t = -\frac{6}{7} \approx -0.86$$

According to the model, there were 7 thousand
Edison students in 1994 and 1997. Model
breakdown has likely occurred for the 1994
estimate.

Chapter 9
Quadratic Functions

Homework 9.1

1. Vertex: (0, 0)

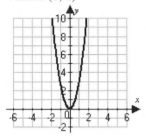

3. Vertex: (0, 0)

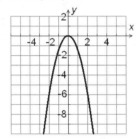

5. Vertex: (0, 5)

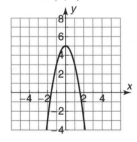

7. Vertex: (1, 0)

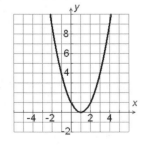

9. Vertex: (–2, 0)

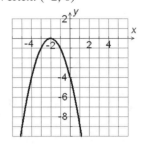

11. Vertex: (–2, –6)

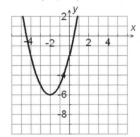

13. Vertex: (1, 3)

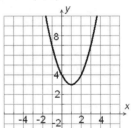

15. Vertex: (–6, –6)

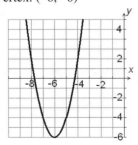

17. Vertex: (6, −2)

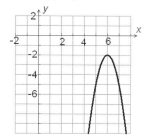

19. Vertex: (2, 3)

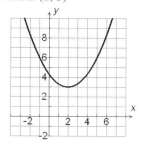

21.

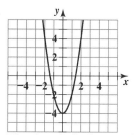

The domain is the set of all real numbers. Since (0, −4) is the minimum point, the range is the set of numbers where $y \geq -4$.

23.

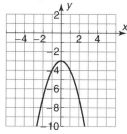

The domain is the set of all real numbers. Since (0, −3) is the maximum point, the range is the set of numbers where $y \leq -3$.

25.

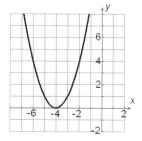

The domain is the set of all real numbers. Since (−4, 0) is the minimum point, the range is the set of numbers where $y \geq 0$.

27.

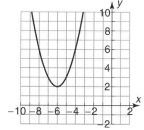

The domain is the set of all real numbers. Since (−6, 2) is the minimum point, the range is the set of numbers where $y \geq 2$.

29.

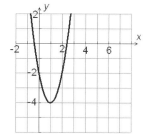

The domain is the set of all real numbers. Since (1, −4) is the minimum point, the range is the set of numbers where $y \geq -4$.

31.

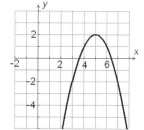

The domain is the set of all real numbers. Since (5, 2) is the maximum point, the range is the set of numbers where $y \leq 2$.

33. a. First make a scattergram of the data.

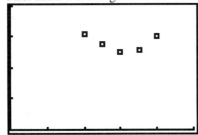

Use the point (6, 2.5) as the vertex.
$$f(t) = a(t-6)^2 + 2.5$$
Now use the point (4, 3.1) to solve for a.
$$3.1 = a((4)-6)^2 + 2.5$$
$$3.1 = a(-2)^2 + 2.5$$
$$3.1 = 4a + 2.5$$
$$0.6 = 4a$$
$$0.15 = a$$
So the equation of f in vertex form is:
$$f(t) = 0.15(t-6)^2 + 2.5$$

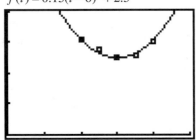

The graph of f is very close to the data points.

b. The vertex of the model is (6, 2.5). The model estimates that the fewest number of insurance claims, 2.5 million, occurred during the year 2006.

c. To find the n-intercept of the model, let $t = 0$ and solve for n.
$$n - f(t) = 0.15(0-6)^2 + 2.5$$
$$n = 0.15(-6)^2 + 2.5$$
$$n = 0.15(36) + 2.5$$
$$n = 5.4 + 2.5$$
$$n = 7.9$$
The n-intercept is (0, 7.9). The model estimates that the number of unemployment insurance claims in the year 2000 was 7.9 million.

d. To find the number of unemployment insurance claims in 2014, let $t = 14$ and solve for $f(14)$.
$$f(14) = 0.15((14)-6)^2 + 2.5$$
$$= 0.15(8)^2 + 2.5$$
$$= 0.15(64) + 2.5$$
$$= 9.6 + 2.5$$
$$= 12.1$$
The model predicts 12.1 million unemployment insurance claims will occur in 2014.

35. a. First make a scattergram of the data.

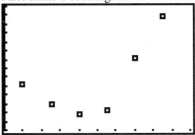

Use the point (8, 297) as the vertex.
$$f(t) = a(t-8)^2 + 297$$
Now use the point (17, 572) to solve for a.
$$572 = a((17)-8)^2 + 297$$
$$572 = a(9)^2 + 297$$
$$572 = 81a + 297$$
$$275 = 81a$$
$$3.40 \approx a$$
So the equation of f in vertex form is:
$$f(t) = 3.40(t-8)^2 + 297$$

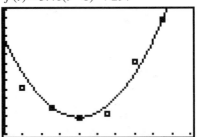

The graph of f is fairly close to the data points.

b. The vertex of the model is (8, 297). The model predicts that in 1998 the U.S. Department of Defense spent the least, at $297 billion.

c. To find the U.S. Department of Defense spending in 2013, let $t = 23$ and solve for f.

$$f(23) = 3.40((23) - 8)^2 + 297$$
$$= 3.40(15)^2 + 297$$
$$= 3.40(225) + 297$$
$$= 765 + 297$$
$$= 1062$$

This model predicts that in 2013 the U.S. Department of Defense will spend about $1062 billion, or about $1.06 trillion.

37. a.

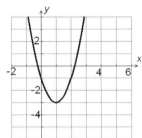

b.

x	y
-2	15
-1	5
0	-1
1	-3
2	-1

c. For each input-output pair, the output variable is 3 less than twice the square of the difference of the input variable and 1.

39. a.

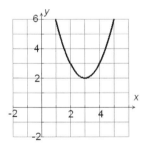

b.
$$3 = (x - 3)^2 + 2$$
$$1 = (x - 3)^2$$
$$\pm 1 = x - 3$$
$$3 \pm 1 = x$$
$$x = 4 \text{ or } x = 2$$

c.
$$2 = (x - 3)^2 + 2$$
$$0 = (x - 3)^2$$
$$0 = x - 3$$
$$3 = x$$

d.
$$1 = (x - 3)^2 + 2$$
$$-1 = (x - 3)^2$$

The next step is to take the square root of both sides. However, this will require taking the square root of -1, which is not a valid step. There is no value of x such that $f(x) = 1$.

41. Answers my vary: Example:
$$y = a(x + 3)^2 + 4$$
where a is any negative number.

43. a. Because the parabola is face up, and the vertex is in the 3rd quadrant: $a > 0$, $h < 0$, $k < 0$.

b. Because the parabola is face down, and the vertex is in the 2nd quadrant: $a < 0$, $h < 0$, $k > 0$.

c. Because the parabola is face up, and the vertex is on the positive x-axis: $a > 0$, $h > 0$, $k = 0$.

d. Because the parabola is face down, and the vertex is on the negative y-axis: $a < 0$, $h = 0$, $k < 0$.

45. Answers may vary. Example:
$$y = a(x + 5)^2 + 3$$
where $a \neq 0$

47. The graph shows that the vertex is $(5, -6)$, so
$$f(x) = a(x - 5)^2 - 6.$$

To solve for a, substitute the point $(1, 4)$ into the equation for f.
$$4 = a((1) - 5)^2 - 6$$
$$4 = a(-4)^2 - 6$$
$$4 = 16a - 6$$
$$10 = 16a$$
$$\frac{5}{8} = a$$

So the equation is:
$$f(x) = \frac{5}{8}(x - 5)^2 - 6$$

49. The value of a for the function f is the opposite of the value of a for the function g since g has a maximum point and f has a minimum point and we can assume that the graphs of f and g have the same "shape". Since the vertex (h, k) of g is $(-7, 3.71)$ and $a = -2.1$, an equation for g is:

$$g(x) = -2.1(x + 7)^2 + 3.71$$

51. It is possible. Example: $y = x^2 + 2$

53. It is possible. Example: $y = x^2 - 2$

55. Both equations have the same vertex (2, 5). From the graph notice this is the only point that lies on both graphs.

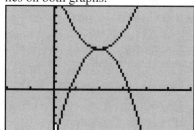

57. a.

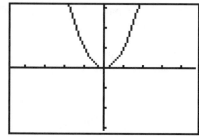

b.

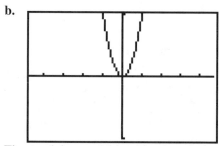

The graph in part (a) is wider than the graph in part (b).

c.

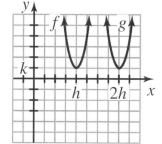

The graph in part (c) is much wider than the graphs in parts (a) and (b).

d. Answers may vary.

59. No, the student is not correct. Moving $y = x^2$ to the left by 4 units would result in $y = (x + 4)^2$. The equation $y = (x - 4)^2$ would move $y = x^2$ to the right by 4 units.

61. Adjust the WINDOW settings. Make your x-min and x-max much larger.

63. a.

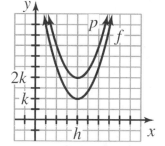

b.

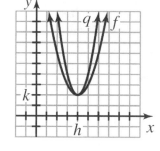

c.

d.

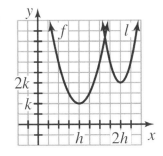

65. Written answers will vary. Example:
To gather some idea of what the parabola will look like, remember that if $a > 0$, the parabola will open upward, whereas if $a < 0$, it will open downward. If $k > 0$, the vertex is always above the x-axis; if $k < 0$, the vertex is always below the x-axis; if $k = 0$, the vertex is on the x-axis. Likewise, if $h > 0$, the vertex is always to the right of the y-axis; if $h < 0$, the vertex is always to the left of the y-axis; if $h = 0$, the vertex is on the y-axis.
To draw the parabola, start at the vertex (h, k). Next make a table of the function, starting, for instance, with $x = h - 5$, up through $x = h + 5$. Plot these points on the graph. Connect the points in a parabola.

67. $f(x) = -2x - 1$

The slope is $m = -2$, and the y-intercept is $(0, -1)$. We first plot $(0, -1)$. From this point we move 1 unit to the right and 2 units down, where we plot the point $(1, -3)$. We then sketch the line that contains these two points.

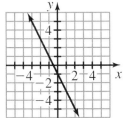

69. $f(x) = -2x^2 - 1$

First, we list some solutions in the table. Then we sketch a curve that contains the points corresponding to the solutions.

x	y
-3	$-2(-3)^2 - 1 = -19$
-2	$-2(-2)^2 - 1 = -9$
-1	$-2(-1)^2 - 1 = -3$
0	$-2(0)^2 - 1 = -1$
1	$-2(1)^2 - 1 = -3$
2	$-2(2)^2 - 1 = -9$
3	$-2(3)^2 - 1 = -19$

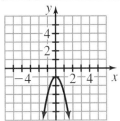

71. a. $y = 2x$

The slope is $m = 2$, and the y-intercept is $(0, 0)$. We first plot $(0, 0)$. From this point we move 1 unit to the right and 2 units up, where we plot the point $(1, 2)$. We then sketch the line that contains these two points.

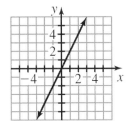

b. $y = x^2$

First, we list some solutions in the table. Then we sketch a curve that contains the points corresponding to the solutions.

x	y
-3	$(-3)^2 = 9$
-2	$(-2)^2 = 4$
-1	$(-1)^2 = 1$
0	$(0)^2 = 0$
1	$(1)^2 = 1$
2	$(2)^2 = 4$
3	$(3)^2 = 9$

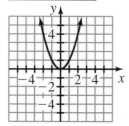

c. The y-intercept is $(0, 0)$ for both curves.

d. The curve $y = x^2$ is steeper. Explanations will vary.

73. $8(3x - 2) = 4(x - 5)$

$24x - 16 = 4x - 20$

$20x - 16 = -20$

$20x = -4$

$x = \dfrac{-4}{20} = -\dfrac{1}{5}$

This is a linear equation in one variable.

75. $8(3x - 2) - 4(x - 5)$

$= 24x - 16 - 4x + 20$

$= 20x + 4$

This is a linear polynomial in one variable.

77. $8(3x - 2)(x - 5) = 8\left(3x^2 - 17x + 10\right)$

$= 24x^2 - 136x + 80$

This is a quadratic polynomial in one variable.

Homework 9.2

1. Since $\dfrac{0 + 10}{2} = 5$, the x-coordinate of the vertex must be 5.

3. Since the points have the same y-coordinate, they are symmetric on the parabola.

Since $\dfrac{0 + 6}{2} = 3$, the x-coordinate of the vertex must be 3.

5. Since the points have the same y-coordinate, they are symmetric on the parabola.

Since $\dfrac{0 + (-7)}{2} = -3.5$, the x-coordinate of the vertex must be -3.5.

7. Since the points have the same y-coordinate, they are symmetric on the parabola.

Since $\dfrac{0 + 7.29}{2} \approx 3.65$, the x-coordinate of the vertex must be 3.65.

9. A symmetric point to the y-intercept has a value of x that is 2 units to the right of $x = 2$ (value of x at the vertex). The value of y is the same as that of the y-intercept, so another point on the parabola is $(4, 9)$.

11. First, find the *y*-intercept by substituting 0 for *x* in the function: $y = 0^2 - 6(0) + 7 = 7$

The *y*-intercept is $(0, 7)$. Next find the symmetric point to $(0, 7)$. Substitute 7 for *y* in the function and solve for *x*:

$7 = x^2 - 6x + 7$

$0 = x^2 - 6x$

$0 = x(x - 6)$

$x = 0$ or $x - 6 = 0$

$x = 0$ or $x = 6$

Therefore, the symmetric points are $(0, 7)$ and $(6, 7)$. Since $\dfrac{0 + 6}{2} = 3$, the *x*-coordinate of the vertex is 3. To find the *y*-coordinate of the vertex, substitute 3 for *x* and solve for *y*:

$y = 3^2 - 6(3) + 7 = -2$. So the vertex is $(3, -2)$.

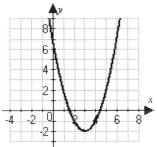

13. First, find the *y*-intercept by substituting 0 for *x* in the function:

$y = 0^2 + 8(0) + 9 = 9$

The *y*-intercept is $(0, 9)$. Next find the symmetric point to $(0, 9)$. Substitute 9 for *y* in the function and solve for *x*:

$9 = x^2 + 8x + 9$

$0 = x^2 + 8x$

$0 = x(x + 8)$

$x = 0$ or $x + 8 = 0$

$x = 0$ or $x = -8$

Therefore, the symmetric points are $(0, 9)$ and $(-8, 9)$. Since $\dfrac{0 + (-8)}{2} = -4$, the *x*-coordinate of the vertex is –4. To find the *y*-coordinate of the vertex, substitute –4 for *x* and solve for *y*:

$y = (-4)^2 + 8(-4) + 9 = -7$. So the vertex is

$(-4, -7)$.

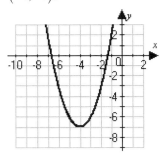

15. First, find the *y*-intercept by substituting 0 for *x* in the function:

$y = -(0)^2 + 8(0) - 10 = -10$

The *y*-intercept is $(0, -10)$. Next find the symmetric point to $(0, -10)$. Substitute –10 for *y* in the function and solve for *x*:

$-10 = -x^2 + 8x - 10$

$0 = -x^2 + 8x$

$0 = -x(x - 8)$

$-x = 0$ or $x - 8 = 0$

$x = 0$ or $x = 8$

Therefore, the symmetric points are $(0, -10)$ and $(8, -10)$. Since $\dfrac{0 + 8}{2} = 4$, the *x*-coordinate of the vertex is 4. To find the *y*-coordinate of the vertex, substitute 4 for *x* and solve for *y*:

$y = -(4)^2 + 8(4) - 10 = 6$. So the vertex is

$(4, 6)$.

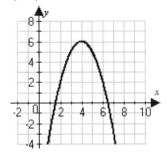

17. First, find the *y*-intercept by substituting 0 for *x* in the function:

$$y = 3(0)^2 + 6(0) - 4 = -4$$

The *y*-intercept is $(0,-4)$. Next find the symmetric point to $(0,-4)$. Substitute –4 for *y* in the function and solve for *x*:

$$-4 = 3x^2 + 6x - 4$$
$$0 = 3x^2 + 6x$$
$$0 = 3x(x+2)$$
$$3x = 0 \text{ or } x + 2 = 0$$
$$x = 0 \text{ or } x = -2$$

Therefore, the symmetric points are $(0,-4)$ and $(-2,-4)$. Since $\dfrac{0+(-2)}{2} = -1$, the *x*-coordinate of the vertex is –1. To find the *y*-coordinate of the vertex, substitute –1 for *x* and solve for *y*:

$$y = 3(-1)^2 + 6(-1) - 4 = -7$$. So the vertex is $(-1,-7)$.

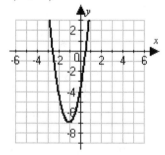

19. First, find the *y*-intercept by substituting 0 for *x* in the function:

$$y = -3(0)^2 + 12(0) - 5 = -5$$

The *y*-intercept is $(0,-5)$. Next find the symmetric point to $(0,-5)$. Substitute -5 for *y* in the function and solve for *x*:

$$-5 = -3x^2 + 12x - 5$$
$$0 = -3x^2 + 12x$$
$$0 = -3x(x-4)$$
$$-3x = 0 \text{ or } x - 4 = 0$$
$$x = 0 \text{ or } x = 4$$

Therefore, the symmetric points are $(0,-5)$ and $(4,-5)$. Since $\dfrac{0+4}{2} = 2$, the *x*-coordinate of the vertex is 2. To find the *y*-coordinate of the vertex, substitute 2 for *x* and solve for *y*:

$$y = -3(2)^2 + 12(2) - 5 = 7$$. So the vertex is $(2,7)$.

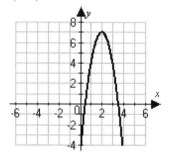

21. First, find the *y*-intercept by substituting 0 for *x* in the function:

$$y = -4(0)^2 - 9(0) - 5 = -5$$

The *y*-intercept is $(0,-5)$. Next find the symmetric point to $(0,-5)$. Substitute -5 for *y* in the function and solve for *x*:

$$-5 = -4x^2 - 9x - 5$$
$$0 = -4x^2 - 9x$$
$$0 = -x(4x+9)$$
$$-x = 0 \text{ or } 4x + 9 = 0$$
$$x = 0 \text{ or } 4x = -9$$
$$x = 0 \text{ or } x = -\frac{9}{4} = -2.25$$

Therefore, the symmetric points are $(0,-5)$ and $(-2.25,-5)$. Since $\dfrac{0+(-2.25)}{2} \approx -1.13$, the *x*-coordinate of the vertex is –1.13. To find the *y*-coordinate of the vertex, substitute –1.13 for *x* and solve for *y*:

$$y = -4(-1.13)^2 - 9(-1.13) - 5 \approx 0.06$$. So the vertex is $(-1.13, 0.06)$.

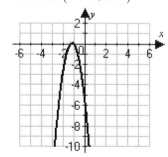

23. First, find the *y*-intercept by substituting 0 for *x* in the function:

$$y = 2(0)^2 - 7(0) + 7 = 7$$

The *y*-intercept is $(0, 7)$. Next find the symmetric point to $(0, 7)$. Substitute 7 for *y* in the function and solve for *x*:

$$7 = 2x^2 - 7x + 7$$
$$0 = 2x^2 - 7x$$
$$0 = x(2x - 7)$$
$$x = 0 \text{ or } 2x - 7 = 0$$
$$x = 0 \text{ or } 2x = 7$$
$$x = 0 \text{ or } x = \frac{7}{2} = 3.5$$

Therefore, the symmetric points are $(0, 7)$ and $(3.5, 7)$. Since $\frac{0 + 3.5}{2} = 1.75$, the *x*-coordinate of the vertex is 1.75. To find the *y*-coordinate of the vertex, substitute 1.75 for *x* and solve for *y*. So the vertex is $(1.75, 0.88)$.

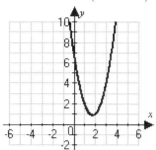

25. First, change the equation to standard form:

$$4x^2 - y + 6 = 8x$$
$$y = 4x^2 - 8x + 6$$

Next, find the *y*-intercept by substituting 0 for *x* in the function:

$$y = 4(0)^2 - 8(0) + 6 = 6$$

The *y*-intercept is $(0, 6)$. Next find the symmetric point to $(0, 6)$. Substitute 6 for *y* in the function and solve for *x*:

$$6 = 4x^2 - 8x + 6$$
$$0 = 4x^2 - 8x$$
$$0 = 4x(x - 2)$$
$$4x = 0 \text{ or } x - 2 = 0$$
$$x = 0 \text{ or } x = 2$$

Therefore, the symmetric points are $(0, 6)$ and

$(2, 6)$. Since $\frac{0 + 2}{2} = 1$, the *x*-coordinate of the vertex is 1. To find the *y*-coordinate of the vertex, substitute 1 for *x* and solve for *y*:

$$y = 4(1)^2 - 8(1) + 6 = 2. \text{ So the vertex is } (1, 2).$$

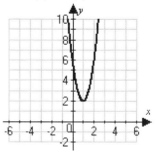

27. First, find the *y*-intercept by substituting 0 for *x* in the function:

$$y = 2.8(0)^2 - 8.7(0) + 4 = 4$$

The *y*-intercept is $(0, 4)$. Next find the symmetric point to $(0, 4)$. Substitute the 4 for *y* in the function and solve for *x*:

$$4 = 2.8x^2 - 8.7x + 4$$
$$0 = 2.8x^2 - 8.7x$$
$$0 = x(2.8x - 8.7)$$
$$x = 0 \text{ or } 2.8x - 8.7 = 0$$
$$x = 0 \text{ or } 2.8x = 8.7$$
$$x = 0 \text{ or } x = \frac{8.7}{2.8} \approx 3.11$$

Therefore, the symmetric points are $(0, 4)$ and $(3.11, 4)$. Since $\frac{0 + 3.11}{2} \approx 1.56$, the *x*-coordinate of the vertex is 1.56. To find the *y*-coordinate of the vertex, substitute 1.56 for *x* and solve for *y*:

$$y = 2.8(1.56)^2 - 8.7(1.56) + 4 \approx -2.76.$$

So the vertex is $(1.56, -2.76)$.

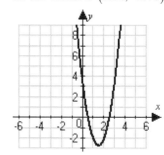

29. First, find the *y*-intercept by substituting 0 for *x* in the function:

$$y = 3.9(0)^2 + 6.9(0) - 3.4 = -3.4$$

The *y*-intercept is $(0, -3.4)$. Next find the symmetric point to $(0, -3.4)$. Substitute -3.4 for *y* in the function and solve for *x*:

$$-3.4 = 3.9x^2 + 6.9x - 3.4$$
$$0 = 3.9x^2 + 6.9x$$
$$0 = x(3.9x + 6.9)$$
$$x = 0 \text{ or } 3.9x + 6.9 = 0$$
$$x = 0 \text{ or } 3.9x = -6.9$$
$$x = 0 \text{ or } x = -\frac{6.9}{3.9} \approx -1.77$$

Therefore, the symmetric points are $(0, -3.4)$ and $(-1.77, -3.4)$. Since $\dfrac{0 + (-1.77)}{2} \approx -0.88$, the *x*-coordinate of the vertex is -0.88. To find the *y*-coordinate of the vertex, substitute -0.88 for *x* and solve for *y*:

$$y = 3.9(-0.88)^2 + 6.9(-0.88) - 3.4 \approx -6.45.$$

So the vertex is $(-0.88, -6.45)$.

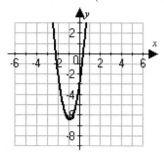

31. First, change the equation to standard form:

$$3.6y - 26.3x = 8.3x^2 - 7.1$$
$$3.6y = 8.3x^2 + 26.3x - 7.1$$
$$y = \frac{8.3x^2 + 26.3x - 7.1}{3.6}$$
$$y \approx 2.31x^2 + 7.31x - 1.97$$

Next, find the *y*-intercept by substituting 0 for *x* in the function:

$$y = 2.31(0)^2 + 7.31(0) - 1.97 = -1.97$$

The *y*-intercept is $(0, -1.97)$. Next find the symmetric point to $(0, -1.97)$. Substitute -1.97 for *y* in the function and solve for *x*:

$$-1.97 = 2.31x^2 + 7.31x - 1.97$$
$$0 = 2.31x^2 + 7.31x$$
$$0 = x(2.31x + 7.31)$$
$$x = 0 \text{ or } 2.31x + 7.31 = 0$$
$$x = 0 \text{ or } 2.31x = -7.31$$
$$x = 0 \text{ or } x = -\frac{7.31}{2.31} \approx -3.16$$

Therefore, the symmetric points are $(0, -1.97)$ and $(-3.16, -1.97)$. Since $\dfrac{0 + (-3.16)}{2} = -1.58$, the *x*-coordinate of the vertex is -1.58. To find the *y*-coordinate of the vertex, substitute -1.58 for *x* and solve for *y*:

$$y = 2.31(-1.58)^2 + 7.31(-1.58) - 1.97 \approx -7.75.$$

So the vertex is $(-1.58, -7.75)$.

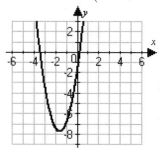

33. Since the *x*-intercepts are symmetric points and $\dfrac{2 + 6}{2} = 4$, the *x*-coordinate of the vertex is 4.

35. Since the *x*-intercepts are symmetric points and $\dfrac{-9 + 4}{2} = -\dfrac{5}{2}$, the *x*-coordinate of the vertex is $-\dfrac{5}{2}$.

37. To find the *x*-intercepts, let $y = 0$ and solve for *x*:

$$0 = 5x^2 - 10x$$
$$0 = 5x(x - 2)$$
$$5x = 0 \text{ or } x - 2 = 0$$
$$x = 0 \text{ or } x = 2$$

The *x*-intercepts are $(0, 0)$ and $(2, 0)$. The *y*-intercept is, therefore, $(0, 0)$. Since the *x*-intercepts are symmetric points and $\dfrac{0 + 2}{2} = 1$, the *x*-coordinate of the vertex is 1. Substitute 1 for x in the function and solve for y:

$y = 5(1)^2 - 10(1) = -5$. So, the vertex is $(1, -5)$.

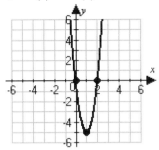

39. To find the x-intercepts, let $y = 0$ and solve for

x:

$0 = -2x^2 + 6x$

$0 = 2x(-x + 3)$

$2x = 0$ or $-x + 3 = 0$

$x = 0$ or $x = 3$

The x-intercepts are $(0, 0)$ and $(3, 0)$. The y-

intercept is, therefore, $(0, 0)$. Since the x-

intercepts are symmetric points and $\dfrac{0+3}{2} = 1.5$,

the x-coordinate of the vertex is 1.5. Substitute

1.5 for x in the function and solve for y:

$y = -2(1.5)^2 + 6(1.5) = 4.5$. So, the vertex is

$(1.5, 4.5)$.

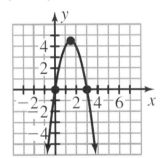

41. To find the x-intercepts, let $y = 0$ and solve for

x:

$0 = x^2 - 10x + 24$

$0 = (x - 6)(x - 4)$

$x - 6 = 0$ or $x - 4 = 0$

$x = 6$ or $x = 4$

The x-intercepts are $(6, 0)$ and $(4, 0)$. To find

the y-intercept, let $x = 0$ and solve for y:

$y = (0)^2 - 10(0) + 24 = 24$. The y-intercept is

$(0, 24)$. Since the x-intercepts are symmetric

points and $\dfrac{6+4}{2} = 5$, the x-coordinate of the

vertex is 5. Substitute 5 for x in the function and

solve for y: $y = (5)^2 - 10(5) + 24 = -1$. So, the

vertex is $(5, -1)$.

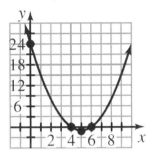

43. To find the x-intercepts, let $y = 0$ and solve for

x:

$0 = x^2 - 8x + 7$

$0 = (x - 7)(x - 1)$

$x - 7 = 0$ or $x - 1 = 0$

$x = 7$ or $x = 1$

The x-intercepts are $(7, 0)$ and $(1, 0)$. To find

the y-intercept, let $x = 0$ and solve for y:

$y = (0)^2 - 8(0) + 7 = 7$. The y-intercept is

$(0, 7)$. Since the x-intercepts are symmetric

points and $\dfrac{7+1}{2} = 4$, the x-coordinate of the

vertex is 4. Substitute 4 for x in the function and

solve for y: $y = (4)^2 - 8(4) + 7 = -9$. So, the

vertex is $(4, -9)$.

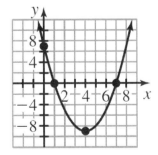

45. To find the *x*-intercepts, let $y = 0$ and solve for *x*:

$$0 = x^2 - 9$$
$$0 = (x-3)(x+3)$$
$$x - 3 = 0 \text{ or } x + 3 = 0$$
$$x = 3 \text{ or } x = -3$$

The *x*-intercepts are $(3, 0)$ and $(-3, 0)$. To find the *y*-intercept, let $x = 0$ and solve for *y*:
$y = (0)^2 - 9 = -9$. The *y*-intercept is $(0, -9)$.

Since the *x*-intercepts are symmetric points and $\dfrac{3 + (-3)}{2} = 0$, the *x*-coordinate of the vertex is 0.

So the vertex is $(0, -9)$.

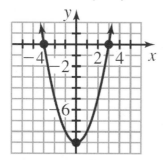

47. a. When the batter hits the ball, $t = 0$.
$$h(0) = -16(0)^2 + 140(0) + 3$$
$$= 0 + 0 + 3$$
$$= 3 \text{ feet}$$

b. The maximum height corresponds to the vertex of the graph.
$$t = -\frac{140}{2(-16)}$$
$$= \frac{-140}{-32}$$
$$= 4.375$$
$$h(4.375) = -16(4.375)^2 + 140(4.375) + 3$$
$$= -16(19.14) + 612.5 + 3$$
$$= -306.25 + 615.5$$
$$= 309.25$$

So after 4.375 seconds the ball is at its maximum height of 309.25 feet.

c.

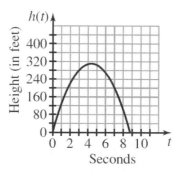

49. a.

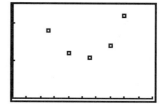

The function is a quadratic function, as the data appear to fit a quadratic function best.

b.

Yes, the function approximates the data very closely.

c. For 2013, $t = 23$.
$$f(23) = 0.031(23)^2 - 0.626(23) + 4.18$$
$$= 6.181$$
The model predicts that about 6.2 million people will move to another state in 2013.

d. The least number of people moved to another state at the $f(t)$ value of the vertex.
$$t = \frac{-b}{2a}$$
$$t = -\frac{-0.626}{2(0.031)}$$
$$\approx 10.10$$
$$f(10.10) = 0.031(10.10)^2 - 0.626(10.10) + 4.18$$
$$\approx 1.02$$
The model estimates that the least number of people that moved to another state was about 1.0 million, and that this happened in 2000.

51. a.

The function is a quadratic function, as the data appear to fit a quadratic function best.

b.

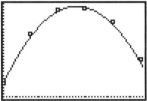

Yes, the function approximates the data very closely.

c. $f(18) = -0.035(18)^2 + 3.25(18) - 26.34$

$= 20.82$

The average annual expenditure of 18-year-old Americans is $20.8 thousand.

d. The highest average annual expenditure corresponds with the vertex of the graph.

$t = -\dfrac{3.25}{2(-0.035)}$

$= \dfrac{-3.25}{-0.07}$

≈ 46.4

$f(46.4) = -0.035(46.4)^2 + 3.25(46.4) - 26.34$

≈ 49.1

The highest average annual expenditure is of 46-year-old Americans at $49.1 thousand.

53. a.

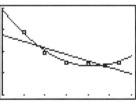

The quadratic function models the data the best.

b.

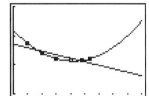

The linear function predicts the lowest student-to-faculty ratios.

c. $15.9 = 0.0119t^2 - 0.5t + 15.9$

$0 = 0.0119t^2 - 0.5t$

$0 = t(0.0119t - 0.5)$

$t = 0$ or $0 = 0.0119t - 0.5$

$0.5 = 0.0119t$

$42 \approx t$

According to the model, during the year 2022, the student-to-faculty ratio will be 15.9.

d. The lowest student-to-faculty ratio corresponds with the vertex of the graph.

$t = -\dfrac{-0.5}{2(0.0119)}$

≈ 21

$f(21) = 0.0119(21)^2 - 0.5(21) + 15.9$

≈ 10.65

The student-to-faculty ratio was at its lowest in 2001 at 10.6.

55. Let w be the width of the fenced in area, l be the length of the fenced in area, and A be the fenced in area. The perimeter and area of the fencing and fenced in area is given by:

$80 = 2w + 2l$

$A = wl$

Solving the first equation for l.

$80 = 2w + 2l$

$80 - 2w = 2l$

$40 - w = l$

Substituting this for l in the area equation:

$A = w(40 - w)$

$= 40w - w^2$

Find the maximum point of the parabola by finding the vertex.

$$w = -\frac{40}{2(-1)}$$

$$= \frac{-40}{-2}$$

$$= 20$$

So the width is 20 feet.

$$A = 40(20) - (20)^2$$

$$= 800 - 400$$

$$= 400$$

The maximum area is 400 square feet.

$$80 = 2(20) + 2l$$

$$80 = 40 + 2l$$

$$40 = 2l$$

$$20 = l$$

The length is 20 feet.

57. Let w be the width of the fenced in area, l be the length of the fenced in area, and A be the fenced in area. The perimeter and area of the fencing and fenced in area is given by:

$$400 = 2w + l$$

$$A = wl$$

Solving the first equation for l.

$$400 = 2w + l$$

$$400 - 2w = l$$

Substituting this for l in the area equation:

$$A = w(400 - 2w)$$

$$= 400w - 2w^2$$

Find the maximum point of the parabola by finding the vertex.

$$w = -\frac{400}{2(-2)}$$

$$= \frac{-400}{-4}$$

$$= 100$$

So the width is 100 feet.

$$A = 400(100) - 2(100)^2$$

$$= 40,000 - 20,000$$

$$= 20,000$$

The maximum area is 20,000 square feet.

$$400 = 2(100) + l$$

$$400 = 200 + l$$

$$200 = l$$

The length is 200 feet.

59. a.

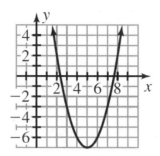

b. Answers may vary. Example:

x	y
3	-3
4	-6
5	-7
6	-6
7	-3

c. For each input-output pair, the output variable is 18 more than the difference between the square of the input and 10 times the input.

61. $f(-5) = -1$

63. When $x = -3, f(x) = 3$.

65. When $x = -2$ or $-4, f(x) = 2$.

67. The maximum value of f is 3.

69. a. $y = (0)^2 + 4(0) - 12$

$$y = -12$$

Solve for x when $y = -12$.

$$-12 = x^2 + 4x - 12$$

$$0 = x^2 + 4x$$

$$0 = x(x + 4)$$

$$0 = x \quad \text{or} \quad 0 = x + 4$$

$$-4 = x$$

Take the average of the y-intercept and its symmetric point:

$$\frac{0 + (-4)}{2} = \frac{-4}{2} = -2$$

The x-coordinate of the vertex is -2.

b.

$$0 = x^2 + 4x - 12$$

$$0 = (x+6)(x-2)$$

$$0 = x + 6 \quad \text{or} \quad 0 = x - 2$$

$$-6 = x \qquad\qquad 2 = x$$

Taking the average of the *x*-intercepts:

$$\frac{(-6)+2}{2} = \frac{-4}{2} = -2$$

The *x*-coordinate of the vertex is –2.

c. Yes, both methods produce the same result.

d. Averaging the *x*-coordinates of the *y*-intercept and its symmetric point is easier, because the function $g(x)$ is very difficult to factor.

e. Averaging the *x*-coordinates of the *y*-intercept and its symmetric point is the only method that can be used, because the function does not have any *x*-intercepts.

f. Answers may vary.

71. (3, 2) is the vertex for both *f* and *k*. The vertex of *g* is approximately (2.7, 1.8). The vertex of *h* is approximately (3.3, 1.7).

73. Answers may vary. See the box "Using Symmetric Points to Graph a Quadratic Function in Standard Form" on page 349 of the text and Examples 5 and 6 on p. 352 of the text.

75.

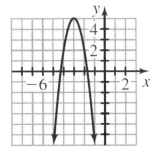

77.

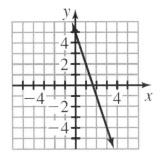

79. a.

$$f(x) = a(x-h)^2 + k$$

$$= a\left(x^2 - 2hx + h^2\right) + k$$

$$= ax^2 - 2ahx + ah^2 + k$$

$$= ax^2 - 2ahx + c$$

b.

$$x = -\frac{b}{2(a)}$$

$$= -\frac{-2ah}{2(a)}$$

$$= \frac{2ah}{2a}$$

$$= h$$

Substituting *h* for *x*.

$$f(h) = ah^2 - 2ahh + ah^2 + k$$

$$= k$$

The vertex of the parabola is (h, k).

81.

$$\frac{\left(3x^4 y^5\right)^3}{18x^7 y^2} = \frac{27x^{12} y^{15}}{18x^7 y^2} = \frac{27x^{12-7} y^{15-2}}{18} = \frac{3x^5 y^{13}}{2}$$

This is an expression in two variables involving exponents.

83.

$$\left(3x^2 - 2y^2\right)^2 = \left(3x^2\right)^2 + 2 \cdot 3x^2 \cdot -2y^2 + \left(-2y^2\right)^2$$

$$= 9x^4 - 12x^2 y^2 + 4y^4$$

This is a fourth-degree polynomial expression in two variables involving exponents.

85.

$$\frac{at-b}{c} = d$$

$$at - b = cd$$

$$at = b + cd$$

$$t = \frac{b+cd}{a}$$

This is an equation in several variables.

Homework 9.3

1. $\sqrt{81} = 9$, because $9^2 = 81$.

3. $\sqrt{121} = 11$, because $11^2 = 121$.

5. $\sqrt{144} = 12$, because $12^2 = 144$.

7. $\sqrt{81} = 9$, because $9^2 = 81$. Therefore, $-\sqrt{81} = -1\left(\sqrt{81}\right) = -1(9) = -9$.

9. $\sqrt{-9}$ is not a real number, because the radicand -9 is negative.

11. $-\sqrt{-25}$ is not a real number, because the radicand -25 is negative.

13. The number 30 is not a perfect square, so $\sqrt{30}$ is irrational.
$$\sqrt{30} \approx 5.48$$

15. The number 78 is not a perfect square, so $\sqrt{78}$ is irrational.
$$\sqrt{78} \approx 8.83$$

17. The number 196 is a perfect square ($196 = 14^2$), so $\sqrt{196}$ is rational.
$$\sqrt{196} = 14$$

19. $\sqrt{20} = \sqrt{4 \cdot 5} = \sqrt{4}\sqrt{5} = 2\sqrt{5}$

21. $\sqrt{45} = \sqrt{9 \cdot 5} = \sqrt{9}\sqrt{5} = 3\sqrt{5}$

23. $\sqrt{27} = \sqrt{9 \cdot 3} = \sqrt{9}\sqrt{3} = 3\sqrt{3}$

25. $\sqrt{50} = \sqrt{25 \cdot 2} = \sqrt{25}\sqrt{2} = 5\sqrt{2}$

27. $\sqrt{300} = \sqrt{100 \cdot 3} = \sqrt{100}\sqrt{3} = 10\sqrt{3}$

29. $-\sqrt{98} = -\sqrt{49 \cdot 2} = -\sqrt{49}\sqrt{2} = -7\sqrt{2}$

31. $\begin{aligned} 4\sqrt{72} &= 4\sqrt{36 \cdot 2} \\ &= 4\sqrt{36}\sqrt{2} \\ &= 4 \cdot 6\sqrt{2} \\ &= 24\sqrt{2} \end{aligned}$

33. $\begin{aligned} 3\sqrt{120} &= 3\sqrt{4 \cdot 30} \\ &= 3\sqrt{4}\sqrt{30} \\ &= 3 \cdot 2\sqrt{30} \\ &= 6\sqrt{30} \end{aligned}$

35. $\sqrt{\dfrac{25}{36}} = \dfrac{\sqrt{25}}{\sqrt{36}} = \dfrac{5}{6}$

37. $\sqrt{\dfrac{121}{4}} = \dfrac{\sqrt{121}}{\sqrt{4}} = \dfrac{11}{2}$

39. $\sqrt{\dfrac{7}{25}} = \dfrac{\sqrt{7}}{\sqrt{25}} = \dfrac{\sqrt{7}}{5}$

41. $\sqrt{\dfrac{19}{64}} = \dfrac{\sqrt{19}}{\sqrt{64}} = \dfrac{\sqrt{19}}{8}$

43. $-\sqrt{\dfrac{8}{49}} = -\dfrac{\sqrt{8}}{\sqrt{49}} = -\dfrac{\sqrt{4 \cdot 2}}{7} = -\dfrac{\sqrt{4}\sqrt{2}}{7} = -\dfrac{2\sqrt{2}}{7}$

45. $\sqrt{\dfrac{20}{81}} = \dfrac{\sqrt{20}}{\sqrt{81}} = \dfrac{\sqrt{4 \cdot 5}}{9} = \dfrac{\sqrt{4}\sqrt{5}}{9} = \dfrac{2\sqrt{5}}{9}$

47. $\sqrt{\dfrac{75}{36}} = \dfrac{\sqrt{75}}{\sqrt{36}} = \dfrac{\sqrt{25 \cdot 3}}{6} = \dfrac{\sqrt{25}\sqrt{3}}{6} = \dfrac{5\sqrt{3}}{6}$

49. $\sqrt{\dfrac{80}{49}} = \dfrac{\sqrt{80}}{\sqrt{49}} = \dfrac{\sqrt{16 \cdot 5}}{7} = \dfrac{\sqrt{16}\sqrt{5}}{7} = \dfrac{4\sqrt{5}}{7}$

51. $\dfrac{2}{\sqrt{3}} = \dfrac{2}{\sqrt{3}} \cdot \dfrac{\sqrt{3}}{\sqrt{3}} = \dfrac{2\sqrt{3}}{\sqrt{9}} = \dfrac{2\sqrt{3}}{3}$

53. $\dfrac{3}{\sqrt{24}} = \dfrac{3}{2\sqrt{6}} = \dfrac{3}{2\sqrt{6}} \cdot \dfrac{\sqrt{6}}{\sqrt{6}} = \dfrac{3\sqrt{6}}{2\sqrt{36}} = \dfrac{3\sqrt{6}}{2 \cdot 6} = \dfrac{\sqrt{6}}{4}$

55. $\sqrt{\dfrac{2}{7}} = \dfrac{\sqrt{2}}{\sqrt{7}} = \dfrac{\sqrt{2}}{\sqrt{7}} \cdot \dfrac{\sqrt{7}}{\sqrt{7}} = \dfrac{\sqrt{14}}{\sqrt{49}} = \dfrac{\sqrt{14}}{7}$

57. $\sqrt{\dfrac{11}{2}} = \dfrac{\sqrt{11}}{\sqrt{2}} = \dfrac{\sqrt{11}}{\sqrt{2}} \cdot \dfrac{\sqrt{2}}{\sqrt{2}} = \dfrac{\sqrt{22}}{\sqrt{4}} = \dfrac{\sqrt{22}}{2}$

59. $\begin{aligned} \sqrt{\dfrac{3}{8}} &= \dfrac{\sqrt{3}}{\sqrt{8}} = \dfrac{\sqrt{3}}{2\sqrt{2}} = \dfrac{\sqrt{3}}{2\sqrt{2}} \cdot \dfrac{\sqrt{2}}{\sqrt{2}} \\ &= \dfrac{\sqrt{6}}{2\sqrt{4}} = \dfrac{\sqrt{6}}{2 \cdot 2} = \dfrac{\sqrt{6}}{4} \end{aligned}$

61. $\begin{aligned} \sqrt{\dfrac{3}{50}} &= \dfrac{\sqrt{3}}{\sqrt{50}} = \dfrac{\sqrt{3}}{5\sqrt{2}} = \dfrac{\sqrt{3}}{5\sqrt{2}} \cdot \dfrac{\sqrt{2}}{\sqrt{2}} \\ &= \dfrac{\sqrt{6}}{5\sqrt{4}} = \dfrac{\sqrt{6}}{5 \cdot 2} = \dfrac{\sqrt{6}}{10} \end{aligned}$

63. $\dfrac{9 + 3\sqrt{2}}{6} = \dfrac{3\left(3 + \sqrt{2}\right)}{3 \cdot 2} = \dfrac{3}{3} \cdot \dfrac{3 + \sqrt{2}}{2} = \dfrac{3 + \sqrt{2}}{2}$

65. $\dfrac{8-4\sqrt{7}}{4} = \dfrac{4\left(2-\sqrt{7}\right)}{4\cdot 1} = \dfrac{4}{4}\cdot\dfrac{2-\sqrt{7}}{1} = 2-\sqrt{7}$

67. $\dfrac{8+12\sqrt{13}}{6} = \dfrac{2\left(4+6\sqrt{13}\right)}{2\cdot 3}$

$\qquad = \dfrac{2}{2}\cdot\dfrac{4+6\sqrt{13}}{3}$

$\qquad = \dfrac{4+6\sqrt{13}}{3}$

69. $\dfrac{4+\sqrt{12}}{8} = \dfrac{4+2\sqrt{3}}{8}$

$\qquad = \dfrac{2\left(2+\sqrt{3}\right)}{2\cdot 4}$

$\qquad = \dfrac{2}{2}\cdot\dfrac{2+\sqrt{3}}{4}$

$\qquad = \dfrac{2+\sqrt{3}}{4}$

71. $\dfrac{10-\sqrt{50}}{20} = \dfrac{10-5\sqrt{2}}{20}$

$\qquad = \dfrac{5\left(2-\sqrt{2}\right)}{5\cdot 4}$

$\qquad = \dfrac{5}{5}\cdot\dfrac{2-\sqrt{2}}{4}$

$\qquad = \dfrac{2-\sqrt{2}}{4}$

73. $\dfrac{9-\sqrt{45}}{6} = \dfrac{9-3\sqrt{5}}{6}$

$\qquad = \dfrac{3\left(3-\sqrt{5}\right)}{3\cdot 2}$

$\qquad = \dfrac{3}{3}\cdot\dfrac{3-\sqrt{5}}{2}$

$\qquad = \dfrac{3-\sqrt{5}}{2}$

75. Since the motorist was traveling on asphalt, the drag factor is $F = 0.75$. The length of the skid mark is given as 210 feet, so $D = 210$.

$S = \sqrt{30FD}$

$\quad = \sqrt{30(0.75)(210)}$

$\quad = \sqrt{4725}$

$\quad = \sqrt{7\cdot 5\cdot 5\cdot 3\cdot 3\cdot 3}$

$\quad = \sqrt{5\cdot 5\cdot 3\cdot 3\cdot 3\cdot 7}$

$\quad = \sqrt{5\cdot 5}\sqrt{3\cdot 3}\sqrt{3\cdot 7}$

$\quad = 5\cdot 3\cdot\sqrt{21}$

$\quad = 15\sqrt{21} \approx 68.7$

The motorist was traveling at about 68.7 miles per hour before braking.

77. a. $f(h) = \sqrt{\dfrac{h}{16}} = \dfrac{\sqrt{h}}{\sqrt{16}} = \dfrac{\sqrt{h}}{4}$

    b. $f(h) = \dfrac{\sqrt{1450}}{4} \approx 9.5$

It will take the baseball about 9.5 seconds to reach the ground.

79. Since $16 < 22 < 25$, we get

$\sqrt{16} < \sqrt{22} < \sqrt{25}$

$4 < \sqrt{22} < 5$

So, $\sqrt{22}$ lies between 4 and 5.

81. Since $64 < 71 < 81$, we get

$\sqrt{64} < \sqrt{71} < \sqrt{81}$

$8 < \sqrt{71} < 9$

So, $\sqrt{71}$ lies between 8 and 9.

83. a. i. 2
    ii. 5
    iii. 8

  b. Each of the numbers 2, 5, and 8 is larger than its principle square root.

  c. i. $\sqrt{0.2}$
    ii. $\sqrt{0.5}$
    iii. $\sqrt{0.8}$

  d. Each of the numbers 0.2, 0.5, and 0.8 is smaller than its principle square root.

   e. Taking the principle square root of a number greater than 1 will result in a smaller result. Taking the principle square root of a number between 0 and 1 (not including 0 or 1) will result in a larger result.

85. No; $\sqrt{10} = \sqrt{2 \cdot 5} = \sqrt{2}\sqrt{5}$

Therefore, $\sqrt{10}$ is $\sqrt{2}$ times as big as $\sqrt{5}$.

87. No, the student is not correct. $\sqrt{-25}$ is not a real number since the radicand -25 is negative. Also note that $(-5)^2 = 25 \neq -25$.

89. In the second line the student is squaring the expression instead of multiplying by $1 = \dfrac{\sqrt{3}}{\sqrt{3}}$.

$$\frac{5}{\sqrt{3}} = \frac{5}{\sqrt{3}} \cdot \frac{\sqrt{3}}{\sqrt{3}} = \frac{5\sqrt{3}}{\sqrt{9}} = \frac{5\sqrt{3}}{3}$$

91. The work is correct, but it may be easier to simplify the denominator first.

$$\frac{3}{\sqrt{20}} = \frac{3}{2\sqrt{5}} = \frac{3}{2\sqrt{5}} \cdot \frac{\sqrt{5}}{\sqrt{5}} = \frac{3\sqrt{5}}{2\sqrt{25}} = \frac{3\sqrt{5}}{2 \cdot 5} = \frac{3\sqrt{5}}{10}$$

93. $12 + 8x = 4 \cdot 3 + 4 \cdot 2x$
$$= 4(3 + 2x)$$

95. $12 + 8\sqrt{3} = 4 \cdot 3 + 4 \cdot 2\sqrt{3}$
$$= 4\left(3 + 2\sqrt{3}\right)$$

97. $f(x) = -2x^2 + 4x + 3$

First we list some solutions of $f(x) = -2x^2 + 4x + 3$. Then we sketch a curve that contains the points corresponding to solutions.

x	$y = -2x^2 + 4x + 3$	(x, y)
-2	$-2(-2)^2 + 4(-2) + 3 = -13$	$(-2, -13)$
-1	$-2(-1)^2 + 4(-1) + 3 = -3$	$(-1, -3)$
0	$-2(0)^2 + 4(0) + 3 = 3$	$(0, 3)$
1	$-2(1)^2 + 4(1) + 3 = 5$	$(1, 5)$
2	$-2(2)^2 + 4(2) + 3 = 3$	$(2, 3)$

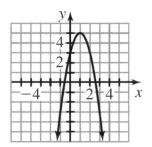

Description: *quadratic function in one varaible*

99. $\qquad x^2 = 6x - 8$
$$x^2 - 6x + 8 = 0$$
$$(x - 4)(x - 2) = 0$$
$$x - 4 = 0 \quad \text{or} \quad x - 2 = 0$$
$$x = 4 \qquad\qquad x = 2$$

The solutions are 2 and 4.
Description: *quadratic equation in one variable*

101. $\sqrt{68} = \sqrt{4 \cdot 17} = \sqrt{4 \cdot 17} = \sqrt{4}\sqrt{17} = 2\sqrt{17}$
Description: *radical expression*

Homework 9.4

1. $x^2 = 4$
$$x = \pm\sqrt{4}$$
$$x = \pm 2$$

3. $x^2 = 0$
$$x = \pm\sqrt{0}$$
$$x = 0$$

5. $t^2 = 15$
$$t = \pm\sqrt{15}$$

7. $x^2 = 20$
$$x = \pm\sqrt{20}$$
$$x = \pm\sqrt{4 \cdot 5}$$
$$x = \pm\sqrt{4} \cdot \sqrt{5}$$
$$x = \pm 2\sqrt{5}$$

9. $x^2 - 28 = 0$

$$x^2 = 28$$
$$x = \pm\sqrt{28}$$
$$x = \pm\sqrt{4 \cdot 7}$$
$$x = \pm\sqrt{4} \cdot \sqrt{7}$$
$$x = \pm2\sqrt{7}$$

11. $4w^2 = 5$

$$w^2 = \frac{5}{4}$$
$$w = \pm\sqrt{\frac{5}{4}}$$
$$w = \pm\frac{\sqrt{5}}{\sqrt{4}}$$
$$w = \pm\frac{\sqrt{5}}{2}$$

13. $5x^2 = 7$

$$x^2 = \frac{7}{5}$$
$$x = \pm\sqrt{\frac{7}{5}}$$
$$x = \pm\frac{\sqrt{7}}{\sqrt{5}} \cdot \frac{\sqrt{5}}{\sqrt{5}}$$
$$x = \pm\frac{\sqrt{35}}{5}$$

15. $8m^2 = 5$

$$m^2 = \frac{5}{8}$$
$$m = \pm\sqrt{\frac{5}{8}}$$
$$m = \pm\frac{\sqrt{5}}{\sqrt{8}} \cdot \frac{\sqrt{2}}{\sqrt{2}}$$
$$m = \pm\frac{\sqrt{10}}{\sqrt{16}}$$
$$m = \pm\frac{\sqrt{10}}{4}$$

17. $2x^2 + 4 = 7$

$$2x^2 = 3$$
$$x^2 = \frac{3}{2}$$
$$x = \pm\sqrt{\frac{3}{2}}$$
$$x = \pm\frac{\sqrt{3}}{\sqrt{2}} \cdot \frac{\sqrt{2}}{\sqrt{2}}$$
$$x = \pm\frac{\sqrt{6}}{2}$$

19. $5x^2 - 3 = 11$

$$5x^2 = 14$$
$$x^2 = \frac{14}{5}$$
$$x = \pm\sqrt{\frac{14}{5}}$$
$$x = \pm\frac{\sqrt{14}}{\sqrt{5}} \cdot \frac{\sqrt{5}}{\sqrt{5}}$$
$$x = \pm\frac{\sqrt{70}}{5}$$

21. $(x+2)^2 = 16$

$$x + 2 = \pm\sqrt{16}$$
$$x + 2 = \pm4$$
$$x + 2 = -4 \quad \text{or} \quad x + 2 = 4$$
$$x = -6 \qquad\qquad x = 2$$

23. $(x-7)^2 = 13$

$$x - 7 = \pm\sqrt{13}$$
$$x = 7 \pm \sqrt{13}$$

25. $(x+2)^2 = 18$

$$x + 2 = \pm\sqrt{18}$$
$$x + 2 = \pm3\sqrt{2}$$
$$x = -2 \pm 3\sqrt{2}$$

27. $(8y+3)^2 = 36$

$\sqrt{(8y+3)^2} = \pm\sqrt{36}$

$8y+3 = \pm 6$

$8y = -3 \pm 6$

$y = \dfrac{-3 \pm 6}{8}$

$y = \dfrac{-9}{8}$ or $y = \dfrac{3}{8}$

29. $(9x-5)^2 = 0$

$\sqrt{(9x-5)^2} = \sqrt{0}$

$9x-5 = 0$

$9x = 5$

$x = \dfrac{5}{9}$

31. $\left(x+\dfrac{3}{4}\right)^2 = \dfrac{41}{16}$

$\sqrt{\left(x+\dfrac{3}{4}\right)^2} = \pm\sqrt{\dfrac{41}{16}}$

$x+\dfrac{3}{4} = \pm\dfrac{\sqrt{41}}{\sqrt{16}}$

$x+\dfrac{3}{4} = \pm\dfrac{\sqrt{41}}{4}$

$x = \dfrac{-3 \pm \sqrt{41}}{4}$

33. $\left(w-\dfrac{7}{3}\right)^2 = \dfrac{5}{9}$

$\sqrt{\left(w-\dfrac{7}{3}\right)^2} = \pm\sqrt{\dfrac{5}{9}}$

$w-\dfrac{7}{3} = \pm\dfrac{\sqrt{5}}{\sqrt{9}}$

$w-\dfrac{7}{3} = \pm\dfrac{\sqrt{5}}{3}$

$w = \dfrac{7 \pm \sqrt{5}}{3}$

35. $5(x-6)^2 + 3 = 33$

$5(x-6)^2 = 30$

$(x-6)^2 = 6$

$\sqrt{(x-6)^2} = \pm\sqrt{6}$

$x-6 = \pm\sqrt{6}$

$x = 6 \pm \sqrt{6}$

37. $-3(x+1)^2 + 2 = -5$

$-3(x+1)^2 = -7$

$(x+1)^2 = \dfrac{7}{3}$

$\sqrt{(x+1)^2} = \pm\sqrt{\dfrac{7}{3}}$

$x+1 = \pm\dfrac{\sqrt{7}}{\sqrt{3}}$

$x+1 = \pm\dfrac{\sqrt{7}}{\sqrt{3}} \cdot \dfrac{\sqrt{3}}{\sqrt{3}}$

$x+1 = \pm\dfrac{\sqrt{21}}{3}$

$x = \dfrac{-3 \pm \sqrt{21}}{3}$

39. Solve for x when $f(x) = 0$

$0 = x^2 - 17$

$x^2 = 17$

$x = \pm\sqrt{17}$

The x-intercepts are $\left(\sqrt{17}, 0\right)$ and $\left(-\sqrt{17}, 0\right)$.

41. Solve for x when $f(x) = 0$

$$0 = 2(x-3)^2 - 7$$

$$7 = 2(x-3)^2$$

$$\frac{7}{2} = (x-3)^2$$

$$\pm\sqrt{\frac{7}{2}} = \sqrt{(x-3)^2}$$

$$\pm\frac{\sqrt{7}}{\sqrt{2}} = x-3$$

$$\pm\frac{\sqrt{7}}{\sqrt{2}} \cdot \frac{\sqrt{2}}{\sqrt{2}} = x-3$$

$$\pm\frac{\sqrt{14}}{2} = x-3$$

$$3 \pm \frac{\sqrt{14}}{2} = x$$

$$\frac{6 \pm \sqrt{14}}{2} = x$$

The x-intercepts are $\left(\dfrac{6-\sqrt{14}}{2}, 0\right)$ and

$\left(\dfrac{6+\sqrt{14}}{2}, 0\right)$.

43. Solve for x when $f(x) = 0$.

$$0 = -4(x-2)^2 - 16$$

$$16 = -4(x-2)^2$$

$$-4 = (x-2)^2$$

The next step would be to take the square root of both sides, resulting in an imaginary number. Since the x-intercept must be a real number, there are no x-intercepts.

45. $\sqrt{-36} = i\sqrt{36} = 6i$

47. $-\sqrt{-45} = -i\sqrt{45} = -i\sqrt{9 \cdot 5} = -3i\sqrt{5}$

49. $\sqrt{-\dfrac{5}{49}} = i\sqrt{\dfrac{5}{49}} = i\dfrac{\sqrt{5}}{\sqrt{49}} = i\dfrac{\sqrt{5}}{7}$

51. $\sqrt{-\dfrac{13}{5}} = i\sqrt{\dfrac{13}{5}} = i\dfrac{\sqrt{13}}{\sqrt{5}} = i\dfrac{\sqrt{13}}{\sqrt{5}} \cdot \dfrac{\sqrt{5}}{\sqrt{5}} = i\dfrac{\sqrt{65}}{5}$

53.
$$x^2 = -49$$

$$\sqrt{x^2} = \pm\sqrt{-49}$$

$$x = \pm i\sqrt{49}$$

$$x = \pm 7i$$

55.
$$x^2 = -18$$

$$\sqrt{x^2} = \pm\sqrt{-18}$$

$$x = \pm i\sqrt{18}$$

$$x = \pm i\sqrt{9 \cdot 2}$$

$$x = \pm 3i\sqrt{2}$$

57.
$$7x^2 + 26 = 5$$

$$7x^2 = -21$$

$$x^2 = -3$$

$$\sqrt{x^2} = \pm\sqrt{-3}$$

$$x = \pm i\sqrt{3}$$

59.
$$(m+4)^2 = -8$$

$$\sqrt{(m+4)^2} = \pm\sqrt{-8}$$

$$m+4 = \pm i\sqrt{8}$$

$$m+4 = \pm 2i\sqrt{2}$$

$$m = -4 \pm 2i\sqrt{2}$$

61.
$$\left(x - \frac{5}{4}\right)^2 = -\frac{3}{16}$$

$$\sqrt{\left(x - \frac{5}{4}\right)^2} = \pm\sqrt{-\frac{3}{16}}$$

$$x - \frac{5}{4} = \pm\frac{\sqrt{-3}}{\sqrt{16}}$$

$$x - \frac{5}{4} = \pm\frac{i\sqrt{3}}{4}$$

$$x = \frac{5 \pm i\sqrt{3}}{4}$$

63. $-2(y+3)^2+1=9$

$$-2(y+3)^2=8$$

$$(y+3)^2=-4$$

$$\sqrt{(y+3)^2}=\pm\sqrt{-4}$$

$$y+3=\pm i\sqrt{4}$$

$$y+3=\pm 2i$$

$$y=-3\pm 2i$$

65. a.

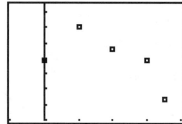

The model should be a quadratic function, as the data appear to fit a quadratic function best.

b.

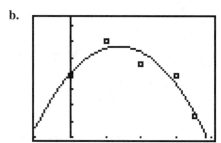

The model fits the data reasonably well.

c. To find the median income of realtors in 2010, find $f(10)$.

$$f(10)=-0.46(10-2.74)^2+51.45$$

$$=-0.46(7.26)^2+51.45$$

$$\approx-24.25+51.45$$

$$\approx27.2$$

The median annual income of realtors is estimated to be $27.2 thousand or $27,200 in 2010.

d. $\quad 39=-0.46(t-2.74)^2+51.45$

$$-12.45=-0.46(t-2.74)^2$$

$$27.07\approx(t-2.74)^2$$

$$\pm\sqrt{27.07}\approx\sqrt{(t-2.74)^2}$$

$$\pm5.2\approx(t-2.74)$$

$$5.2\approx t-2.74 \quad \text{or} \quad -5.2\approx t-2.74$$

$$7.94\approx t \qquad \text{or} \quad -2.46\approx t$$

The median annual income of realtors was $39 thousand in $2000-2\approx1998$ and $2000+8\approx2008$.

e. The maximum median annual income of realtors in the modeled time period is given by the vertex, (h, k).
$h=2.74$; $k=51.45$;
so the vertex is $(2.74, 51.45)$.
The vertex indicates that, in $t=2.74\approx3$, or the year 2003, realtors earned the highest median annual income, $51.45 thousand, or $51,450.

67. a.

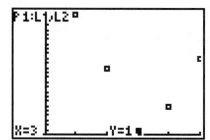

Use the point $(3,1)$ as the vertex.

$$y=a(x-3)^2+1$$

Use the point $(1, 25)$ to solve for a:

$$y=a(x-3)^2+1$$

$$25=a(1-3)^2+1$$

$$24=a(-2)^2$$

$$6=a$$

$$y=6(x-3)^2+1$$

or, $f(t)=6(t-3)^2+1$

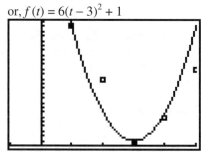

The graph fits the data reasonably well.

b. The vertex is $(3,1)$. This indicates that the number of poetry books published in Iraq was at its lowest (1 book) in 2003.

c. $f(6) = 6(6-3)^2 + 1$

$f(6) = 6(3)^2 + 1$

$f(6) = 6(9) + 1$

$f(6) = 55$

This indicates that in 2006, the model estimates 55 poetry books were published in Iraq.

d. $y = 6(x-3)^2 + 1$

$85 = 6(x-3)^2 + 1$

$84 = 6(x-3)^2$

$14 = (x-3)^2$

$\pm\sqrt{14} = \sqrt{(x-3)^2}$

$\pm\sqrt{14} = x-3$

$3 \pm \sqrt{14} = x$

$x = 3 + \sqrt{14}$ or $x = 3 - \sqrt{14}$

$\approx 3 + (3.74)$ $\approx 3 - (3.74)$

$\approx 3 + 3.74$ $\approx 3 - 3.74$

≈ 6.74 ≈ -0.74

The model estimates that in the years $2000 - 1 \approx 1999$ and $2000 + 7 \approx 2007$, 85 poetry books were published in Iraq.

69. No, the student did not solve it correctly. There is still an x on the right-hand side. The student should have factored the left hand side first.

$x^2 - 10x + 25 = 0$

$(x-5)(x-5) = 0$

$(x-5)^2 = 0$

$x - 5 = 0$

$x = 5$

71. The graphs of the two equations meet when $x \approx 1.4$ or 4.2.

73. The graph of the equation meets the line $y = 2$ when $x = 2$ or 4.

75. The graphs of the equations meet approximately at the points $(1.1, -3.5)$ and $(4.7, -1.7)$.

77. a. The vertex of the graph is $(3, 5)$.

b. Since $2 > 0$, the graph of f opens upward.

c. **i.** The equation has two solutions. Since the vertex is $(3,5)$ and the graph opens upward, there must be two values of x that produce a y-value of 8.

ii. The equation has one solution ($x = 3$) because y = 5 at the vertex of the graph.

iii. The equation has no solutions, because the line $y = 1$ is below the vertex of the equation and the equation opens upward.

79. a. $25x^2 - 49 = 0$

$x^2 - \dfrac{49}{25} = 0$

$x^2 - \left(\dfrac{7}{5}\right)^2 = 0$

$\left(x - \dfrac{7}{5}\right)\left(x + \dfrac{7}{5}\right) = 0$

$x - \dfrac{7}{5} = 0 \qquad x + \dfrac{7}{5} = 0$

$x = \dfrac{7}{5} \qquad\qquad x = -\dfrac{7}{5}$

b. $25x^2 - 49 = 0$

$25x^2 = 49$

$x^2 = \dfrac{49}{25}$

$\sqrt{x^2} = \pm\sqrt{\dfrac{49}{25}}$

$x = \pm\dfrac{\sqrt{49}}{\sqrt{25}}$

$x = \pm\dfrac{7}{5}$

c. Both solutions are the same.

d. Answers may vary.

81. a. Yes it can be solved with the square root property.

$(x+4)^2 = 5$

$\sqrt{(x+4)^2} = \pm\sqrt{5}$

$x + 4 = \pm\sqrt{5}$

$x = -4 \pm \sqrt{5}$

b. No, it cannot be solved by factoring.

c. No, not all equations that can be solved with the square root property can be solved by factoring. Not all equations involving quadratic terms will necessarily be factorable.

83. $a^2 + b^2 = c^2$

$$a^2 = c^2 - b^2$$

$$a = \pm\sqrt{c^2 - b^2}$$

85. $(mt + b)^2 = p$

$$\sqrt{(mt + b)^2} = \pm\sqrt{p}$$

$$mt + b = \pm\sqrt{p}$$

$$mt = -b \pm \sqrt{p}$$

$$t = \frac{-b \pm \sqrt{p}}{m}$$

87. Answers may vary.

89. a. $x^2 - 36 = 0$

$$(x - 6)(x + 6) = 0$$

$$x - 6 = 0 \quad \text{or} \quad x + 6 = 0$$

$$x = 6 \qquad x = -6$$

The solutions are -6 and 6.

b. $\sqrt{36} = 6$, because $6^2 = 36$

c. Answers may vary.

91. $x^2 = 4x + 12$

$$x^2 - 4x - 12 = 0$$

$$(x - 6)(x + 2) = 0$$

$$x - 6 = 0 \quad \text{or} \quad x + 2 = 0$$

$$x = 6 \qquad x = -2$$

The solutions are -2 and 6.

93. $y^2 - 81 = 0$

$$y^2 = 81$$

$$y = \pm\sqrt{81}$$

$$y = \pm 9$$

The solutions are -9 and 9.

95. $(x - 2)^2 = 24$

$$x - 2 = \pm\sqrt{24}$$

$$x - 2 = \pm 2\sqrt{6}$$

$$x = 2 \pm 2\sqrt{6}$$

The solutions are $2 - 2\sqrt{6}$ and $2 + 2\sqrt{6}$.

97. $3x^2 + 4 = 15$

$$3x^2 = 11$$

$$x^2 = \frac{11}{3}$$

$$x = \pm\sqrt{\frac{11}{3}}$$

$$x = \pm\frac{\sqrt{11}}{\sqrt{3}} \cdot \frac{\sqrt{3}}{\sqrt{3}}$$

$$x = \pm\frac{\sqrt{33}}{3}$$

The solutions are $-\dfrac{\sqrt{33}}{3}$ and $\dfrac{\sqrt{33}}{3}$.

99. $2x^2 - 15 = -7x$

$$2x^2 + 7x - 15 = 0$$

$$(2x - 3)(x + 5) = 0$$

$$2x - 3 = 0 \quad \text{or} \quad x + 5 = 0$$

$$2x = 3 \qquad x = -5$$

$$x = \frac{3}{2}$$

The solutions are -5 and $\dfrac{3}{2}$.

101. $5(t - 1)^2 - 3 = 4$

$$(t - 1)^2 = \frac{7}{5}$$

$$t - 1 = \pm\sqrt{\frac{7}{5}}$$

$$t = 1 \pm \sqrt{\frac{7}{5}}$$

$$t = \frac{5 \pm \sqrt{35}}{5}$$

The solutions are $\dfrac{5 - \sqrt{35}}{5}$ and $\dfrac{5 + \sqrt{35}}{5}$.

103. $2w^3 + 3w^2 - 18w - 27 = w^2(2w + 3) - 9(2w + 3)$

$$= (w^2 - 9)(2w + 3)$$

$$= (w + 3)(w - 3)(2w + 3)$$

This is a cubic polynomial in one variable.

105. From problem 103 we know that:
$$2w^3 + 3w^2 - 18w - 27 = (w-3)(w+3)(2w+3)$$
So:
$$0 = 2w^3 + 3w^2 - 18w - 27$$
$$= (w-3)(w+3)(2w+3)$$

$$w - 3 = 0 \qquad w + 3 = 0$$
$$w = 3 \qquad w = -3$$

$$2w + 3 = 0$$
$$2w = -3$$
$$w = -\frac{3}{2}$$

This is a cubic equation in one variable.

107. $(5w^2 - 2)(4w + 3) = 20w^3 + 15w^2 - 8w - 6$

This is a cubic polynomial in one variable.

Homework 9.5

1. $\left(\dfrac{12}{2}\right)^2 = 6^2 = 36 = c$

This expression is $x^2 + 12x + 36$ and its factored form is $(x+6)^2$.

3. $\left(\dfrac{-14}{2}\right)^2 = (-7)^2 = 49 = c$

This expression is $x^2 - 14x + 49$ and its factored form is $(x-7)^2$.

5. $\left(\dfrac{7}{2}\right)^2 = \dfrac{7^2}{2^2} = \dfrac{49}{4} = c$

This expression is $x^2 + 7x + \dfrac{49}{4}$ and its factored form is $\left(x + \dfrac{7}{2}\right)^2$.

7. $\left(\dfrac{-3}{2}\right)^2 = \dfrac{(-3)^2}{2^2} = \dfrac{9}{4} = c$

This expression is $x^2 - 3x + \dfrac{9}{4}$ and its factored form is $\left(x - \dfrac{3}{2}\right)^2$.

9. $\left(\dfrac{1}{2} \cdot \dfrac{1}{2}\right)^2 = \left(\dfrac{1}{4}\right)^2 = \dfrac{1^2}{4^2} = \dfrac{1}{16} = c$

This expression is $x^2 + \dfrac{1}{2}x + \dfrac{1}{16}$ and its factored form is $\left(x + \dfrac{1}{4}\right)^2$.

11. $\left(-\dfrac{4}{5} \cdot \dfrac{1}{2}\right)^2 = \left(\dfrac{-4}{10}\right)^2 = \dfrac{(-4)^2}{(10)^2} = \dfrac{16}{100} = \dfrac{4}{25} = c$

This expression is $x^2 - \dfrac{4}{5}x + \dfrac{4}{25}$ and its factored form is $\left(x - \dfrac{2}{5}\right)^2$.

13. Since $\left(\dfrac{6}{2}\right)^2 = 3^2 = 9$, add 9 to both sides of the equation.
$$x^2 + 6x = 1$$
$$x^2 + 6x + 9 = 1 + 9$$
$$(x+3)^2 = 10$$
$$x + 3 = \pm\sqrt{10}$$
$$x = -3 \pm \sqrt{10}$$

15. Since $\left(\dfrac{2}{2}\right)^2 = 1^2 = 1$, add 1 to both sides of the equation.
$$p^2 - 2p = 19$$
$$p^2 - 2p + 1 = 19 + 1$$
$$(p-1)^2 = 20$$
$$p - 1 = \pm\sqrt{20}$$
$$p = 1 \pm 2\sqrt{5}$$

17. $x^2 + 12x = -4$

Since $\left(\dfrac{12}{2}\right)^2 = 6^2 = 36$, we add 36 to both sides

of the equation so that the left side is a perfect square trinomial.

$x^2 + 12x + 36 = -4 + 36$

$(x+6)^2 = 32$

$x + 6 = \pm\sqrt{32}$

$x = -6 \pm 4\sqrt{2}$

The solutions are $-6 - 4\sqrt{2}$ and $-6 + 4\sqrt{2}$.

19. $x^2 - 10x - 7 = 0$

$x^2 - 10x = 7$

Since $\left(\dfrac{-10}{2}\right)^2 = (-5)^2 = 25$, we add 25 to both

sides of the equation so that the left side is a perfect square trinomial.

$x^2 - 10x + 25 = 7 + 25$

$(x-5)^2 = 32$

$x - 5 = \pm\sqrt{32}$

$x - 5 = \pm 4\sqrt{2}$

$x = 5 \pm 4\sqrt{2}$

The solutions are $5 - 4\sqrt{2}$ and $5 + 4\sqrt{2}$.

21. Since $\left(\dfrac{4}{2}\right)^2 = 2^2 = 4$, add 4 to both sides of the

equation.

$x^2 + 4x - 24 = 0$

$x^2 + 4x = 24$

$x^2 + 4x + 4 = 28$

$(x+2)^2 = 28$

$(x+2)^2 = 28$

$x + 2 = \pm\sqrt{28}$

$x = -2 \pm 2\sqrt{7}$

23. Since $\left(\dfrac{-7}{2}\right)^2 = \dfrac{(-7)^2}{2^2} = \dfrac{49}{4}$, add $\dfrac{49}{4}$ to both

sides of the equation.

$x^2 - 7x = 3$

$x^2 - 7x + \dfrac{49}{4} = 3 + \dfrac{49}{4}$

$\left(x - \dfrac{7}{2}\right)^2 = \dfrac{12}{4} + \dfrac{49}{4}$

$\left(x - \dfrac{7}{2}\right)^2 = \dfrac{61}{4}$

$x - \dfrac{7}{2} = \pm\sqrt{\dfrac{61}{4}}$

$x - \dfrac{7}{2} = \pm\dfrac{\sqrt{61}}{2}$

$x = \dfrac{7}{2} \pm \dfrac{\sqrt{61}}{2}$

$x = \dfrac{7 \pm \sqrt{61}}{2}$

25. Since $\left(\dfrac{5}{2}\right)^2 = \dfrac{5^2}{2^2} = \dfrac{25}{4}$, add $\dfrac{25}{4}$ to both sides of

the equation.

$t^2 + 5t - 4 = 0$

$t^2 + 5t = 4$

$t^2 + 5t + \dfrac{25}{4} = 4 + \dfrac{25}{4}$

$\left(t + \dfrac{5}{2}\right)^2 = \dfrac{41}{4}$

$t + \dfrac{5}{2} = \pm\sqrt{\dfrac{41}{4}}$

$t + \dfrac{5}{2} = \pm\dfrac{\sqrt{41}}{\sqrt{4}}$

$t + \dfrac{5}{2} = \pm\dfrac{\sqrt{41}}{2}$

$t = \dfrac{-5 \pm \sqrt{41}}{2}$

27. Since $\left(\dfrac{-5}{2}\cdot\dfrac{1}{2}\right)^2=\left(\dfrac{-5}{4}\right)^2=\dfrac{(-5)^2}{4^2}=\dfrac{25}{16}$, add $\dfrac{25}{16}$

to both sides of the equation.

$$x^2-\frac{5}{2}x=\frac{1}{2}$$

$$x^2-\frac{5}{2}x+\frac{25}{16}=\frac{1}{2}+\frac{25}{16}$$

$$\left(x-\frac{5}{4}\right)^2=\frac{8}{16}+\frac{25}{16}$$

$$\left(x-\frac{5}{4}\right)^2=\frac{33}{16}$$

$$x-\frac{5}{4}=\pm\sqrt{\frac{33}{16}}$$

$$x-\frac{5}{4}=\pm\frac{\sqrt{33}}{4}$$

$$x=\frac{5}{4}\pm\frac{\sqrt{33}}{4}$$

$$x=\frac{5\pm\sqrt{33}}{4}$$

29. $5p^2+10p=35$

$$p^2+2p=7$$

Since $\left(\dfrac{2}{2}\right)^2=1^2=1$, we add 1 to both sides of

the equation so that the left side is a perfect square trinomial.

$$p^2+2p+1=7+1$$

$$\left(p+1\right)^2=8$$

$$p+1=\pm\sqrt{8}$$

$$p+1=\pm2\sqrt{2}$$

$$p=-1\pm2\sqrt{2}$$

The solutions are $-1-2\sqrt{2}$ and $-1+2\sqrt{2}$.

31. $4x^2-24x+4=0$

$$4x^2-24x=-4$$

$$x^2-6x=-1$$

Since $\left(\dfrac{-6}{2}\right)^2=(-3)^2=9$, we add 9 to both sides

of the equation so that the left side is a perfect square trinomial.

$$x^2-6x+9=-1+9$$

$$\left(x-3\right)^2=8$$

$$x-3=\pm\sqrt{8}$$

$$x-3=\pm2\sqrt{2}$$

$$x=3\pm2\sqrt{2}$$

The solutions are $3-2\sqrt{2}$ and $3+2\sqrt{2}$.

33. First write the equation with an x^2 coefficient of 1:

$$2x^2+8x=3$$

$$x^2+4x=\frac{3}{2}$$

Since $\left(\dfrac{4}{2}\right)^2=2^2=4$, add 4 to both sides of the

equation.

$$x^2+4x=\frac{3}{2}$$

$$x^2+4x+4=\frac{3}{2}+4$$

$$(x+2)^2=\frac{11}{2}$$

$$x+2=\pm\sqrt{\frac{11}{2}}$$

$$x+2=\pm\frac{\sqrt{11}}{\sqrt{2}}$$

$$x+2=\pm\frac{\sqrt{11}}{\sqrt{2}}\cdot\frac{\sqrt{2}}{\sqrt{2}}$$

$$x+2=\pm\frac{\sqrt{22}}{2}$$

$$x=\frac{-4\pm\sqrt{22}}{2}$$

35. First write the equation with an x^2 coefficient of 1:

$$2r^2 - r - 7 = 0$$

$$r^2 - \frac{1}{2}r - \frac{7}{2} = 0$$

Since $\left(-\frac{1}{2} \cdot \frac{1}{2}\right)^2 = \left(-\frac{1}{4}\right)^2 = \frac{1}{16}$, add $\frac{1}{16}$ to both sides of the equation.

$$r^2 - \frac{1}{2}r - \frac{7}{2} = 0$$

$$r^2 - \frac{1}{2}r = \frac{7}{2}$$

$$r^2 - \frac{1}{2}r + \frac{1}{16} = \frac{7}{2} + \frac{1}{16}$$

$$\left(r - \frac{1}{4}\right)^2 = \frac{57}{16}$$

$$r - \frac{1}{4} = \pm\sqrt{\frac{57}{16}}$$

$$r - \frac{1}{4} = \pm\frac{\sqrt{57}}{\sqrt{16}}$$

$$r - \frac{1}{4} = \pm\frac{\sqrt{57}}{4}$$

$$r = \frac{1 \pm \sqrt{57}}{4}$$

37. First write the equation with an x^2 coefficient of 1:

$$3x^2 + 4x - 5 = 0$$

$$x^2 + \frac{4}{3}x - \frac{5}{3} = 0$$

Since $\left(\frac{4}{3} \cdot \frac{1}{2}\right)^2 = \left(\frac{2}{3}\right)^2 = \frac{2^2}{3^2} = \frac{4}{9}$, add $\frac{4}{9}$ to both sides of the equation.

$$x + \frac{2}{3} = \pm\sqrt{\frac{19}{9}}$$

$$x + \frac{2}{3} = \pm\frac{\sqrt{19}}{\sqrt{9}}$$

$$x + \frac{2}{3} = \pm\frac{\sqrt{19}}{3}$$

$$x = \frac{-2 \pm \sqrt{19}}{3}$$

$$x^2 + \frac{4}{3}x - \frac{5}{3} = 0$$

$$x^2 + \frac{4}{3}x = \frac{5}{3}$$

$$x^2 + \frac{4}{3}x + \frac{4}{9} = \frac{5}{3} + \frac{4}{9}$$

$$\left(x + \frac{2}{3}\right)^2 = \frac{19}{9}$$

39. First write the equation with an x^2 coefficient of 1:

$$6x^2 - 8x = -1$$

$$x^2 - \frac{4}{3}x = -\frac{1}{6}$$

Since $\left(-\frac{4}{3} \cdot \frac{1}{2}\right)^2 = \left(\frac{2}{3}\right)^2 = \frac{2^2}{3^2} = \frac{4}{9}$, add $\frac{4}{9}$ to both sides of the equation.

$$x^2 - \frac{4}{3}x = -\frac{1}{6}$$

$$x^2 - \frac{4}{3}x + \frac{4}{9} = -\frac{1}{6} + \frac{4}{9}$$

$$\left(x - \frac{2}{3}\right)^2 = \frac{5}{18}$$

$$x - \frac{2}{3} = \pm\sqrt{\frac{5}{18}}$$

$$x - \frac{2}{3} = \pm\frac{\sqrt{5}}{\sqrt{18}}$$

$$x - \frac{2}{3} = \pm\frac{\sqrt{5}}{3\sqrt{2}}$$

$$x - \frac{2}{3} = \pm\frac{\sqrt{5}}{3\sqrt{2}} \cdot \frac{\sqrt{2}}{\sqrt{2}}$$

$$x - \frac{2}{3} = \pm\frac{\sqrt{10}}{6}$$

$$x = \frac{4 \pm \sqrt{10}}{6}$$

41. First write the equation with an x^2 coefficient of 1:

$$8w^2 + 4w - 3 = 0$$

$$w^2 + \frac{1}{2}w - \frac{3}{8} = 0$$

Since $\left(\frac{1}{2} \cdot \frac{1}{2}\right)^2 = \left(\frac{1}{4}\right)^2 = \frac{1}{16}$ add $\frac{1}{16}$ to both sides of the equation.

$$w^2 + \frac{1}{2}w - \frac{3}{8} = 0$$

$$w^2 + \frac{1}{2}w = \frac{3}{8}$$

$$w^2 + \frac{1}{2}w + \frac{1}{16} = \frac{3}{8} + \frac{1}{16}$$

$$\left(w + \frac{1}{4}\right)^2 = \frac{7}{16}$$

$$w + \frac{1}{4} = \pm\sqrt{\frac{7}{16}}$$

$$w + \frac{1}{4} = \pm\frac{\sqrt{7}}{\sqrt{16}}$$

$$w + \frac{1}{4} = \pm\frac{\sqrt{7}}{4}$$

$$w = \frac{-1 \pm \sqrt{7}}{4}$$

43. Since $\left(\frac{2}{2}\right)^2 = 1^2 = 1$, add 1 to both sides of the equation.

$$x^2 + 2x = -7$$

$$x^2 + 2x + 1 = -7 + 1$$

$$\left(x + 1\right)^2 = -6$$

$$x + 1 = \pm\sqrt{-6}$$

$$x = -1 \pm i\sqrt{6}$$

45. Since $\left(\frac{6}{2}\right)^2 = 3^2 = 9$, add 9 to both sides of the equation.

$$x^2 - 6x + 17 = 0$$

$$x^2 - 6x = -17$$

$$x^2 - 6x + 9 = -17 + 9$$

$$\left(x - 3\right)^2 = -8$$

$$x - 3 = \pm\sqrt{-8}$$

$$x = 3 \pm 2i\sqrt{2}$$

47. Since $\left(\frac{3}{2}\right)^2 = \frac{3^2}{2^2} = \frac{9}{4}$, add $\frac{9}{4}$ to both sides of the equation.

$$k^2 + 3k + 4 = 0$$

$$k^2 + 3k = -4$$

$$k^2 + 3k + \frac{9}{4} = -4 + \frac{9}{4}$$

$$\left(k + \frac{3}{2}\right)^2 = \frac{-7}{4}$$

$$k + \frac{3}{2} = \pm\sqrt{\frac{-7}{4}}$$

$$k + \frac{3}{2} = \pm\frac{\sqrt{-7}}{\sqrt{4}}$$

$$k + \frac{3}{2} = \pm\frac{i\sqrt{7}}{2}$$

$$k = \frac{-3 \pm i\sqrt{7}}{2}$$

49. Since $\left(\dfrac{2}{3}\cdot\dfrac{1}{2}\right)^2=\left(\dfrac{1}{3}\right)^2=\dfrac{1^2}{3^2}=\dfrac{1}{9}$, add $\dfrac{1}{9}$ to both sides of the equation.

$$x^2+\frac{2}{3}x+\frac{7}{3}=0$$

$$x^2+\frac{2}{3}x=-\frac{7}{3}$$

$$x^2+\frac{2}{3}x+\frac{1}{9}=-\frac{7}{3}+\frac{1}{9}$$

$$\left(x+\frac{1}{3}\right)^2=-\frac{20}{9}$$

$$x+\frac{1}{3}=\pm\sqrt{\frac{-20}{9}}$$

$$x+\frac{1}{3}=\pm\frac{\sqrt{-20}}{\sqrt{9}}$$

$$x+\frac{1}{3}=\pm\frac{2i\sqrt{5}}{3}$$

$$x=\frac{-1\pm2i\sqrt{5}}{3}$$

51. First write the equation with an x^2 coefficient of one:

$$4r^2-3r=-5$$

$$r^2-\frac{3}{4}r=-\frac{5}{4}$$

Since $\left(-\dfrac{3}{4}\cdot\dfrac{1}{2}\right)^2=\left(-\dfrac{3}{8}\right)^2=\dfrac{(-3)^2}{8^2}=\dfrac{9}{64}$, add $\dfrac{9}{64}$ to both sides of the equation.

$$r^2-\frac{3}{4}r=-\frac{5}{4}$$

$$r^2-\frac{3}{4}r+\frac{9}{64}=-\frac{5}{4}+\frac{9}{64}$$

$$\left(r-\frac{3}{8}\right)^2=-\frac{71}{64}$$

$$r-\frac{3}{8}=\pm\sqrt{-\frac{71}{64}}$$

$$r-\frac{3}{8}=\pm\frac{\sqrt{-71}}{\sqrt{64}}$$

$$r-\frac{3}{8}=\pm\frac{i\sqrt{71}}{8}$$

$$r=\frac{3\pm i\sqrt{71}}{8}$$

53. First write the equation with an x^2 coefficient of one:

$$4p^2+6p+3=0$$

$$p^2+\frac{3}{2}p+\frac{3}{4}=0$$

Since $\left(\dfrac{3}{2}\cdot\dfrac{1}{2}\right)^2=\left(\dfrac{3}{4}\right)^2=\dfrac{3^2}{4^2}=\dfrac{9}{16}$, add $\dfrac{9}{16}$ to both sides of the equation.

$$p^2+\frac{3}{2}p+\frac{3}{4}=0$$

$$p^2+\frac{3}{2}p=-\frac{3}{4}$$

$$p^2+\frac{3}{2}p+\frac{9}{16}=-\frac{3}{4}+\frac{9}{16}$$

$$\left(p+\frac{3}{4}\right)^2=-\frac{3}{16}$$

$$p+\frac{3}{4}=\pm\sqrt{-\frac{3}{16}}$$

$$p+\frac{3}{4}=\pm\frac{\sqrt{-3}}{\sqrt{16}}$$

$$p+\frac{3}{4}=\pm\frac{i\sqrt{3}}{4}$$

$$p=\frac{-3\pm i\sqrt{3}}{4}$$

55. Solve for x when $f(x)=0$:

$$0=x^2-8x+3$$

$$x^2-8x=-3$$

$$x^2-8x+16=-3+16$$

$$(x-4)^2=13$$

$$x-4=\pm\sqrt{13}$$

$$x=4\pm\sqrt{13}$$

The x-intercepts are

$(4-\sqrt{13},0)$ and $(4+\sqrt{13},0)$.

57. Solve for x when $f(x) = 0$:

$$0 = 2x^2 - 5x - 4$$

$$0 = x^2 - \frac{5}{2}x - 2$$

$$x^2 - \frac{5}{2}x = 2$$

$$x^2 - \frac{5}{2}x + \frac{25}{16} = 2 + \frac{25}{16}$$

$$\left(x - \frac{5}{4}\right)^2 = \frac{57}{16}$$

$$x - \frac{5}{4} = \pm\sqrt{\frac{57}{16}}$$

$$x - \frac{5}{4} = \pm\frac{\sqrt{57}}{\sqrt{16}}$$

$$x - \frac{5}{4} = \pm\frac{\sqrt{57}}{4}$$

$$x = \frac{5 \pm \sqrt{57}}{4}$$

The x-intercepts are

$\left(\frac{5 - \sqrt{57}}{4}, 0\right)$ and $\left(\frac{5 + \sqrt{57}}{4}, 0\right)$.

59. Solve for x when $f(x) = 0$:

$$0 = x^2 + 10x + 25$$

$$(x + 5)^2 = 0$$

$$x + 5 = 0$$

$$x = -5$$

The x-intercept is the vertex, $(-5, 0)$.

61. $x^2 - 9 = 0$

$$x^2 = 9$$

$$x = \pm\sqrt{9}$$

$$x = \pm 3$$

The solutions are -3 and 3.

63. $r^2 = 11r - 30$

$$r^2 - 11r + 30 = 0$$

$$(r - 6)(r - 5) = 0$$

$$r - 6 = 0 \quad \text{or} \quad r - 5 = 0$$

$$r = 6 \qquad r = 5$$

The solutions are 5 and 6.

65. $(x - 5)^2 = 32$

$$x - 5 = \pm\sqrt{32}$$

$$x - 5 = \pm 4\sqrt{2}$$

$$x = 5 \pm 4\sqrt{2}$$

The solutions are $5 - 4\sqrt{2}$ and $5 + 4\sqrt{2}$.

67. $3x^2 + 5x = 12$

$$3x^2 + 5x - 12 = 0$$

$$(3x - 4)(x + 3) = 0$$

$$3x - 4 = 0 \quad \text{or} \quad x + 3 = 0$$

$$3x = 4 \qquad x = -3$$

$$x = \frac{4}{3}$$

The solutions are -3 and $\frac{4}{3}$.

69. $x^2 = 13$

$$x = \pm\sqrt{13}$$

The solutions are $-\sqrt{13}$ and $\sqrt{13}$.

71. $t^2 - 6t - 3 = 0$

$$t^2 - 6t = 3$$

Since $\left(\frac{-6}{2}\right)^2 = (-3)^2 = 9$, we add 9 to both sides

of the equation so that the left side is a perfect square trinomial.

$$t^2 - 6t + 9 = 3 + 9$$

$$(t - 3)^2 = 12$$

$$t - 3 = \pm\sqrt{12}$$

$$t - 3 = \pm 2\sqrt{3}$$

$$t = 3 \pm 2\sqrt{3}$$

The solutions are $3 - 2\sqrt{3}$ and $3 + 2\sqrt{3}$.

73. No, the student did not solve the equation correctly. The student should have first divided both sides by 4 and then completed the square and extracted the roots. The correct solution is:

$$4x^2 + 6x = 1$$

$$x^2 + \frac{3}{2}x = \frac{1}{4}$$

$$x^2 + \frac{3}{2}x + \frac{9}{16} = \frac{1}{4} + \frac{9}{16}$$

$$\left(x + \frac{3}{4}\right)^2 = \frac{4}{16} + \frac{9}{16}$$

$$\left(x + \frac{3}{4}\right)^2 = \frac{13}{16}$$

$$x + \frac{3}{4} = \pm\sqrt{\frac{13}{16}}$$

$$x + \frac{3}{4} = \pm\frac{\sqrt{13}}{\sqrt{16}}$$

$$x + \frac{3}{4} = \pm\frac{\sqrt{13}}{4}$$

$$x = -\frac{3}{4} \pm \frac{\sqrt{13}}{4}$$

$$x = \frac{-3 \pm \sqrt{13}}{4}$$

75. a.

$$3 = x^2 + 6x + 13$$

$$-10 = x^2 + 6x$$

$$-10 + 9 = x^2 + 6x + 9$$

$$-1 = (x + 3)^2$$

The next step is to take the square root of both sides. However, this will produce imaginary numbers. There is no real number such that $f(x) = 3$.

b.

$$4 = x^2 + 6x + 13$$

$$-9 = x^2 + 6x$$

$$-9 + 9 = x^2 + 6x + 9$$

$$0 = (x + 3)^2$$

$$0 = x + 3$$

$$-3 = x$$

When $x = -3$, $f(x) = 4$.

c.

$$6 = x^2 + 6x + 13$$

$$-7 = x^2 + 6x$$

$$-7 + 9 = x^2 + 6x + 9$$

$$2 = (x + 3)^2$$

$$\pm\sqrt{2} = x + 3$$

$$-3 \pm \sqrt{2} = x$$

When $x = -3 \pm \sqrt{2}$ $f(x) = 6$.

77. When $x = 1$ or 3, both sides of the equation are the same.

79. When $x = 2$ or 3, the left side of the equation is equal to -2.

81. The two equations have the points $(0, -0.5)$ and $(5, -8)$ in common.

83. a.

$$x^2 - 6x + 8 = 0$$

$$(x - 4)(x - 2) = 0$$

$$x - 4 = 0 \quad \text{or} \quad x - 2 = 0$$

$$x = 4 \qquad\qquad x = 2$$

The solutions are 2 and 4.

b.

$$x^2 - 6x + 8 = 0$$

$$x^2 - 6x = -8$$

Since $\left(\dfrac{-6}{2}\right)^2 = (-3)^2 = 9$, we add 9 to both sides of the equation so that the left side is a perfect square trinomial.

$$x^2 - 6x + 9 = -8 + 9$$

$$(x - 3)^2 = 1$$

$$x - 3 = \pm\sqrt{1}$$

$$x - 3 = \pm 1$$

$$x - 3 = -1 \quad \text{or} \quad x - 3 = 1$$

$$x = 2 \qquad\qquad x = 4$$

The solutions are 2 and 4.

c. Answers may vary.

85. a. Yes;

$x^2 + 4x = 7$

Since $\left(\dfrac{4}{2}\right)^2 = 2^2 = 4$, we add 4 to both sides

of the equation so that the left side is a perfect square trinomial.

$x^2 + 4x + 4 = 7 + 4$

$(x+2)^2 = 11$

$x + 2 = \pm\sqrt{11}$

$x = -2 \pm \sqrt{11}$

The solutions are $-2 - \sqrt{11}$ and $-2 + \sqrt{11}$.

b. No; the solutions involve radicals, so it is not possible to factor the express $x^2 + 4x - 7$ over the set of integers.

c. A quadratic equation of the form $x^2 + bx + c = 0$ can be solved by factoring if $b^2 - 4c$ is a perfect square. (see section 9.5)

87. Answers may vary.

89. $w^2 - 10w + 25 = (w-5)^2$

91. $x^2 + \dfrac{5}{3}x + \dfrac{25}{36} = \left(x + \dfrac{5}{6}\right)^2$

93. $-5x^2(x-4)^2 = -5x^2\left(x^2 - 2(4)(x) + 4^2\right)$

$= -5x^2\left(x^2 - 8x + 16\right)$

$= -5x^4 + 40x^3 - 80x^2$

Description: *fourth degree polynomial in one variable*

95. $2(x-4)^2 + 5 = 11$

$2(x-4)^2 = 6$

$(x-4)^2 = 3$

$x - 4 = \pm\sqrt{3}$

$x = 4 \pm \sqrt{3}$

The solutions are $4 - \sqrt{3}$ and $4 + \sqrt{3}$.

Description: *quadratic equation in one variable*

97. $p^2 - 8pq + 16q^2 = p^2 - 2(4q)p + (4q)^2$

$= (p - 4q)^2$

Description: *quadratic (or second degree) polynomial in two variables*

Homework 9.6

1. $2x^2 + 5x + 3 = 0$

$a = 2, b = 5, c = 3$

$x = \dfrac{-5 \pm \sqrt{5^2 - 4(2)(3)}}{2(2)}$

$= \dfrac{-5 \pm \sqrt{25 - 24}}{4}$

$= \dfrac{-5 \pm \sqrt{1}}{4}$

$= \dfrac{-5 \pm 1}{4}$

$x = \dfrac{-5-1}{4}$ or $x = \dfrac{-5+1}{4}$

$= \dfrac{-6}{4}$ $= \dfrac{-4}{4}$

$= -\dfrac{3}{2}$ $= -1$

The solutions are $-\dfrac{3}{2}$ and -1.

3. $x^2 + 3x - 5 = 0$

$a = 1, b = 3, c = -5$

$x = \dfrac{-3 \pm \sqrt{3^2 - 4(1)(-5)}}{2(1)}$

$= \dfrac{-3 \pm \sqrt{9 + 20}}{2}$

$= \dfrac{-3 \pm \sqrt{29}}{2}$

The solutions are $\dfrac{-3 \pm \sqrt{29}}{2}$.

5. $3w^2 - 5w - 3 = 0$

$a = 3, b = -5, c = -3$

$$w = \frac{-(-5) \pm \sqrt{(-5)^2 - 4(3)(-3)}}{2(3)}$$

$$= \frac{5 \pm \sqrt{25 + 36}}{6}$$

$$= \frac{5 \pm \sqrt{61}}{6}$$

The solutions are $\dfrac{5 \pm \sqrt{61}}{6}$.

7. $3x^2 - 6x + 1 = 0$

$a = 3, \ b = -6, \ c = 1$

$$x = \frac{-(-6) \pm \sqrt{(-6)^2 - 4(3)(1)}}{2(3)}$$

$$x = \frac{6 \pm \sqrt{24}}{6}$$

$$x = \frac{6 \pm 2\sqrt{6}}{6}$$

$$x = \frac{3 \pm \sqrt{6}}{3}$$

9. $t^2 = 4t + 3$

$t^2 - 4t - 3 = 0$

$a = 1, \ b = -4, \ c = -3$

$$x = \frac{-(-4) \pm \sqrt{(-4)^2 - 4(1)(-3)}}{2(1)}$$

$$x = \frac{4 \pm \sqrt{28}}{2}$$

$$x = \frac{4 \pm 2\sqrt{7}}{2}$$

$$x = 2 \pm \sqrt{7}$$

11. $4x^2 - 2x = 3$

$4x^2 - 2x - 3 = 0$

$a = 4, \ b = -2, \ c = -3$

$$x = \frac{-(-2) \pm \sqrt{(-2)^2 - 4(4)(-3)}}{2(4)}$$

$$= \frac{2 \pm \sqrt{52}}{8}$$

$$= \frac{2 + 2\sqrt{13}}{8}$$

$$= \frac{1 \pm \sqrt{13}}{4}$$

$$x = \frac{1 + \sqrt{13}}{4} \ \text{ or } \ x = \frac{1 - \sqrt{13}}{4}$$

13. $3x^2 - 17 = 0$

$a = 3, \ b = 0, c = -17$

$$x = \frac{0 \pm \sqrt{(0)^2 - 4(3)(-17)}}{2(3)}$$

$$x = \pm \frac{\sqrt{204}}{6}$$

$$x = \pm \frac{2\sqrt{51}}{6}$$

$$x = \pm \frac{\sqrt{51}}{3}$$

15. $2y^2 = -5y$

$2y^2 + 5y = 0$

$a = 2, \ b = 5, \ c = 0$

$$x = \frac{-(5) \pm \sqrt{(5)^2 - 4(2)(0)}}{2(2)}$$

$$x = \frac{-5 \pm \sqrt{25}}{4}$$

$$x = \frac{-5 \pm 5}{4}$$

$$x = 0 \ \text{ or } \ x = -\frac{5}{2}$$

17.
$$\frac{2}{3}x^2 - \frac{5}{6}x = \frac{1}{3}$$

$$\frac{2}{3}x^2 - \frac{5}{6}x - \frac{1}{3} = 0$$

$$a = \frac{2}{3}, \ b = -\frac{5}{6}, \ c = -\frac{1}{3}$$

$$x = \frac{-\left(-\frac{5}{6}\right) \pm \sqrt{\left(-\frac{5}{6}\right)^2 - 4\left(\frac{2}{3}\right)\left(-\frac{1}{3}\right)}}{2\left(\frac{2}{3}\right)}$$

$$x = \frac{\frac{5}{6} \pm \sqrt{\frac{25}{36} + \frac{8}{9}}}{\frac{4}{3}}$$

$$x = \frac{\frac{5}{6} \pm \sqrt{\frac{57}{36}}}{\frac{4}{3}}$$

$$x = \frac{\frac{5}{6} \pm \frac{\sqrt{57}}{\sqrt{36}}}{\frac{4}{3}}$$

$$x = \frac{\frac{5}{6} \pm \frac{\sqrt{57}}{6}}{\frac{4}{3}}$$

$$x = \frac{5 \pm \sqrt{57}}{8}$$

19. $(3x+2)(x-1) = 1$

$$3x^2 - x - 2 = 1$$

$$3x^2 - x - 3 = 0$$

$$a = 3, \ b = -1, \ c = -3$$

$$x = \frac{-(-1) \pm \sqrt{(-1)^2 - 4(3)(-3)}}{2(3)}$$

$$x = \frac{1 \pm \sqrt{37}}{6}$$

21.
$$2x^2 = 5x + 4$$

$$2x^2 - 5x - 4 = 0$$

$$a = 2, \ b = -5, \ c = -4$$

$$x = \frac{-(-5) \pm \sqrt{(-5)^2 - 4(2)(-4)}}{2(2)}$$

$$x = \frac{5 \pm \sqrt{57}}{4}$$

$$x \approx \frac{5 + 7.55}{4} \ \text{ or } \ x \approx \frac{5 - 7.55}{4}$$

$$x \approx 3.14 \ \text{ or } \ x \approx -0.64$$

23.
$$2.85p^2 - 7.12p = 4.49$$

$$2.85p^2 - 7.12p - 4.49 = 0$$

$$a = 2.85, b = -7.12, c = -4.49$$

$$p = \frac{-(-7.12) \pm \sqrt{(-7.12)^2 - 4(2.85)(-4.49)}}{2(2.85)}$$

$$p = \frac{7.12 \pm \sqrt{101.88}}{5.7}$$

$$p \approx \frac{7.12 + 10.09}{5.7} \ \text{ or } \ p \approx \frac{7.12 - 10.09}{5.7}$$

$$p \approx 3.02 \ \text{ or } \ p \approx -0.52$$

25. $-5.4x(x+9.8) + 4.1 = 3.2 - 6.9x$

$$-5.4x^2 - 52.92x + 4.1 - 3.2 + 6.9x = 0$$

$$-5.4x^2 - 46.02x + 0.9 = 0$$

$$a = -5.4, \ b = -46.02, \ c = 0.9$$

$$x = \frac{-(-46.02) \pm \sqrt{(-46.02)^2 - 4(-5.4)(0.9)}}{2(-5.4)}$$

$$x = \frac{46.02 \pm \sqrt{2137.2804}}{-10.8}$$

$$x \approx \frac{46.02 + 46.23}{-10.8} \ \text{ or } \ x \approx \frac{46.02 - 46.23}{-10.8}$$

$$x \approx -8.54 \ \text{ or } \ x \approx 0.02$$

27. $0 = 2x^2 - x - 7$

$$x = \frac{-(-1) \pm \sqrt{(-1)^2 - 4(2)(-7)}}{2(2)}$$

$$x = \frac{1 \pm \sqrt{57}}{4}$$

The *x*-intercepts are
$$\left(\frac{1-\sqrt{57}}{4}, 0\right) \text{ and } \left(\frac{1+\sqrt{57}}{4}, 0\right).$$

29. $0 = 3x^2 + 2x + 5$

$$x = \frac{-(2) \pm \sqrt{(2)^2 - 4(3)(5)}}{2(3)}$$

$$x = \frac{-2 \pm \sqrt{-56}}{6}$$

The only way to take the square root of a negative number is to use imaginary numbers. Therefore, there are no x-intercepts.

31. $0 = x^2 + 2x - 5$

$$x = \frac{-(2) \pm \sqrt{(2)^2 - 4(1)(-5)}}{2(1)}$$

$$x = \frac{-2 \pm \sqrt{24}}{2}$$

$$x = \frac{-2 \pm 2\sqrt{6}}{2}$$

$$x = -1 \pm \sqrt{6}$$

The x-intercepts are
$(-1 - \sqrt{6}, 0)$ and $(-1 + \sqrt{6}, 0)$.

33. $x^2 - 3x + 8 = 0$
$a = 1,\ b = -3,\ c = 8$

$$x = \frac{-(-3) \pm \sqrt{(-3)^2 - 4(1)(8)}}{2(1)}$$

$$x = \frac{3 \pm \sqrt{-23}}{2}$$

$$x = \frac{3 \pm i\sqrt{23}}{2}$$

35. $-w^2 + 2w = 5$
$-w^2 + 2w - 5 = 0$
$a = -1,\ b = 2,\ c = -5$

$$w = \frac{-(2) \pm \sqrt{(2)^2 - 4(-1)(-5)}}{2(-1)}$$

$$w = \frac{-2 \pm \sqrt{-16}}{-2}$$

$$w = \frac{-2 \pm 4i}{-2}$$

$$w = 1 \pm 2i$$

37. $\dfrac{1}{4} x^2 = 2x - \dfrac{9}{2}$

$$\frac{1}{4} x^2 - 2x + \frac{9}{2} = 0$$

$$a = \frac{1}{4},\ b = -2,\ c = \frac{9}{2}$$

$$x = \frac{-(-2) \pm \sqrt{(-2)^2 - 4\left(\frac{1}{4}\right)\left(\frac{9}{2}\right)}}{2\left(\frac{1}{4}\right)}$$

$$x = \frac{2 \pm \sqrt{-\frac{1}{2}}}{\frac{1}{2}}$$

$$x = 4 \pm 2i\sqrt{\frac{1}{2}}$$

$$x = 4 \pm 2i \frac{\sqrt{1}}{\sqrt{2}}$$

$$x = 4 \pm 2i \frac{\sqrt{1}}{\sqrt{2}} \cdot \frac{\sqrt{2}}{\sqrt{2}}$$

$$x = 4 \pm 2i \frac{\sqrt{2}}{2}$$

$$x = 4 \pm i\sqrt{2}$$

39. $3x(3x - 2) = -2$

$$9x^2 - 6x = -2$$

$$9x^2 - 6x + 2 = 0$$

$$a = 9,\ b = -6,\ c = 2$$

$$x = \frac{-(-6) \pm \sqrt{(-6)^2 - 4(9)(2)}}{2(9)}$$

$$x = \frac{6 \pm \sqrt{-36}}{18}$$

$$x = \frac{6 \pm 6i}{18}$$

$$x = \frac{1 \pm i}{3}$$

41.
$$3k^2 = 4k - 5$$
$$3k^2 - 4k + 5 = 0$$
$$a = 3, b = -4, c = 5$$
$$k = \frac{-(-4) \pm \sqrt{(-4)^2 - 4(3)(5)}}{2(3)}$$
$$k = \frac{4 \pm \sqrt{-44}}{6}$$
$$k = \frac{4 \pm 2i\sqrt{11}}{6}$$
$$k = \frac{2 \pm i\sqrt{11}}{3}$$

43. $4x^2 - 80 = 0$
$$4x^2 = 80$$
$$x^2 = 20$$
$$x = \pm\sqrt{20}$$
$$x = \pm 2\sqrt{5}$$

45. $5(w+3)^2 + 2 = 8$
$$5(w+3)^2 = 6$$
$$(w+3)^2 = \frac{6}{5}$$
$$w + 3 = \pm\sqrt{\frac{6}{5}}$$
$$w + 3 = \pm\frac{\sqrt{6}}{\sqrt{5}}$$
$$w + 3 = \pm\frac{\sqrt{6}}{\sqrt{5}} \cdot \frac{\sqrt{5}}{\sqrt{5}}$$
$$w + 3 = \pm\frac{\sqrt{30}}{5}$$
$$w = \frac{-15 \pm \sqrt{30}}{5}$$

47.
$$m^2 = -12m - 36$$
$$m^2 + 12m + 36 = 0$$
$$(m+6)^2 = 0$$
$$m + 6 = 0$$
$$m = -6$$

49.
$$-24x^2 + 18x = -60$$
$$-24x^2 + 18x + 60 = 0$$
$$a = -24, b = 18, c = 60$$
$$x = \frac{-(18) \pm \sqrt{(18)^2 - 4(-24)(60)}}{2(-24)}$$
$$x = \frac{-18 \pm \sqrt{6084}}{-48}$$
$$x = \frac{-18 \pm 78}{-48}$$
$$x = -\frac{5}{4} \text{ or } x = 2$$

51. $\frac{1}{3}x^2 - \frac{3}{2}x = \frac{1}{6}$
$$2x^2 - 9x = 1$$
$$2x^2 - 9x - 1 = 0$$
$$a = 2, \ b = -9, \ c = -1$$
$$x = \frac{-(-9) \pm \sqrt{(-9)^2 - 4(2)(-1)}}{2(2)}$$
$$x = \frac{9 \pm \sqrt{89}}{4}$$

53. $(x-5)(x+2) = 3(x-1) + 2$
$$x^2 - 3x - 10 = 3x - 3 + 2$$
$$x^2 - 6x = 9$$
$$x^2 - 6x + 9 = 9 + 9$$
$$(x-3)^2 = 18$$
$$x - 3 = \pm\sqrt{18}$$
$$x - 3 = \pm 3\sqrt{2}$$
$$x = 3 \pm 3\sqrt{2}$$

55. $25r^2 = 49$
$$r^2 = \frac{49}{25}$$
$$r = \pm\sqrt{\frac{49}{25}}$$
$$r = \pm\frac{\sqrt{49}}{\sqrt{25}}$$
$$r = \pm\frac{7}{5}$$

57.
$$(x-1)^2 + (x+2)^2 = 6$$
$$x^2 - 2x + 1 + x^2 + 4x + 4 = 6$$
$$2x^2 + 2x + 5 = 6$$
$$2x^2 + 2x - 1 = 0$$
$$a = 2,\ b = 2,\ c = -1$$
$$x = \frac{-(2) \pm \sqrt{(2)^2 - 4(2)(-1)}}{2(2)}$$
$$x = \frac{-2 \pm \sqrt{12}}{4}$$
$$x = \frac{-2 \pm 2\sqrt{3}}{4}$$
$$x = \frac{-1 \pm \sqrt{3}}{2}$$

59. $4x^2 = -25$
$$x^2 = -\frac{25}{4}$$
$$x = \pm\sqrt{-\frac{25}{4}}$$
$$x = \pm\frac{\sqrt{-25}}{\sqrt{4}}$$
$$x = \pm\frac{5i}{2}$$

61.
$$-2t^2 + 5t = 6$$
$$-2t^2 + 5t - 6 = 0$$
$$a = -2,\ b = 5,\ c = -6$$
$$t = \frac{-(5) \pm \sqrt{(5)^2 - 4(-2)(-6)}}{2(-2)}$$
$$t = \frac{-5 \pm \sqrt{-23}}{-4}$$
$$t = \frac{5 \pm i\sqrt{23}}{4}$$

63. $(x-6)^2 + 5 = -43$
$$(x-6)^2 = -48$$
$$x - 6 = \pm\sqrt{-48}$$
$$x - 6 = \pm 4i\sqrt{3}$$
$$x = 6 \pm 4i\sqrt{3}$$

65. $(y-2)(y-5) = -4$
$$y^2 - 7y + 10 = -4$$
$$y^2 - 7y = -14$$
$$y^2 - 7y + \frac{49}{4} = -14 + \frac{49}{4}$$
$$\left(y - \frac{7}{2}\right)^2 = \frac{-7}{4}$$
$$y - \frac{7}{2} = \pm\sqrt{\frac{-7}{4}}$$
$$y - \frac{7}{2} = \pm\frac{\sqrt{-7}}{\sqrt{4}}$$
$$y - \frac{7}{2} = \pm\frac{i\sqrt{7}}{2}$$
$$y = \frac{7 \pm i\sqrt{7}}{2}$$

67. Since $(4)^2 - 4(3)(-5) = 76 > 0$, there are 2 real solutions.

69. Since $(-5)^2 - 4(2)(7) = -31 < 0$, there are 2 imaginary solutions.

71. Since $(-12)^2 - 4(4)(9) = 0$, there is 1 real solution.

73. a. Substitute 3 for $f(x)$:
$$3 = x^2 - 4x + 8$$
$$x^2 - 4x + 5 = 0$$
$$a = 1, b = -4, c = 5$$
$$b^2 - 4ac = (-4)^2 - 4(1)(5) = 16 - 20 = -4 < 0$$
So, there are no real number solutions, which means there are no points on f at $y = 3$.

b. Substitute 4 for $f(x)$:
$$4 = x^2 - 4x + 8$$
$$x^2 - 4x + 4 = 0$$
$$a = 1, b = -4, c = 4$$
$$b^2 - 4ac = (-4)^2 - 4(1)(4) = 16 - 16 = 0$$
So, there is one solution to the equation, which means there is one point on f at $y = 4$.

c. Substitute 5 for $f(x)$:

$5 = x^2 - 4x + 8$

$x^2 - 4x + 3 = 0$

$a = 1, b = -4, c = 3$

$b^2 - 4ac = (-4)^2 - 4(1)(3) = 16 - 12 = 4 > 0$

So, there are two real number solutions, which means there are two points on f at $y = 5$.

d.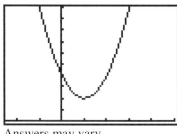

Answers may vary.

75. Solve for x when $f(x) = 2$:

$2 = x^2 - 6x + 7$

$x^2 - 6x + 5 = 0$

$(x - 5)(x - 1) = 0$

$x - 5 = 0$ or $x - 1 = 0$

$x = 5$ or $x = 1$

Therefore, two points at height 2 are $(1, 2)$ and $(5, 2)$. Since these points are symmetric and the average of the x-coordinates at these points is

$\dfrac{1+5}{2} = 3$ the x-coordinate of the vertex is 3.

Substitute 3 for x in $f(x)$ to find the y-coordinate of the vertex:

$f(3) = 3^2 - 6(3) + 7 = -2$

So the vertex is $(3, -2)$.

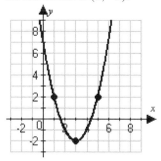

77. a.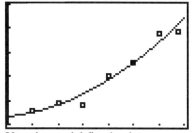

Yes, the model fits the data very well.

b. To find the capacity of the U.S. nuclear power plants in 2006, let $t = 36$ and solve for f.

$f(36) = 0.027(36)^2 + 0.22(36) + 53.3$

$= 0.027(1296) + 7.92 + 53.3$

$= 34.992 + 61.22$

$= 96.212$

The model estimates that U.S. nuclear power plants were working at 96% capacity in 2006.

c. To find the year when U.S. power plants will be working at full capacity, substitute 100 for f and solve for t.

$100 = 0.027t^2 + 0.22t + 53.3$

$0 = 0.027t^2 + 0.22t - 46.7$

$a = 0.027, b = 0.22, c = -46.7$

$t = \dfrac{-(0.22) \pm \sqrt{(0.22)^2 - 4(0.027)(-46.7)}}{2(0.027)}$

$t = \dfrac{-0.22 \pm \sqrt{5.09}}{0.054}$

$t \approx \dfrac{-0.22 \pm 2.26}{0.054}$

$t \approx 37.78$ or $t \approx -45.93$

$1970 - 46 = 1924$, which is before nuclear power plants existed, so model breakdown has occurred for that value of x. The model predicts that in $1970 + 38 = 2008$, U.S. power plants will be working at full capacity.

d. Answers may vary.

79. a.

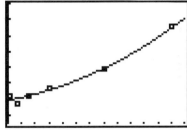

The model fits the data very well.

b. To find the percentage of women police officers in Glen Ellyn, Illinois, let $t = 27.04$ and solve for f.

$$f(27.04) = 0.00006(27.04)^2$$
$$+0.012(27.04) + 7.88$$
$$\approx 0.044 + 0.324 + 7.88$$
$$\approx 8.25$$

The model predicts that Glen Ellyn would have about 8.25% of police officers who are women.

c.

$$10 = 0.00006t^2 + 0.012t + 7.88$$
$$0 = 0.00006t^2 + 0.012t - 2.12$$
$$a = 0.00006, b = 0.012, c = -2.12$$
$$t = \frac{-(0.012) \pm \sqrt{(0.012)^2 - 4(0.00006)(-2.12)}}{2(0.00006)}$$
$$t \approx \frac{-0.012 \pm 0.02555}{0.00012}$$
$$t \approx -312.92 \text{ or } t \approx 112.92$$

The model predicts that 10% of police officers will be women in cities with populations of about 112.9 thousand people. The population size of −312.9 does not make sense, so model breakdown has occurred for that value.

81. a.
$$h(3) = -16(3)^2 + 52(3) + 4$$
$$= -16(9) + 156 + 4$$
$$= -144 + 160$$
$$= 16$$

After 3 seconds the stone's height is 16 feet.

b.
$$30 = -16t^2 + 52t + 4$$
$$26 = -16t^2 + 52t$$
$$-\frac{13}{8} = t^2 - \frac{13}{4}t$$
$$-\frac{13}{8} + \frac{169}{64} = t^2 - \frac{13}{4}t + \frac{169}{64}$$
$$\frac{65}{64} = \left(t - \frac{13}{8}\right)^2$$
$$\pm\sqrt{\frac{65}{64}} = t - \frac{13}{8}$$
$$\pm\frac{\sqrt{65}}{\sqrt{64}} = t - \frac{13}{8}$$
$$\pm\frac{\sqrt{65}}{8} = t - \frac{13}{8}$$
$$\frac{13 \pm \sqrt{65}}{8} = t$$
$$t \approx 2.63 \text{ or } t \approx 0.62$$

The stone is at a height of 30 feet at 0.62 second and 2.63 seconds.

c.
$$0 = -16t^2 + 52t + 4$$
$$a = -16, b = 52, c = 4$$
$$t = \frac{-(52) \pm \sqrt{(52)^2 - 4(-16)(4)}}{2(-16)}$$
$$t = \frac{-52 \pm \sqrt{2960}}{-32}$$
$$t \approx 3.33 \text{ or } t \approx -0.08$$

Since we are looking for the time the stone hit the ground after it was thrown, we should not use −0.08 seconds.

The stone will hit the ground 3.33 seconds after being thrown.

83. The graphs of the two equations meet when $x = -2$ or 1.3.

85. The graph of the equation is equal to 4 when $x = \pm 2.4$.

87. The graphs of the two equations meet at the points $(-3.4, -3.4)$ and $(2.0, -1.2)$.

89. The student did not solve the equation correctly because they did not change the form into $ax^2 + bx + c = 0$ first. Here is the correct way:

$2x^2 + 5x = 1$

$2x^2 + 5x - 1 = 0$

So, $a = 2$, $b = 5$, $c = -1$

$x = \dfrac{-5 \pm \sqrt{(5)^2 - 4(2)(-1)}}{2(2)}$

$x = \dfrac{-5 \pm \sqrt{33}}{4}$

91. a. $mx + b = 0$

$mx + b - b = 0 - b$

$mx = -b$

$\dfrac{mx}{m} = -\dfrac{b}{m}$

$x = -\dfrac{b}{m}$

b. $7x + 21 = 0$

So, $m = 7$ and $b = 21$. Using the formula from part a:

$x = -\dfrac{21}{7} = -3$

Solving for x in the usual way:

$7x + 21 = 0$

$7x + 21 - 21 = 0 - 21$

$7x = -21$

$\dfrac{7x}{7} = -\dfrac{21}{7}$

$x = -3$

93. Factor:

$x^2 - x - 20 = 0$

$(x - 5)(x + 4) = 0$

$x - 5 = 0$ or $x + 4 = 0$

$x = 5$ or $x = -4$

Completing the square:

$x^2 - x = 20$

$x^2 - x + \dfrac{1}{4} = 20 + \dfrac{1}{4}$

$\left(x - \dfrac{1}{2}\right)^2 = \dfrac{81}{4}$

$x - \dfrac{1}{2} = \pm\sqrt{\dfrac{81}{4}}$

$x - \dfrac{1}{2} = \pm\dfrac{9}{2}$

$x = \dfrac{1}{2} + \dfrac{9}{2}$ or $x = \dfrac{1}{2} - \dfrac{9}{2}$

$x = \dfrac{10}{2}$ or $x = -\dfrac{8}{2}$

$x = 5$ or $x = -4$

Quadratic formula:

$x^2 - x - 20 = 0$

$x = \dfrac{-(-1) \pm \sqrt{(-1)^2 - 4(1)(-20)}}{2(1)}$

$x = \dfrac{1 \pm \sqrt{81}}{2}$

$x = \dfrac{1 \pm 9}{2}$

$x = \dfrac{1 + 9}{2}$ or $x = \dfrac{1 - 9}{2}$

$x = 5$ or $x = -4$

95. Answers may vary.

97. $(x + 2)(x - 5) = x^2 - 5x + 2x - 10$
$= x^2 - 3x - 10$

99.
$$(x+2)(x-5)=3$$
$$x^2-5x+2x-10=3$$
$$x^2-3x=13$$
$$x^2-3x+\frac{9}{4}=13+\frac{9}{4}$$
$$\left(x-\frac{3}{2}\right)^2=\frac{61}{4}$$
$$x-\frac{3}{2}=\pm\sqrt{\frac{61}{4}}$$
$$x-\frac{3}{2}=\pm\frac{\sqrt{61}}{\sqrt{4}}$$
$$x-\frac{3}{2}=\pm\frac{\sqrt{61}}{2}$$
$$x=\frac{3\pm\sqrt{61}}{2}$$

101.
$$-4(x-2)^2+3=-1$$
$$-4(x-2)^2=-4$$
$$(x-2)^2=1$$
$$x-2=\pm\sqrt{1}$$
$$x-2=\pm1$$
$$x=2\pm1=3,1$$

103.
$$-4(x-2)^2+3=-4(x^2-4x+4)+3$$
$$=-4x^2+16x-16+3$$
$$=-4x^2+16x-13$$

105. $8x^2-18x+9=(4x-3)(2x-3)$
This is a quadratic polynomial in one variable.

107.
$$f(-2)=8(-2)^2-18(-2)+9$$
$$=8(4)+36+9$$
$$=32+45$$
$$=77$$
This is a quadratic function.

109.
$$0=8x^2-18x+9$$
$$0=(4x-3)(2x-3)$$
$$0=4x-3 \qquad 0=2x-3$$
$$3=4x \quad \text{or} \quad 3=2x$$
$$\frac{3}{4}=x \qquad\qquad \frac{3}{2}=x$$
This is a quadratic equation in one variable.

Homework 9.7

1. Add the first and third equations:
$$x+y+z=0$$
$$\underline{x+2y-z=-7}$$
$$2x+3y=-7 \quad (4)$$
Add the second and the third equations:
$$x-y+z=6$$
$$\underline{x+2y-z=-7}$$
$$2x+y=-1 \quad (5)$$
Subtract the two new equations:
$$2x+3y=-7$$
$$\underline{-2x-y=1}$$
$$2y=-6$$
$$y=-3$$
Solve for x:
$$2x+3(-3)=-7$$
$$2x-9=-7$$
$$2x=2$$
$$x=1$$
Solve for z:
$$(1)+(-3)+z=0$$
$$1-3+z=0$$
$$-2+z=0$$
$$z=2$$
The solution of the system is the point $(1,-3,2)$.

3. Multiply the first equation by 2 and add it to the second equation.
$$2x+2y-2z=-2$$
$$\underline{2x-2y+3z=8}$$
$$4x+z=6 \quad (4)$$

Add equations (1) and (3):
$$x+y-z=-1$$
$$\underline{2x-y+2z=9}$$
$$3x+z=8 \quad (5)$$

Subtract equations (4) and (5).
$$4x+z=6$$
$$\underline{-3x-z=-8}$$
$$x=-2$$

Solve for z:

$$4(-2) + z = 6$$
$$-8 + z = 6$$
$$z = 14$$

Solve for y:
$$(-2) + y - (14) = -1$$
$$-2 + y - 14 = -1$$
$$y - 16 = -1$$
$$y = 15$$

The solution of the system is the point $(-2, 15, 14)$.

5. Add the first and third equations:
$$3x - y + 2z = 0$$
$$\underline{x + y + 6z = 0}$$
$$4x \qquad + 8z = 0 \quad (4)$$

Add 3 times the first equation to the second equation:
$$9x - 3y + 6z = 0$$
$$\underline{2x + 3y + 8z = 8}$$
$$11x \qquad + 14z = 8 \quad (5)$$

Subtract 11 times the fourth equation from 4 times the fifth equation:
$$44x + 56z = 32$$
$$\underline{-44x - 88z = 0}$$
$$-32z = 32$$
$$z = -1$$

Solve for x:
$$4x + 8(-1) = 0$$
$$4x - 8 = 0$$
$$4x = 8$$
$$x = 2$$

Solve for y:
$$(2) + y + 6(-1) = 0$$
$$2 + y - 6 = 0$$
$$y - 4 = 0$$
$$y = 4$$

The solution to the system is the point $(2, 4, -1)$.

7. Add the first and second equations:
$$2x + y + z = 3$$
$$\underline{2x - y - z = 9}$$
$$4x \qquad = 12$$
$$x \qquad = 3$$

Add the first and third equations:
$$2x + y + z = 3$$
$$\underline{x + y - z = 0}$$
$$3x + 2y \qquad = 3$$

Solve for y:
$$3(3) + 2y = 3$$
$$9 + 2y = 3$$
$$2y = -6$$
$$y = -3$$

Solve for z:
$$(3) + (-3) - z = 0$$
$$3 - 3 - z = 0$$
$$-z = 0$$
$$z = 0$$

The solution to the system is the point $(3, -3, 0)$.

9. Add the first equation to 2 times the second equation:
$$2x + 2y + z = 1$$
$$\underline{-2x + 2y + 4z = 6}$$
$$4y + 5z = 7 \quad (4)$$

Add the second equation to the third equation:
$$-x + y + 2z = 3$$
$$\underline{x + 2y + 4z = 0}$$
$$3y + 6z = 3 \quad (5)$$

Subtract 4 times the fifth equation from 3 times the fourth equation.
$$12y + 15z = 21$$
$$\underline{-12y - 24z = -12}$$
$$-9z = 9$$
$$z = -1$$

Solve for y:
$$3y + 6(-1) = 3$$
$$3y - 6 = 3$$
$$3y = 9$$
$$y = 3$$

Solve for x:
$$-x + (3) + 2(-1) = 3$$
$$-x + 3 - 2 = 3$$
$$-x + 1 = 3$$
$$x = -2$$

The solution to the system is the point $(-2, 3, -1)$.

11. Add the first and second equations:
$$2x - y + 2z = 6$$
$$3x + y - z = 5$$
$$\overline{5x \qquad + z = 11} \quad (4)$$

Add 2 times the first equation to the third equation:
$$4x - 2y + 4z = 12$$
$$x + 2y + z = 3$$
$$\overline{5x \qquad + 5z = 15} \quad (5)$$

Subtract the fourth equation from the fifth equation:
$$5x + 5z = 15$$
$$-5x - z = -11$$
$$\overline{\qquad 4z = 4}$$
$$z = 1$$

Solve for x:
$$5x + (1) = 11$$
$$5x + 1 = 11$$
$$5x = 10$$
$$x = 2$$

Solve for y:
$$(2) + 2y + (1) = 3$$
$$2 + 2y + 1 = 3$$
$$2y + 3 = 3$$
$$2y = 0$$
$$y = 0$$

The solution to the system is the point $(2, 0, 1)$.

13. Add 2 times the first equation to 3 times the second equation:
$$2x \qquad - 6z = 12$$
$$3y + 6z = 6$$
$$\overline{2x + 3y \qquad = 18} \quad (4)$$

Add 5 times the second equation to 2 times the third equation:
$$5y + 10z = 10$$
$$14x - 6y - 10z = 28$$
$$\overline{14x - y \qquad = 38} \quad (5)$$

Add the fourth equation to 3 times the fifth equation:
$$2x + 3y = 18$$
$$42x - 3y = 114$$
$$\overline{44x \qquad = 132}$$
$$x \qquad = 3$$

Solve for y:
$$14(3) - y = 38$$
$$42 - y = 38$$
$$-y = -4$$
$$y = 4$$

Solve for z:
$$(3) - 3z = 6$$
$$-3z = 3$$
$$z = -1$$

The solution to the system is the point $(3, 4, -1)$.

15. Add the first equation to the second equation:
$$2x - y \qquad = -8$$
$$y + 3z = 22$$
$$\overline{2x \qquad + 3z = 14} \quad (4)$$

Add the fourth equation to 3 times the third equation:
$$2x + 3z = 14$$
$$3x - 3z = -24$$
$$\overline{5x \qquad = -10}$$
$$x \qquad = -2$$

Solve for z:

$$(-2) - z = -8$$
$$-z = -6$$
$$z = 6$$

Solve for y:

$$2(-2) - y = -8$$
$$-4 - y = -8$$
$$-y = -4$$
$$y = 4$$

The solution to the system is the point $(-2, 4, 6)$.

17. Substitute the given points into $y = ax^2 + bx + c$.

$$(1, 6): 6 = a(1)^2 + b(1) + c$$
$$(2, 11): 11 = a(2)^2 + b(2) + c$$
$$(3, 18): 18 = a(3)^2 + b(3) + c$$

Simplify these equations:

$$a + b + c = 6 \qquad (1)$$
$$4a + 2b + c = 11 \qquad (2)$$
$$9a + 3b + c = 18 \qquad (3)$$

Eliminate c by multiplying both sides of equation (1) by -1:

$$-a - b - c = -6 \qquad (4)$$

Adding the left sides and right sides of equations (2) and (4) gives:

$$3a + b = 5 \qquad (5)$$

Adding the left sides and right sides of equations (3) and (4) gives:

$$8a + 2b = 12 \qquad (6)$$

Simplify:

$$4a + b = 6 \qquad (7)$$

Eliminate b by multiplying equation (5) by -1 and add each side to the corresponding side of equation (7):

$$a = 1$$

Next, substitute 1 for a in equation (5):

$$3(1) + b = 5$$
$$b = 2$$

Then, substitute 1 for a and 2 for b in equation

(1):

$$a + b + c = 6$$
$$1 + 2 + c = 6$$
$$c = 3$$

Therefore, $a = 1$, $b = 2$, and $c = 3$. So, the equation is $y = x^2 + 2x + 3$.

19. Substitute the given points into $y = ax^2 + bx + c$.

$$(1, 9): 9 = a(1)^2 + b(1) + c$$
$$(2, 7): 7 = a(2)^2 + b(2) + c$$
$$(4, -15): -15 = a(4)^2 + b(4) + c$$

Simplify these equations:

$$a + b + c = 9 \qquad (1)$$
$$4a + 2b + c = 7 \qquad (2)$$
$$16a + 4b + c = -15 \qquad (3)$$

Eliminate c by multiplying both sides of equation (1) by -1:

$$-a - b - c = -9 \qquad (4)$$

Adding the left sides and right sides of equations (2) and (4) gives:

$$3a + b = -2 \qquad (5)$$

Adding the left sides and right sides of equations (3) and (4) gives:

$$15a + 3b = -24 \qquad (6)$$

Simplify:

$$5a + b = -8 \qquad (7)$$

Eliminate b by multiplying equation (5) by -1 and add each side to the corresponding side of equation (7):

$$2a = -6$$
$$a = -3$$

Next, substitute -3 for a in equation (5):

$$3(-3) + b = -2$$
$$b = 7$$

Then, substitute -3 for a and 7 for b in equation (1):

$$a + b + c = 9$$
$$-3 + 7 + c = 9$$
$$c = 5$$

Therefore, $a = -3$, $b = 7$, and $c = 5$. So, the equation is $y = -3x^2 + 7x + 5$.

21. Substitute the given points into $y = ax^2 + bx + c$.

$$(2, 2): 2 = a(2)^2 + b(2) + c$$
$$(3, 11): 11 = a(3)^2 + b(3) + c$$
$$(4, 24): 24 = a(4)^2 + b(4) + c$$

Simplify these equations:

$$4a + 2b + c = 2 \qquad (1)$$
$$9a + 3b + c = 11 \qquad (2)$$
$$16a + 4b + c = 24 \qquad (3)$$

Eliminate c by multiplying both sides of equation (1) by –1:

$$-4a - 2b - c = -2 \qquad (4)$$

Adding the left sides and right sides of equations (2) and (4) gives:

$$5a + b = 9 \qquad (5)$$

Adding the left sides and right sides of equations (3) and (4) gives:

$$12a + 2b = 22 \qquad (6)$$

Simplify:

$$6a + b = 11 \qquad (7)$$

Eliminate b by multiplying equation (5) by –1 and add each side to the corresponding side of equation (7):

$$a = 2$$

Next, substitute 2 for a in equation (5):

$$5(2) + b = 9$$
$$b = -1$$

Then, substitute 2 for a and –1 for b in equation (1):

$$4a + 2b + c = 2$$
$$4(2) + 2(-1) + c = 2$$
$$8 - 2 + c = 2$$
$$c = -4$$

Therefore, $a = 2$, $b = -1$, and $c = -4$. So, the equation is $y = 2x^2 - x - 4$.

23. Substitute the given points into $y = ax^2 + bx + c$.

$$(1, -3): -3 = a(1)^2 + b(1) + c$$
$$(3, 9): 9 = a(3)^2 + b(3) + c$$
$$(5, 29): 29 = a(5)^2 + b(5) + c$$

Simplify these equations:

$$a + b + c = -3 \qquad (1)$$
$$9a + 3b + c = 9 \qquad (2)$$
$$25a + 5b + c = 29 \qquad (3)$$

Eliminate c by multiplying both sides of equation (1) by –1:

$$-a - b - c = 3 \qquad (4)$$

Adding the left sides and right sides of equations (2) and (4) gives:

$$8a + 2b = 12 \qquad (5)$$

Simplify:

$$4a + b = 6 \qquad (6)$$

Adding the left sides and right sides of equations (3) and (4) gives:

$$24a + 4b = 32 \qquad (7)$$

Simplify:

$$6a + b = 8 \qquad (8)$$

Eliminate b by multiplying equation (6) by –1 and add each side to the corresponding side of equation (8):

$$2a = 2$$
$$a = 1$$

Next, substitute 1 for a in equation (6):

$$4(1) + b = 6$$
$$b = 2$$

Then, substitute 1 for a and 2 for b in equation (1):

$$a + b + c = -3$$
$$1 + 2 + c = -3$$
$$c = -6$$

Therefore, $a = 1$, $b = 2$, and $c = -6$. So, the equation is $y = x^2 + 2x - 6$.

25. Substitute the given points into $y = ax^2 + bx + c$.

$(3,7): 7 = a(3)^2 + b(3) + c$

$(4,0): 0 = a(4)^2 + b(4) + c$

$(5,-11): -11 = a(5)^2 + b(5) + c$

Simplify these equations:

$9a + 3b + c = 7$ $\qquad (1)$

$16a + 4b + c = 0$ $\qquad (2)$

$25a + 5b + c = -11$ $\qquad (3)$

Eliminate c by multiplying both sides of equation (1) by -1:

$-9a - 3b - c = -7$ $\qquad (4)$

Adding the left sides and right sides of equations (2) and (4) gives:

$7a + b = -7$ $\qquad (5)$

Adding the left sides and right sides of equations (3) and (4) gives:

$16a + 2b = -18$ $\qquad (6)$

Simplify:

$8a + b = -9$ $\qquad (7)$

Eliminate b by multiplying equation (5) by -1 and add each side to the corresponding side of equation (7):

$a = -2$

Next, substitute -2 for a in equation (5):

$7(-2) + b = -7$

$b = 7$

Then, substitute -2 for a and 7 for b in equation (1):

$9a + 3b + c = 7$

$9(-2) + 3(7) + c = 7$

$-18 + 21 + c = 7$

$c = 4$

Therefore, $a = -2$, $b = 7$, and $c = 4$. So, the equation is $y = -2x^2 + 7x + 4$.

27. Substitute the given points into $y = ax^2 + bx + c$.

$(2,-5): -5 = a(2)^2 + b(2) + c$

$(4,3): 3 = a(4)^2 + b(4) + c$

$(5,13): 13 = a(5)^2 + b(5) + c$

Simplify these equations:

$4a + 2b + c = -5$ $\qquad (1)$

$16a + 4b + c = 3$ $\qquad (2)$

$25a + 5b + c = 13$ $\qquad (3)$

Eliminate c by multiplying both sides of equation (1) by -1:

$-4a - 2b - c = 5$ $\qquad (4)$

Adding the left sides and right sides of equations (2) and (4) gives:

$12a + 2b = 8$ $\qquad (5)$

Simplify:

$6a + b = 4$ $\qquad (6)$

Adding the left sides and right sides of equations (3) and (4) gives:

$21a + 3b = 18$ $\qquad (7)$

Simplify:

$7a + b = 6$ $\qquad (8)$

Eliminate b by multiplying equation (6) by -1 and add each side to the corresponding side of equation (8):

$a = 2$

Next, substitute 2 for a in equation (6):

$6(2) + b = 4$

$b = -8$

Then, substitute 2 for a and -8 for b in equation (1):

$4a + 2b + c = -5$

$4(2) + 2(-8) + c = -5$

$8 - 16 + c = -5$

$c = 3$

Therefore, $a = 2$, $b = -8$, and $c = 3$. So, the equation is $y = 2x^2 - 8x + 3$.

29. Substitute the given points into $y = ax^2 + bx + c$.

$(0,4): 4 = a(0)^2 + b(0) + c$

$(2,8): 8 = a(2)^2 + b(2) + c$

$(3,1): 1 = a(3)^2 + b(3) + c$

Simplify these equations:

$$c = 4 \qquad (1)$$

$$4a + 2b + c = 8 \qquad (2)$$

$$9a + 3b + c = 1 \qquad (3)$$

Since $c = 4$, substitute 4 for c in equations (2) and (3):

$$4a + 2b + 4 = 8$$

$$9a + 3b + 4 = 1$$

Simplifying these equations gives:

$$4a + 2b = 4 \qquad (4)$$

$$9a + 3b = -3 \qquad (5)$$

To eliminate b, multiply both sides of equation (4) by -3 and both sides of equation (5) by 2:

$$-12a - 6b = -12 \qquad (6)$$

$$18a + 6b = -6 \qquad (7)$$

Adding the left and the right sides of equations (6) and (7) gives:

$$6a = -18$$

$$a = -3$$

Next, substitute -3 for a in equation (4):

$$4(-3) + 2b = 4$$

$$2b = 16$$

$$b = 8$$

Therefore, $a = -3$, $b = 8$, and $c = 4$. So, the equation is $y = -3x^2 + 8x + 4$.

31. Substitute the given points into $y = ax^2 + bx + c$.

$(0,-1): -1 = a(0)^2 + b(0) + c$

$(1,3): 3 = a(1)^2 + b(1) + c$

$(2,13): 13 = a(2)^2 + b(2) + c$

Simplify these equations:

$$c = -1 \qquad (1)$$

$$a + b + c = 3 \qquad (2)$$

$$4a + 2b + c = 13 \qquad (3)$$

Since $c = -1$, substitute -1 for c in equations (2) and (3):

$$a + b + (-1) = 3$$

$$4a + 2b + (-1) = 13$$

Simplifying these equations gives:

$$a + b = 4 \qquad (4)$$

$$4a + 2b = 14 \qquad (5)$$

To eliminate b, multiply both sides of equation (4) by -2 and add each side to the corresponding side in equation (5):

$$2a = 6$$

$$a = 3$$

Next, substitute 3 for a in equation (4):

$$3 + b = 4$$

$$b = 1$$

Therefore, $a = 3$, $b = 1$, and $c = -1$. So, the equation is $y = 3x^2 + x - 1$.

33. Substitute the given points into $y = ax^2 + bx + c$.

$(1,1): 1 = a(1)^2 + b(1) + c$

$(2,4): 4 = a(2)^2 + b(2) + c$

$(3,9): 9 = a(3)^2 + b(3) + c$

Simplify these equations:

$$a + b + c = 1 \qquad (1)$$

$$4a + 2b + c = 4 \qquad (2)$$

$$9a + 3b + c = 9 \qquad (3)$$

Eliminate c by multiplying both sides of equation (1) by -1:

$$-a - b - c = -1 \qquad (4)$$

Adding the left sides and right sides of equations (2) and (4) gives:

$$3a + b = 3 \qquad (5)$$

Adding the left sides and right sides of equations (3) and (4) gives:

$$8a + 2b = 8 \qquad (6)$$

Simplify:
$4a+b=4$ (7)

Eliminate b by multiplying equation (5) by –1 and add each side to the corresponding side of equation (7):
$a=1$
Next, substitute 1 for a in equation (5):
$3(1)+b=3$
$b=0$
Then, substitute 1 for a and 0 for b in equation (1):
$a+b+c=1$
$1+0+c=1$
$c=0$
Therefore, $a = 1$, $b = 0$, and $c = 0$. So, the equation is $y=x^2$.

35. Substitute the given points into $y=ax^2+bx+c$.
$(0,4):4=a(0)^2+b(0)+c$
$(1,0):0=a(1)^2+b(1)+c$
$(2,0):0=a(2)^2+b(2)+c$

Simplify these equations:
$c=4$ (1)
$a+b+c=0$ (2)
$4a+2b+c=0$ (3)

Since $c = 4$, substitute 4 for c in equations (2) and (3):
$a+b+4=0$
$4a+2b+4=0$

Simplify these equations:
$a+b=-4$ (4)
$4a+2b=-4$ (5)

Eliminate b by multiplying equation (4) by –2 and add each side to the corresponding side of equation (5):
$2a=4$
$a=2$
Next, substitute 2 for a in equation (4):
$2+b=-4$
$b=-6$
Therefore, $a = 2$, $b = –6$, and $c = 4$. So, the

equation is $y=2x^2-6x+4$.

37. Three possible points are (2, 8), (3, 4), and (6, 4). Substitute the given points into $y=ax^2+bx+c$.
$(2,8):8=a(2)^2+b(2)+c$
$(3,4):4=a(3)^2+b(3)+c$
$(6,4):4=a(6)^2+b(6)+c$

Simplify these equations:
$4a+2b+c=8$ (1)
$9a+3b+c=4$ (2)
$36a+6b+c=4$ (3)

Eliminate c by multiplying both sides of equation (1) by –1:
$-4a-2b-c=-8$ (4)
Adding the left sides and right sides of equations (2) and (4) gives:
$5a+b=-4$ (5)

Adding the left sides and right sides of equations (3) and (4) gives:
$32a+4b=-4$ (6)

Simplify:
$8a+b=-1$ (7)

Eliminate b by multiplying equation (5) by –1 and add each side to the corresponding side of equation (7):
$3a=3$
$a=1$
Next, substitute 1 for a in equation (5):
$5(1)+b=-4$
$b=-9$
Then, substitute 1 for a and –9 for b in equation (1):
$4a+2b+c=8$
$4(1)+2(-9)+c=8$
$4-18+c=8$
$c=22$
Therefore, $a = 1$, $b = –9$, and $c = 22$. So, the equation is $y=x^2-9x+22$.

39. Solve for a in $y = a(x-h)^2 + k$ by substituting 5 for h and 8 for k since (5, 8) is the vertex, and substitute 4 for x and 6 for y since (4, 6) lies on the parabola:

$$y = a(x-h)^2 + k$$
$$6 = a(4-5)^2 + 8$$
$$6 = a + 8$$
$$a = -2$$

Since $a = -2$, $y = -2(x-5)^2 + 8$, or expanding the solution:

$$y = -2(x-5)(x-5) + 8$$
$$= -2(x^2 - 10x + 25) + 8$$
$$= -2x^2 + 20x - 50 + 8$$
$$= -2x^2 + 20x - 42$$

41. a.

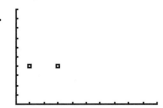

b. Answers may vary. Example:

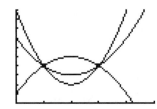

c. Answers may vary. Example:
$$y = (x-2)^2 + 3$$
$$y = -(x-2)^2 + 5$$
$$y = 2(x-2)^2 + 2$$

d. Answers may vary.

43. Answers may vary. Example:
$(0,2)$, $(1,1)$, and $(3,5)$.

The equation of the parabola through these points is $y = x^2 - 2x + 2$.

45.
$$m = \frac{-6-1}{1-(-2)} = -\frac{7}{3}$$

$$y - 1 = -\frac{7}{3}(x+2)$$
$$y - 1 = -\frac{7}{3}x - \frac{14}{3}$$
$$y = -\frac{7}{3}x - \frac{11}{3}$$

47. Linear: $L = 2x + 2$ since the slope is 2 and the y-intercept is (0, 2);
Quadratic: answers may vary. Example:
$Q = 2x^2 + 2$.

49. Substitute the given points into
$f(x) = ax^2 + bx + c$.

$$(1,1): 1 = a(1)^2 + b(1) + c$$
$$(2,2): 2 = a(2)^2 + b(2) + c$$
$$(3,3): 3 = a(3)^2 + b(3) + c$$

Simplify these equations:
$$a + b + c = 1 \qquad (1)$$
$$4a + 2b + c = 2 \qquad (2)$$
$$9a + 3b + c = 3 \qquad (3)$$

Eliminate c by multiplying both sides of equation (1) by -1:
$$-a - b - c = -1 \qquad (4)$$

Adding the left sides and right sides of equations (2) and (4) gives:
$$3a + b = 1 \qquad (5)$$

Adding the left sides and right sides of equations (3) and (4) gives:
$$8a + 2b = 2 \qquad (6)$$

Simplify:
$$4a + b = 1 \qquad (7)$$

Eliminate b by multiplying equation (5) by -1 and add each side to the corresponding side of equation (7):
$$a = 0$$

Next, substitute 0 for a in equation (5):
$$3(0) + b = 1$$
$$b = 1$$

Then, substitute 0 for a and 1 for b in equation (1):

$a+b+c=1$

$0+1+c=1$

$c=0$

Therefore, $a = 0$, $b = 1$, and $c = 0$. So, the equation is $f(x) = x$, which is a linear function.

51. Since the parabola has a vertex of (5, –7) it has the form: $f(x) = a(x-5)^2 - 7$. Now substitute the point (8, 11) and solve for a:

$11 = a((8)-5)^2 - 7$

$11 = a(3)^2 - 7$

$11 = 9a - 7$

$18 = 9a$

$2 = a$

The equation of the parabola is:

$f(x) = 2(x-5)^2 - 7$ or $f(x) = 2x^2 - 20x + 43$.

53. $2x^2 - 10x + 7 = 0$

$$x = \frac{-(-10) \pm \sqrt{(-10)^2 - 4(2)(7)}}{2(2)}$$

$$x = \frac{10 \pm \sqrt{44}}{4}$$

$$x = \frac{10 \pm 2\sqrt{11}}{4}$$

$$x = \frac{5 \pm \sqrt{11}}{2}$$

This is a quadratic equation in one variable.

55. $f(2) = 2(2)^2 - 10(2) + 7$

$= 2(4) - 20 + 7$

$= 8 - 13$

$= -5$

This is a quadratic function.

57.

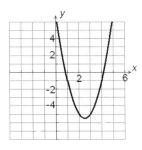

This is a quadratic function.

Homework 9.8

1. a. A quadratic function would be reasonable.

b. A linear function would be reasonable.

c. A quadratic function would be reasonable.

d. None of the mentioned types of functions would be reasonable for this scattergram.

3.

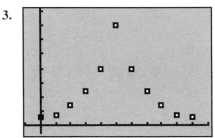

The data do not suggest a quadratic relationship based on the scattergram above. A quadratic function is not a reasonable function.

5. By hand:

Substitute the points (4, 15.1), (6, 16.3), and (8, 15.2) into $f(t) = at^2 + bt + c$.

$(4, 15.1): 15.1 = a(4)^2 + b(4) + c$

$(6, 16.3): 16.3 = a(6)^2 + b(6) + c$

$(8, 15.2): 15.2 = a(8)^2 + b(8) + c$

Simplify these equations:

$16a + 4b + c = 15.1 \qquad (1)$

$36a + 6b + c = 16.3 \qquad (2)$

$64a + 8b + c = 15.2 \qquad (3)$

Eliminate c by multiplying both sides of equation (1) by -1:

$-16a - 4b - c = -15.1 \qquad (4)$

Adding the left sides and right sides of equations (2) and (4) gives:

$20a + 2b = 1.2 \qquad (5)$

Simplify:

$10a + b = 0.6 \qquad (6)$

Adding the left sides and right sides of equations (3) and (4) gives:

$48a + 4b = 0.1 \qquad (7)$

Simplify:

$12a + b = 0.025 \qquad (8)$

Eliminate b by multiplying equation (6) by -1 and add each side to the corresponding side of equation (8):

$$2a = -0.575$$
$$a = -0.2875$$

Next, substitute -0.2875 for a in equation (6):

$$10(-0.2875) + b = 0.6$$
$$b = 3.475$$

Then, substitute -0.2875 for a and 3.475 for b in equation (1):

$$16(-0.2875) + 4(3.475) + c = 15.1$$
$$-4.6 + 13.9 + c = 15.1$$
$$c = 5.8$$

Therefore, $a = -0.2875$, $b = 3.475$, and $c = 5.8$.
So, the equation of the parabola
is $f(t) \approx -0.29t^2 + 3.48t + 5.8$.

By regression:

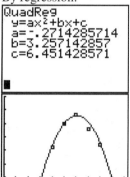

The equation of the parabola is
$f(t) = -0.27t^2 + 3.26t + 6.45$.
Answers may vary.

7. By hand:
Substitute the points $(5, 82)$, $(15, 52)$, and $(50, 5)$
into $f(t) = at^2 + bt + c$.

$$(5, 82): 82 = a(5)^2 + b(5) + c$$
$$(15, 52): 52 = a(15)^2 + b(15) + c$$
$$(50, 5): 5 = a(50)^2 + b(50) + c$$

Simplify these equations:

$$25a + 5b + c = 82 \qquad (1)$$
$$225a + 15b + c = 52 \qquad (2)$$
$$2500a + 50b + c = 5 \qquad (3)$$

Eliminate c by multiplying both sides of equation (1) by -1:

$$-25a - 5b - c = -82 \qquad (4)$$

Adding the left sides and right sides of equations (2) and (4) gives:

$$200a + 10b = -30 \qquad (5)$$

Simplify:

$$20a + b = -3 \qquad (6)$$

Adding the left sides and right sides of equations (3) and (4) gives:

$$2475a + 45b = -77 \qquad (7)$$

Eliminate b by multiplying equation (6) by -45 and add each side to the corresponding side of equation (7):

$$1575a = 58$$
$$a \approx 0.037$$

Next, substitute 0.037 for a in equation (6):

$$20(0.037) + b = -3$$
$$b = -3.74$$

Then, substitute 0.037 for a and -3.74 for b in equation (1):

$$25(0.037) + 5(-3.74) + c = 82$$
$$0.925 - 18.7 + c = 82$$
$$c \approx 99.78$$

Therefore, $a = 0.037$, $b = -3.74$, and $c = 99.78$.
So, the equation of the parabola
is $f(t) = 0.037t^2 - 3.74t + 99.78$.

By regression:

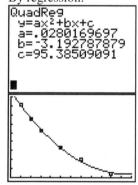

The equation of the parabola
is $f(t) = 0.028t^2 - 3.19t + 95.39$.
Answers may vary.

9. By hand:

Substitute the points (9, 2.6), (13, 22.8), and (16, 52.5) into $f(t) = at^2 + bt + c$.

$(9, 2.6): 2.6 = a(9)^2 + b(9) + c$

$(13, 22.8): 22.8 = a(13)^2 + b(13) + c$

$(16, 52.5): 52.5 = a(16)^2 + b(16) + c$

Simplify these equations:

$81a + 9b + c = 2.6$ $\qquad (1)$

$169a + 13b + c = 22.8$ $\qquad (2)$

$256a + 16b + c = 52.5$ $\qquad (3)$

Eliminate c by multiplying both sides of equation (1) by -1:

$-81a - 9b - c = -2.6$ $\qquad (4)$

Adding the left sides and right sides of equations (2) and (4) gives:

$88a + 4b = 20.2$ $\qquad (5)$

Simplify:

$22a + b = 5.05$ $\qquad (6)$

Adding the left sides and right sides of equations (3) and (4) gives:

$175a + 7b = 49.9$ $\qquad (7)$

Eliminate b by multiplying equation (6) by -7 and add each side to the corresponding side of equation (7):

$21a = 14.55$

$a \approx 0.69$

Next, substitute 0.69 for a in equation (6):

$22(0.69) + b = 5.05$

$b = -10.13$

Then, substitute 0.69 for a and -10.13 for b in equation (1):

$9(0.69) + 3(-10.13) + c = 2.6$

$6.21 - 30.39 + c = 2.6$

$c = 26.78$

Therefore, $a = 0.69$, $b = -10.13$, and $c = 26.78$. So, the equation of the parabola is $f(t) = 0.69t^2 - 10.13t + 26.78$.

By regression:

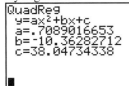

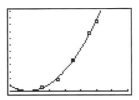

The equation of the parabola is $f(t) = 0.71t^2 - 10.36t + 38.05$. Answers may vary.

11. a. By regression:

$f(t) = 9.9t^2 - 8.9t + 278.2$

b.

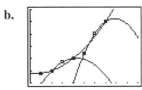

The graph of $f(t) = 9.9t^2 - 8.9t + 278.2$ gives the best model of the data. It involves data points over the greatest number of years.

13. a. By regression:

Linear: $f(t) = 3.1t + 46.2$

Quadratic: $f(t) = -3.07t^2 + 15.39t + 40.06$

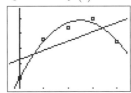

The quadratic model comes closer to the points in the scattergram.

b. Mark Cuban and the Mavericks would like the linear model to be the most accurate for future seasons. Explanations may vary. One possibility follows: The number of win would continue to go up under the linear model.

15. a. By regression:

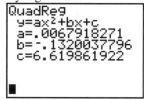

The equation is
$f(t) = 0.0068t^2 - 0.13t + 6.62$.

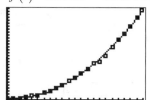

The model fits the data well.

b. i.

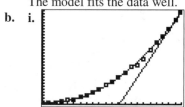

The quadratic function describes the population better for these years, as it includes all of the data.

ii.

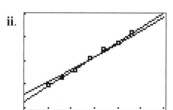

The linear function describes the population better for these years, as it is designed for these data.

iii. Answers may vary.

iv. It appears to be linear. Answers may vary.

17. a. By regression:
$f(t) = 0.18t^2 + 0.2t + 3.9$
$g(t) = 0.87t + 11.1$

b.

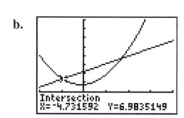

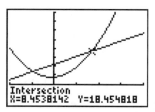

The points of intersection are $(-4.73, 6.98)$ and $(8.45, 18.45)$. The point $(-4.73, 6.98)$ means that in $2000 - 5 = 1995$, 7.0 million cases of both brands of beer were sold. The point $(8.45, 18.45)$ means that in $2000 + 8 = 2008$, 18.5 million cases of both brands of beer were sold.

19. If the point (c, d) is below the parabola, then the model overestimates the value of p when $t = c$. Explanations may vary.

21. Answers may vary. Sample: It is more desirable to find a quadratic model whose graph contains several(but not all) data points;

23. Answers may vary.

25. a.

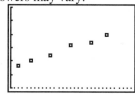

b. Answers may vary depending on the data points selected to create the model. We use the points $(5, 110)$ and $(20, 117)$ to find an equation of the form $M = mt + b$. We begin by finding the slope:
$$m = \frac{117 - 110}{20 - 5} = \frac{7}{15} \approx 0.47$$
So, the equation of the line is of the form $M = 0.47t + b$. To find b, we substitute the coordinates of the point $(5, 110)$ into the equation and solve for b:
$$M = 0.47t + b$$
$$110 = 0.47(5) + b$$
$$110 = 2.35 + b$$
$$107.65 = b$$
So, the equation is $M = 0.47t + 107.65$.

c. Answers may vary [depending on the equation found in part (b).] The year 2015 is represented by $t = 35$, so we substitute 35 for t in the equation:

$M = 0.47t + 107.65$

$M = 0.47(35) + 107.65 = 124.1$

We predict that the male birth rate in China in 2015 will be 124.1 male births per 100 female births.

d. Answers may vary [depending on the equation found in part (b)]. We substitute 100 for M in our linear model:

$M = 0.47t + 107.65$

$100 = 0.47t + 107.65$

$-7.65 = 0.47t$

$t = \dfrac{-7.65}{0.47} \approx -16.27$

We predict that the number of male and female births was equal in the year $1980 + (-16.27) \approx 1964$.

27. $\dfrac{1}{2}x - \dfrac{2}{3}y = 2$

$\dfrac{4}{3}x + \dfrac{5}{2}y = 31$

$3x - 4y = 12$

$8x + 15y = 186$

$3x = 12 + 4y$

$x = 4 + \dfrac{4}{3}y$

$8\left(4 + \dfrac{4}{3}y\right) + 15y = 186$

$32 + \dfrac{32}{3}y + 15y = 186$

$\dfrac{77}{3}y = 154$

$y = 6$

$x = 4 + \dfrac{4}{3}(6) = 12$

$(12, 6)$

This is a system of linear equations in two variables.

29. $\dfrac{1}{2}x - \dfrac{2}{3}y = 2$

$-\dfrac{2}{3}y = 2 - \dfrac{1}{2}x$

$y = \dfrac{3}{4}x - 3$

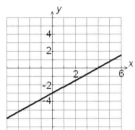

This is a linear equation in two variables.

31. $m = \dfrac{-7 + 2}{-2 + 5} = -\dfrac{5}{3}$

$y = -\dfrac{5}{3}x + b$

$-2 = -\dfrac{5}{3}(-5) + b$

$-2 = \dfrac{25}{3} + b$

$b = -\dfrac{31}{3}$

$y = -\dfrac{5}{3}x - \dfrac{31}{3}$

This is a linear equation in two variables.

Homework 9.9

1. a. The n-intercept is found when $t = 0$.

$f(0) = 0.031(0)^2 - 0.626(0) + 4.18$

$= 4.18$

In 1990, about 4.2 million people moved to another state.

b. $f(15) = 0.031(15)^2 - 0.626(15) + 4.18$

$= 1.765$

In 2005, the model estimates that about 1.8 million people moved to another state. This involved interpolation because 2005 is between given ordered pairs.

c. $f(24) = 0.031(24)^2 - 0.626(24) + 4.18$

$= 7.012$

In 2014, the model predicts that about 7 million people moved to another state. This involved extrapolation because 2014 is beyond 2006, the last year data were provided.

d. $7.9 = 0.031t^2 - 0.626t + 4.18$

$0 = 0.031t^2 - 0.626t - 3.72$

$a = 0.031, \ b = -0.626, \ c = -3.72$

$t \approx \dfrac{-(-0.626) \pm \sqrt{(-0.626)^2 - 4(0.031)(-3.72)}}{2(0.031)}$

$t \approx \dfrac{0.626 \pm 0.924}{0.062}$

$\approx 25, \ -4.8$

The model predicts that about 7.9 million people will move to another state in 1990 + 25 = 2015.

3. a. Use a calculator to find the quadratic regression equation for this set of data.

$f(a) = -0.0313a^2 + 4.03a - 47.05$

```
QuadReg
 y=ax2+bx+c
 a=-.0313095238
 b=4.031785714
 c=-47.04770833
```

b. The a-intercepts occur when $f(a) = 0$. Use the quadratic formula to solve for a.

$a = \dfrac{-4.03 \pm \sqrt{(4.03)^2 - 4(-0.0313)(-47.05)}}{2(-0.0313)}$

$= \dfrac{-4.03 \pm \sqrt{10.35024}}{-0.0626}$

$a \approx \dfrac{-4.03 + 3.2172}{-0.0626}$ or $a \approx \dfrac{-4.03 - 3.2172}{-0.0626}$

$a \approx 12.98$ or $a \approx 115.77$

The a-intercepts are therefore (12.98, 0) and (115.77, 0).

Simplifying, $a \approx 13$ or $a \approx 116$. These values represent ages at which 0% own a home.

c. Model breakdown occurs for values less than 12.98 and greater than 115.77. These represent ages at which less than 0% own a home. The legal age for home ownership and human life expectancy also would factor into which values are reasonable.

d. The vertex represents the highest point of a downward-pointing parabola. The x-value of the vertex is given

by $-\dfrac{b}{2a} = -\dfrac{4.03}{-0.0626} = 64.4$ years old.

$f(64.4) = -0.0313(64.4)^2 + 4.03(64.4) - 47.05$,

≈ 82.7

or approximately 83% of 65-year-olds own their own home.

e. Solve for a for $f(a) = 50$.

$50 = -0.0313(a)^2 + 4.03a - 47.05$

$0 = -0.0313(a)^2 + 4.03a - 97.05$

Use the quadratic formula to solve for a.

$a = \dfrac{-4.03 \pm \sqrt{(4.03)^2 - 4(-0.0313)(-97.05)}}{2(-0.0313)}$

$\approx \dfrac{-4.03 \pm \sqrt{4.09}}{-0.0626}$

$a \approx \dfrac{-4.03 + 2.022}{-0.0626}$ or $a \approx \dfrac{-4.03 - 2.022}{-0.0626}$

$a \approx 32.1$ or $a \approx 96.7$

Simplifying, $a \approx 32$ or $a \approx 97$. These values represent ages in years at which 50% own a home.

5. a. $f(224) = 0.0068(224)^2 - 0.13(224) + 6.62$

≈ 318.70

In 2014, the U.S. population will be about 318.7 million people.

b. $0.0068t^2 - 0.13t + 6.62 = 325$

$0.0068t^2 - 0.13t - 318.38 = 0$

$a = 0.0068, b = -0.13, c = -318.38$

$$t = \frac{0.13 \pm \sqrt{(-0.13)^2 - 4(0.0068)(-318.38)}}{2(0.0068)}$$

$$\approx \frac{0.13 \pm 2.9456}{0.0136}$$

$$\approx -207.03, \ 226.15$$

The negative value for t indicates that the U.S. population was 325 million in 1790 − 207 = 1583, so model breakdown has occurred. The U.S. population will be 325 million people in 1790 + 226 = 2016.

c.

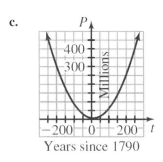

d. The t coordinate of the vertex for the model is given by $-\dfrac{b}{2a} = -\dfrac{-0.13}{2(0.0068)} = 9.56$,

which means that in 1790 + 9.56 ≈ 1800, the U.S. population will reach a minimum value. This minimum value is given by the model as

$$f(9.56) = 0.0068(9.56)^2 - 0.13(9.56) + 6.62$$

$$\approx 6.00$$

However, the census data for 1790 and 1800 are both lower than 6 million. Therefore, model breakdown occurs for years prior to 1800.

e. The graph should indicate that, for low values of t, the population should be small but slowly growing, while at large values of t, the population should level off at a maximum value (that is, there should not be an infinite-growth curve for a finite system). Between these two nearly horizontal curves, the growth should follow a quadratic or exponential function that closely models the data. An example of such a qualitative graph would be the following:

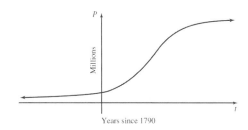

7. a. By regression:

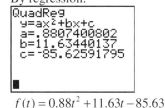

$$f(t) = 0.88t^2 + 11.63t - 85.63$$

b. $0.88t^2 + 11.63t - 85.63 = 755$

$0.88t^2 + 11.63t - 840.63 = 0$

$a = 0.88, b = 11.63, c = -840.63$

$$t = \frac{-11.63 \pm \sqrt{(11.63)^2 - 4(0.88)(-840.63)}}{2(0.88)}$$

$$\approx \frac{-11.63 \pm 55.63}{1.76}$$

$$\approx 25, \ -38.2$$

Barry Bonds will reach 755 home runs in 1980 + 25 = 2005.

c. $f(25) = 0.88(25)^2 + 11.63(25) - 85.63$

$$= 755.12$$

$$f(26) = 0.88(26)^2 + 11.63(26) - 85.63$$

$$- 811.63$$

$$f(26) - f(25) = 811.63 - 755.12 = 56.51$$

Yes, as he will hit enough home runs in 2006 to reach the record.

d. Answers may vary.

9. a.

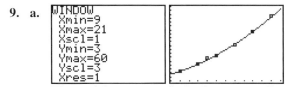

The model appears to fit the data very well.

389

b. Substitute 45 for I and solve for t.

$$45 = 0.175t^2 - 1.1t + 3.8$$

$$0 = 0.175t^2 - 1.1t - 41.2$$

$$a = 0.175, b = -1.1, c = -41.2$$

$$t = \frac{-(-1.1) \pm \sqrt{(-1.1)^2 - 4(0.175)(-41.2)}}{2(0.175)}$$

$$= \frac{1.1 \pm \sqrt{30.05}}{0.35}$$

$$t \approx -12.52 \quad \text{or} \quad t \approx 18.81$$

The model predicts that people whose median annual income is $45 thousand have about 19 years of full-time equivalent education (model breakdown occurs for $t \approx -12.52$ because the number of years of education cannot be negative).

c. i. With only a high school diploma, the median income is $15.7 thousand.

$$4(15.7) = 62.8$$

So, over 4 years the student would earn an estimated $62,800.

ii. Each year of college is estimated to cost $6836.

$$4(6836) = 27,344$$

So, four years of college would cost the student $27,344.

iii. Let $x =$ the number of years the student would work after college. Then the high school graduate would work for $x + 4$ years.

We need to find when the total earnings for a high school graduate would equal the total earnings of a college graduate, less the cost of college.

$$15.7(x+4) = 31.0x - 27.344$$

$$15.7x + 62.8 = 31.0x - 27.344$$

$$90.144 = 15.3x$$

$$x = \frac{90.144}{15.3} \approx 5.9$$

The student would need to work for about 5.9 years after college to be in the same financial position as if he had not gone to college.

iv. High School:

$$37(15.7) = 580.9$$

Bachelor's:

$$33(31.0) - 27.344 = 995.656$$

Difference:

$$995.656 - 580.9 = 414.756$$

So, the student will earn $414,756 (71.4%) more in his lifetime if he gets a Bachelor's degree than if he does not go to college.

v. Underestimate; our estimate is based on the assumption that the difference in income remains constant. Since those with larger incomes saw larger growth in income, the difference in income will actually increase.

11. $f(t) = 0.18t^2 + 0.2t + 3.9$

$$g(t) = 0.87t + 11.1$$

$$0.18t^2 + 0.2t + 3.9 = 0.87t + 11.1$$

$$0.18t^2 - 0.67t - 7.2 = 0$$

$$a = 0.18, b = -0.67, c = -7.2$$

$$t = \frac{0.67 \pm \sqrt{(-0.67)^2 - 4(0.18)(-7.2)}}{2(0.18)}$$

$$\approx \frac{0.67 \pm 2.37}{0.36}$$

$$\approx 8.44, \ -4.72$$

In $2000 + 8 = 2008$ and in $2000 - 5 = 1995$, the sales of the two brands will be equal.

13. a. By regression:

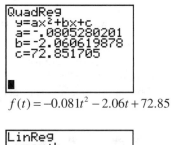

$$f(t) = -0.081t^2 - 2.06t + 72.85$$

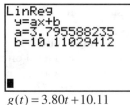

$$g(t) = 3.80t + 10.11$$

b. $f(t) = -0.081t^2 - 2.06t + 72.85$

$g(t) = 3.80t + 10.11$

$-0.081t^2 - 2.06t + 72.85 = 3.80t + 10.11$

$-0.081t^2 - 5.86t + 62.74 = 0$

$a = -0.081, b = -5.86, c = 62.74$

$$t = \frac{5.86 \pm \sqrt{(-5.86)^2 - 4(-0.081)(62.74)}}{2(-0.081)}$$

$$\approx \frac{5.86 \pm 7.39}{-0.162}$$

$$\approx -81.79, \ 9.44$$

As electronic voting machines did not exist in 1990 − 82 = 1908, the positive root is the only meaningful result. In 1990 + 9 = 1999, the percentage of voters using optical scan or other modern electrical system equaled the percentage of people using punch cards or lever machines. No, 1999 was not a major election year. 2000 is the closest election year.

c. $h(t) = 100 - (f + g)(t)$ represents the percentage of voters using the three other ways to vote.

d. $h(t)$

$= 100 - (f + g)(t)$

$= 100 - \left[\begin{array}{l} (-0.081t^2 - 2.06t + 72.85) \\ +(3.80t + 10.11) \end{array} \right]$

$= 100 - (-0.081t^2 + 1.74t + 82.96)$

$= 0.081t^2 - 1.74t + 17.04$

e. $h(17) = 0.081(17)^2 - 1.74(17) + 17.04$

≈ 10.87

In 1990 + 17 = 2007, about 10.9% of registered voters used voting methods other than punch cards, lever machines, optical scan or other modern electronic systems.

15. $p = 250 - 5n$

$R = pn = 250n - 5n^2$

$n = -\dfrac{b}{2a} = -\dfrac{250}{2(-5)} = 25$

A group of 25 people would maximize the bus company's revenue.

17. $p = 28 - 0.2n$

$R = pn = 28n - 0.2n^2$

$n = -\dfrac{b}{2a} = -\dfrac{28}{2(-0.2)} = 70$

A party of 70 people would maximize the restaurant's revenue.

19. $160 = 2l + 2w$

$l = 80 - w$

$A = lw = 80w - w^2$

$w = -\dfrac{b}{2a} = -\dfrac{80}{2(-1)} = 40$

$l = 80 - 40 = 40$

The dimensions are 40 feet long by 40 feet wide. The area is 1600 square feet.

21. Answers may vary.

23. a. The linear regression equation is
$f(t) = 0.51t + 41.28$.

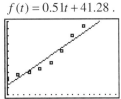

The quadratic regression equation is
$f(t) = 0.038t^2 - 0.021t + 42.35$.

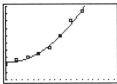

The quadratic equation model fits the data better.

b. Linear: $f(6) = 0.51(6) + 41.28 = 44.34$

Quadratic:

$f(6) = 0.038(6)^2 - 0.021(6) + 42.35$

$= 43.592$

The quadratic model estimate is better as it is closer to the actual percentage.

c. The p-intercept of the linear model is (0, 41.28). The p-intercept of the quadratic model is (0, 42.35). The p-intercept of the quadratic model is better because it is closer to the actual value.

d. Linear: $60 = 0.51t + 41.28$

$18.72 = 0.51t$

$36.71 \approx t$

According to the linear model, 60% of law degrees will be earned by women in 1990 + 37 = 2027.

Quadratic:

$0.038t^2 - 0.02t + 42.35 = 60$

$0.038t^2 - 0.02t - 17.65 = 0$

$a = 0.038, b = -0.02, c = -17.65$

$$t = \frac{0.02 \pm \sqrt{(-0.02)^2 - 4(0.038)(-17.65)}}{2(0.038)}$$

$$\approx \frac{0.02 \pm 1.638}{0.076}$$

$$\approx 21.82, \ -21.29$$

Only the positive root is meaningful. In 1990 + 22 = 2012, 60% of law degrees will be earned by women.

The quadratic model's result is earlier than the linear model's result because it increases at a greater rate.

25. Answers may vary.

27. Answers may vary.

29. Answers may vary.

31. Answers may vary.

Chapter 9 Review Exercises

1.

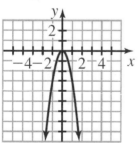

2.

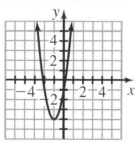

3.

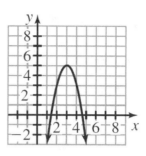

4.

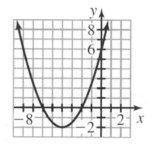

5. Since the parabola has a maximum point, $a < 0$. Since the vertex is in quadrant II, $h < 0$ and $k > 0$.

6. Vertex: $(2, -5)$

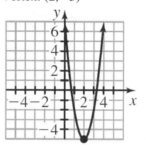

7. Vertex: $(2, 13)$

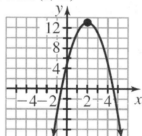

8. Vertex (2.5, −3.25)

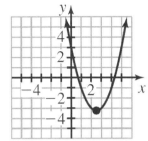

9. Vertex: (1.43, −6.25)

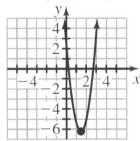

10. $\sqrt{196} = 14$ because $14^2 = 196$

11. $\sqrt{64} = 8$ because $8^2 = 64$. Therefore, $-\sqrt{64} = -1\left(\sqrt{64}\right) = -1(8) = -8$

12. $\sqrt{95} \approx 9.75$

13. $-7.29\sqrt{38.36} \approx -45.15$

14. $\sqrt{18} = \sqrt{9 \cdot 2} = \sqrt{9}\sqrt{2} = 3\sqrt{2}$

15. $\sqrt{98} = \sqrt{49 \cdot 2} = \sqrt{49}\sqrt{2} = 7\sqrt{2}$

16. $-3\sqrt{50} = -3\sqrt{25 \cdot 2} = -3 \cdot 5\sqrt{2} = -15\sqrt{2}$

17. $\sqrt{\dfrac{5}{9}} = \dfrac{\sqrt{5}}{\sqrt{9}} = \dfrac{\sqrt{5}}{3}$

18. $\dfrac{4}{\sqrt{7}} = \dfrac{4}{\sqrt{7}} \cdot \dfrac{\sqrt{7}}{\sqrt{7}} = \dfrac{4\sqrt{7}}{\sqrt{49}} = \dfrac{4\sqrt{7}}{7}$

19. $\sqrt{\dfrac{7}{3}} = \dfrac{\sqrt{7}}{\sqrt{3}} = \dfrac{\sqrt{7}}{\sqrt{3}} \cdot \dfrac{\sqrt{3}}{\sqrt{3}} = \dfrac{\sqrt{21}}{3}$

20.
$$\sqrt{\dfrac{5}{32}} = \dfrac{\sqrt{5}}{\sqrt{32}} = \dfrac{\sqrt{5}}{\sqrt{16}\sqrt{2}} = \dfrac{\sqrt{5}}{4\sqrt{2}}$$
$$= \dfrac{\sqrt{5}}{4\sqrt{2}} \cdot \dfrac{\sqrt{2}}{\sqrt{2}} = \dfrac{\sqrt{10}}{4 \cdot 2}$$
$$= \dfrac{\sqrt{10}}{8}$$

21. The student squared the numerator and denominator instead of multiplying the expression by $1 = \dfrac{\sqrt{7}}{\sqrt{7}}$ to rationalize the denominator.
$$\dfrac{3}{\sqrt{7}} = \dfrac{3}{\sqrt{7}} \cdot \dfrac{\sqrt{7}}{\sqrt{7}} = \dfrac{3\sqrt{7}}{\sqrt{49}} = \dfrac{3\sqrt{7}}{7}$$

22. $3x^2 - 2x - 2 = 0$
$$x = \dfrac{2 \pm \sqrt{(-2)^2 - 4(3)(-2)}}{2(3)}$$
$$x = \dfrac{2 \pm \sqrt{28}}{6}$$
$$x = \dfrac{2 \pm 2\sqrt{7}}{6}$$
$$x = \dfrac{1 \pm \sqrt{7}}{3}$$

23. $5x^2 = 7$
$$x^2 = \dfrac{7}{5}$$
$$= \pm\sqrt{\dfrac{7}{5}}$$
$$= \pm\dfrac{\sqrt{7}}{\sqrt{5}}$$
$$= \pm\dfrac{\sqrt{7}}{\sqrt{5}} \cdot \dfrac{\sqrt{5}}{\sqrt{5}}$$
$$= \pm\dfrac{\sqrt{35}}{5}$$

24. $5(p-3)^2 + 4 = 7$

$5p^2 - 30p + 42 = 0$

$p = \dfrac{30 \pm \sqrt{(-30)^2 - 4(5)(42)}}{2(5)}$

$p = \dfrac{30 \pm \sqrt{60}}{10}$

$p = \dfrac{30 \pm 2\sqrt{15}}{10}$

$p = \dfrac{15 \pm \sqrt{15}}{5}$

25. $(t+1)(t-7) = 4$

$t^2 - 6t - 11 = 0$

$x = \dfrac{6 \pm \sqrt{(-6)^2 - 4(1)(-11)}}{2(1)}$

$x = \dfrac{6 \pm \sqrt{80}}{2}$

$x = \dfrac{6 \pm 4\sqrt{5}}{2}$

$x = 3 \pm 2\sqrt{5}$

26. $2x^2 = 4 - 5x$

$2x^2 + 5x - 4 = 0$

$x = \dfrac{-5 \pm \sqrt{5^2 - 4(2)(-4)}}{2(2)}$

$x = \dfrac{-5 \pm \sqrt{57}}{4}$

27. $4x - x^2 = 1$

$x^2 - 4x + 1 = 0$

$x = \dfrac{4 \pm \sqrt{(-4)^2 - 4(1)(1)}}{2(1)}$

$x = \dfrac{4 \pm \sqrt{12}}{2}$

$x = \dfrac{4 \pm 2\sqrt{3}}{2}$

$x = 2 \pm \sqrt{3}$

28. $2x^2 - x = \dfrac{3}{2}$

$2(2x^2 - x) = 2\left(\dfrac{3}{2}\right)$

$4x^2 - 2x = 3$

$4x^2 - 2x - 3 = 0$

$a = 4, b = -2, c = -3$

$x = \dfrac{-(-2) \pm \sqrt{(-2)^2 - 4(4)(-3)}}{2(4)}$

$= \dfrac{2 \pm \sqrt{4+48}}{8} = \dfrac{2 \pm \sqrt{52}}{8}$

$= \dfrac{2 \pm 2\sqrt{13}}{8} = \dfrac{2(1 \pm \sqrt{13})}{2(4)}$

$= \dfrac{1 \pm \sqrt{13}}{4}$

The solutions are $\dfrac{1 \pm \sqrt{13}}{4}$.

29. $2x(x-1) = 5$

$2x^2 - 2x = 5$

$2x^2 - 2x - 5 = 0$

$a = 2, b = -2, c = -5$

$x = \dfrac{-(-2) \pm \sqrt{(-2)^2 - 4(2)(-5)}}{2(2)}$

$= \dfrac{2 \pm \sqrt{4+40}}{4} = \dfrac{2 \pm \sqrt{44}}{4}$

$= \dfrac{2 \pm 2\sqrt{11}}{4} = \dfrac{2(1 \pm \sqrt{11})}{2(2)}$

$= \dfrac{1 \pm \sqrt{11}}{2}$

The solutions are $\dfrac{1 \pm \sqrt{11}}{2}$.

30. $5x^2 - 6x = 2$

$5x^2 - 6x - 2 = 0$

$x = \dfrac{6 \pm \sqrt{(-6)^2 - 4(5)(-2)}}{2(5)}$

$x = \dfrac{6 \pm \sqrt{76}}{10}$

$x = \dfrac{6 \pm 2\sqrt{19}}{10}$

$x = \dfrac{3 \pm \sqrt{19}}{5}$

31. $7r^2 - 20 = 0$

$7r^2 = 20$

$r^2 = \dfrac{20}{7}$

$r = \pm\sqrt{\dfrac{20}{7}}$

$ = \pm\dfrac{\sqrt{20}}{\sqrt{7}}$

$ = \pm\dfrac{\sqrt{20}}{\sqrt{7}} \cdot \dfrac{\sqrt{7}}{\sqrt{7}}$

$ = \pm\dfrac{\sqrt{140}}{7}$

$ = \pm\dfrac{2\sqrt{35}}{7}$

32. $(t+2)^2 + (t-3)^2 = 15$

$2t^2 - 2t - 2 = 0$

$t = \dfrac{2 \pm \sqrt{(-2)^2 - 4(2)(-2)}}{2(2)}$

$t = \dfrac{2 \pm \sqrt{20}}{4}$

$t = \dfrac{2 \pm 2\sqrt{5}}{4}$

$t = \dfrac{1 \pm \sqrt{5}}{2}$

33. $5(5x^2 - 8) = 9$

$25x^2 - 40 = 9$

$25x^2 = 49$

$x^2 = \dfrac{49}{25}$

$x = \pm\sqrt{\dfrac{49}{25}}$

$x = \pm\dfrac{7}{5}$

34. $\dfrac{3}{2}x^2 - \dfrac{3}{4}x = \dfrac{1}{2}$

$6x^2 - 3x - 2 = 0$

$x = \dfrac{3 \pm \sqrt{(-3)^2 - 4(6)(-2)}}{2(6)}$

$x = \dfrac{3 \pm \sqrt{57}}{12}$

35. $2.7x^2 - 5.1x = 9.8$

$2.7x^2 - 5.1x - 9.8 = 0$

$x = \dfrac{-(-5.1) \pm \sqrt{(-5.1)^2 - 4(2.7)(-9.8)}}{2(2.7)}$

$ \approx \dfrac{5.1 \pm 11.48}{5.4}$

$x \approx -1.18 \ \text{ or } \ x \approx 3.07$

36. $1.7(x^2 - 2.3) = 3.4 - 2.8x$

$1.7x^2 - 3.91 = 3.4 - 2.8x$

$1.7x^2 + 2.8x - 7.31 = 0$

$x = \dfrac{-2.8 \pm \sqrt{2.8^2 - 4(1.7)(-7.31)}}{2(1.7)}$

$ \approx \dfrac{-2.8 \pm 7.586}{3.4}$

$x \approx -3.05 \ \text{ or } \ x \approx 1.41$

37. $\sqrt{-45} = \sqrt{9 \cdot 5 \cdot -1} = \sqrt{9} \cdot \sqrt{5} \cdot \sqrt{-1} = 3i\sqrt{5}$

38. $\sqrt{-\dfrac{7}{2}} = \dfrac{\sqrt{-7}}{\sqrt{2}} = \dfrac{\sqrt{7}\sqrt{-1}}{\sqrt{2}} \cdot \dfrac{\sqrt{2}}{\sqrt{2}}$

$\phantom{\sqrt{-\dfrac{7}{2}}} = \dfrac{\sqrt{14}\sqrt{-1}}{\sqrt{4}} = \dfrac{i\sqrt{14}}{2}$

39. $-2(x+4)^2 = 9$

$-2x^2 - 16x - 41 = 0$

$x = \dfrac{16 \pm \sqrt{(-16)^2 - 4(-2)(-41)}}{2(-2)}$

$x = \dfrac{16 \pm \sqrt{-72}}{-4}$

$x = \dfrac{16 \pm 6i\sqrt{2}}{-4}$

$x = \dfrac{-8 \pm 3i\sqrt{2}}{2}$

40. $2x^2 = 4x - 7$

$2x^2 - 4x + 7 = 0$

$x = \dfrac{4 \pm \sqrt{(-4)^2 - 4(2)(7)}}{2(2)}$

$x = \dfrac{4 \pm \sqrt{-40}}{4}$

$x = \dfrac{4 \pm 2i\sqrt{10}}{4}$

$x = \dfrac{2 \pm i\sqrt{10}}{2}$

41. $x^2 + 6x - 4 = 0$

$x^2 + 6x = 4$

$x^2 + 6x + 9 = 4 + 9$

$(x+3)^2 = 13$

$x + 3 = \pm\sqrt{13}$

$x = -3 \pm \sqrt{13}$

42. $x^2 - 5x = 2$

$x^2 - 5x + \dfrac{25}{4} = 2 + \dfrac{25}{4}$

$\left(x - \dfrac{5}{2}\right)^2 = \dfrac{33}{4}$

$x - \dfrac{5}{2} = \pm\dfrac{\sqrt{33}}{2}$

$x = \dfrac{5}{2} \pm \dfrac{\sqrt{33}}{2} = \dfrac{5 \pm \sqrt{33}}{2}$

43. $3x^2 - 18x - 27 = 0$

$3(x^2 - 6x - 9) = 0$

$x^2 - 6x - 9 = 0$

$x^2 - 6x = 9$

$x^2 - 6x + 9 = 9 + 9$

$(x-3)^2 = 18$

$x - 3 = \pm\sqrt{18}$

$x - 3 = \pm 3\sqrt{2}$

$x = 3 \pm 3\sqrt{2}$

44. $2t^2 = -3t + 6$

$2t^2 + 3t = 6$

$t^2 + \dfrac{3}{2}t = 3$

$t^2 + \dfrac{3}{2}t + \dfrac{9}{16} = 3 + \dfrac{9}{16}$

$\left(t + \dfrac{3}{4}\right)^2 = \dfrac{57}{16}$

$t + \dfrac{3}{4} = \pm\sqrt{\dfrac{57}{16}}$

$t + \dfrac{3}{4} = \pm\dfrac{\sqrt{57}}{4}$

$t = \dfrac{-3 \pm \sqrt{57}}{4}$

45. Solve for x when $h(x) = 0$:

$3x^2 + 2x - 2 = 0$

$x = \dfrac{-2 \pm \sqrt{2^2 - 4(3)(-2)}}{2(3)}$

$x = \dfrac{-2 \pm \sqrt{28}}{6}$

$x = \dfrac{-2 \pm 2\sqrt{7}}{6}$

$x = \dfrac{-1 \pm \sqrt{7}}{3}$

The x-intercepts are $\left(\dfrac{-1 - \sqrt{7}}{3}, 0\right)$ and

$\left(\dfrac{-1 + \sqrt{7}}{3}, 0\right)$.

46. Solve for x when $k(x) = 0$:

$-5x^2 + 3x - 1 = 0$

$x = \dfrac{-3 \pm \sqrt{3^2 - 4(-5)(-1)}}{2(-5)}$

$x = \dfrac{-3 \pm \sqrt{-11}}{-10}$

Since the square root of a negative number is not a real number, there are no real number solutions. Therefore, there are no x-intercepts.

47. Factor:

$x^2 - 2x - 8 = 0$

$(x - 4)(x + 2) = 0$

$x - 4 = 0$ or $x + 2 = 0$

$x = 4$ or $x = -2$

Completing the square:

$x^2 - 2x - 8 = 0$

$x^2 - 2x = 8$

$x^2 - 2x + 1 = 8 + 1$

$(x - 1)^2 = 9$

$x - 1 = \pm\sqrt{9}$

$x - 1 = \pm 3$

$x - 1 = 3$ or $x - 1 = -3$

$x = 4$ or $x = -2$

Quadratic Formula:

$x^2 - 2x - 8 = 0$

$x = \dfrac{-(-2) \pm \sqrt{(-2)^2 - 4(1)(-8)}}{2(1)}$

$x = \dfrac{2 \pm \sqrt{36}}{2}$

$x = \dfrac{2 \pm 6}{2}$

$x = \dfrac{2 + 6}{2} = \dfrac{8}{2}$ or $x = \dfrac{2 - 6}{2} = \dfrac{-4}{2}$

$x = 4$ or $x = -2$

48. $3x^2 - 5x + 4 = 0$

$(-5)^2 - 4(3)(4) = -23 < 0$

There are no real solutions. So, there are two imaginary solutions.

49. a. $3x^2 - 6x + 7 = 3$

$3x^2 - 6x + 4 = 0$

$x = \dfrac{-(-6) \pm \sqrt{(-6)^2 - 4(3)(4)}}{2(3)}$

$x = \dfrac{6 \pm \sqrt{-12}}{6}$

Since the square root of a negative is not a real number, there are no real number solutions. There is no such value for x.

b. $3x^2 - 6x + 7 = 4$

$3x^2 - 6x + 3 = 0$

$x = \dfrac{-(-6) \pm \sqrt{(-6)^2 - 4(3)(3)}}{2(3)}$

$x = \dfrac{6 \pm \sqrt{0}}{6}$

$x = \dfrac{6}{6} = 1$

There is one real solution.

c. $3x^2 - 6x + 7 = 5$

$3x^2 - 6x + 2 = 0$

$x = \dfrac{-(-6) \pm \sqrt{(-6)^2 - 4(3)(2)}}{2(3)}$

$x = \dfrac{6 \pm \sqrt{12}}{6}$

$x = \dfrac{6 \pm 2\sqrt{3}}{6}$

$x = \dfrac{3 \pm \sqrt{3}}{3}$

There are two real solutions.

d. Answers may vary.

50. $x = -0.6$ and $x = 1$

51. $x = -3$ or $x = 5$

52. $(-2.0, -1.3)$ and $(5.4, -3.8)$

53. $7 - 2x^2 = x^2 - x - 8$

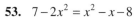
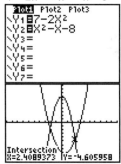
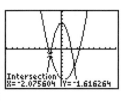

The intersection points are approximately $(-2.08, -1.62)$ and $(2.41, -4.61)$, whose x-coordinates are -2.08 and 2.41. Therefore, -2.08 and 2.41 are the approximate solutions to the equation.

54. Multiply the first equation by 2, and then subtract the second equation from the first equation.

$2x + 4y - 6z = -8$

$\underline{2x - y + z = 3}$

$\quad 5y - 7z = -11 \quad (4)$

Multiply the first equation by 3, and then subtract the third equation from the first equation:

$3x + 6y - 9z = -12$

$\underline{3x + 2y + z = 10}$

$\quad 4y - 10z = -22 \quad (5)$

Multiply (4) by 2 so that the right side equals the right side of (5) and then isolate:

$10y - 14z = -22$

$4y - 10z = -22$

$4y - 10z = 10y - 14z$

$4z = 6y$

$y = \dfrac{2}{3}z$

Solve for z:

$5\left(\dfrac{2}{3}z\right) - 7z = -11$

$\dfrac{10}{3}z - 7z = -11$

$\dfrac{10z - 21z}{3} = -11$

$\dfrac{-11z}{3} = -11$

$z = 3$

Solve for y:

$y = \dfrac{2}{3}(3) = 2$

Solve for x:

$x + 2(2) - 3(3) = -4$

$x = 1$

The solution to the system is the point $(1, 2, 3)$.

55. Isolate x in the first and second equations, and solve the third equation for x:

$2x - 3z = -4$

$-3z = -4 - 2x$

$z = \dfrac{4 + 2x}{3}$

$3x + y = 0$

$y = -3x$

$x - 4(-3x) + 2\left(\dfrac{4 + 2x}{3}\right) = 17$

$x + 12x + \dfrac{8 + 4x}{3} = 17$

$3x + 36x + 8 + 4x = 51$

$43x = 43$

$x = 1$

Solve for y:

$y = -3(1) = -3$

Solve for z:

$z = \dfrac{4 + 2(1)}{3} = 2$

The solution to the system is the point $(1, -3, 2)$.

56. Substitute the given points into $y = ax^2 + bx + c$.

$(1, 4): 4 = a(1)^2 + b(1) + c$

$(2, 3): 3 = a(2)^2 + b(2) + c$

$(3, -2): -2 = a(3)^2 + b(3) + c$

Simplify these equations:

$a + b + c = 4 \qquad (1)$

$4a + 2b + c = 3 \qquad (2)$

$9a + 3b + c = -2 \qquad (3)$

Eliminate c by multiplying both sides of equation (1) by -1:

$-a - b - c = -4 \qquad (4)$

Adding the left sides and right sides of equations (2) and (4) gives:

$3a + b = -1 \qquad (5)$

Adding the left sides and right sides of equations (3) and (4) gives:

$8a + 2b = -6 \qquad (6)$

Simplify:

$4a + b = -3 \qquad (7)$

Eliminate b by multiplying equation (5) by -1 and add each side to the corresponding side of equation (7):

$a = -2$

Next, substitute -2 for a in equation (5):

$3(-2) + b = -1$

$\qquad b = 5$

Then, substitute -2 for a and 5 for b in equation (1):

$a + b + c = 4$

$(-2) + (5) + c = 4$

$-2 + 5 + c = 4$

$\qquad c = 1$

Therefore, $a = -2$, $b = 5$, and $c = 1$. So, the equation is $y = -2x^2 + 5x + 1$.

57. Substitute the given points into $y = ax^2 + bx + c$.

$(2, 9): 9 = a(2)^2 + b(2) + c$

$(3, 18): 18 = a(3)^2 + b(3) + c$

$(5, 48): 48 = a(5)^2 + b(5) + c$

Simplify these equations:

$4a + 2b + c = 9 \qquad (1)$

$9a + 3b + c = 18 \qquad (2)$

$25a + 5b + c = 48 \qquad (3)$

Eliminate c by multiplying both sides of equation (1) by -1:

$-4a - 2b - c = -9 \qquad (4)$

Adding the left sides and right sides of equations (2) and (4) gives:

$5a + b = 9 \qquad (5)$

Adding the left sides and right sides of equations (3) and (4) gives:

$21a + 3b = 39 \qquad (6)$

Simplify:

$7a + b = 13 \qquad (7)$

Eliminate b by multiplying equation (5) by -1 and add each side to the corresponding side of equation (7):

$2a = 4$

$a = 2$

Next, substitute 2 for a in equation (5):

$5(2) + b = 9$

$\qquad b = -1$

Then, substitute 2 for a and -1 for b in equation (1):

$4a + 2b + c = 9$

$4(2) + 2(-1) + c = 9$

$8 - 2 + c = 9$

$\qquad c = 3$

Therefore, $a = 2$, $b = -1$, and $c = 3$. So, the equation is $y = 2x^2 - x + 3$.

58. Substitute the given points into $y = ax^2 + bx + c$.

$(0, 5): 5 = a(0)^2 + b(0) + c$

$(2, 3): 3 = a(2)^2 + b(2) + c$

$(4, -15): -15 = a(4)^2 + b(4) + c$

Simplify these equations:

$c = 5 \qquad (1)$

$4a + 2b + c = 3 \qquad (2)$

$16a + 4b + c = -15 \qquad (3)$

Since $c = 5$, substitute 5 for c in equations (2) and (3):

$4a + 2b + (5) = 3$

$16a + 4b + (5) = -15$

Simplifying these equations gives:

$4a + 2b = -2 \qquad (4)$

$16a + 4b = -20 \qquad (5)$

To eliminate b, multiply both sides of equation (4) by -2 and add each side to the corresponding side in equation (5):

$8a = -16$

$\ a = -2$

Next, substitute -2 for a in equation (4):

$4a + 2b = -2$

$4(-2) + 2b = -2$

$\qquad 2b = 6$

$\qquad b = 3$

Therefore, $a = -2$, $b = 3$, and $c = 5$. So, the equation is $y = -2x^2 + 3x + 5$.

59. Linear:

$$\text{slope} = m = \frac{2-4}{1-0} = -2$$

$$y - \text{intercept} = (0,4)$$

So, $y = -2x + 4$

Quadratic:

Answers may vary. Example: $y = -2x^2 + 4$

60. Substitute the given points into $y = ax^2 + bx + c$.

$$(0,7): 7 = a(0)^2 + b(0) + c$$

$$(2,1): 1 = a(2)^2 + b(2) + c$$

$$(5,7): 7 = a(5)^2 + b(5) + c$$

Simplify these equations:

$$c = 7 \qquad (1)$$

$$4a + 2b + c = 1 \qquad (2)$$

$$25a + 5b + c = 7 \qquad (3)$$

Since $c = 7$, substitute 7 for c in equations (2) and (3):

$$4a + 2b + (7) = 1$$

$$25a + 5b + (7) = 7$$

Simplifying these equations gives:

$$4a + 2b = -6 \qquad (4)$$

$$25a + 5b = 0 \qquad (5)$$

Simplify these equations:

$$2a + b = -3 \qquad (6)$$

$$5a + b = 0 \qquad (7)$$

To eliminate b, multiply both sides of equation (6) by -1 and add each side to the corresponding side in equation (7):

$$3a = 3$$

$$a = 1$$

Next, substitute 1 for a in equation (6):

$$2a + b = -3$$

$$2(1) + b = -3$$

$$b = -5$$

Therefore, $a = 1$, $b = -5$, and $c = 7$. So, the equation is $y = x^2 - 5x + 7$.

61. a. Since the function is in the form $h(t) = at^2 + bt + c$ and $a = -16 < 0$, the vertex is the maximum point. Find the $h(t)$-coordinate of the vertex.

$$h(0) = -16(0)^2 + 100(0) + 3 = 3$$

So, the h-intercept is (0, 3). Next, find the

symmetric point by substituting 3 for $h(t)$ in the function and solve for t:

$$3 = -16t^2 + 100t + 3$$

$$0 = -16t^2 + 100t$$

$$0 = -4t(4t - 25)$$

$$-4t = 0 \quad \text{or} \quad 4t - 25 = 0$$

$$t = 0 \quad \text{or} \quad 4t = 25$$

$$t = 0 \quad \text{or} \quad t = \frac{25}{4} = 6.25$$

The symmetric points are (0, 3) and (6.25, 3). Since the average of the t-coordinates is $\frac{0 + 6.25}{2} = 3.125$, the t-coordinate of the vertex is 3.125. Substitute 3.125 for t in the function to find the h-coordinate of the vertex:

$$h(3.125) = -16(3.125)^2 + 100(3.125) + 3$$

$$= 159.25$$

So the vertex is (3.125, 159.25), which means that the maximum height of the ball is 159.25 feet and it is reached in 3.125 seconds.

b. Solve for t when $h(t) = 3$. From part a, we see that when $h(t) = 3$, t is either 0 or 6.25. In this case, the fielder had 6.25 seconds to get into position.

c.

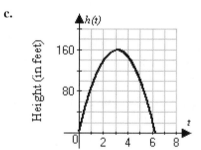

62. $l + 2w = 180$

$$l = 180 - 2w$$

$$A = lw = 180w - 2w^2$$

$$w = -\frac{180}{2(-2)} = 45$$

$$l = 180 - 2(45) = 90$$

$$A = (90)(45) = 4050$$

The rectangle should be 90 feet long and 45 feet wide. The area is 4050 square feet.

63. a. By regression:

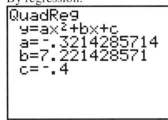

$$f(t) = -0.32t^2 + 7.22t - 0.40$$

b. The t coordinate of the vertex for the model is given by $-\dfrac{b}{2a} = -\dfrac{7.22}{2(-0.32)} = 11.28$, which means that in $2000 + 11 = 2011$, the percentage of military personnel having served more than one tour of duty in Iraq and Afghanistan will reach a maximum. This maximum value is given by the model as

$$f(11.28) = -0.32(11.28)^2 + 7.22(11.28) - 0.40$$
$$= 40.33$$

The vertex $(11.28, 40.33)$ indicates that the maximum percentage of personnel having served more than one tour of duty will be about 40% in 2011.

c. Solve for t for $f(t) = 37$.

$$37 = -0.32t^2 + 7.22t - 0.40$$

$$0 = -0.32t^2 + 7.22t - 37.40$$

$$t = \frac{-7.22 \pm \sqrt{(7.22)^2 - 4(-0.32)(-37.40)}}{2(-0.32)}$$

$$\approx \frac{-7.22 \pm 2.06}{-0.64}$$

$$\approx 8.06, \ 14.5$$

In $2000 + 8 = 2008$, and again in $2000 + 15 = 2015$, 37% of military personnel will have served more than one tour of duty.

d. For $t = 10$,

$$f(10) = -0.32(10)^2 + 7.22(10) - 0.40$$
$$= 39.8$$

In 2009, the number of military personnel having served more than one tour of duty in Iraq and Afghanistan was about 40%.

64. a. By regression:

$$f(t) = -0.084t^2 - 1.29t + 70.56$$
$$g(t) = 0.13t^2 - 0.52t + 2.26$$

b. $-0.084t^2 - 1.29t + 70.56$
$$= 0.13t^2 - 0.52t + 2.26$$
$$0.214t^2 + 0.77t - 68.3 = 0$$

$$t = \frac{-0.77 \pm \sqrt{(0.77)^2 - 4(0.214)(-68.3)}}{2(0.214)}$$

$$\approx \frac{-0.77 \pm 7.68}{0.428}$$

$$\approx 16.1, \ -19.7$$

The internet was not in existence in $1990 - 20 = 1970$, so only the positive root is meaningful. In $1990 + 16 = 2006$, the percentage of Americans who get their news every day from the nightly news programs was equal to the percentage of Americans who get their news every day on the Internet.

Chapter 9 Test

1.

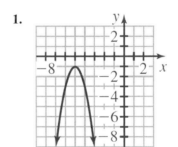

2. Since the vertex lies on the x-axis when $x > 0$, $h > 0$ and $k = 0$. Since the parabola is turned upward (has a minimum point), $a > 0$.

3. Answers may vary. Example: $y = -(x - 2)^2 - 7$

4. Vertex: $(-1, 5)$

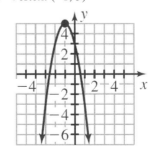

5. a. To find the x-intercepts, solve for x when
$f(x) = 0$

$$0 = x^2 - 2x - 8$$
$$0 = (x-4)(x+2)$$
$$x - 4 = 0 \text{ or } x + 2 = 0$$
$$x = 4 \text{ or } x = -2$$
$$(-2, 0), (4, 0)$$

b. Since the x-intercepts are symmetric points, the average of the x-coordinates for these points is the x-coordinate of the vertex, which is $\dfrac{4 + (-2)}{2} = 1$. Substitute 1 for x in the function to find the y-coordinate of the vertex:

$$y = (1)^2 - 2(1) - 8 = -9$$
So, the vertex is $(1, -9)$.

c.

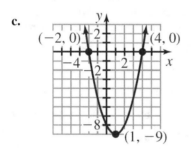

6. $\sqrt{32} = \sqrt{16 \cdot 2} = \sqrt{16}\sqrt{2} = 4\sqrt{2}$

7. $\sqrt{\dfrac{20}{75}} = \dfrac{\sqrt{20}}{\sqrt{75}} = \dfrac{2\sqrt{5}}{5\sqrt{3}} = \dfrac{2\sqrt{5}}{5\sqrt{3}} \cdot \dfrac{\sqrt{3}}{\sqrt{3}} = \dfrac{2\sqrt{15}}{15}$

8. $x^2 - 3x - 10 = 0$
$$(x-5)(x+2) = 0$$
$$x - 5 = 0 \text{ or } x + 2 = 0$$
$$x = 5 \text{ or } x = -2$$

9. $6x^2 = 100$
$$x^2 = \dfrac{100}{6}$$
$$x^2 = \dfrac{50}{3}$$
$$x = \pm\sqrt{\dfrac{50}{3}}$$
$$x = \pm\dfrac{\sqrt{50}}{\sqrt{3}}$$
$$x = \pm\dfrac{5\sqrt{2}}{\sqrt{3}} \cdot \dfrac{\sqrt{3}}{\sqrt{3}}$$
$$x = \pm\dfrac{5\sqrt{6}}{3}$$

10. $4(r-3)^2 + 1 = 7$
$$4r^2 - 24r + 30 = 0$$
$$r = \dfrac{24 \pm \sqrt{(-24)^2 - 4(4)(30)}}{2(4)}$$
$$= \dfrac{24 \pm \sqrt{96}}{8}$$
$$= \dfrac{24 \pm 4\sqrt{6}}{8}$$
$$= \dfrac{6 \pm \sqrt{6}}{2}$$

11. $\dfrac{5}{6}x^2 - \dfrac{1}{2}x = \dfrac{2}{3}$
$$5x^2 - 3x - 4 = 0$$
$$x = \dfrac{3 \pm \sqrt{(-3)^2 - 4(5)(-4)}}{2(5)}$$
$$= \dfrac{3 \pm \sqrt{89}}{10}$$

12. $(x-3)(x+5) = 6$
$$x^2 + 5x - 3x - 15 = 6$$
$$x^2 + 2x - 21 = 0$$
$$x^2 + 2x = 21$$
$$x^2 + 2x + 1 = 21 + 1$$
$$(x+1)^2 = 22$$
$$x + 1 = \pm\sqrt{22}$$
$$x = -1 \pm \sqrt{22}$$

13. $2x(x+5) = 4x-3$

$2x^2 + 10x = 4x - 3$

$2x^2 + 6x + 3 = 0$

$x = \dfrac{-6 \pm \sqrt{6^2 - 4(2)(3)}}{2(2)}$

$x = \dfrac{-6 \pm \sqrt{12}}{4}$

$x = \dfrac{-6 \pm 2\sqrt{3}}{4}$

$x = \dfrac{-3 \pm \sqrt{3}}{2}$

14. $3x^2 - 6x = 1$

$3x^2 - 6x - 1 = 0$

$x = \dfrac{6 \pm \sqrt{(-6)^2 - 4(3)(-1)}}{2(3)}$

$= \dfrac{6 \pm \sqrt{48}}{6}$

$= \dfrac{6 \pm 4\sqrt{3}}{6}$

$= \dfrac{3 \pm 2\sqrt{3}}{3}$

15. $3.7x^2 = 2.4 - 5.9x$

$3.7x^2 + 5.9x - 2.4 = 0$

$x = \dfrac{-5.9 \pm \sqrt{(5.9)^2 - 4(3.7)(-2.4)}}{2(3.7)}$

$\approx \dfrac{-5.9 \pm 8.4}{7.4}$

$\approx 0.34, \ -1.93$

16. $3x^2 - 6x = -5$

$3x^2 - 6x + 5 = 0$

$x = \dfrac{6 \pm \sqrt{(-6)^2 - 4(3)(5)}}{2(3)}$

$= \dfrac{6 \pm \sqrt{-24}}{6}$

$= \dfrac{6 \pm 2i\sqrt{6}}{6}$

$= \dfrac{3 \pm i\sqrt{6}}{3}$

17. $-2(p+4)^2 = 24$

$-2p^2 - 16p - 56 = 0$

$x = \dfrac{16 \pm \sqrt{(-16)^2 - 4(-2)(-56)}}{2(-2)}$

$= \dfrac{16 \pm \sqrt{-192}}{-4}$

$= \dfrac{16 \pm 8i\sqrt{3}}{-4}$

$= -4 \pm 2i\sqrt{3}$

18. $x^2 - 8x - 2 = 0$

$x^2 - 8x = 2$

$x^2 - 8x + 16 = 2 + 16$

$(x-4)^2 = 18$

$x - 4 = \pm\sqrt{18}$

$x - 4 = \pm 3\sqrt{2}$

$x = 4 \pm 3\sqrt{2}$

19. $2(x^2 - 4) = -3x$

$x^2 - 4 = -\dfrac{3}{2}x$

$x^2 + \dfrac{3}{2}x = 4$

$x^2 + \dfrac{3}{2}x + \dfrac{9}{16} = 4 + \dfrac{9}{16}$

$\left(x + \dfrac{3}{4}\right)^2 = \dfrac{73}{16}$

$x + \dfrac{3}{4} = \pm\sqrt{\dfrac{73}{16}}$

$x + \dfrac{3}{4} = \pm\dfrac{\sqrt{73}}{4}$

$x = \dfrac{-3 \pm \sqrt{73}}{4}$

20. Solve for x when $f(x) = 0$:

$$3x^2 - 8x + 1 = 0$$

$$x = \frac{-(-8) \pm \sqrt{(-8)^2 - 4(3)(1)}}{2(3)}$$

$$x = \frac{8 \pm \sqrt{52}}{6}$$

$$x = \frac{8 \pm 2\sqrt{13}}{6}$$

$$x = \frac{4 \pm \sqrt{13}}{3}$$

The x-intercepts are $\left(\frac{4-\sqrt{13}}{3}, 0\right)$ and

$\left(\frac{4+\sqrt{13}}{3}, 0\right)$.

21. $-2(x-3)^2 + 5 = 0$

$$-2x^2 + 12x - 13 = 0$$

$$x = \frac{-12 \pm \sqrt{(12)^2 - 4(-2)(-13)}}{2(-2)}$$

$$= \frac{-12 \pm \sqrt{40}}{-4}$$

$$\approx \frac{-12 \pm 6.32}{-4}$$

$$= 4.58, \ 1.42$$

The x-intercepts are (1.42, 0) and (4.58, 0). The vertex is (3, 5).

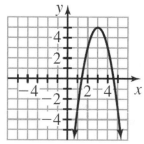

22. $b^2 - 4ac = 0$

$$(-4)^2 - 4(a)(4a) = 0$$

$$16 - 16a^2 = 0$$

$$16a^2 = 16$$

$$a^2 = 1$$

$$a = \pm 1$$

23. Substitute the given points into $y = ax^2 + bx + c$.

$$(1,4): 4 = a(1)^2 + b(1) + c$$

$$(2,9): 9 = a(2)^2 + b(2) + c$$

$$(3,16): 16 = a(3)^2 + b(3) + c$$

Simplify these equations:

$$a + b + c = 4 \qquad (1)$$

$$4a + 2b + c = 9 \qquad (2)$$

$$9a + 3b + c = 16 \qquad (3)$$

Eliminate c by multiplying both sides of equation (1) by -1:

$$-a - b - c = -4 \qquad (4)$$

Adding the left sides and right sides of equations (2) and (4) gives:

$$3a + b = 5 \qquad (5)$$

Adding the left sides and right sides of equations (3) and (4) gives:

$$8a + 2b = 12 \qquad (6)$$

Simplify:

$$4a + b = 6 \qquad (7)$$

Eliminate b by multiplying equation (5) by -1 and add each side to the corresponding side of equation (7):

$$a = 1$$

Next, substitute 1 for a in equation (5):

$$3(1) + b = 5$$

$$b = 2$$

Then, substitute 1 for a and 2 for b in equation (1):

$$a + b + c = 4$$

$$1 + 2 + c = 4$$

$$c = 1$$

Therefore, $a = 1$, $b = 2$, and $c = 1$. So, the equation is $y = x^2 + 2x + 1$.

24. Using the equation $y = a(x - h)^2 + k$, substitute 5 for h and 3 for k since the vertex is (5, 3). Also, substitute 3 for x and 11 for y since (3, 11) lies on the parabola.

$$y = a(x - h)^2 + k$$
$$11 = a(3 - 5)^2 + 3$$
$$11 = a(-2)^2 + 3$$
$$11 = 4a + 3$$
$$8 = 4a$$
$$a = 2$$

So, the equation is $y = 2(x - 5)^2 + 3$.

25. a.
$$x^2 - 6x + 11 = 1$$
$$x^2 - 6x + 10 = 0$$
$$x = \frac{-(-6) \pm \sqrt{(-6)^2 - 4(1)(10)}}{2(1)}$$
$$x = \frac{6 \pm \sqrt{-4}}{2}$$

Since the square root of a negative is not a real number, there are no real number solutions. There is no such value for x.

b.
$$x^2 - 6x + 11 = 2$$
$$x^2 - 6x + 9 = 0$$
$$x = \frac{-(-6) \pm \sqrt{(-6)^2 - 4(1)(9)}}{2(1)}$$
$$x = \frac{6 \pm \sqrt{0}}{2}$$
$$x = \frac{6}{2} = 3$$

There is one real solution.

c.
$$x^2 - 6x + 11 = 3$$
$$x^2 - 6x + 8 = 0$$
$$x = \frac{-(-6) \pm \sqrt{(-6)^2 - 4(1)(8)}}{2(1)}$$
$$x = \frac{6 \pm \sqrt{4}}{2}$$
$$x = \frac{6 \pm 2}{2}$$
$$x = \frac{8}{2} \text{ or } x = \frac{4}{2}$$
$$x = 4 \text{ or } x = 2$$

There are two real solutions.

26. Multiply the first equation by –2, and then add the first and second equations:

$$-2x - 8y - 6z = -4$$
$$\underline{2x + y + z = 10}$$
$$-7y - 5z = 6$$

Add the first and third equations:

$$x + 4y + 3z = 2$$
$$\underline{-x + y + 2z = 8}$$
$$5y + 5z = 10$$

Isolate y:
$$5y + 5z = 10$$
$$5y = 10 - 5z$$
$$y = 2 - z$$

Solve for z:
$$-7(2 - z) - 5z = 6$$
$$-14 + 7z - 5z = 6$$
$$2z = 20$$
$$z = 10$$

Solve for y:
$$y = 2 - 10 = -8$$

Solve for x:
$$x + 4(-8) + 3(10) = 2$$
$$x - 32 + 30 = 2$$
$$x = 4$$

The solution to the system is the point (4, –8, 10).

27. Add the first and second equations:

$$2x - 3y \quad\quad = 4$$
$$\underline{\quad\quad 3y + 2z = 2}$$
$$2x \quad\quad + 2z = 6$$

Isolate z:

$$2x + 2z = 6$$
$$2x = 6 - 2z$$
$$x = 3 - z$$

Solve for z:

$$x - z = -5$$
$$3 - z - z = -5$$
$$3 - 2z = -5$$
$$-2z = -8$$
$$z = 4$$

Solve for y:

$$3y + 2(4) = 2$$
$$3y + 8 = 2$$
$$3y = -6$$
$$y = -2$$

Solve for x:

$$x = 3 - 4 = -1$$

The solution to the system is the point $(-1, -2, 4)$.

28. Using a graphing calculator, find that the maximum point of the parabola is approximately $(2.50, 103)$.

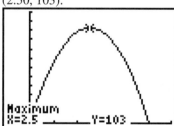

So, the maximum height reached by the ball is 103 feet at 2.5 seconds.

29. a. By regression:

$$f(t) = -0.028t^2 + 2.54t - 15.92$$

b. $f(30) = -0.028(30)^2 + 2.54(30) - 15.92$

$$= 35.08$$

About 35% of 30-year-old Americans feel that they are taking a great risk by entering personal information into a pop-up ad.

c. $-0.028t^2 + 2.54t - 15.92 = 30$

$$-0.028t^2 + 2.54t - 45.92 = 0$$

$$t = \frac{-2.54 \pm \sqrt{(2.54)^2 - 4(-0.028)(-45.92)}}{2(-0.028)}$$

$$\approx \frac{-2.54 \pm 1.1439}{-0.056}$$

$$\approx 24.93,\ 65.78$$

30% of 25-year-old Americans and 30% of 66-year-old Americans feel that they are taking a great risk when entering personal information into a pop-up ad.

d. $-0.028t^2 + 2.54t - 15.92 = 0$

$$t = \frac{-2.54 \pm \sqrt{(2.54)^2 - 4(-0.028)(-15.92)}}{2(-0.028)}$$

$$\approx \frac{-2.54 \pm 2.1607}{-0.056}$$

$$\approx 6.77,\ 83.94$$

The t-intercepts are therefore $(6.79, 0)$ and $(83.93, 0)$. These mean that there are no 7-year-old or 84-year-old Americans who feel that they are taking a great risk when entering personal information into a pop-up ad. Model breakdown has occurred.

e. $t = -\dfrac{2.54}{2(-0.028)} = 45.36$

$$f(45.36)$$

$$= -0.028(45.36)^2 + 2.54(45.36) - 15.92$$

$$= 41.68$$

The vertex is $(45.36, 41.68)$. This means that the age at which the maximum percentage, 42%, of Americans who feel that they are taking a great risk is 45 years.

30. $p = 40 - 0.25x$

$$R = px = 40x - 0.25x^2$$

$$x = -\frac{40}{2(-0.25)} = 80$$

A group of 80 people would maximize the boat owner's revenue.

Cumulative Review of Chapters 1-9

1. $-3-6 = -9$

Over the past two hours, the change in temperature was $-9°F$.

2. We substitute -2 for a, 8 for b, and -4 for c.

$$ac^2 - \frac{b}{c} = (-2)(-4)^2 - \frac{8}{(-4)}$$
$$= (-2)(16) - \frac{8}{(-4)}$$
$$= -32 - (-2)$$
$$= -32 + 2$$
$$= -30$$

3. We substitute -2 for a, 8 for b, and -4 for c.

$$\frac{a+bc}{ab-c} = \frac{-2+8(-4)}{-2(8)-(-4)} = \frac{-2+(-32)}{-16+4} = \frac{-34}{-12} = \frac{17}{6}$$

4. Slope of ski run $A = \frac{130 \text{ yards}}{610 \text{ yards}} \approx 0.21$

Slope of ski run $B = \frac{165 \text{ yards}}{700 \text{ yards}} \approx 0.24$

Thus, ski run B is steeper since it has a larger slope.

5. Using the slope formula with $(x_1, y_1) = (-5,-4)$ and $(x_2, y_2) = (-1,-2)$, the slope is

$$m = \frac{y_2 - y_1}{x_2 - x_1} = \frac{-2-(-4)}{-1-(-5)} = \frac{-2+4}{-1+5} = \frac{2}{4} = \frac{1}{2}.$$

The slope is positive, so the line is increasing.

6. $81x^2 - 49 = 0$

$$81x^2 = 49$$
$$x^2 = \frac{49}{81}$$
$$\sqrt{x^2} = \pm\sqrt{\frac{49}{81}}$$
$$x = \pm\frac{7}{9}$$

7. $\frac{5x}{6} - \frac{2}{3} = \frac{7}{4}$

$$10x - 8 = 21$$
$$10x = 29$$
$$x = \frac{29}{10}$$

8. $5x^2 - 2x = 4$

$$5x^2 - 2x - 4 = 0$$
$$x = \frac{2 \pm \sqrt{(-2)^2 - 4(5)(-4)}}{2(5)}$$
$$= \frac{2 \pm \sqrt{84}}{10}$$
$$= \frac{2 \pm 2\sqrt{21}}{10}$$
$$= \frac{1 \pm \sqrt{21}}{5}$$

9. $2(3t^2 - 10) = -7t$

$$3t^2 - 10 = -\frac{7t}{2}$$
$$3t^2 + \frac{7t}{2} - 10 = 0$$
$$6t^2 + 7t - 20 = 0$$
$$t = \frac{-7 \pm \sqrt{(7)^2 - 4(6)(-20)}}{2(6)}$$
$$= \frac{-7 \pm \sqrt{529}}{12}$$
$$= \frac{-7 \pm 23}{12}$$
$$t = \frac{4}{3} \qquad t = -\frac{5}{2}$$

10. $(2p-5)(3p+4) = 5p-2$

$$6p^2 - 7p - 20 = 5p - 2$$
$$6p^2 - 12p - 18 = 0$$
$$6(p^2 - 2p - 3) = 0$$
$$6(p-3)(p+1) = 0$$
$$p = 3 \qquad p = -1$$

11. $2(5x+2)-1=9(x-3)-(3x-8)$

$10x+4-1=9x-27-3x+8$

$10x+3=6x-19$

$4x=-22$

$x=-\dfrac{11}{2}$

12. $2x(3x-4)+5=4-x^2$

$6x^2-8x+5=4-x^2$

$7x^2-8x+1=0$

$(7x-1)(x-1)=0$

$x=\dfrac{1}{7} \quad x=1$

13. $\qquad w^2=5w+24$

$w^2-5w-24=0$

$(w-8)(w+3)=0$

$w-8=0 \quad \text{or} \quad w+3=0$

$w=8 \quad \text{or} \quad w=-3$

So, the solutions are -3 and 8.

This is a quadratic (or second-degree) equation.

14. $\qquad (2r-1)(3r-2)=1$

$6r^2-4r-3r+2=1$

$6r^2-7r+2=1$

$6r^2-7r+1=0$

$(6r-1)(r-1)=0$

$6r-1=0 \quad \text{or} \quad r-1=0$

$6r=1 \quad \text{or} \quad r=1$

$r=\dfrac{1}{6}$

So, the solutions are $\dfrac{1}{6}$ and 1.

This is a quadratic (or second-degree) equation.

15. $3x^2-7=13$

$3x^2=20$

$x^2=\dfrac{20}{3}$

$x=\pm\sqrt{\dfrac{20}{3}}$

$x=\pm\dfrac{\sqrt{20}}{\sqrt{3}}$

$x=\pm\dfrac{2\sqrt{5}}{\sqrt{3}}\cdot\dfrac{\sqrt{3}}{\sqrt{3}}$

$x=\pm\dfrac{2\sqrt{15}}{3}$

So, the solutions are $\pm\dfrac{2\sqrt{15}}{3}$.

This is a quadratic (or second-degree) equation.

16. $(x+4)^2=60$

$x+4=\pm\sqrt{60}$

$x+4=\pm2\sqrt{15}$

$x=-4\pm2\sqrt{15}$

So, the solutions are $-4\pm2\sqrt{15}$.

This is a quadratic (or second-degree) equation.

17. $3x^2-5x-4=0$

We solve by using the quadratic formula with $a=3$, $b=-5$, and $c=-4$.

$x=\dfrac{-b\pm\sqrt{b^2-4ac}}{2a}$

$=\dfrac{-(-5)\pm\sqrt{(-5)^2-4(3)(-4)}}{2(3)}$

$=\dfrac{5\pm\sqrt{25+48}}{6}=\dfrac{5\pm\sqrt{73}}{6}$

So, the solutions are $\dfrac{5\pm\sqrt{73}}{6}$.

This is a quadratic (or second-degree) equation.

18. $\qquad 2x(x+3)=-3$

$2x^2+6x=-3$

$2x^2+6x+3=0$

We solve by using the quadratic formula with $a=2$, $b=6$, and $c=3$.

$$x = \frac{-b \pm \sqrt{b^2 - 4ac}}{2a} = \frac{-(6) \pm \sqrt{(6)^2 - 4(2)(3)}}{2(2)}$$

$$= \frac{-6 \pm \sqrt{36 - 24}}{4} = \frac{-6 \pm \sqrt{12}}{4} = \frac{-6 \pm 2\sqrt{3}}{4}$$

$$= \frac{2(-3 \pm \sqrt{3})}{4} = \frac{-3 \pm \sqrt{3}}{2}$$

So, the solutions are $\dfrac{-3 \pm \sqrt{3}}{2}$.

This is a quadratic (or second-degree) equation.

19. $a = \dfrac{v - v_0}{t}$

$$a \cdot t = \frac{v - v_0}{t} \cdot t$$

$$at = v - v_0$$

$$\frac{at}{a} = \frac{v - v_0}{a}$$

$$t = \frac{v - v_0}{a}$$

20. $2x^2 - 6x = -5$

$$2x^2 - 6x + 5 = 0$$

$$x = \frac{6 \pm \sqrt{(-6)^2 - 4(2)(5)}}{2(2)}$$

$$= \frac{6 \pm \sqrt{-4}}{4}$$

$$= \frac{6 \pm 2i}{4}$$

$$= \frac{3 \pm i}{2}$$

21. $2x^2 + 3x - 6 = 0$

$$2x^2 + 3x = 6$$

$$x^2 + \frac{3}{2}x = 3$$

$$x^2 + \frac{3}{2}x + \frac{9}{16} = 3 + \frac{9}{16}$$

$$\left(x + \frac{3}{4}\right)^2 = \frac{48}{16} + \frac{9}{16}$$

$$\left(x + \frac{3}{4}\right)^2 = \frac{57}{16}$$

$$x + \frac{3}{4} = \pm\sqrt{\frac{57}{16}}$$

$$x + \frac{3}{4} = \pm\frac{\sqrt{57}}{4}$$

$$x = -\frac{3}{4} \pm \frac{\sqrt{57}}{4}$$

$$x = \frac{-3 \pm \sqrt{57}}{4}$$

22. Substitute $y = 3x - 1$ in $2x - 3y = -11$.

$$2x - 3(3x - 1) = -11$$

$$2x - 9x + 3 = -11$$

$$-7x = -14$$

$$x = 2$$

Substitute 2 for x in one of the original equations to solve for y:

$$y = 3x - 1$$

$$= 3(2) - 1$$

$$= 5$$

The solution is $(2, 5)$.

23. $2x - 7y = 3$ Equation (1)

$-5x + 3y = 7$ Equation (2)

To eliminate the x terms, we multiply both sides of equation (1) by 5 and we multiply both sides of equation (2) by 2, yielding the system

$$10x - 35y = 15$$

$$-10x + 6y = 14$$

The coefficients of the x terms are equal in absolute value and opposite in sign. Add the left and rights sides of the equations and solve for y.

$$10x - 35y = 15$$

$$\underline{-10x + 6y = 14}$$

$$-29y = 29$$

$$y = -1$$

Substitute –1 in for y in equation (1) and solve for x:

$$2x - 7(-1) = 3$$
$$2x = -4$$
$$x = -2$$

So the solution is $(-2, -1)$.

24. In order to eliminate y, multiply $\frac{1}{2}x - y = \frac{5}{2}$ by $-\frac{3}{5}$. This gives $-\frac{3}{10}x + \frac{3}{5}y = -\frac{15}{10}$. Add the left sides and the right sides of the equations:

$$-\frac{3}{10}x + \frac{3}{5}y = -\frac{15}{10}$$
$$\frac{2}{5}x - \frac{3}{5}y = \frac{6}{5}$$

This yields:

$$-\frac{3}{10}x + \frac{2}{5}x = -\frac{15}{10} + \frac{6}{5}$$
$$-\frac{3}{10}x + \frac{4}{10}x = -\frac{15}{10} + \frac{12}{10}$$
$$\frac{1}{10}x = -\frac{3}{10}$$
$$\frac{10}{1} \cdot \frac{1}{10}x = -\frac{3}{10} \cdot \frac{10}{1}$$
$$x = -3$$

Substitute –3 for x in one of the original equations to solve for y:

$$\frac{1}{2}(-3) - y = \frac{5}{2}$$
$$-\frac{3}{2} - y = \frac{5}{2}$$
$$y = -\frac{3}{2} - \frac{5}{2}$$
$$y = -\frac{8}{2} = -4$$

So the solution is $(-3, -4)$.

25. Multiply the first equation by 2 and add the first and second equations:

$$4x - 2y + 6z = 2$$
$$\underline{3x + 2y - z = -6}$$
$$7x \qquad + 5z = -4$$

Multiply the first equation by –3 and add the first and third equations:

$$-6x + 3y - 9z = -3$$
$$\underline{4x - 3y + 2z = -7}$$
$$-2x \qquad -7z = -10$$

Isolate z:

$$-2x - 7z = -10$$
$$-7z = 2x - 10$$
$$z = \frac{10 - 2x}{7}$$

Solve for x:

$$7x + 5\left(\frac{10 - 2x}{7}\right) = -4$$
$$7x + \frac{50 - 10x}{7} = -4$$
$$49x + 50 - 10x = -28$$
$$39x = -78$$
$$x = -2$$

Solve for z:

$$z = \frac{10 - 2(-2)}{7} = 2$$

Solve for y:

$$4(-2) - 2y + 6(2) = 2$$
$$-8 - 2y + 12 = 2$$
$$-2y = -2$$
$$y = 1$$

The solution to the system is the point $(-2, 1, 2)$.

26. $2(3x - 4) < 5 - 3(6x + 5)$

$$2(3x - 4) < 5 - 3(6x + 5)$$
$$6x - 8 < 5 - 18x - 15$$
$$6x - 8 < -18x - 10$$
$$24x < -2$$
$$x < -\frac{1}{12}$$
$$\left(-\infty, -\frac{1}{12}\right)$$

27. $3x - 2y \ge 2$

First, we get y by itself on one side of the inequality:
$$3x - 2y \ge 2$$
$$-2y \ge -3x + 2$$
$$\frac{-2y}{-2} \le \frac{-3x + 2}{-2}$$
$$y \le \frac{3}{2}x - 1$$

The graph of $y \le \frac{3}{2}x - 1$ is the line $y = \frac{3}{2}x - 1$ and the region below the line. We use a solid line along the boarder to indicate that the points on the line are solutions to $3x - 2y \ge 2$.

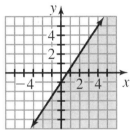

28. $y > \frac{1}{4}x - 3$

$y \ge -2x$

First we sketch the graph of $y > \frac{1}{4}x - 3$ and the graph of $y \ge -2x$. The graph of $y > \frac{1}{4}x - 3$ is the region above the line $y = \frac{1}{4}x - 3$ (graph the line with a dashed line). The graph of $y \ge -2x$ is the line $y = -2x$ and the region above the line (graph the line with a solid line). The graph of the solution set of the system is the intersection of the graphs of the inequalities.

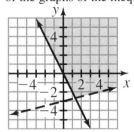

29. $(3x - 4y)^2 = 9x^2 - 24xy + 16y^2$

30. $(5p - 7q)(5p + 7q) = 25p^2 - 49q^2$

31. $-3x(x^2 - 5)(x^3 + 8)$
$$= -3x(x^5 + 8x^2 - 5x^3 - 40)$$
$$= -3x(x^5 - 5x^3 + 8x^2 - 40)$$
$$= -3x^6 + 15x^4 - 24x^3 + 120x$$

32. $(x^2 - 3x - 4)(x^2 + 4x - 5)$
$$= x^4 + 4x^3 - 5x^2 - 3x^3 - 12x^2 +$$
$$15x - 4x^2 - 16x + 20$$
$$= x^4 + x^3 - 21x^2 - x + 20$$

33. $f(x) = -2(x - 5)^2 + 3$
$$= -2(x - 5)(x - 5) + 3$$
$$= -2(x^2 - 5x - 5x + 25) + 3$$
$$= -2(x^2 - 10x + 25) + 3$$
$$= -2x^2 + 20x - 50 + 3$$
$$= -2x^2 + 20x - 47$$

34. $m^4 - 16n^4 = (m^2 - 4n^2)(m^2 + 4n^2)$
$$= (m + 2n)(m - 2n)(m^2 + 4n^2)$$

35. $x^3 - 13x^2 + 40x = x(x^2 - 13x + 40)$
$$= x(x - 8)(x - 5)$$

36. $8p^2 + 22pq - 21q^2 = (4p - 3q)(2p + 7q)$

37. $x^3 + 4x^2 - 9x - 36 = (x^2 - 9)(x + 4)$
$$= (x - 3)(x + 3)(x + 4)$$

38. $128a^3 + 250 = 2(64a^3 + 125)$
$$= 2((4a)^3 + (5)^3)$$
$$= 2(4a + 5)(16a^2 - 20a + 25)$$

39. $3p^3t - 6p^2t^2 - 45pt^3 = 3pt(p^2 - 2pt - 15t^2)$
$$= 3pt(p - 5t)(p + 3t)$$

40. Since the y-intercept is $(0, 20)$ and as x increases by 1, $f(x)$ decreases by 3, so the slope is -3:
$$f(x) = -3x + 20$$

41. As x increases by 1, $g(x)$ increases by a factor of 5, so the slope is 5. We substitute $m = 5$ and

$(x_1, y_1) = (1, 4)$ into the slope intercept form and solve for b:
$$y = mx + b$$
$$4 = 5 \cdot 1 + b$$
$$-1 = b$$
Therefore $g(x) = 5x - 1$

42. For the function k, as x increases by 1, $k(x)$ increases by 4, so the slope is 4.

43. $g(1) = 4$, so $x = 1$.

44. $h(7) = 56$

45.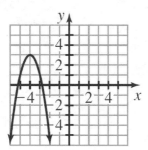

46.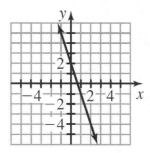

47. First, change the form into $y = mx + b$
$$2x - 5y = 20$$
$$-5y = -2x + 20$$
$$y = \frac{2}{5}x - 4$$

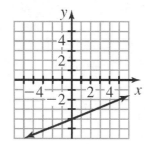

48.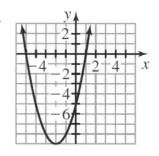

49. The domain goes from -3 to 5, inclusive. The range goes from -2 to 4, inclusive. This is a function.

50. We substitute $m = -\frac{2}{5}$ and $(x_1, y_1) = (-3, 4)$ into the point slope form and solve for y:
$$y - y_1 = m(x - x_1)$$
$$y - 4 = -\frac{2}{5}(x - (-3))$$
$$y - 4 = -\frac{2}{5}(x + 3)$$
$$y - 4 = -\frac{2}{5}x - \frac{6}{5}$$
$$y = -\frac{2}{5}x - \frac{6}{5} + 4$$
$$y = -\frac{2}{5}x + \frac{14}{5}$$

51. We begin by finding the slope of the line:
$$m = \frac{-3 - 4}{6 - (-2)} = \frac{-7}{8} = -\frac{7}{8}$$

Then we substitute $m = -\frac{7}{8}$ and $(x_1, y_1) = (-2, 4)$ into the point slope form and solve for y:
$$y - y_1 = m(x - x_1)$$
$$y - 4 = -\frac{7}{8}(x - (-2))$$
$$y - 4 = -\frac{7}{8}(x + 2)$$
$$y - 4 = -\frac{7}{8}x - \frac{7}{4}$$
$$y = -\frac{7}{8}x - \frac{7}{4} + 4$$
$$y = -\frac{7}{8}x + \frac{9}{4}$$

52. First, change the form of the equation given to $y = mx + b$.

$$3x - 4y = 5$$

$$-4y = -3x + 5$$

$$y = \frac{3}{4}x - \frac{5}{4}$$

The slope of the perpendicular line will be $-\frac{4}{3}$. So

the equation of the perpendicular line will be

$y = -\frac{4}{3}x + b$. Substitute the given point into this

equation to solve for b.

$$6 = -\frac{4}{3}(-2) + b$$

$$6 = \frac{8}{3} + b$$

$$b = 6 - \frac{8}{3}$$

$$b = \frac{18}{3} - \frac{8}{3}$$

$$b = \frac{10}{3}$$

So, the equation is $y = -\frac{4}{3}x + \frac{10}{3}$.

53. Substitute the given points into $y = ax^2 + bx + c$.

$$(1, -1) : -1 = a(1)^2 + b(1) + c$$

$$(2, 4) : 4 = a(2)^2 + b(2) + c$$

$$(4, 20) : 20 = a(4)^2 + b(4) + c$$

Simplify these equations:

$$a + b + c = -1 \qquad (1)$$

$$4a + 2b + c = 4 \qquad (2)$$

$$16a + 4b + c = 20 \qquad (3)$$

Eliminate c by multiplying both sides of equation (1) by -1:

$$-a - b - c = 1 \qquad (4)$$

Adding the left sides and right sides of equations (2) and (4) gives:

$$3a + b = 5 \qquad (5)$$

Adding the left sides and right sides of equations (3) and (4) gives:

$$15a + 3b = 21 \qquad (6)$$

Simplify:

$$5a + b = 7 \qquad (7)$$

Eliminate b by multiplying equation (5) by -1 and add each side to the corresponding side of equation (7):

$$2a = 2$$

$$a = 1$$

Next, substitute 1 for a in equation (5):

$$3(1) + b = 5$$

$$b = 2$$

Then, substitute 1 for a and 2 for b in equation (1):

$$a + b + c = -1$$

$$1 + 2 + c = -1$$

$$c = -4$$

Therefore, $a = 1$, $b = 2$, and $c = -4$. So, the equation is $y = x^2 + 2x - 4$.

54. a. Linear:

$$\text{slope} = m = \frac{6 - 3}{1 - 0} = 3$$

$$y - \text{intercept} = (0, 3)$$

So, $f(x) = 3x + 3$

Quadratic:

Answers may vary. Example:

$g(x) = 3x^2 + 3$.

b.

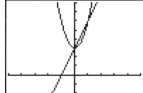

55. $f(-3) = -(-3)^2 + 6(-3) - 5 = -32$

56. $-x^2 + 6x - 5 = 3$

$$x^2 - 6x + 8 = 0$$

$$(x - 4)(x - 2) = 0$$

$$x - 4 = 0 \text{ or } x - 2 = 0$$

$$x = 4 \text{ or } x = 2$$

57. To find the x-intercepts, let $f(x) = 0$ and solve for x:

$$-x^2 + 6x - 5 = 0$$

$$x^2 - 6x + 5 = 0$$

$$(x - 5)(x - 1) = 0$$

$$x - 5 = 0 \text{ or } x - 1 = 0$$

$$x = 5 \text{ or } x = 1$$

The x-intercepts are (1, 0) and (5, 0).

58.

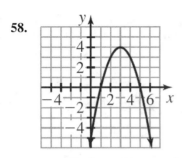

59. $5x^2 y^6 \left(2x^3 y\right)^3 = 5x^2 y^6 \cdot 8x^9 y^3$

$\qquad = 40x^{11} y^9$

60. $\left(\dfrac{3x^5 y^7}{2w^3}\right)^4 = \dfrac{81x^{20} y^{28}}{16w^{12}}$

61. Let x = the amount invested at 6%, so $12{,}000 - x$ = the amount invested at 11%.

$0.06x + (12000 - x)(0.11) = 845$

$0.06x + 1320 - 0.11x = 845$

$0.05x = 475$

$x = 9500$

$12000 - 9500 = 2500$

$9500 is invested at 6% and $2500 is invested at 11%.

62. a. By regression:

$f(a) = 0.0086a^2 - 1.35a + 61.33$

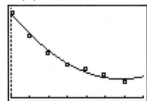

The quadratic equation models the data closely .

b. The p-intercept is (0, 61.33). This means that about 61% of newborn male drivers were speeding when they became involved in fatal crashes. Model breakdown has occurred.

c. We substitute 23 for a in the model:

$f(23) = 0.0086(23)^2 - 1.35(23) + 61.3$

$\qquad \approx 34.7994$

Thus, we estimate that approximately 35% of 23-year-old male drivers were speeding when they became involved in a fatal crash.

d. We substitute 25 for p and solve for a:

$25 = 0.0086a^2 - 1.35a + 61.3$

$0 = 0.0086a^2 - 1.35a + 36.3$

To solve, we use the quadratic formula with $a = 0.0086$, $b = -1.35$, and $c = 36.3$:

$a = \dfrac{-(-1.35) \pm \sqrt{(-1.35)^2 - 4(0.0086)(36.3)}}{2(0.0086)}$

$a = \dfrac{1.35 \pm \sqrt{0.57378}}{0.0172}$

$a \approx 34.45$ or $a \approx 122.53$

We disregard 122.53. We predict that 25% of 34-year-old male drivers were speeding when they became involved in a fatal crash.

e. Use $a = 0.0086$ and $b = -1.35$ to find the vertex.

$-\dfrac{b}{2a} = -\dfrac{-1.35}{2(0.0086)} \approx 78.49$

Substitute $a = 78.49$ into the equation and solve for $f(a)$.

$f(78.49) = 0.0086(78.49)^2 - 1.35(78.49) + 61.33$

$\qquad \approx 8.35$

The vertex is about (78.49, 8.35). This means that the lowest percentage, about 8%, of 78 years old male drivers were speeding when they became involved in a fatal crash, model breakdown has occurred.

63. a. Since the airplane is descending at a rate of 1350 feet per minute, we can model the situation by a linear equation. The slope is -1350 feet per minute. Since the altitude of the plane as 27,500 feet before beginning its descent, the f-intercept is (0, 27500). So, a reasonable model is

$f(t) = -1350t + 27{,}500$.

b. We substitute 7 for t in our model:

$A = -1350(7) + 27{,}500 = 18{,}050$

The plane's altitude 7 minutes after it has begun it descent will be 18,050 feet.

c. We substitute 1200 for A in our model and solve for t:

$1200 = -1350t + 27{,}500$

$-26{,}300 = -1350t$

$t = \dfrac{-26{,}300}{-1350} \approx 19.48$

The plane's altitude will be 1200 feet about 19.48 minutes after it begins its descent.

d. The slope is $m = -1350$. It means that the airplane descends by 1350 feet per minute.

e. We find the t-intercept by substituting 0 for A and solving for t:

$$0 = -1350t + 27,500$$

$$1350t = 27,500$$

$$t = \frac{27500}{1350} \approx 20.37$$

The t-intercept is approximately (20.37, 0). It means that the airplane will land on the ground (altitude will be 0 feet) about 20.4 minutes after it begins its descent.

64. a. $m = \dfrac{13 - 29}{25 - 5} = -0.8$

$$y = -0.8x + b$$

$$29 = -0.8(5) + b$$

$$b = 33$$

$$f(t) = -0.8t + 33$$

b. The slope of the graph is –0.8. This means that the percentage of union members who work in manufacturing is decreasing by 0.8 percent per year.

c. $f(33) = -0.8(33) + 33 = 6.6$

In 1980 + 33 = 2013, about 7% of union members will work in manufacturing.

d. $-0.8t + 33 = 100$

$$-0.8t = 67$$

$$t = -83.75$$

In 1980 – 84 = 1896, 100% of union members were working in manufacturing. Model breakdown has occurred.

e. To find the t-intercept of the model, let $p = 0$ and solve for t.

$$-0.8t + 33 = 0$$

$$-0.8t = -33$$

$$t = 41.25$$

The t-intercept is (41.25, 0). In 1980 + 41 = 2021, no union members will be working manufacturing. Model breakdown has likely occurred.

f. For $t < -83.75$ and $t > 41.25$, there is model breakdown.

65. a. First, draw a scattergram of the data for f. The linear regression equation,

$f(t) = -2.61t + 76.89$, is the best model for this data.

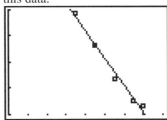

First, draw a scattergram of the data for g. The linear regression equation,

$g(t) = 2.08t + 46.36$, is the best model for this data.

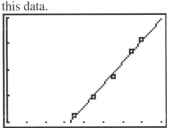

b. $f(24) = -2.61(24) + 76.89 = 14.25$

$g(24) = 2.08(24) + 46.36 = 96.28$

In the year 1990 + 24 = 2014, the pregnancy rate will be about 14.3 for every 1000 among 15–17-year-old women. In that same year, the pregnancy rate will be about 96.3 for every 1000 among 35–39-year-old women.

c. For some value of t, $f(t) = g(t)$.

$$-2.61t + 76.89 = 2.08t + 46.36$$

$$30.53 = 4.69t$$

$$t = 6.51$$

$$f(6.51) = -2.61(6.51) + 76.89 = 59.9$$

$$g(6.51) = 2.08(6.51) + 46.36 = 59.9$$

In 1990 + 7 = 1997, the two pregnancy rates were equal, at nearly 60 pregnancies per 1000 women.

d. Because the pregnancy rate for women 15–17 years of age is decreasing, it would have been greater than the pregnancy rate for women 35–39-years of age before 1997, when the two rates became equal.

415

Chapter 10
Exponential Functions

Homework 10.1

1. $b^{-4} = \dfrac{1}{b^4}$

3. $\dfrac{1}{b^{-2}} = b^2$

5. $\dfrac{b^{-3}}{c^5} = b^{-3} \cdot \dfrac{1}{c^5} = \dfrac{1}{b^3} \cdot \dfrac{1}{c^5} = \dfrac{1}{b^3 c^5}$

7. $\dfrac{c^{-4}}{b^{-2}} = c^{-4} \cdot \dfrac{1}{b^{-2}} = \dfrac{1}{c^4} \cdot b^2 = \dfrac{b^2}{c^4}$

9. $\dfrac{4b^{-9}}{-6c^4 d^{-1}} = \dfrac{4}{-6c^4} \cdot b^{-9} \cdot \dfrac{1}{d^{-1}}$

$= -\dfrac{2}{3c^4} \cdot \dfrac{1}{b^9} \cdot d^1$

$= -\dfrac{2d}{3b^9 c^4}$

11. $2^{-1} = \dfrac{1}{2}$

13. $2^{-1} + 3^{-1} = \dfrac{1}{2} + \dfrac{1}{3} = \dfrac{3}{6} + \dfrac{2}{6} = \dfrac{5}{6}$

15. $7^{-902} 7^{900} = 7^{900-902} = 7^{-2} = \dfrac{1}{7^2} = \dfrac{1}{49}$

17. $13^{500} 13^{-500} = 13^{500+(-500)} = 13^0 = 1$

19. $\left(b^{-2}\right)^7 = b^{-2(7)} = b^{-14} = \dfrac{1}{b^{14}}$

21. $\left(-4b^{-1}\right)\left(3b^{-8}\right) = -4 \cdot 3 \cdot b^{-1} b^{-8} = -12b^{-9} = -\dfrac{12}{b^9}$

23. $\left(-4b^3 c^{-7}\right)\left(-b^{-5} c^4\right) = (-4)(-1) b^3 b^{-5} c^{-7} c^4$

$= 4b^{-2} c^{-3}$

$= \dfrac{4}{b^2 c^3}$

25. $\dfrac{b^{-3}}{b^5} = b^{-3-5} = b^{-8} = \dfrac{1}{b^8}$

27. $\dfrac{b^3}{b^{-2}} = b^{3-(-2)} = b^{3+2} = b^5$

29. $\dfrac{7b^{-3}}{4b^{-9}} = \dfrac{7b^{-3-(-9)}}{4} = \dfrac{7b^{-3+9}}{4} = \dfrac{7b^6}{4}$

31. $\dfrac{2^{-1}}{2^4} = 2^{-1-4} = 2^{-5} = \dfrac{1}{2^5} = \dfrac{1}{32}$

33. $\dfrac{5^{-6}}{5^{-4}} = 5^{-6-(-4)} = 5^{-6+4} = 5^{-2} = \dfrac{1}{5^2} = \dfrac{1}{25}$

35. $\dfrac{3^4 b^{-8}}{3^2 b^{-3}} = 3^{4-2} b^{-8-(-3)} = 3^2 b^{-5} = \dfrac{3^2}{b^5} = \dfrac{9}{b^5}$

37. $\left(2b^{-1}\right)^{-5} = 2^{-5} \left(b^{-1}\right)^{-5} = \dfrac{1}{2^5} \cdot b^5 = \dfrac{b^5}{32}$

39. $\left(b^{-2} c^5\right)^{-6} = \left(b^{-2}\right)^{-6} \left(c^5\right)^{-6} = b^{12} c^{-30} = \dfrac{b^{12}}{c^{30}}$

41. $3\left(b^5 c\right)^{-2} = 3b^{5(-2)} c^{-2} = 3b^{-10} c^{-2} = \dfrac{3}{b^{10} c^2}$

43.
$\left(2b^4 c^{-2}\right)^5 \left(3b^{-3} c^{-4}\right)^{-2}$

$= (2)^5 \left(b^4\right)^5 \left(c^{-2}\right)^5 (3)^{-2} \left(b^{-3}\right)^{-2} \left(c^{-4}\right)^{-2}$

$= 32b^{4 \cdot 5} c^{-2 \cdot 5} \dfrac{1}{3^2} b^{-3(-2)} c^{-4(-2)}$

$= 32b^{20} c^{-10} \dfrac{1}{9} b^6 c^8$

$= 32\left(\dfrac{1}{9}\right) b^{20} b^6 c^{-10} c^8$

$= \dfrac{32b^{26}}{9c^2}$

45. $\dfrac{-12b^{-6} c^5}{14b^4 c^5} = \dfrac{-6b^{-6-4} c^{5-5}}{7} = \dfrac{-6b^{-10} c^0}{7} = -\dfrac{6}{7b^{10}}$

47. $\dfrac{15b^{-7}c^{-3}d^8}{-45c^2b^{-6}d^8} = \dfrac{b^{-7-(-6)}c^{-3-2}d^{8-8}}{-3}$

$\qquad = \dfrac{b^{-1}c^{-5}d^0}{-3}$

$\qquad = \dfrac{1}{-3bc^5}$ or $-\dfrac{1}{3bc^5}$

49. $\dfrac{\left(-5b^{-3}c^4\right)\left(4b^{-5}c^{-1}\right)}{80b^2c^{17}} = \dfrac{-20b^{-3+(-5)}c^{4+(-1)}}{80b^2c^{17}}$

$\qquad = -\dfrac{b^{-8}c^3}{4b^2c^{17}}$

$\qquad = -\dfrac{b^{-8-2}c^{3-17}}{4}$

$\qquad = -\dfrac{b^{-10}c^{-14}}{4}$

$\qquad = -\dfrac{1}{4b^{10}c^{14}}$

51. $\dfrac{\left(24b^3c^{-6}\right)\left(49b^{-1}c^{-2}\right)}{\left(28b^2c^4\right)\left(14b^{-5}c\right)} = \dfrac{24 \cdot 49 b^{3+(-1)}c^{-6+(-2)}}{28 \cdot 14 b^{2+(-5)}c^{4+1}}$

$\qquad = \dfrac{3b^2c^{-8}}{b^{-3}c^5}$

$\qquad = 3b^{2-(-3)}c^{-8-5}$

$\qquad = 3b^5c^{-13}$

$\qquad = \dfrac{3b^5}{c^{13}}$

53. $\dfrac{\left(3b^5c^{-2}\right)^3}{2^{-1}b^{-3}c} = \dfrac{3^3b^{5\cdot3}c^{-2\cdot3}}{2^{-1}b^{-3}c}$

$\qquad = \dfrac{27b^{15}c^{-6}}{2^{-1}b^{-3}c}$

$\qquad -27(2)b^{15-(-3)}c^{-6-1}$

$\qquad = 54b^{18}c^{-7}$

$\qquad = \dfrac{54b^{18}}{c^7}$

55. $\dfrac{\left(2b^{-4}c\right)^{-3}}{\left(2b^2c^{-5}\right)^2} = \dfrac{2^{-3}b^{-4\cdot-3}c^{-3}}{2^2b^{2\cdot2}c^{-5\cdot2}}$

$\qquad = \dfrac{2^{-3}b^{12}c^{-3}}{2^2b^4c^{-10}}$

$\qquad = \dfrac{b^{12-4}c^{-3-(-10)}}{8 \cdot 4}$

$\qquad = \dfrac{b^8c^7}{32}$

57. $\left(\dfrac{6b^5c^{-2}}{7b^2c^4}\right)^2 = \dfrac{6^2b^{5\cdot2}c^{-2\cdot2}}{7^2b^{2\cdot2}c^{4\cdot2}}$

$\qquad = \dfrac{36b^{10}c^{-4}}{49b^4c^8}$

$\qquad = \dfrac{36b^{10-4}c^{-4-8}}{49}$

$\qquad = \dfrac{36b^6c^{-12}}{49}$

$\qquad = \dfrac{36b^6}{49c^{12}}$

59. $\left(\dfrac{5b^4c^{-3}}{15b^{-2}c^{-1}}\right)^{-4} = \left(\dfrac{b^4c^{-3}}{3b^{-2}c^{-1}}\right)^{-4}$

$\qquad = \dfrac{b^{4(-4)}c^{-3(-4)}}{3^{-4}b^{-2(-4)}c^{-1(-4)}}$

$\qquad = \dfrac{3^4b^{-16}c^{12}}{b^8c^4}$

$\qquad = \dfrac{81c^{12-4}}{b^{16+8}}$

$\qquad = \dfrac{81c^8}{b^{24}}$

61. $b^{-1}c^{-1} = \dfrac{1}{bc}$

63. $\dfrac{1}{b^{-1}} + \dfrac{1}{c^{-1}} = b + c$

65. $b^{4n}b^{3n} = b^{4n+3n} = b^{7n}$

67. $\dfrac{b^{7n-1}}{b^{2n+3}} = b^{(7n-1)-(2n+3)} = b^{7n-1-2n-3} = b^{5n-4}$

69. $f(3) = 2(3)^3 = 2(27) = 54$

71. $f(-4) = 2(3)^{-4} = \dfrac{2}{3^4} = \dfrac{2}{81}$

73. $g(a+2) = 4^{a+2} = 4^a \cdot 4^2 = 16\left(4^a\right)$

75. $g(2a) = 4^{2a} = \left(4^2\right)^a = 16^a$

77. a.

x	$f(x)$
-3	$f(-3) = 2^{-3} = \dfrac{1}{2^3} = \dfrac{1}{8} = 0.125$
-2	$f(-2) = 2^{-2} = \dfrac{1}{2^2} = \dfrac{1}{4} = 0.25$
-1	$f(-1) = 2^{-1} = \dfrac{1}{2} = 0.5$
0	$f(0) = 2^0 = 1$
1	$f(1) = 2^1 = 2$
2	$f(2) = 2^2 = 4$
3	$f(3) = 2^3 = 8$
4	$f(4) = 2^4 = 16$

b.

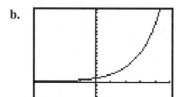

c. $2^{\frac{1}{2}} \approx 1.4$

79. a. $s = dt^{-1}$

$$s = \frac{d}{t}$$

b. $s = \dfrac{d}{t} = \dfrac{186}{3} = 62$

This result means that an object that travels 186 miles in 3 hours at a constant speed is traveling at a speed of 62 miles per hour.

81. a. $f(d) = 5760d^{-2}$

$$f(d) = \frac{5760}{d^2}$$

b. $f(8) = \dfrac{5760}{8^2} = \dfrac{5760}{84} = 90$

This result means that the sound level is 90 decibels at a distance of 8 yards from the amplifier.

83. For 4.9×10^4 the decimal point must move four places to the right. Thus, the standard decimal is 49,000.

85. For 8.59×10^{-3} the decimal point must move three places to the left. Thus, the standard decimal is 0.00859.

87. For 2.95×10^{-4} the decimal point must move four places to the left. Thus, the standard decimal is 0.000295.

89. For -4.512×10^8 the decimal point must move eight places to the right. Thus, the standard decimal is $-451,200,000$.

91. For 45,700,000 the decimal point needs to be moved seven places to the left so that the new number is between 1 and 10. Thus, the scientific notation is 4.57×10^7.

93. For 0.0000659 the decimal point needs to be moved five places to the right so that the new number is between 1 and 10. Thus, the scientific notation is 6.59×10^{-5}.

95. For $-5,987,000,000,000$ the decimal point needs to be moved twelve places to the left so that the absolute value of the new number is between 1 and 10. Thus, the scientific notation is -5.987×10^{12}.

97. For 0.000001 the decimal point needs to be moved six places to the right so that the new number is between 1 and 10. Thus, the scientific notation is 1×10^{-6}.

99. $6.3\text{E-}6 = \dfrac{6.3}{1,000,000} = 0.0000063$

$1.3\text{E-}4 = \dfrac{1.3}{10,000} = 0.00013$

$3.2\text{E}6 = 3.2 \cdot 1,000,000 = 3,200,000$

$6.4\text{E}7 = 6.4 \cdot 10,000,000 = 64,000,000$

101. $3.6 \times 10^9 = 3.6 \cdot 1,000,000,000$
$= 3,600,000,000$ years

103. $6.3 \times 10^{-8} = 6.3 \cdot \dfrac{1}{100,000,000}$
$= 0.000000063$ mole per liter

105. $10,080,000 = 1.008 \times 10,000,000$
$= 1.008 \times 10^7$ gallons

107. $0.00000047 = \dfrac{4.7}{10,000,000}$
$= 4.7 \times 10^{-7}$ meter

109. a.

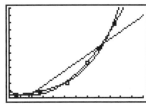

The quadratic model
$n = 0.0066t^2 - 0.12t + 0.85$ and the
exponential model $n = 0.30(1.078)^t$
describe the function well. The linear model
does not fit the data as well.

b. $n = 0.30(1.078)^{54} \approx 17.3$

The model predicts the number of bald eagle
pairs to be 17.3 thousand in 2014.

c. $n = 0.21(54) - 1.66 \approx 9.7$

The linear model predicts the number of
bald eagle pairs to be 9.7 thousand in 2014.
The exponential model grows at a much
faster rate than the linear model.

$n = 0.0066(54)^2 - 0.12(54) + 0.85 \approx 13.6$

The quadratic model predicts the total
number of bald eagle pairs to be 13.6
thousand in 2014. The exponential model
grows at a slightly faster rate than the
quadratic model.

111. Student B is correct. Student A did not distribute
the −1 exponent to the base 5 correctly. It should
have been 5^{-1} and not −5. Student A mistakenly
multiplied 5 by −1.

113. The student moved 3 to the denominator with
b^{-2}.

$$\frac{3b^{-2}c^4}{d^7} = \frac{3c^4}{b^2 d^7}$$

115. $-2^2 = -4$

$2(-1) = -2$

$\left(\dfrac{1}{2}\right)^2 = \dfrac{1}{4}$

$\dfrac{1}{2}$

$2^{-1} = \dfrac{1}{2}$

$\left(\dfrac{1}{2}\right)^{-1} = \dfrac{2}{1} = 2$

$(-2)^2 = 4$

$2^2 = 4$

The "ties" are $2^{-1} = \dfrac{1}{2}$ and $(-2)^2 = 2^2$.

117. a. $5^0 = 4^0 = 3^0 = 2^0 = 1^0 = 1$

It is reasonable to assume that $0^0 = 1$.

b. $0^5 = 0^4 = 0^3 = 0^2 = 0^1 = 0$

It is reasonable to assume that $0^0 = 0$.

c. Answers may vary. It is a good idea to leave
0^0 meaningless, since depending on the
reasoning used, we get different values for
0^0.

119. Answers may vary.

b^m means that the base b is multiplied by itself
m times. Also, b^n means that the base b is
multiplied by itself n times. So, if we multiply m
factors of b by n factors of b, we will have a total
of $m + n$ factors of b.

$\left(b^m\right)^n$ means that there are n factors of b^m.

Since each b^m has m factors of b, we have a total
of $m \cdot n$ or mn factors of b.

121. $f(3) = 2(3) = 6$

123. $g(3) = 3^2 = 9$

125. $h(3) = 2^3 = 8$

127. $y = 3x + 1$

$y = 2x - 4$

$3x + 1 = 2x - 4$

$x = -5$

$y = 3(-5) + 1 = -15 + 1 = -14$

The solution is $(-5, -14)$.
This is a linear system in two variables.

129. $3x + 1 = 2x - 4$

$x = -5$

This is a linear equation in one variable.

131. $5(3x+1)(2x-4) = 5(6x^2 - 12x + 2x - 4)$

$= 5(6x^2 - 10x - 4)$

$= 30x^2 - 50x - 20$

This is a quadratic expression in one variable.

Homework 10.2

1. $16^{1/2} = 4$, since $4^2 = 16$

3. $1000^{1/3} = 10$, since $10^3 = 1000$

5. $49^{1/2} = 7$, since $7^2 = 49$

7. $125^{1/3} = 5$, since $5^3 = 125$

9. $8^{4/3} = \left(8^{1/3}\right)^4 = 2^4 = 16$

11. $9^{3/2} = \left(9^{1/2}\right)^3 = 3^3 = 27$

13. $32^{2/5} = \left(32^{1/5}\right)^2 = 2^2 = 4$

15. $4^{5/2} = \left(4^{1/2}\right)^5 = 2^5 = 32$

17. $27^{-1/3} = \dfrac{1}{27^{1/3}} = \dfrac{1}{3}$

19. $-36^{-1/2} = -\dfrac{1}{36^{1/2}} = -\dfrac{1}{6}$

21. $4^{-5/2} = \dfrac{1}{4^{5/2}} = \dfrac{1}{\left(4^{1/2}\right)^5} = \dfrac{1}{2^5} = \dfrac{1}{32}$

23.
$$(-27)^{-4/3} = \dfrac{1}{(-27)^{4/3}}$$
$$= \dfrac{1}{\left((-27)^{1/3}\right)^4}$$
$$= \dfrac{1}{(-3)^4} = \dfrac{1}{81}$$

25. $2^{\frac{1}{4}} 2^{\frac{3}{4}} = 2^{\frac{1}{4} + \frac{3}{4}} = 2^{\frac{4}{4}} = 2^1 = 2$

27. $\left(3^{\frac{1}{2}} 2^{\frac{3}{2}}\right)^2 = 3^{\left(\frac{1}{2}\right)(2)} 2^{\left(\frac{3}{2}\right)(2)} = 3^1 \cdot 2^3 = 3 \cdot 8 = 24$

29. $\dfrac{7^{\frac{1}{3}}}{7^{-\frac{5}{3}}} = 7^{\frac{1}{3} - \left(-\frac{5}{3}\right)} = 7^{\frac{6}{3}} = 7^2 = 49$

31. $f\left(\dfrac{3}{4}\right) = 81^{\frac{3}{4}} = \left(81^{\frac{1}{4}}\right)^3 = 3^3 = 27$

33. $g\left(\dfrac{1}{3}\right) = 4(27)^{\frac{1}{3}} = 4 \cdot 3 = 12$

35. $g\left(-\dfrac{4}{3}\right) = 4(27)^{-\frac{4}{3}} = \dfrac{4}{27^{\frac{4}{3}}} = \dfrac{4}{81}$

37. $h\left(\dfrac{3}{2}\right) = -2(4)^{\frac{3}{2}} = -2\left(4^{\frac{1}{2}}\right)^3$
$$= -2(2)^3 = -2 \cdot 8 = -16$$

39. $f\left(-\dfrac{3}{4}\right) = 16^{-\frac{3}{4}} = \dfrac{1}{16^{\frac{3}{4}}} = \dfrac{1}{\left(16^{\frac{1}{4}}\right)^3} = \dfrac{1}{2^3} = \dfrac{1}{8}$

$f\left(-\dfrac{1}{2}\right) = 16^{-\frac{1}{2}} = \dfrac{1}{16^{\frac{1}{2}}} = \dfrac{1}{4}$

$f\left(-\dfrac{1}{4}\right) = 16^{-\frac{1}{4}} = \dfrac{1}{16^{\frac{1}{4}}} = \dfrac{1}{2}$

$f(0) = 16^0 = 1$

$f\left(\dfrac{1}{4}\right) = 16^{\frac{1}{4}} = 2$

$f\left(\dfrac{1}{2}\right) = 16^{\frac{1}{2}} = 4$

$f\left(\dfrac{3}{4}\right) = 16^{\frac{3}{4}} = \left(16^{\frac{1}{4}}\right)^3 = 2^3 = 8$

$f(1) = 16^1 = 16$

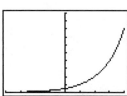

41. $b^{\frac{7}{6}} b^{\frac{5}{6}} = b^{\frac{7}{6} + \frac{5}{6}} = b^{\frac{12}{6}} = b^2$

43. $b^{\frac{3}{5}} b^{-\frac{13}{5}} = b^{\frac{3}{5} + \left(-\frac{13}{5}\right)} = b^{-\frac{10}{5}} = b^{-2} = \dfrac{1}{b^2}$

45. $\left(16b^8\right)^{1/4} = (16)^{1/4} \left(b^8\right)^{1/4} = 2b^{8\left(\frac{1}{4}\right)} = 2b^2$

47.
$$4\left(25b^8 c^{14}\right)^{-1/2} = \frac{4}{\left(25b^8 c^{14}\right)^{1/2}}$$
$$= \frac{4}{(25)^{1/2}\left(b^8\right)^{1/2}\left(c^{14}\right)^{1/2}}$$
$$= \frac{4}{5\left(b^{8\left(\frac{1}{2}\right)}\right)\left(c^{14\left(\frac{1}{2}\right)}\right)}$$
$$= \frac{4}{5b^4 c^7}$$

49.
$$\left(b^{3/5}c^{-1/4}\right)\left(b^{2/5}c^{-7/4}\right) = b^{\frac{3}{5}+\frac{2}{5}}c^{-\frac{1}{4}+\left(-\frac{7}{4}\right)}$$
$$= b^{\frac{5}{5}}c^{-\frac{8}{4}}$$
$$= b^1 c^{-2}$$
$$= \frac{b}{c^2}$$

51.
$$(5bcd)^{1/5}(5bcd)^{4/5} = (5bcd)^{\frac{1}{5}+\frac{4}{5}}$$
$$= (5bcd)^{\frac{5}{5}} = 5bcd$$

53.
$$\left[\left(3b^5\right)^3\left(3b^9 c^8\right)\right]^{1/4}$$
$$= \left(3b^5\right)^{3/4}\left(3b^9 c^8\right)^{1/4}$$
$$= (3)^{3/4}\left(b^5\right)^{3/4}(3)^{1/4}\left(b^9\right)^{1/4}\left(c^8\right)^{1/4}$$
$$= 3^{3/4} b^{15/4} 3^{1/4} b^{9/4} c^2$$
$$= 3^{3/4+1/4} b^{15/4+9/4} c^2$$
$$= 3b^6 c^2$$

55.
$$\frac{b^{-2/5}c^{11/8}}{b^{18/5}c^{-5/8}} = \frac{c^{11/8-(-5/8)}}{b^{2/5+18/5}} = \frac{c^{16/8}}{b^{20/5}} = \frac{c^2}{b^4}$$

57.
$$\left(\frac{9b^3 c^{-2}}{25b^{-5}c^4}\right)^{-1/2} = \left(\frac{9b^3 b^5}{25c^2 c^4}\right)^{-1/2}$$
$$= \left(\frac{9b^{3+5}}{25c^{2+4}}\right)^{-1/2}$$
$$= \left(\frac{9b^8}{25c^6}\right)^{-1/2}$$
$$= \left(\frac{25c^6}{9b^8}\right)^{1/2}$$
$$= \frac{(25)^{1/2}\left(c^6\right)^{1/2}}{(9)^{1/2}\left(b^8\right)^{1/2}} = \frac{5c^3}{3b^4}$$

59. $32^{1/5} b^{3/7} b^{2/5} = 2b^{3/7+2/5} = 2b^{(15+14)/35} = 2b^{29/35}$

61.
$$\frac{b^{5/6}}{b^{1/4}} = b^{\frac{5}{6}-\frac{1}{4}} = b^{\frac{10}{12}-\frac{3}{12}} = b^{7/12}$$

63.
$$\frac{\left(9b^5\right)^{3/2}}{\left(27b^4\right)^{2/3}} = \frac{(9)^{3/2}\left(b^5\right)^{3/2}}{(27)^{2/3}\left(b^4\right)^{2/3}}$$
$$= \frac{27b^{15/2}}{9b^{8/3}}$$
$$= 3b^{(45-16)/6}$$
$$= 3b^{\frac{29}{6}}$$

65.
$$\left(\frac{8b^{2/3}}{2b^{4/5}}\right)^{3/2} = \left(\frac{4b^{2/3}}{b^{4/5}}\right)^{3/2}$$
$$= \frac{(4)^{3/2}\left(b^{2/3}\right)^{3/2}}{\left(b^{4/5}\right)^{3/2}}$$
$$= \frac{\left(4^{1/2}\right)^3 b}{b^{6/5}}$$
$$= 2^3 b^{1-\frac{6}{5}}$$
$$= 8b^{-1/5} = \frac{8}{b^{1/5}}$$

67.
$$\frac{\left(8bc^3\right)^{1/3}}{\left(81b^{-5}c^3\right)^{3/4}} = \frac{(8)^{1/3} b^{1/3}\left(c^3\right)^{1/3}}{(81)^{3/4}\left(b^{-5}\right)^{3/4}\left(c^3\right)^{3/4}}$$
$$= \frac{2b^{1/3}c}{27b^{-15/4}c^{9/4}}$$
$$= \frac{2b^{\frac{1}{3}+\frac{15}{4}}c^{1-\frac{9}{4}}}{27}$$
$$= \frac{2b^{\frac{4}{12}+\frac{45}{12}}c^{-\frac{5}{4}}}{27}$$
$$= \frac{2b^{49/12}}{27c^{5/4}}$$

69.
$$b^{2/5}\left(b^{8/5}+b^{3/5}\right) = b^{2/5}b^{8/5}+b^{2/5}b^{3/5}$$
$$= b^{\frac{2}{5}+\frac{8}{5}}+b^{\frac{2}{5}+\frac{3}{5}}$$
$$= b^{\frac{10}{5}}+b^{\frac{5}{5}}$$
$$= b^2 + b$$

71. a.

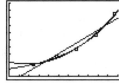

The quadratic model
$n = 0.0087t^2 - 0.32t + 19.95$ and the
exponential model $n = 10.1(1.02)^t$ fit the
data well. The linear model does not fit the
data well.

b. The exponential function describes the
situation best for the years before 1916. The
linear function produces a negative number
of countries for the years before 1916, and
the quadratic equation produces an
increasing number of countries for the years
before 1916 (both of which are impossible).

c. $n = 10.1(1.02)^{114} \approx 96.55$

About 97 countries will participate in the
2014 Winter Olympics.

d.

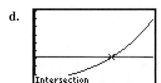

42 countries participated in the Winter
Olympics in 1972.

73. Answers may vary. $5^{1/n}$ may be represented by
$\sqrt[n]{5}$. So, when $n = 2$, $\sqrt[n]{5} = \sqrt[2]{5}$, which is
equivalent to $\sqrt{5}$.

75. Answers may vary. For $k = 1$,
$N \times 10^k = N \times 10^1 = N \times 10$, which moves the
decimal point of the number N to the right by 1
place. Similarly, for $k = 2$, $N \times 10^2 = N \times 100$,
which moves the decimal point of the number N
to the right by 2 places, and so on.

77. $f\left(\dfrac{1}{3}\right) = 8 \cdot \dfrac{1}{3} = \dfrac{8}{3}$

79. $g\left(\dfrac{1}{3}\right) = 8^{1/3} = 2$

81. $f\left(-\dfrac{5}{3}\right) = 8 \cdot -\dfrac{5}{3} = -\dfrac{40}{3}$

83. $g\left(-\dfrac{5}{3}\right) = 8^{-5/3} = \dfrac{1}{8^{5/3}} = \dfrac{1}{32}$

85. $2p^3 - 3p^2 - 18p + 27$
$= p^2(2p - 3) - 9(2p - 3)$
$= (p^2 - 9)(2p - 3)$
$= (p + 3)(p - 3)(2p - 3)$

This is a cubic expression in one variable.

87.

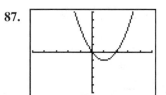

This is a quadratic function in one variable.

89. $x(3x - 2) = 4$
$3x^2 - 2x = 4$
$3x^2 - 2x - 4 = 0$
$a = 3, b = -2, c = -4$

$x = \dfrac{-(-2) \pm \sqrt{(-2)^2 - 4(3)(-4)}}{2(3)}$

$x = \dfrac{2 \pm \sqrt{52}}{6} = \dfrac{2 \pm 2\sqrt{13}}{6} = \dfrac{1 \pm \sqrt{13}}{3}$

$x = 1.5352, -0.8685$

This is a quadratic equation in one variable.

Homework 10.3

1. $y = 3^x$

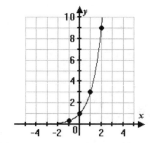

3. $y = 10^x$

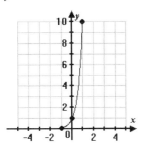

5. $y = 3(2)^x$

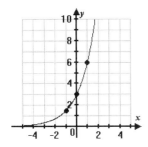

7. $y = 6(3)^x$

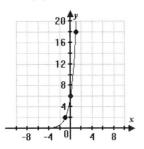

9. $y = 15\left(\dfrac{1}{3}\right)^x$

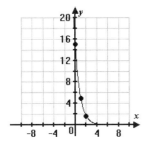

11. $y = 12\left(\dfrac{1}{2}\right)^x$

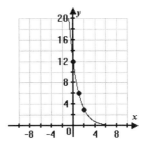

13. $f(x) = 2^x, g(x) = -2^x$

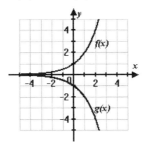

15. $f(x) = 4(3)^x, g(x) = -4(3)^x$

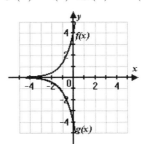

17. $f(x) = 8\left(\dfrac{1}{2}\right)^x, g(x) = -8\left(\dfrac{1}{2}\right)^x$

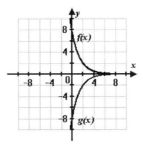

19.

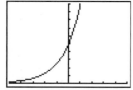

Domain: All real numbers
Range: $y > 0$

21.

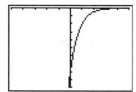

Domain: All real numbers
Range: $y < 0$

23. a. $a < 0$ and $b > 1$
negative output and exponential growth

b. $a > 0$ and $b > 1$
positive output and exponential growth

c. $a > 0$ and $0 < b < 1$
positive output and exponential decay

d. $a < 0$ and $0 < b < 1$
negative output and exponential decay

25. Answers may vary. Consider the following example. The family of exponential curves, $f(x) = ab^x$, where $b = \dfrac{1}{2}$ and the coefficient is an integer between -4 and 4, inclusive, excluding 0.

$f(x) = -4\left(\dfrac{1}{2}\right)^x$ $j(x) = 4\left(\dfrac{1}{2}\right)^x$

$g(x) = -3\left(\dfrac{1}{2}\right)^x$ $k(x) = 3\left(\dfrac{1}{2}\right)^x$

$h(x) = -2\left(\dfrac{1}{2}\right)^x$ $l(x) = 2\left(\dfrac{1}{2}\right)^x$

$i(x) = -1\left(\dfrac{1}{2}\right)^x$ $m(x) = 1\left(\dfrac{1}{2}\right)^x$

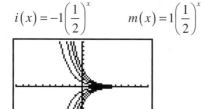

27. Since the y-intercept is $(0, 3)$, we know that the equation is of the form $f(x) = 3(b)^x$. Since the point $(1, 6)$ lies on the graph, we know that when x is 1, $f(x)$ is 6. Therefore, $6 = 3b$, and $b = 2$. The equation is $f(x) = 3(2)^x$.

29. Answers may vary. Consider the following example.

$f(x) = 2\left(\dfrac{2}{3}\right)^x$ $h(x) = 2(2)^x$

$g(x) = 4\left(\dfrac{9}{8}\right)^x$ $k(x) = 3\left(\dfrac{1}{2}\right)^x$

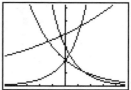

31. a.

x	$f(x)$
0	4
1	8
2	16
3	32
4	64

b.

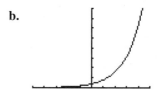

c. For each input–output pair, the output is 4 times 2 raised to the power equal to the input.

33.

x	$f(x)$	$g(x)$	$h(x)$	$k(x)$
0	162	3	2	800
1	54	12	10	400
2	18	48	50	200
3	6	192	250	100
4	2	768	1250	50

35.

x	$f(x)$	$g(x)$	$h(x)$	$k(x)$
0	5	160	162	2
1	10	80	54	12
2	20	40	18	72
3	40	20	6	432
4	80	10	2	2592

37. $f(-3) = 8$

39. $f(0) = 1$

41. $x = -2$

43. $x = 0$

45. $f(3) = 24$

47. $f(5) = 96$

49. $x = 0$

51. $x = 3$

53. a.

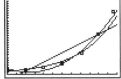

The quadratic and exponential models fit the data well. The linear model does not fit the data well.

b. The exponential function describes the situation best before years before 1950. The linear function describes negative ticket prices for years before 1950, and the quadratic function describes increasing ticket prices for years before 1950, both of which are impossible.

c. $p = 1.21(1.051)^{64} \approx 29.20$

The average ticket price in 2014 will be about $29.20.

d. The average ticket prices to all major league games will reach $48.80 in 2024.

55. $y = 7^x$

No x-intercept; y-intercept: (0, 1)

57. $y = 3\left(\dfrac{1}{5}\right)^x$

No x-intercept; y-intercept: (0, 3)

59. a. $f(0) = 100$, y-intercept (0, 100)

$g(0) = 5$, y-intercept (0, 5)

b. Since $g(x)$ has a larger base (3 versus 2), $g(x)$

will increase faster than $f(x)$.

c. Eventually $g(x)$ will be much greater than $f(x)$. For every increase in x of one, $g(x)$ increases by a factor of three, while $f(x)$ increases by a factor of two.

d.

X	Y1	Y2
0	100	5
1	200	15
2	400	45
3	800	135
4	1600	405
5	3200	1215
6	6400	3645

X=0

X	Y1	Y2
7	12800	10935
8	25600	32805
9	51200	98415
10	102400	295245
11	204800	885735
12	409600	2.66E6
13	819200	7.97E6

X=7

61. $f(2) = 2^2 + 3^2 = 4 + 9 = 13$

63. $f(-2) = 2^{-2} + 3^{-2} = \dfrac{1}{4} + \dfrac{1}{9} = \dfrac{9}{36} + \dfrac{4}{36} = \dfrac{13}{36}$

65. $3 = 3^x$
$3^1 = 3^x$
$1 = x$ or $x = 1$

67. $1 = 3^x$
$3^0 = 3^x$
$0 = x$ or $x = 0$

69. $f(x) = 3^x 3^x$, $g(x) = 3^{2x}$
$g(x) = 3^{2x}$
$= 3^{x+x}$
$= 3^x 3^x$.
$= f(x)$

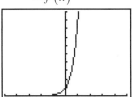

The graphs coincide. f and g are equivalent functions.

71. $f(x) = 2^{3x}, g(x) = 8^x$

$$g(x) = 8^x = (2^3)^x = 2^{3x} = f(x)$$

The graphs coincide. f and g are equivalent functions.

73. $f(x) = 2^{x+3}, g(x) = 8(2)^x$

$$g(x) = 8(2)^x = 2^3(2)^x = 2^{3+x} = 2^{x+3} = f(x)$$

The graphs coincide. f and g are equivalent functions.

75. $f(x) = 2^0, g(x) = 3^0$

$$\begin{aligned} g(x) &= 3^0 \\ &= 1 \\ &= 2^0 \\ &= f(x) \end{aligned}$$

The graphs coincide. f and g are equivalent functions.

77. $f(x) = 5^{x/3}, g(x) = (5^{1/3})^x$

$$\begin{aligned} g(x) &= (5^{1/3})^x \\ &= 5^{(1/3)(x)} \\ &= 5^{x/3} \\ &= f(x) \end{aligned}$$

The graphs coincide. f and g are equivalent functions.

79. $f(x) = x^{1/2}, g(x) = \sqrt{x}$

$$f(x) = x^{1/2} = \sqrt{x} = g(x)$$

The graphs coincide. f and g are equivalent functions.

81. a. $f(3+4) = 2^{3+4} = 2^7 = 128$

$$f(3) + f(4) = 2^3 + 2^4 = 8 + 16 = 24$$
$$f(3+4) \neq f(3) + f(4)$$

The statement is not true.

b. $f(x+y) = 2^{x+y} = 2^x \cdot 2^y$

$$f(x) + f(y) = 2^x + 2^y$$
$$2^x \cdot 2^y \neq 2^x + 2^y$$

The statement is not true.

83. Answers may vary. If $b > 1$, then f is increasing because b increases as it is multiplied by itself x times. If $0 < b < 1$, then f is decreasing because b decreases toward 0 as it is multiplied by itself x times.

85. Answers may vary. If $f(x) = -ab^x$, then $-f(x) = ab^x$. Since $g(x)$ also equals ab^x, $g(x) = -f(x)$. This means that for the same x-value, f and g return opposite y-values. Therefore, functions f and g would reflect each other across the x-axis at each x.

87. a.

Translate the graph of f 4 units to the right to get the graph of g. Translate the graph of f 4 units to the left to get the graph of h.

b.

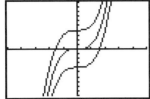

Translate the graph of *f* 4 units down to get the graph of *g*. Translate the graph of *f* 4 units up to get the graph of *h*.

c. Yes, the translations of x^3 match the translations of x^2. In each case add a constant to *f* to move the graph up or down; add a constant to *x* to move the graph left or right. The up and down movement is consistent with the sign, while the right and left movement is opposite its sign.

d.

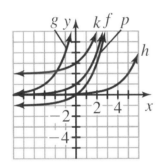

89.

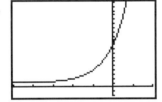

91.

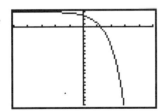

93. $0 = 8 + 4x$
$-8 = 4x$
$x = -2$
$y = 8 + 4(0)$
$y = 8$

The *x*-intercept is (−2, 0) and the *y*-intercept is (0, 8).

95.
$$y = 8\left(\frac{1}{4}\right)^0 = 8$$
$$0 = 8\left(\frac{1}{4}\right)^x$$

There is no *x*-intercept as the graph does not cross the *x*-axis. The *y*-intercept is (0, 8).

97. $f(x) = 13 - 4x$, which is linear.
$g(x) = 4(3)^x$, which is exponential.
$h(x) = 48\left(\frac{1}{2}\right)^x$, which is exponential.
$k(x)$ is neither linear nor exponential.

99.

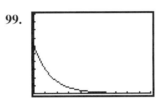

This is an exponential function.

101.
$$f(-2) = 6\left(\frac{1}{2}\right)^{-2} = 6(2)^2 = 6 \cdot 4 = 24$$

This is an exponential function.

103.
$$\frac{\left(8b^{-6}c\right)^{1/3}}{\left(16b^{12}c^{-2}\right)^{-1/4}} = \frac{8^{1/3}b^{-6/3}c^{1/3}}{16^{-1/4}b^{-12/4}c^{2/4}}$$
$$= \frac{2b^{-2}c^{1/3}}{2^{-1}b^{-3}c^{1/2}}$$
$$= \frac{2 \cdot 2}{b^{-3+2}c^{1/2-1/3}}$$
$$= \frac{4}{bc^{1/6}}$$

This is a polynomial expression involving exponents in two variables.

Homework 10.4

1. The y-intercept of f is $(0, 4)$. As the value of x increases by 1, the value of y is multiplied by 2. By the base multiplier property, we know that f is an exponential function with base 2.
$f(x) = 4(2)^x$
The y-intercept of g is $(0, 36)$. As x increases by 1, the value of y is multiplied by $\dfrac{1}{3}$.

$g(x) = 36\left(\dfrac{1}{3}\right)^x$

The y-intercept of h is $(0, 5)$. As x increases by 1, the value of y is multiplied by 10.
$h(x) = 5(10)^x$
The y-intercept of k is $(0, 250)$. As x increases by 1, the value of y is multiplied by $\dfrac{1}{5}$.

$k(x) = 250\left(\dfrac{1}{5}\right)^x$

3. The y-intercept of f is $(0, 100)$. As x increases by 1, the value of y is multiplied by $\dfrac{1}{2}$. f is exponential with base $\dfrac{1}{2}$.

$f(x) = 100\left(\dfrac{1}{2}\right)^x$

The y-intercept of g is $(0, 100)$. As x increases by 1, the value of y decreases by 50. g is linear with slope of -50.
$g(x) = -50x + 100$
The y-intercept of h is $(0, 2)$. As x increases by 1, the value of y increases by 4. h is linear with a slope of 4.
$h(x) = 4x + 2$
The y-intercept of k is $(0, 2)$. As x increases by 1, the value of y is multiplied by 3. k is exponential with base 3.
$k(x) = 2(3)^x$

5. $b^2 = 16$
$b = \pm(16)^{1/2}$
$b = \pm 4$

7. $b^3 = 27$
$b = 27^{1/3}$
$b = 3$

9. $3b^5 = 96$
$b^5 = 32$
$b = 32^{1/5}$
$b = 2$

11. $35b^4 = 15$
$b^4 \approx 0.429$
$b \approx \pm(0.429)^{1/4}$
$b \approx \pm 0.81$

13. $3.6b^3 = 42.5$
$b^3 \approx 11.81$
$b \approx 11.81^{1/3}$
$b \approx 2.28$

15. $32.7b^6 + 8.1 = 392.8$
$32.7b^6 = 384.7$
$b^6 \approx 11.765$
$b \approx \pm(11.765)^{1/6}$
$b \approx \pm 1.51$

17. $\dfrac{1}{4}b^3 - \dfrac{1}{2} = \dfrac{9}{4}$
$4\left(\dfrac{1}{4}b^3 - \dfrac{1}{2}\right) = 4\left(\dfrac{9}{4}\right)$
$b^3 - 2 = 9$
$b^3 = 11$
$b = 11^{1/3}$
$b \approx 2.22$

19. $\dfrac{b^6}{b^2} = 81$
$b^{6-2} = 81$
$b^4 = 81$
$b = \pm(81)^{1/4}$
$b = \pm 3$

21. $\dfrac{b^8}{b^3} = \dfrac{79}{5}$
$b^{8-3} = \dfrac{79}{5}$
$b^5 = \dfrac{79}{5}$
$b = \left(\dfrac{79}{5}\right)^{1/5}$
$b \approx 1.74$

23. $b^n + k = p$

$\quad b^n = p - k$

$\quad b = \left(p - k \right)^{1/n}$

25. $\dfrac{b^n}{a} + k = p$

$\quad \dfrac{b^n}{a} = p - k$

$\quad b^n = a\left(p - k \right)$

$\quad b^n = ap - ak$

$\quad b = \left(ap - ak \right)^{1/n}$

27. (0, 4) and (1, 8)

The y-intercept is (0, 4), and the equation if of the form $y = 4b^x$. Substitute 1 for x and 8 for y.

$8 = 4b^1$

$4b = 8$

$\quad b = 2$

The equation is $y = 4(2)^x$.

29. (0, 3) and (5, 100)

The y-intercept is (0, 3), and the equation is of the form $y = 3b^x$. Substitute 5 for x and 100 for y to find b.

$100 = 3b^5$

$3b^5 = 100$

$\quad b^5 = \dfrac{100}{3}$

$\quad b = \left(\dfrac{100}{3} \right)^{1/5}$

$\quad b \approx 2.02$

The equation is $y = 3(2.02)^x$.

31. (0, 87) and (6, 14)

The y-intercept is (0, 87), and the equation is of the form $y = 87b^x$. Substitute 6 for x and 14 for y to find b.

$14 = 87b^6$

$\quad b^6 = \dfrac{14}{87}$

$\quad b = \left(\dfrac{14}{87} \right)^{1/6}$

$\quad b \approx 0.74$

The equation is $y = 87(0.74)^x$.

33. (0, 5.5) and (2, 73.9)

The y-intercept is (0, 5.5), and the equation is of the form $y = 5.5b^x$. Substitute 2 for x and 73.9 for y to find b.

$73.9 = 5.5b^2$

$5.5b^2 = 73.9$

$\quad b^2 = \dfrac{73.9}{5.5}$

$\quad b = \left(\dfrac{73.9}{5.5} \right)^{1/2}$

$\quad b \approx 3.67$

The equation is $y = 5.5(3.67)^x$.

35. (0, 7.4) and (3, 1.3)

The y-intercept is (0, 7.4), and the equation is of the form $y = 7.4b^x$. Substitute 3 for x and 1.3 for y to find b.

$1.3 = 7.4b^3$

$7.4b^3 = 1.3$

$\quad b^3 = \dfrac{1.3}{7.4}$

$\quad b = \left(\dfrac{1.3}{7.4} \right)^{1/3}$

$\quad b \approx 0.56$

The equation is $y = 7.4(0.56)^x$.

37. (0, 39.18) and (15, 3.66)

The y-intercept is (0, 39.18), and the equation is of the form $y = 39.18b^x$. Substitute 15 for x and 3.66 for y to find b.

$3.66 = 39.18b^{15}$

$39.18b^{15} = 3.66$

$\quad b^{15} = \dfrac{3.66}{39.18}$

$\quad b = \left(\dfrac{3.66}{39.18} \right)^{1/15}$

$\quad b \approx 0.85$

The equation is $y = 39.18(0.85)^x$.

39. The points (0, 4) and (1, 2) lie on the graph. Use these points to determine the equation of the exponential curve. The y-intercept is (0, 4), and the equation is of the form $y = 4b^x$. Substitute 1 for x and 2 for y to find b.

$2 = 4b^1$

$4b^1 = 2$

$\quad b = \dfrac{2}{4} = \dfrac{1}{2}$

The equation is $y = 4\left(\dfrac{1}{2} \right)^x$.

41. (1, 4) and (2, 12)

We can form a system of equations since both points satisfy $y = a(b)^x$.

$4 = ab^1$
$12 = ab^2$

Combining the two equations yields the following.

$\dfrac{12}{4} = \dfrac{ab^2}{ab^1}$

$3 = b$

Use b and one of the points to solve for a. Substitute 1 for x and 4 for y.

$4 = a(3)^1$

$a(3)^1 = 4$

$3a = 4$

$a \approx 1.33$

The equation of the curve is $y = 1.33(3)^x$.

43. (3, 4) and (5, 9)

We can form a system of equations since both points satisfy $y = a(b)^x$.

$4 = ab^3$
$9 = ab^5$

Combining the two equations yields the following.

$\dfrac{9}{4} = \dfrac{ab^5}{ab^3}$

$\dfrac{9}{4} = b^2$

$b = \left(\dfrac{9}{4}\right)^{1/2}$

$b = \dfrac{3}{2} = 1.5$

Use b and one of the points to solve for a. Substitute 3 for x and 4 for y.

$4 = a(1.5)^3$

$a = \dfrac{4}{(1.5)^3}$

$a \approx 1.19$

The equation of the curve is $y = 1.19(1.5)^x$.

.

45. (10, 329) and (30, 26)

We can form a system of equations since both points satisfy $y = a(b)^x$.

$329 = ab^{10}$

$26 = ab^{30}$

Combining the two equations yields the

following.

$\dfrac{26}{329} = \dfrac{ab^{30}}{ab^{10}}$

$\dfrac{26}{329} = b^{20}$

$b = \left(\dfrac{26}{329}\right)^{1/20}$

$b \approx 0.88$

Use b and one of the points to solve for a. Substitute 10 for x and 329 for y.

$329 \approx a(0.88)^{10}$

$a \approx \dfrac{329}{(0.88)^{10}}$

$a \approx 1181.32$

The equation of the curve is $y = 1181.32(0.88)^x$.

47. (5, 8.1) and (9, 2.4)

We can form a system of equations since both points satisfy $y = a(b)^x$.

$8.1 = ab^5$

$2.4 = ab^9$

Combining the two equations yields the following.

$\dfrac{2.4}{8.1} = \dfrac{ab^9}{ab^5}$

$\dfrac{2.4}{8.1} = b^4$

$b \approx 0.74$

Use b and one of the points to solve for a. Substitute 5 for x and 8.1 for y.

$8.1 \approx a(0.74)^5$

$a \approx \dfrac{2.4}{(0.74)^5}$

$a \approx 36.50$

The equation of the curve is $y = 36.50(0.74)^x$.

49. $(13, 24.71)$ and $(21, 897.35)$

We can form a system of equations since both points satisfy $y = a(b)^x$.

$897.35 = ab^{21}$

$24.71 = ab^{13}$

Combining the two equations yields the following.

$\dfrac{897.35}{24.71} = \dfrac{ab^{21}}{ab^{13}}$

$\dfrac{897.35}{24.71} = b^8$

$b \approx 1.57$

Use b and one of the points to solve for a. Substitute 13 for x and 24.71 for y.

$24.71 \approx a(1.57)^{13}$

$a \approx \dfrac{24.71}{(1.57)^{13}}$

$a \approx 0.070$

The equation of the curve is $y = 0.070(1.57)^x$.

51. $(2, 73.8)$ and $(7, 13.2)$

We can form a system of equations since both points satisfy $y = a(b)^x$.

$13.2 = ab^7$

$73.8 = ab^2$

Combining the two equations yields the following.

$\dfrac{13.2}{73.8} = \dfrac{ab^7}{ab^2}$

$\dfrac{13.2}{73.8} = b^5$

$b \approx 0.71$

Use b and one of the points to solve for a. Substitute 2 for x and 73.8 for y.

$73.8 \approx a(0.71)^2$

$a \approx \dfrac{73.8}{(0.71)^2}$

$a \approx 146.40$

The equation of the curve is $y = 146.40(0.71)^x$.

53. The points $(1, 2)$ and $(3, 5)$ lie on the exponential curve. Use the points to form a system of equations since both points satisfy the equation $y = a(b)^x$.

$5 = ab^3$

$2 = ab^1$

Combining the two equations yields the

following.

$\dfrac{5}{2} = \dfrac{ab^3}{ab^1}$

$\dfrac{5}{2} = b^2$

$b \approx 1.58$

Use b and one of the points to solve for a. Substitute 1 for x and 2 for y.

$2 \approx a(1.58)^1$

$a \approx \dfrac{2}{1.58}$

$a \approx 1.27$

The equation of the curve is $y = 1.27(1.58)^x$.

55. Both the exponential equations have the coefficient 6. Therefore they both have the same y-intercept $(0, 6)$. Thus, the solution is $(0, 6)$.

57. a. i. Yes. Answers may vary. The equation $y = 2(2)^x$ contains the point $(0, 2)$.

ii. No. Answers may vary. For $(2, 0)$ to be a solution to an exponential equation, the equation must be of the form $0 = a(b)^2$. However, since $a \neq 0$ and $b > 0$ in all exponential equations, $(2, 0)$ can never be found on an exponential curve.

b. No. Answers may vary. Create a system of equations based on $y = a(b)^x$.

$1 = ab^3$

$-1 = ab^2$

Combining the two equations yields the following.

$\dfrac{1}{-1} = \dfrac{ab^3}{ab^2}$

$-1 = b$

Since $b = -1$, the equation is not exponential.

59. Answers may vary. One possible answer is as follows. The base multiplier property states that when $y = ab^x$, if the value of x increases by 1, the value of y is multiplied by the base b. This makes sense because increasing x by 1 is the same as multiplying by another factor b, due to the nature of exponents. For example, if $y = 5(3)^x$, y is 45 when x is 2. If you increase x by 1, y becomes 135, which is the same as the product of 45 and 3.

61. $\dfrac{b^7}{b^2} = b^{7-2} = b^5$

63. $\dfrac{b^7}{b^2} = 76$
$b^5 = 76$
$b = (76)^{1/5}$
$b \approx 2.38$

65. $\dfrac{8b^3}{6b^{-1}} = \dfrac{4b^3}{3b^{-1}} = \dfrac{4b^{3-(-1)}}{3} = \dfrac{4b^4}{3}$

67. $\dfrac{8b^3}{6b^{-1}} = \dfrac{3}{7}$
$\dfrac{4b^4}{3} = \dfrac{3}{7}$
$b^4 = \dfrac{9}{28}$
$b = \pm\left(\dfrac{9}{28}\right)^{1/4}$
$b \approx \pm 0.75$

69. L is a linear function of the form $y = mx + b$.
The y-intercept is $(0, 2)$, so $b = 2$ and the equation is of the form $y = mx + 2$.
Substitute 1 for x and 6 for y to find m.
$6 = m(1) + 2$
$6 = m + 2$
$4 = m$
The equation for the linear function is
$L(x) = 4x + 2$.
Q is a quadratic function of the form
$y = ax^2 + bx + c$. The y-intercept is $(0, 2)$, so
$c = 2$ and the equation is of the form
$y = ax^2 + bx + 2$.
Substitute 1 for x and 6 for y to find a and b.
$6 = a(1)^2 + b(1) + 2$
$6 = a + b + 2$
$4 = a + b$
Let $a = b = 2$.
The equation for the quadratic function is
$Q(x) = 2x^2 + 2x + 2$. Answers may vary.
E is an exponential function of the form $y = ab^x$.
The y-intercept is $(0, 2)$, so $a = 2$ and the equation is of the form $y = 2b^x$.
Substitute 1 for x and 6 for y to find b.

$6 = 2b^1$
$\dfrac{6}{2} = b^1$
$3 = b$
The equation for the exponential function is
$E(x) = 2(3)^x$.

71. A linear function has the form $y = mx + b$.
Substitute for x and y and solve.
$6 = 7m + b$
$3 = 5m + b$
$3 = 2m$
$m = \dfrac{3}{2}$
Solve for b.
$6 = 7\left(\dfrac{3}{2}\right) + b$
$6 = \dfrac{21}{2} + b$
$b = -\dfrac{9}{2}$
The equation for the linear function is
$y = \dfrac{3}{2}x - \dfrac{9}{2}$.
An exponential function has the form $y = ab^x$.
Substitute for x and y and solve.
$\dfrac{6}{3} = \dfrac{ab^7}{ab^5}$
$2 = b^2$
$b \approx \pm 1.41$
Solve for a.
$6 = a(1.41)^7$
$a \approx 0.54$
The equation for the exponential function is
$y = 0.54(1.41)^x$.

So, the function could be either linear or exponential.

73. a. $L(x) = 2x + 100$, $E(x) = 3(2)^x$
To find the y-intercept, set $x = 0$.
$L(0) = 2(0) + 100 = 100$
The y-intercept of L is $(0, 100)$.
$E(0) = 3(2)^0 = 3(1) = 3$
The y-intercept of E is $(0, 3)$.

b. *L* is linear. By the slope addition property, when *x* increases by 1, the value of *y* increases by 2. *E* is exponential. By the base multiplier property, when *x* increases by 1, the value of *y* is multiplied by 2.

c. The exponential function, *E*, will eventually dominate. *L* increases by a fixed amount for every change in *x*, while *E* increases by an increasing amount for every change in *x*.

d.

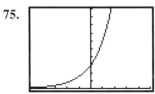

75.

This is an exponential function in one variable.

77.

$$f(-3) = 3(2)^{-3} = \frac{3}{2^3} = \frac{3}{8} = 0.375$$

This is an exponential function in one variable.

79.

$$\frac{8b^{-3}c^6}{12b^2c^3} = \frac{2b^{-3-2}c^{6-3}}{3}$$
$$= \frac{2b^{-5}c^3}{3}$$
$$= \frac{2c^3}{3b^5}$$

This is an expression in two variables involving exponents.

Homework 10.5

1. a. Complete a table for *f(t)* based on the assumption that the total number of people triples each day.

t (days)	*f(t)* (people)
0	40
1	120
2	360
3	1080
4	3240

For every increase of 1 in *t*, *f(t)* is multiplied by 3. *f(t)* is exponential with base 3 and *y*-

intercept 40. The equation is $f(t) = 40(3)^t$.

b. $f(10) = 40(3)^{10} = 2,361,960$ people

c. $f(15) = 40(3)^{15} = 573,956,280$
Model breakdown has occurred, since this is well over the entire population of the United States.

3. a. Complete a table for *f(t)* based on the assumption that the total number of Web pages doubles each year.

t (years)	*f(t)* (trillions of web pages)
0	1
1	2
2	4
3	8
4	16

For every increase in *t* of 1, *f(t)* is multiplied by 2. *f(t)* is exponential with base 2 and *y*-intercept 1. The equation is $f(t) = (2)^t$.

b. Since 2014 is 6 years after 2008, find *f(6)*.
$f(6) = (2)^6 = 64$
In the year 2014, 64 trillion Web pages will be indexed.

c. First convert pages to inches.

$$64,000,000,000 \text{ pages} \cdot \frac{2 \text{ inches}}{500 \text{ pages}}$$
$$= 256,000,000 \text{ inches}$$
Now, convert inches to miles.

$$256,000,000 \text{ inches} \times \frac{\text{foot}}{12 \text{ inches}} \times \frac{\text{mile}}{5280 \text{ feet}}$$
$$\approx 4,040,404 \text{ miles}$$
The pile would be about 4.04 million miles.

5. a. Complete a table for *h(t)*, assuming that revenue grows by 2.14 times the previous year's revenue.

t (years)	*h(t)* ($ millions)
0	500
1	500(2.14) = 1070
2	1070(2.14) = 2289.8
3	2289.8(2.14) ≈ 4900.17
4	4900.17(2.14) ≈ 10,486.37

For every increase in *t* of 1, *h(t)* is multiplied by 2.14. *h(t)* is exponential with base 2.14 and *y*-intercept 500. The equation is $h(t) = 500(2.14)^t$.

b. The *r*-intercept is the value of *a* in the equation $h(t) = ab^t$. In this case, the *r*-intercept is (0, 500). This means that revenue from ring tones was $500 million in 2005, the first year.

c. The base, *b*, of the model is 2.14. Each year, the revenue increases by 2.14 times that of the previous year's revenue.

d. Since 2014 is 9 years after 2005, find *h*(9).
$h(9) = 500(2.14)^9 \approx 470,646$.
If revenue continues at 2.14 times the revenue of the previous year, revenue from ring tones will be about $471 billion in 2014.

7. a. Complete a table for *D*(*t*), assuming that the number of subscribers increases by 50% per year.

t (years)	*D*(*t*) (thousands of subscribers)
0	2.5
1	2.5(1.5) = 3.75
2	3.75(1.5) = 5.625
3	5.625(1.5) ≈ 8.44
4	8.44(1.5) ≈ 12.66

For every increase in *t* of 1, *D*(*t*) is multiplied by 1.5. *D*(*t*) is exponential with base 1.5 and *y*-intercept 2.5. The equation is $D(t) = 2.5(1.5)^t$.

b. Complete a table for *S*(*t*), assuming that the number of subscribers increases by 120% per year.

t (years)	*S*(*t*) (thousands of subscribers)
0	1.71
1	1.71(2.2) = 3.762
2	3.762(2.2) ≈ 8.28
3	8.28(2.2) ≈ 18.22
4	18.22(2.2) ≈ 40.08

For every increase in *t* of 1, *S*(*t*) is multiplied by 2.2. *S*(*t*) is exponential with base 2.2 and *y*-intercept 1.71. The equation is $S(t) = 1.71(2.2)^t$.

c.

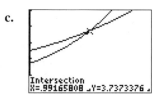

Intersection
X=.99165808 _Y=3.7373376

The point of intersection is about (0.99, 3.74). It means that the number of stand-alone TiVo subscribers will equal the number of DirectTV® subscribers in about 1 year, or 2008, with about 3.74 million subscribers.

9. a. Complete a table for *f*(*t*), assuming 8% interest compounded annually.

t (years)	*f*(*t*) ($)
0	3000
1	3000(1.08) = 3240
2	3240(1.08) = 3499.20
3	3499(1.08) ≈ 3799.14

As the value of *t* increases by 1, the value of *f*(*t*) is multiplied by 1.08. *f*(*t*) is exponential with base 1.08 and *y*-intercept 3000. The equation is $f(t) = 3000(1.08)^t$.

b. The base, *b*, of the model is 1.08. The base minus one is the interest rate.
$b - 1 = 1.08 - 1 = 0.08 = 8\%$
The account balance increases by 8% per year.

c. The coefficient, *a*, is the *y*-intercept. In this model, it is the initial amount invested, $3000.

d. $f(15) = 3000(1.08)^{15} \approx 9516.51$
In 15 years, the account's value will be $9516.51.

11. a. Complete the table for $f(t)$.

t	$f(t)$ ($)
0	4000
6	$4000(2) = 4000(2)^1$
12	$4000(2)(2) = 4000(2)^2$
18	$4000(2)(2)(2) = 4000(2)^3$
t	$4000(2)^{t/6}$

As the value of t increases by 6, the value of $f(t)$ is multiplied by 2. $f(t)$ is exponential with base 2, has a y-intercept of 4000, and an exponent $\dfrac{t}{6}$ which allows t to remain in years even though the doubling occurs every 6 years. The equation is $f(t) = 4000(2)^{t/6}$.

b. $f(20) = 4000(2)^{20/6} \approx 40{,}317.47$

In 20 years, the investment will be worth $40,317.47.

13. The first 3 years could be modeled using an exponential function with base 1.06 and y-intercept 5000. The equation is $f(t) = 5000(1.06)^t$. After 3 years, there would be $f(3) = 5000(1.06)^3 = \$5955.08$ in the account. Then, all of this money is put into an account earning 8% interest (compounded annually) for 5 years. This can be modeled using an exponential function with base 1.08 and y-intercept 5955.08. The equation is $g(t) = 5955.08(1.08)^t$. After 5 years, there will be $g(5) = 5955.08(1.08)^5 = \$8749.97$. This is the value of the investment after 8 years.

15. a. Complete a table for $g(t)$ based on the assumption that the sales are cut in half each year.

t (years)	$g(t)$ (sales)
0	984
1	492
2	246
3	123
4	61.5

When the value of t increases by 1, the value of $g(t)$ is multiplied by 0.5. $g(t)$ is exponential with base 0.5 and y-intercept 984. The equation is $g(t) = 984(0.5)^t$.

b. The coefficient, a, is the s-intercept. In this model, it is the number of new textbooks sold in 2006, which is 984.

c. $g(3) = 984(0.5)^3 = 123$
In this situation, it means that the college bookstore will sell 123 new textbooks in 2009.

d. The half-life of new textbook sales is 1 year, as textbook sales are half of the previous year's sales.

17. a. As the value of t increases by 1600, the value of $f(t)$ is multiplied by $\dfrac{1}{2}$. $f(t)$ is exponential with base $\dfrac{1}{2}$, a y-intercept of 100, and an exponent $\dfrac{t}{1600}$ which allows t to remain in years even though the halving occurs every 1600 years. The equation is

$$f(t) = 100\left(\dfrac{1}{2}\right)^{t/1600}$$

b. $f(100) = 100\left(\dfrac{1}{2}\right)^{100/1600} = 95.76$

This means that after 100 years, 95.76% of the radium will remain.

c. $f(3200) = 100\left(\dfrac{1}{2}\right)^{3200/1600} = 25$

This means that after 3200 years, 25% of the radium will remain. This result can be found without using the equation. We know that after 1600 years, one half of the radium will remain. In an additional 1600 years (for a total of 3200 years), one half of the one half of the radium will remain. We know that $\dfrac{1}{2} \cdot \dfrac{1}{2} = \dfrac{1}{4}$ or 25% will remain.

19. a. As the value of t increases by 7.56, the value of $f(t)$ is multiplied by $\frac{1}{2}$. $f(t)$ is exponential with base $\frac{1}{2}$, a y-intercept of 100, and an exponent $\frac{t}{7.56}$ which allows t to remain in days even though the halving occurs every 7.56 days. The equation is

$$f(t) = 100\left(\frac{1}{2}\right)^{t/7.56}.$$

b.

$$f(3) = 100\left(\frac{1}{2}\right)^{3/7.56} = 75.95$$

This means that after 3 days, 75.95% of the iodine-131 will remain.

c.

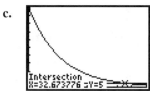

Intersection
X=32.673776 Y=5

A patient can safely spend a lot of time near a child after 33 days.

21. As the value of t increases by 6, the value of $f(t)$ is multiplied by $\frac{1}{2}$. $f(t)$ is exponential with base $\frac{1}{2}$, a y-intercept of 80, and an exponent $\frac{t}{6}$. The equation is $f(t) = 80\left(\frac{1}{2}\right)^{t/6}$.

$$f(14) = 80\left(\frac{1}{2}\right)^{14/6} = 15.87$$

After 14 hours, 15.87 milligrams of caffeine will remain in the bloodstream.

23. a. The graph passes through $p = 50$ when $t = 10$. So, the half-life of the element is 10 years.

b. $f(t)$ is exponential with base $\frac{1}{2}$, a y-intercept of 100, and an exponent $\frac{t}{10}$. The equation is $f(t) = 100\left(\frac{1}{2}\right)^{t/10}$.

$$f(40) = 100\left(\frac{1}{2}\right)^{40/10} = 6.25$$

After 40 years, 6.25% of the element will remain in the tank.

25. $f(t)$ is exponential with base b, a y-intercept of 0.08, and an exponent t. The equation is $f(t) = 0.08b^t$. When $t = 5$, $f(5) = 4.2$. Solve for b.

$$f(5) = 0.08b^5$$
$$0.08b^5 = 4.2$$
$$b^5 = 52.5$$
$$b \approx 2.21$$
$$f(11) = 0.08(2.21)^{11} \approx 491.4$$

Sales of MP3 players will reach $491.4 billion in 2011.

27. $f(t)$ is exponential with base b, coefficient a, and exponent t. It passes through the points $(1, 1)$ and $(27, 5000)$.

$$1 = ab^1$$
$$5000 = ab^{27}$$
$$\frac{5000}{1} = \frac{ab^1}{ab^{27}}$$
$$5000 = b^{26}$$
$$b \approx 1.39$$
$$1 = a(1.39)^1$$
$$a \approx 0.72$$

So, the equation is $f(t) = 0.72(1.39)^t$. Since 2013 is 33 years after 1980, we find $f(33)$.

$$f(33) = 0.72(1.39)^{33}$$
$$f(33) \approx 37,742$$

There will be 37,742 restaurants in 2013.

29. a. Use a linear function to model the data.

b. There are no functions that can model this data.

c. Use an exponential function to model this data.

d. Use a quadratic function to model this data.

31.

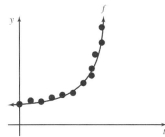

Decrease the base, *b*, of the model to slow the growth of the function so that it will pass through the middle of the data points.

33. a.

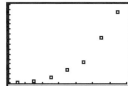

The data points appear to bend upwards, so model with an exponential function. Use an exponential regression.

The equation is $f(t) = 100.84(1.41)^t$.
Compare this model to the data.

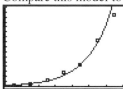

The model appears to fit the data well.

b. The rate of growth is the base, *b*, minus 1.
$b - 1 = 1.41 - 1 = 0.41$, or 41% growth per year.

c. $f(4) = 100.84(1.41)^4 \approx 398.57$
According to the model, there were 399 Starbucks stores in $1990 + 4 = 1994$.

d. $f(18) = 100.84(1.41)^{18} \approx 48,930$
According to the model, there will be 48,930 Starbucks stores in 2008. Because the actual number of stores in 2008 was only 15,256, the rate of growth of stores between 1991–2003 must decrease for the period 2003–2008.

e.

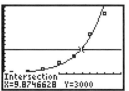

In $1990 + 9.87 \approx 2000$, there were about 3000 Starbucks stores.

35. a. *h* is exponential with base *b*, coefficient *a*, and exponent *t*. It passes through the points (0, 1.27) and (4, 0.66).
The *y*-intercept is (0, 1.27), and the equation is of the form $y = 1.27b^x$. Substitute 4 for *x* and 0.66 for *y* to find *b*.

$$0.66 = 1.27b^4$$
$$1.27b^4 = 0.66$$
$$b^4 = \frac{0.66}{1.27}$$
$$b = \left(\frac{0.66}{1.27}\right)^{1/4}$$
$$b \approx 0.849$$

So, the equation is $h = 1.27(0.849)^t$.

By regression: $r = 1.26(0.847)^t$

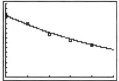

The models fit the data well.

b. The *p*-intercept is (0, 1.26). It means that PDA revenue is $1.26 million in 2000.

c. $1 - 0.847 = 0.153 = 15.3\%$
The percentage rate of decay of revenue from PDAs is 15.3%.

d. $r = 1.26(0.847)^2 \approx 0.90$
According to the model, revenue from PDAs in 2002 is $0.90 million. This is interpolation, as you are calculating an amount within the given values.
$0.90 - 0.88 = 0.02$
The error is $0.02 million.

e. $r = 1.26(0.847)^{13} \approx 0.15$
The predicted revenue from PDAs in 2013 is $0.15 million. This is extrapolation, as the estimate occurs outside the given values.

37. a. By regression: The linear equation is
$L(t) = 0.062t - 0.33$, the quadratic equation
is $Q(t) = 0.00051t^2 - 0.0086t + 1.8$, and the
exponential equation is $E(t) = 1.2(1.0162)^t$.

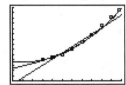

The quadratic and exponential functions
model the data well. The linear model does
not fit the data well.

b. The exponential model gives the best
estimate of the world population for the
years before 1900. The linear model gives
negative population values for the years
before 1900, and the quadratic model gives
increasing population values for the years
before 1900 (both of which are impossible).

c. $a = 1.20$
This is the *p*-intercept of the function. It
corresponds to the world population of 1.20
billion people in the year 1900.

d. $b = 1.0162$
This is the rate (1.62%) at which the world
population is increasing per year.

e. $f(114) = 1.20(1.0162)^{114} = 7.496$
This means that the world population will be
7.496 billion in the year 2014.

39. a. By regression: The linear equation is
$L(t) = 8.03t - 294.74$, the quadratic
equation is $Q(t) = 0.37t^2 - 28.88t + 569.75$,
and the exponential equation is
$E(t) = 0.66(1.096)^t$.

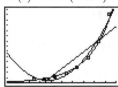

The quadratic and exponential functions
model the data well. The linear model does
not fit the data well.

b. The exponential model best models the
situation for ages between 20 and 30. The
linear model gives negative monthly rates for

ages between 20 and 30, and the quadratic
model gives increasing monthly rates for
ages between 20 and 30 (both of which are
impossible).

c. The slope of the graph of *L* is 8.03, which
means that the monthly rate increases by
$8.03 per year of age. Model breakdown has
occurred.
$$x = -\frac{b}{2a} = -\frac{28.88}{2(0.37)} \approx 39.03$$
$$0.37(39.03)^2 - 28.88(39.03) + 569.75 \approx 6.20$$
The vertex of the graph of *Q* is (39.03, 6.20),
which means that the minimum monthly rate
is $6.20 for 39-year-old employees. Model
breakdown has occurred The base *b* of *E* is
1.096, which means that the monthly rate
increases by 9.6% per year in age.

d. $L(47) = 8.03(47) - 294.74 = 82.67$
The linear function estimates a monthly rate
of $82.67.
$$Q(47) = 0.37(47)^2 - 28.88(47) + 569.75$$
$$= 29.72$$
The quadratic function estimates a monthly
rate of $29.72.
$E(47) = 0.66(1.096)^{47} = 49.05$
The exponential function estimates a
monthly rate of $49.05.
The exponential estimate is closest to the
actual amount of $46.00.

e. Men would pay higher monthly rates
because there is a higher likelihood that the
man will die at a younger age than a woman.

41. a.

Year	Population	Population Ratio
1790	3.9	
1800	5.3	1.36
1810	7.2	1.36
1820	9.6	1.33
1830	12.9	1.34
1840	17.1	1.33
1850	23.2	1.36
1860	31.4	1.35

b. The ratios stay approximately the same, with
the average being about 1.35.

c. It is better to use an exponential model. The
populations appear to be increasing by a
constant multiplicative factor.

d. As the value of *t* (years) increases by 10, the value of *f*(*t*) (population) is multiplied by approximately 1.35. Thus, the base is about $1.35^{1/10} \approx 1.03$, the *y*-intercept is 3.94, and the exponent is *t*. The equation is

$$f(t) = 3.94(1.03)^t .$$

e.

Year	Population	Population Ratio
1860	31.4	
1870	39.8	1.27
1880	50.2	1.26
1890	62.9	1.25
1900	76.0	1.21

f. It is not likely that *f* gives reasonable population estimates after 1860. The population ratio changes from approximately 1.35 to 1.25. This indicates that model breakdown may occur in years after 1860.

g. $f(218) = 3.94(1.03)^{218} \approx 2477.5$

The model predicts that the population of the United States was approximately 2477.5 million (or 2.4775 billion) in the year 2008. The actual population was 305 million. The error in the estimate is 2477.5 − 305.0 = 2172.5 million (or 2.1725 billion).

43. a.

Use an exponential regression.

The equation is *f*(*t*) = 232.22(1.082)*ᵗ*.

b. $f(54) = 232.22(1.082)^{54} \approx 16{,}374.64$
The federal debt will be about $16,375 billion, or $16.375 trillion, in 2014.

c. $16{,}374{,}640{,}000{,}000 \div 322{,}000{,}000 \approx$ 50,852.92
Each person would have to pay about $50,853.

d. $f(90) = 232.22(1.082)^{90} \approx 279{,}481.52$

In 2050, the federal debt will be about $279,482 billion, or $279.5 trillion.

e. $279{,}481{,}520{,}000{,}000 \div 420{,}000{,}000 \approx$ 665,432.19
Each person would have to pay about $665,432.
People want to reduce or eliminate the debt now because it will grow exponentially and be a much larger size in the future.

45. a. Use an exponential regression.

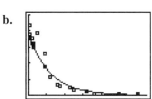

The equation is *f*(*p*) = 37,313(0.92)*ᵖ*.

b.

For the majority of the points, the model fits the data fairly well.

c. *b* = 0.92
This means that for every 1% increase in population involved in agriculture, there is a decrease of 1.00 − 0.92 = 0.08 or 8.0% of GNP per person.

d. Japan's data point is farthest away vertically from the regression line. This data point is far above the regression line. This suggests that the workers in Japan make much more money than workers in other countries with similar agricultural make-ups.

47. If $f(t) = ab^t$, where *a* > 0, models a quantity at time *t*, then the percent rate of change is constant. In particular, if *b* > 1, then the quantity grows exponentially at a rate of *b* − 1 percent (in decimal form) per unit of time. If 0 < *b* < 1, then the quantity decays exponentially at a rate of 1 − *b* percent (in decimal form) per unit of time.

49. a. $C(t) = 800(1.03)^t$

b. $S(t) = 24t + 800$

c. $C(1) = 800(1.03)^1 = 824$
$C(2) = 800(1.03)^2 = 848.72$
$S(1) = 800(1 + 0.03(1)) = 824$
$S(2) = 800(1 + 0.03(2)) = 848$
$C(1)$ and $S(1)$ are equal because they are both 800(1.03). However, $C(2) = 800(1.0609)$, whereas $S(2) = 800(1.06)$.

d. $C(20) = 800(1.03)^{20} = 1444.89$
$S(20) = 800(1 + 0.03(20)) = 1280$
For $C(20)$, interest has compounded for 20 years, whereas for $S(20)$ simple interest has accumulated for 20 years. That is why $C(20)$ is much higher than $S(20)$.

51. a. By regression, the quadratic equation is
$f(a) = -0.0217a^2 + 1.96a - 18.63$.

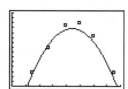

The quadratic equation fits the data well.

b. $f(20) = -0.0217(20)^2 + 1.96(20) - 18.63$
$= 11.89$
About 11.9% of 20-year-old Americans listen to talk radio.

c. $20 = -0.0217a^2 + 1.96a - 18.63$
$0 = -0.0217a^2 + 1.96a - 38.63$
$a = -0.0217, b = 1.96, c = -38.63$

$$a = \frac{-1.96 \pm \sqrt{(1.96)^2 - 4(-0.0217)(-38.63)}}{2(-0.0217)}$$

$$a = \frac{1.96 \pm \sqrt{0.4885}}{0.0434} = 29.1, 61.3$$

20% of 29-year-old and 61-year-old Americans listen to talk radio

d.
$$a = -\frac{b}{2a} = -\frac{1.96}{2(-0.0217)} \approx 45.2$$

$$f(45.2) = -0.0217(45.2)^2 + 1.96(45.2) - 18.6$$
$$\approx 25.65$$

The vertex is (45.2, 25.65), which means that 45-year-old Americans have the highest percentage of people who listen to talk radio, at about 25.6%. This fits with the table of data.

e. $0 = -0.0217a^2 + 1.96a - 18.63$
$a = -0.0217, b = 1.96, c = -18.63$

$$a = \frac{-1.96 \pm \sqrt{(1.96)^2 - 4(-0.0217)(-18.63)}}{2(-0.0217)}$$

$$a = \frac{1.96 \pm \sqrt{2.225}}{0.0434} = 10.80, 79.53$$

The a-intercepts are (10.80, 0) and (79.53, 0). This means that there are no 11-year-old or 80-year-old Americans who listen to talk radio.

53. Answers may vary.
$f(x) = 2(3)^x$
$f(3) = 2(3)^3 = 54$

55. Answers may vary.
$y = 4x + 1$

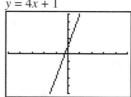

57. Answers may vary.
$y = 3(2)^x$

59. Answers may vary.
The growth of a population of frogs is modeled by the exponential expression $85(1.02)^t$. In 8 years, the population of frogs will be $85(1.02)^8 = 99.6$.

Chapter 10 Review Exercises

1. $\dfrac{2^{-400}}{2^{-405}} = 2^{-400-(-405)}$
$= 2^5$
$= 32$

2. $\left(8b^{-3}c^5\right)\left(6b^{-9}c^{-2}\right) = \dfrac{48c^{5-2}}{b^{3+9}} = \dfrac{48c^3}{b^{12}}$

3. $\dfrac{4b^{-3}c^{12}}{16b^{-4}c^3} = \dfrac{b^{-3-(-4)}c^{12-3}}{4}$

$\qquad = \dfrac{bc^9}{4}$

4. $\left(2b^{-5}c^{-2}\right)^3\left(3b^4c^{-6}\right)^{-2} = 2^3b^{-15}c^{-6}\,3^{-2}b^{-8}c^{12}$

$\qquad\qquad = \dfrac{2^3b^{-15+(-8)}c^{-6+12}}{3^2}$

$\qquad\qquad = \dfrac{8b^{-23}c^6}{9}$

$\qquad\qquad = \dfrac{8c^6}{9b^{23}}$

5. $\left(37b^{-3}c^4\right)^{-97}\left(37b^{-3}c^4\right)^{97} = 37^{-97+97}b^{291-291}c^{-388+388}$

$\qquad\qquad = 37^0b^0c^0$

$\qquad\qquad = 1$

6. $\dfrac{\left(20b^{-2}c^{-9}\right)\left(27b^5c^3\right)}{\left(18b^3c^{-1}\right)\left(30b^{-1}c^{-4}\right)} = \dfrac{20\cdot27b^{-2+5}c^{-9+3}}{18\cdot30b^{3+(-1)}c^{-1+(-4)}}$

$\qquad\qquad = \dfrac{540b^3c^{-6}}{540b^2c^{-5}}$

$\qquad\qquad = b^{3-2}c^{-6-(-5)}$

$\qquad\qquad = bc^{-1}$

$\qquad\qquad = \dfrac{b}{c}$

7. $32^{4/5} = \left(32^{1/5}\right)^4$

$\qquad = 2^4$

$\qquad = 16$

8. $16^{-3/4} = \dfrac{1}{16^{3/4}}$

$\qquad = \dfrac{1}{\left(16^{1/4}\right)^3}$

$\qquad = \dfrac{1}{2^3}$

$\qquad = \dfrac{1}{8}$

9. $b^{-4/5}\cdot b^{2/3} = b^{-4/5+2/3}$

$\qquad = b^{-2/15}$

$\qquad = \dfrac{1}{b^{2/15}}$

10. $\dfrac{b^{-1/3}}{b^{4/3}} = b^{-\frac{1}{3}-\frac{4}{3}}$

$\qquad = b^{-\frac{5}{3}}$

$\qquad = \dfrac{1}{b^{5/3}}$

11. $\dfrac{\left(16b^8c^{-4}\right)^{1/4}}{\left(25b^{-6}c^4\right)^{3/2}} = \dfrac{16^{1/4}b^{8(1/4)}c^{-4(1/4)}}{25^{3/2}b^{-6(3/2)}c^{4(3/2)}}$

$\qquad\qquad = \dfrac{2b^2c^{-1}}{\left(25^{1/2}\right)^3b^{-9}c^6}$

$\qquad\qquad = \dfrac{2b^{2-(-9)}c^{-1-6}}{5^3}$

$\qquad\qquad = \dfrac{2b^{11}c^{-7}}{125}$

$\qquad\qquad = \dfrac{2b^{11}}{125c^7}$

12. $\left(\dfrac{32b^2c^5}{2b^{-6}c^1}\right)^{1/4} = \left(16b^{2-(-6)}c^{5-1}\right)^{1/4}$

$\qquad\qquad = \left(16b^8c^4\right)^{1/4}$

$\qquad\qquad = 16^{1/4}b^{8(1/4)}c^{4(1/4)}$

$\qquad\qquad = 2b^2c$

13. $\left(8^{2/3}b^{-1/3}c^{3/4}\right)\left(64^{-1/3}b^{1/2}c^{-5/2}\right)$

$= 8^{2/3}64^{-1/3}b^{-1/3}b^{1/2}c^{3/4}c^{-5/2}$

$= \left(8^{1/3}\right)^2\left(64^{1/3}\right)^{-1}b^{-\frac{1}{3}+\frac{1}{2}}c^{\frac{3}{4}+\left(-\frac{5}{2}\right)}$

$= 2^24^{-1}b^{-\frac{2}{6}+\frac{3}{6}}c^{\frac{3}{4}+\left(-\frac{10}{4}\right)}$

$= 4\left(\dfrac{1}{4}\right)b^{1/6}c^{-7/4}$

$= \dfrac{b^{1/6}}{c^{7/4}}$

14. $b^{2n-1}b^{4n+3} = b^{(2n-1)+(4n+3)}$

$\qquad = b^{2n-1+4n+3}$

$\qquad = b^{6n+2}$

15. $\dfrac{b^{n/2}}{b^{n/3}} = b^{\frac{n}{2}-\frac{n}{3}}$

$\qquad = b^{\frac{3n}{6}-\frac{2n}{6}}$

$\qquad = b^{n/6}$

441

16. $3^{2x} = \left(3^2\right)^x$

$\quad = 9^x$

17. $f(-2) = 3(5)^{-2}$

$\quad = \dfrac{3}{5^2}$

$\quad = \dfrac{3}{25}$

18. $g(a+2) = 6^{a+2}$

$\quad = 6^a \cdot 6^2$

$\quad = 36 \cdot 6^a$

19. $f\left(\dfrac{1}{2}\right) = 49^{1/2}$

$\quad = 7$

20. $g\left(-\dfrac{3}{4}\right) = 2(81)^{-3/4}$

$\quad = \dfrac{2}{81^{3/4}}$

$\quad = \dfrac{2}{\left(81^{1/4}\right)^3}$

$\quad = \dfrac{2}{3^3}$

$\quad = \dfrac{2}{27}$

21. $4.4487 \times 10^7 = 4.4487 \cdot 10,000,000$

$\qquad\qquad\quad = 44,487,000$

22. $3.85 \times 10^{-5} = 3.85 \cdot \dfrac{1}{100,000}$

$\qquad\qquad\quad = 0.0000385$

23. $54,000,000 = 5.4 \times 10^7$

24. $-0.00897 = -8.97 \times 10^{-3}$

25. $f(x) = 2(3)^x$

x	$f(x)$
-1	$\dfrac{2}{3}$
0	2
1	6
2	18

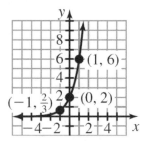

26. $k(x) = -18\left(\dfrac{1}{3}\right)^x$

x	$k(x)$
-1	-54
0	-18
1	-6
2	-2

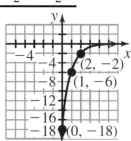

27. $h(x) = -3(2)^x$

x	$h(x)$
-1	-1.5
0	-3
1	-6
2	-12

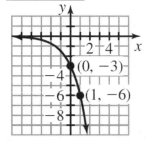

domain: all real numbers
range: $y < 0$

28.

$$g(x) = 12\left(\frac{1}{2}\right)^x$$

x	$g(x)$
−1	24
0	12
1	6
2	3

domain: all real numbers
range: $y > 0$

29. $b^3 = 8$
$b = 8^{1/3}$
$b = 2$

30. $2b^5 = 60$
$b^5 = 30$
$b = 30^{1/5}$
$b \approx 1.97$

31. $3.9b^7 = 283.5$
$b^7 \approx 72.69$
$b \approx 72.69^{1/7}$
$b \approx 1.84$

32. $5b^4 - 13 = 67$
$5b^4 - 80$
$b^4 = 16$
$b = \pm(16)^{1/4}$
$b = \pm 2$

33.
$$\frac{1}{3}b^2 - \frac{1}{5} = \frac{2}{3}$$
$$15\left(\frac{1}{3}b^2 - \frac{1}{5}\right) = 15\left(\frac{2}{3}\right)$$
$$5b^2 - 3 = 10$$
$$5b^2 = 13$$
$$b^2 = \frac{13}{5}$$
$$b = \pm\left(\frac{13}{5}\right)^{1/2}$$
$$b \approx \pm 1.61$$

34. $\dfrac{b^7}{b^2} = \dfrac{83}{6}$
$b^{7-2} = \dfrac{83}{6}$
$b^5 = \dfrac{83}{6}$
$b = \left(\dfrac{83}{6}\right)^{1/5}$
$b \approx 1.69$

35. $f(x)$ is linear. As x increases by 1, $f(x)$ decreases by 4. The linear equation is $f(x) = -4x + 34$.
$g(x)$ is exponential. As x increases by 1, $g(x)$ is multiplied by 3. The exponential equation is $g(x) = \dfrac{5}{3}(3)^x$.

$h(x)$ does not appear to be linear or exponential. $k(x)$ is exponential. As x increases by 1, $k(x)$ is multiplied by $\dfrac{1}{2}$. The exponential equation is

$k(x) = 192\left(\dfrac{1}{2}\right)^x$.

36. $f(4) = 18$

37. $h(3) = 6$

38. When $g(x) = 5$, $x = 1$.

39. When $k(x) = 6$, $x = 5$.

40. (0, 2) and (5, 3)

The y-intercept is (0, 2), and the equation is of the form $y = 2b^x$. Substitute 5 for x and 3 for y to find b.

$$3 = 2b^5$$
$$b^5 = \frac{3}{2}$$
$$b = \left(\frac{3}{2}\right)^{1/5}$$
$$b \approx 1.08$$

The equation is $y = 2(1.08)^x$.

41. (0, 3.8) and (4, 113.2)

The y-intercept is (0, 3.8), and the equation is of the form $y = 3.8b^x$. Substitute 4 for x and 113.2 for y to find b.

$$113.2 = 3.8b^4$$
$$b^4 = \frac{113.2}{3.8}$$
$$b = \left(\frac{113.2}{3.8}\right)^{1/4}$$
$$b \approx 2.34$$

The equation is $y = 3.8(2.34)^x$.

42. (3, 30) and (9, 7)

We can form a system of equations since both points satisfy $y = a(b)^x$.

$$30 = ab^3$$
$$7 = ab^9$$

Combining the two equations yields the following.

$$\frac{7}{30} = \frac{ab^9}{ab^3}$$
$$\frac{7}{30} = b^6$$
$$b = \left(\frac{7}{30}\right)^{1/6}$$
$$b \approx 0.78$$

Use b and one of the points to solve for a. Substitute 3 for x and 30 for y.

$$30 = a(0.78)^3$$
$$a = \frac{30}{(0.78)^3}$$
$$a \approx 63.22$$

The equation of the curve is $y = 63.22(0.78)^x$.

43. (5, 6.9) and (20, 78.6)

We can form a system of equations since both points satisfy $y = a(b)^x$.

$$6.9 = ab^5$$
$$78.6 = ab^{20}$$

Combining the two equations yields the following.

$$\frac{78.6}{6.9} = \frac{ab^{20}}{ab^5}$$
$$\frac{78.6}{6.9} = b^{15}$$
$$b = \left(\frac{78.6}{6.9}\right)^{1/15}$$
$$b \approx 1.18$$

Use b and one of the points to solve for a. Substitute 5 for x and 6.9 for y.

$$6.9 = a(1.18)^5$$
$$a = \frac{6.9}{(1.18)^5}$$
$$a \approx 3.02$$

The equation of the curve is $y = 3.02(1.18)^x$.

44.

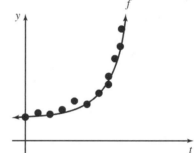

First, increase the value of the coefficient a to raise the y-intercept until it matches the data point at $t = 0$. Then, decrease the value of the base b to slow the increase of the function until it passes through the middle of the data points.

45. a. For every increase of t by 1, $f(t)$ is multiplied by 1.07. $f(t)$ is exponential with base 1.07. Since \$2000 is the initial investment, $a = 2000$. The equation is $f(t) = 2000(1.07)^t$.

b. $f(5) = 2000(1.07)^5 = 2805.10$

The value of the account after 5 years will be \$2805.10.

46. a. Since sales double every year, $g(t)$ must be exponential with base 2 and exponent t. In the first year, total sales were $17,000, so let $a = 17$. The equation is of the form

$$g(t) = 17(2)^t.$$

b. $g(6) = 17(2)^6 = 1088$

In 2013, the corporation's total sales will be $1,088,000.

47. a. For every increase in t of 5730 years, the value of $f(t)$ is multiplied by $\frac{1}{2}$. $f(t)$ is exponential with base $\frac{1}{2}$ and exponent $\frac{t}{5730}$. Since at time $t = 0$, 100% of the carbon-14 remains, $a = 100$. The equation is

$$f(t) = 100\left(\frac{1}{2}\right)^{t/5730}.$$

b. $f(100) = 100\left(\frac{1}{2}\right)^{100/5730} \approx 98.80$

After 100 years, 98.8% of the carbon-14 remains in the tank.

48. We know that $a = 0.12$.
Use $t = 17$ and $f(17) = 1.07$ to solve for b.
$$1.07 = 0.12b^{17}$$
$$b^{17} \approx 8.917$$
$$b \approx 1.14$$
Solve for $t = 23$ (for 2013).
$$f(23) = 0.12(1.14)^{23} \approx 2.44$$
The ad revenue for Latino newspapers will be about $2.44 billion in 2013.

49. a.

b. Use exponential regression.
ExpReg
 y=a*b^x
 a=58.84149993
 b=1.175764854

The equation is $f(t) = 58.84(1.18)^t$.

c. The coefficient a is 58.84. This means that there were approximately 59 stores in 1990.

d. The base b is 1.18. This means that the number of Kohl's stores is increasing by 18% per year.

e. $f(24) = 58.84(1.18)^{24} \approx 3124.9$

According to the model, in 2014 there will be approximately 3125 Kohl's stores.

50. a.

Use an exponential regression.
ExpReg
 y=a*b^x
 a=.9602081862
 b=1.444315754

The equation is $f(t) = 0.96(1.444)^t$.

b. The percentage rate of growth of the percentage of cell phone-only households is about 44.4% per year.

c. $f(12) = 0.96(1.444)^{12} = 78.9$
The percent of cell phone-only households in 2012 will be about 78.9%.

d.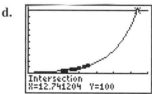
Intersection
X=12.741204 Y=100

According to the model, all households will have only cell phones by 2013. Model breakdown has likely occurred.

Chapter 10 Test

1.
$$32^{2/5} = \left(32^{1/5}\right)^2$$
$$= 2^2$$
$$= 4$$

2.
$$-8^{-4/3} = -\frac{1}{8^{4/3}}$$
$$= -\frac{1}{\left(8^{1/3}\right)^4}$$
$$= -\frac{1}{(2)^4}$$
$$= -\frac{1}{16}$$

3.
$$\left(2b^3 c^8\right)^3 = 2^3 b^{3 \cdot 3} c^{8 \cdot 3}$$
$$= 8b^9 c^{24}$$

4.
$$\left(\frac{4b^{-3}c}{25b^5 c^{-9}}\right)^0 = 1$$

5.
$$\frac{b^{1/2}}{b^{1/3}} = b^{\frac{1}{2} - \frac{1}{3}}$$
$$= b^{\frac{3}{6} - \frac{2}{6}}$$
$$= b^{1/6}$$

6.
$$\frac{25b^{-9} c^{-8}}{35b^{-10} c^{-3}} = \frac{5b^{-9-(-10)} c^{-8-(-3)}}{7}$$
$$= \frac{5bc^{-5}}{7}$$
$$= \frac{5b}{7c^5}$$

7.
$$\left(\frac{6b\left(b^3 c^{-2}\right)}{3b^2 c^5}\right)^2 = \left(\frac{2bb^3 c^{-2}}{b^2 c^5}\right)^2$$
$$= \left(2b^{1+3-2} c^{-2-5}\right)^2$$
$$= \left(2b^2 c^{-7}\right)^2$$
$$= 2^2 b^{2 \cdot 2} c^{-7 \cdot 2}$$
$$= \frac{4b^4}{c^{14}}$$

8.
$$\frac{\left(25b^8 c^{-6}\right)^{3/2}}{\left(7b^{-2}\right)\left(2c^3\right)^{-1}} = \frac{25^{3/2} 2b^{8(3/2)} b^2 c^{-6(3/2)} c^3}{7}$$
$$= \frac{\left(25^{1/2}\right)^3 2b^{12} b^2 c^{-9} c^3}{7}$$
$$= \frac{5^3 \cdot 2b^{12+2} c^{-9+3}}{7}$$
$$= \frac{125 \cdot 2b^{14} c^{-6}}{7}$$
$$= \frac{250b^{14}}{7c^6}$$

9.
$$8^{x/3} 2^{x+3} = 8(4)^x$$
$$\left(2^3\right)^{x/3} 2^{x+3} = 2^3 \left(2^2\right)^x$$
$$2^{3(x/3)} 2^{x+3} = 2^3 \left(2^{2x}\right)$$
$$2^x 2^{x+3} = 2^3 \left(2^{2x}\right)$$
$$2^{x+x+3} = 2^{3+2x}$$
$$2^{2x+3} = 2^{2x+3}$$

10.
$$f(-2) = 4^{-2}$$
$$= \frac{1}{4^2}$$
$$= \frac{1}{16}$$

11.
$$f\left(-\frac{3}{2}\right) = 4^{-3/2}$$
$$= \frac{1}{4^{3/2}}$$
$$= \frac{1}{\left(4^{1/2}\right)^3}$$
$$= \frac{1}{2^3}$$
$$= \frac{1}{8}$$

12. $f(x) = -5(2)^x$

x	f(x)
−1	−2.5
0	−5
1	−10
2	−20

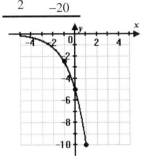

The domain is all real numbers. The range is all negative real numbers.

13. $f(x) = 18\left(\dfrac{1}{3}\right)^x$

x	g(x)
−1	54
0	18
1	6
2	2
3	2/3

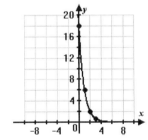

The domain is all real numbers. The range is all positive real numbers.

14. Answers may vary. One example is as follows.

$f(x) = 2\left(\dfrac{2}{3}\right)^x \qquad h(x) = 3(2)^x$

$g(x) = 4\left(\dfrac{9}{8}\right)^x \qquad k(x) = 3\left(\dfrac{1}{2}\right)^x$

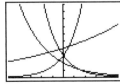

15. For every increase of 1 in *t*, the value of *f(t)* is

multiplied by $\dfrac{1}{2}$. $f(t)$ is exponential with base $\dfrac{1}{2}$ and *y*-intercept 160. $f(t) = 160\left(\dfrac{1}{2}\right)^x$.

16.
$$3b^6 + 5 = 84$$
$$3b^6 = 79$$
$$b^6 = 26.33$$
$$b = \pm(26.33)^{1/6}$$
$$b = \pm 1.72$$

17. (0, 70) and (6, 20)

The *y*-intercept is (0, 70), so the equation is of the form $y = 70b^x$. Substitute 6 for *x* and 20 for *y* to find *b*.

$$20 = 70b^6$$
$$\frac{20}{70} = b^6$$
$$b = \left(\frac{20}{70}\right)^{1/6}$$
$$b \approx 0.81$$

The equation is $y = 70(0.81)^x$.

18. (4, 9) and (7, 50)

We can form a system of equations since both points satisfy $y = a(b)^x$.

$$50 = ab^7$$
$$9 = ab^4$$

Combining the two equations yields the following.

$$\frac{50}{9} = \frac{ab^7}{ab^4}$$
$$\frac{50}{9} = b^3$$
$$b = \left(\frac{50}{9}\right)^{1/3}$$
$$b \approx 1.77$$

Use *b* and one of the points to solve for *a*. Substitute 4 for *x* and 9 for *y*.

$$9 = a(1.77)^4$$
$$a = \frac{9}{(1.77)^4}$$
$$a \approx 0.92$$

The equation of the curve is $y = 0.92(1.77)^x$.

19. $f(0) = 6$

20. When $f(x) = 3$, $x = 1$.

21. From the graph, we see that the points (0, 6) and (1, 3) lie on the curve. The y-intercept is (0, 6), so the equation is of the form $y = 6b^x$. Substitute 1 for x and 3 for y to find b.

$3 = 6b^1$

$b = \dfrac{1}{2}$

The equation is $y = 6\left(\dfrac{1}{2}\right)^x$.

22. a. Complete a table for $f(t)$.

t (weeks)	$f(t)$ (leaves)
0	400
1	1200
2	3600
3	10,800
4	32,400

For every increase of 1 in t, the value of $f(t)$ is multiplied by 3. $f(t)$ is exponential with base 3 and y-intercept 400. The equation is $f(t) = 400(3)^t$.

b. $f(6) = 400(3)^6 = 291,600$
There will be 291,600 leaves on the tree 6 weeks after March 1.

c. $f(52) = 400(3)^{52} = 2.58 \times 10^{27}$
The model predicts there will be 2.58×10^{27} leaves on the tree 1 year after March 1. This is unrealistic, model breakdown has occurred.

23. a. Use an exponential regression.

```
ExpReg
 y=a*b^x
 a=3.783231608
 b=1.269169475

■
```

The equation is $f(t) = 3.78(1.27)^t$.

b. The base b is 1.27, so the percent growth in the number of complaints of fraudulent tax returns filed is 27%.

c. $a = 3.78$ is the y-intercept. This means that there were approximately 3780 complaints of fraudulent tax returns filed in 2000.

d. $f(13) = 3.78(1.27)^{13} \approx 84.52$
The model predicts there will be about 84,520 complaints of fraudulent tax returns filed in 2013.

Chapter 11
Logarithmic Functions

Homework 11.1

1. $f^{-1}(7) = 4$, since $f(4) = 7$.

3. $f(4) = 6$

5. $f^{-1}(4) = 5$, since $f(5) = 4$.

7.

x	$f^{-1}(x)$
2	6
4	5
6	4
8	3
10	2

9. $g(2) = 6$

11. $g^{-1}(2) = 1$, since $f(1) = 2$.

13.

x	$g^{-1}(x)$
2	1
6	2
18	3
54	4
162	5
486	6

15.

x	$f^{-1}(x)$
4	6
10	5
16	4
22	3
28	2
34	1

17. Answers may vary. Begin by creating a table of values for $f(x)$, then build a table for $f^{-1}(x)$ from that information.

x	$f(x)$
0	3
1	6
2	12
3	24
4	48

x	$f^{-1}(x)$
3	0
6	1
12	2
24	3
48	4

19. $f(3) = 3(2)^3$

$\quad = 3(8)$

$\quad = 24$

21. $f^{-1}(3) = 0$, since $f(0) = 3$.

23.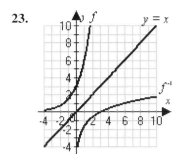

25.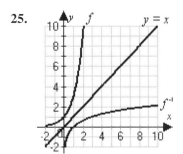

27.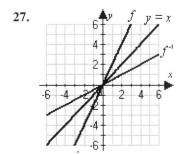

449

29.

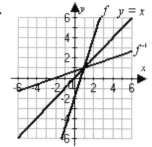

31.

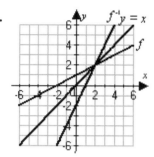

33.

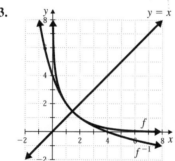

35.

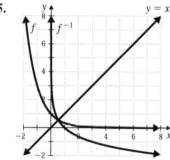

37. Since g sends 2 to 1, $g(2) = 1$.

39. Since g sends 6 to 2, g^{-1} sends 2 back to 6. So, $g^{-1}(2) = 6$.

41. Since g sends 0 to 0, g^{-1} sends 0 back to 0. So, $g^{-1}(0) = 0$.

43. Since f sends 2 to 1, $f(2) = 1$.

45. Since f sends 3 to 4, f^{-1} sends 4 back to 3. So, $f^{-1}(4) = 3$.

47.

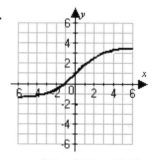

49. a. $f(t) = 0.77t - 43.18$

Replace $f(t)$ with p.

$p = 0.77t - 43.18$

Solve for t.

$p = 0.77t - 43.18$

$p + 43.18 = 0.77t$

$\dfrac{p + 43.18}{0.77} = t$

An approximate equation is $t = 1.30p + 56.08$.

Replace t with $f^{-1}(p)$.

$f^{-1}(p) = 1.30p + 56.08$

b. $f(100) = 0.77(100) - 43.18$

$= 33.82$

According to the model, in 2000, 33.82% of births were outside of marriage.

c. $f^{-1}(100) = 1.30(100) + 56.08$

$= 186.08$

According to the inverse model, all births will be outside marriage in 2086. This is likely a model breakdown.

d. The slope of $f^{-1}(p)$ is 1.30. This means that the rate of change of t with respect to p is 1.30. According to the model f^{-1}, 1.30 years pass for each 1% increase in outside of marriage births.

51. a. Using the linear regression feature, $f(t) = 6.03t + 51.10$.

b. $f(t) = 6.03t + 51.10$

Replace *f(t)* with *n*.

$n = 6.03t + 51.10$

Solve for *t*.

$n - 51.10 = 6.03t$

$\dfrac{n - 51.10}{6.03} = t$

An approximate equation is

$0.17n - 8.47 = t$.

Replace *t* with $f^{-1}(n)$.

$f^{-1}(n) = 0.17n - 8.47$

c. $f(t) = 6.03t + 51.10$

$135 = 6.03t + 51.10$

$\dfrac{83.9}{6.03} = \dfrac{6.03t}{6.03}$

$13.91 \approx t$

$2000 + 13.91 \approx 2014$.

d. $f^{-1}(n) = 0.17n - 8.47$

$f^{-1}(135) = 0.17(135) - 8.47$

$= 14.48$

$2000 + 14.48 \approx 2014$.

e. The results are the same, when rounding is accounted for.

53. a. Using the linear regression feature,

$f(a) = 2.17a + 581.49$.

b. $f(a) = 2.17a + 581.49$

Replace *f(a)* with *c*.

$c = 2.17a + 581.49$

Solve for *t*.

$c - 581.49 = 2.17t$

$\dfrac{c - 581.49}{2.17} = t$

An approximate equation is

$0.46c - 267.97 = t$.

Replace *t* with $f^{-1}(a)$.

$f^{-1}(c) = 0.46c - 267.97$

c. $f^{-1}(677) = 0.46(677) - 267.97$

$= 43.45$

According to the model, the age of adults whose average credit score is 677 points is about 43 years.

d. $f^{-1}(830) = 0.46(830) - 267.97$

$= 113.83$

According to the model, the age of adults whose average credit score is 830 points is about 114 years.

e. The slope of the graph of f^{-1} is 0.46 and it represents a credit score increase by 1 point for each age increase of 0.46 years.

55. $f(x) = x + 8$

Replace $f(x)$ with *y*.

$y = x + 8$

Solve for *x*.

$y - 8 = x$

Replace *x* with $f^{-1}(y)$.

$f^{-1}(y) = y - 8$

Write equation in terms of *x*.

$f^{-1}(x) = x - 8$

57. $f(x) = -4x$

Replace $f(x)$ with *y*.

$y = -4x$

Solve for *x*.

$\dfrac{y}{-4} = x$

Replace *x* with $f^{-1}(y)$.

$f^{-1}(y) = -\dfrac{y}{4}$

Write equation in terms of *x*.

$f^{-1}(x) = -\dfrac{x}{4}$

$= -\dfrac{1}{4}x$

59.

$f(x) = \dfrac{x}{7}$

Replace $f(x)$ with y.

$y = \dfrac{x}{7}$

Solve for x.

$7y = x$

Replace x with $f^{-1}(y)$.

$f^{-1}(y) = 7y$

Write equation in terms of x.

$f^{-1}(x) = 7x$

61. $f(x) = -6x - 2$

Replace $f(x)$ with y.

$y = -6x - 2$

Solve for x.

$y + 2 = -6x$

$-6x = y + 2$

$x = \dfrac{y + 2}{-6}$

$x = -\dfrac{1}{6}y - \dfrac{2}{6}$

Replace x with $f^{-1}(y)$.

$f^{-1}(y) = -\dfrac{1}{6}y - \dfrac{1}{3}$

Write equation in terms of x.

$f^{-1}(x) = -\dfrac{1}{6}x - \dfrac{1}{3}$

63. $f(x) = 0.4x - 7.9$

Replace $f(x)$ with y.

$y = 0.4x - 7.9$

Solve for x.

$y + 7.9 = 0.4x$

$\dfrac{y + 7.9}{0.4} = x$

$x = \dfrac{y}{0.4} + \dfrac{7.9}{0.4}$

Replace x with $f^{-1}(y)$.

$f^{-1}(y) = 2.5y + 19.75$

Write equation in terms of x.

$f^{-1}(x) = 2.5x + 19.75$

65.

$f(x) = \dfrac{7}{3}x + 1$

Replace $f(x)$ with y.

$y = \dfrac{7}{3}x + 1$

Solve for x.

$y - 1 = \dfrac{7}{3}x$

$\dfrac{3}{7}(y - 1) = x$

$x = \dfrac{3y - 3}{7}$

Replace x with $f^{-1}(y)$.

$f^{-1}(y) = \dfrac{3}{7}y - \dfrac{3}{7}$

Write equation in terms of x.

$f^{-1}(x) = \dfrac{3}{7}x - \dfrac{3}{7}$

67.

$f(x) = -\dfrac{5}{6}x - 3$

Replace $f(x)$ with y.

$y = -\dfrac{5}{6}x - 3$

Solve for x.

$y + 3 = -\dfrac{5}{6}x$

$-\dfrac{6}{5}(y + 3) = x$

$x = \dfrac{-6y - 18}{5}$

Replace x with $f^{-1}(y)$.

$f^{-1}(y) = -\dfrac{6}{5}y - \dfrac{18}{5}$

Write equation in terms of x.

$f^{-1}(x) = -\dfrac{6}{5}x - \dfrac{18}{5}$

69.
$$f(x) = \frac{6x-2}{5}$$
Replace $f(x)$ with y.
$$y = \frac{6x-2}{5}$$
Solve for x.
$$5y = 6x - 2$$
$$5y + 2 = 6x$$
$$\frac{5y+2}{6} = x$$
$$x = \frac{5y}{6} + \frac{2}{6}$$
Replace x with $f^{-1}(y)$.
$$f^{-1}(y) = \frac{5}{6}y + \frac{1}{3}$$
Write equation in terms of x.
$$f^{-1}(x) = \frac{5}{6}x + \frac{1}{3}$$

71. $f(x) = 7 - 8(x+1)$
Replace $f(x)$ with y.
$$y = 7 - 8(x+1)$$
Solve for x.
$$y = 7 - 8x - 8$$
$$y = -8x - 1$$
$$y + 1 = -8x$$
$$\frac{y+1}{-8} = x$$
$$x = -\frac{1}{8}y - \frac{1}{8}$$
Replace x with $f^{-1}(y)$.
$$f^{-1}(y) = -\frac{1}{8}y - \frac{1}{8}$$
Write equation in terms of x.
$$f^{-1}(x) = -\frac{1}{8}x - \frac{1}{8}$$

73. $f(x) = x$

Replace $f(x)$ with y.
$$y = x$$
Solve for x.
$$x = y$$
Replace x with $f^{-1}(y)$.
$$f^{-1}(y) = y$$
Write equation in terms of x.
$$f^{-1}(x) = x$$

75. $f(x) = x^3$
Replace $f(x)$ with y.
$$y = x^3$$
Solve for x.
$$\sqrt[3]{y} = x$$
Replace x with $f^{-1}(y)$.
$$f^{-1}(y) = \sqrt[3]{y} = y^{\frac{1}{3}}$$
Write equation in terms of x.
$$f^{-1}(x) = \sqrt[3]{x} \text{ or } f^{-1}(x) = x^{\frac{1}{3}}$$

77. a. $f(x) = 5x - 9$
Replace $f(x)$ with y.
$$y = 5x - 9$$
Solve for x.
$$\frac{y+9}{5} = \frac{5x}{5}$$
$$\frac{1}{5}y + \frac{9}{5} = x$$
Replace x with $f^{-1}(y)$.
$$f^{-1}(y) = \frac{1}{5}y + \frac{9}{5}$$
Write equation in terms of x.
$$f^{-1}(x) = \frac{1}{5}x + \frac{9}{5}$$

b. $f(x) = 5x - 9$
$$f(4) = 5(4) - 9$$
$$= 11$$

c.
$$f^{-1}(x) = \frac{1}{5}x + \frac{9}{5}$$
$$f^{-1}(4) = \frac{1}{5}(4) + \frac{9}{5}$$
$$= \frac{13}{5}$$

79. a. $f(x) = 3x - 5$

Replace $f(x)$ with y.

$y = 3x - 5$

Solve for x.

$$\frac{y+5}{3} = \frac{3x}{3}$$

$$\frac{1}{3}y + \frac{5}{3} = x$$

Replace x with $f^{-1}(y)$.

$$f^{-1}(y) = \frac{1}{3}y + \frac{5}{3}$$

Write equation in terms of x.

$$f^{-1}(x) = \frac{1}{3}x + \frac{5}{3}$$

b. Answers may vary.

x	$f^{-1}(x)$
-2	$\frac{1}{3}(-2) + \frac{5}{3} = 1$
0	$\frac{1}{3}(0) + \frac{5}{3} = \frac{5}{3}$
1	$\frac{1}{3}(1) + \frac{5}{3} = 2$
4	$\frac{1}{3}(4) + \frac{5}{3} = 3$
7	$\frac{1}{3}(7) + \frac{5}{3} = 4$

c.

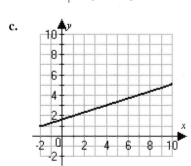

d. For each input-output pair, the output is $\frac{5}{3}$

more than $\frac{1}{3}$ times the input.

81. Answers may vary. One example follows. It makes sense that $g(x) = x - 5$ is the inverse function of $f(x) = x + 5$ because addition and subtraction are inverse operations of each other (or, 5 and -5 are additive inverses).

83. $f(x) = 3$ is not one-to-one. For example, $f(1) = 3$ and $f(2) = 3$. So, the inverse of f would send 3 to both 1 and 2, making the inverse of f not a function. Since f^{-1} is not a function, f is not invertible.

85. a. $f(x) = mx + b$

Replace $f(x)$ with y.

$y = mx + b$

Solve for x.

$y - b = mx$

$$\frac{y-b}{m} = x$$

$$x = \frac{y-b}{m}$$

$$x = \frac{1}{m}y - \frac{b}{m}$$

Replace x with $f^{-1}(y)$.

$$f^{-1}(y) = \frac{1}{m}y - \frac{b}{m}$$

Write equation in terms of x.

$$f^{-1}(x) = \frac{1}{m}x - \frac{b}{m}$$

b. The function $f(x)$ given in part a is a linear function with nonzero slope (since $m \neq 0$). The inverse function is also a linear function as its slope is nonzero ($\frac{1}{m}$ is nonzero since $m \neq 0$).

87. a

Intersection
X=4   Y=5

The point of intersection is (4, 5).

b. $f(x) = 2x - 3$

Replace $f(x)$ with y.

$y = 2x - 3$

Solve for x.

$$\frac{y+3}{2} = \frac{2x}{2}$$

$$\frac{1}{2}y + \frac{3}{2} = x$$

Replace x with $f^{-1}(y)$.

$$f^{-1}(y) = \frac{1}{2}y + \frac{3}{2}$$

Write equation in terms of x.

$$f^{-1}(x) = \frac{1}{2}x + \frac{3}{2}$$

c. $g(x) = \frac{1}{2}x + 3$

Replace $g(x)$ with y.

$y = \frac{1}{2}x + 3$

Solve for x.

$$2(y-3) = 2\left(\frac{1}{2}x\right)$$

$$2y - 6 = x$$

Replace x with $g^{-1}(y)$.

$$g^{-1}(y) = 2y - 6$$

Write equation in terms of x.

$$g^{-1}(x) = 2x - 6$$

d.

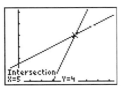

The point of intersection is (5, 4).

e. The x- and y-coordinates are exchanged. An inverse function exchanges the input and output values.

89. Multiply the first equation by 4 and the second equation by 5. Then add the equations.

$$12x - 20y = 40$$
$$\underline{35x + 20y = 195}$$
$$47x = 235$$
$$x = 5$$

Solve for y.

$$3x - 5y = 10$$
$$3(5) - 5y = 10$$
$$15 - 5y = 10$$
$$\frac{-5y}{-5} = \frac{-5}{-5}$$
$$y = 1$$

The solution is (5, 1). The two equations form a linear system in two variables.

91.

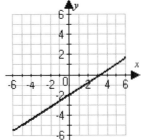

This is a linear equation in two variables.

93. $12x^3 - 20x^2 - 27x + 45$

$$= 4x^2(3x - 5) - 9(3x - 5)$$
$$= (4x^2 - 9)(3x - 5)$$
$$= (2x + 3)(2x - 3)(3x - 5)$$

This is a cubic polynomial in one variable.

Homework 11.2

1. $\log_9(81) = 2$, since $9^2 = 81$.

3. $\log_3(27) = 3$ since $3^3 = 27$.

5. $\log_4(256) = 4$ since $4^4 = 256$.

7. $\log_6(216) = 3$ since $6^3 = 216$.

9. $\log(100) = 2$ since $10^2 = 100$.

11. $\log_4\left(\frac{1}{4}\right) = -1$ since $4^{-1} = \frac{1}{4}$.

13. $\log_2\left(\frac{1}{8}\right) = -3$ since $2^{-3} = \frac{1}{8}$.

15. $\log\left(\dfrac{1}{10,000}\right) = -4$ since $10^{-4} = \dfrac{1}{10,000}$.

17. $\log_5(1) = 0$ since $5^0 = 1$.

19. $\log_9(9) = 1$ since $9^1 = 9$.

21. $\log_9(3) = \dfrac{1}{2}$ since $9^{\frac{1}{2}} = 3$.

23. $\log_8(2) = \dfrac{1}{3}$ since $8^{\frac{1}{3}} = 2$.

25. $\log_7\left(\sqrt{7}\right) = \dfrac{1}{2}$ since $7^{\frac{1}{2}} = \sqrt{7}$.

27. $\log_5\left(\sqrt[4]{5}\right) = \dfrac{1}{4}$ since $5^{\frac{1}{4}} = \sqrt[4]{5}$.

29. $\log_2(\log_2(16)) = \log_2(4)$ since $2^4 = 16$
$\qquad\qquad\qquad = 2$ since $2^2 = 4$.

31. $\log_{10}(\log_{10}(10)) = \log_{10}(1)$ since $10^1 = 10$
$\qquad\qquad\qquad\quad = 0$ since $10^0 = 1$.

33. $\log_b(b) = 1$ since $b^1 = b$.

35. $\log_b\left(b^4\right) = 4$ since $b^4 = b^4$.

37. $\log_b\left(\dfrac{1}{b^5}\right) = -5$ since $b^{-5} = \dfrac{1}{b^5}$.

39. $\log_b\left(\sqrt{b}\right) = \dfrac{1}{2}$ since $b^{\frac{1}{2}} = \sqrt{b}$.

41. $\log_b(\log_b(b)) = \log_b(1)$ since $b^1 = b$.
$\qquad\qquad\qquad = 0$ since $b^0 = 1$.

43. $f(x) = 3^x$
$\quad f^{-1}(x) = \log_3(x)$

45. $h(x) = 10^x$
$\quad h^{-1}(x) = \log(x)$

47. $f(x) = \log_5(x)$
$\quad f^{-1}(x) = 5^x$

49. $h(x) = \log(x)$
$\quad h^{-1}(x) = 10^x$

51. $f(2) = 2^2$
$\qquad = 4$

53. $f^{-1}(2) = \log_2(2)$
$\qquad\quad = 1$, since $2^1 = 2$.

55. $g(3) = \log_3(3)$
$\qquad = 1$

57. $g^{-1}(3) = 3^3$
$\qquad\quad = 27$

59. $f(1) = 3$
61. $f^{-1}(1) = \log_3(1)$
$\qquad\quad = 0$

63.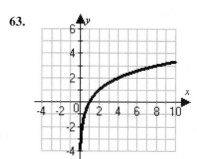

65.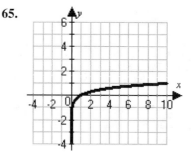

67.

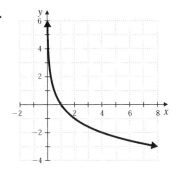

69. a

71. d

73. a.

x	$f(x) = \log_5(x)$
$\dfrac{1}{5}$	$\log_5\left(\dfrac{1}{5}\right) = -1$
1	$\log_5(1) = 0$
5	$\log_5(5) = 1$
25	$\log_5(25) = 2$
125	$\log_5(125) = 3$

b.

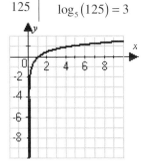

c. For each input-output pair, the output is the logarithm, base 5, of the input.

75. a. $x = 2$, since $5^2 = 25$.

b. $\log_5(25) = 2$, since $5^2 = 25$.

c. 5^2 and $\log_5(25)$ are inverses of each other.

77. a.
$$R = \log\left(\frac{1.6 \times 10^9 A_0}{A_0}\right)$$
$$= \log\left(1.6 \times 10^9\right)$$
$$= 9.2$$
The Richter number for the Indian Ocean earthquake was 9.2.

b.
$$R = \log\left(\frac{6.3 \times 10^7 A_0}{A_0}\right)$$
$$= \log\left(6.3 \times 10^7\right)$$
$$= 7.8$$
The Richter number for the Mexico City earthquake was 7.8.

c.
$$\frac{1.6 \times 10^9}{6.3 \times 10^7} = 25.40$$
The ratio of the Indian Ocean earthquake's amplitude to the Mexico City earthquake's amplitude is 25.40.

79.
$$L = 10\log\left(\frac{1}{I_0}\right)$$

Sound	Intensity of Sound (W/m^2)	Decibel Reading (L)
Faintest sound heard by humans	10^{-12}	0
Whisper	10^{-10}	20
Inside a running car	10^{-8}	40
Conversation	10^{-6}	60
Noisy street corner	10^{-4}	80
Soft-rock concert	10^{-2}	100
Threshold of pain	1	120

81. Answers may vary. Make a table of values for $f(x) = 5^x$, and then build a table for $f^{-1}(x)$.

x	$f(x)$
0	1
1	5
2	25
3	125
4	625

so

x	$f^{-1}(x)$
1	0
5	1
25	2
125	3
625	4

Another name for $f^{-1}(x)$ is $\log_5(x)$.

83. a.

x	$f(x) = \log_2(x)$	$g(x) = 2x$	$h(x) = x^2$	$k(x) = 2^x$
1	0	2	1	2
2	1	4	4	4
4	2	8	16	16
8	3	16	64	256
16	4	32	256	65,536

b. The outputs of k are growing the fastest, followed by h. The outputs of f are growing at the slowest rate.

85. $x^2 = 5 - 3x$

$x^2 + 3x - 5 = 0$

$a = 1, b = 3, c = -5$

$x = \dfrac{-3 \pm \sqrt{3^2 - 4(1)(-5)}}{2(1)}$

$x = \dfrac{-3 \pm \sqrt{29}}{2}$

This is an quadratic equation in one variable.

87. $6x^2 - x - 1 = (3x+1)(2x-1)$

This is a quadratic polynomial in one variable.

89. $(2x-3)^2 - (3x-2)^2$

$= (2x)^2 + 2(2x)(-3) + (-3)^2 -$

$\quad \left((3x)^2 + 2(3x)(-2) + (-2)^2 \right)$

$= 4x^2 - 12x + 9 - \left(9x^2 - 12x + 4 \right)$

$= 4x^2 - 12x + 9 - 9x^2 + 12x - 4$

$= -5x^2 + 5$

This is a quadratic polynomial in one variable.

Homework 11.3

1. $\log_3(243) = 5$

$3^5 = 243$

3. $\log(100) = 2$

$10^2 = 100$

5. $\log_b(a) = c$

$b^c = a$

7. $\log(m) = n$

$10^n = m$

9. $5^3 = 125$

$\log_5(125) = 3$

11. $10^3 = 1000$

$\log(1000) = 3$

13. $y^w = x$

$\log_y(x) = w$

15. $10^p = q$

$\log(q) = p$

17. $\log_4(x) = 2$

$4^2 = x$

$x = 16$

19. $\log(x) = -2$

$10^{-2} = x$

$x = \dfrac{1}{100}$

$\quad = 0.01$

21. $\log_4(x) = 0$

$4^0 = x$

$x = 1$

23. $\log_{27}(t) = \dfrac{4}{3}$

$27^{\frac{4}{3}} = t$

$t = 81$

25. $2\log_8(2x-5) = 4$

$\log_8(2x-5) = 2$

$8^2 = 2x - 5$

$\dfrac{64+5}{2} = \dfrac{2x}{2}$

$\dfrac{69}{2} = x$

27. $4\log_{81}(x) - 3 = -2$

$$\frac{4\log_{81}(x)}{4} = \frac{1}{4}$$

$$\log_{81}(x) = \frac{1}{4}$$

$$81^{\frac{1}{4}} = x$$

$$3 = x$$

29. $\log_2\left(\log_3(y)\right) = 3$

$$2^3 = \log_3(y)$$

$$8 = \log_3(y)$$

$$3^8 = y$$

$$6561 = y$$

31. $\log_6\left(x^3\right) = 2$

$$6^2 = x^3$$

$$36 = x^3$$

$$36^{\frac{1}{3}} = x$$

$$3.3019 \approx x$$

33. $\log_b(49) = 2$

$$b^2 = 49$$

$$b = 49^{\frac{1}{2}}$$

$$b = 7$$

35. $\log_b(8) = 3$

$$b^3 = 8$$

$$b = 8^{\frac{1}{3}}$$

$$b = 2$$

37. $\log_b(16) = 5$

$$b^5 = 16$$

$$b = 16^{\frac{1}{5}}$$

$$b \approx 1.7411$$

39. $4^x = 9$

$$\log\left(4^x\right) = \log(9)$$

$$x\log(4) = \log(9)$$

$$x = \frac{\log(9)}{\log(4)}$$

$$x \approx 1.5850$$

41. $5\left(4^x\right) = 80$

$$4^x = 16$$

$$\log\left(4^x\right) = \log(16)$$

$$x\log(4) = \log(16)$$

$$x = \frac{\log(16)}{\log(4)}$$

$$x = 2$$

43. $3.83(2.18)^t = 170.91$

$$2.18^t = \frac{170.91}{3.83}$$

$$\log\left(2.18^t\right) = \log\left(\frac{170.91}{3.83}\right)$$

$$t\log(2.18) = \log\left(\frac{170.91}{3.83}\right)$$

$$t = \frac{\log\left(\frac{170.91}{3.83}\right)}{\log(2.18)}$$

$$t \approx 4.8738$$

45. $8 + 5(2)^x = 79$

$$5\left(2^x\right) = 71$$

$$2^x = \frac{71}{5}$$

$$\log\left(2^x\right) = \log\left(\frac{71}{5}\right)$$

$$x\log(2) = \log\left(\frac{71}{5}\right)$$

$$x = \frac{\log\left(\frac{71}{5}\right)}{\log(2)}$$

$$x \approx 3.8278$$

47.
$$2^{4x+5} = 17$$
$$\log\left(2^{4x+5}\right) = \log(17)$$
$$(4x+5)\log(2) = \log(17)$$
$$4x+5 = \frac{\log(17)}{\log(2)}$$
$$4x = \frac{\log(17)}{\log(2)} - 5$$
$$x = \frac{\left(\dfrac{\log(17)}{\log(2)} - 5\right)}{4}$$
$$x \approx -0.2281$$

49.
$$6(3)^x - 7 = 85 + 4(3)^x$$
$$6(3)^x - 4(3)^x = 92$$
$$\frac{2(3)^x}{2} = \frac{92}{2}$$
$$(3)^x = 46$$
$$x\log(3) = \log(46)$$
$$x = \frac{\log(46)}{\log(3)}$$
$$x \approx 3.4850$$

51.
$$4^{3p} \cdot 4^{2p-1} = 100$$
$$4^{5p-1} = 100$$
$$\log\left(4^{5p-1}\right) = \log(100)$$
$$(5p-1)\log(4) = 2$$
$$5p-1 = \frac{2}{\log(4)}$$
$$5p = \frac{2}{\log(4)} + 1$$
$$p = \frac{\left(\dfrac{2}{\log(4)} + 1\right)}{5}$$
$$p \approx 0.8644$$

53. $3^x = -8$

No real-number solution. 3 raised to any power will *always* be positive.

55. $\log_4(x) = 3$
$$4^3 = x$$
$$x = 64$$

57. $3(4)^t + 15 = 406$
$$\frac{3(4)^t}{3} = \frac{391}{3}$$
$$\log\left(4^t\right) = \log\left(\frac{391}{3}\right)$$
$$t = \frac{\log\left(\dfrac{391}{3}\right)}{\log(4)}$$
$$t \approx 3.5130$$

59. $\log_b(73) = 5$
$$b^5 = 73$$
$$b = 73^{\frac{1}{5}}$$
$$b \approx 2.3587$$

61. $3\log_{27}(y-1) = 2$
$$\log_{27}(y-1) = \frac{2}{3}$$
$$27^{\frac{2}{3}} = y-1$$
$$9+1 = y$$
$$10 = y$$

63.
$$3(2)^{4x-2} = 83$$
$$\log\left(2^{4x-2}\right) = \log\left(\frac{83}{3}\right)$$
$$(4x-2)\log(2) = \log\left(\frac{83}{3}\right)$$
$$4x-2 = \frac{\log\left(\dfrac{83}{3}\right)}{\log(2)}$$
$$\frac{4x}{4} = \frac{\dfrac{\log\left(\dfrac{83}{3}\right)}{\log(2)} + 2}{4}$$
$$x \approx 1.6975$$

65.

$x = 1$ because $y = 2^x$ and $y = 4\left(\dfrac{1}{2}\right)^x$ intersect at $x = 1$.

67.

$x = 0$ and $x \approx 3.7$ because $y = 4\left(\dfrac{1}{2}\right)^x$ intersects

$y = 4 - x$ in two points with the given x-values.

69.

$x = 2$ because $y = 4\left(\dfrac{1}{2}\right)^x$ is 1 when $x = 2$.

71. Graph $y = 3^x$ and $y = 5 - x$. Then use the intersect feature on a graphing calculator. The x-coordinate, 1.2122, is the approximate solution of the equation $3^x = 5 - x$.

73. Graph $y = 7\left(\dfrac{1}{2}\right)^x$ and $y = 2x$. Then use the intersect feature on a graphing calculator. The x-coordinate, 1.3618, is the approximate solution of the equation

$7\left(\dfrac{1}{2}\right)^x = 2x$.

75. Graph $y = \log(x+1)$ and $y = 3 - \dfrac{2}{5}x$. Then use the intersect feature on a graphing calculator. The x-coordinate, 5.4723, is the approximate solution of the equation

$\log(x+1) = 3 - \dfrac{2}{5}x$.

77. 2. Functions representing each side of the equation have the same y-value when $x = 2$.

79. 5. Functions representing each side of the equation have the same y-value when $x = 5$.

81. (3, 1.5). Functions representing each equation in the system have the same x- and y-values at (3, 1.5).

83. Line 3 includes an error.

$\log[3(8^x)] \neq x\log[3(8)]$

The power property for logarithms would only work in this case if *both* the 3 and the 8 were raised to the x power. The first step the student should have made was to divide both sides of the equation by 3.

$3(8^x) = 7$

$8^x = \dfrac{7}{3}$

Then take the log of both sides and solve for x.

$\log(8^x) = \log\left(\dfrac{7}{3}\right)$

$x\log(8) = \log\left(\dfrac{7}{3}\right)$

$x = \dfrac{\log\left(\dfrac{7}{3}\right)}{\log(8)}$

$x \approx 0.4075$

85.

$ab^x = c$

$ab^x = c$

$b^x = \dfrac{c}{a}$

$\log(b^x) = \log\left(\dfrac{c}{a}\right)$

$x\log(b) = \log\left(\dfrac{c}{a}\right)$

$x = \dfrac{\log\left(\dfrac{c}{a}\right)}{\log(b)}$

87.

$ab^{kx} + d = c$

$ab^{kx} = c - d$

$b^{kx} = \dfrac{c - d}{a}$

$\log(b^{kx}) = \log\left(\dfrac{c-d}{a}\right)$

$kx\log(b) = \log\left(\dfrac{c-d}{a}\right)$

$kx = \dfrac{\log\left(\dfrac{c-d}{a}\right)}{\log(b)}$

$x = \dfrac{\log\left(\dfrac{c-d}{a}\right)}{k\log(b)}$

89. $f(4) = 4^{(4)} = 256$

91.
$$4^x = 3$$
$$\log(4^x) = \log(3)$$
$$x \log(4) = \log(3)$$
$$x = \frac{\log(3)}{\log(4)}$$
$$x \approx 0.7925$$

93. $g(8) = \log_2(8)$
$$= 3$$

95. $\log_2(a) = 5$
$$2^5 = a$$
$$a = 32$$

97. a. False. $\dfrac{\log_2(4)}{\log_2(16)} \neq \dfrac{4}{16}$ because we cannot divide out logarithms of different numbers.
$$\frac{\log_2(4)}{\log_2(16)} = \frac{2}{4}$$
$$= \frac{1}{2}$$
$$\neq \frac{4}{16}$$

b. False. We cannot divide out logarithms of different numbers.
$$\frac{\log_3(1)}{\log_3(27)} = \frac{0}{3}$$
$$= 0$$
$$\neq \frac{1}{27}$$

c. False. We cannot divide out logarithms of different numbers.
$$\frac{\log(1000)}{\log(10000)} = \frac{3}{4}$$
$$\neq \frac{1000}{10000}$$

d. False. We cannot divide out logarithms of different numbers.

99. a. The part of the line $y = 1$ where $x > 0$.

b. We cannot take the logarithm of a negative number.

c. $f(x) = \log(x^3) - 3\log(x) + 1$
$$= 3\log(x) - 3\log(x) + 1$$
$$= 1$$

101. Answers may vary. One example follows. For $x > 0$, $b > 0$, and $b \neq 1$,
$$\log_b(x^p) = p \log_b(x)$$
This does not imply $x^p = px$.
$$x^p \overset{?}{=} px$$
$$\log(x^p) \overset{?}{=} \log(px)$$
$$p \log(x) \neq \log(px)$$

103.
$$5(3p - 7) - 9p = -4p + 23$$
$$15p - 35 - 9p = -4p + 23$$
$$10p = 58$$
$$p = \frac{58}{10}$$
$$p = \frac{29}{5}$$

105.
$$5b^6 - 88 = 56$$
$$\frac{5b^6}{5} = \frac{144}{5}$$
$$b = \left(\frac{144}{5}\right)^{\frac{1}{6}}$$
$$b \approx \pm 1.7508$$

107.
$$6x^2 - 3x = 5 - x$$
$$6x^2 - 2x - 5 = 0$$
$$a = 6, b = -2, c = -5$$
$$x = \frac{-(-2) \pm \sqrt{(-2)^2 - 4(6)(-5)}}{2(6)}$$
$$x = \frac{2 \pm \sqrt{124}}{12}$$
$$x = \frac{2 \pm 2\sqrt{31}}{12}$$
$$x = \frac{1 \pm \sqrt{31}}{6}$$
$$x \approx -0.7613, 1.0946$$

109. $\log_2(x) = -5$
$$2^{-5} = x$$
$$\frac{1}{32} = x$$

This is a logarithmic equation in one variable.

111.

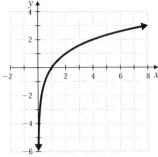

This is a logarithmic function.

113. $f(16) = \log_2(16) = 4$

This is a logarithmic function.

Homework 11.4

1. a. $V = f(t)$

We know we can model the situation well by using an exponential model $f(t) = ab^t$. The V-intercept is $(0, 2000)$, so $a = 2000$ and $f(t) = 2000b^t$. Since the interest rate is 5%, the base must be 1.05, so $f(t) = 2000(1.05)^t$.

b. The V-intercept is $(0, 2000)$. The original $(t = 0)$ value in the account was $2000.

c. $f(t) = 2000(1.05)^t$
$f(5) = 2000(1.05)^5$
$\quad\quad = 2552.56$
In 5 years, the investment will be worth $2,552.56.

d. $2000(1.05)^t = 3000$
$\quad\quad 1.05^t = 1.5$
$\quad \log(1.05^t) = \log(1.5)$
$\quad t\log(1.05) = \log(1.5)$
$$t = \frac{\log(1.5)}{\log(1.05)}$$
$\quad\quad t \approx 8.3104$
The balance will be $3000 after 8.31 years.

3. $f(t) = 9300(1.06)^t$

$9300(1.06)^t = 13700$
$\quad\quad 1.06^t \approx 1.473$
$\quad \log(1.06^t) = \log(1.473)$
$\quad t\log(1.06) = \log(1.473)$
$$t = \frac{\log(1.473)}{\log(1.06)}$$
$\quad\quad \approx 6.65$
The balance will be $13,700 after 6.65 years.

5. $f(t) = 6000(1.10)^t$

$6000(1.10)^t = 12000$
$\quad\quad 1.10^t = 2$
$\quad \log(1.10^t) = \log(2)$
$\quad t\log(1.10) = \log(2)$
$$t = \frac{\log(2)}{\log(1.10)}$$
$\quad\quad \approx 7.27$
The balance will double after 7.27 years. The interest is compounded annually so that interest on previous year's interest earnings also grow at 10% per year.

7. $f(t) = 6.5(1.26)^t$

$6.5(1.26)^t = 33$
$\quad\quad 1.26^t \approx 5.08$
$\quad \log(1.26^t) = \log(5.08)$
$\quad t\log(1.26) = \log(5.08)$
$$t = \frac{\log(5.08)}{\log(1.26)}$$
$\quad\quad t \approx 7.03$
The annual production of ethanol reaches 33 billion in $2007 + 7 = 2014$.

9. a. We know we can model the situation well by using an exponential model $f(t) = ab^t$. Let $p = f(t)$, the total number of people. The p-intercept is $(0, 30)$, and the base is 3.
$f(t) = 30(3)^t$

b. $f(t) = 30(3)^t$
$f(8) = 30(3)^8$
$\quad\quad = 196830$
The total number of Americans who will have heard the rumor after 8 days is 196,830.

c.

$$30(3)^t = 305,000,000$$

$$(3)^t = \frac{305,000,000}{30}$$

$$\log(3^t) = \log\left(\frac{305,000,000}{30}\right)$$

$$t\log(3) = \log\left(\frac{305,000,000}{30}\right)$$

$$t = \frac{\log\left(\frac{305,000,000}{30}\right)}{\log(3)}$$

$$t \approx 14.69$$

The model predicts that all Americans will have heard the rumor after about 15 days.

11. a. Use an exponential decay model $T = f(d) = ab^d$. The T-intercept is $(0, 8)$ so $a = 8$. For every increase of 5 decibels d, the exposure time is halved so the base is $\frac{1}{2}$ and the exponent is $\frac{d}{5}$.

$$f(d) = 8\left(\frac{1}{2}\right)^{\frac{d}{5}}$$

b.

$$f(24) = 8\left(\frac{1}{2}\right)^{\frac{24}{5}}$$

$$= 0.2872$$

The model predicts that at 114 decibels, the bands could play for 0.29 hours (about 17.4 minutes!) without the fans experiencing hearing loss. The average rock concert lasts longer than 18 minutes, so the model predicts that these fans experience hearing loss.

c. $f^{-1}(3)$

$$3 = 8\left(\frac{1}{2}\right)^{\frac{d}{5}}$$

$$\left(\frac{1}{2}\right)^{\frac{d}{5}} = \frac{3}{8}$$

$$\log\left(\frac{1}{2}^{\frac{d}{5}}\right) = \log\left(\frac{3}{8}\right)$$

$$\frac{d}{5}\log\left(\frac{1}{2}\right) = \log\left(\frac{3}{8}\right)$$

$$\frac{d}{5} = \frac{\log\left(\frac{3}{8}\right)}{\log\left(\frac{1}{2}\right)}$$

$$t = \frac{5\log\left(\frac{3}{8}\right)}{\log\left(\frac{1}{2}\right)}$$

$$t \approx 7.08$$

To play for 3 hours, the rock bands should play at 97 decibels.

13. Use the exponential model $y = ab^t$ with 1975 as year 0. Substituting the data point $(0.21, 0)$ yields $a = 0.21$. Solve for b using \$8.25 million in 2007, when $t = 32$.

$$y = ab^t$$

$$8.25 = 0.21(b)^{32}$$

$$\frac{8.25}{0.21} = (b)^{32}$$

$$\left(\frac{8.25}{0.21}\right)^{\frac{1}{32}} = b$$

$$1.122 \approx b$$

The model is $y = 0.21(1.122)^t$.

Predict when the prize is \$20 million.

$$20 = 0.21(1.122)^t$$

$$\frac{20}{0.21} = \frac{0.21(1.122)^t}{0.21}$$

$$\log\left(\frac{20}{0.21}\right) = \log(1.122)^t$$

$$\frac{\log\left(\frac{20}{0.21}\right)}{\log(1.122)} = \frac{t\log(1.122)}{\log(1.122)}$$

$$39.58 \approx t$$

The prize is \$20 million in $1975 + 40 = 2015$.

15. Use the exponential model $y = ab^t$ with 1990 as year 0. This provides the data point $(471, 0)$ so that $a = 471$. Solve for b using 19 million in 2007, when $t = 17$.

$$y = ab^t$$
$$19 = 471(b)^{17}$$
$$19 = 471(b)^{17}$$
$$\frac{19}{471} = (b)^{17}$$
$$\left(\frac{19}{471}\right)^{\frac{1}{17}} = b$$
$$0.83 \approx b$$

The model is $y = 471(0.83)^t$.

Predict when the harvest is 6 million.

$$6 = 471(0.83)^t$$
$$\frac{6}{471} = \frac{471(0.83)^t}{471}$$
$$\log\left(\frac{6}{471}\right) = \log(0.83)^t$$
$$\frac{\log\left(\frac{6}{471}\right)}{\log(0.83)} = \frac{t\log(0.83)}{\log(0.83)}$$
$$23.42 \approx t$$

The harvest is 6 million in 1990 + 23 = 2013.

17. a. Use the points (2, 105) and (5, 441) to find an equation of the form $y = ab^t$.

$$105 = ab^2$$
$$441 = ab^5$$

Divide and solve for b.

$$105 = ab^2$$
$$441 = ab^5$$
$$\frac{105}{441} = b^{-3}$$
$$\left(\frac{105}{441}\right)^{-\frac{1}{3}} = \left(b^{-3}\right)^{-\frac{1}{3}}$$
$$1.61 \approx b$$

Solve for a.

$$105 = a(1.61)^2$$
$$\frac{105}{(1.61)^2} = a$$
$$40.51 \approx a$$

The model is $f(t) = 40.51(1.61)^t$. (Your equation may be slightly different if you chose different points.) Use the graphing

calculator to check your results.

b. $b = 1.61$

The number of U.S. visas issued to Ethiopian orphans is growing exponentially by about 61% per year.

c. $f(14) = 40.51(1.61)^{14}$
$$\approx 31{,}851.1$$

In 2014, about 31,851 U.S. visas will be issued to Ethiopian orphans.

d.
$$f(t) = 40.51(1.61)^t$$
$$100{,}000 = 40.51(1.61)^t$$
$$\frac{100{,}000}{40.51} = \frac{40.51(1.61)^t}{40.51}$$
$$\log\left(\frac{100{,}000}{40.51}\right) = \log(1.61)^t$$
$$\frac{\log\left(\frac{100{,}000}{40.51}\right)}{\log(1.61)} = \frac{t\log(1.61)}{\log(1.61)}$$
$$16.40 \approx t$$

In 2000 + 16 = 2016, 100,000 U.S. visas will be issued to Ethiopian orphans.

19. a. Use the points (20, 120) and (100, 24,441) to find an equation of the form $y = ab^t$.

$$120 = ab^{20}$$
$$24{,}441 = ab^{100}$$

Divide and solve for b.

$$120 = ab^{20}$$
$$24{,}441 = ab^{100}$$
$$\frac{120}{24{,}441} = b^{-80}$$
$$\left(\frac{120}{24{,}441}\right)^{-\frac{1}{80}} = \left(b^{-80}\right)^{-\frac{1}{80}}$$
$$1.069 \approx b$$

Solve for a.

$$120 = a(1.069)^{20}$$
$$\frac{120}{(1.069)^{20}} = a$$
$$31.6 \approx a$$

The model is $f(t) = 31.6(1.069)^t$. (Your equation may be slightly different if you chose different points.) Use the graphing calculator to check your results.

b.
$$f(t) = 31.6(1.069)^t$$
$$f(-9) = 31.6(1.069)^{-9}$$
$$\approx 17.33$$
According to the model, in 1891, the tuition rate would have been about $17.33.

c.
$$f(t) = 31.6(1.069)^t$$
$$43,950 = 31.6(1.069)^t$$
$$\frac{43,950}{31.6} = (1.069)^t$$
$$\log\left(\frac{43,950}{31.6}\right) = \log(1.069)^t$$
$$\frac{\log\left(\dfrac{43,950}{31.6}\right)}{\log(1.069)} = \frac{t\log(1.069)}{\log(1.069)}$$
$$108.5 \approx t$$
Stanford's tuition rate will be $43,950 in 1900 + 109 = 2009 (according to this model).
(Your equation may be slightly different if you chose different points.) Use the graphing calculator to check your results.

d. First calculate the tuition rate for different years.
$$f(10) = 31.6(1.069)^{10} \approx 61.58$$
$$f(20) = 31.6(1.069)^{20} \approx 120.02$$
$$f(30) = 31.6(1.069)^{30} \approx 233.89$$
Then determine the difference between the tution rates to calculate the annual increase.
$$\frac{120.02 - 61.58}{20 - 10} = \frac{58.44}{10} = 5.844$$
$$\frac{233.89 - 120.02}{30 - 20} = \frac{113.87}{10} \approx 11.39$$
The annual increase in tuition rate increased over time.
Now determine the percentage growth in tuition rate over time.
$$\frac{120.02 - 61.58}{61.58} = \frac{58.44}{61.58} \approx 0.949$$
$$\frac{233.89 - 120.02}{120.02} = \frac{113.87}{120.02} \approx 0.949$$
The percentage growth in tuition stayed constant over time.

e.
$$f(t) = 31.6(1.069)^t$$
$$1,000,000 = 31.6(1.069)^t$$
$$\frac{1,000,000}{31.6} = (1.069)^t$$
$$\log\left(\frac{1,000,000}{31.6}\right) = \log(1.069)^t$$
$$\frac{\log\left(\dfrac{1,000,000}{31.6}\right)}{\log(1.069)} = \frac{t\log(1.069)}{\log(1.069)}$$
$$155.3 \approx t$$
Stanford's tuition rate will be $1 million per year in 1900 + 155 = 2055 (according to this model).

21. a. Use the points (8, 350) and (16, 33) to find an equation of the form $y = ab^t$.
$$350 = ab^8$$
$$33 = ab^{16}$$
Divide and solve for b.
$$350 = ab^8$$
$$33 = ab^{16}$$
$$\frac{350}{33} = b^{-8}$$
$$\left(\frac{350}{33}\right)^{-\frac{1}{8}} = \left(b^{-8}\right)^{-\frac{1}{8}}$$
$$0.74 \approx b$$
Solve for a.
$$350 = a(0.74)^8$$
$$\frac{350}{(0.74)^8} = a$$
$$3892 \approx a$$
The model is $f(t) = 3892(0.74)^t$. (Your equation may be slightly different if you chose different points.) Use the graphing calculator to check your results.

b.
$$f(t) = 3892(0.74)^t$$
$$f(33) = 3892(0.74)^{33}$$
$$\approx 0.19$$
In 2013, the model predicts that there will be about 0.19 thousand, or 190, polio cases.

c.

$$f(t) = 3892(0.74)^t$$

$$0.001 = 3892(0.74)^t$$

$$\frac{0.001}{3892} = (0.74)^t$$

$$\log\left(\frac{0.001}{3892}\right) = \log(0.74)^t$$

$$\frac{\log\left(\dfrac{0.001}{3892}\right)}{\log(0.74)} = \frac{t\log(0.74)}{\log(0.74)}$$

$$50.40 \approx t$$

There will be 1 case of polio in 1980 + 50 = 2030 (according to this model). (Your equation may be slightly different if you chose different points.) Use the graphing calculator to check your results.

d. Half the number of cases in 1980, or half of 3892 thousand, is 1946 thousand.

$$f(t) = 3892(0.74)^t$$

$$1946 = 3892(0.74)^t$$

$$\frac{1946}{3892} = (0.74)^t$$

$$\log\left(\frac{1946}{3892}\right) = \log(0.74)^t$$

$$\frac{\log\left(\dfrac{1}{2}\right)}{\log(0.74)} = \frac{t\log(0.74)}{\log(0.74)}$$

$$2.30 \approx t$$

This model predicts there will be half as many cases of polio in 2.30 years.

23. a.

$$f(t) = 1.2(1.0162)^t$$

$$9.3 - 1.2(1.0162)^t$$

$$1.0162^t = \frac{9.3}{1.2}$$

$$\log(1.0162^t) = \log\left(\frac{9.3}{1.2}\right)$$

$$t\log(1.0162) = \log\left(\frac{9.3}{1.2}\right)$$

$$t = \frac{\log\left(\dfrac{9.3}{1.2}\right)}{\log(1.0162)}$$

$$t \approx 127.4219$$

The model predicts the world population will reach 9.3 billion in 1900 + 127 = 2027.

b.

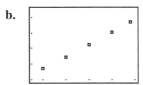

A linear function would best fit these data points. Using the linear regression feature on a graphing calculator, $g(t) = 0.08t - 1.91$.

c.

$$g(t) = 0.08t - 1.91$$

$$9.3 = 0.08t - 1.91$$

$$\frac{9.3 + 1.91}{0.08} = \frac{0.08t}{0.08}$$

$$140 \approx t$$

The year the population reaches 9.3 billion is 1900 + 140 = 2040, which is after the model in part a. of 2027. This is because the linear increase is more gradual than the exponential increase in part (a).

d.

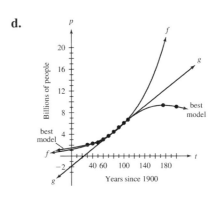

25. a. By regression:

Linear: $f(t) = 0.54t - 35.83$

Quadratic: $f(t) = 0.024t^2 - 3.16t + 106.03$

Exponential: $f(t) = 0.00067(1.119)^t$

(Your equations may be slightly different if you calculated the answers manually.)

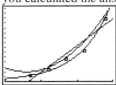

The exponential equation models fits the data best.

b. The exponential function best models the situation for ages less than 65 years. The linear function has negative values for ages less than 65 years, and the quadratic function has increasing values for ages less than 65 years (both of which are not possible).

c.
$$f(t) = 0.00067(1.119)^t$$
$$f(70) = 0.00067(1.119)^{70}$$
$$\approx 1.75$$
Based on this model, about 1.8% of 70-year-old seniors have severe memory impairment. (Your equation may be slightly different if you chose different points.) Use the graphing calculator to check your results.

d.
$$f(t) = 0.00067(1.119)^t$$
$$10 = 0.00067(1.119)^t$$
$$\frac{10}{0.00067} = (1.119)^t$$
$$\log\left(\frac{10}{0.00067}\right) = \log(1.119)^t$$
$$\frac{\log\left(\frac{10}{0.00067}\right)}{\log(1.119)} = \frac{t\log(1.119)}{\log(1.119)}$$
$$85.48 \approx t$$
This model predicts 10% of seniors will have severe memory impairment at age 85. (Your equation may be slightly different if you chose different points.) Use the graphing calculator to check your results.

e. The base b is 1.119 and it represents the percentage of seniors with severe memory impairment increases by 11.9% for each additional year of age. (Your equation may be slightly different if you chose different points.) Use the graphing calculator to check your results.

f. No. The linear relationship shows a change in the number of seniors with severe memory impairment, whereas the exponential relationship shows a change in the percentage of seniors with severe memory impairment.

27. a. Using a graphing calculator and the exponential regression feature gives:
$$E(s) = 0.36(1.0036)^s$$
$$R(s) = 0.037(1.0049)^s$$

b.
$$E(1425) = 0.36(1.0036)^{1425} \approx 60.3\%$$
$$R(1425) = 0.037(1.0049)^{1425} \approx 39.2\%$$

c. Half = 50%
Use $E(s)$ for early decision applicants.

$$E(s) = 50$$
$$0.36(1.0036)^s = 50$$
$$1.0036^s = \frac{50}{0.36}$$
$$\log(1.0036^s) = \log\left(\frac{50}{0.36}\right)$$
$$s\log(1.0036) = \log\left(\frac{50}{0.36}\right)$$
$$s = \frac{\log\left(\frac{50}{0.36}\right)}{\log(1.0036)}$$
$$s \approx 1373$$
Use $R(s)$ for regular decision applicants.
$$R(s) = 50$$
$$0.037(1.0049)^s = 50$$
$$1.0049^s = \frac{50}{0.037}$$
$$\log(1.0049^s) = \log\left(\frac{50}{0.037}\right)$$
$$s\log(1.0049) = \log\left(\frac{50}{0.037}\right)$$
$$s = \frac{\log\left(\frac{50}{0.037}\right)}{\log(1.0049)}$$
$$s \approx 1475$$

d. 1475 − 1373 = 102 points

e.
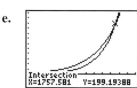
(1757.58, 199.19). Students who score 1758 points on their SAT have the same chance (199%) of being selected from the early decision and regular decision systems. Model breakdown has occurred. A solution to the Challenge problem follows.

$$0.36(1.0036)^s = 0.037(1.0049)^s$$

$$\frac{(1.0036)^s}{(1.0049)^s} = \frac{0.037}{0.36}$$

$$\left(\frac{1.0036}{1.0049}\right)^s = \frac{0.037}{0.36}$$

$$\log\left(\frac{1.0036}{1.0049}\right)^s = \log\left(\frac{0.037}{0.36}\right)$$

$$\frac{s\log\left(\frac{1.0036}{1.0049}\right)}{\log\left(\frac{1.0036}{1.0049}\right)} = \frac{\log\left(\frac{0.037}{0.36}\right)}{\log\left(\frac{1.0036}{1.0049}\right)}$$

$$s \approx 1757.58$$

29. a. Use the exponential model $f(t) = ab^t$.

At $t = 0$, 100% of the gallium citrate-67 remains. Substitute $(0, 100)$.

$$100 = ab^0$$
$$100 = a$$

To solve for b, substitute $(3.25, 50)$.

$$50 = 100(b)^{3.25}$$

$$\frac{50}{100} = (b)^{3.25}$$

$$\left(\frac{1}{2}\right)^{\frac{1}{3.25}} = b$$

The equation is $f(t) = 100\left(\frac{1}{2}\right)^{\frac{t}{3.25}}$.

b.

$$f(t) = 100\left(\frac{1}{2}\right)^{\frac{2}{3.25}}$$
$$= 65.28$$

After 2 days, 65.28% of the gallium citrate-67 remains.

c.

$$f(t) = 100\left(\frac{1}{2}\right)^{\frac{t}{3.25}}$$

$$0.39 = 100\left(\frac{1}{2}\right)^{\frac{t}{3.25}}$$

$$\log\left(\frac{0.39}{100}\right) = \log\left(\frac{1}{2}\right)^{\frac{t}{3.25}}$$

$$\frac{\log\left(\frac{0.39}{100}\right)}{\log\left(\frac{1}{2}\right)} = \frac{\frac{t}{3.25}\log\left(\frac{1}{2}\right)}{\log\left(\frac{1}{2}\right)}$$

$$\frac{\log\left(\frac{0.39}{100}\right)}{\log\left(\frac{1}{2}\right)} = \frac{t}{3.25}$$

$$3.25\left(\frac{\log\left(\frac{0.39}{100}\right)}{\log\left(\frac{1}{2}\right)}\right) = t$$

$$26.0 \approx t$$

After 26 days, 0.39% of the gallium citrate-67 remains.

31. Use an exponential decay model $f(t) = ab^t$. Every 5730 years the amount of carbon-14 is halved, so the base is $\frac{1}{2}$ and the exponent is $\frac{t}{5730}$. 24.46% of the carbon-14 remains, so $f(t) = 24.46$:

$$f(t) = 100\left(\frac{1}{2}\right)^{\frac{t}{5730}}$$

$$24.46 = 100\left(\frac{1}{2}\right)^{\frac{t}{5730}}$$

$$\log\left(\frac{24.46}{100}\right) = \log\left(\frac{1}{2}\right)^{\frac{t}{5730}}$$

$$\frac{\log\left(\frac{24.46}{100}\right)}{\log\left(\frac{1}{2}\right)} = \frac{\frac{t}{5730}\log\left(\frac{1}{2}\right)}{\log\left(\frac{1}{2}\right)}$$

$$\frac{\log\left(\frac{24.46}{100}\right)}{\log\left(\frac{1}{2}\right)} = \frac{t}{5730}$$

$$5730\left(\frac{\log\left(\frac{24.46}{100}\right)}{\log\left(\frac{1}{2}\right)}\right) = t$$

$$11640.5 \approx t$$

The ice sheet advanced about 11,641 years ago.

33. a. Since 50% of the wood's carbon-14 remains, one half-life has passed. The half-life of carbon-14 is 5730 years. The age of the wood is 5730 years.

b. Since 25% of the wood's carbon-14 remains, two half-lives have passed (half of 100% is 50% and then half of 50% is 25%). The age of the wood is $2 \cdot 5730$ or 11,460 years.

c. After three half-lives have passed 12.5% of the wood's carbon-14 remains. This corresponds to $3 \cdot 5730$ or 17,190 years passing. The wood has only 10% of its carbon-14 remaining, so guess a little longer than 17,190 years.

$$f(t) = 100\left(\frac{1}{2}\right)^{\frac{t}{5730}}$$

$$10 = 100\left(\frac{1}{2}\right)^{\frac{t}{5730}}$$

$$\left(\frac{1}{2}\right)^{\frac{t}{5730}} = 0.1$$

$$\log\left(\frac{1}{2}\right)^{\frac{t}{5730}} = \log(0.1)$$

$$\frac{t}{5730}\log\left(\frac{1}{2}\right) = -1$$

$$t = \frac{-5730}{\log\left(\frac{1}{2}\right)}$$

$$t \approx 19035$$

The age of the wood is 19,035 years.

35. Use an exponential decay model $f(t) = ab^t$. Let $P = f(t)$ be the percentage of remaining of the element at t years. The P-intercept is $(0, 100)$. Every 100 years the amount of the element is halved so the base is $\frac{1}{2}$ and the exponent is $\frac{t}{100}$.

$$f(t) = 100\left(\frac{1}{2}\right)^{\frac{t}{100}}$$

Find $f^{-1}(0.01)$.

$$0.01 = 100\left(\frac{1}{2}\right)^{\frac{t}{100}}$$

$$\left(\frac{1}{2}\right)^{\frac{t}{100}} = 0.0001$$

$$\log\left(\frac{1}{2}\right)^{\frac{t}{100}} = \log(0.0001)$$

$$\frac{t}{100}\log\left(\frac{1}{2}\right) = -4$$

$$\frac{t}{100} = \frac{-4}{\log\left(\frac{1}{2}\right)}$$

$$t = \frac{-400}{\log\left(\frac{1}{2}\right)}$$

$$t \approx 1328.77$$

The tank must remain intact for 1329 years.

37. a. Use the linear regression feature of a graphing calculator. The linear model is $L(t) = -5.51t + 122.84$.

Use the quadratic regression feature of a graphing calculator. The quadratic model is $Q(t) = 0.044t^2 - 6.51t + 125.88$.

Use the exponential regression feature of a graphing calculator. The exponential model is $E(t) = 177.7(0.876)^t$.

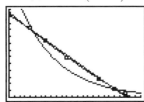

The linear and quadratic models appear to fit the data better as shown in the graph above.

b. Linear:
$$45 = -5.51t + 122.84$$
$$45 - 122.84 = -5.51t$$
$$\frac{-77.84}{-5.51} = \frac{-5.51t}{-5.51}$$
$$14.13 \approx t$$
The bar of soap weighed 45 grams after 14 days of use.
Quadratic:
$$45 = 0.044t^2 - 6.51t + 125.88$$
$$0.044t^2 - 6.51t + 80.88 = 0$$
$$a = 0.044, b = -6.51, c = 80.88$$
$$t = \frac{-(-6.51) \pm \sqrt{(-6.51)^2 - 4(0.044)(80.88)}}{2(0.044)}$$
$$t \approx \frac{6.51 \pm 5.31}{0.088}$$
$$t \approx 13.6, 134.3$$
We reject the second values, so the bar of soap weighed 45 grams after 14 days of use.

c. Linear: -5.51;
The slope shows that the weight of the soap bar decreases by 5.51 grams each day.
Quadratic:
$$-\frac{b}{2a} = -\frac{-6.51}{2(0.044)} \approx 73.98$$
$$Q(73.98)$$
$$= 0.044(73.98)^2 - 6.51(73.98) + 125.88$$
$$\approx -114.92$$

The vertex is $(73.98, -114.92)$, which means that the bar of soap weighs about -115 grams after 74 days, and will begin to increase in weight from this point on. Model breakdown has occurred.

d. Linear:
$$0 = -5.51t + 122.84$$
$$0 - 122.84 = -5.51t$$
$$\frac{-122.84}{-5.51} = \frac{-5.51t}{-5.51}$$
$$22.3 \approx t$$
There is no soap left after the 22nd day of use. Model breakdown has occurred, because in fact there was enough soap left on the 23rd day for the bar to break into two pieces.
Quadratic:
$$0 = 0.044t^2 - 6.51t + 125.88$$
$$a = 0.044, b = -6.51, c = 125.88$$
$$t = \frac{-(-6.51) \pm \sqrt{(-6.51)^2 - 4(0.044)(125.88)}}{2(0.044)}$$
$$t \approx \frac{6.51 \pm 4.50}{0.088}$$
$$t \approx 22.8, 125.1$$
There is no soap left after the 23rd day of use. Model breakdown has occurred, because in fact there was enough soap left on the 23rd day for the bar to break into two pieces.

39. $(x-5)(x+2) = 3x$
$$x^2 - 3x - 10 = 3x$$
$$x^2 - 6x - 10 = 0$$
$$x^2 - 6x = 10$$
$$x^2 - 6x + 9 = 10 + 9$$
$$(x-3)^2 = 19$$
$$x - 3 = \pm\sqrt{19}$$
$$x = 3 \pm \sqrt{19}$$
This is a quadratic equation in one variable.

41. $7x^2 + 3 = 8$
$$7x^2 = 5$$
$$x^2 = \frac{5}{7}$$
$$x = \pm\sqrt{\frac{5}{7}} = \pm 0.7143$$
This is a quadratic equation in one variable.

43. $\dfrac{2}{3}x^2 = \dfrac{1}{2}x + \dfrac{5}{6}$

$\dfrac{2}{3}x^2 - \dfrac{1}{2}x - \dfrac{5}{6} = 0$

$6\left(\dfrac{2}{3}x^2 - \dfrac{1}{2}x - \dfrac{5}{6}\right) = 6(0)$

$4x^2 - 3x - 5 = 0$

$a = 4, b = -3, c = -5$

$x = \dfrac{-(-3) \pm \sqrt{(-3)^2 - 4(4)(-5)}}{2(4)}$

$x = \dfrac{3 \pm \sqrt{89}}{8}$

$x = 1.5542, -0.8042$

This is a quadratic equation in one variable.

Homework 11.5

1. $\log_b(x) + \log_b(3x)$

$= \log_b\left[(x)(3x)\right]$

$= \log_b\left(3x^2\right)$

3. $\log_b(8x) - \log_b(2)$

$= \log_b\left(\dfrac{8x}{2}\right)$

$= \log_b(4x)$

5. $4\log_b(t) + \log_b(5t)$

$= \log_b(t)^4 + \log_b(5t)$

$= \log_b\left[(t^4)(5t)\right]$

$= \log_b\left(5t^5\right)$

7. $\log_b\left(3x^2\right) - 5\log_b(x)$

$= \log_b\left(3x^2\right) - \log_b(x)^5$

$= \log_b\left(\dfrac{3x^2}{x^5}\right)$

$= \log_b\left(\dfrac{3}{x^3}\right)$

9. $2\log_b(3x) + 3\log_b\left(x^3\right)$

$= \log_b(3x)^2 + \log_b\left(x^3\right)^3$

$= \log_b\left[\left(9x^2\right)\left(x^9\right)\right]$

$= \log_b\left(9x^{11}\right)$

11. $3\log_b(2m) + 5\log_b\left(m^2\right) - \log_b(3m)$

$= \log_b(2m)^3 + \log_b\left(m^2\right)^5 - \log_b(3m)$

$= \log_b\left[\dfrac{\left(8m^3\right)\left(m^{10}\right)}{3m}\right]$

$= \log_b\left(\dfrac{8m^{12}}{3}\right)$

13. $\log_5(6x) + \log_5(x) = 2$

$\log_5\left[(6x)(x)\right] = 2$

$5^2 = 6x^2$

$\dfrac{25}{6} = x^2$

$\left(\dfrac{25}{6}\right)^{\frac{1}{2}} = x$

$2.0412 \approx x$

15. $\log_2(9x) - \log_2(3) = 5$

$\log_2\left(\dfrac{9x}{3}\right) = 5$

$2^5 = \dfrac{9x}{3}$

$32 = 3x$

$\dfrac{32}{3} = x$

$10.6667 \approx x$

17.
$$\log_7\left(w^2\right) + 2\log_7\left(3w\right) = 2$$
$$\log_7\left(w^2\right) + \log_7\left(3w\right)^2 = 2$$
$$\log_7\left[\left(w^2\right)\left(9w^2\right)\right] = 2$$
$$7^2 = 9w^4$$
$$\frac{49}{9} = w^4$$
$$\left(\frac{49}{9}\right)^{\frac{1}{4}} = w$$
$$1.5275 \approx w$$

19.
$$\log\left(x^{13}\right) - 2\log\left(x^4\right) = 1$$
$$\log\left(x^{13}\right) - \log\left(x^4\right)^2 = 1$$
$$\log\left(\frac{x^{13}}{x^8}\right) = 1$$
$$\log\left(x^5\right) = 1$$
$$10^1 = x^5$$
$$\left(10\right)^{\frac{1}{5}} = x$$
$$1.5849 \approx x$$

21.
$$3\log\left(x^2\right) + 4\log\left(2x\right) = 2$$
$$\log\left(x^2\right)^3 + \log\left(2x\right)^4 = 2$$
$$\log\left[\left(x^6\right)\left(16x^4\right)\right] = 2$$
$$10^2 = 16x^{10}$$
$$\left(\frac{100}{16}\right)^{\frac{1}{10}} = x$$
$$1.2011 \approx x$$

23.
$$3\log_5\left(p^4\right) - 5\log_5\left(2p\right) = 3$$
$$\log_5\left(p^4\right)^3 - \log_5\left(2p\right)^5 = 3$$
$$\log_5\left(\frac{p^{12}}{32p^5}\right) = 3$$
$$5^3 = \frac{p^7}{32}$$
$$\left(4000\right)^{\frac{1}{7}} = p$$
$$3.2702 \approx p$$

25.
$$\log_3\left(7\right) = \frac{\log(7)}{\log(3)}$$
$$\approx 1.7712$$

27.
$$\log_9\left(3.58\right) = \frac{\log(3.58)}{\log(9)} \approx 0.5804$$

29.
$$\log_8\left(\frac{1}{70}\right) = \frac{\log\left(\frac{1}{70}\right)}{\log(8)} \approx -2.0431$$

31. Graph $y = \log\left(x+5\right) + \log\left(x+2\right)$ and $y = 3-x$. Then use "intersect."

The x-coordinate, 1.6204, is the approximate solution of the equation $\log\left(x+5\right) + \log\left(x+2\right) = 3-x$.

33. Given $\log_5\left(x+3\right) + \log_2\left(x+4\right) = -2x+9$, use the change of base formula to graph
$$y = \frac{\log\left(x+3\right)}{\log 5} + \frac{\log\left(x+4\right)}{\log 2} \text{ and } y = -2x+9.$$

The x-coordinate, 2.6031, is the approximate solution of the equation $\log_5\left(x+3\right) - \log_2\left(x+4\right) = -2x+9$.

35. Given $\log_2\left(x+4\right) + \log_3\left(x+5\right) = 2^x+1$, use the change of base formula to graph
$$y = \frac{\log\left(x+4\right)}{\log 2} + \frac{\log\left(x+5\right)}{\log 3} \text{ and } y = 2^x+1.$$

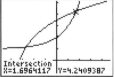

The x-coordinates, -2.6876 and 1.6964, are the approximate solutions of the equation $\log_2\left(x+4\right) + \log_3\left(x+5\right) = 2^x+1$.

37. $\dfrac{\log_2(x)}{\log_2(7)} = \log_7(x)$

39. $\dfrac{\log_b(r)}{\log_b(s)} = \log_s(r)$

41. All three students did the problem correctly.

43. $g(17) = \log_{12}(17)$

$\qquad = \dfrac{\log(17)}{\log(12)}$

$\qquad \approx 1.1402$

45. $g(8) = \log_{12}(8)$

$\qquad = \dfrac{\log(8)}{\log(12)}$

$\qquad \approx 0.8368$

47. $\log_b(b^2) = 2$

$\log_b\left(\dfrac{b^6}{b^4}\right) = \log_b(b^2) = 2$

$\log_b(b^6) = 6$

$\log_b(b^6) - \log_b(b^4) = \log_b\left(\dfrac{b^6}{b^4}\right)$

$\qquad\qquad\qquad\qquad = \log_b(b^2)$

$\qquad\qquad\qquad\qquad = 2$

$\dfrac{\log_b(b^6)}{\log_b(b^4)} = \dfrac{6}{4} = 1.5$

The expressions $\log_b(b^2)$, $\log_b\left(\dfrac{b^6}{b^4}\right)$, 2, and

$\log_b(b^6) - \log_b(b^4)$ are all equal.

49.
$\log_b(x) - \log_b(x) = \log_b\left(\dfrac{x}{x}\right)$

$\qquad\qquad\qquad\quad = \log_b(1)$

$\qquad\qquad\qquad\quad = 0$

51. a. $\log_2(x^3) + \log_2(x^5)$

$\qquad = \log_2[(x^3)(x^5)]$

$\qquad = \log_2(x^8)$

b. $\log_2(x^3) + \log_2(x^5) = 7$

$\qquad \log_2[(x^3)(x^5)] = 7$

$\qquad\qquad \log_2(x^8) = 7$

$\qquad\qquad\qquad x^8 = 2^7$

$\qquad\qquad\qquad x = \left(2^7\right)^{\frac{1}{8}}$

$\qquad\qquad\qquad x \approx 1.8340$

c. Answers may vary. Simplifying an expression involves combining separate logarithms into one logarithm. Solving the equation involves simplifying and using the definition of a logarithm to modify the statement into an exponential equation that can then be solved.

d. Answers may vary. Simplifying an expression allows you to combine similar variables and reduce coefficients to their simplest forms, making the process of solution easier.

53. $\log_2\left(x^4\right) + \log_2\left(x^3\right)$

$\qquad \log_2\left[\left(x^4\right)\left(x^3\right)\right]$

$\qquad\qquad \log_2\left(x^7\right)$

55. $\log_2\left(x^4\right) + \log_2\left(x^3\right) = 4$

$\qquad \log_2\left[\left(x^4\right)\left(x^3\right)\right] = 4$

$\qquad\qquad \log_2\left(x^7\right) = 4$

$\qquad\qquad\qquad 2^4 = x^7$

$\qquad\qquad\left(2^4\right)^{\frac{1}{7}} = x$

$\qquad\qquad 1.4860 \approx x$

57. $2\log_9\left(x^3\right) - 3\log_9\left(2x\right) = 2$

$\log_9\left(x^3\right)^2 - \log_9\left(2x\right)^3 = 2$

$\log_9\left(\dfrac{x^6}{8x^3}\right) = 2$

$9^2 = \dfrac{x^3}{8}$

$9^2 = \dfrac{x^3}{8}$

$\left(9^2 \cdot 8\right)^{\frac{1}{3}} = x$

$8.6535 \approx x$

59. $2\log_9\left(x^3\right) - 3\log_9\left(2x\right)$

$\log_9\left(x^3\right)^2 - \log_9\left(2x\right)^3$

$\log_9\left(\dfrac{x^6}{8x^3}\right)$

$\log_9\left(\dfrac{x^3}{8}\right)$

61. $\left(16b^{16}c^{-7}\right)^{\frac{1}{4}}\left(27b^{27}c^5\right)^{\frac{1}{3}}$

$= \left(16^{\frac{1}{4}}b^{\frac{16}{4}}c^{-\frac{7}{4}}\right)\left(27^{\frac{1}{3}}b^{\frac{27}{3}}c^{\frac{5}{3}}\right)$

$= \left(2b^4 c^{-\frac{7}{4}}\right)\left(3b^9 c^{\frac{5}{3}}\right)$

$= 6b^{13}c^{-\frac{21}{12}+\frac{20}{12}}$

$= 6b^{13}c^{-\frac{1}{12}}$

$= \dfrac{6b^{13}}{c^{\frac{1}{12}}}$

63. $3\log_b\left(2x^5\right) + 2\log_b\left(3x^4\right)$

$= \log_b\left(2x^5\right)^3 + \log_b\left(3x^4\right)^2$

$= \log_b\left[\left(8x^{15}\right)\left(9x^8\right)\right]$

$= \log_b\left(72x^{23}\right)$

65. Substitute $3x - 7$ for y in the second equation.

$y = -2x + 3$

$3x - 7 = -2x + 3$

$5x = 10$

$x = 2$

Solve for y when $x = 2$.

$y = 3x - 7$

$y = 3(2) - 7$

$y = -1$

The solution is $(2, -1)$.

67. Substitute $\log_2(x) + 2$ for y in the first equation.

$y = \log_2\left(4x^2\right) - 3$

$\log_2(x) + 2 = \log_2\left(4x^2\right) - 3$

$\log_2(x) - \log_2\left(4x^2\right) = -5$

$\log_2\left(\dfrac{x}{4x^2}\right) = -5$

$2^{-5} = \dfrac{1}{4x}$

$\dfrac{1}{32} = \dfrac{1}{4x}$

$4x = 32$

$x = 8$

Solve for y when $x = 8$.

$y = \log_2(x) + 2$

$= \log_2(8) + 2$

$= \dfrac{\log(8)}{\log(2)} + 2$

$= 3 + 2 = 5$

The solution is $(8, 5)$.

69. Substitute $\dfrac{2}{3}x - 2$ for y in the first equation.

$2x - 3\left(\dfrac{2}{3}x - 2\right) = 6$

$2x - 2x + 6 = 6$

$6 = 6$

True

The solution is all points on the line $y = \dfrac{2}{3}x - 2$.

$\left.\begin{array}{l} 2x - 3y = 6 \\ y = \dfrac{2}{3}x - 2 \end{array}\right\}$ is a dependent linear system of

equations in two variables.

71.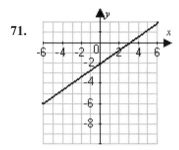

This is a linear equation in two variables.

73. $f(x) = -\dfrac{4}{3}x - 1$

Replace $f(x)$ with y:

$y = -\dfrac{4}{3}x - 1$

Solve for x:

$y + 1 = -\dfrac{4}{3}x$

$\dfrac{-3(y+1)}{4} = x$

$x = -\dfrac{3y}{4} - \dfrac{3}{4}$

Replace x with $f^{-1}(y)$:

$f^{-1}(y) = -\dfrac{3y}{4} - \dfrac{3}{4}$

Write equation in terms of x:

$f^{-1}(x) = -\dfrac{3x}{4} - \dfrac{3}{4}$

$f^{-1}(2) = -\dfrac{3 \cdot 2}{4} - \dfrac{3}{4} = -\dfrac{9}{4}$

This is a linear function in one variable.

Homework 11.6

1. $\ln(54.8) \approx 4.0037$

3. $\ln\left(\dfrac{1}{2}\right) \approx -0.6931$

5. $\ln(e^4) = 4$

7. $\ln(e) = \ln(e^1) = 1$

9. $\ln\left(\dfrac{1}{e}\right) = \ln(e^{-1}) = -1$

11. $\dfrac{1}{2}\ln(e^6) = \dfrac{1}{2}(6) = 3$

13. $\ln(x) = 2$

$e^2 = x$

$7.3891 \approx x$

15. $\ln(p + 5) = 3$

$e^3 = p + 5$

$e^3 - 5 = p$

$p \approx 15.0855$

17. $7e^x = 44$

$e^x = \dfrac{44}{7}$

$x = \ln\left(\dfrac{44}{7}\right)$

$x \approx 1.8383$

19. $5\ln(3x) + 2 = 7$

$\dfrac{5\ln(3x)}{5} = \dfrac{5}{5}$

$\ln(3x) = 1$

$3x = e^1$

$x = \dfrac{e}{3}$

$x \approx 0.9061$

21. $4e^{3m-1} = 68$

$e^{3m-1} = 17$

$3m - 1 = \ln(17)$

$3m = \ln(17) + 1$

$m = \dfrac{\ln(17) + 1}{3}$

$m \approx 1.2777$

23. $e^{3x-5} \cdot e^{2x} = 135$

$e^{5x-5} = 135$

$5x - 5 = \ln(135)$

$\dfrac{5x}{5} = \dfrac{\ln(135) + 5}{5}$

$x \approx 1.9811$

25.

$$3.1^x = 49.8$$
$$\ln(3.1^x) = \ln(49.8)$$
$$x\ln(3.1) = \ln(49.8)$$
$$x = \frac{\ln(49.8)}{\ln(3.1)}$$
$$x \approx 3.4541$$

27. $3(6^x) - 1 = 97$

$$3(6^x) = 98$$
$$6^x = \frac{98}{3}$$
$$\ln(6^x) = \ln\left(\frac{98}{3}\right)$$
$$x\ln(6) = \ln\left(\frac{98}{3}\right)$$
$$x = \frac{\ln\left(\frac{98}{3}\right)}{\ln(6)}$$
$$x \approx 1.9458$$

29. $5e^x - 20 = 2e^x + 67$

$$3e^x = 87$$
$$e^x = 29$$
$$x = \ln(29)$$
$$x \approx 3.3673$$

31. $\ln(4x) + \ln(3x^4)$

$$= \ln\left[(4x)(3x^4)\right]$$
$$= \ln(12x^5)$$

33. $\ln(25x^4) - \ln(5x^3)$

$$= \ln\left(\frac{25x^4}{5x^3}\right)$$
$$= \ln(5x)$$

35. $2\ln(w^4) + 3\ln(2w)$

$$= \ln(w^4)^2 + \ln(2w)^3$$
$$= \ln\left[(w^8)(8w^3)\right]$$
$$= \ln(8w^{11})$$

37. $3\ln(3x) - 2\ln(x^2)$

$$= \ln(3x)^3 - \ln(x^2)^2$$
$$= \ln(27x^3) - \ln(x^4)$$
$$= \ln\left(\frac{27x^3}{x^4}\right)$$
$$= \ln\left(\frac{27}{x}\right)$$

39. $3\ln(2k) + 4\ln(k^2) - \ln(k^7)$

$$= \ln(2k)^3 + \ln(k^2)^4 - \ln(k^7)$$
$$= \ln\left[\frac{(8k^3)(k^8)}{(k^7)}\right]$$
$$= \ln(8k^4)$$

41. $\ln(3x) + \ln(x) = 4$

$$\ln[(3x)(x)] = 4$$
$$\ln(3x^2) = 4$$
$$3x^2 = e^4$$
$$x^2 = \frac{e^4}{3}$$
$$x = \left(\frac{e^4}{3}\right)^{\frac{1}{2}}$$
$$x \approx 4.2661$$

43. $\ln(4x^5) - 2\ln(x^2) = 5$

$$\ln(4x^5) - \ln(x^2)^2 = 5$$
$$\ln(4x^5) - \ln(x^4) = 5$$
$$\ln\left(\frac{4x^5}{x^4}\right) = 5$$
$$\ln(4x) = 5$$
$$4x = e^5$$
$$x = \frac{e^5}{4}$$
$$x \approx 37.1033$$

45. $2\ln(3x) + 2\ln\left(x^3\right) = 8$

$\ln(3x)^2 + \ln\left(x^3\right)^2 = 8$

$\ln\left(9x^2\right) + \ln\left(x^6\right) = 8$

$\ln\left[\left(9x^2\right)\left(x^6\right)\right] = 8$

$\ln\left(9x^8\right) = 8$

$9x^8 = e^8$

$x^8 = \dfrac{e^8}{9}$

$x = \left(\dfrac{e^8}{9}\right)^{\frac{1}{8}}$

$x \approx 2.0654$

47. $5\ln\left(2m\right) - 3\ln\left(m^4\right) = 7$

$\ln\left(2m\right)^5 - \ln\left(m^4\right)^3 = 7$

$\ln\left(32m^5\right) - \ln\left(m^{12}\right) = 7$

$\ln\left(\dfrac{32m^5}{m^{12}}\right) = 7$

$\ln\left(\dfrac{32}{m^7}\right) = 7$

$\dfrac{32}{m^7} = e^7$

$\dfrac{1}{m^7} = \dfrac{e^7}{32}$

$m^{-7} = \dfrac{e^7}{32}$

$m = \left(\dfrac{e^7}{32}\right)^{-\frac{1}{7}}$

$x \approx 0.6036$

49. Graph $y = e^x$ and $y = 5 - x$. Then use "intersect."

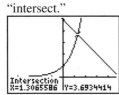

The *x*-coordinate, 1.3066, is the approximate solution of the equation $e^x = 5 - x$.

51. Graph $y = 3\ln(x + 2)$ and $y = -2x + 6$. Then use "intersect."

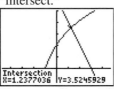

The *x*-coordinate, 1.2377 is the approximate solution of the equation $3\ln(x + 2) = -2x + 6$.

53. Graph $y = 3\ln(x + 3)$ and $y = 0.7x + 2$. Then use "intersect."

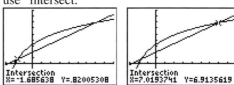

The *x*-coordinates, -1.6856 and 7.0194, are the approximate solutions of the equation $3\ln(x + 3) = 0.7x + 2$.

55. $f(x) = 4\ln(x)$

$f\left(e^5\right) = 4\ln\left(e^5\right)$

$= 4 \cdot 5$

$= 20$

57. $f(x) = 4\ln(x)$

$-8 = 4\ln\left(x\right)$

$\dfrac{-8}{4} = \dfrac{4\ln\left(x\right)}{4}$

$-2 = \ln(x)$

$x = e^{-2}$

$x \approx 0.1353$

59. $\ln(e) = 1$ because $e^1 = e$.

61. $ae^{bx} = c$

$e^{bx} = \dfrac{c}{a}$

$bx = \ln\left(\dfrac{c}{a}\right)$

$x = \dfrac{\ln\left(\dfrac{c}{a}\right)}{b}$ or $x = \dfrac{\ln(c) - \ln(a)}{b}$

63. $3\ln(x) = 3\ln(x)$

$\ln(x^7) - \ln(x^4) = \ln\left(\dfrac{x^7}{x^4}\right) = \ln(x^3) = 3\ln(x)$

$\dfrac{\ln(x^7)}{\ln(x^4)} = \log_{x^4}(x^7)$

$2\ln(x)\ln(x) = 2[\ln(x)]^2$

$\ln(x^3) = 3\ln(x)$

$\ln(3x) = \ln(3x)$

$3\ln(x)$, $\ln(x^7) - \ln(x^4)$, and $\ln(x^3)$ are all equal.

65. a.

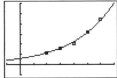

The function appears to be a reasonable model.

b. $f(t) = 0.15e^{0.33t}$
$ = 0.15e^{0.33(14)}$
$ \approx 15.22$
The annual sales in 2014 are predicted to be $15.22 billion.

c. $f(t) = 0.15e^{0.33t}$
$30 = 0.15e^{0.33t}$
$\dfrac{30}{0.15} = e^{0.33t}$
$\ln\left(\dfrac{30}{0.15}\right) = 0.33t$
$\dfrac{\ln\left(\dfrac{30}{0.15}\right)}{0.33} = t$
$16.06 \approx t$
The annual sales is predicted to reach $30 billion in 2016.

67. a. The time when the person bought it is $t = 0$.
$70 + 137e^{-0.66(0)} = 70 + 137e^0$
$\phantom{70 + 137e^{-0.66(0)}} = 70 + 137$
$\phantom{70 + 137e^{-0.66(0)}} = 207$
The temperature was 207°F when the coffee was purchased

b. $180 = 70 + 137e^{-0.06t}$

$110 = 137e^{-0.06t}$

$e^{-0.06t} = \dfrac{110}{137}$

$\ln\left(e^{-0.06t}\right) = \ln\left(\dfrac{110}{137}\right)$

$-0.06t\ln(e) = \ln\left(\dfrac{110}{137}\right)$

$-0.06t = \ln\left(\dfrac{110}{137}\right)$

$t = \dfrac{\ln\left(\dfrac{110}{137}\right)}{-0.06}$

$t \approx 3.6583$

He will be able to drink the coffee in about 3.66 minutes.

c.

Y1=70+137e^(-0.06X)

X=145 . . . . Y=70.022822

Looking at the graph of y we can see that as t gets larger, y approaches 70. So the temperature of the store is 70°F.

69. a. The poles are at $x = 10$ or $x = -10$
$h(10) = 16.67(e^{0.03(10)} + e^{-0.03(10)})$
$ \approx 16.67(1.34986 + 0.740818)$
$ \approx 16.67(2.090678)$
$ \approx 34.85$
The poles are about 34.85 feet high.

b. $h(6) = 16.67(e^{0.03(6)} + e^{-0.03(6)})$
$h(6) \approx 16.67(1.197217 + 0.835270)$
$ \approx 16.67(2.032487)$
$ \approx 33.88$
The cable is about 33.88 feet high when it is 6 feet away from the center (or 4 feet to the left of the rightmost pole).

c. The shortest height happens in the center, where $x = 0$.
$h(0) = 16.67(e^{0.03(0)} + e^{-0.03(0)})$
$ = 16.67(1 + 1)$
$ = 16.67(2)$
$ = 33.34$
The minimum height of the cable is 33.34 feet.

71. a. i.
$$3^x = 58$$
$$\ln(3^x) = \ln(58)$$
$$\frac{x\ln(3)}{\ln(3)} = \frac{\ln(58)}{\ln(3)}$$
$$x \approx 3.6960$$

ii.
$$3^x = 58$$
$$\log(3^x) = \log(58)$$
$$\frac{x\log(3)}{\log(3)} = \frac{\log(58)}{\log(3)}$$
$$x \approx 3.6960$$

iii. Both results are the same.

b. i. Answers may vary. Sample of the form $b^x = c$.

$$5^x = 25$$
$$\ln(5^x) = \ln(25)$$
$$\frac{x\ln(5)}{\ln(5)} = \frac{\ln(25)}{\ln(5)}$$
$$x = 2$$

ii.
$$5^x = 25$$
$$\log(5^x) = \log(25)$$
$$\frac{x\log(5)}{\log(5)} = \frac{\log(25)}{\log(5)}$$
$$x = 2$$

iii. Both results are the same.

c. We can take either the common logarithm or the natural logarithm to solve an exponential equation.

73. $\ln(x^8) - \ln(x^3)$
$$= \ln\left(\frac{x^8}{x^3}\right)$$
$$= \ln(x^5)$$

75. $\ln(x^8) - \ln(x^3) = 4$
$$\ln\left(\frac{x^8}{x^3}\right) = 4$$
$$\ln(x^5) = 4$$
$$x^5 = e^4$$
$$x = \left(e^4\right)^{\frac{1}{5}}$$
$$x \approx 2.2255$$

77. $3e^x - 5 = 7$
$$\frac{3e^x}{3} = \frac{12}{3}$$
$$e^x = 4$$
$$x = \ln(4)$$
$$x \approx 1.3863$$

79. $7 - 3(2t - 4) = 5t + 6$
$$7 - 6t + 12 = 5t + 6$$
$$\frac{-11t}{-11} = \frac{-13}{-11}$$
$$t = \frac{13}{11}$$

81. $25x^3 - 4x = 12 - 75x^2$
$$25x^3 + 75x^2 - 4x - 12 = 0$$
$$25x^2(x + 3) - 4(x + 3) = 0$$
$$(25x^2 - 4)(x + 3) = 0$$
$$(5x + 2)(5x - 2)(x + 3) = 0$$

$5x + 2 = 0$	$5x - 2 = 0$	$x + 3 = 0$
$5x = -2$	$5x = 2$	$x = -3$
$x = -\frac{2}{5} = -0.4$	$x = \frac{2}{5} = 0.4$	

83. $\dfrac{b^7}{b^3} = 16$
$$b^4 = 16$$
$$b = (16)^{\frac{1}{4}}$$
$$b = \pm 2$$

85. Answers may vary.
One example is $5x^2 - 2x + 1$.

87. Answers may vary.
One example is $\log(2x-1)=5$.

$\log(2x-1)=5$

$10^5=2x-1$

$\dfrac{10^5+1}{2}=x$

89. Answers may vary.
One example is $f(x)=5x+2$.

Chapter 11 Review Exercises

1. $f(2)=4$

2. $f^{-1}(2)=1$

3.

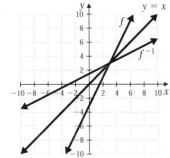

4.

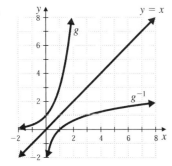

5. a. Using the linear regression feature, $f(t)=0.85t-65.24$.

b. Replace $f(t)$ with p.

$p=0.85t-65.24$

Solve for t.

$p=0.85t-65.24$

$\dfrac{p+65.24}{0.85}=t$

$1.18p+76.75\approx t$

An approximate equation is

$t=1.18p+76.75$.

Replace t with $f^{-1}(p)$.

$f^{-1}(p)=1.18p+76.75$

c. $f(100)=0.85(100)-65.24$

$=85-65.24$

$=19.76$

19.76% of Americans were obese in 2000.

d. $f^{-1}(100)=1.18(100)+76.75$

≈ 194.8

In 1900 + 195 = 2095, all Americans will be obese.

e. The slope is 1.18, which means that the percentage of American adults who are obsese is increasing by 1 percentage point every 1.18 years.

6. $f(x)=3x$

Replace $f(x)$ with y.

$y=3x$

Solve for x.

$x=\dfrac{1}{3}y$

Replace x with $f^{-1}(y)$.

$f^{-1}(y)=\dfrac{1}{3}y$

Write in terms of x.

$f^{-1}(x)=\dfrac{1}{3}x$

7.
$$g(x) = \frac{4x - 7}{8}$$

Replace $g(x)$ with y.

$$y = \frac{4x - 7}{8}$$

Solve for x.

$$4x - 7 = 8y$$
$$4x = 8y + 7$$
$$x = \frac{8y + 7}{4}$$

Replace x with $g^{-1}(y)$.

$$g^{-1}(y) = 2y + \frac{7}{4}$$

Write in terms of x.

$$g^{-1}(x) = 2x + \frac{7}{4}$$

8. $\log_5(25) = 2$, since $5^2 = 25$.

9. $\log(100,000) = 5$, since $10^5 = 100,000$.

10. $\log_3\left(\frac{1}{9}\right) = -2$, since $3^{-2} = \frac{1}{9}$.

11. $\ln\left(\frac{1}{e^3}\right) = \ln(e^{-3})$

$\qquad = -3$

12. $\log_6\left(\sqrt{6}\right) = \frac{1}{2}$, since $6^{\frac{1}{2}} = \sqrt{6}$.

13. $\log_4\left(\sqrt[3]{4}\right) = \frac{1}{3}$, since $4^{\frac{1}{3}} = \sqrt[3]{4}$.

14. $\log(0.001) = -3$, since $10^{-3} = 0.001$.

15. $\log_3(7) = \frac{\log(7)}{\log(3)}$

$\qquad \approx 1.7712$

16. $\ln(5) \approx 1.6094$

17. $\log_b(b) = 1$, since $b^1 = b$.

18. $\log_b(b^7) = 7$, since $b^7 = b^7$

19. $\log_b(1) = 0$, since $b^0 = 1$.

20. $h(x) = 3^x$
$h^{-1}(x) = \log_3(x)$

21. $f(x) = 10^x$
$f^{-1}(x) = \log_{10}(x)$

22. $g(x) = \log_4(x)$
$g^{-1}(x) = 4^x$

23. $h(x) = \log(x)$
$h^{-1}(x) = 10^x$

24.

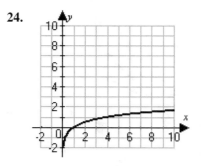

25. $\log_d(k) = t$

26. $y^r = w$

27. $6(2)^x = 30$
$$2^x = 5$$
$$\log(2^x) = \log(5)$$
$$x\log(2) = \log(5)$$
$$x = \frac{\log(5)}{\log(2)}$$
$$x \approx 2.3219$$

28. $\log_3(x) = -4$
$$x = 3^{-4}$$
$$x = \frac{1}{81}$$

29. $4.3(9.8)^x - 3.3 = 8.2$

$4.3(9.8)^x = 11.5$

$9.8^x = \dfrac{11.5}{4.3}$

$\log(9.8^x) = \log\left(\dfrac{11.5}{4.3}\right)$

$x\log(9.8) = \log\left(\dfrac{11.5}{4.3}\right)$

$x = \dfrac{\log\left(\dfrac{11.5}{4.3}\right)}{\log(9.8)}$

$x \approx 0.4310$

30. $\log_b(83) = 6$

$b^6 = 83$

$b = 83^{\frac{1}{6}}$

$b \approx 2.0886$

31. $5\log_{32}(m) - 3 = -1$

$\log_{32}(m)^5 = 2$

$m^5 = 32^2$

$m = \left(32^2\right)^{\frac{1}{5}}$

$m = 4$

32. $5(4)^{3r-7} = 40$

$4^{3r-7} = 8$

$\log(4^{3r-7}) = \log(8)$

$(3r - 7)\log(4) = \log(8)$

$3r - 7 = \dfrac{\log(8)}{\log(4)}$

$3r = \dfrac{\log(8)}{\log(4)} + 7$

$r = \dfrac{\dfrac{\log(8)}{\log(4)} + 7}{3}$

$r \approx 2.8333$

33. $2^{4t} \cdot 2^{3t-5} = 94$

$2^{7t-5} = 94$

$\log\left(2^{7t-5}\right) = \log(94)$

$(7t - 5)\log(2) = \log(94)$

$7t - 5 = \dfrac{\log(94)}{\log(2)}$

$7t = \dfrac{\log(94)}{\log(2)} + 5$

$t = \dfrac{\dfrac{\log(94)}{\log(2)} + 5}{7}$

≈ 1.6507

34. $\log_b(32) = 5$

$32 = b^5$

$b = 32^{1/5}$

$b = 2$

35. $x = 4$ because $y = \log_2(x)$ and $y = -\dfrac{3}{4}x + 5$ intersect at $x = 4$.

36. $x = 0$ because $y = 2^x - 3$ is -2 when $x = 0$.

37. The solution to the system $y = \log_2(x)$ and $y = -\dfrac{3}{4}x + 5$ is the point of intersection on the graph, $(4, 2)$.

38. $f(x) = 3^x$

$f(4) = 3^4$

$= 81$

39. $f(x) = 3^x$, so $f^{-1}(x) = \log_3(x)$

$f^{-1}(25) = \log_3(25)$

$= \dfrac{\log(25)}{\log(3)}$

≈ 2.9299

40.
$$f(x) = 3^x$$
$$6 = 3^x$$
$$\log(6) = \log\left(3^x\right)$$
$$\log(6) = x\log(3)$$
$$\frac{\log(6)}{\log(3)} = x$$
$$1.6309 \approx x$$

41. $f(x) = 3^x$, so $f^{-1}(x) = \log_3(x)$
Substitute using $f^{-1}(x) = 6$.
$$6 = \log_3(x)$$
$$3^6 = x$$
$$729 = x$$

42. a. Use an exponential model $f(t) = ab^t$. Let $V = f(t)$, where V is the value of the account. The V-intercept is (0, 8000), so $a = 8000$. Since the interest rate is 5%, the base is $b = 1.05$. $f(t) = 8000(1.05)^t$.

b. $f(9) = 8000(1.05)^9 \approx 12410.63$
The balance in the account after 9 years is $12,410.63.

c. The balance will have doubled when it is $16,000. Find $f^{-1}(16000)$
$$16000 = 8000(1.05)^t$$
$$1.05^t = 2$$
$$\log(1.05^t) = \log(2)$$
$$t\log(1.05) = \log(2)$$
$$t = \frac{\log(2)}{\log(1.05)}$$
$$t \approx 14.2067$$
The balance will be doubled in 14.2 years.

43. a. Use an exponential model $f(t) = ab^t$. Let $n = f(t)$ be the number of leaves. The n-intercept is (0, 30), so $a = 30$. The number of leaves quadruples every week so the base, $b = 4$. $f(t) = 30(4)^t$.

b. $f(5) = 30(4)^5 = 30720$
There are 30,720 leaves on the tree 5 weeks after April 1.

c.
$$f^{-1}(10000)$$
$$100000 = 30(4)^t$$
$$4^t = \frac{100000}{30}$$
$$\log(4^t) = \log\left(\frac{10000}{3}\right)$$
$$t\log(4) = \log\left(\frac{10000}{3}\right)$$
$$t = \frac{\log\left(\dfrac{10000}{3}\right)}{\log(4)}$$
$$t \approx 5.85$$
There are 100,000 leaves on the tree about 5.9 weeks after April 1.

44. a. Exponential regression on a graphing calculator yields the equation
$$f(t) = 0.12(1.085)^t$$

b. 0.12; the national health spending in 1970 was 0.12 trillion dollars.

c. The percentage rate of growth is 8.5% per year.

d. $f(44) = 0.12(1.085)^{44} \approx 4.35$
The national health spending in 2014 ($t = 44$) will be about 4.35 trillion dollars.

e.
$$f(t) = 0.12(1.085)^t$$
$$5 = 0.12(1.085)^t$$
$$\frac{5}{0.12} = \frac{0.12(1.085)^t}{0.12}$$
$$\log\left(\frac{5}{0.12}\right) = \log(1.085)^t$$
$$\log\left(\frac{5}{0.12}\right) = t\log(1.085)$$
$$\frac{\log\left(\dfrac{5}{0.12}\right)}{\log(1.085)} = t$$
$$45.72 \approx t$$
National health spending will be 5 trillion dollars in 1970 + 46 = 2016.

45. a. Exponential regression on a graphing calculator yields the equation
$$f(n) = 9.33(1.31)^n.$$

b. 1.31. As each cassette is added to the bag the length increases by 31%

c. 9.33. The initial length of the rubber band is 9.33 inches.

d. $f(8) = 9.33(1.31)^8 \approx 80.92$

The rubber band is stretched to 80.92 inches with 8 cassettes.
There are two scenarios which might cause model breakdown. The rubber band reaches a point where it can stretch no farther, or the rubber band breaks.

e.
$$f^{-1}(139)$$
$$139 = 9.33(1.31)^n$$
$$1.31^n = \frac{139}{9.33}$$
$$\log(1.31^n) = \log\left(\frac{139}{9.33}\right)$$
$$n\log(1.31) = \log\left(\frac{139}{9.33}\right)$$
$$n = \frac{\log\left(\frac{139}{9.33}\right)}{\log(1.31)}$$
$$n \approx 10.00$$

It would take 10 cassettes to stretch the rubber band to 139 inches. If model breakdown occurs with 8 cassettes, then it definitely occurs with 10. Either the rubber band has stopped stretching with the addition of the last two cassettes, or the rubber band is broken.

46. Use an exponential decay model $f(t) = ab^t$.
Every 5.3 years the amount of cobalt-60 is halved, so the base is $\frac{1}{2}$ and the exponent is $\frac{t}{5.3}$.
15% of the cobalt-60 remains, so $f(t) = 15$:

$$f(t) = 100\left(\frac{1}{2}\right)^{\frac{t}{5.3}}$$
$$15 = 100\left(\frac{1}{2}\right)^{\frac{t}{5.3}}$$
$$\left(\frac{15}{100}\right) = \left(\frac{1}{2}\right)^{\frac{t}{5.3}}$$
$$\log\left(\frac{15}{100}\right) = \left(\frac{t}{5.3}\right)\log\left(\frac{1}{2}\right)$$
$$(5.3)\frac{\log\left(\frac{15}{100}\right)}{\log\left(\frac{1}{2}\right)} = \frac{t}{5.3}(5.3)$$
$$14.51 \approx t$$

About 15% of the cobalt-60 remains after 14.5 years.

47. $\log_b(p) + \log_b(6p) - \log_b(2p)$
$$\log_b[p(6p)] - \log_b(2p)$$
$$\log_b(6p^2) - \log_b(2p)$$
$$\log_b\left(\frac{6p^2}{2p}\right)$$
$$\log_b(3p)$$

48. $3\log_b(2x) + 2\log_b(3x)$
$$\log_b(2x)^3 + \log_b(3x)^2$$
$$\log_b[(2x)^3(3x)^2]$$
$$\log_b[72x^5]$$

49. $4\log_b\left(x^2\right) - 2\log_b\left(x^5\right)$
$$\log_b\left(x^2\right)^4 - \log_b\left(x^5\right)^2$$
$$\log_b\left(\frac{x^8}{x^{10}}\right)$$
$$\log_b\left(\frac{1}{x^2}\right)$$

50. $\dfrac{\log_b(w)}{\log_b(y)} = \log_y(w)$

51. $\log_b(b^5) - \log_b(b^2) = 5 - 2 = 3$

$3 = 3$

$\dfrac{\log_b(b^5)}{\log_b(b^2)} = \dfrac{5}{2}$

$\log_b(b^3) = 3$

$\log_b(b^5) = 5$

$\log_b\left(\dfrac{b^5}{b^2}\right) = \log_b(b^3)$

$= 3$

The expressions $\log_b(b^5) - \log_b(b^2) = 5 - 2 = 3$,

3, $\log_b(b^3) = 3$, and $\log_b\left(\dfrac{b^5}{b^2}\right) = \log_b(b^3) = 3$ are

all equal.

52. $\log_2(x^2) + \log_2(2x) = 4$

$\log_2(x^2 \cdot 2x) = 4$

$\log_2(2x^3) = 4$

$2x^3 = 2^4$

$2x^3 = 16$

$x^3 = 8$

$x = 2$

53. $2\log_9(3w) + 3\log_9(w^2) = 5$

$\log_9(3w)^2 + \log_9(w^2)^3 = 5$

$\log_9\left[(9w^2)(w^6)\right] = 5$

$\log_9(9w^8) = 5$

$9w^8 = 9^5$

$w^8 = \dfrac{9^5}{9}$

$w = \left(9^4\right)^{\frac{1}{8}}$

$= \pm 3$

Substitute each answer into the original equation. Because the equation is defined only for $w = 3$, the only solution is 3.

54. $5\log_6(2x) - 3\log_6(4x) = 2$

$\log_6(2x)^5 - \log_6(4x)^3 = 2$

$\log_6\left(\dfrac{32x^5}{64x^3}\right) = 2$

$\log_6\left(\dfrac{x^2}{2}\right) = 2$

$\dfrac{x^2}{2} = 6^2$

$x^2 = 2 \cdot 36$

$x = (72)^{\frac{1}{2}}$

≈ 8.4853

55. $3\ln(4x) + 2\ln(2x)$

$= \ln(4x)^3 + \ln(2x)^2$

$= \ln\left[(64x^3)(4x^2)\right]$

$= \ln(256x^5)$

56. $\ln(2m^7) - 4\ln(m^3) + 3\ln(m^2)$

$= \ln(2m^7) - \ln(m^3)^4 + \ln(m^2)^3$

$= \ln\left[\dfrac{(2m^7)(m^6)}{(m^{12})}\right]$

$= \ln(2m)$

57. $4e^x = 75$

$e^x = \dfrac{75}{4}$

$x = \ln\left(\dfrac{75}{4}\right)$

≈ 2.9312

58. $-3\ln(p) + 7 = 1$

$-3\ln(p) = -6$

$\ln(p) = 2$

$e^2 = p$

$7.3891 \approx p$

59. $\ln(3x+1) = 2$

$3x+1 = e^2$

$3x = e^2 - 1$

$x = \dfrac{e^2 - 1}{3} \approx 2.1297$

60. $3\ln(t^5) - 5\ln(2t) = 7$

$\ln(t^5)^3 - \ln(2t)^5 = 7$

$\ln\left(\dfrac{t^{15}}{32t^5}\right) = 7$

$\dfrac{t^{10}}{32} = e^7$

$t^{10} = 32e^7$

$t = (32e^7)^{\frac{1}{10}}$

≈ 2.8479

61. $e^{3x-8} = 12$

$3x - 8 = \ln(12)$

$3x = 8 + \ln(12)$

$x = \dfrac{8 + \ln(12)}{3} \approx 3.4950$

Chapter 11 Test

1.

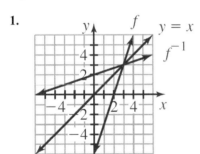

2.

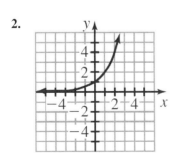

3. a. Using the linear regression feature on a graphing calculator, $f(t) = 4.09t + 42.28$.

b. $f(5) = 4.09(5) + 42.28 = 62.73$

An adult ticket cost about \$62.73 in 2005.

c. Replace $f(t)$ with p.

$f(t) = 4.09t + 42.28$

Solve for t.

$p = 4.09t + 42.28$

$p - 42.28 = 4.09t$

$\dfrac{p - 42.28}{4.09} = \dfrac{4.09t}{4.09}$

$0.24p - 10.34 \approx t$

An approximate equation is

$t = 0.24p - 10.34$.

Replace t with $f^{-1}(p)$.

$f^{-1}(p) = 0.24p - 10.34$

d. $f^{-1}(p) = 0.24p - 10.34$

$f^{-1}(100) = 0.24(100) - 10.34$

$= 13.66$

An adult one-day ticket will be \$100 in $1990 + 14 = 2014$.

e. 0.24; the slope shows that the ticket price increases by \$1 every 0.24 years.

4. $g(x) = 2x - 9$

Replace $g(x)$ with y.

$y = 2x - 9$

Solve for x:

$2x = y + 9$

$x = \dfrac{y + 9}{2}$

Replace x with $g^{-1}(y)$.

$g^{-1}(y) = \dfrac{1}{2}y + \dfrac{9}{2}$

Write in terms of x.

$g^{-1}(x) = \dfrac{1}{2}x + \dfrac{9}{2}$

5. $\log_2(16) = 4$, since $2^4 = 16$.

6. $\log_4\left(\dfrac{1}{64}\right) = -3$, since $4^{-3} = \dfrac{1}{64}$.

7.
$$\log_7(10) = \frac{\log(10)}{\log(7)}$$
$$\approx 1.1833$$

8. $\log(0.1) = -1$, since $10^{-1} = 0.1$.

9. $\log_b(\sqrt{b}) = \frac{1}{2}$, since $b^{\frac{1}{2}} = \sqrt{b}$.

10. $\ln\left(\frac{1}{e^2}\right) = -2$, since $e^{-2} = \frac{1}{e^2}$.

11. $h(x) = 4^x$
$$h^{-1}(x) = \log_4(x)$$

12. $f(x) = \log_5(x)$
$$f^{-1}(x) = 5^x$$

13. $\log_s(w) = t$

14. $c^d = a$

15. $\log_b(50) = 4$
$$b^4 = 50$$
$$b = (50)^{\frac{1}{4}}$$
$$\approx 2.6591$$

16. $6(2)^x - 9 = 23$
$$6(2)^x = 32$$
$$2^x = \frac{32}{6}$$
$$\log(2^x) = \log\left(\frac{32}{6}\right)$$
$$x\log(2) = \log\left(\frac{32}{6}\right)$$
$$x = \frac{\log\left(\frac{32}{6}\right)}{\log(2)}$$
$$\approx 2.4150$$

17.
$$\log_4(7p+5) = -\frac{3}{2}$$
$$7p+5 = 4^{-\frac{3}{2}}$$
$$7p = 4^{-\frac{3}{2}} - 5$$
$$p = \frac{4^{-\frac{3}{2}} - 5}{7}$$
$$= -0.6964$$

18. Graph $y = 4^x - 8$ and $y = -\frac{1}{2}x + 3$. Then use "intersect."

Intersection
X=1.6726743 Y=2.1636629

The *x*-coordinate, 1.67, is the approximate solution of the equation
$$4^x - 8 = -\frac{1}{2}x + 3.$$

19. a. By regression:
Linear: $f(t) = 605.05t - 5640.44$
Quadratic:
$f(t) = 13.67t^2 - 219.34t + 1153.34$
Exponential: $f(t) = 650.17(1.074)^t$
(Your equations may be slightly different if you calculated the answers manually.)
The quadratic model fits the data quite well; the exponential model fits the data fairly well; the linear model does not fit the data well.

b. The exponential function.

c. The base is 1.074. The tuition rate is growing at a rate of about 7.4% per year. (Your answer may be slightly different if you chose different points.)

d. $f(t) = 650.17(1.074)^{64}$
$$\approx 62,705$$
According to this model, the tuition in 2014 is predicted to be $62,705. (Your answer may be slightly different if you chose different points.)

e.

$$f(t) = 650.17(1.074)^t$$

$$70000 = 650.17(1.074)^t$$

$$\frac{70000}{650.17} = \frac{650.17(1.074)^{tt}}{650.17}$$

$$\log\left(\frac{70000}{650.17}\right) = \log(1.074)^t$$

$$\frac{\log\left(\frac{70000}{650.17}\right)}{\log(1.074)} = \frac{t\log(1.074)}{\log(1.074)}$$

$$65.54 \approx t$$

According to this model, the tuition is predicted to be $70,000 in 1950 + 66 = 2016. (Your answer may be slightly different if you chose different points.)

20. Use an exponential decay model $f(t) = ab^t$. Every 5730 years the amount of carbon-14 is halved so the base is $\frac{1}{2}$ and the exponent is $\frac{t}{5730}$. 78.04% of the carbon-14 remains, so $f(t)$ = 78.04:

$$f(t) = 100\left(\frac{1}{2}\right)^{\frac{t}{5730}}$$

$$78.04 = 100\left(\frac{1}{2}\right)^{\frac{t}{5730}}$$

$$\left(\frac{78.04}{100}\right) = \left(\frac{1}{2}\right)^{\frac{t}{5730}}$$

$$\log\left(\frac{78.04}{100}\right) = \left(\frac{t}{5730}\right)\log\left(\frac{1}{2}\right)$$

$$(5730)\frac{\log\left(\frac{78.04}{100}\right)}{\log\left(\frac{1}{2}\right)} = \frac{t}{5730}(5760)$$

$$2049.70 \approx t$$

The mummy is about 2050 years old.

21. $\log_b(x^3) + \log_b(5x)$

$$\log_b[x^3(5x)]$$

$$\log_b(5x^4)$$

22. $3\log_b\left(4p^2\right) - 2\log_b\left(8w^5\right) + \log_b\left(2p^4\right)$

$$\log_b\left(4p^2\right)^3 - \log_b\left(8w^5\right)^2 + \log_b\left(2p^4\right)$$

$$\log_b\left[\frac{\left(64p^6\right)\left(2p^4\right)}{64w^{10}}\right]$$

$$\log_b\left(\frac{2p^{10}}{w^{10}}\right)$$

23. $\log_3(x) + \log_3(2x) = 5$

$$\log_3[x(2x)] = 5$$

$$\log_3(2x^2) = 5$$

$$2x^2 = 3^5$$

$$x^2 = \frac{243}{2}$$

$$x = \left(\frac{243}{2}\right)^{\frac{1}{2}}$$

$$\approx 11.0227$$

24. $2\log_4(x^4) - 3\log_4(3x) = 3$

$$\log_4(x^4)^2 - \log_4(3x)^3 = 3$$

$$\log_4(x^8) - \log_4(27x^3) = 3$$

$$\log_4\left(\frac{x^8}{27x^3}\right) = 3$$

$$\log_4\left(\frac{x^5}{27}\right) = 3$$

$$\frac{x^5}{27} = 4^3$$

$$x^5 = 27 \cdot 4^3$$

$$x = \left(27 \cdot 4^3\right)^{\frac{1}{5}}$$

$$\approx 4.4413$$

25. $2\ln(5w) + 3\ln\left(w^6\right)$

$$\ln(5w)^2 + \ln\left(w^6\right)^3$$

$$\ln\left[\left(25w^2\right)\left(w^{18}\right)\right]$$

$$\ln\left(25w^{20}\right)$$

26. $2e^{3x-1} = 54$

$$e^{3x-1} = 27$$
$$\ln(e^{3x-1}) = \ln(27)$$
$$(3x-1)\ln e = \ln(27)$$
$$3x-1 = \ln(27)$$
$$3x = \ln(27)+1$$
$$x = \frac{\ln(27)+1}{3}$$
$$\approx 1.4319$$

27. $7\ln(x-2)-1 = 4$

$$7\ln(x-2) = 5$$
$$\ln(x-2) = \frac{5}{7}$$
$$x-2 = e^{\frac{5}{7}}$$
$$x = e^{\frac{5}{7}}+2$$
$$\approx 4.0427$$

Cumulative Review of Chapters 1 – 11

1. $2(4)^{5x-1} = 17$

$$(4)^{5x-1} = \frac{17}{2}$$
$$\log(4^{5x-1}) = \log\left(\frac{17}{2}\right)$$
$$(5x-1)\log(4) = \log\left(\frac{17}{2}\right)$$
$$5x-1 = \frac{\log\left(\frac{17}{2}\right)}{\log(4)}$$
$$5x = \frac{\log\left(\frac{17}{2}\right)}{\log(4)}+1$$
$$x = \frac{\frac{\log\left(\frac{17}{2}\right)}{\log(4)}+1}{5}$$
$$\approx 0.5087$$

2. $(x-2)(x+4) = 7$

$$x^2+2x-8 = 7$$
$$x^2+2x-15 = 0$$
$$(x+5)(x-3) = 0$$
$$x+5 = 0 \text{ or } x-3 = 0$$
$$x = -5 \qquad x = 3$$

3. $\log_3(x-5) = 4$

$$x-5 = 3^4$$
$$x = 81+5$$
$$x = 86$$

4. $3b^7-18 = 7$

$$3b^7 = 25$$
$$b^7 = \frac{25}{3}$$
$$b = \left(\frac{25}{3}\right)^{\frac{1}{7}}$$
$$\approx 1.3538$$

5. $3x^2 = 7-2x$

$$3x^2+2x-7 = 0$$
$$a = 3, b = 2, c = -7$$
$$x = \frac{-2\pm\sqrt{(2)^2-4(3)(-7)}}{2(3)}$$
$$x = \frac{-2\pm\sqrt{88}}{6} = \frac{-1\pm\sqrt{22}}{3}$$
$$x = 1.2301, -1.8968$$

6. $8+2e^x = 15$

$$2e^x = 7$$
$$e^x = \frac{7}{2}$$
$$\ln(e^x) = \ln\left(\frac{7}{2}\right)$$
$$x = \ln\left(\frac{7}{2}\right)$$
$$\approx 1.2528$$

7. $2(x-5)^2 - 1 = 6$

$2(x^2 - 10x + 25) - 1 = 6$

$2x^2 - 20x + 50 - 1 = 6$

$2x^2 - 20x + 49 = 6$

$2x^2 - 20x + 43 = 0$

$a = 2, b = -20, c = 43$

$x = \dfrac{-(-20) \pm \sqrt{(-20)^2 - 4(2)(43)}}{2(2)}$

$x = \dfrac{20 \pm \sqrt{56}}{4} = \dfrac{10 + \sqrt{14}}{2}$

$x = 6.8708, 3.1292$

8. $4\log_5(3x^2) + 3\log_5(6x^4) = 3$

$\log_5(3x^2)^4 + \log_5(6x^4)^3 = 3$

$\log_5(81x^8) + \log_5(216x^{12}) = 3$

$\log_5[(81x^8)(216x^{12})] = 3$

$\log_5(17496x^{20}) = 3$

$17496x^{20} = 5^3$

$x^{20} = \dfrac{125}{17496}$

$x = \pm\left(\dfrac{125}{17496}\right)^{\frac{1}{20}}$

$\approx \pm 0.7811$

9. $7 - 3(4w - 2) = 2(3w + 5) - 4(2w + 1)$

$7 - 12w + 6 = 6w + 10 - 8w - 4$

$13 - 12w = -2w + 6$

$7 = 10w$

$\dfrac{7}{10} = w$

10. $3x(2x - 1) + 1 = 2 - 4x^2$

$6x^2 - 3x + 1 = 2 - 4x^2$

$10x^2 - 3x - 1 = 0$

$(5x + 1)(2x - 1) = 0$

$5x + 1 = 0 \quad$ or $\quad 2x - 1 = 0$

$5x = -1 \qquad\qquad 2x = 1$

$x = -\dfrac{1}{5} = -0.2 \quad x = \dfrac{1}{2} = 0.5$

11. $2\ln(12x^9) - \ln(3x^3) = 5$

$\ln(12x^9)^2 - \ln(3x^3) = 5$

$\ln(144x^{18}) - \ln(3x^3) = 5$

$\ln\left(\dfrac{144x^{18}}{3x^3}\right) = 5$

$\ln(48x^{15}) = 5$

$48x^{15} = e^5$

$x^{15} = \dfrac{e^5}{48}$

$x = \left(\dfrac{e^5}{48}\right)^{1/15} \approx 1.0782$

12. $5x^2 - 4x = -3$

$5x^2 - 4x + 3 = 0$

$a = 5, b = -4, c = 3$

$x = \dfrac{-(-4) \pm \sqrt{(-4)^2 - 4(5)(3)}}{2(5)}$

$x = \dfrac{4 \pm \sqrt{-44}}{10} = \dfrac{4 \pm 2i\sqrt{11}}{10} = \dfrac{2}{5} \pm \dfrac{i\sqrt{11}}{5}$

13. $2x^2 + 5x - 2 = 0$

$2x^2 + 5x = 2$

$x^2 + \dfrac{5}{2}x = 1$

$x^2 + \dfrac{5}{2}x + \dfrac{25}{16} = 2 + \dfrac{25}{16}$

$\left(x + \dfrac{5}{4}\right)^2 = \dfrac{41}{16}$

$x + \dfrac{5}{4} = \pm\sqrt{\dfrac{41}{16}}$

$x + \dfrac{5}{4} = \pm\dfrac{\sqrt{41}}{4}$

$x = \dfrac{-5 \pm \sqrt{41}}{4}$

14. $(at - b)^2 = c$

$at - b = \pm\sqrt{c}$

$at = b \pm \sqrt{c}$

$t = \dfrac{b \pm \sqrt{c}}{a}$

15.

$x = 1$ because $y = 3^x$ and $y = 9\left(\dfrac{1}{3}\right)^x$ intersect

at $x = 1$.

16.

$x = 2$ because $y = 9\left(\dfrac{1}{3}\right)^x$ and $y = x - 1$

intersect at $x = 2$.

17. Substitute $x = 2y - 5$ into $4x - 5y = -14$.

$$4(2y - 5) - 5y = -14$$
$$8y - 20 - 5y = -14$$
$$3y = 6$$
$$y = 2$$

Find x.

$$x = 2(2) - 5$$
$$= -1$$

The solution is $(-1, 2)$.

18. Simplify $3(2 - 4x) = -10 - 2y$.

$$3(2 - 4x) = -10 - 2y$$
$$6 - 12x = -10 - 2y$$
$$-12x + 2y = -16$$

Multiply equation (2) by 6 and add.

$$-12x + 2y = -16$$
$$\underline{12x - 18y = -48}$$
$$-16y = -64$$
$$y = 4$$

Find x.

$$2x - 3(4) = -8$$
$$2x - 12 + 12 = -8 + 12$$
$$2x = 4$$
$$x = 2$$

The solution is $(2, 4)$.

19. $2x + 3y - 2z = 3$ (1)

$3x - y + 4z = 2$ (2) .

$5x - 2y + 3z = -5$ (3)

Multiply (2) by 3 and add to (1).

$11x + 10z = 9$ (4)

Multiply (2) by -2 and add to (3).

$-x - 5z = -9$ (5)

Isolate x in (5) and substitute in (4) to solve for z.

$$-x - 5z = -9$$
$$-x = 5z - 9$$
$$x = -5z + 9$$
$$11(-5z + 9) + 10z = 9$$
$$-55z + 99 + 10z = 9$$
$$-45z + 99 = 9$$
$$-45z = -90$$
$$z = 2$$

Substitute $z = 2$ into (5) and solve for x.

$$-x - 5(2) = -9$$
$$-x - 10 = -9$$
$$-x = 1$$
$$x = -1$$

Substitute $x = -1$ and $z = 2$ into (1) and solve for y.

$$2(-1) + 3y - 2(2) = 3$$
$$-2 + 3y - 4 = 3$$
$$3y = 9$$
$$y = 3$$

The solution is $x = -1$, $y = 3$, $z = 2$.

20. $4x - 3y = 24$

$$4x - 3(0) = 24$$
$$4x = 24$$
$$x = 6$$

The x-intercept is $(6, 0)$.

21. $y = 2x^2 - 5x - 12$

$$0 = 2x^2 - 5x - 12$$
$$0 = (2x + 3)(x - 4)$$
$$2x + 3 = 0 \quad x - 4 = 0$$
$$2x = -3 \qquad x = 4$$
$$x = -\frac{3}{2}$$

The x-intercepts are $(4, 0)$ and $(-1.5, 0)$.

22. $2x^2(3x - 5)(2x - 4)$

$$= 2x^2\left(6x^2 - 12x - 10x + 20\right)$$
$$= 2x^2\left(6x^2 - 22x + 20\right)$$
$$= 12x^4 - 44x^3 + 40x^2$$

23. $(4mt + 7r)(4mt - 7r) = (4mt)^2 - (7r)^2$
$$= 16m^2t^2 - 49r^2$$

24. $(5m-3n)^2 = (5m)^2 + 2\cdot5m\cdot(-3n) + (3n)^2$
$$= 25m^2 - 30mn + 9n^2$$

25. $f - g = 2x^2 - x + 5 - (3x^2 + 2x - 4)$
$$= 2x^2 - x + 5 - 3x^2 - 2x + 4$$
$$= -x^2 - 3x + 9$$
$(f-g)(-3) = -(-3)^2 - 3(-3) + 9$
$$= -9 + 9 + 9$$
$$= 9$$

26. $f \cdot g = (2x^2 - x + 5)(3x^2 + 2x - 4)$
$$= 6x^4 + 4x^3 - 8x^2 - 3x^3 - 2x^2 + 4x + 15x^2 f + 10x - 20$$
$$= 6x^4 + x^3 + 5x^2 + 14x - 20$$
$(f \cdot g)(2) = 6(2)^4 + (2)^3 + 5(2)^2 + 14(2) - 20$
$$= 96 + 8 + 20 + 28 - 20$$
$$= 132$$

27. $12x^3 - 20x^2 - 27x + 45$
$$= 4x^2(3x-5) - 9(3x-5)$$
$$= (4x^2 - 9)(3x - 5)$$
$$= (2x+3)(2x-3)(3x-5)$$

28. $3x^3y^2 + 6x^2y^3 - 24xy^4$
$$= 3xy^2(x^2 + 2xy - 8y^2)$$
$$= 3xy^2(x+4y)(x-2y)$$

29. $27x^3 + 64 = (3x)^3 + (4)^3$
$$= (3x+4)\left((3x)^2 - 3x \cdot 4 + (4)^2\right)$$
$$= (3x+4)(9x^2 - 12x + 16)$$

30. $8x - 3 \geq -3(4x-5)$
$$8x - 3 \geq -12x + 15$$
$$20x \geq 18$$
$$x \geq \frac{18}{20}$$
$$x \geq \frac{9}{10}$$
$$\left[\frac{9}{10}, \infty\right)$$

31. $5x - 3y > 6$
$$5x - 3y - 5x > 6 - 5x$$
$$-3y > -5x + 6$$
$$\frac{-3y}{-3} < \frac{-5x}{-3} + \frac{6}{-3}$$
$$y < \frac{5}{3}x - 2$$

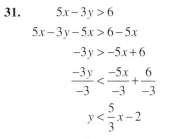

32.

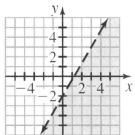

33. $(4b^{-3}c^2)^3(5b^{-7}c^{-1})^2$
$$(64b^{-9}c^6)(25b^{-14}c^{-2})$$
$$(64 \cdot 25)(b^{-9} \cdot b^{-14})(c^6 \cdot c^{-2})$$
$$1600b^{-23}c^4$$
$$\frac{1600c^4}{b^{23}}$$

34.
$$\frac{8b^{\frac{1}{3}}c^{-\frac{1}{2}}}{6b^{-\frac{1}{2}}c^{\frac{3}{4}}}$$

$$= \frac{4b^{\frac{1}{3}-\left(-\frac{1}{2}\right)}c^{-\frac{1}{2}-\frac{3}{4}}}{3}$$

$$= \frac{4b^{\frac{2}{6}+\frac{3}{6}}c^{-\frac{2}{4}-\frac{3}{4}}}{3}$$

$$= \frac{4b^{\frac{5}{6}}c^{-\frac{5}{4}}}{3}$$

$$= \frac{4b^{\frac{5}{6}}}{3c^{\frac{5}{4}}}$$

35. $4\log_b\left(x^7\right) - 2\log_b\left(7x\right)$

$$= \log_b\left(x^7\right)^4 - \log_b\left(7x\right)^2$$

$$= \log_b\left(x^{28}\right) - \log_b\left(49x^2\right)$$

$$= \log_b\left(\frac{x^{28}}{49x^2}\right)$$

$$= \log_b\left(\frac{x^{26}}{49}\right)$$

36. $3\ln\left(p^6\right) + 4\ln\left(p^2\right)$

$$= \ln\left(p^6\right)^3 + \ln\left(p^2\right)^4$$

$$= \ln\left(p^{18}\right) + \ln\left(p^8\right)$$

$$= \ln\left[\left(p^{18}\right)\left(p^8\right)\right]$$

$$= \ln\left(p^{26}\right)$$

37. $f(x) = 5(3)^x$

38. $g(x) = 3x + 25$

39. 76

40. $k^{-1}(5) = 8$, since $k(8) = 5$.

41.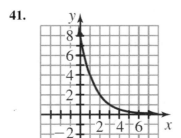

42.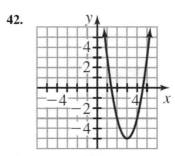

43.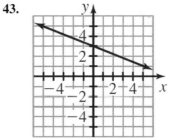

44.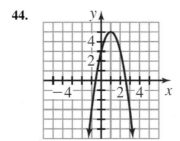

45.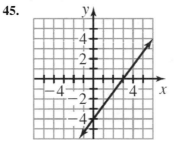

46.

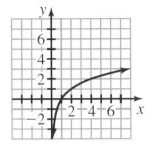

47. First find the slope.

$$m = \frac{-3-7}{5+4}$$

$$= -\frac{10}{9}$$

So $y = -\frac{10}{9}x + b$. Substitute a point, say $(-4, 7)$, to solve for b.

$$7 = -\frac{10}{9}(-4) + b$$

$$7 = \frac{40}{9} + b$$

$$7 - \frac{40}{9} = b$$

$$\frac{63}{9} - \frac{40}{9} = b$$

$$b = \frac{23}{9}$$

So the equation is $y = -\frac{10}{9}x + \frac{23}{9}$.

48. Substitute given points into $y = ax^2 + bx + c$.

$$(2,4): 4 = a(2)^2 + b(2) + c$$

$$(3,14): 14 = a(3)^2 + b(3) + c$$

$$(4,30): 30 = a(4)^2 + b(4) + c$$

Simplify these equations:

$$4a + 2b + c = 4 \qquad (1)$$

$$9a + 3b + c = 14 \qquad (2)$$

$$16a + 4b + c = 30 \qquad (3)$$

Eliminate c by multiplying both sides of equation (1) by -1:

$$-4a - 2b - c = -4 \qquad (4)$$

Adding the left sides and right sides of equations (2) and (4) gives:

$$5a + b = 10 \qquad (5)$$

Adding the left sides and right sides of equations

(3) and (4) gives:

$$12a + 2b = 26 \qquad (6)$$

Simplify:

$$6a + b = 13 \qquad (7)$$

Eliminate b by multiplying equation (5) by -1 and add each side to the corresponding side of equation (7):

$$a = 3$$

Next, substitute 3 for a in equation (5):

$$5(3) + b = 10$$

$$b = -5$$

Then, substitute 3 for a and -5 for b in equation (1):

$$4a + 2b + c = 4$$

$$4(3) + 2(-5) + c = 4$$

$$12 - 10 + c = 4$$

$$c = 2$$

Therefore, $a = 3$, $b = -5$, and $c = 2$. So, the equation is $y = 3x^2 - 5x + 2$.

49. Both points satisfy the equation $y = ab^x$. This produces a system of equations.

$$13 = ab^7$$

$$85 = ab^3$$

Combine the equations.

$$\frac{13}{85} = \frac{ab^7}{ab^3}$$

$$\frac{13}{85} = b^4$$

$$b = \left(\frac{13}{85}\right)^{\frac{1}{4}}$$

$$b \approx 0.62536$$

Substitute this value of the base into the equation $y = a(0.62536)^x$. Substitute $(3, 85)$ to find a.

$$85 = a(0.62536)^3$$

$$a = \frac{85}{(0.62536)^3}$$

$$a \approx 347.56$$

So the equation is $y = 347.56(0.63)^x$.

50.

$$f(-4) = 2(3)^{-4} = \frac{2}{81}$$

51.

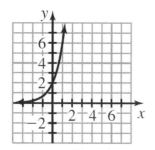

52.

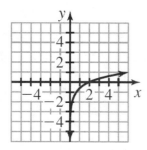

53. $f^{-1}(35)$

$$2(3)^x = 35$$

$$3^x - \frac{35}{2}$$

$$\log(3^x) = \log\left(\frac{35}{2}\right)$$

$$x\log(3) = \log\left(\frac{35}{2}\right)$$

$$x = \frac{\log\left(\frac{35}{2}\right)}{\log(3)}$$

$$\approx 2.6053$$

54. $\log_3\left(\frac{1}{81}\right) = -4$, since $3^{-4} = \frac{1}{81}$.

55. $\log_b\left(\sqrt[7]{b}\right) = \frac{1}{7}$, since $b^{\frac{1}{7}} = \sqrt[7]{b}$.

56. $f(-1) = 1$

57. The y-intercept is $(0, 2)$. So the equation is $y = 2b^x$. Substitute $(-1, 1)$ to find b.

$$1 = 2b^{-1}$$

$$b^{-1} = \frac{1}{2}$$

$$b = \left(\frac{1}{2}\right)^{-1}$$

$$b = 2$$

So the equation is $f(x) = 2(2)^x$ or $f(x) = (2)^{x+1}$.

58.

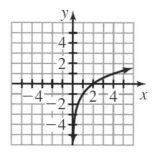

59. $f^{-1}(2)$

$$2 = 2(2)^x$$

$$2^x = 1$$

$$\log(2^x) = \log(1)$$

$$x\log(2) = 0$$

$$x = \frac{0}{\log(2)}$$

$$= 0$$

60. $f(x) = \frac{2}{7}x - 3$

Replace $f(x)$ with y.

$$y = \frac{2}{7}x - 3$$

Solve for x.

$$y + 3 = \frac{2}{7}x$$

$$\frac{7}{2}(y + 3) = x$$

$$x = \frac{7}{2}y + \frac{21}{2}$$

Replace x with $f^{-1}(y)$.

$$f^{-1}(y) = \frac{7}{2}y + \frac{21}{2}$$

Replace y with x.

$$f^{-1}(x) = \frac{7}{2}x + \frac{21}{2}$$

61. $g(x) = 8^x$

Replace $g(x)$ with y:

$y = 8^x$

Solve for x:

$\log(y) = \log(8^x)$

$\log(y) = x \log(8)$

$x = \dfrac{\log(y)}{\log(8)} = \log_8(y)$

Replace x with $g^{-1}(y)$:

$g^{-1}(y) == \log_8(y)$

Replace y with x:

$g^{-1}(x) = \log_8(x)$

62. a. The y-intercept for both functions is $(0, 2)$.

b. For f, as the value of x increases by 1, the value of $f(x)$ increases by 3.

For g, as the value of x increases by 1, the value of $g(x)$ is multiplied by 3.

c. g. Raising 3 to a large power (as happens in g for large x values) will yield a larger number than multiplying that number by 3 (as happens in f).

d.

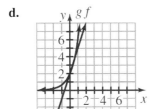

63. a. $f(2) = 3(2)$

$\qquad = 6$

$g(2) = 3^2$

$\qquad = 9$

b. Find f^{-1}.

$f(x) = 3x$

Replace $f(x)$ with y.

$y = 3x$

Solve for x:

$x = \dfrac{1}{3} y$

Replace x with $f^{-1}(y)$.

$f^{-1}(y) = \dfrac{1}{3} y$

Replace y with x.

$f^{-1}(x) = \dfrac{1}{3} x$

Find g^{-1}.

$g(x) = 3^x$

Replace $g(x)$ with y:

$y = 3^x$

Solve for x:

$\log(y) = \log(3^x)$

$\log(y) = x \log(3)$

$x = \dfrac{\log(y)}{\log(3)} = \log_3(y)$

Replace x with $g^{-1}(y)$:

$g^{-1}(y) == \log_3(y)$

Replace y with x:

$g^{-1}(x) = \log_3(x)$

c. $f^{-1}(81) = \dfrac{1}{3}(81) = 27$

$g^{-1}(81) = \log_3(81) = 4$, since $3^4 - 81$

64. a. $U(x) = 0.69x + 19.95$

$B(x) = 0.45x + 29.95$

b. The slope of the graph of U is 0.69, so U-Haul charges \$0.69 per mile. The slope of the graph of B is 0.45, so Budget charges \$0.45 per mile.

c. $0.69x + 19.95 = 0.45x + 29.95$

$0.24x = 10$

$x = \dfrac{10}{0.24}$

≈ 41.67 miles

65. Write the system.
$$x + y = 15000$$
$$43x + 60y = 721500$$
Use substitution.
$$43(15000 - y) + 60y = 721500$$
$$645000 - 43y + 60y = 721500$$
$$17y = 76500$$
$$y = 4500$$
Find x.
$$x + 4500 = 15000$$
$$x = 10500$$
10,500 tickets at \$43 and 4500 tickets at \$60

66. a. $f(t) = 35(1.17)^t$, where $t = 0$ in 2007.

b. The n-intercept is the value when $t = 0$, which is 35. This represents the number in thousands of homes built by Habitat for Humanity in 2007.

c. 1.17; the number of homes built by Habitat for Humanity has increased by 17% per year.

d.
$$f(t) = 35(1.17)^t$$
$$90 = 35(1.17)^t$$
$$\frac{90}{35} = \frac{35(1.17)^t}{35}$$
$$\log\left(\frac{90}{35}\right) = \log(1.17)^t$$
$$\frac{\log\left(\frac{90}{35}\right)}{\log(1.17)} = \frac{t\log(1.17)}{\log(1.17)}$$
$$6.02 \approx t$$
The model predicts that there will be 90 thousand homes built in $2007 + 6 = 2013$.

67. a. By regression, the linear equation is $f(t) = -1.06t + 67.34$, the quadratic equation is $f(t) = 0.023t^2 - 2.49t + 82.86$, and the exponential equation is $f(t) = 78.48(0.97)^t$.

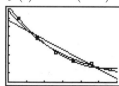

The exponential and quadratic models fit the data best.

b. The exponential equation best models the situation for years after 2006. The linear model is in negative values for years after 2006, and the quadratic model is increasing for years after 2006.

c. The n-intercept is (0, 78.48), which means there were about 78.5 thousand tuberculosis cases in the United States in 1950.

d. The percent rate of decay is $1 - 0.97 = 0.03$, or about 3%. The number of tuberculosis cases is decreasing by about 3% per year.

e. $f(11) = 78.48(0.97)^{11}$
$$= 56.14$$
There were 56,140 tuberculosis cases in 1961.

f. To find $f^{-1}(11)$, substitute 11 for f and solve for t.
$$f(t) = 78.48(0.97)^t$$
$$11 = 78.48(0.97)^t$$
$$\frac{11}{78.48} = \frac{78.48(0.97)^t}{78.48}$$
$$\log\left(\frac{11}{78.48}\right) = \log(0.97)^t$$
$$\frac{\log\left(\frac{11}{78.48}\right)}{\log(0.97)} = \frac{t\log(0.97)}{\log(0.97)}$$
$$64.51 \approx t$$
There will be 11,000 tuberculosis cases in $1950 + 65 = 2015$.

g. In 1950, $t = 0$.

$$f(0) = 78.48(0.97)^0$$
$$= 78.48$$

So, there are 78,480 tuberculosis cases in 1950.

Find when 39,240 cases (which is exactly half 78,480) are predicted,

$$f(t) = 78.48(0.97)^t$$
$$39.24 = 78.48(0.97)^t$$
$$\frac{39.24}{78.48} = \frac{78.48(0.97)^t}{78.48}$$
$$\log\left(\frac{39.24}{78.48}\right) = \log(0.97)^t$$
$$\frac{\log\left(\frac{39.24}{78.48}\right)}{\log(0.97)} = \frac{t\log(0.97)}{\log(0.97)}$$
$$22.76 \approx t$$

The approximate half-life of the number of cases is 22.76 years.

68. a. Using the linear regression feature on a graphing calculator, $f(t) = 1.3t + 102.5$.

b. The slope is 1.3. The slope means the average maximum speed increases by 1.3 miles per hour each year.

c.
$$f(t) = 1.3t + 102.5$$
$$0 = 1.3t + 102.5$$
$$\frac{-102.5}{1.3} = \frac{1.3t}{1.3}$$
$$-78.85 \approx t$$

The *t*-intercept, $(-78.85, 0)$, tells when the average maximum speed was 0, which was $1980 - 79 = 1901$. Model breakdown has occurred.

d. $f(33) = 1.3(33) + 102.5 = 145.4$

In $1980 + 33 = 2013$, the average maximum speed will be about 145 miles per hour.

e. Replace *f(t)* with *s*.
$$s = 1.3t + 102.5$$
Solve for *t*.

$$s = 1.3t + 102.5$$
$$s - 102.5 = 1.3t$$
$$\frac{s - 102.5}{1.3} = \frac{1.3t}{1.3}$$
$$0.77s - 78.85 \approx t$$

Replace t with $f^{-1}(s)$.

An approximate equation is
$$f^{-1}(s) = 0.77s - 78.85.$$

f. $f^{-1}(148) = 0.77(148) - 78.85 = 35.11$

In $1980 + 35 = 2015$, the average maximum speed will be 148 miles per hour.

69. a. Using the quadratic regression feature on a graphing calculator,
$$f(t) = -0.0195t^2 + 1.58t - 10.20.$$

b. $-0.0195t^2 + 1.58t - 10.20 = 0$

$a = -0.0195, b = 1.58, c = -10.2$

$$t = \frac{-1.58 \pm \sqrt{(1.58)^2 - 4(-0.0195)(-10.2)}}{2(-0.0195)}$$
$$t = \frac{1.58 \pm \sqrt{1.7008}}{0.039}$$
$$t = 7.07, 73.95$$

The t-intercepts are (7.7, 0) and (73.95 0). This means that there are no 7-year-olds or 74-year-olds visting online trading sites. Model breakdown has occurred.

c.
$$-\frac{b}{2a} = -\frac{1.58}{2(-0.0195)} = 40.51$$

$f(40.51)$
$$= -0.0195(40.51)^2 + 1.58(40.5)1 - 10.20$$
$$= 21.8$$

The vertex is (40.51, 21.8). According to the model, this means that about 21.8% of 41-year-old adults visit online trading sites, the highest percentage for any age group. In reality, the highest percentage occurs among 25 to 34-year-olds, at 22.9%.

d. $f(19) = -0.0195(19)^2 + 1.58(19) - 10.20$
$$\approx 12.78$$

About 12.8% of 19-year-old Americans visit online trading sites.

e. $18 = -0.0195t^2 + 1.58t - 10.20$

$-0.0195t^2 + 1.58t - 28.2 = 0$

$a = -0.0195, b = 1.58, c = -28.2$

$$t = \frac{-1.58 \pm \sqrt{(1.58)^2 - 4(-0.0195)(-28.2)}}{2(-0.0195)}$$

$$t = \frac{1.58 \pm \sqrt{0.2968}}{0.039}$$

$t \approx 26.54, 54.48$

This groups includes 27-year-old and 54-year-old Americans.

Chapter 12
Rational Functions

1.
$$f(-1) = \frac{(-1)+1}{(-1)^2 - 9}$$
$$= \frac{0}{1-9}$$
$$= \frac{0}{-8}$$
$$= 0$$

$$f(2) = \frac{(2)+1}{(2)^2 - 9}$$
$$= \frac{3}{4-9}$$
$$= \frac{3}{-5}$$
$$= -\frac{3}{5}$$

$$f(3) = \frac{(3)+1}{(3)^2 - 9}$$
$$= \frac{4}{9-9}$$
$$= \frac{4}{0}$$
$f(3)$ is undefined.

3.
$$f(-1) = \frac{(-1)^3 - 8}{2(-1)^2 + 3(-1) - 1}$$
$$= \frac{-1-8}{2-3-1}$$
$$= \frac{-9}{-2}$$
$$= \frac{9}{2}$$

$$f(0) = \frac{(0)^3 - 8}{2(0)^2 + 3(0) - 1}$$
$$= \frac{0-8}{-1}$$
$$= \frac{-8}{-1}$$
$$= 8$$

$$f(3) = \frac{(3)^3 - 8}{2(3)^2 + 3(3) - 1}$$
$$= \frac{27-8}{2(9)+9-1}$$
$$= \frac{19}{26}$$

5. The only value that will make the function undefined (i.e., the denominator 0) is 0. Therefore, the domain is the set of all real numbers except 0.

7. Since there are no values that will make the function undefined, the domain is the set of all real numbers.

9. $x + 3 = 0$
$x = -3$
Since -3 is the only value that will make the function undefined, the domain is the set of all real numbers except -3.

11. $2x + 1 = 0$
$2x = -1$
$$x = -\frac{1}{2}$$
The domain is the set of all real numbers except $-\frac{1}{2}$.

13. $x^2 - 3x - 10 = 0$
$(x-5)(x+2) = 0$
$x - 5 = 0 \qquad x + 2 = 0$
$x = 5 \qquad x = -2$
The domain is the set of all real numbers

except 5 and -2.

15.
$$x^2 - 16 = 0$$
$$(x+4)(x-4) = 0$$
$$x+4=0 \quad \text{or} \quad x-4=0$$
$$x=-4 \quad \text{or} \quad x=4$$
The domain is the set of all real numbers except -4 and 4.

17.
$$4x^2 - 25 = 0$$
$$(2x-5)(2x+5) = 0$$
$$2x-5=0 \quad 2x+5=0$$
$$2x=5 \quad 2x=-5$$
$$x=\frac{5}{2} \quad x=-\frac{5}{2}$$
The domain is the set of all real numbers except $\dfrac{5}{2}$ and $-\dfrac{5}{2}$.

19. $x^2 + 1 = 0$
$$x^2 = -1$$
This equation has no real number solution. The domain is the set of all real numbers.

21. $2x^2 - 7x - 15 = 0$
$$(x-5)(2x+3) = 0$$
$$x-5=0 \quad 2x+3=0$$
$$x=5 \quad 2x=-3$$
$$x=5 \quad x=-\frac{3}{2}$$
The domain is the set of all real numbers except 5 and $-\dfrac{3}{2}$.

23. $x^2 - 3x + 6 = 0$
$$x = \frac{-(-3) \pm \sqrt{(-3)^2 - 4(1)(6)}}{6}$$
$$= \frac{3 \pm \sqrt{9-24}}{6}$$
$$= \frac{3 \pm \sqrt{-15}}{6}$$
Since the solution is not real, the domain is the set of all real numbers.

25. $3x^2 - 2x - 7 = 0$
$$x = \frac{2 \pm \sqrt{4 - 4(3)(-7)}}{6}$$
$$x = \frac{2 \pm \sqrt{4+84}}{6}$$
$$x = \frac{2 \pm \sqrt{88}}{6}$$
$$x = \frac{2 \pm \sqrt{4 \cdot 22}}{6}$$
$$x = \frac{2 \pm 2\sqrt{22}}{6}$$
$$x = \frac{1 \pm \sqrt{22}}{3}$$
The domain is the set of all real numbers except $\dfrac{1+\sqrt{22}}{3}$ and $\dfrac{1-\sqrt{22}}{3}$.

27.
$$4x^3 - 8x^2 - 9x + 18 = 0$$
$$4x^2(x-2) - 9(x-2) = 0$$
$$(x-2)\left(4x^2 - 9\right) = 0$$
$$(x-2)(2x-3)(2x+3) = 0$$
$$x-2=0 \quad 2x-3=0 \quad 2x+3=0$$
$$x=2 \quad 2x=3 \quad 2x=-3$$
$$x=2 \quad x=\frac{3}{2} \quad x=-\frac{3}{2}$$
The domain is the set of all real numbers except 2, $\dfrac{3}{2}$ and $-\dfrac{3}{2}$.

29. $f(x) = \dfrac{4x}{6} = \dfrac{\cancel{2} \cdot 2 \cdot x}{\cancel{2} \cdot 3} = \dfrac{2x}{3}$

31. $f(x) = \dfrac{20x^7}{15x^4} = \dfrac{\cancel{5} \cdot 4 \cdot \cancel{x} \cdot \cancel{x} \cdot \cancel{x} \cdot \cancel{x} \cdot x \cdot x \cdot x}{\cancel{5} \cdot 3 \cdot \cancel{x} \cdot \cancel{x} \cdot \cancel{x} \cdot \cancel{x}}$
$$= \frac{4x^3}{3}$$

33. $f(x) = \dfrac{4x-28}{5x-35} = \dfrac{4\cancel{(x-7)}}{5\cancel{(x-7)}}$
$$= \frac{4}{5}$$

35.
$$f(x) = \frac{x^2 + 7x + 10}{x^2 - 7x - 18} = \frac{(x+5)(x+2)}{(x-9)(x+2)}$$
$$= \frac{x+5}{x-9}$$

37.
$$f(x) = \frac{x^2 - 49}{x^2 - 14x + 49} = \frac{(x-7)(x+7)}{(x-7)(x-7)}$$
$$= \frac{x+7}{x-7}$$

39.
$$f(x) = \frac{16x^2 - 25}{8x^2 - 22x + 15} = \frac{(4x-5)(4x+5)}{(4x-5)(2x-3)}$$
$$= \frac{4x+5}{2x-3}$$

41.
$$f(x) = \frac{x-5}{5-x} = \frac{x-5}{-1(x-5)}$$
$$= \frac{1}{-1}$$
$$= -1$$

43.
$$f(x) = \frac{4x-12}{18-6x} = \frac{4(x-3)}{-6(x-3)}$$
$$= \frac{4}{-6}$$
$$= -\frac{2}{3}$$

45.
$$f(x) = \frac{6x-18}{9-x^2} = \frac{6(x-3)}{(3-x)(3+x)}$$
$$= \frac{6(x-3)}{-1(x-3)(x+3)}$$
$$= -\frac{6}{x+3}$$

47.
$$f(x) = \frac{x^3 + 4x^2}{7x^2 + 28x}$$
$$= \frac{x^2(x+4)}{7x(x+4)}$$
$$= \frac{x \cdot x \cdot (x+4)}{7 \cdot x \cdot (x+4)}$$
$$= \frac{x}{7}$$

49.
$$f(x) = \frac{x^2 + 2x - 35}{-x^2 + 3x + 10} = \frac{x^2 + 2x - 35}{-1(x^2 - 3x - 10)}$$
$$= \frac{(x-5)(x+7)}{-1(x-5)(x+2)}$$
$$= -\frac{x+7}{(x+2)}$$

51.
$$f(x) = \frac{3x^3 + 21x^2 + 36x}{x^2 - 9} = \frac{3x(x^2 + 7x + 12)}{(x-3)(x+3)}$$
$$= \frac{3x(x+4)(x+3)}{(x-3)(x+3)}$$
$$= \frac{3x(x+4)}{x-3}$$

53.
$$f(x) = \frac{3x^2 + 9x + 6}{6x^2 + 5x - 1}$$
$$= \frac{3(x^2 + 3x + 2)}{(6x-1)(x+1)}$$
$$= \frac{3(x+2)(x+1)}{(6x-1)(x+1)}$$
$$= \frac{3(x+2)}{6x-1}$$

55.
$$f(x) = \frac{x^2 - 2x - 8}{4x^3 + 8x^2 - 9x - 18}$$
$$= \frac{(x-4)(x+2)}{4x^2(x+2) - 9(x+2)}$$
$$= \frac{(x-4)(x+2)}{(4x^2 - 9)(x+2)}$$
$$= \frac{(x-4)(x+2)}{(2x-3)(2x+3)(x+2)}$$
$$= \frac{x-4}{(2x-3)(2x+3)}$$

57.
$$f(x) = \frac{x^3 + 8}{x^2 - 4} = \frac{x^3 + 2^3}{(x-2)(x+2)}$$
$$= \frac{(x+2)(x^2 - 2x + 4)}{(x-2)(x+2)}$$
$$= \frac{x^2 - 2x + 4}{x-2}$$

503

59.
$$f(x) = \frac{3x^2 + 7x - 6}{27x^3 - 8} = \frac{(3x-2)(x+3)}{(3x)^3 - (2)^3}$$

$$= \frac{\cancel{(3x-2)}(x+3)}{\cancel{(3x-2)}(9x^2 + 6x + 4)}$$

$$= \frac{x+3}{9x^2 + 6x + 4}$$

$$\left(\frac{f}{g}\right)(3) = \frac{3+4}{3-6}$$

$$= \frac{7}{-3}$$

$$= -\frac{7}{3}$$

61.
$$\frac{18x^3 y}{27x^2 y^4} = \frac{2 \cdot \cancel{3} \cdot \cancel{3} \cdot \cancel{x} \cdot \cancel{x} \cdot x \cdot \cancel{y}}{3 \cdot \cancel{3} \cdot \cancel{3} \cdot \cancel{x} \cdot \cancel{x} \cdot \cancel{y} \cdot y \cdot y \cdot y}$$

$$= \frac{2 \cdot x}{3 \cdot y \cdot y \cdot y}$$

$$= \frac{2x}{3y^3}$$

63.
$$\frac{x^2 - 6xy + 9y^2}{x^2 - 3xy} = \frac{(x-3y)\cancel{(x-3y)}}{x\cancel{(x-3y)}}$$

$$= \frac{x-3y}{x}$$

65.
$$\frac{6a^2 + ab - 2b^2}{3a^2 - 7ab - 6b^2} = \frac{\cancel{(3a+2b)}(2a-b)}{\cancel{(3a+2b)}(a-3b)}$$

$$= \frac{2a-b}{a-3b}$$

67.
$$\frac{p^3 - q^3}{p^2 - q^2} = \frac{\cancel{(p-q)}(p^2 + pq + q^2)}{\cancel{(p-q)}(p+q)}$$

$$= \frac{p^2 + pq + q^2}{p+q}$$

69.
$$\left(\frac{f}{g}\right)(x) = \frac{x^2 + 2x - 8}{x^2 - 8x + 12}$$

$$= \frac{(x+4)\cancel{(x-2)}}{(x-6)\cancel{(x-2)}}$$

$$= \frac{x+4}{x-6}$$

71.
$$\left(\frac{h}{f}\right)(x) = \frac{3x^2 + 17x + 20}{x^2 + 2x - 8}$$

$$= \frac{(3x+5)\cancel{(x+4)}}{\cancel{(x+4)}(x-2)}$$

$$= \frac{3x+5}{x-2}$$

$$\left(\frac{h}{f}\right)(4) = \frac{3(4)+5}{4-2}$$

$$= \frac{17}{2}$$

73.
$$\left(\frac{f}{h}\right)(x) = \frac{3x^3 - x^2}{9x^2 - 1}$$

$$= \frac{x^2 \cancel{(3x-1)}}{\cancel{(3x-1)}(3x+1)}$$

$$= \frac{x^2}{3x+1}$$

$$\left(\frac{f}{h}\right)(-2) = \frac{(-2)^2}{3(-2)+1}$$

$$= \frac{4}{-6+1}$$

$$= -\frac{4}{5}$$

75.
$$\left(\frac{k}{g}\right)(x) = \frac{27x^3 + 1}{18x^3 + 12x^2 + 2x}$$

$$= \frac{\cancel{(3x+1)}(9x^2 - 3x + 1)}{\cancel{(3x+1)}(6x^2 + 2x)}$$

$$= \frac{9x^2 - 3x + 1}{2x(3x+1)}$$

$$\left(\frac{k}{g}\right)(-1) = \frac{9(-1)^2 - 3(-1)+1}{6(-1)^2 + 2(-1)}$$

$$= \frac{9+3+1}{6-2}$$

$$= \frac{13}{4}$$

77. a. Percentage of people who received food stamps t years after 1990:

$$P(t) = \frac{F(t)}{U(t)} \times 100$$

$$= \frac{100 \cdot F(t)}{U(t)}$$

$$= \frac{100\left(0.465t^2 - 9.5t + 66\right)}{0.0068t^2 + 2.58t + 251.9}$$

$$= \frac{46.5t^2 - 950t + 6{,}600}{0.0068t^2 + 2.58t + 251.9}$$

The assumption that neither model will break down for a large domain of t has been assumed.

b. In the year 2004, $t = 14$:

$$P(14) \approx 8.34$$

According to the model, about 8.3% of Americans received food stamps in the year 2004. The actual percent is:

$$\frac{23.9}{293.7} \times 100\% = 8.14\%$$

The result of using the model is an overestimate.

c. $P(17) \approx 13.1\%$, which represents the approximate percent of Americans who received food stamps in the year 1990 + 17 = 2007.

79. a. Using the quadratic regression feature of a graphing calculator, we get

$$A(t) = 0.058t^2 - 0.82t + 3.6$$

b.
$$P(t) = \frac{U(t)}{A(t)} \cdot 100$$

$$= \frac{100 \cdot U(t)}{A(t)}$$

$$= \frac{100\left(0.047t^2 - 0.77t + 3.5\right)}{0.058t^2 - 0.82t + 3.6}$$

$$= \frac{4.7t^2 - 77t + 350}{0.058t^2 - 0.82t + 3.6}$$

c. $P(34) \approx 74\%$, which represents the approximate percent of cumulative unredeemed frequent-flier miles for the year 1980 + 34 = 2014.

d.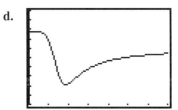

Using the "minimum" option on the graphing calculator, the minimum value for P can be found.

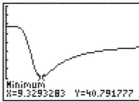

The minimum value for $P(t)$ between $t = 0$ and $t = 35$ is 40.79%, which occurs at $t = 9.33$. This means that, in the year 1980 + 9 = 1989, the percentage of cumulative unredeemed frequent-flier miles reached a minimum of just under 41%.

e. The percentage of cumulative unredeemed miles has been increasing since the year 1990. The graph decreases from about 1980 to 1989, then increases after 1989.

81. Answers may vary. Three examples are:

$$f(x) = \frac{1}{(x-3)(x+3)}$$

$$g(x) = \frac{4x^2}{9-x^2}$$

$$h(x) = \frac{3x^2+5}{\left(\dfrac{x}{3}\right)^2 - 1}$$

83. Domain: -3, -2, -1, 0, 1, 2, 3; range: 50.4, 25.2, 16.8, 12.6, 10.08, 8.4, 7.2

85. The student is incorrect about 2 and 4, which are in the domain because they do not make the denominator 0. The only values that must be excluded are 5 and 1 because for these values the denominator equals 0.

87.

original	student's
$\dfrac{2(3+4)+3}{(3+4)(3-1)}$	$\dfrac{5}{3-1}$
$\dfrac{2(7)+3}{7(2)}$	$\dfrac{5}{2}$
$\dfrac{14+3}{14}$	
$\dfrac{17}{14}$	

The results are not the same, so the original expression is not equivalent to the student's expression.

89. Answers may vary. In general, the denominator is set equal to zero. Any solution to this equation cannot be part of the domain of the function.

91. The domain is all real numbers.

93. The domain is all real numbers.

95.
$$x^2 - 4x - 21 = 0$$
$$(x-7)(x+3) = 0$$
$$x - 7 = 0 \qquad x + 3 = 0$$
$$x = 7 \qquad x = -3$$
The domain of f is all real numbers except 7 and -3.
The function $f(x)$ is a rational function in one variable.

97.
$$3x^3 + 5x^2 = 12x + 20$$
$$3x^3 + 5x^2 - 12x - 20 = 0$$
$$3x^3 - 12x + 5x^2 - 20 = 0$$
$$3x(x^2 - 4) + 5(x^2 - 4) = 0$$
$$(x^2 - 4)(3x + 5) = 0$$
$$(x-2)(x+2)(3x+5) = 0$$
$$x - 2 = 0 \quad x + 2 = 0 \quad 3x + 5 = 0$$
$$x = 2 \qquad x = -2 \qquad x = -\frac{5}{3}$$

The solutions are 2, -2, and $-\dfrac{5}{3}$.

$3x^3 + 5x^2 = 12x + 20$ is a cubic equation in one variable.

99.
$$8x^3 - 125$$
$$(2x)^3 - (5)^3$$
$$(2x - 5)(4x^2 + 10x + 25)$$

$8x^3 - 125$ is a cubic polynomial in one variable.

Homework 12.2

1. $\dfrac{3}{x} \cdot \dfrac{5}{x} = \dfrac{3 \cdot 5}{x \cdot x} = \dfrac{15}{x^2}$

3. $\dfrac{x}{6} \div \dfrac{3}{2x} = \dfrac{x}{6} \cdot \dfrac{2x}{3} = \dfrac{x \cdot \cancel{2} \cdot x}{\cancel{2} \cdot 3 \cdot 3} = \dfrac{x \cdot x}{3 \cdot 3} = \dfrac{x^2}{9}$

5. $\dfrac{6a^2}{7} \cdot \dfrac{21}{5a^8} = \dfrac{2 \cdot 3 \cdot a^2 \cdot 3 \cdot \cancel{7}}{\cancel{7} \cdot 5 \cdot a^8} = \dfrac{2 \cdot 3 \cdot 3}{5 \cdot a^{8-2}} = \dfrac{18}{5a^6}$

7. $\dfrac{2}{x-3} \cdot \dfrac{x-4}{x+5} = \dfrac{2(x-4)}{(x-3)(x+5)}$

9. $\dfrac{k-2}{k-6} \div \dfrac{k+6}{k+4} = \dfrac{k-2}{k-6} \cdot \dfrac{k+4}{k+6} = \dfrac{(k-2)(k+4)}{(k-6)(k+6)}$

11. $\dfrac{6}{7x-14} \cdot \dfrac{5x-10}{9} = \dfrac{2 \cdot 3}{7(x-2)} \cdot \dfrac{5(x-2)}{3 \cdot 3}$

$= \dfrac{2 \cdot \cancel{3} \cdot 5\cancel{(x-2)}}{7\cancel{(x-2)} \cdot \cancel{3} \cdot 3}$

$= \dfrac{2 \cdot 5}{7 \cdot 3}$

$= \dfrac{10}{21}$

13. $\dfrac{3x+18}{x-6} \div \dfrac{x+6}{2x-12} = \dfrac{3x+18}{x-6} \cdot \dfrac{2x-12}{x+6}$

$= \dfrac{3(x+6)}{x-6} \cdot \dfrac{2(x-6)}{x+6}$

$= \dfrac{3\cancel{(x+6)} \cdot 2\cancel{(x-6)}}{\cancel{(x-6)} \cdot \cancel{(x+6)}}$

$= \dfrac{3 \cdot 2}{1}$

$= 6$

15. $\dfrac{4w^6}{w+3} \cdot \dfrac{w+5}{2w^2} = \dfrac{2 \cdot 2 \cdot w^6 \cdot (w+5)}{(w+3) \cdot 2 \cdot w^2}$

$= \dfrac{2 \cdot w^{6-2} \cdot (w+5)}{(w+3)}$

$= \dfrac{2w^4(w+5)}{w+3}$

17. $\dfrac{(x-4)(x+1)}{(x-7)(x+2)} \cdot \dfrac{5(x+2)}{3(x-4)} = \dfrac{\cancel{(x-4)}(x+1) \cdot 5\cancel{(x+2)}}{(x-7)\cancel{(x+2)} \cdot 3\cancel{(x-4)}}$

$= \dfrac{(x+1) \cdot 5}{(x-7) \cdot 3}$

$= \dfrac{5(x+1)}{3(x-7)}$

19. $\dfrac{4(x-4)^2}{(x+5)^2} \div \dfrac{14(x-4)}{15(x+5)} = \dfrac{4(x-4)^2}{(x+5)^2} \cdot \dfrac{15(x+5)}{14(x-4)}$

$= \dfrac{\cancel{2} \cdot 2 \cdot (x-4)^{\cancel{2}5} \cdot 3 \cdot 5 \cdot \cancel{(x+5)}}{(x+5)^{\cancel{2}} \cdot \cancel{2} \cdot 7 \cdot \cancel{(x-4)}}$

$= \dfrac{2 \cdot (x-4) \cdot 3 \cdot 5}{(x+5) \cdot 7}$

$= \dfrac{30(x-4)}{7(x+5)}$

21. $\dfrac{4t^7}{3t-9} \cdot \dfrac{5t-15}{8t^3} = \dfrac{4t^7}{3(t-3)} \cdot \dfrac{5(t-3)}{8t^3}$

$= \dfrac{2 \cdot 2 \cdot t^7 \cdot 5\cancel{(t-3)}}{3\cancel{(t-3)} \cdot 2 \cdot 2 \cdot 2 \cdot t^3}$

$= \dfrac{t^{7-3} \cdot 5}{3 \cdot 2}$

$= \dfrac{5t^4}{6}$

23. $\dfrac{8x^2}{x^2-49} \div \dfrac{4x^5}{3x+21} = \dfrac{8x^2}{x^2-49} \cdot \dfrac{3x+21}{4x^5}$

$= \dfrac{8x^2}{(x-7)(x+7)} \cdot \dfrac{3(x+7)}{4x^5}$

$= \dfrac{2 \cdot 2 \cdot 2 \cdot x^2 \cdot 3\cancel{(x+7)}}{(x-7)\cancel{(x+7)} \cdot 2 \cdot 2 \cdot x^5}$

$= \dfrac{2 \cdot 3}{(x-7)x^{5-2}}$

$= \dfrac{6}{x^3(x-7)}$

25. $\dfrac{15a^4b}{8ab^5} \div \dfrac{25ab^3}{4a} = \dfrac{15a^4b}{8ab^5} \cdot \dfrac{4a}{25ab^3}$

$= \dfrac{3 \cdot \cancel{5} \cdot a^4 \cdot b \cdot \cancel{2 \cdot 2} \cdot a}{\cancel{2 \cdot 2} \cdot 2 \cdot a \cdot b^5 \cdot \cancel{5} \cdot 5 \cdot a \cdot b^3}$

$= \dfrac{3 \cdot a^{4+1-1-1}}{2 \cdot 5 \cdot b^{5+3-1}}$

$= \dfrac{3a^3}{10b^7}$

27. $\dfrac{2x-12}{x+1} \cdot \dfrac{4x+4}{18-3x} = \dfrac{2(x-6)}{\cancel{(x+1)}} \cdot \dfrac{4\cancel{(x+1)}}{3(6-x)}$

$= \dfrac{8(x-6)}{3(6-x)}$

$= \dfrac{8\cancel{(x-6)}}{-3\cancel{(x-6)}}$

$= -\dfrac{8}{3}$

29.

$$\frac{2k^2-32}{k^2-2k-24} \div \frac{k+6}{k^2-7k+6}$$

$$=\frac{2k^2-32}{k^2-2k-24} \cdot \frac{k^2-7k+6}{k+6}$$

$$=\frac{2\left(k^2-16\right)}{(k-6)(k+4)} \cdot \frac{(k-6)(k-1)}{(k+6)}$$

$$=\frac{2(k-4)\cancel{(k+4)}}{\cancel{(k-6)}\cancel{(k+4)}} \cdot \frac{\cancel{(k-6)}(k-1)}{(k+6)}$$

$$=\frac{2(k-4)(k-1)}{k+6}$$

31.

$$\frac{2a^2+3ab}{3a-6b} \cdot \frac{a^2-4b^2}{2ab+3b^2}$$

$$=\frac{a\left(2a+3b\right)}{3\left(a-2b\right)} \cdot \frac{\left(a-2b\right)(a+2b)}{b\left(2a+3b\right)}$$

$$=\frac{a(a+2b)}{3b}$$

33.

$$\frac{4-x}{x^2+10x+25} \div \frac{3x^2-9x-12}{25-x^2}$$

$$=\frac{4-x}{x^2+10x+25} \cdot \frac{25-x^2}{3x^2-9x-12}$$

$$=\frac{(4-x)}{(x+5)(x+5)} \cdot \frac{(5-x)(5+x)}{3\left(x^2-3x-4\right)}$$

$$=\frac{-1\cdot\left(x-4\right)}{(x+5)\cancel{(x+5)}} \cdot \frac{(5-x)\cancel{(5+x)}}{3\cancel{(x-4)}(x+1)}$$

$$=\frac{-(5-x)}{3(x+5)(x+1)}$$

$$=\frac{x-5}{3(x+5)(x+1)}$$

35.

$$\frac{t^2-8t+16}{t^2-2t-3} \cdot \frac{3-t}{t^2-16}$$

$$=\frac{\cancel{(t-4)}(t-4)}{\cancel{(t-3)}(t+1)} \cdot \frac{-1\cdot\cancel{(t-3)}}{\cancel{(t-4)}(t+4)}$$

$$=\frac{-(t-4)}{(t+1)(t+4)}$$

$$=\frac{4-t}{(t+1)(t+4)}$$

37.

$$\frac{-x^2+7x-10}{2x^2+5x-12} \div \frac{-x^2+4}{8x^2-18}$$

$$=\frac{-x^2+7x-10}{2x^2+5x-12} \cdot \frac{8x^2-18}{-x^2+4}$$

$$=\frac{-1(x^2-7x+10)}{(2x-3)(x+4)} \cdot \frac{2(4x^2-9)}{-1(x^2-4)}$$

$$=\frac{\cancel{-1}(x-5)\cancel{(x-2)}}{\cancel{(2x-3)}(x+4)} \cdot \frac{2\cancel{(2x-3)}(2x+3)}{\cancel{-1}\cancel{(x-2)}(x+2)}$$

$$=\frac{2(x-5)(2x+3)}{(x+4)(x+2)}$$

39.

$$\frac{-4x-6}{36-x^2} \cdot \frac{4x+24}{6x^2+x-12}$$

$$=\frac{-2(2x+3)}{-1(x^2-36)} \cdot \frac{4(x+6)}{(3x-4)(2x+3)}$$

$$=\frac{\cancel{-2}\cancel{(2x+3)}}{\cancel{-1}\cancel{(x+6)}(x-6)} \cdot \frac{4\cancel{(x+6)}}{(3x-4)\cancel{(2x+3)}}$$

$$=\frac{8}{(x-6)(3x-4)}$$

41.

$$\frac{9x^2-16}{x+2} \div \left(3x^2+5x-12\right)$$

$$=\frac{9x^2-16}{x+2} \cdot \frac{1}{3x^2+5x-12}$$

$$=\frac{\cancel{(3x-4)}(3x+4)}{(x+2)} \cdot \frac{1}{\cancel{(3x-4)}(x+3)}$$

$$=\frac{3x+4}{(x+2)(x+3)}$$

43. $\dfrac{6m^2-17m-14}{m^2+6m+9} \cdot \dfrac{9-m^2}{4m^2-49}$

$= \dfrac{(2m-7)(3m+2)}{(m+3)(m+3)} \cdot \dfrac{(3-m)(3+m)}{(2m-7)(2m+7)}$

$= \dfrac{(3m+2)(3-m)}{(m+3)(2m+7)} = -\dfrac{(3m+2)(m-3)}{(m+3)(2m+7)}$

45. $\dfrac{x^2-4x-32}{x^2+7x+12} \div \dfrac{x^2-2x-48}{x^2+3x-4}$

$= \dfrac{x^2-4x-32}{x^2+7x+12} \cdot \dfrac{x^2+3x-4}{x^2-2x-48}$

$= \dfrac{(x-8)(x+4)}{(x+3)(x+4)} \cdot \dfrac{(x+4)(x-1)}{(x-8)(x+6)}$

$= \dfrac{(x+4)(x-1)}{(x+3)(x+6)}$

47. $\dfrac{p^2+4pt-12t^2}{p^2+pt-12t^2} \cdot \dfrac{p^2+7pt+12t^2}{p^2-7pt+10t^2}$

$= \dfrac{(p+6t)(p-2t)}{(p+4t)(p-3t)} \cdot \dfrac{(p+4t)(p+3t)}{(p-2t)(p-5t)}$

$= \dfrac{(p+6t)(p+3t)}{(p-3t)(p-5t)}$

49. $\dfrac{2x^2-xy-3y^2}{3xy-5y^2} \div \dfrac{4x^2-9y^2}{3x^2-14xy+15y^2}$

$= \dfrac{2x^2-xy-3y^2}{3xy-5y^2} \cdot \dfrac{3x^2-14xy+15y^2}{4x^2-9y^2}$

$= \dfrac{(2x-3y)(x+y)}{y(3x-5y)} \cdot \dfrac{(3x-5y)(x-3y)}{(2x-3y)(2x+3y)}$

$= \dfrac{(x+y)(x-3y)}{y(2x+3y)}$

51. $\dfrac{3x^3-15x^2+18x}{x^2+16x+64} \cdot \dfrac{x^2-64}{4x^4-28x^3+40x^2}$

$= \dfrac{3x(x^2-5x+6)}{(x+8)(x+8)} \cdot \dfrac{(x-8)(x+8)}{4x^2(x^2-7x+10)}$

$= \dfrac{3 \cdot x\,(x-2)(x-3)}{(x+8)(x+8)} \cdot \dfrac{(x-8)(x+8)}{4x \cdot x\,(x-2)(x-5)}$

$= \dfrac{3(x-3)(x-8)}{4x(x+8)(x-5)}$

53. $\dfrac{w^2-2w-8}{12w^4+32w^3-12w^2} \div \dfrac{w^2-9w+20}{12w^3+54w^2+54w}$

$= \dfrac{w^2-2w-8}{12w^4+32w^3-12w^2} \cdot \dfrac{12w^3+54w^2+54w}{w^2-9w+20}$

$= \dfrac{(w-4)(w+2)}{4w^2(3w^2+8w-3)} \cdot \dfrac{6w(2w^2+9w+9)}{(w-4)(w-5)}$

$= \dfrac{(w-4)(w+2)}{4w^2(3w-1)(w+3)} \cdot \dfrac{6w(2w+3)(w+3)}{(w-4)(w-5)}$

$= \dfrac{3 \cdot 2w\,(w+2)(2w+3)}{2w \cdot 2w\,(3w-1)(w-5)}$

$= \dfrac{3(w+2)(2w+3)}{2w(3w-1)(w-5)}$

55. $\dfrac{x^2+4x-5}{x^3+6x^2-4x-24} \cdot \dfrac{x^2+8x+12}{x^2+10x+25}$

$= \dfrac{(x+5)(x-1)}{x^2(x+6)-4(x+6)} \cdot \dfrac{(x+2)(x+6)}{(x+5)(x+5)}$

$= \dfrac{(x+5)(x-1)}{(x+6)(x^2-4)} \cdot \dfrac{(x+2)(x+6)}{(x+5)(x+5)}$

$= \dfrac{(x+5)(x-1)}{(x+6)(x-2)(x+2)} \cdot \dfrac{(x+2)(x+6)}{(x+5)(x+5)}$

$= \dfrac{x-1}{(x-2)(x+5)}$

57.

$$\frac{18x^3 + 27x^2 - 8x - 12}{3x^2 - x - 2} \div \left(6x^2 + 5x - 6\right)$$

$$= \frac{18x^3 + 27x^2 - 8x - 12}{3x^2 - x - 2} \cdot \frac{1}{6x^2 + 5x - 6}$$

$$= \frac{9x^2(2x+3) - 4(2x+3)}{(3x+2)(x-1)} \cdot \frac{1}{(2x+3)(3x-2)}$$

$$= \frac{(2x+3)(9x^2 - 4)}{(3x+2)(x-1)} \cdot \frac{1}{(2x+3)(3x-2)}$$

$$= \frac{\cancel{(2x+3)}\cancel{(3x-2)}\cancel{(3x+2)}}{\cancel{(3x+2)}(x-1)} \cdot \frac{1}{\cancel{(2x+3)}\cancel{(3x-2)}}$$

$$= \frac{1}{x-1}$$

59.

$$\frac{k^3 - 8}{k^3 + 27} \cdot \frac{k^2 - 9}{k^2 - 4}$$

$$= \frac{\cancel{(k-2)}\left(k^2 + 2k + 4\right)}{\cancel{(k+3)}\left(k^2 - 3k + 9\right)} \cdot \frac{(k-3)\cancel{(k+3)}}{\cancel{(k-2)}(k+2)}$$

$$= \frac{(k-3)\left(k^2 + 2k + 4\right)}{(k+2)\left(k^2 - 3k + 9\right)}$$

61.

$$\frac{8x^3 - 27}{3x^2 - 6x + 12} \div \frac{8x^2 + 12x + 18}{6x^3 + 48}$$

$$= \frac{8x^3 - 27}{3x^2 - 6x + 12} \cdot \frac{6x^3 + 48}{8x^2 + 12x + 18}$$

$$= \frac{(2x-3)\left(4x^2 + 6x + 9\right)}{3\left(x^2 - 2x + 4\right)} \cdot \frac{6\left(x^3 + 8\right)}{2\left(4x^2 + 6x + 9\right)}$$

$$= \frac{(2x-3)\cancel{\left(4x^2 + 6x + 9\right)}}{3\cancel{\left(x^2 - 2x + 4\right)}} \cdot \frac{6(x+2)\cancel{\left(x^2 - 2x + 4\right)}}{2\cancel{\left(4x^2 + 6x + 9\right)}}$$

$$= \frac{\cancel{6}(2x-3)(x+2)}{\cancel{6}}$$

$$= (2x-3)(x+2)$$

63.

$$\frac{a^2 + ab - 2b^2}{a^3 + b^3} \cdot \frac{a^2 + 2ab + b^2}{a^2 - b^2}$$

$$= \frac{(a+2b)\cancel{(a-b)}}{\cancel{(a+b)}\left(a^2 - ab + b^2\right)} \cdot \frac{\cancel{(a+b)}\cancel{(a+b)}}{\cancel{(a-b)}\cancel{(a+b)}}$$

$$= \frac{a+2b}{a^2 - ab + b^2}$$

65.

$$(f \cdot g)(x) = \frac{x^2 - 6x - 16}{x^2 + 3x - 40} \cdot \frac{x^2 - 64}{x^2 - 3x - 10}$$

$$= \frac{(x-8)\cancel{(x+2)}}{\cancel{(x+8)}(x-5)} \cdot \frac{(x-8)\cancel{(x+8)}}{(x-5)\cancel{(x+2)}}$$

$$= \frac{(x-8)(x-8)}{(x-5)(x-5)}$$

$$= \frac{(x-8)^2}{(x-5)^2}$$

$$= \left(\frac{x-8}{x-5}\right)^2$$

$$(f \cdot g)(6) = \left(\frac{6-8}{6-5}\right)^2$$

$$= \left(\frac{-2}{1}\right)^2$$

$$= 4$$

67.

$$\left(\frac{g}{f}\right)(x) = \frac{x^2 - 64}{x^2 - 3x - 10} \div \frac{x^2 - 6x - 16}{x^2 + 3x - 40}$$

$$= \frac{x^2 - 64}{x^2 - 3x - 10} \cdot \frac{x^2 + 3x - 40}{x^2 - 6x - 16}$$

$$= \frac{\cancel{(x-8)}(x+8)}{\cancel{(x-5)}(x+2)} \cdot \frac{(x+8)\cancel{(x-5)}}{\cancel{(x-8)}(x+2)}$$

$$= \frac{(x+8)(x+8)}{(x+2)(x+2)}$$

$$= \left(\frac{x+8}{x+2}\right)^2$$

$$\left(\frac{g}{f}\right)(7) = \left(\frac{7+8}{7+2}\right)^2$$

$$= \left(\frac{15}{9}\right)^2$$

$$= \left(\frac{5}{3}\right)^2$$

$$= \frac{25}{9}$$

$$= \frac{12k^3}{k^2-4} \div \frac{2k^7}{-6(k-2)(k+2)}$$

$$= \frac{12k^3}{k^2-4} \cdot \frac{-6(k-2)(k+2)}{2k^7}$$

$$= \frac{12\cancel{k^3}}{\cancel{(k-2)}\,\cancel{(k+2)}} \cdot \frac{-\cancel{2}\cdot 3\,\cancel{(k-2)}\,\cancel{(k+2)}}{\cancel{2}\cdot\cancel{k^3}\cdot k^4}$$

$$= -\frac{36}{k^4}$$

69.
$$\left(\frac{f}{g}\right)(x) = \frac{1-x^2}{x^2-3x-28} \div \frac{x^2-8x+7}{x^2+5x+4}$$

$$= \frac{1-x^2}{x^2-3x-28} \cdot \frac{x^2+5x+4}{x^2-8x+7}$$

$$= \frac{-1\cdot \cancel{(x-1)}(1+x)}{(x-7)\cancel{(x+4)}} \cdot \frac{\cancel{(x+4)}(x+1)}{(x-7)\cancel{(x-1)}}$$

$$= \frac{-(1+x)(x+1)}{(x-7)(x-7)}$$

$$= -\left(\frac{x+1}{x-7}\right)^2$$

$$\left(\frac{f}{g}\right)(4) = -\left(\frac{4+1}{4-7}\right)^2$$

$$= -\left(\frac{5}{-3}\right)^2$$

$$= -\frac{25}{9}$$

71.
$$\left(\frac{20x^7}{x^2-9} \div \frac{x^2-14x+24}{5x-15}\right) \cdot \frac{x^2+x-6}{8x^{13}}$$

$$= \left(\frac{20x^7}{x^2-9} \cdot \frac{5x-15}{x^2-14x+24}\right) \cdot \frac{x^2+x-6}{8x^{13}}$$

$$= \frac{\cancel{4}\cdot 5\cancel{x^7}}{(x+3)\cancel{(x-3)}} \cdot \frac{5\cancel{(x-3)}}{(x-12)\cancel{(x-2)}} \cdot \frac{\cancel{(x-2)}(x+3)}{\cancel{4}\cdot 2\cdot \cancel{x^7}\cdot x^6}$$

$$= \frac{25}{2x^6(x-12)}$$

73.
$$\frac{12k^3}{k^2-4} \div \left(\frac{22k^6}{-6k+12} \cdot \frac{k}{11k+22}\right)$$

$$= \frac{12k^3}{k^2-4} \div \left(\frac{\cancel{11}\cdot 2k^6}{-6(k-2)} \cdot \frac{k}{\cancel{11}(k+2)}\right)$$

75.
$$\left(\left(\frac{x-4}{x+5}\right)^2 \cdot \left(\frac{x+5}{x-1}\right)^2\right) \div \left(\frac{x-4}{x-1}\right)^2$$

$$= \left(\left(\frac{x-4}{x+5}\right)^2 \cdot \left(\frac{x+5}{x-1}\right)^2\right) \cdot \left(\frac{x-1}{x-4}\right)^2$$

$$= \frac{\cancel{(x-4)^2}}{\cancel{(x+5)^2}} \cdot \frac{\cancel{(x+5)^2}}{\cancel{(x-1)^2}} \cdot \frac{\cancel{(x-1)^2}}{\cancel{(x-4)^2}}$$

$$= 1$$

77. $\dfrac{3 \text{ feet}}{1} \cdot \dfrac{12 \text{ inches}}{1 \text{ foot}} = 36 \text{ inches}$

The height of the net is 36 inches at the center.

79. $\dfrac{10 \text{ kilometers}}{1} \cdot \dfrac{1 \text{ mile}}{1.61 \text{ kilometers}} \approx 6.21 \text{ miles}$

The race is 6.21 miles long.

81. $\dfrac{9.8 \text{ pounds}}{1 \text{ year}} \cdot \dfrac{16 \text{ ounces}}{1 \text{ pound}} \cdot \dfrac{1 \text{ year}}{365 \text{ days}} \approx 0.43 \dfrac{\text{ounces}}{\text{day}}$

Americans consumed an average of 0.43 ounces of fish and shellfish per day.

83. $\dfrac{6.29 \text{ km}}{1 \text{ liter}} \cdot \dfrac{1 \text{ mile}}{1.61 \text{ km}} \cdot \dfrac{0.946 \text{ liter}}{1 \text{ quart}} \cdot \dfrac{4 \text{ quarts}}{1 \text{ gallon}}$

$\approx 14.78 \dfrac{\text{miles}}{\text{gallon}}$

The car's gas mileage is 14.78 miles per gallon.

85. $\dfrac{71.2 \text{ mg}}{12 \text{ ounces}} \cdot \dfrac{1 \text{ gram}}{1000 \text{ mg}} \cdot \dfrac{8 \text{ ounces}}{1 \text{ cup}} \cdot \dfrac{4 \text{ cups}}{1 \text{ quart}} \cdot \dfrac{4 \text{ quarts}}{1 \text{ gallon}}$

$\approx 0.76 \dfrac{\text{grams}}{\text{gallon}}$

There is 0.76 gram of caffeine in 1 gallon of Jolt®.

87. $\dfrac{x^3}{12} \cdot \dfrac{3}{x} = \dfrac{x^3 \cdot \cancel{3}}{2 \cdot 2 \cdot \cancel{3} \cdot x} = \dfrac{x^{3-1}}{2 \cdot 2} = \dfrac{x^2}{4}$

89. $\dfrac{x-2}{x^2-3x-18} \div \dfrac{x+4}{x^2+4x+3}$

$= \dfrac{x-2}{x^2-3x-18} \cdot \dfrac{x^2+4x+3}{x+4}$

$= \dfrac{x-2}{(x-6)(x+3)} \cdot \dfrac{(x+3)(x+1)}{x+4}$

$= \dfrac{(x-2)\cancel{(x+3)}(x+1)}{(x-6)\cancel{(x+3)}(x+4)}$

$= \dfrac{(x-2)(x+1)}{(x-6)(x+4)}$

91. Answers may vary. One possibility follows: The student failed to simplify. The correct answer is:

$\dfrac{x+2}{x+4} \cdot \dfrac{x+4}{x+6} = \dfrac{(x+2)\cancel{(x+4)}}{\cancel{(x+4)}(x+6)} = \dfrac{x+2}{x+6}$

93. Answers may vary. One possibility follows: Substitute 0 for x:

$\dfrac{x}{3} \cdot \dfrac{x+4}{x-7} = \dfrac{x^2+4}{3x-7}$

$\dfrac{0}{3} \cdot \dfrac{0+4}{0-7} \overset{?}{=} \dfrac{0^2+4}{3(0)-7}$

$0 \overset{?}{=} -\dfrac{4}{7}$ False

Since the result is false, the result is incorrect. The correct multiplication is:

$\dfrac{x}{3} \cdot \dfrac{x+4}{x-7} = \dfrac{x(x+4)}{3(x-7)}$ or $\dfrac{x^2+4x}{3x-21}$

95. a. $T(50) = \dfrac{420}{50} = 8.4$ hours

This represents the driving time, in hours.

b. $T(55) = \dfrac{420}{55} = 7.64$ hours

$T(60) = \dfrac{420}{60} = 7.00$ hours

$T(65) = \dfrac{420}{65} = 6.46$ hours

$T(70) = \dfrac{420}{70} = 6.00$ hours

c. T is decreasing for $s > 0$. This makes sense because the faster a person drives, the less time it will take to arrive at the destination (as shown in part b).

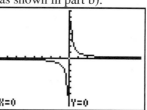

97. a. $\dfrac{1}{x} \div \dfrac{1}{x} = \dfrac{1}{x} \cdot \dfrac{x}{1}$

$= \dfrac{x}{x}$

$= 1$

b. $\dfrac{1}{x} \div \left(\dfrac{1}{x} \div \dfrac{1}{x} \right) = \dfrac{1}{x} \div \left(\dfrac{1}{x} \cdot \dfrac{x}{1} \right)$

$= \dfrac{1}{x} \div 1$

$= \dfrac{1}{x}$

c. $\dfrac{1}{x} \div \left(\dfrac{1}{x} \div \left(\dfrac{1}{x} \div \dfrac{1}{x} \right) \right) = \dfrac{1}{x} \div \left(\dfrac{1}{x} \div 1 \right)$

$= \dfrac{1}{x} \div \dfrac{1}{x}$

$= 1$

d. $\dfrac{1}{x} \div \left(\dfrac{1}{x} \div \left(\dfrac{1}{x} \div \left(\dfrac{1}{x} \div \dfrac{1}{x} \right) \right) \right)$

$= \dfrac{1}{x} \div \left(\dfrac{1}{x} \div \left(\dfrac{1}{x} \div 1 \right) \right)$

$= \dfrac{1}{x} \div \left(\dfrac{1}{x} \div \dfrac{1}{x} \right)$

$= \dfrac{1}{x} \div 1$

$= \dfrac{1}{x}$

e. $\underbrace{\dfrac{1}{x} \div \left(\dfrac{1}{x} \div \left(\dfrac{1}{x} \div \cdots \div \left(\dfrac{1}{x} \div \left(\dfrac{1}{x} \div \dfrac{1}{x} \right) \right) \right) \cdots \right)}_{n \text{ division symbols}}$

The answer will be 1 if n is odd, $\dfrac{1}{x}$, if n is even.

99. $(f \cdot g)(x) = 8^x \cdot 2^x$

$= \left(2^3\right)^x \cdot 2^x$

$= 2^{3x} \cdot 2^x$

$= 2^{3x+x}$

$= 2^{4x}$

$= \left(2^4\right)^x$

$= 16^x$

$\left(\dfrac{f}{g}\right)(x) = \dfrac{8^x}{2^x}$

$= \dfrac{\left(2^3\right)^x}{2^x}$

$= \dfrac{2^{3x}}{2^x}$

$= 2^{3x-x}$

$= 2^{2x}$

$= \left(2^2\right)^x$

$= 4^x$

101. $(f \cdot g)(x) = 12(6)^x \cdot 3(2)^x$

$= 12 \cdot 3(6)^x (2)^x$

$= 36(6 \cdot 2)^x$

$= 36(12)^x$

$\left(\dfrac{f}{g}\right)(x) = \dfrac{12(6)^x}{3(2)^x}$

$= 4\left(\dfrac{6}{2}\right)^x$

$= 4(3)^x$

103. $4\log_b\left(2x^2\right) - 2\log_b\left(3x^3\right) = \log_b\left(2x^2\right)^4 - \log_b\left(3x^3\right)^2$

$= \log_b\left(16x^8\right) - \log_b\left(9x^6\right)$

$= \log_b\left(\dfrac{16x^8}{9x^6}\right)$

$= \log_b\left(\dfrac{16x^2 \cdot \cancel{x^6}}{9 \cdot \cancel{x^6}}\right)$

$= \log_b\left(\dfrac{16x^2}{9}\right)$

$4\log_b\left(2x^2\right) - 2\log_b\left(3x^3\right)$ is a logarithmic expression in two variables.

105. $\log_2(x-3) + \log_2(x-2) = 3$

$\log_2\left[(x-3)(x-2)\right] = 3$

$2^3 = (x-3)(x-2)$

$8 = x^2 - 5x + 6$

$0 = x^2 - 5x - 2$

$x = \dfrac{-(-5) \pm \sqrt{(-5)^2 - 4(1)(-2)}}{2(1)}$

$= \dfrac{5 \pm \sqrt{25 + 8}}{2}$

$= \dfrac{5 + \sqrt{33}}{2}, \; \cancel{\dfrac{5 - \sqrt{33}}{2}}$

The solution is $\dfrac{5 + \sqrt{33}}{2} \approx 5.3723$.

$\log_2(x-3) + \log_2(x-2) = 3$ is a logarithmic equation in one variable.

107. $5(4)^x - 23 = 81$

$5(4)^x = 104$

$(4)^x = \dfrac{104}{5}$

$x = \log_4\left(\dfrac{104}{5}\right)$

$x = \log_4(20.8)$

$x = \dfrac{\log_{10} 20.8}{\log_{10} 4}$

$x \approx 2.1893$

$5(4)^x - 23 = 81$ is an exponential equation in one variable.

Homework 12.3

1. $\dfrac{7}{x} + \dfrac{2}{x} = \dfrac{7+2}{x} = \dfrac{9}{x}$

3. $\dfrac{9x}{x-2} - \dfrac{2x}{x-2} = \dfrac{9x-2x}{x-2} = \dfrac{7x}{x-2}$

5. $\dfrac{t^2}{t+5} + \dfrac{7t+10}{t+5} = \dfrac{t^2+7t+10}{t+5} = \dfrac{(t+5)(t+2)}{t+5} = t+2$

7. $\dfrac{x}{x^2-9} - \dfrac{3}{x^2-9} = \dfrac{x-3}{x^2-9} = \dfrac{x-3}{(x-3)(x+3)} = \dfrac{1}{x+3}$

9. $\dfrac{x^2}{x+1} - \dfrac{2x+3}{x+1} = \dfrac{x^2-(2x+3)}{x+1}$

$\qquad = \dfrac{x^2-2x-3}{x+1}$

$\qquad = \dfrac{(x-3)(x+1)}{x+1}$

$\qquad = x-3$

11. $\dfrac{c^2-5c}{c^2+5c+6} + \dfrac{4c-12}{c^2+5c+6} = \dfrac{c^2-5c+4c-12}{c^2+5c+6}$

$\qquad = \dfrac{c^2-c-12}{c^2+5c+6}$

$\qquad = \dfrac{(c-4)(c+3)}{(c+3)(c+2)}$

$\qquad = \dfrac{c-4}{c+2}$

13. $\dfrac{3x^2+9x}{x^2+10x+21} - \dfrac{2x^2+x-15}{x^2+10x+21}$

$\qquad = \dfrac{3x^2+9x-(2x^2+x-15)}{x^2+10x+21}$

$\qquad = \dfrac{3x^2+9x-2x^2-x+15}{x^2+10x+21}$

$\qquad = \dfrac{x^2+8x+15}{x^2+10x+21}$

$\qquad = \dfrac{\cancel{(x+3)}(x+5)}{\cancel{(x+3)}(x+7)}$

$\qquad = \dfrac{x+5}{x+7}$

15. $\dfrac{3}{x} + \dfrac{5}{2x} = \dfrac{3}{x} \cdot \dfrac{2}{2} + \dfrac{5}{2x} = \dfrac{6}{2x} + \dfrac{5}{2x} = \dfrac{6+5}{2x} = \dfrac{11}{2x}$

17. $\dfrac{5}{2b} - \dfrac{3}{8} = \dfrac{5}{2b} - \dfrac{3}{2\cdot2\cdot2}$

$\qquad = \dfrac{5}{2b} \cdot \dfrac{4}{4} - \dfrac{3}{2\cdot2\cdot2} \cdot \dfrac{b}{b}$

$\qquad = \dfrac{20}{8b} - \dfrac{3b}{8b}$

$\qquad = \dfrac{20-3b}{8b}$

$\qquad = \dfrac{-3b+20}{8b}$

19. $\dfrac{5x}{6} + \dfrac{3}{4x} = \dfrac{5x}{2\cdot3} + \dfrac{3}{2\cdot2\cdot x}$

$\qquad = \dfrac{5x}{2\cdot3} \cdot \dfrac{2x}{2x} + \dfrac{3}{2\cdot2\cdot x} \cdot \dfrac{3}{3}$

$\qquad = \dfrac{10x^2}{12x} + \dfrac{9}{12x}$

$\qquad = \dfrac{10x^2+9}{12x}$

21. $\dfrac{2}{x^6} - \dfrac{4}{x^2} = \dfrac{2}{x^6} - \dfrac{4}{x^2} \cdot \dfrac{x^4}{x^4}$

$\qquad = \dfrac{2}{x^6} - \dfrac{4x^4}{x^6}$

$\qquad = \dfrac{2-4x^4}{x^6}$

23.

$$\frac{3}{10x^6} + \frac{5}{12x^4} = \frac{3}{10x^6} \cdot \frac{6}{6} + \frac{5}{12x^4} \cdot \frac{5x^2}{5x^2}$$

$$= \frac{18}{60x^6} + \frac{25x^2}{60x^6}$$

$$= \frac{18 + 25x^2}{60x^6}$$

25.

$$\frac{7}{4a^2b} - \frac{5}{6ab^3} = \frac{7}{4a^2b} \cdot \frac{3b^2}{3b^2} - \frac{5}{6ab^3} \cdot \frac{2a}{2a}$$

$$= \frac{21b^3}{12a^2b^3} - \frac{10a}{12a^2b^3}$$

$$= \frac{21b^3 - 10a}{12a^2b^3}$$

27.

$$\frac{5}{4x} + \frac{2}{x+3} = \frac{5}{4x} \cdot \frac{x+3}{x+3} + \frac{2}{x+3} \cdot \frac{4x}{4x}$$

$$= \frac{5(x+3)}{4x(x+3)} + \frac{8x}{4x(x+3)}$$

$$= \frac{5(x+3) + 8x}{4x(x+3)}$$

$$= \frac{5x + 15 + 8x}{4x(x+3)}$$

$$= \frac{13x + 15}{4x(x+3)}$$

29.

$$\frac{3}{x+1} + \frac{4}{x-2} = \frac{3}{x+1} \cdot \left(\frac{x-2}{x-2}\right) + \frac{4}{x-2} \cdot \left(\frac{x+1}{x+1}\right)$$

$$= \frac{3x-6}{(x+1)(x-2)} + \frac{4x+4}{(x+1)(x-2)}$$

$$= \frac{7x-2}{(x+1)(x-2)}$$

31.

$$\frac{3x}{x-2} - \frac{5}{x+3} = \frac{3x}{x-2} \cdot \frac{x+3}{x+3} - \frac{5}{x+3} \cdot \frac{x-2}{x-2}$$

$$= \frac{3x(x+3)}{(x-2)(x+3)} - \frac{5(x-2)}{(x+3)(x-2)}$$

$$= \frac{3x(x+3) - 5(x-2)}{(x-2)(x+3)}$$

$$= \frac{3x^2 + 9x - 5x + 10}{(x-2)(x+3)}$$

$$= \frac{3x^2 + 4x + 10}{(x-2)(x+3)}$$

33.

$$\frac{1}{a+b} + \frac{1}{a-b} = \frac{1}{a+b} \cdot \frac{a-b}{a-b} + \frac{1}{a-b} \cdot \frac{a+b}{a+b}$$

$$= \frac{a-b}{(a+b)(a-b)} + \frac{a+b}{(a-b)(a+b)}$$

$$= \frac{a-b+a+b}{(a+b)(a-b)}$$

$$= \frac{2a}{(a+b)(a-b)}$$

35.

$$\frac{c}{2c-8} - \frac{3}{c-4} = \frac{c}{2(c-4)} - \frac{3}{c-4}$$

$$= \frac{c}{2(c-4)} - \frac{3}{c-4} \cdot \frac{2}{2}$$

$$= \frac{c}{2(c-4)} - \frac{6}{2(c-4)}$$

$$= \frac{c-6}{2(c-4)}$$

37.

$$\frac{2x}{5x-25} + \frac{4}{3x-15} = \frac{2x}{5(x-5)} + \frac{4}{3(x-5)}$$

$$= \frac{2x}{5(x-5)} \cdot \frac{3}{3} + \frac{4}{3(x-5)} \cdot \frac{5}{5}$$

$$= \frac{6x}{15(x-5)} + \frac{20}{15(x-5)}$$

$$= \frac{6x+20}{15(x-5)}$$

$$= \frac{2(3x+10)}{15(x-5)}$$

39.
$$\frac{6}{k^2-1}+\frac{3}{k+1}=\frac{6}{(k-1)(k+1)}+\frac{3}{k+1}$$

$$=\frac{6}{(k-1)(k+1)}+\frac{3}{k+1}\cdot\frac{k-1}{k-1}$$

$$=\frac{6}{(k-1)(k+1)}+\frac{3(k-1)}{(k+1)(k-1)}$$

$$=\frac{6+3(k-1)}{(k-1)(k+1)}$$

$$=\frac{6+3k-3}{(k+1)(k-1)}$$

$$=\frac{3k+3}{(k+1)(k-1)}$$

$$=\frac{3(k+1)}{(k+1)(k-1)}$$

$$=\frac{3}{k-1}$$

41.
$$\frac{3x-1}{x^2+2x-15}-\frac{2}{x+5}=\frac{3x-1}{(x+5)(x-3)}-\frac{2}{x+5}$$

$$=\frac{3x-1}{(x+5)(x-3)}-\frac{2}{x+5}\cdot\frac{x-3}{x-3}$$

$$=\frac{3x-1}{(x+5)(x-3)}-\frac{2(x-3)}{(x+5)(x-3)}$$

$$=\frac{3x-1-2(x-3)}{(x+5)(x-3)}$$

$$=\frac{3x-1-2x+6}{(x+5)(x-3)}$$

$$=\frac{x+5}{(x+5)(x-3)}$$

$$=\frac{1}{x-3}$$

43.
$$\frac{3}{x^2-25}+\frac{5}{x^2-5x}=\frac{3}{(x+5)(x-5)}+\frac{5}{x(x-5)}$$

$$=\frac{3}{(x-5)(x+5)}\cdot\frac{x}{x}+\frac{5}{x(x-5)}\cdot\left(\frac{x+5}{x+5}\right)$$

$$=\frac{3x}{x(x-5)(x+5)}+\frac{5x+25}{x(x-5)(x+5)}$$

$$=\frac{8x+25}{x(x-5)(x+5)}$$

45.
$$\frac{2}{x^2-9}+\frac{3}{x^2-7x+12}$$

$$=\frac{2}{(x+3)(x-3)}+\frac{3}{(x-4)(x-3)}$$

$$=\frac{2}{(x+3)(x-3)}\cdot\left(\frac{x-4}{x-4}\right)+\frac{3}{(x-4)(x-3)}\cdot\left(\frac{x+3}{x+3}\right)$$

$$=\frac{2x-8}{(x+3)(x-3)(x-4)}+\frac{3x+9}{(x+3)(x-3)(x-4)}$$

$$=\frac{5x+1}{(x+3)(x-3)(x-4)}$$

47.
$$\frac{5}{3t-6}-\frac{2}{5t+15}=\frac{5}{3(t-2)}-\frac{2}{5(t+3)}$$

$$=\frac{5}{3(t-2)}\cdot\frac{5(t+3)}{5(t+3)}-\frac{2}{5(t+3)}\cdot\frac{3(t-2)}{3(t-2)}$$

$$=\frac{25(t+3)}{15(t-2)(t+3)}-\frac{6(t-2)}{15(t+3)(t-2)}$$

$$=\frac{25(t+3)-6(t-2)}{15(t-2)(t+3)}$$

$$=\frac{25t+75-6t+12}{15(t-2)(t+3)}$$

$$=\frac{19t+87}{15(t-2)(t+3)}$$

49.
$$2+\frac{k-3}{k+1}=\frac{2}{1}\cdot\left(\frac{k+1}{k+1}\right)+\frac{k-3}{k+1}$$

$$=\frac{2k+2}{k+1}+\frac{k-3}{k+1}$$

$$=\frac{3k-1}{k+1}$$

51.
$$2-\frac{2x+4}{x^2+3x+2}=\frac{2}{1}-\frac{2(x+2)}{(x+2)(x+1)}$$

$$=\frac{2}{1}-\frac{2}{x+1}=\frac{2}{1}\cdot\left(\frac{x+1}{x+1}\right)-\frac{2}{x+1}$$

$$=\frac{2x+2}{x+1}-\frac{2}{x+1}=\frac{2x}{x+1}$$

53.
$$\frac{8}{x-6}-\frac{4}{6-x}=\frac{8}{x-6}+\frac{4}{x-6}$$

$$=\frac{12}{x-6}$$

55.

$$\frac{2x+1}{x^2-4x-21}+\frac{3}{14-2x}$$

$$=\frac{2x+1}{(x-7)(x+3)}+\frac{3}{-2(x-7)}$$

$$=\frac{2x+1}{(x-7)(x+3)}-\frac{3}{2(x-7)}$$

$$=\frac{2x+1}{(x-7)(x+3)}\cdot\frac{2}{2}-\frac{3}{2(x-7)}\cdot\left(\frac{x+3}{x+3}\right)$$

$$=\frac{4x+2}{2(x-7)(x+3)}-\frac{3x+9}{2(x-7)(x+3)}$$

$$=\frac{4x+2-3x-9}{2(x-7)(x+3)}$$

$$=\frac{x-7}{2(x-7)(x+3)}$$

$$=\frac{1}{2(x+3)}$$

57.

$$\frac{-2c}{7-2c}-\frac{c+1}{4c^2-49}$$

$$=\frac{2c}{(2c-7)}-\frac{(c+1)}{(2c-7)(2c+7)}$$

$$=\frac{2c}{(2c-7)}\cdot\frac{(2c+7)}{(2c+7)}-\frac{(c+1)}{(2c-7)(2c+7)}$$

$$=\frac{2c(2c+7)-(c+1)}{(2c-7)(2c+7)}$$

$$=\frac{4c^2+14c-c-1}{(2c-7)(2c+7)}$$

$$=\frac{4c^2+13c-1}{(2c-7)(2c+7)}$$

59.

$$\frac{2a}{a^2-b^2}+\frac{b}{ab-b^2}$$

$$=\frac{2a}{(a-b)(a+b)}+\frac{b}{b(a-b)}$$

$$=\frac{2a}{(a-b)(a+b)}\cdot\frac{b}{b}+\frac{b}{b(a-b)}\cdot\frac{(a+b)}{(a+b)}$$

$$=\frac{2ab+b(a+b)}{b(a-b)(a+b)}$$

$$=\frac{3ab+b^2}{b(a-b)(a+b)}$$

$$=\frac{\not b\,(3a+b)}{\not b\,(a-b)(a+b)}$$

$$=\frac{3a+b}{(a-b)(a+b)}$$

61.

$$\frac{x}{x^2+5x+6}-\frac{3}{x^2+7x+12}$$

$$=\frac{x}{(x+2)(x+3)}\cdot\frac{(x+4)}{(x+4)}$$

$$\qquad-\frac{3}{(x+3)(x+4)}\cdot\frac{(x+2)}{(x+2)}$$

$$=\frac{x(x+4)-3(x+2)}{(x+2)(x+3)(x+4)}$$

$$=\frac{x^2+x-6}{(x+2)(x+3)(x+4)}$$

$$=\frac{(x-2)(x+3)}{(x+2)(x+3)(x+4)}$$

$$=\frac{x-2}{(x+2)(x+4)}$$

63.

$$\frac{x-1}{x+2}+\frac{x+2}{x-1}=\left(\frac{x-1}{x+2}\right)\left(\frac{x-1}{x-1}\right)+\left(\frac{x+2}{x-1}\right)\left(\frac{x+2}{x+2}\right)$$

$$=\frac{x^2-2x+1}{(x+2)(x-1)}+\frac{x^2+4x+4}{(x+2)(x-1)}$$

$$=\frac{2x^2+2x+5}{(x+2)(x-1)}$$

65. $\dfrac{y-5}{y-3} - \dfrac{y+3}{y+5}$

$= \left(\dfrac{y-5}{y-3}\right)\left(\dfrac{y+5}{y+5}\right) - \left(\dfrac{y+3}{y+5}\right)\left(\dfrac{y-3}{y-3}\right)$

$= \dfrac{y^2-25}{(y-3)(y+5)} - \dfrac{y^2-9}{(y-3)(y+5)}$

$= \dfrac{y^2-25-y^2+9}{(y-3)(y+5)}$

$= \dfrac{-16}{(y-3)(y+5)}$

67. $\dfrac{x+4}{x^2-7x+10} - \dfrac{5}{x^2-25}$

$= \dfrac{x+4}{(x-2)(x-5)} - \dfrac{5}{(x-5)(x+5)}$

$= \dfrac{(x+4)}{(x-2)(x-5)} \cdot \dfrac{(x+5)}{(x+5)} - \dfrac{5}{(x-5)(x+5)} \cdot \dfrac{(x-2)}{(x-2)}$

$= \dfrac{(x+4)(x+5) - 5(x-2)}{(x-2)(x-5)(x+5)}$

$= \dfrac{x^2+9x+20-5x+10}{(x-2)(x-5)(x+5)}$

$= \dfrac{x^2+4x+30}{(x-2)(x-5)(x+5)}$

69. $\dfrac{x+2}{(x-4)(x+3)^2} + \dfrac{x-1}{(x-4)(x+1)(x+3)}$

$= \left(\dfrac{x+2}{(x-4)(x+3)^2}\right)\left(\dfrac{x+1}{x+1}\right)$

$\quad + \left(\dfrac{x-1}{(x-4)(x+1)(x+3)}\right)\left(\dfrac{x+3}{x+3}\right)$

$= \dfrac{x^2+3x+2}{(x-4)(x+1)(x+3)^2} + \dfrac{x^2+2x-3}{(x-4)(x+1)(x+3)^2}$

$= \dfrac{2x^2+5x-1}{(x-4)(x+1)(x+3)^2}$

71. $\dfrac{c+2}{c^2-4} + \dfrac{3c}{c^2-2c} = \dfrac{c+2}{(c+2)(c-2)} + \dfrac{3c}{c(c-2)}$

$\qquad\qquad = \dfrac{1}{c-2} + \dfrac{3}{c-2}$

$\qquad\qquad = \dfrac{4}{c-2}$

73. $\dfrac{x-1}{4x^2+20x+25} - \dfrac{x+4}{6x^2+17x+5}$

$= \dfrac{x-1}{(2x+5)(2x+5)} - \dfrac{x+4}{(2x+5)(3x+1)}$

$= \left(\dfrac{x-1}{(2x+5)(2x+5)}\right)\left(\dfrac{3x+1}{3x+1}\right) -$

$\qquad \left(\dfrac{x+4}{(2x+5)(3x+1)}\right)\left(\dfrac{2x+5}{2x+5}\right)$

$= \dfrac{3x^2-2x-1}{(3x+1)(2x+5)^2} - \dfrac{2x^2+13x+20}{(3x+1)(2x+5)^2}$

$= \dfrac{3x^2-2x-1-2x^2-13x-20}{(3x+1)(2x+5)^2}$

$= \dfrac{x^2-15x-21}{(3x+1)(2x+5)^2}$

75. $\dfrac{3x-1}{x^2+4x+4} + \dfrac{2x+1}{3x^2+5x-2}$

$= \dfrac{3x-1}{(x+2)(x+2)} - \dfrac{2x+1}{(3x-1)(x+2)}$

$= \left(\dfrac{3x-1}{(x+2)(x+2)}\right)\left(\dfrac{3x-1}{3x-1}\right)$

$\quad + \left(\dfrac{2x+1}{(3x-1)(x+2)}\right)\left(\dfrac{x+2}{x+2}\right)$

$= \dfrac{9x^2-6x+1}{(3x-1)(x+2)^2} + \dfrac{2x^2+5x+2}{(3x-1)(x+2)^2}$

$= \dfrac{9x^2-6x+1+2x^2+5x+2}{(3x-1)(x+2)^2}$

$= \dfrac{11x^2-x+3}{(3x-1)(x+2)^2}$

77.
$$\frac{3p}{p^2 - 2pq - 24q^2} - \frac{2q}{p^2 - 3pq - 18q^2}$$
$$= \frac{3p}{(p-6q)(p+4q)} - \frac{2q}{(p-6q)(p+3q)}$$
$$= \frac{3p}{(p-6q)(p+4q)} \cdot \frac{(p+3q)}{(p+3q)}$$
$$\qquad - \frac{2q}{(p-6q)(p+3q)} \cdot \frac{(p+4q)}{(p+4q)}$$
$$= \frac{3p(p+3q) - 2q(p+4q)}{(p-6q)(p+4q)(p+3q)}$$
$$= \frac{3p^2 + 9pq - 2pq - 8q^2}{(p-6q)(p+4q)(p+3q)}$$
$$= \frac{3p^2 + 7pq - 8q^2}{(p-6q)(p+4q)(p+3q)}$$

79.
$$\frac{x-1}{6x^2 - 24x} + \frac{5}{3x^3 - 6x^2 - 24x}$$
$$= \frac{x-1}{6x(x-4)} + \frac{5}{3x(x^2 - 2x - 8)}$$
$$= \frac{x-1}{6x(x-4)} + \frac{5}{3x(x-4)(x+2)}$$
$$= \left(\frac{x-1}{6x(x-4)}\right)\left(\frac{x+2}{x+2}\right)$$
$$\qquad + \left(\frac{5}{3x(x-4)(x+2)}\right)\left(\frac{2}{2}\right)$$
$$= \frac{x^2 + x - 2}{6x(x-4)(x+2)} + \frac{10}{6x(x-4)(x+2)}$$
$$= \frac{x^2 + x + 8}{6x(x-4)(x+2)}$$

81.
$$\left(\frac{2}{x^2 - 4} + \frac{3}{x+2}\right) - \frac{1}{2x-4}$$
$$= \left(\frac{2}{(x+2)(x-2)} + \frac{3}{x+2}\right) - \frac{1}{2(x-2)}$$
$$= \left(\frac{2}{(x+2)(x-2)} + \left(\frac{3}{x+2}\right)\left(\frac{x-2}{x-2}\right)\right) - \frac{1}{2(x-2)}$$
$$= \left(\frac{2}{(x+2)(x-2)} + \frac{3x-6}{(x+2)(x-2)}\right) - \frac{1}{2(x-2)}$$

$$\frac{3x-4}{(x+2)(x-2)} - \frac{1}{2(x-2)}$$
$$= \left(\frac{3x-4}{(x+2)(x-2)}\right)\left(\frac{2}{2}\right) - \left(\frac{1}{2(x-2)}\right)\left(\frac{x+2}{x+2}\right)$$
$$= \frac{6x-8}{2(x+2)(x-2)} - \frac{x+2}{2(x+2)(x-2)}$$
$$= \frac{5x-10}{2(x+2)(x-2)}$$
$$= \frac{5(x-2)}{2(x+2)(x-2)}$$
$$= \frac{5}{2(x+2)}$$

83.
$$\frac{3}{t+1} - \left(\frac{2t-3}{t^2 + 6t + 5} + \frac{2}{t+5}\right)$$
$$= \frac{3}{t+1} - \left(\frac{2t-3}{(t+5)(t+1)} + \frac{2}{t+5}\right)$$
$$= \frac{3}{t+1} - \left(\frac{2t-3}{(t+5)(t+1)} + \left(\frac{2}{t+5}\right)\left(\frac{t+1}{t+1}\right)\right)$$
$$= \frac{3}{t+1} - \left(\frac{2t-3}{(t+5)(t+1)} + \frac{2t+2}{(t+5)(t+1)}\right)$$
$$= \frac{3}{t+1} - \frac{4t-1}{(t+5)(t+1)}$$
$$= \left(\frac{3}{t+1}\right)\left(\frac{t+5}{t+5}\right) - \frac{4t-1}{(t+5)(t+1)}$$
$$= \frac{3t+15}{(t+1)(t+5)} - \frac{4t-1}{(t+1)(t+5)}$$
$$= \frac{3t+15 - 4t + 1}{(t+1)(t+5)}$$
$$= \frac{-t+16}{(t+1)(t+5)}$$

85.
$$f(x) + g(x) = \frac{x+3}{x-4} + \frac{x+4}{x-3}$$
$$= \left(\frac{x+3}{x-4}\right)\left(\frac{x-3}{x-3}\right) + \left(\frac{x+4}{x-3}\right)\left(\frac{x-4}{x-4}\right)$$
$$= \frac{x^2 - 9}{(x-4)(x+3)} + \frac{x^2 - 16}{(x-4)(x-3)}$$
$$= \frac{2x^2 - 25}{(x-4)(x-3)}$$

87.
$$g(x) - f(x) = \frac{x+4}{x-3} - \frac{x+3}{x-4}$$

$$= \left(\frac{x+4}{x-3}\right)\left(\frac{x-4}{x-4}\right) - \left(\frac{x+3}{x-4}\right)\left(\frac{x-3}{x-3}\right)$$

$$= \frac{x^2-16}{(x-3)(x-4)} - \frac{x^2-9}{(x-3)(x-4)}$$

$$= \frac{x^2-16-x^2+9}{(x-3)(x-4)}$$

$$= \frac{-7}{(x-3)(x-4)}$$

89.

$$f(x) - g(x) = \frac{x-2}{x^2-2x-8} - \frac{x+1}{3x+6}$$

$$= \frac{x-2}{(x-4)(x+2)} - \frac{x+1}{3(x+2)}$$

$$= \left(\frac{x-2}{(x-4)(x+2)}\right)\left(\frac{3}{3}\right) - \left(\frac{x+1}{3(x+2)}\right)\left(\frac{x-4}{x-4}\right)$$

$$= \frac{3x-6}{3(x-4)(x+2)} - \frac{x^2-3x-4}{3(x-4)(x+2)}$$

$$= \frac{3x-6-x^2+3x+4}{3(x-4)(x+2)}$$

$$= \frac{-x^2+6x-2}{3(x-4)(x+2)}$$

91. a. The total illumination is represented by:

$$\frac{18}{d^2} + \frac{18}{(2d)^2}$$

b.

$$\frac{18}{d^2} + \frac{18}{(2d)^2} = \frac{18}{d^2} + \frac{18}{4d^2}$$

$$= \frac{18}{d^2} \cdot \frac{4}{4} + \frac{18}{4d^2}$$

$$= \frac{72}{4d^2} + \frac{18}{4d^2}$$

$$= \frac{90}{4d^2}$$

$$= \frac{45}{2d^2}$$

c. Substitute 1.2 for *d*:

$$\frac{45}{2(1.2)^2} = \frac{45}{2(1.44)} = \frac{45}{2.88} \approx 15.63$$

This means that the total illumination is 15.63 W/m^2 when the person is 1.2 meters away from the closer light and $2(1.2) = 2.4$ meters away from the other light.

93. The student did not multiply each expression by "1". The expression $\frac{2}{x+1}$ should have been multiplied by $\frac{x+2}{x+2}$ not $\frac{1}{x+2}$ and the expression $\frac{3}{x+2}$ should have been multiplied by $\frac{x+1}{x+1}$ not $\frac{1}{x+1}$. The correct addition is:

$$\frac{2}{x+1} + \frac{3}{x+2}$$

$$= \frac{2}{x+1} \cdot \frac{x+2}{x+2} + \frac{3}{x+2} \cdot \frac{x+1}{x+1}$$

$$= \frac{2x+4}{(x+1)(x+2)} + \frac{3x+3}{(x+1)(x+2)}$$

$$= \frac{5x+7}{(x+1)(x+2)}$$

95. The student did not subtract the entire numerator in the second expression. The student only subtracted $5x$ and not the 1. The correct subtraction is:

$$\frac{9x}{x-3} - \frac{5x+1}{x-3} = \frac{9x-5x-1}{x-3}$$

$$= \frac{4x-1}{x-3}$$

97. Answers may vary. The two rational expressions must have the same denominator in order to be added, so each expression must be multiplied by a fraction equal to "1," which introduces the necessary terms in each denominator that make them equal.

99.

$$(f+g)(x) = (6x^2-4x+3) + (2x^2-7x-5)$$

$$= 6x^2-4x+3+2x^2-7x-5$$

$$= 8x^2-11x-2$$

$$(f-g)(x) = (6x^2-4x+3) - (2x^2-7x-5)$$

$$= 6x^2-4x+3-2x^2+7x+5$$

$$= 4x^2+3x+8$$

101.

$$(f+g)(x) = \left[2(5)^x\right] + \left[-3(5)^x\right]$$
$$= 2(5)^x - 3(5)^x$$
$$= (2-3) \cdot (5)^x$$
$$= -(5)^x$$

$$(f-g)(x) = \left[2(5)^x\right] - \left[-3(5)^x\right]$$
$$= 2(5)^x + 3(5)^x$$
$$= (2+3) \cdot (5)^x$$
$$= 5 \cdot (5)^x$$
$$= 5^1 \cdot 5^x$$
$$= 5^{x+1}$$

103.

$$\frac{4x+5}{x+2} + \left(\frac{3x+15}{x^2-4} \cdot \frac{x^2-2x}{x^2+7x+10}\right)$$
$$= \frac{4x+5}{x+2} + \left(\frac{3(x+5)}{(x+2)(x-2)} \cdot \frac{x(x-2)}{(x+5)(x+2)}\right)$$
$$= \frac{4x+5}{x+2} + \frac{3x}{(x+2)^2}$$
$$= \left(\frac{4x+5}{x+2}\right)\left(\frac{x+2}{x+2}\right) + \frac{3x}{(x+2)^2}$$
$$= \frac{4x^2+13x+10}{(x+2)^2} + \frac{3x}{(x+2)^2}$$
$$= \frac{4x^2+16x+10}{(x+2)^2}$$
$$= \frac{2(2x^2+8x+5)}{(x+2)^2}$$

105.

$$\frac{5x+5}{3x+6} \cdot \left(\frac{x^2+4x}{x^2+2x+1} + \frac{4}{x^2+2x+1}\right)$$
$$= \frac{5(x+1)}{3(x+2)} \cdot \left(\frac{x^2+4x+4}{x^2+2x+1}\right)$$
$$= \frac{5(x+1)}{3(x+2)} \cdot \frac{(x+2)(x+2)}{(x+1)(x+1)}$$
$$= \frac{5(x+2)}{3(x+1)}$$

107.

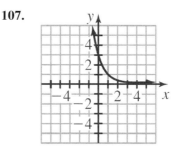

$f(x) = 3\left(\dfrac{1}{3}\right)^x$ is an exponential function.

109.

$$5b^4 = 66$$
$$5b^4 - 66 = 0$$
$$5\left(b^4 - \frac{66}{5}\right) = 0$$
$$5\left(b^2 - \frac{\sqrt{330}}{5}\right)\left(b^2 + \frac{\sqrt{330}}{5}\right) = 0$$
$$b^2 - \frac{\sqrt{330}}{5} = 0$$
$$b^2 - 3.6332 \approx 0$$
$$b^2 \approx 3.6332$$
$$b \approx \pm\sqrt{3.6332}$$
$$b \approx \pm 1.9061$$

$5b^4 = 66$ is a fourth-degree polynomial equation in one variable.

111.

$$y = ab^x$$
$$(3, 95):$$
$$95 = a \cdot b^3$$
$$a = \frac{95}{b^3}$$
$$(7, 2):$$
$$2 = a \cdot b^7$$

$$2 = \left(\frac{95}{b^3}\right) \cdot b^7$$

$$2 = 95b^4$$

$$b^4 = \frac{2}{95}$$

$$b \approx \sqrt[4]{\frac{2}{95}}$$

$$a \approx \frac{95}{\left(\sqrt[4]{\frac{2}{95}}\right)^3} \approx 1718.87$$

$$y \approx 1718.87(0.38)^x$$

The equation is $y \approx 1718.87(0.38)^x$. It is an exponential equation in two variables.

Homework 12.4

1.
$$\frac{\frac{4}{5}}{\frac{8}{3}} = \frac{4}{5} \div \frac{8}{3} = \frac{4}{5} \cdot \frac{3}{8} = \frac{2 \cdot 2}{5} \cdot \frac{3}{2 \cdot 2 \cdot 2}$$

$$= \frac{2 \cdot 2 \cdot 3}{5 \cdot 2 \cdot 2 \cdot 2} = \frac{3}{5 \cdot 2} = \frac{3}{10}$$

3.
$$\frac{\frac{x}{4}}{\frac{x}{7}} = \frac{x}{4} \div \frac{x}{7} = \frac{x}{4} \cdot \frac{7}{x} = \frac{x \cdot 7}{4 \cdot x} = \frac{7}{4}$$

5.
$$\frac{\frac{6}{5x}}{\frac{3}{7x}} = \frac{6}{5x} \div \frac{3}{7x} = \frac{6}{5x} \cdot \frac{7x}{3} = \frac{2 \cdot 3}{5x} \cdot \frac{7x}{3}$$

$$= \frac{2 \cdot 3 \cdot 7 \cdot x}{5 \cdot x \cdot 3} = \frac{2 \cdot 7}{5} = \frac{14}{5}$$

7.
$$\frac{\frac{w}{6}}{\frac{w^2}{9}} = \frac{w}{6} \div \frac{w^2}{9} = \frac{w}{6} \cdot \frac{9}{w^2} = \frac{w}{2 \cdot 3} \cdot \frac{3 \cdot 3}{w^2}$$

$$= \frac{w \cdot 3 \cdot 3}{2 \cdot 3 \cdot w^2} = \frac{3}{2 \cdot w^{2-1}} = \frac{3}{2w}$$

9.
$$\frac{\frac{15x^3}{8}}{\frac{25x^5}{12}} = \frac{15x^3}{8} \div \frac{25x^5}{12} = \frac{15x^3}{8} \cdot \frac{12}{25x^5}$$

$$= \frac{3 \cdot 5 \cdot x^3}{2 \cdot 2 \cdot 2} \cdot \frac{2 \cdot 2 \cdot 3}{5 \cdot 5 \cdot x^5} = \frac{3 \cdot 5 \cdot x^3 \cdot 2 \cdot 2 \cdot 3}{2 \cdot 2 \cdot 2 \cdot 5 \cdot 5 \cdot x^5}$$

$$= \frac{3 \cdot 3}{2 \cdot 5 \cdot x^{5-3}} = \frac{9}{10x^2}$$

11.
$$\frac{\frac{4a^2}{5b}}{\frac{6a}{15b^3}} = \frac{4a^2}{5b} \div \frac{6a}{15b^3}$$

$$= \frac{4a^2}{5b} \cdot \frac{15b^3}{6a}$$

$$= \frac{60a^2b^3}{30ab}$$

$$= 2ab^2$$

13.
$$\frac{\frac{14}{x^2-9}}{\frac{21}{x-3}} = \frac{14}{x^2-9} \div \frac{21}{x-3} = \frac{14}{x^2-9} \cdot \frac{x-3}{21}$$

$$= \frac{2 \cdot 7}{(x-3)(x+3)} \cdot \frac{x-3}{3 \cdot 7}$$

$$= \frac{2 \cdot 7 \cdot (x-3)}{(x-3)(x+3) \cdot 3 \cdot 7}$$

$$= \frac{2}{(x+3) \cdot 3} = \frac{2}{3(x+3)}$$

15.
$$\frac{\frac{5a-10}{4}}{\frac{3a-6}{2}} = \frac{5a-10}{4} \div \frac{3a-6}{2} = \frac{5a-10}{4} \cdot \frac{2}{3a-6}$$

$$= \frac{5(a-2)}{2 \cdot 2} \cdot \frac{2}{3(a-2)} = \frac{5 \cdot (a-2) \cdot 2}{2 \cdot 2 \cdot 3 \cdot (a-2)}$$

$$= \frac{5}{2 \cdot 3} = \frac{5}{6}$$

17.
$$\frac{\dfrac{3x-3}{2x+10}}{\dfrac{6x^2-6}{4x+20}} = \frac{3x-3}{2x+10} \div \frac{6x^2-6}{4x+20}$$

$$= \frac{3x-3}{2x+10} \cdot \frac{4x+20}{6x^2-6}$$

$$= \frac{3(x-1)}{2(x+5)} \cdot \frac{4(x+5)}{6(x^2-1)}$$

$$= \frac{12(x-1)(x+5)}{12(x+5)(x-1)(x+1)}$$

$$= \frac{1}{x+1}$$

19.
$$\frac{\dfrac{x^2-49}{3x^2-9x}}{\dfrac{x^2-5x-14}{7x-21}} = \frac{x^2-49}{3x^2-9x} \cdot \frac{7x-21}{x^2-5x-14}$$

$$= \frac{(x+7)(x-7)}{3x(x-3)} \cdot \frac{7(x-3)}{(x-7)(x+2)}$$

$$= \frac{7(x+7)}{3x(x+2)}$$

21.
$$\frac{\dfrac{25x^2-4}{9x^2-16}}{\dfrac{25x^2-20x+4}{9x^2-24x+16}} = \frac{25x^2-4}{9x^2-16} \div \frac{25x^2-20x+4}{9x^2-24x+16}$$

$$= \frac{25x^2-4}{9x^2-16} \cdot \frac{9x^2-24x+16}{25x^2-20x+4}$$

$$= \frac{(5x-2)(5x+2)}{(3x-4)(3x+4)} \cdot \frac{(3x-4)(3x-4)}{(5x-2)(5x-2)}$$

$$= \frac{(5x+2)(3x-4)}{(3x+4)(5x-2)}$$

23.
$$\frac{\dfrac{4}{x}+\dfrac{2}{x}}{\dfrac{9}{x}-\dfrac{7}{x}} = \frac{\dfrac{4}{x}+\dfrac{2}{x}}{\dfrac{9}{x}-\dfrac{7}{x}} \cdot \frac{x}{x} = \frac{\dfrac{4}{x}\cdot x+\dfrac{2}{x}\cdot x}{\dfrac{9}{x}\cdot x-\dfrac{7}{x}\cdot x} = \frac{4+2}{9-7} = \frac{6}{2} = 3$$

25.
$$\frac{\dfrac{3}{8}+\dfrac{1}{4}}{\dfrac{1}{2}+\dfrac{5}{8}} = \frac{\dfrac{3}{8}+\dfrac{1}{4}}{\dfrac{1}{2}+\dfrac{5}{8}} \cdot \frac{8}{8} = \frac{\dfrac{3}{8}\cdot 8+\dfrac{1}{4}\cdot 8}{\dfrac{1}{2}\cdot 8+\dfrac{5}{8}\cdot 8} = \frac{3+2}{4+5} = \frac{5}{9}$$

27.
$$\frac{\dfrac{7}{4x}+\dfrac{1}{x}}{\dfrac{3}{2x}+\dfrac{5}{x}} = \frac{\dfrac{7}{4x}+\dfrac{1}{x}}{\dfrac{3}{2x}+\dfrac{5}{x}} \cdot \frac{4x}{4x} = \frac{\dfrac{7}{4x}\cdot 4x+\dfrac{1}{x}\cdot 4x}{\dfrac{3}{2x}\cdot 4x+\dfrac{5}{x}\cdot 4x}$$

$$= \frac{7+4}{6+20} = \frac{11}{26}$$

29.
$$\frac{\dfrac{5}{3r}-\dfrac{3}{2r}}{\dfrac{1}{2r}-\dfrac{4}{3r}} = \frac{\dfrac{5}{3r}-\dfrac{3}{2r}}{\dfrac{1}{2r}-\dfrac{4}{3r}} \cdot \frac{6r}{6r} = \frac{\dfrac{5}{3r}\cdot 6r-\dfrac{3}{2r}\cdot 6r}{\dfrac{1}{2r}\cdot 6r-\dfrac{4}{3r}\cdot 6r}$$

$$= \frac{10-9}{3-8} = \frac{1}{-5} = -\frac{1}{5}$$

31.
$$\frac{\dfrac{2}{3}-\dfrac{4}{3x}}{\dfrac{5}{6x}} = \frac{\dfrac{2}{3}-\dfrac{4}{3x}}{\dfrac{5}{6x}} \cdot \frac{6x}{6x} = \frac{\dfrac{2}{3}\cdot 6x-\dfrac{4}{3x}\cdot 6x}{\dfrac{5}{6x}\cdot 6x}$$

$$= \frac{4x-8}{5} = \frac{4(x-2)}{5}$$

33.
$$\frac{\dfrac{2}{x^3}-\dfrac{3}{x}}{\dfrac{5}{x^3}+\dfrac{4}{x^2}} = \frac{\left(\dfrac{2}{x^3}-\dfrac{3}{x}\right)}{\left(\dfrac{5}{x^3}+\dfrac{4}{x^2}\right)} \cdot \frac{x^3}{x^3}$$

$$= \frac{2-3x^2}{5+4x}$$

35.
$$\frac{4+\dfrac{3}{x}}{\dfrac{2}{x}-3} = \frac{\left(4+\dfrac{3}{x}\right)}{\left(\dfrac{2}{x}-3\right)} \cdot \frac{x}{x}$$

$$= \frac{4x+3}{2-3x}$$

37.
$$\frac{\dfrac{5}{2x^3}-4}{\dfrac{1}{6x^3}-3} = \frac{\left(\dfrac{5}{2x^3}-4\right)}{\left(\dfrac{1}{6x^3}-3\right)} \cdot \frac{6x^3}{6x^3}$$

$$= \frac{3(5-8x^3)}{1-18x^3}$$

39.
$$\frac{\dfrac{a^2}{b}-b}{\dfrac{1}{b}-\dfrac{1}{a}}=\frac{\left(\dfrac{a^2}{b}-b\right)}{\left(\dfrac{1}{b}-\dfrac{1}{a}\right)}\cdot\frac{ab}{ab}$$

$$=\frac{a^3-ab^2}{a-b}$$

$$=\frac{a\left(a^2-b^2\right)}{a-b}$$

$$=\frac{a(a-b)(a+b)}{(a-b)}$$

$$=a(a+b)$$

41.
$$\frac{\dfrac{1}{x}-\dfrac{8}{x^2}+\dfrac{15}{x^3}}{\dfrac{1}{x}-\dfrac{5}{x^2}}=\frac{\left(\dfrac{1}{x}-\dfrac{8}{x^2}+\dfrac{15}{x^3}\right)}{\left(\dfrac{1}{x}-\dfrac{5}{x^2}\right)}\cdot\frac{x^3}{x^3}$$

$$=\frac{x^2-8x+15}{x^2-5x}$$

$$=\frac{(x-5)(x-3)}{x(x-5)}$$

$$=\frac{x-3}{x}$$

43.
$$\frac{\dfrac{x}{x-4}-\dfrac{2x}{x+1}}{\dfrac{x}{x+1}-\dfrac{2x}{x-4}}=\frac{\left(\dfrac{x}{x-4}-\dfrac{2x}{x+1}\right)}{\left(\dfrac{x}{x+1}-\dfrac{2x}{x-4}\right)}\cdot\frac{(x-4)(x+1)}{(x-4)(x+1)}$$

$$=\frac{x(x+1)-2x(x-4)}{x(x-4)-2x(x+1)}$$

$$=\frac{x^2+x-2x^2+8x}{x^2-4x-2x^2-2x}$$

$$=\frac{-x^2+9x}{-x^2-6x}$$

$$=\frac{-x(x-9)}{-x(x+6)}$$

$$=\frac{x-9}{x+6}$$

45.
$$\frac{p+\dfrac{2}{p-4}}{p-\dfrac{3}{p-4}}=\frac{\left(p+\dfrac{2}{p-4}\right)}{\left(p-\dfrac{3}{p-4}\right)}\cdot\frac{(p-4)}{(p-4)}$$

$$=\frac{p(p-4)+2}{p(p-4)-3}$$

$$=\frac{p^2-4p+2}{p^2-4p-3}$$

47.
$$\frac{\dfrac{1}{x+3}-\dfrac{1}{x}}{3}=\left(\frac{\dfrac{1}{x+3}-\dfrac{1}{x}}{3}\right)\cdot\left(\frac{x(x+3)}{x(x+3)}\right)$$

$$=\frac{x-(x+3)}{3x(x+3)}$$

$$=\frac{-3}{3x(x+3)}$$

$$=\frac{-1}{x(x+3)}$$

49.
$$\frac{\dfrac{3}{a+b}-\dfrac{3}{a-b}}{2ab}$$

$$=\frac{\left(\dfrac{3}{a+b}-\dfrac{3}{a-b}\right)}{2ab}\cdot\frac{(a+b)(a-b)}{(a+b)(a-b)}$$

$$=\frac{3(a-b)-3(a+b)}{2ab(a+b)(a-b)}$$

$$=\frac{3a-3b-3a-3b}{2ab(a+b)(a-b)}$$

$$=\frac{-6b}{2ab(a+b)(a-b)}$$

$$=\frac{-3}{a(a+b)(a-b)}$$

51.
$$\frac{\dfrac{1}{(x+2)^2}-\dfrac{1}{x^2}}{2}=\left(\frac{\dfrac{1}{(x+2)^2}-\dfrac{1}{x^2}}{2}\right)\cdot\frac{x^2(x+2)^2}{x^2(x+2)^2}$$

$$=\frac{x^2-(x+2)^2}{2x^2(x+2)^2}$$

$$=\frac{x^2-(x^2+4x+4)}{2x^2(x+2)^2}$$

$$=\frac{-4x-4}{2x^2(x+2)^2}$$

$$=\frac{-4(x+1)}{2x^2(x+2)^2}$$

$$=\frac{-2(x+1)}{x^2(x+2)^2}$$

53.
$$\frac{\dfrac{6}{2x-8}+\dfrac{10}{x^2-4x}}{\dfrac{1}{x^2-x-12}-\dfrac{2}{x^2-16}}$$

$$=\frac{\dfrac{6}{2(x-4)}+\dfrac{10}{x(x-4)}}{\dfrac{1}{(x-4)(x+3)}-\dfrac{2}{(x-4)(x+4)}}$$

$$=\frac{\dfrac{6}{2(x-4)}\cdot\dfrac{x}{x}+\dfrac{10}{x(x-4)}\cdot\dfrac{2}{2}}{\dfrac{1}{(x-4)(x+3)}\cdot\dfrac{(x+4)}{(x+4)}-\dfrac{2}{(x-4)(x+4)}\cdot\dfrac{(x+3)}{(x+3)}}$$

$$=\frac{\dfrac{6x+20}{2x(x-4)}}{\dfrac{x+4}{(x-4)(x+3)(x+4)}-\dfrac{2x+6}{(x-4)(x+3)(x+4)}}$$

$$=\frac{\dfrac{6x+20}{2x(x-4)}}{\dfrac{x+4-2x-6}{(x-4)(x+3)(x+4)}}\cdot\frac{2x(x-4)(x+3)(x+4)}{2x(x-4)(x+3)(x+4)}$$

$$=\frac{(6x+20)(x+3)(x+4)}{(-x-2)\cdot 2x}$$

$$=\frac{2(3x+10)(x+3)(x+4)}{-2x(x+2)}$$

$$=-\frac{(3x+10)(x+3)(x+4)}{x(x+2)}$$

55.
$$\frac{\dfrac{x+7}{x^2+7x+10}-\dfrac{6}{x^2+2x}}{\dfrac{x+1}{x^2+7x+10}+\dfrac{6}{x^2+5x}}$$

$$=\frac{\dfrac{x+7}{(x+5)(x+2)}-\dfrac{6}{x(x+2)}}{\dfrac{x+1}{(x+5)(x+2)}+\dfrac{6}{x(x+5)}}$$

$$=\frac{\dfrac{x+7}{(x+5)(x+2)}\cdot\dfrac{x}{x}-\dfrac{6}{x(x+2)}\cdot\dfrac{(x+5)}{(x+5)}}{\dfrac{x+1}{(x+5)(x+2)}\cdot\dfrac{x}{x}+\dfrac{6}{x(x+5)}\cdot\dfrac{(x+2)}{(x+2)}}$$

$$=\frac{\dfrac{x^2+7x}{x(x+5)(x+2)}-\dfrac{6x+30}{x(x+5)(x+2)}}{\dfrac{x^2+x}{x(x+5)(x+2)}+\dfrac{6x+12}{x(x+5)(x+2)}}$$

$$=\frac{\dfrac{x^2+7x-6x-30}{x(x+5)(x+2)}}{\dfrac{x^2+x+6x+12}{x(x+5)(x+2)}}$$

$$=\frac{\dfrac{x^2+x-30}{x(x+5)(x+2)}}{\dfrac{x^2+7x+12}{x(x+5)(x+2)}}$$

$$=\frac{x^2+x-30}{x(x+5)(x+2)}\cdot\frac{x(x+5)(x+2)}{x^2+7x+12}$$

$$=\frac{x^2+x-30}{x^2+7x+12}$$

$$=\frac{(x+6)(x-5)}{(x+3)(x+4)}$$

57.
$$\left(\frac{f}{g}\right)(x)=\frac{\dfrac{5x+10}{x^2-6x+9}}{\dfrac{4x+8}{x^2-4x+3}}$$

$$=\frac{\dfrac{5(x+2)}{(x-3)(x-3)}}{\dfrac{4(x+2)}{(x-3)(x-1)}}$$

$$=\frac{5(x+2)}{(x-3)(x-3)}\cdot\frac{(x-3)(x-1)}{4(x+2)}$$

$$=\frac{5(x-1)}{4(x-3)}$$

59.

$$\left(\dfrac{f}{g}\right)(x) = \dfrac{\left(\dfrac{x}{2} - \dfrac{2}{x}\right)}{\left(\dfrac{3}{2} + \dfrac{3}{x}\right)}$$

$$= \dfrac{\left(\dfrac{x}{2} - \dfrac{2}{x}\right)}{\left(\dfrac{3}{2} + \dfrac{3}{x}\right)} \cdot \dfrac{2x}{2x}$$

$$= \dfrac{x^2 - 4}{3x + 6}$$

$$= \dfrac{(x-2)(x+2)}{3(x+2)}$$

$$= \dfrac{x-2}{3}$$

61.

$$\left(\dfrac{f}{g}\right)(x) = \dfrac{\dfrac{2x}{x^2 - 25} + \dfrac{x+5}{x-5}}{\dfrac{x-5}{x+5} + \dfrac{3x}{x^2 - 25}}$$

$$= \dfrac{\left(\dfrac{2x}{(x-5)(x+5)} + \dfrac{x+5}{x-5}\right)}{\left(\dfrac{x-5}{x+5} + \dfrac{3x}{(x-5)(x+5)}\right)} \cdot \dfrac{(x-5)(x+5)}{(x-5)(x+5)}$$

$$= \dfrac{2x + (x+5)(x+5)}{(x-5)(x-5) + 3x}$$

$$= \dfrac{2x + x^2 + 10x + 25}{x^2 - 10x + 25 + 3x}$$

$$= \dfrac{x^2 + 12x + 25}{x^2 - 7x + 25}$$

63. The student must add the two expressions in the parentheses before taking the reciprocals. The correct simplification is below:

65. Method 1

$$\dfrac{\dfrac{6}{x^2} - \dfrac{5}{x}}{\dfrac{2}{x^2} + \dfrac{3}{2x}} = \dfrac{\dfrac{6}{x^2} - \dfrac{5}{x} \cdot \dfrac{x}{x}}{\dfrac{2}{x^2} \cdot \dfrac{2}{2} + \dfrac{3}{2x} \cdot \dfrac{x}{x}} = \dfrac{\dfrac{6}{x^2} - \dfrac{5x}{x^2}}{\dfrac{4}{2x^2} + \dfrac{3x}{2x^2}}$$

$$= \dfrac{\dfrac{6 - 5x}{x^2}}{\dfrac{4 + 3x}{2x^2}} = \dfrac{6 - 5x}{x^2} \div \dfrac{4 + 3x}{2x^2} = \dfrac{6 - 5x}{x^2} \cdot \dfrac{2x^2}{4 + 3x}$$

$$= \dfrac{2(6 - 5x)}{4 + 3x}$$

Method 2

$$\dfrac{\dfrac{6}{x^2} - \dfrac{5}{x}}{\dfrac{2}{x^2} + \dfrac{3}{2x}} = \dfrac{\left(\dfrac{6}{x^2} - \dfrac{5}{x}\right)}{\left(\dfrac{2}{x^2} + \dfrac{3}{2x}\right)} \cdot \dfrac{2x^2}{2x^2} = \dfrac{12 - 10x}{4 + 3x}$$

$$= \dfrac{2(6 - 5x)}{4 + 3x}$$

Answers may vary.

67. A complex rational expression is a rational expression that has rational expressions in the numerator and in the denominator. Written examples may vary.

69.

$$\dfrac{8x^{-2}y^5}{6x^{-7}y^8} = \dfrac{4x^{-2-(-7)}}{3y^{8-5}}$$

$$= \dfrac{4x^5}{3y^3}$$

71.

$$\frac{x^{-1}+x^{-2}}{x^{-2}-x^{-1}}=\frac{\dfrac{1}{x}+\dfrac{1}{x^2}}{\dfrac{1}{x^2}-\dfrac{1}{x}}$$

$$=\frac{\left(\dfrac{1}{x}+\dfrac{1}{x^2}\right)}{\left(\dfrac{1}{x^2}-\dfrac{1}{x}\right)}\cdot\frac{x^2}{x^2}$$

$$=\frac{x+1}{1-x}$$

73.

$$\frac{2b^{-2}-4b}{8b^{-1}-6b}\cdot\frac{b^2}{b^2}=\frac{2-4b^3}{8b-6b^3}$$

$$=\frac{2\left(1-2b^3\right)}{2b\left(4-3b^2\right)}$$

$$=\frac{1-2b^3}{b\left(4-3b^2\right)}$$

75. a.

$$H_e=\frac{1}{\dfrac{1}{H_p}+\dfrac{1}{H_b}}$$

$$=\frac{1}{\dfrac{H_b+H_p}{H_bH_p}}$$

$$=\frac{H_bH_p}{H_b+H_p}$$

b.

$$H_e=\frac{H_bH_p}{H_b+H_p}$$

$$=\frac{(623)(87.4)}{623+87.4}$$

$$\approx 76.6 \text{ days}$$

77.

$$\frac{x-2}{x^2-2x-24}+\frac{x+4}{x^2-8x+12}=$$

$$=\frac{x-2}{(x+4)(x-6)}+\frac{x+4}{(x-6)(x-2)}$$

$$=\frac{(x-2)}{(x+4)(x-6)}\cdot\frac{(x-2)}{(x-2)}$$

$$+\frac{(x+4)}{(x-6)(x-2)}\cdot\frac{(x+4)}{(x+4)}$$

$$=\frac{\left(x^2-4x+4\right)+\left(x^2+8x+16\right)}{(x+4)(x-6)(x-2)}$$

$$=\frac{2x^2+4x+20}{(x+4)(x-6)(x-2)}$$

$\dfrac{x-2}{x^2-2x-24}+\dfrac{x+4}{x^2-8x+12}$ is a rational expression in one variable.

79.

$$\frac{x-2}{x^2-2x-24}\cdot\frac{x+4}{x^2-8x+12}$$

$$=\frac{(x-2)}{(x-6)(x+4)}\cdot\frac{(x+4)}{(x-6)(x-2)}$$

$$=\frac{1}{(x-6)^2}$$

$\dfrac{x-2}{x^2-2x-24}\cdot\dfrac{x+4}{x^2-8x+12}$ is a rational expression in one variable.

81.

$$x^2-2x-24-0$$

$$(x-6)(x+4)=0$$

$$x-6=0 \qquad x+4=0$$

$$x=6 \qquad x=-4$$

The domain is all real numbers except 6 and −4.

The function $f(x)$ is a rational function.

Homework 12.5

1.

$$\frac{3}{x}-2=\frac{7}{x}$$

We note that 0 is an excluded value.

$$x \cdot \left(\frac{3}{x} - 2 \right) = x \cdot \left(\frac{7}{x} \right)$$

$$x \cdot \frac{3}{x} - x \cdot 2 = x \cdot \frac{7}{x}$$

$$3 - 2x = 7$$

$$-2x = 4$$

$$x = -2$$

Since -2 is not an excluded value, we conclude that -2 is the solution of the equation.

3.
$$5 - \frac{4}{x} = 3 + \frac{2}{x}$$

We note that 0 is an excluded value.

$$x \cdot \left(5 - \frac{4}{x} \right) = x \cdot \left(3 + \frac{2}{x} \right)$$

$$x \cdot 5 - x \cdot \frac{4}{x} = x \cdot 3 + x \cdot \frac{2}{x}$$

$$5x - 4 = 3x + 2$$

$$2x = 6$$

$$x = 3$$

Since 3 is not an excluded value, we conclude that 3 is the solution of the equation.

5.
$$\frac{5}{p-1} = \frac{2p+1}{p-1}$$

We note that 1 is an excluded value.

$$(p-1) \cdot \left(\frac{5}{p-1} \right) = (p-1) \cdot \left(\frac{2p+1}{p-1} \right)$$

$$5 = 2p + 1$$

$$4 = 2p$$

$$2 = p$$

Since 2 is not an excluded value, we conclude that 2 is the solution of the equation.

7.
$$\frac{8x+4}{x+2} = \frac{5x-2}{x+2}$$

We note that -2 is an excluded value.

$$(x+2) \cdot \left(\frac{8x+4}{x+2} \right) = (x+2) \cdot \left(\frac{5x-2}{x+2} \right)$$

$$8x + 4 = 5x - 2$$

$$3x = -6$$

$$x = -2$$

Our result -2 is not a solution because it is an excluded value. Since this is the only possible solution, we conclude that no number is a solution. That is, the solution is the empty set.

9.
$$\frac{w+2}{w-4} + 3 = \frac{2}{w-4}$$

We note that 4 is an excluded value.

$$(w-4) \cdot \left(\frac{w+2}{w-4} + 3 \right) = (w-4) \cdot \left(\frac{2}{w-4} \right)$$

$$(w-4) \cdot \frac{w+2}{w-4} + (w-4) \cdot 3 = 2$$

$$w + 2 + 3w - 12 = 2$$

$$4w - 10 = 2$$

$$4w = 12$$

$$w = 3$$

Since 3 is not an excluded value, we conclude that 3 is the solution of the equation.

11.
$$\frac{2}{x} + \frac{5}{4} = \frac{3}{x}$$

We note that 0 is an excluded value.

$$4x \cdot \left(\frac{2}{x} + \frac{5}{4} \right) = 4x \cdot \left(\frac{3}{x} \right)$$

$$4x \cdot \frac{2}{x} + 4x \cdot \frac{5}{4} = 4x \cdot \frac{3}{x}$$

$$8 + 5x = 12$$

$$5x = 4$$

$$x = \frac{4}{5}$$

Since $\frac{4}{5}$ is not an excluded value, we conclude that $\frac{4}{5}$ is the solution of the equation.

13.
$$\frac{5}{6x} - \frac{1}{2} = \frac{3}{4x}$$

We note that 0 is an excluded value.

$$12x \cdot \left(\frac{5}{6x} - \frac{1}{2} \right) = 12x \cdot \left(\frac{3}{4x} \right)$$

$$12x \cdot \frac{5}{6x} - 12x \cdot \frac{1}{2} = 12x \cdot \frac{3}{4x}$$

$$2 \cdot 5 - 6x \cdot 1 = 3 \cdot 3$$

$$10 - 6x = 9$$

$$-6x = -1$$

$$x = \frac{-1}{-6}$$

$$x = \frac{1}{6}$$

Since $\frac{1}{6}$ is not an excluded value, we conclude that

$\dfrac{1}{6}$ is the solution of the equation.

15. $\dfrac{4}{x-2}=\dfrac{2}{x+3}$

We note that -3 and 2 are excluded values.

$$(x-2)(x+3)\cdot\left(\dfrac{4}{x-2}\right)=(x-2)(x+3)\cdot\left(\dfrac{2}{x+3}\right)$$

$$(x+3)\cdot 4=(x-2)\cdot 2$$

$$4x+12=2x-4$$

$$2x=-16$$

$$x=-8$$

Since -8 is not an excluded value, we conclude that -8 is the solution of the equation.

17. $\dfrac{2r+7}{4r}=\dfrac{5}{3}$

We note that 0 is an excluded value.

$$12r\cdot\left(\dfrac{2r+7}{4r}\right)=12r\cdot\left(\dfrac{5}{3}\right)$$

$$3\cdot(2r+7)=4r\cdot 5$$

$$6r+21=20r$$

$$21=14r$$

$$r=\dfrac{21}{14}$$

$$r=\dfrac{3}{2}$$

Since $\dfrac{3}{2}$ is not an excluded value, we conclude that $\dfrac{3}{2}$ is the solution of the equation.

19. $\dfrac{5}{x+3}+\dfrac{3}{4}=2$

We note that -3 is an excluded value.

$$4(x+3)\cdot\left(\dfrac{5}{x+3}+\dfrac{3}{4}\right)=4(x+3)\cdot(2)$$

$$4(x+3)\cdot\dfrac{5}{x+3}+4(x+3)\cdot\dfrac{3}{4}=8(x+3)$$

$$4\cdot 5+(x+3)\cdot 3=8x+24$$

$$20+3x+9=8x+24$$

$$3x+29=8x+24$$

$$-5x=-5$$

$$x=1$$

Since 1 is not an excluded value, we conclude that 1 is the

solution of the equation.

21. $\dfrac{2}{x-3}+\dfrac{1}{x+3}=\dfrac{5}{x^2-9}$

$$\dfrac{2}{x-3}+\dfrac{1}{x+3}=\dfrac{5}{(x-3)(x+3)}$$

We note that -3 and 3 are excluded values.

$$(x-3)(x+3)\cdot\left(\dfrac{2}{x-3}+\dfrac{1}{x+3}\right)=$$

$$(x-3)(x+3)\cdot\left(\dfrac{5}{(x-3)(x+3)}\right)$$

$$(x-3)(x+3)\cdot\dfrac{2}{x-3}+(x-3)(x+3)\cdot\dfrac{1}{x+3}=5$$

$$(x+3)\cdot 2+(x-3)\cdot 1=5$$

$$2x+6+x-3=5$$

$$3x+3=5$$

$$3x=2$$

$$x=\dfrac{2}{3}$$

Since $\dfrac{2}{3}$ is not an excluded value, we conclude that $\dfrac{2}{3}$ is the solution of the equation.

23. $\dfrac{4}{x+2}+\dfrac{3}{x+1}=\dfrac{3}{x^2+3x+2}$

$$\dfrac{4}{x+2}+\dfrac{3}{x+1}=\dfrac{3}{(x+2)(x+1)}$$

We note that -2 and -1 are excluded values.

$$(x+2)(x+1)\cdot\left(\dfrac{4}{x+2}+\dfrac{3}{x+1}\right)$$

$$=(x+2)(x+1)\cdot\left(\dfrac{3}{(x+2)(x+1)}\right)$$

$$(x+2)(x+1)\cdot\dfrac{4}{x+2}+(x+2)(x+1)\cdot\dfrac{3}{x+1}=3$$

$$(x+1)\cdot 4+(x+2)\cdot 3=3$$

$$4x+4+3x+6=3$$

$$7x+10=3$$

$$7x=-7$$

$$x=-1$$

Our result -1 is not a solution because it is an excluded value. Since this is the only possible solution, we conclude that no number is a solution. That is, the solution is the empty set.

25.

$$\frac{5}{x^2-4}+\frac{2}{x+2}=\frac{4}{x-2}$$

$$\frac{5}{(x-2)(x+2)}+\frac{2}{x+2}=\frac{4}{x-2}$$

We note that -2 and 2 are excluded values.

$$(x-2)(x+2)\cdot\left(\frac{5}{(x-2)(x+2)}+\frac{2}{x+2}\right)$$

$$=(x-2)(x+2)\cdot\left(\frac{4}{x-2}\right)$$

$$(x-2)(x+2)\cdot\frac{5}{(x-2)(x+2)}+(x-2)(x+2)\cdot\frac{2}{x+2}$$

$$=(x+2)\cdot4$$

$$5+(x-2)\cdot2=4x+8$$

$$5+2x-4=4x+8$$

$$2x+1=4x+8$$

$$-2x=7$$

$$x=-\frac{7}{2}$$

Since $-\frac{7}{2}$ is not an excluded value, we conclude that $-\frac{7}{2}$ is the solution of the equation.

27.

$$2+\frac{4}{k-2}=\frac{8}{k^2-2k}$$

$$2+\frac{4}{k-2}=\frac{8}{k(k-2)}$$

$$k(k-2)\left(2+\frac{4}{k-2}\right)=k(k-2)\frac{8}{k(k-2)}$$

$$2k(k-2)+4k=8$$

$$2k^2-4k+4k=8$$

$$2k^2=8$$

$$k^2=4$$

$$k=\pm2$$

$k=2$ makes the denominators $k-2$ and k^2-2k equal 0. The solution is $k=-2$.

29.

$$\frac{-48}{x^2-2x-15}-\frac{6}{x+3}=\frac{7}{x-5}$$

$$(x-5)(x+3)\cdot\left(\frac{-48}{(x-5)(x+3)}-\frac{6}{x+3}\right)$$

$$=\frac{7}{x-5}\cdot(x-5)(x+3)$$

$$-48-6(x-5)=7(x+3)$$

$$-48-6x+30=7x+21$$

$$-6x-18=7x+21$$

$$-13x=39$$

$$x=-3$$

$x=-3$ makes the denominators $x^2-2x-15$ and $x+3$ equal 0. This equation has no solution.

31.

$$\frac{x^2-23}{2x^2-5x-3}+\frac{2}{x-3}=\frac{-1}{2x+1}$$

$$(2x+1)(x-3)\left(\frac{(x^2-23)}{(2x+1)(x-3)}+\frac{2}{x-3}\right)$$

$$=\frac{-1(2x+1)(x-3)}{2x+1}$$

$$x^2-23+2(2x+1)=-(x-3)$$

$$x^2-23+4x+2=-x+3$$

$$x^2+5x-24=0$$

$$(x+8)(x-3)=0$$

$$x+8=0 \qquad x-3=0$$

$$x=-8 \qquad x=3$$

$x=3$ makes the denominators $2x^2-5x-3$ and $x-3$ equal 0. The solution is $x=-8$.

33.

$$\frac{w+7}{w^2-9}=\frac{-w+2}{w-3}$$

$$(w-3)(w+3)\frac{w+7}{(w-3)(w+3)}=\frac{(w-3)(w+3)(-w+2)}{w-3}$$

$$w+7=(w+3)(-w+2)$$

$$w+7=-w^2-3w+2w+6$$

$$w^2+2w+1=0$$

$$(w+1)^2=0$$

$$w=-1$$

The solution is $w=-1$.

35.
$$x^2 \cdot \left(3 + \frac{2}{x}\right) = \frac{4}{x^2} \cdot x^2$$
$$3x^2 + 2x = 4$$
$$3x^2 + 2x - 4 = 0$$
$$x = \frac{-2 \pm \sqrt{2^2 - 4(3)(-4)}}{2(3)}$$
$$x = \frac{-2 \pm \sqrt{4 + 48}}{6}$$
$$= \frac{-2 \pm \sqrt{52}}{6}$$
$$= \frac{-2 \pm 2\sqrt{13}}{6}$$
$$= \frac{-1 \pm \sqrt{13}}{3}$$

The solutions are $x = \dfrac{-1 \pm \sqrt{13}}{3}$.

37.
$$\frac{5}{r^2 - 3r + 2} - \frac{1}{r - 2} = \frac{r + 6}{3r - 3}$$
$$\frac{5}{(r - 2)(r - 1)} - \frac{1}{r - 2} = \frac{r + 6}{3(r - 1)}$$
$$3(r - 2)(r - 1)\left(\frac{5}{(r - 2)(r - 1)} - \frac{1}{r - 2}\right)$$
$$= 3(r - 2)(r - 1)\frac{r + 6}{3(r - 1)}$$
$$15 - 3(r - 1) = (r - 2)(r + 6)$$
$$15 - 3r + 3 = r^2 + 6r - 2r - 12$$
$$18 - 3r = r^2 + 4r - 12$$
$$0 = r^2 + 7r - 30$$
$$0 = (r + 10)(r - 3)$$
The solutions are $r = 3$ and $r = -10$.

39.
$$\frac{2x}{x + 1} - \frac{3}{2} = \frac{-2}{x + 2}$$
$$2(x + 1)(x + 2)\left(\frac{2x}{x + 1} - \frac{3}{2}\right) = \frac{2(x + 1)(x + 2)(-2)}{x + 2}$$
$$4x(x + 2) - 3(x + 2)(x + 1) = -4(x + 1)$$
$$4x^2 + 8x - 3(x^2 + 3x + 2) = -4x - 4$$
$$4x^2 + 8x - 3x^2 - 9x - 6 = -4x - 4$$
$$x^2 + 3x - 2 = 0$$

$$x = \frac{-(3) \pm \sqrt{(3)^2 - 4(1)(-2)}}{2(1)} = \frac{-3 \pm \sqrt{17}}{2}$$
The solutions are $x = \dfrac{-3 \pm \sqrt{17}}{2}$.

41.
$$\frac{x - 4}{x^2 - 7x + 12} - \frac{x + 2}{x - 3} = 0$$
$$\frac{x - 4}{x^2 - 7x + 12} = \frac{x + 2}{x - 3}$$
$$\frac{x - 4}{(x - 4)(x - 3)} = \frac{x + 2}{x - 3}$$
$$\frac{1}{x - 3} = \frac{x + 2}{x - 3}$$
$$\left(\frac{x - 3}{1}\right) \cdot \frac{1}{x - 3} = \frac{x + 2}{x - 3} \cdot \left(\frac{x - 3}{1}\right)$$
$$1 = x + 2$$
$$-1 = x$$
The solution is $x = -1$.

43.
$$\frac{t}{t - 3} = 2 - \frac{5}{3 - t}$$
$$(t - 3) \cdot \frac{t}{t - 3} = \left(2 + \frac{5}{t - 3}\right) \cdot (t - 3)$$
$$t = 2(t - 3) + 5$$
$$t = 2t - 6 + 5$$
$$-t = -1$$
$$t = 1$$
The solution is $t = 1$.

45.
$$\frac{12}{9 - x^2} + \frac{3}{x + 3} = \frac{2}{x - 3}$$
$$\frac{12}{(3 - x)(3 + x)} + \frac{3}{3 + x} = \frac{2}{3 - x}$$
$$(3 - x)(3 + x) \cdot \left(\frac{12}{(3 - x)(3 + x)} + \frac{3}{3 + x}\right)$$
$$= \frac{2}{3 - x} \cdot (3 - x)(3 + x)$$
$$12 + 3(3 - x) = 2(3 + x)$$
$$12 + 9 - 3x = 6 + 2x$$
$$15 = 5x$$
$$3 = x$$
$x = 3$ makes the denominators $9 - x^2$ and $x - 3$ equal 0. This equation has no solution.

47.

$$\frac{x+2}{x-3} - \frac{x-3}{x+2} = \frac{5x}{x^2-x-6}$$

$$(x-3)(x+2)\left(\frac{x+2}{x-3} - \frac{x-3}{x+2}\right) = \frac{(x-3)(x+2)5x}{(x-3)(x+2)}$$

$$(x+2)^2 - (x-3)^2 = 5x$$

$$x^2 + 4x + 4 - (x^2 - 6x + 9) = 5x$$

$$10x - 5 = 5x$$

$$5x = 5$$

$$x = 1$$

The solution is $x = 1$.

49.

$$\frac{2y}{y-2} - \frac{2y-5}{y^2-7y+10} = \frac{-4}{y-5}$$

$$(y-2)(y-5)\cdot\left(\frac{2y}{y-2} - \frac{2y-5}{(y-2)(y-5)}\right) = \frac{-4}{y-5}\cdot(y-2)(y-5)$$

$$2y(y-5) - (2y-5) = -4(y-2)$$

$$2y^2 - 10y - 2y + 5 = -4y + 8$$

$$2y^2 - 8y - 3 = 0$$

$$y = \frac{-(-8)\pm\sqrt{(-8)^2 - 4(2)(-3)}}{2(2)}$$

$$= \frac{8\pm\sqrt{88}}{4}$$

$$= \frac{8\pm 2\sqrt{22}}{4}$$

$$= \frac{4\pm\sqrt{22}}{2}$$

The solutions are $y = \dfrac{4\pm\sqrt{22}}{2}$.

51.

$$\frac{x-2}{x^2-2x-3} + \frac{x+5}{x^2-1} = \frac{x+3}{x^2-4x+3}$$

$$\frac{x-2}{(x-3)(x+1)} + \frac{x+5}{(x-1)(x+1)} = \frac{x+3}{(x-3)(x-1)}$$

$$(x-3)(x-1)(x+1)\cdot\left(\frac{x-2}{(x-3)(x+1)} + \frac{x+5}{(x-1)(x+1)}\right)$$

$$= \frac{(x+3)(x-3)(x-1)(x+1)}{(x-3)(x-1)}$$

$$(x-2)(x-1) + (x+5)(x-3) = (x+3)(x+1)$$

$$x^2 - 3x + 2 + x^2 + 2x - 15 = x^2 + 4x + 3$$

$$x^2 - 5x - 16 = 0$$

$$x = \frac{-(-5)\pm\sqrt{(-5)^2 - 4(1)(-16)}}{2(1)}$$

$$= \frac{5\pm\sqrt{89}}{2}$$

The solutions are $x = \dfrac{5\pm\sqrt{89}}{2}$.

53.

$$\frac{5}{x} - \frac{2}{x^2} = 4$$

$$x^2\cdot\left(\frac{5}{x} - \frac{2}{x^2}\right) = 4\cdot x^2$$

$$5x - 2 = 4x^2$$

$$4x^2 - 5x + 2 = 0$$

$$x = \frac{-(-5)\pm\sqrt{(-5)^2 - 4(4)(2)}}{2(4)}$$

$$= \frac{5\pm\sqrt{-7}}{8}$$

$$= \frac{5\pm i\sqrt{7}}{8}$$

The complex solutions are $x = \dfrac{5\pm i\sqrt{7}}{8}$.

55.

$$\frac{2}{t-5} - \frac{3t}{t+5} = \frac{35}{t^2-25}$$

$$(t-5)(t+5)\cdot\left(\frac{2}{t-5} - \frac{3t}{t+5}\right) = \frac{35(t-5)(t+5)}{(t-5)(t+5)}$$

$$2(t+5) - 3t(t-5) = 35$$

$$2t + 10 - 3t^2 + 15t = 35$$

$$3t^2 - 17t + 25 = 0$$

$$t = \frac{-(-17)\pm\sqrt{(-17)^2 - 4(3)(25)}}{2(3)}$$

$$= \frac{17\pm\sqrt{-11}}{6}$$

$$= \frac{17\pm i\sqrt{11}}{6}$$

The complex solutions are $t = \dfrac{17\pm i\sqrt{11}}{6}$.

57.

$$\frac{x-1}{3x-12}+\frac{-x+1}{x-5}=\frac{4x}{x^2-9x+20}$$

$$\frac{x-1}{3(x-4)}+\frac{-x+1}{x-5}=\frac{4x}{(x-4)(x-5)}$$

$$3(x-4)(x-5)\cdot\left(\frac{x-1}{3(x-4)}+\frac{-x+1}{x-5}\right)=\frac{3(x-4)(x-5)4x}{(x-4)(x-5)}$$

$$(x-5)(x-1)+3(x-4)(-x+1)=12x$$

$$x^2-6x+5+3(-x^2+5x-4)=12x$$

$$x^2-6x+5-3x^2+15x-12=12x$$

$$-2x^2-3x-7=0$$

$$2x^2+3x+7=0$$

$$x=\frac{-3\pm\sqrt{3^2-4(2)(7)}}{2(2)}$$

$$=\frac{-3\pm\sqrt{-47}}{4}$$

$$=\frac{-3\pm i\sqrt{47}}{4}$$

The complex solutions are $x=\dfrac{-3\pm i\sqrt{47}}{4}$.

59.

$$4=\frac{3}{x-5}$$

$$(x-5)4=(x-5)\frac{3}{x-5}$$

$$4x-20=3$$

$$4x=23$$

$$x=\frac{23}{4}$$

The solution for $f(x)=4$ is $x=\dfrac{23}{4}$.

61.

$$-1=\frac{5}{x-1}+\frac{3}{x+1}$$

$$(x-1)(x+1)\cdot(-1)=(x-1)(x+1)\left(\frac{5}{x-1}+\frac{3}{x+1}\right)$$

$$-1(x^2-1)=5(x+1)+3(x-1)$$

$$-x^2+1=5x+5+3x-3$$

$$-x^2+1=8x+2$$

$$0=x^2+8x+1$$

$$x=\frac{-8\pm\sqrt{64-4(1)(1)}}{2}$$

$$=\frac{-8\pm\sqrt{60}}{2}$$

$$=\frac{-8\pm\sqrt{4\cdot15}}{2}$$

$$=\frac{-8\pm2\sqrt{15}}{2}$$

$$=-4\pm\sqrt{15}$$

$$\approx-0.13\text{ and }-7.87$$

The solutions for $f(x)=-1$ are $x=-4\pm\sqrt{15}$. The approximate solutions are $x\approx-0.13$ and $x\approx-7.87$.

63.

$$0=\frac{x-1}{x-5}-\frac{x+2}{x+3}$$

$$(x-5)(x+3)\cdot0=(x-5)(x+3)\left(\frac{x-1}{x-5}-\frac{x+2}{x+3}\right)$$

$$0=(x+3)(x-1)-(x-5)(x+2)$$

$$0=x^2+2x-3-(x^2-3x-10)$$

$$0=x^2+2x-3-x^2+3x+10$$

$$0=5x+7$$

$$-7=5x$$

$$-\frac{7}{5}=x$$

The x-intercept is $\left(-\dfrac{7}{5},0\right)$.

65.

$$F=\frac{mv^2}{r}$$

$$r\cdot F=\frac{mv^2}{r}\cdot r$$

$$\frac{Fr}{F}=\frac{mv^2}{F}$$

$$r=\frac{mv^2}{F}$$

67.

$$F=\frac{-GMm}{r^2}$$

$$r^2\cdot F=\frac{-GMm}{r^2}\cdot r^2$$

$$\frac{r^2F}{-Gm}=\frac{-GMm}{-Gm}$$

$$M=-\frac{r^2F}{Gm}$$

69.

$$P = \frac{A}{1+rt}$$

$$(1+rt) \cdot P = \left(\frac{A}{1+rt}\right) \cdot (1+rt)$$

$$P + Prt = A$$

$$\frac{Prt}{Pr} = \frac{A-P}{Pr}$$

$$t = \frac{A-P}{Pr}$$

71.

$$74.5 = \frac{4.7t^2 - 77t + 350}{0.058t^2 - 0.82t + 3.6}$$

$$74.5\left(0.058t^2 - 0.82t + 3.6\right) = 4.7t^2 - 77t + 350 \qquad \text{y}$$

$$4.321t^2 - 61.09t + 268.2 = 4.7t^2 - 77t + 350$$

$$0 \approx 0.38t^2 - 15.91t + 81.8$$

$$t \approx \frac{-(-15.91) \pm \sqrt{(-15.91)^2 - 4(0.38)(81.8)}}{2(0.38)}$$

$$\approx \frac{15.91 \pm \sqrt{128.79}}{0.76}$$

$$\approx \frac{15.91 \pm 11.35}{0.76} \approx 6 \text{ and } 36$$

Assuming that the model does not break down for low values of t, 74.5% of the cumulative awarded miles were redeemed in 1980 + 6 = 1986, and will be redeemed in the year 1980 + 36 = 2016.

73. a.

$$P(t) = \frac{B(t)}{(N+B)(t)} \cdot 100$$

$$= \frac{100 \cdot B(t)}{(N+B)(t)}$$

$$= \frac{100\left(-0.036t^2 + 0.176t + 1.28\right)}{-0.036t^2 + 0.346t + 4.28}$$

$$= \frac{-3.6t^2 + 17.6t + 128}{-0.036t^2 + 0.346t + 4.28}$$

b.

$$P(8) = \frac{-3.6(8)^2 + 17.6(8) + 128}{-0.036(8)^2 + 0.346(8) + 4.28}$$

$$\approx 8.09$$

This means that in the year 2000 + 8 = 2008, about 8.1% of Mattel's sales were Barbie toys.

c.

$$\frac{-3.6t^2 + 17.6t + 128}{-0.036t^2 + 0.346t + 4.28} = 15$$

$$-3.6t^2 + 17.6t + 128 = 15\left(-0.036t^2 + 0.346t + 4.28\right)$$

$$-3.6t^2 + 17.6t + 128 = -0.54t^2 + 5.19t + 64.2$$

$$-3.06t^2 + 12.41t + 63.8 = 0$$

$$t = \frac{-(12.41) \pm \sqrt{(12.41)^2 - 4(-3.06)(63.8)}}{2(-3.06)} \approx$$

$$\approx \frac{-12.41 \pm \sqrt{934.92}}{-6.12}$$

$$\approx \frac{-12.41 \pm 30.58}{-6.12}$$

$$\approx -2.97 \text{ and } 7.02$$

This means that in the years 1997 and 2007, 15% of Mattel's sales were Barbie toys.

d.

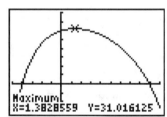

The maximum point on the graph of P over the interval $-5 < t < 10$ is approximately $(1.38, 31)$. This point shows that in the year 2001, the percent sales for Barbie toys reached a maximum of about 31%.

75.
The graphs of $y = \dfrac{5}{x-2}$ and $y = x^2 - 6x + 10$ intersect at approximately $(4.2, 2.3)$. The solution of the equation is $x \approx 4.2$.

77.
The graphs of $y = \dfrac{5}{x-2}$ and $y = 4$ intersect at approximately $(3.3, 4)$. The solution of the equation is $x \approx 3.3$.

79.
The graphs of $y = \dfrac{5}{x-2}$ and $y = -x^2 + x - 1$ intersect at approximately $(-0.6, -1.9)$. The solution of the system is approximately $(-0.6, -1.9)$.

81.

$$2 = \frac{0+a}{0+b} \qquad \text{and} \qquad \frac{5}{2} = \frac{1+a}{1+b}$$

$$2 = \frac{a}{b} \qquad 2(1+b)\frac{5}{2} = 2(1+b)\frac{1+a}{1+b}$$

$$2b = a \qquad 5(1+b) = 2(1+a)$$

By substituting $2b$ for a in the second equation we get the following:

$$5(1+b) = 2(1+2b)$$
$$5+5b = 2+4b$$
$$b = -3$$

By substituting -3 in the first equation for b we get:

$$2 = \frac{a}{-3}$$
$$-6 = a$$

The value for a is -6, and the value for b is -3, so

$$f(x) = \frac{x-6}{x-3}.$$

83. A more efficient way would be to start by subtracting $\dfrac{4}{x+2}$ from both sides of the equation. Then, cross multiply:

$$\frac{4}{x+2} - \frac{2}{x} = \frac{1}{x+2}$$

$$\frac{4}{\cancel{x+2}} - \frac{2}{x} - \frac{4}{\cancel{x+2}} = \frac{1}{x+2} - \frac{4}{x+2}$$

$$\frac{-2}{x} = \frac{-3}{x+2}$$

$$-2(x+2) = -3x$$

$$-2x-4 = -3x$$

$$-4 = -x$$

$$x = 4$$

85. Answers may vary. One possibility follows: The student has simplified the right side of the equation but has not solved the equation. The correct solution is:

$$\frac{7}{x^2+x-20} = \frac{4}{x+5} - \frac{2}{x-4}$$

$$\frac{7}{(x+5)(x-4)} = \frac{4}{x+5} - \frac{2}{x-4}$$

We note that -5 and 4 are excluded values.

$$(x+5)(x-4) \cdot \left(\frac{7}{(x+5)(x-4)} \right)$$

$$= (x+5)(x-4) \cdot \left(\frac{4}{x+5} - \frac{2}{x-4} \right)$$

$$7 = (x+5)(x-4) \cdot \left(\frac{4}{x+5} \right) - (x+5)(x-4) \cdot \left(\frac{2}{x-4} \right)$$

$$7 = (x-4) \cdot 4 - (x+5) \cdot 2$$

$$7 = 4x-16-2x-10$$

$$7 = 2x-26$$

$$33 = 2x$$

$$x = \frac{33}{2}$$

Since $\dfrac{33}{2}$ is not an excluded value, we conclude that $\dfrac{33}{2}$ is the solution of the equation.

87. Answers may vary. One possibility follows: When simplifying a rational expression, we cannot multiply it by the LCD because doing so will cause a non-equivalent expression. We can multiply the numerator and denominator of the rational expression by the same expression, but generally will not be the LCD.

When solving a rational equation, we can multiply both sides of the equation by the LCD. Doing so will gives a simpler equation to solve, but we have to be sure to discard any solutions that are excluded values.

89.
$$\frac{5}{x} + \frac{4}{x+1} - \frac{3}{x} = \frac{5}{x} \cdot \frac{(x+1)}{(x+1)} + \frac{4}{x+1} \cdot \frac{x}{x} - \frac{3}{x} \cdot \frac{(x+1)}{(x+1)}$$

$$= \frac{5(x+1) + 4x - 3(x+1)}{x(x+1)}$$

$$= \frac{5x+5+4x-3x-3}{x(x+1)}$$

$$= \frac{6x+2}{x(x+1)}$$

91.
$$\frac{5}{t}+\frac{4}{t+1}=\frac{3}{t}$$
$$t(t+1)\cdot\left(\frac{5}{t}+\frac{4}{t+1}\right)=\frac{3}{t}\cdot t(t+1)$$
$$5(t+1)+4t=3(t+1)$$
$$5t+5+4t=3t+3$$
$$6t=-2$$
$$t=-\frac{1}{3}$$

The solution is $-\frac{1}{3}$.

93.
$$\frac{x+2}{x^2-5x+6}-\frac{x+1}{x^2-4}=\frac{4}{x^2-x-6}$$
$$\frac{x+2}{(x-2)(x-3)}-\frac{x+1}{(x-2)(x+2)}=\frac{4}{(x-3)(x+2)}$$
$$(x-2)(x+2)(x-3)\cdot\left(\frac{x+2}{(x-2)(x-3)}-\frac{x+1}{(x-2)(x+2)}\right)$$
$$=\frac{4(x-2)(x+2)(x-3)}{(x-3)(x+2)}\cdot$$
$$(x+2)^2-(x+1)(x-3)=4(x-2)$$
$$x^2+4x+4-(x^2-2x-3)=4x-8$$
$$6x+7=4x-8$$
$$2x=-15$$
$$x=-\frac{15}{2}$$

The solution is $-\frac{15}{2}$.

95.
$$\frac{x+2}{x^2-5x+6}-\frac{x+1}{x^2-4}+\frac{4}{x^2-x-6}$$
$$\frac{x+2}{(x-2)(x-3)}-\frac{x+1}{(x-2)(x+2)}+\frac{4}{(x-3)(x+2)}$$
$$\frac{x+2}{(x-2)(x-3)}\cdot\frac{(x+2)}{(x+2)}-\frac{x+1}{(x-2)(x+2)}\cdot\frac{(x-3)}{(x-3)}$$
$$+\frac{4}{(x-3)(x+2)}\cdot\frac{(x-2)}{(x-2)}$$
$$=\frac{(x+2)^2-(x+1)(x-3)+4(x-2)}{(x-2)(x-3)(x+2)}$$
$$=\frac{x^2+4x+4-(x^2-2x-3)+4x-8}{(x-2)(x-3)(x+2)}$$
$$=\frac{10x-1}{(x-2)(x-3)(x+2)}$$

97.
$$2p^3-p^2=8p-4$$
$$2p^3-p^2-8p+4=0$$
$$2p^3-8p-p^2+4=0$$
$$2p(p^2-4)-1\cdot(p^2-4)=0$$
$$(p^2-4)(2p-1)=0$$
$$(p-2)(p+2)(2p-1)=0$$
$$p=2 \quad p=-2 \quad p=\frac{1}{2}$$

99.
$$2(4)^x+3=106$$
$$2(4)^x=103$$
$$(4)^x=51.5$$
$$x=\log_4 51.5$$
$$=\frac{\log_{10}(51.5)}{\log_{10}(4)}$$
$$\approx 2.8433$$

101.
$$\log_3(5x-4)-\log_3(2x-3)=2$$
$$\log_3\left(\frac{5x-4}{2x-3}\right)=2$$
$$3^2=\frac{5x-4}{2x-3}$$
$$9\cdot(2x-3)=\frac{5x-4}{2x-3}\cdot(2x-3)$$
$$18x-27=5x-4$$
$$13x=23$$
$$x=\frac{23}{13}$$

103.

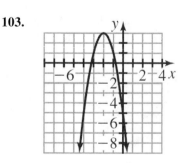

$f(x)=-2(x+2)^2+3$ is a quadratic function with a vertex at $(-2, 3)$.

105.
$$-2(x+2)^2 + 3 = -15$$
$$-2(x+2)^2 = -18$$
$$(x+2)^2 = 9$$
$$\sqrt{(x+2)^2} = \sqrt{9}$$
$$|x+2| = 3$$

$x+2 = 3$ and $x+2 = -3$
$x = 1$ and $x = -5$

$-2(x+2)^2 + 3 = -15$ is a quadratic equation in one variable with solutions $x = 1$ and $x = -5$.

107.
$$-2(x+2)^2 + 3 = -2(x^2 + 4x + 4) + 3$$
$$= -2x^2 - 8x - 8 + 3$$
$$= -2x^2 - 8x - 5$$

$-2(x+2)^2 + 3$ is a quadratic expression in one variable.

Homework 12.6

1. **a.** $C(n) = 1250 + 350n$

b. $M(n) = \dfrac{1250 + 350n}{n}$

c. $M(30) = \dfrac{1250 + 350(30)}{30}$
$\approx \$391.67$

d.
$$400 = \dfrac{1250 + 350n}{n}$$
$$400n = 1250 + 350n$$
$$50n = 1250$$
$$n = 25$$
The minimum number of students needed to go on the trip is 25.

3. **a.** $T(n) = 500 + 50n$

b. $M(n) = \dfrac{500 + 50n}{n}$

c. $M(270) = \dfrac{500 + 50(270)}{270}$
$\approx \$51.85$

If 270 people attend the reunion, the mean cost per person is \$51.85.

d.
$$60 = \dfrac{500 + 50n}{n}$$
$$60n = 500 + 50n$$
$$10n = 500$$
$$n = 50$$
For the mean cost per person to be \$60, 50 people would have to attend the reunion.

e.

f. As n gets very large, $M(n)$ decreases but never drops below 50. This makes sense in terms of the restaurant fees because each person pays \$50 plus an equal share of \$500 – the cost for the band. So the more people who attend (i.e., as n gets larger), the closer the mean cost per person gets to \$50.

5. **a.** $C(n) = 90000 + 7000n$

b. $B(n) = \dfrac{90000 + 7000n}{n}$

c. $P(n) = \dfrac{90000 + 7000n}{n} + 2000$
$$= \dfrac{90000 + 7000n}{n} + \dfrac{2000}{1} \cdot \dfrac{n}{n}$$
$$= \dfrac{90000 + 7000n}{n} + \dfrac{2000n}{n}$$
$$= \dfrac{90000 + 9000n}{n}$$

d. $P(40) = \dfrac{90000 + 9000(40)}{40}$
$= 11250$
If the manufacturer produces and sells 40 cars, it would have to charge \$11250 for each car in order to make a profit of \$2000 per car.

e. As the values of *n* get very large, $P(n)$ gets close to 9000. If a very large number of cars are produced and sold, the price per car can be just a little more than \$9000 to insure a profit of \$2000 per car.

7. a. By using the linear regression feature of a graphing calculator, we get the equation:
$$I(t) = 413.73t + 4064.65$$

b.
$$M(t) = \frac{I(t)}{H(t)}$$
$$= \frac{413.73t + 4064.65}{0.0015t + 0.091}$$

c. $M(t)$ is measured in dollars per household. This makes sense, since $I(t)$ is measured in billions of dollars and $H(t)$ is measured in billions of households.

d.
$$108,000 = \frac{413.73t + 4064.65}{0.0015t + 0.091}$$
$$108,000(0.0015t + 0.091) = 413.73t + 4064.65$$
$$162t + 9828 = 413.73t + 4064.65$$
$$5763.35 = 251.73t$$
$$22.89 \approx t$$
The mean household income should reach $108,000 in the year 1990 + 23 = 2013.

e.

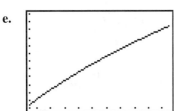

$M(t)$ is increasing over the interval $5 < t < 25$. This means that the average annual income per household is steadily increasing between 1995 and 2015.

9. a. By using the quadratic regression feature of a graphing calculator, we get the equation:
$$N(t) = 0.11t^2 - 1.09t + 8.9$$

b.
$$M(t) = \frac{C(t)}{N(t)}$$
$$= \frac{64t^2 - 788t + 5750}{0.11t^2 - 1.09t + 8.9}$$

c. $M(t)$ is measured in dollars per decision. This makes sense, since $C(t)$ is measured in millions of dollars and $N(t)$ is measured in millions of decisions.

d.
$$M(24) = \frac{64(24)^2 - 788(24) + 5750}{0.11(24)^2 - 1.09(24) + 8.9}$$
$$= \frac{23,702}{46.1}$$
$$\approx 514.14$$
In 2014, the mean cost per decision is $514.14.

e.
$$\frac{64t^2 - 788t + 5750}{0.11t^2 - 1.09t + 8.9} = 520$$
$$64t^2 - 788t + 5750 = 520\left(0.11t^2 - 1.09t + 8.9\right)$$
$$64t^2 - 788t + 5750 = 57.2t^2 - 566.8t + 4628$$
$$6.8t^2 - 221.2t + 1122 = 0$$
$$a = 6.8, b = -221.2, c = 1122$$
$$t = \frac{-(-221.2) \pm \sqrt{(-221.2)^2 - 4(6.8)(1122)}}{2(6.8)}$$
$$t = \frac{221.2 \pm \sqrt{18,411.04}}{13.6}$$
$$t \approx 26, 6$$
The mean cost per decision will be $520 in 2016.

11. a. By using the linear regression feature of a graphing calculator, we get the equation:
$$B(t) = 288.6t - 1493$$

b.
$$E(t) = W(t) + M(t)$$
$$= (0.17t + 5.59) + (0.076t + 5.38)$$
$$= 0.246t + 10.97$$

c.
$$A(t) = \frac{B(t)}{E(t)}$$
$$= \frac{288.6t - 1493}{0.246t + 10.97}$$

d. In the year 2013, $t = 33$, so:
$$A(33) = \frac{288.6(33) - 1493}{0.246(33) + 10.97}$$
$$\approx 420.73$$
The mean amount of money spent on books per student in the year 2013 will be about

$420.73.

e. $\dfrac{288.6t - 1493}{0.246t + 10.97} = 440$

$288.6t - 1493 = 440(0.246t + 10.97)$

$288.6t - 1493 = 108.24t + 4826.8$

$180.36t = 6319.8$

$t \approx 35.04$

The mean amount of money spent on books per student will reach about $440 in the year $1980 + 35 = 2015$.

13. a. Using quadratic regression, we get the following equations:

$W(t) = 0.30t^2 + 6.99t + 456.39$

$M(t) = 0.24t^2 - 1.19t + 478.36$

b. $W(t) + M(t)$

$= (0.30t^2 + 6.99t + 456.39) + (0.24t^2 - 1.19t + 478.36)$

$= 0.54t^2 + 5.80t + 934.75$

The input, t, represents the number of years since 1980. The output, $W(t) + M(t)$, represents the total number of people who earned a bachelors degree in that year.

c. $P(t) = \dfrac{M(t)}{W(t) + M(t)}$

$= \left(\dfrac{0.24t^2 - 1.19t + 478.36}{0.54t^2 + 5.80t + 934.75} \right) 100$

$= \dfrac{24t^2 - 119t + 47836}{0.54t^2 + 5.80t + 934.75}$

d. $41 = \dfrac{24t^2 - 119t + 47836}{0.54t^2 + 5.80t + 934.75}$

$41(0.54t^2 + 5.80t + 934.75)$

$= 24t^2 - 119t + 47836$

$22.14t^2 + 237.80t + 38324.75$

$= 24t^2 - 119t + 47836$

$0 = 1.86t^2 - 356.80t + 9511.25$

$t = \dfrac{356.80 \pm \sqrt{(-356.80)^2 - 4(1.86)(9511.25)}}{2(1.86)}$

$= \dfrac{356.80 \pm \sqrt{56542.54}}{3.72}$

$\approx \dfrac{356.80 \pm 237.79}{3.72}$

$\approx \dfrac{356.80 - 237.79}{3.72} \qquad \approx \dfrac{356.80 + 237.79}{3.72}$

$t \approx 31.99 \qquad\qquad t \approx 159.84$

The possibility of model breakdown makes the larger solution unrealistic. Therefore, in the year $1980 + 32 = 2012$, 41% of the people who earn bachelor's degrees will be men.

e.

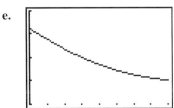

The graph of P is decreasing over the interval $0 < t < 40$. The number of bachelor's degrees earned by women has been increasing at a faster rate compared to men, which accounts for the decrease in the percentage of bachelor's degrees earned by men.

15. a. Using quadratic regression, we get the following equation:

$C(t) = 0.14t^2 + 0.65t + 7.69$

$F(t) = 1.98t^2 - 0.45t + 121.54$

b. $C(t) + F(t)$

$= (0.14t^2 + 0.65t + 7.69) + (1.98t^2 - 0.45t + 121.54)$

$= 2.12t^2 + 0.20t + 129.23$

The input, t, represents the number of years since 2000. The output, $C(t) + F(t)$, represents the total sales at all limited-service restaurants in billions of dollars.

c.

$$P(t) = \left(\frac{C(t)}{C(t) + F(t)}\right)100$$

$$= \frac{0.14t^2 + 0.65t + 7.69}{2.12t^2 + 0.20t + 129.23} \cdot 100$$

$$= \frac{14t^2 + 65t + 769}{2.12t^2 + 0.20t + 129.23}$$

d.

$$8.0 = \frac{14t^2 + 65t + 769}{2.12t^2 + 0.20t + 129.23}$$

$$8.0(2.12t^2 + 0.20t + 129.23) = 14t^2 + 65t + 769$$

$$16.96t^2 + 1.60t + 1033.84 = 14t^2 + 65t + 769$$

$$0 = 2.96t^2 - 63.40t + 264.84$$

$$t = \frac{63.40 \pm \sqrt{(-63.40)^2 - 4(2.96)(264.84)}}{2(2.96)}$$

$$\approx \frac{63.40 \pm \sqrt{883.85}}{5.92}$$

$$\approx \frac{63.40 \pm 29.73}{5.92}$$

$$\approx \frac{63.40 - 29.73}{5.92} \qquad \approx \frac{63.40 + 29.73}{5.92}$$

$$t \approx 5.68 \qquad\qquad t \approx 15.73$$

The first time 8% of sales at all limited-service restaurants from coffeehouses and doughnut shops occurred was around 2000 + 6 = 2006. The next time sales will be at 8% will be around 2000 + 16 = 2016.

17. Using $t = \dfrac{d}{s}$ gives the following:

$$t = \frac{85}{60} \approx 1.4 \text{ hours}$$

19. a.

$$T(a) = \frac{253}{a + 75} + \frac{410}{a + 65}$$

b.

$$T(3) = \frac{253}{3 + 75} + \frac{410}{3 + 65}$$

$$= \frac{253}{78} + \frac{410}{68}$$

$$\approx 3.24 + 6.03$$

$$\approx 9.3 \text{ hours}$$

c. Using a graphing calculator table:

X	Y1
3	9.273
4	9.1446
5	9.0196
5.1	9.0073
■	8.9951

X=5.2

The equation yields a time of $T(a) = 9$ hours for a value of $a \approx 5.2$. So, the student would have to exceed the speed limit by about 5.2 mph for a 9 hour driving time.

21. a.

$$T(a) = \frac{83}{a + 70} + \frac{37}{a + 65}$$

b.

$$T(0) = \frac{83}{0 + 70} + \frac{37}{0 + 65}$$

$$= \frac{83}{70} + \frac{37}{65}$$

$$\approx 1.1857 + 0.5692$$

$$\approx 1.75 \text{ hours}$$

$$T(10) = \frac{83}{10 + 70} + \frac{37}{10 + 65}$$

$$= \frac{83}{80} + \frac{37}{75}$$

$$\approx 1.04 + 0.49$$

$$\approx 1.53 \text{ hours}$$

This means that if the student drives the speed limit, her driving time will be about 1.75 hours. If she drives 10 mph over the speed limit, her driving time will be about 1.53 hours.

c. $T(0) - T(10) = 0.22$

This shows the amount of time she will save if she drives 10 mph over the speed limit.

d.

$$1.6 = \frac{83}{a + 70} + \frac{37}{a + 65}$$

$$1.6(a + 70)(a + 65)$$

$$= \left(\frac{83}{a + 70} + \frac{37}{a + 65}\right)(a + 70)(a + 65)$$

$$1.6a^2 + 216a + 7280$$

$$= 83a + 5395 + 37a + 2590$$

$$1.6a^2 + 96a - 705 = 0$$

$$a = \frac{-96 \pm \sqrt{(96)^2 - 4(1.6)(-705)}}{2(1.6)}$$

$$a = \frac{-96 \pm \sqrt{13728}}{3.2}$$

The only solution that makes sense in this context for exceeding the speed limit is the

positive value $\frac{-96 + \sqrt{13728}}{3.2} \approx 6.61$ miles per

hour. This means that the student's driving time will be 1.6 hours if she exceeds the speed limit by 6.61 miles per hour.

23. a. $\frac{164}{a+70} + \frac{121}{a+65}$

$$= \left(\frac{164}{a+70}\right)\left(\frac{a+65}{a+65}\right) + \left(\frac{121}{a+65}\right)\left(\frac{a+70}{a+70}\right)$$

$$= \frac{164a + 10660}{(a+70)(a+65)} + \frac{121a + 8470}{(a+70)(a+65)}$$

$$= \frac{285a + 19130}{(a+70)(a+65)}$$

b. $\frac{285(10) + 19130}{(10+70)(10+65)} = \frac{2850 + 19130}{(80)(75)}$

$$= \frac{21980}{6000}$$

$$\approx 3.66 \text{ hours}$$

25. a. Linear:
$$L(t) = 0.525t - 12.22$$

Exponential:
$$E(t) = 0.43(1.056)^t$$

Quadratic:
$$Q(t) = 0.01t^2 - 0.47t + 6.1$$

The percentage of Americans who have shingles does not increase at a constant rate from year to year. So, the linear model would be the worst fit. The quadratic or exponential models provide a better fit of the data.

b. There is model breakdown for the linear model, because the model takes on negative values for ages less than 23 years. There is model breakdown also for the quadratic model, because it shows a decrease in the percent of Americans who have shingles, up to age 23. The exponential model is the best

fit of the data.

c. $25 = 0.43(1.056)^t$

$$\frac{25}{0.43} = (1.056)^t$$

$$58.14 \approx (1.056)^t$$

$$\log(58.14) \approx t \log(1.056)$$

$$t \approx \frac{\log(58.14)}{\log(1.056)}$$

$t \approx 74.56$

So, 25% of people of about age 75 have shingles.

d. The base of the exponential model is 1.056, which means that the number of Americans who have shingles increases by about 6% for each additional year that a person lives.

e. $f(t) = 0.43(1.056)^{85} \approx 44.15$

The model predicts that about 44.15% of Americans age 85 will have shingles. If the new vaccine reduces the number of shingles cases by 51%, then only about $44.15(1 - 0.51) = 21.6\%$ of people age 85 will have shingles.

27. $75x^3 - 50x^2 - 12x + 8$

$$= 25x^2(3x - 2) - 4(3x - 2)$$

$$= (3x - 2)(25x^2 - 4)$$

$$= (3x - 2)(5x - 2)(5x + 2)$$

$75x^3 - 50x^2 - 12x + 8$ is a third-degree polynomial (cubic) expression in one variable.

29. $75x^3 - 50x^2 = 12x - 8$

$$75x^3 - 50x^2 - 12x + 8 = 0$$

$$25x^2(3x - 2) - 4(3x - 2) = 0$$

$$(3x - 2)(25x^2 - 4) = 0$$

$$(3x - 2)(5x - 2)(5x + 2) = 0$$

$$x = \frac{2}{3}, x = \frac{2}{5} \text{ or } x = -\frac{2}{5}$$

$75x^3 - 50x^2 = 12x - 8$ is a third-degree

polynomial (cubic) equation in one variable.

31.

$$\left(x^2 + 2x - 3\right)\left(3x^2 - x - 4\right)$$

$$= 3x^2\left(x^2 + 2x - 3\right) - x\left(x^2 + 2x - 3\right) -$$

$$4\left(x^2 + 2x - 3\right)$$

$$= 3x^4 + 6x^3 - 9x^2 - x^3 - 2x^2 + 3x -$$

$$4x^2 - 8x + 12$$

$$= 3x^4 + 5x^3 - 15x^2 - 5x + 12$$

$\left(x^2 + 2x - 3\right)\left(3x^2 - x - 4\right)$ is a fourth-degree polynomial expression in one variable.

Homework 12.7

1. Let x be the cost for 6 months' use of AOL.

$$\frac{95.60}{4} = \frac{x}{6}$$

$$12\left(\frac{95.60}{4}\right) = 12\left(\frac{x}{6}\right)$$

$$286.80 = 2x$$

$$143.40 = x$$

The person will pay \$143.40 for 6 months' use of AOL.

3. Let x be the number of cups that contain 7 grams of sugar.

$$\frac{0.75}{4} = \frac{x}{7}$$

$$28\left(\frac{0.75}{4}\right) = 28\left(\frac{x}{7}\right)$$

$$5.25 = 4x$$

$$1.31 \approx x$$

Approximately 1.31 cubs of Post Grape-Nuts Flakes® cereal contains 7 grams of sugar.

5. Let x be the number of ounces of acid in 6 ounces of the solution.

$$\frac{10}{4} = \frac{6}{x}$$

$$4x\left(\frac{10}{4}\right) = 4x\left(\frac{6}{x}\right)$$

$$10x = 24$$

$$x = 2.4$$

There are 2.4 ounces of acid in 6 ounces of the solution.

7. Let x be the enrollment at the college.

$$\frac{3}{5} = \frac{21,720}{x}$$

$$5x\left(\frac{3}{5}\right) = 5x\left(\frac{21,720}{x}\right)$$

$$3x = 108,600$$

$$x = 36,200$$

The enrollment at the college is 36,200 students.

9. Let x be the number of inches on the map that represent 270 miles.

$$\frac{1.25}{50} = \frac{x}{270}$$

$$1350\left(\frac{1.25}{50}\right) = 1350\left(\frac{x}{270}\right)$$

$$33.75 = 5x$$

$$6.75 = x$$

On the map, 6.75 inches represent 270 miles.

11. Let x be the number of U.S. dollars that can be exchanged for 260 euros.

$$\frac{4.05}{5} = \frac{260}{x}$$

$$5x\left(\frac{4.05}{5}\right) = 5x\left(\frac{260}{x}\right)$$

$$4.05x = 1300$$

$$x \approx 320.99$$

Approximately 320.99 U.S. dollars can be exchanged for 260 euros.

13. Let x be the weight of the person on Earth who weights 28.5 pounds on the Moon.

$$\frac{29.8}{180} = \frac{28.5}{x}$$

$$180x\left(\frac{29.8}{180}\right) = 180x\left(\frac{28.5}{x}\right)$$

$$29.8x = 5130$$

$$x \approx 172$$

The person's weighs approximately 172 pounds on Earth if she weights 28.5 pounds on the Moon.

15. a. Let x be the amount the person will pay for 7 months of phone service.

$$\frac{175.50}{3} = \frac{x}{7}$$

$$21\left(\frac{175.50}{3}\right) = 21\left(\frac{x}{7}\right)$$

$$1228.50 = 3x$$

$$409.50 = x$$

The person will pay $409.50 for 7 months of phone service.

b. Answers may vary. One possibility follows: We assumed that the person's monthly bill for phone service is constant. If the person begins to make a lot of long-distance calls during the 7-month period, then our estimate will be an underestimate.

17. a. Let x be the number of adults in Deerfield, Illinois who have online access at home.

$$\frac{x}{13,590} = \frac{1335}{2022}$$

$$13,590\left(\frac{x}{13,590}\right) = 13,590\left(\frac{1335}{2022}\right)$$

$$x \approx 8973$$

Approximately 8973 adults in Deerfield, Illinois have online access at home.

b. Answers may vary. One possibility follows: We assumed that the ratio of adults in Deerfield, Illinois who have online access at home is the same as that for the entire United States. Since the median household income for Deerfield, Illinois is a lot higher than the median income for the United States, the estimate from part (a) is likely to be an underestimate, since adults from Deerfield would be more likely to afford online access.

19. $\dfrac{26 \text{ tons}}{40 \text{ mph}} = 0.65$ tons per mph

$\dfrac{55 \text{ tons}}{60 \text{ mph}} \approx 0.92$ tons per mph

No, the speed and the force of impact are not proportional for a 4000-pound car, since the ratios are not the same.

21. a. $\dfrac{27,764}{1294} \approx 21.5$

The ratio of the FTE enrollment to the number of FTE faculty at LSU in fall 2003 was 21.5:1. This ratio is greater than 17:1.

b. Let x by the number of FTE faculty who would need to be hired for the 17:1 ratio.

$$\frac{27,764}{1294+x} = \frac{17}{1}$$

$$(1294+x)\left(\frac{27,764}{1294+x}\right) = (1294+x)\left(\frac{17}{1}\right)$$

$$27,764 = 21,998 + 17x$$

$$5766 = 17x$$

$$339.2 \approx x$$

LSU would need to hire approximately 339.2 FTE faculty to achieve the 17:1 ratio.

$$339.2 \text{ FTE} \cdot \left(\frac{\$73,125}{\text{FTE}}\right) = \$24,804,000$$

The cost would be about $24.8 million in order to achieve the 17:1 ratio.

c. Let x be the reduction in FTE enrollment for the 17:1 ratio.

$$\frac{27,764-x}{1294} = \frac{17}{1}$$

$$1294\left(\frac{27,764-x}{1294}\right) = 1294\left(\frac{17}{1}\right)$$

$$27,764-x = 21,998$$

$$-x = -5766$$

$$x = 5766$$

FTE enrollment would need to be reduced by 5766 students in order to achieve the 17:1 ratio.

$$5766 \text{ FTE} \cdot \left(\frac{\$3345}{\text{FTE}}\right) = \$19,287,270$$

The cost would be about $19.3 million in order to achieve the 17:1 ratio.

d. The cheaper way to reduce the ratio would be to reduce the FTE enrollment.

23. $\dfrac{3}{x} = \dfrac{8}{13}$

$\dfrac{3}{x} \cdot 13x = \dfrac{8}{13} \cdot 13x$

$39 = 8x$

$\dfrac{39}{8} = x$

$4.88 \approx x$

The length is approximately 4.88 inches.

25. $\dfrac{x}{8} = \dfrac{13}{7}$

$\dfrac{x}{8} \cdot 8 = \dfrac{13}{7} \cdot 8$

$x = \dfrac{104}{7}$

$x \approx 14.86$

The length is approximately 14.86 meters.

27. $\dfrac{9}{x} = \dfrac{8}{5}$

$\dfrac{9}{x} \cdot 5x = \dfrac{8}{5} \cdot 5x$

$45 = 8x$

$\dfrac{45}{8} = x$

$5.63 \approx x$

The length is approximately 5.63 feet.

29. a. $\dfrac{y}{x} = k$

$\dfrac{y}{x} \cdot x = k \cdot x$

$y = kx$

The y-intercept is $(0, 0)$.

b. $C = 15t$

The variable t and C are proportional. Explanations may vary. One possibility follows: Since $\dfrac{C}{t} = 15$, a constant, the variables t and C are proportional.

c. $C = 10t + 25$

The variable t and C are not proportional. Explanations may vary. One possibility follows: Since $\dfrac{C}{t}$ is not a constant, the variables t and C are not proportional.

d. Substitute 2 for t: $C = 10(2) + 25 = 45$

It costs $45 to rent a bike for 2 hours.

Substitute 3 for t: $C = 10(3) + 25 = 55$

It costs $55 to rent a bike for 3 hours.

For 2 hours, the ratio is $\dfrac{\$45}{2 \text{ hours}} = \$22.50$ per hour. For 3 hours, the ratio is $\dfrac{\$45}{3 \text{ hours}} = \$15.00$ per hour. Since the ratios are not the same, the variable t and C are not proportional. This conclusion agrees with our conclusion in part (c).

31. a. The slope is $\dfrac{n}{m}$.

b. The slope is $\dfrac{q}{p}$.

c. Answers may vary. One possibility follows: Since the triangles are similar, we have:

$\dfrac{n}{q} = \dfrac{m}{p}$

$\dfrac{n}{q} \cdot pq = \dfrac{m}{p} \cdot pq$

$np = mq$

$\dfrac{np}{mp} = \dfrac{mq}{mp}$

$\dfrac{n}{m} = \dfrac{q}{p}$

d. Answers may vary. One possibility follows: The results from parts (a), (b), and (c) show that for any two distinct points on a line will have slopes that are proportional. Thus, the slope will simplify to the same result no matter which two points are used.

33. $2x^2 + 7x - 15 = 0$

$(2x - 3)(x + 5) = 0$

$2x - 3 = 0$ or $x + 5 = 0$

$2x = 3$ or $x = -5$

$x = \dfrac{3}{2}$

The solutions are -5 and $\dfrac{3}{2}$. This is a quadratic (or second-degree) equation in one variable.

35. $2x^2 + 7x - 15 = (2x-3)(x+5)$

This is a quadratic (or second-degree) polynomial in one variable.

37. Substitute -2 for x and simplify:

$$f(x) = 2x^2 + 7x - 15$$
$$f(-2) = 2(-2)^2 + 7(-2) - 15$$
$$= 2(4) + 7(-2) - 15$$
$$= 8 - 14 - 15$$
$$= -21$$

This is a quadratic function.

Homework 12.8

1. $I = kt$

3. $w = \dfrac{k}{x+4}$

5. w varies inversely as r.

7. T varies directly as the square root of w.

9. $c = ku$

To find k, solve the following equation:
$$12 = k(3)$$
$$4 = k$$
$$c = 4u$$

11. $w = \dfrac{k}{\sqrt{t}}$

To find k, solve the following equation:
$$3 = \frac{k}{\sqrt{16}}$$
$$3 = \frac{k}{4}$$
$$12 = k$$
$$w = \frac{12}{\sqrt{t}}$$

13. $y = kx$

To find k, solve the following equation:
$$12 = k(4)$$
$$3 = k$$
$$y = 3x$$

Substitute 9 for x and solve for y to get the required value:
$$y = 3(9) = 27$$

15. $G = \dfrac{k}{r}$

To find k, solve the following equation:
$$G = \frac{k}{r}$$
$$8 = \frac{k}{3}$$
$$24 = k$$
$$G = \frac{24}{r}$$

Substitute 4 for r and solve for G to get the required value:
$$G = \frac{24}{r} = \frac{24}{4} = 6$$

17. $p = kx^2$

To find k, solve the following equation:
$$6 = k(2)^2$$
$$6 = 4k$$
$$\frac{6}{4} = k$$
$$\frac{3}{2} = k$$
$$p = \frac{3}{2}x^2$$

Substitute 24 for p and solve for x to get the required value:
$$p = \frac{3}{2}x^2$$
$$24 = \frac{3}{2}x^2$$
$$48 = 3x^2$$
$$16 = x^2$$
$$x = \pm 4$$

19. $I = \dfrac{k}{r+2}$

To find k, solve the following equation:
$$I = \frac{k}{r+2}$$
$$9 = \frac{k}{3+2}$$
$$9 = \frac{k}{5}$$
$$45 = k$$
$$I = \frac{45}{r+2}$$

Substitute 7 for I and solve for r to get the required value.

$$I = \frac{45}{r+2}$$

$$7 = \frac{45}{r+2}$$

$$7(r+2) = 45$$

$$7r + 14 = 45$$

$$7r = 31$$

$$r = \frac{31}{7}$$

21. As the value of w increases, the value of B will also increase for the given situation.

23. As the value of p increases, the value of w will decrease for the given situation.

25. If the GDP rises, the transaction demand will also rise.

27. A tall person will have less nerve conduction than a short person.

29. Answers may vary. One possibility follows: This quotation means that as one's knowledge of the facts increases, one's degree of emotion about the issue decreases.

31. Let c be the cost of tuition and h be the number of credit hours a student takes.

$c = kh$

Let $c = 1530$ and $h = 15$.

$1530 = k(15)$

$102 = k$

Therefore, $c = 102h$

$c = 102(12)$

$= \$1224$

33. Let t be the tension in the string and r be the radius of the circle.

$$t = \frac{k}{r}$$

Let $t = 80$ and $r = 60$.

$$80 = \frac{k}{60}$$

$$4800 = k$$

Therefore, $t = \dfrac{4800}{r}$

$$t = \frac{4800}{50}$$

$$= 96 \text{ newtons}$$

35. Let d be the distance an object falls and t be the time in motion.

$d = kt^2$

Let $d = 144.9$ and $t = 3$.

$144.9 = k \cdot 3^2$

$144.9 = 9k$

$16.1 = k$

Therefore, $d = 16.1t^2$

$d = 16.1(3.4)^2 = 186.116$ feet

37. Let i be the intensity of radiation and d be the distance from the machine.

$$i = \frac{k}{d^2}$$

Let $i = 90$ and $d = 2.5$.

$$90 = \frac{k}{2.5^2}$$

$$90 = \frac{k}{6.25}$$

$$562.5 = k$$

Therefore, $i = \dfrac{562.5}{d^2}$

$$45 = \frac{562.5}{d^2}$$

$$45d^2 = 562.5$$

$$d^2 = 12.5$$

$$d \approx 3.54 \text{ meters}$$

39. a. $F = kw$

To find k solve the following equation:

$50 = k(120)$

$$\frac{5}{12} = k$$

The equation is $F = \dfrac{5}{12}w$.

b. $F = \dfrac{5}{12} \cdot 150 = 62.5$ pounds

c. Answers may vary. The carpet increases resistance to the applied force. So k would be larger for a carpeted floor than a wood floor.

41. a. $T = kd$

Let $T = 3$ and $d = 3313$.

$3 = k(3313)$

$0.000906 \approx k$

Therefore, $T \approx 0.000906d$.

b. $4 = 0.000906d$

$d \approx 4415$ feet

c. For every additional foot away the lightning strikes, it takes another 0.000906 seconds to hear the thunder.

d. Answers may vary. The equation indicates that thunder travels 1 mile in about 4.78 seconds. A better rule of thumb is that, for every five seconds after you see the lightning, the thunder travels a mile further.

43. a. $w = f(d) = \dfrac{k}{d^2}$

$200 = \dfrac{k}{4^2}$

$200 = \dfrac{k}{16}$

$3200 = k$

Therefore, $w = f(d) = \dfrac{3200}{d^2}$.

b. If sea level is about 4 thousand miles from the center of the Earth, then 1 thousand miles above the surface would be a total of 5 thousand miles from the center of the Earth.

$w = \dfrac{3200}{5^2} = 128$ pounds

c. $1 = \dfrac{3200}{d^2}$

$d^2 = 3200$

$d = \sqrt{3200}$

≈ 56.569

An astronaut would weigh 1 pound at a distance of about 56,569 miles from the center of Earth.

d. $f(239) = \dfrac{3200}{239^2}$

≈ 0.056 pounds

Model breakdown as occurred. At the moon's surface, the gravitational effect of the moon is greater than that of Earth. This needs to be taken into account for the information to be accurate.

e. Answers may vary. The equation would have a slightly smaller value for k, because k is directly proportional to the astronaut's weight, and the distance is the same in both situations.

45. a.

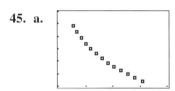

b. The model should be of the form

$F(L) = \dfrac{k}{L}$.

To find k take the average of all products LF from the table.
The sum of the products is 36467.715.
Divide this sum by 13 (the total number of notes in the table) to get the average.

$\dfrac{36467.715}{13} \approx 2805.21$

So $F(L) = \dfrac{2805.21}{L}$

The graph below shows the equation graphed along with the scattergram of the data. By inspection, it appears the model fits the data extremely well.

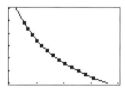

c. F varies inversely as L.

d. $F(7.58) = \dfrac{2805.21}{7.58} \approx 370.1\,\text{hertz}$

e.

$$(eq1)\,F = \frac{2805.21}{a}$$

$$(eq2)\,F = \frac{2805.21}{\frac{1}{2}a}$$

$$= 2805.21 \div \tfrac{1}{2}a$$

$$= 2805.21 \cdot \tfrac{2}{a}$$

$$= 2\left(\frac{2805.21}{a}\right)$$

Equation 2 is 2 times equation 1. So when we halved the effective length the frequency doubled.

47. a.

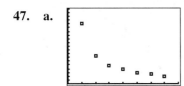

b. The model should be of the form

$f(d) = \dfrac{k}{d}$. To find k take the average

of all products dh from the table.

$$k = \frac{10\cdot16+20\cdot7.3+30\cdot4.8+40\cdot3.8+50\cdot3+60\cdot2.5+70\cdot2}{7}$$

$$\approx 148.86$$

So $f(d) = \dfrac{148.86}{d}$

c. The apparent height varies inversely with the distance.

d. This makes sense in this case because the farther you are from the garage (i.e. the bigger d is) the smaller the apparent height $f(d)$ is.

e.

$$f(100) = \frac{148.86}{100} = 1.4886 \text{ inches}$$

f.

$$f(1) = \frac{148.86}{1} = 148.86 \text{ inches}$$

49. a. $T = k\sqrt{L}$

b. $\dfrac{T}{\sqrt{L}} = k$

c.

L	T	$\dfrac{T}{\sqrt{L}}$
5	0.50	0.22
10	0.63	0.20
15	0.88	0.23
20	1.00	0.22
25	1.13	0.23
32.5	1.25	0.22
45	1.50	0.22
60	1.75	0.23
85	2.00	0.22
110	2.25	0.21

A reasonable value for k is the average of column 3, which is approximately 0.22.

d. $T = 0.22\sqrt{L}$

e. The following is the scattergram and the graph of T.

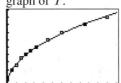

The model fits the data very well

f. $T = 0.22\sqrt{130} \approx 2.51$ seconds

51. $f(L) = 5L$

$k = 5$

53. $f(n) = \dfrac{2}{n}$

$k = 2$

55. $f(r) = 2\pi r$

$k = 2\pi$

57. a. f is an increasing function

The number of CD's sold increases as more money is spent on advertising.

b. The number of CD's sold does not vary directly as the amount of money spent on advertising. "Varies directly" usually implies a linear relationship. A linear model would not fit this data well.

c. Answers may vary. The first statement indicates a direct, increasing linear relationship between the variables, while the second statement could refer to an increasing logarithmic, exponential, or quadratic function as well as an increasing linear function.

59. False. As a person gets older, the person doesn't necessarily keep getting taller. At some point we stop growing.

61. True. Coffee will get cooler the longer the time passes since it has been poured.

63. $y = kx$

Solving this equation for x we get the following:

$\dfrac{y}{k} = x$

Yes, it follows that x varies directly as y.

The variation constant is $\dfrac{1}{k}$.

65. a. If y varies directly as x, x and y are linearly related. This relationship takes the form of $y = kx$, which is a linear relationship.

b. No. Just because w and t are linearly related doesn't mean they are directly related. The relationship may be either $w = kt$ or $w = \dfrac{k}{t}$.

67. $n = kt$

$310 = k(5)$

$62 = k$

$n = 62t$

The slope of the model is 62. This indicates that the typist can type 62 words per minute.

69. Answers may vary. Example:

$x + y = 2$

$x - y = 0$

$y = x$

$x + y = 2$

$x = 1$

$y = 1$

71. Answers may vary. Example:

$\dfrac{x - 2}{2x + 2} - \dfrac{2x}{2x + 2} =$

$\dfrac{x - 2 - 2x}{2x + 2} = \dfrac{-2 - x}{2x + 2}$

73. Answers may vary. Example:

$y = x^2$

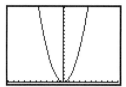

75. Answers may vary. Example:

$y = e^x$

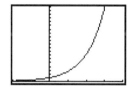

Chapter 12 Review Exercises

1. $f(x) = \dfrac{5x - 3}{2x^2 - 3x + 1}$

$f(0) = \dfrac{5(0) - 3}{2(0)^2 - 3(0) + 1}$

$f(0) = -3$

$f(2) = \dfrac{5(2) - 3}{2(2)^2 - 3(2) + 1}$

$f(2) = \dfrac{7}{3}$

2. $3x - 5 = 0$

$3x = 5$

$x = \dfrac{5}{3}$

The domain is the set of all real numbers except $\dfrac{5}{3}$.

3. $4x^2 - 49 = 0$

$(2x - 7)(2x + 7) = 0$

$$2x-7=0 \quad \text{or} \quad 2x+7=0$$
$$2x=7 \qquad\qquad 2x=-7$$
$$x=\frac{7}{2} \qquad\qquad x=-\frac{7}{2}$$

The domain is the set of all real numbers except $\frac{7}{2}$ and $-\frac{7}{2}$.

4.
$$x^2-6x+8=0$$
$$(x-4)(x-2)=0$$
$$x-4=0 \quad \text{or} \quad x-2=0$$
$$x=4 \quad \text{or} \qquad x=2$$

The domain is the set of all real numbers except 2 and 4.

5. $12x^2+13x-35=0$
$$x=\frac{-13\pm\sqrt{169-4(12)(-35)}}{24}$$
$$=\frac{-13\pm\sqrt{169+1680}}{24}$$
$$=\frac{-13\pm\sqrt{1849}}{24}$$
$$=\frac{-13\pm43}{24}$$

The solutions are $\frac{-13+43}{24}=\frac{5}{4}$ and

$\frac{-13-43}{24}=-\frac{7}{3}$. The domain is the set of all real

numbers except $\frac{5}{4}$ and $-\frac{7}{3}$.

6. The function will be defined for all x except where the denominator is 0.

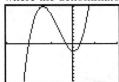

The "intersect" function on the calculator was used to find all instances where the denominator function crosses the x-axis. These values were:

$$x=\{-2,\pm\frac{1}{3}\}$$

7.
$$\frac{3x-12}{x^2-6x+8}=\frac{3(x-4)}{(x-2)(x-4)}$$
$$=\frac{3}{x-2}$$

8.
$$\frac{16-x^2}{2x^3-16x^2+32x}=\frac{(4+x)(4-x)}{2x(x^2-8x+16)}$$
$$=\frac{(4+x)(4-x)}{2x(x-4)(x-4)}$$
$$=\frac{-x-4}{2x(x-4)}$$

9.
$$\frac{x^2-8x+12}{3x^2-16x-12}=\frac{(x-6)(x-2)}{(3x+2)(x-6)}=\frac{x-2}{3x+2}$$

10.
$$\frac{x^2+10x+25}{2x^3-3x^2-50x+75}=\frac{(x+5)(x+5)}{x^2(2x-3)-25(2x-3)}$$
$$=\frac{(x+5)(x+5)}{(x^2-25)(2x-3)}$$
$$=\frac{(x+5)(x+5)}{(x-5)(x+5)(2x-3)}$$
$$=\frac{x+5}{(x-5)(2x-3)}$$

11.
$$\frac{x+2}{x^3+8}=\frac{x+2}{(x+2)(x^2-2x+4)}$$
$$=\frac{1}{(x^2-2x+4)}$$

12.
$$\frac{6a^2-17ab+5b^2}{3a^2-4ab+b^2}=\frac{(3a-b)(2a-5b)}{(3a-b)(a-b)}$$
$$=\frac{2a-5b}{a-b}$$

13.
$$\frac{3x+6}{2x-4}\cdot\frac{5x-10}{6x+12}=\frac{3(x+2)}{2(x-2)}\cdot\frac{5(x-2)}{6(x+2)}$$
$$=\frac{15}{12}$$
$$=\frac{5}{4}$$

14.
$$\frac{25b^3}{b^2-b}\cdot\frac{b^2-1}{35b}=\frac{5\cdot5\cdot b\cdot b\cdot b}{b(b-1)}\cdot\frac{(b-1)(b+1)}{5\cdot7\cdot b}$$
$$=\frac{5\cdot5\cdot b\cdot b\cdot b\cdot(b-1)(b+1)}{b\cdot(b-1)\cdot5\cdot7\cdot b}$$
$$=\frac{5\cdot b\cdot(b+1)}{7}$$
$$=\frac{5b(b+1)}{7}$$

15.
$$\frac{x^2-49}{9-x^2}\cdot\frac{2x^3+8x^2-42x}{5x-35}$$
$$=\frac{(x-7)(x+7)}{-(x^2-9)}\cdot\frac{2x(x^2+4x-21)}{5(x-7)}$$
$$=\frac{(x-7)(x+7)}{-(x+3)(x-3)}\cdot\frac{2x(x+7)(x-3)}{5(x-7)}$$
$$=-\frac{2x(x+7)^2}{5(x+3)}$$

16.
$$\frac{p^3-t^3}{p^2-t^2}\cdot\frac{p^2+6pt+5t^2}{p^2t+pt^2+t^3}$$
$$=\frac{(p-t)(p^2+pt+t^2)}{(p-t)(p+t)}\cdot\frac{(p+5t)(p+t)}{t(p^2+pt+t^2)}$$
$$=\frac{p+5t}{t}$$

17.
$$\frac{x^2-4}{x^2+3x+2}\div\frac{4x^2-24x+32}{x^2-5x+4}$$
$$=\frac{x^2-4}{x^2+3x+2}\cdot\frac{x^2-5x+4}{4x^2-24x+32}$$
$$=\frac{(x-2)(x+2)}{(x+2)(x+1)}\cdot\frac{(x-4)(x-1)}{4(x^2-6x+8)}$$
$$=\frac{(x-2)(x+2)}{(x+2)(x+1)}\cdot\frac{(x-4)(x-1)}{4(x-4)(x-2)}$$
$$=\frac{(x-2)}{(x+1)}\cdot\frac{(x-1)}{4(x-2)}$$
$$=\frac{x-1}{4(x+1)}$$

18.
$$\frac{7t+14}{t-7}\div(3t^2+2t-8)=\frac{7t+14}{t-7}\cdot\frac{1}{3t^2+2t-8}$$
$$=\frac{7(t+2)}{t-7}\cdot\frac{1}{(3t-4)(t+2)}$$
$$=\frac{7(t+2)}{(t-7)\cdot(3t-4)(t+2)}$$
$$=\frac{7}{(t-7)(3t-4)}$$

19.
$$\frac{4-x}{4x}\div\frac{16-x^2}{16x^2}=\frac{4-x}{4x}\cdot\frac{16x^2}{16-x^2}$$
$$=\frac{4-x}{4x}\cdot\frac{16x^2}{(4-x)(4+x)}$$
$$=\frac{4x}{4+x}$$

20.
$$\frac{8x^3+4x^2-18x-9}{x^2-6x+9}\div\frac{4x^2+8x+3}{x^2-9}$$
$$=\frac{8x^3+4x^2-18x-9}{x^2-6x+9}\cdot\frac{x^2-9}{4x^2+8x+3}$$
$$=\frac{4x^2(2x+1)-9(2x+1)}{(x-3)(x-3)}\cdot\frac{(x-3)(x+3)}{(2x+1)(2x+3)}$$
$$=\frac{(2x+1)(4x^2-9)}{(x-3)(x-3)}\cdot\frac{(x-3)(x+3)}{(2x+1)(2x+3)}$$
$$=\frac{(2x+1)(2x-3)(2x+3)}{(x-3)(x-3)}\cdot\frac{(x-3)(x+3)}{(2x+1)(2x+3)}$$
$$=\frac{(2x-3)(x+3)}{x-3}$$

21.
$$\frac{5}{x^2+7x+6}+\frac{2x}{x^2-3x-4}$$
$$=\frac{5}{(x+6)(x+1)}+\frac{2x}{(x-4)(x+1)}$$
$$=\frac{5}{(x+6)(x+1)}\cdot\frac{x-4}{x-4}+\frac{2x}{(x-4)(x+1)}\cdot\frac{x+6}{x+6}$$
$$=\frac{5(x-4)}{(x+6)(x+1)(x-4)}+\frac{2x(x+6)}{(x-4)(x+1)(x+6)}$$
$$=\frac{5(x-4)+2x(x+6)}{(x-4)(x+1)(x+6)}$$
$$=\frac{5x-20+2x^2+12x}{(x-4)(x+1)(x+6)}$$
$$=\frac{2x^2+17x-20}{(x-4)(x+1)(x+6)}$$

22.
$$\frac{x}{x^2-5x+6}+\frac{3}{3-x}$$
$$=\frac{x}{(x-3)(x-2)}-\frac{3}{x-3}$$
$$=\frac{x}{(x-3)(x-2)}-\frac{3}{(x-3)}\cdot\frac{(x-2)}{(x-2)}$$
$$=\frac{x-3x+6}{(x-3)(x-2)}=\frac{-2x+6}{(x-3)(x-2)}=\frac{-2(x-3)}{(x-3)(x-2)}$$
$$=\frac{-2}{x-2}$$

23.
$$\frac{x}{2x^3-3x^2-5x}+\frac{2}{x^3-x}$$
$$=\frac{x}{x(2x^2-3x-5)}+\frac{2}{x(x^2-1)}$$
$$=\frac{x}{x(2x-5)(x+1)}+\frac{2}{x(x-1)(x+1)}$$
$$=\frac{x}{x(2x-5)(x+1)}\cdot\frac{(x-1)}{(x-1)}$$
$$+\frac{2}{x(x-1)(x+1)}\cdot\frac{(2x-5)}{(2x-5)}$$
$$=\frac{x^2-x}{x(2x-5)(x+1)(x-1)}$$
$$+\frac{4x-10}{x(2x-5)(x+1)(x-1)}$$
$$=\frac{x^2+3x-10}{x(2x-5)(x+1)(x-1)}$$
$$=\frac{(x-2)(x+5)}{x(2x-5)(x+1)(x-1)}$$

24.
$$\frac{x-1}{x^2-4}+\frac{x+3}{x^2-4x+4}$$
$$=\frac{x-1}{(x-2)(x+2)}+\frac{x+3}{(x-2)(x-2)}$$
$$=\frac{(x-1)(x-2)}{(x-2)(x-2)(x+2)}+\frac{(x+2)(x+3)}{(x-2)(x-2)(x+2)}$$
$$=\frac{(x-1)(x-2)+(x+2)(x+3)}{(x-2)(x-2)(x+2)}$$
$$=\frac{x^2-3x+2+x^2+5x+6}{(x-2)^2(x+2)}$$
$$=\frac{2x^2+2x+8}{(x-2)^2(x+2)}$$
$$=\frac{2(x^2+x+4)}{(x-2)^2(x+2)}$$

25.
$$\frac{3}{4x-12}-\frac{x}{x^2-2x-3}$$
$$=\frac{3}{4(x-3)}-\frac{x}{(x-3)(x+1)}$$
$$=\frac{3}{4(x-3)}\cdot\frac{(x+1)}{(x+1)}-\frac{x}{(x-3)(x+1)}\cdot\frac{(4)}{(4)}$$
$$=\frac{3x+3-4x}{4(x-3)(x+1)}=\frac{-x+3}{4(x-3)(x+1)}$$
$$=\frac{-(x-3)}{4(x-3)(x+1)}=\frac{-1}{4(x+1)}$$

26. $\dfrac{x-4}{x^2+2x-3}-\dfrac{x+2}{x^2-6x+5}$

$=\dfrac{x-4}{(x+3)(x-1)}-\dfrac{x+2}{(x-5)(x-1)}$

$=\dfrac{x-4}{(x+3)(x-1)}\cdot\dfrac{x-5}{x-5}-\dfrac{x+2}{(x-5)(x-1)}\cdot\dfrac{x+3}{x+3}$

$=\dfrac{(x-4)(x-5)}{(x+3)(x-1)(x-5)}-\dfrac{(x+2)(x+3)}{(x-5)(x-1)(x+3)}$

$=\dfrac{(x-4)(x-5)-(x+2)(x+3)}{(x+3)(x-1)(x-5)}$

$=\dfrac{x^2-5x-4x+20-(x^2+3x+2x+6)}{(x-5)(x-1)(x+3)}$

$=\dfrac{x^2-5x-4x+20-x^2-3x-2x-6}{(x-5)(x-1)(x+3)}$

$=\dfrac{-14x+14}{(x-5)(x-1)(x+3)}$

$=\dfrac{-14(x-1)}{(x-5)(x-1)(x+3)}$

$=\dfrac{-14}{(x-5)(x+3)}=-\dfrac{14}{(x-5)(x+3)}$

27. $\dfrac{x+1}{25-x^2}-\dfrac{x-4}{2x^2-14x+20}$

$=-\dfrac{x+1}{x^2-25}-\dfrac{x-4}{2x^2-14x+20}$

$=-\dfrac{x+1}{(x-5)(x+5)}-\dfrac{x-4}{2(x^2-7x+10)}$

$=-\dfrac{x+1}{(x-5)(x+5)}-\dfrac{x-4}{2(x-5)(x-2)}$

$=-\dfrac{(x+1)}{(x-5)(x+5)}\cdot\dfrac{2(x-2)}{2(x-2)}-\dfrac{(x-4)}{2(x-5)(x-2)}\cdot\dfrac{(x+5)}{(x+5)}$

$=-\dfrac{2(x^2-x-2)}{2(x-5)(x+5)(x-2)}-\dfrac{x^2+x-20}{2(x-5)(x-2)(x+5)}$

$=\dfrac{-2x^2+2x+4-x^2-x+20}{2(x-5)(x+5)(x-2)}$

$=\dfrac{-3x^2+x+24}{2(x-5)(x+5)(x-2)}=\dfrac{-(3x+8)(x-3)}{2(x-5)(x+5)(x-2)}$

28. $\dfrac{2m}{m^2-3mn-10n^2}-\dfrac{4n}{m^2+8mn+12n^2}$

$=\dfrac{2m}{(m-5n)(m+2n)}-\dfrac{4n}{(m+6n)(m+2n)}$

$=\dfrac{2m(m+6n)}{(m-5n)(m+2n)(m+6n)}-\dfrac{4n(m-5n)}{(m+6n)(m+2n)(m-5n)}$

$=\dfrac{2m^2+12mn-4mn+20n^2}{(m+6n)(m+2n)(m-5n)}$

$=\dfrac{2m^2+8mn+20n^2}{(m+6n)(m+2n)(m-5n)}$

$=\dfrac{2\left(m^2+4mn+10n^2\right)}{(m+6n)(m+2n)(m-5n)}$

29. $\dfrac{2}{x-5}-\left(\dfrac{x^2+5x+6}{3x^2-75}\div\dfrac{x^2+2x}{3x+15}\right)$

$=\dfrac{2}{x-5}-\left(\dfrac{x^2+5x+6}{3x^2-75}\cdot\dfrac{3x+15}{x^2+2x}\right)$

$=\dfrac{2}{x-5}-\left(\dfrac{(x+3)(x+2)}{3(x^2-25)}\cdot\dfrac{3(x+5)}{x(x+2)}\right)$

$=\dfrac{2}{x-5}-\left(\dfrac{(x+3)(x+2)}{3(x+5)(x-5)}\cdot\dfrac{3(x+5)}{x(x+2)}\right)$

$=\dfrac{2}{x-5}-\dfrac{x+3}{x(x-5)}$

$=\dfrac{2}{x-5}\cdot\left(\dfrac{x}{x}\right)-\dfrac{x+3}{x(x-5)}$

$=\dfrac{2x-x+3}{x(x-5)}$

$=\dfrac{x+3}{x(x-5)}$

30. $\dfrac{2x-8}{3x+4}\cdot\left(\dfrac{x-2}{x+1}-\dfrac{x+3}{x-4}\right)$

$=\dfrac{2(x-4)}{3x+4}\cdot\left(\dfrac{(x-2)(x-4)-(x+1)(x+3)}{(x+1)(x-4)}\right)$

$=\dfrac{2(x-4)}{3x+4}\cdot\left(\dfrac{x^2-6x+8-\left(x^2+4x+3\right)}{(x+1)(x-4)}\right)$

$=\dfrac{2(x-4)}{3x+4}\cdot\left(\dfrac{-10x+5}{(x+1)(x-4)}\right)$

$=\dfrac{2(x-4)}{3x+4}\cdot\left(\dfrac{-5(2x-1)}{(x+1)(x-4)}\right)$

$=\dfrac{-10(2x-1)}{(3x+4)(x+1)}$

31. $f(x)g(x)=\dfrac{x^2-x-2}{x^2+5x+6}\cdot\dfrac{x+3}{x+2}$

$=\dfrac{(x-2)(x+1)}{(x+2)(x+3)}\cdot\dfrac{(x+3)}{(x+2)}$

$=\dfrac{(x-2)(x+1)}{(x+2)^2}$

32. $\dfrac{f(x)}{g(x)}=\dfrac{x^2-x-2}{x^2+5x+6}\div\dfrac{x+3}{x+2}$

$=\dfrac{x^2-x-2}{x^2+5x+6}\cdot\dfrac{x+2}{x+3}$

$=\dfrac{(x-2)(x+1)}{(x+2)(x+3)}\cdot\dfrac{x+2}{x+3}$

$=\dfrac{(x-2)(x+1)}{(x+3)^2}$

33. $f(x)+g(x)=\dfrac{x^2-x-2}{x^2+5x+6}+\dfrac{x+3}{x+2}$

$=\dfrac{(x-2)(x+1)}{(x+2)(x+3)}+\dfrac{x+3}{x+2}$

$=\dfrac{(x-2)(x+1)}{(x+2)(x+3)}+\dfrac{(x+3)}{(x+2)}\cdot\dfrac{(x+3)}{(x+3)}$

$=\dfrac{x^2-x-2}{(x+2)(x+3)}+\dfrac{x^2+6x+9}{(x+2)(x+3)}$

$=\dfrac{2x^2+5x+7}{(x+2)(x+3)}$

34. $f(x)-g(x)=\dfrac{x^2-x-2}{x^2+5x+6}-\dfrac{x+3}{x+2}$

$=\dfrac{x^2-x-2}{(x+2)(x+3)}-\dfrac{x+3}{x+2}$

$=\dfrac{x^2-x-2}{(x+2)(x+3)}-\dfrac{(x+3)}{(x+2)}\cdot\dfrac{(x+3)}{(x+3)}$

$=\dfrac{x^2-x-2}{(x+2)(x+3)}-\dfrac{x^2+6x+9}{(x+2)(x+3)}$

$=\dfrac{x^2-x-2-x^2-6x-9}{(x+2)(x+3)}=\dfrac{-7x-11}{(x+2)(x+3)}$

35. Answers may vary. One possibility follows: The student failed to distribute the subtraction properly through the numerator of the second rational expression. The correct difference is:

$\dfrac{2x}{x+4}-\dfrac{7x-3}{x+4}=\dfrac{2x-(7x-3)}{x+4}$

$=\dfrac{2x-7x+3}{x+4}=\dfrac{-5x+3}{x+4}$

36. $\dfrac{0.62\text{ pound}}{1}\cdot\dfrac{16\text{ ounces}}{1\text{ pound}}=9.92$ ounces

A TI-84 graphing calculator weighs 9.92 ounces.

37. $\dfrac{121\text{ gallons}}{1\text{ year}}\cdot\dfrac{4\text{ quarts}}{1\text{ gallon}}\cdot\dfrac{4\text{ cups}}{1\text{ quart}}\cdot\dfrac{1\text{ year}}{365\text{ days}}$

$\approx 5.30\ \dfrac{\text{cups}}{\text{day}}$

Americans consume an average 5.30 cups of water per day.

38. $\dfrac{\dfrac{12}{x^2}}{\dfrac{9}{x^3}}=\dfrac{12}{x^2}\div\dfrac{9}{x^3}=\dfrac{12}{x^2}\cdot\dfrac{x^3}{9}=\dfrac{2\cdot2\cdot3}{x^2}\cdot\dfrac{x^3}{3\cdot3}$

$=\dfrac{2\cdot2\cdot3\cdot x^3}{x^2\cdot3\cdot3}=\dfrac{2\cdot2\cdot x^{3-2}}{3}=\dfrac{4x}{3}$

39.
$$\dfrac{\dfrac{x-2}{x^2-9}}{\dfrac{x^2-4}{x+3}} = \dfrac{\dfrac{x-2}{(x-3)(x+3)}}{\dfrac{(x-2)(x+2)}{x+3}}$$

$$= \dfrac{x-2}{(x-3)(x+3)} \div \dfrac{(x-2)(x+2)}{x+3}$$

$$= \dfrac{x-2}{(x-3)(x+3)} \cdot \dfrac{x+3}{(x-2)(x+2)}$$

$$= \dfrac{1}{(x-3)(x+2)}$$

40.
$$\dfrac{5-\dfrac{2}{w}}{1-\dfrac{3}{w}} = \dfrac{5-\dfrac{2}{w}}{1-\dfrac{3}{w}} \cdot \dfrac{w}{w} = \dfrac{5 \cdot w - \dfrac{2}{w} \cdot w}{1 \cdot w - \dfrac{3}{w} \cdot w} = \dfrac{5w-2}{w-3}$$

41.
$$\dfrac{\dfrac{4}{3x^4}-\dfrac{2}{6x^2}}{\dfrac{1}{2x}+\dfrac{1}{4}} = \left(\dfrac{\dfrac{4}{3x^4}-\dfrac{2}{6x^2}}{\dfrac{1}{2x}+\dfrac{1}{4}}\right) \cdot \dfrac{12x^4}{12x^4}$$

$$= \dfrac{16-4x^2}{6x^3+3x^4} = \dfrac{-4(x^2-4)}{3x^3(2+x)}$$

$$= \dfrac{-4(x+2)(x-2)}{3x^3(x+2)} = \dfrac{-4(x-2)}{3x^3}$$

42.
$$\dfrac{1}{x+5}-\dfrac{2}{x-2} = \dfrac{-14}{x^2+3x-10}$$

$$\dfrac{1}{x+5}-\dfrac{2}{x-2} = \dfrac{-14}{(x+5)(x-2)}$$

$$(x+5)(x-2)\left(\dfrac{1}{x+5}-\dfrac{2}{x-2}\right)$$

$$= (x+5)(x-2)\dfrac{-14}{(x+5)(x-2)}$$

$$x-2-2(x+5) = -14$$
$$x-2-2x-10 = -14$$
$$-x-12 = -14$$
$$-x = -2$$
$$x = 2$$

$x = 2$ makes the denominators $x - 2$ and $x^2 + 3x - 10$ equal 0. This equation has no solution.

43.
$$\dfrac{x}{x+2}+\dfrac{3}{x+4} = \dfrac{14}{x^2+6x+8}$$

$$\dfrac{x}{x+2}+\dfrac{3}{x+4} = \dfrac{14}{(x+2)(x+4)}$$

$$(x+2)(x+4)\left(\dfrac{x}{x+2}+\dfrac{3}{x+4}\right)$$

$$= (x+2)(x+4)\dfrac{14}{(x+2)(x+4)}$$

$$x(x+4)+3(x+2) = 14$$
$$x^2+4x+3x+6 = 14$$
$$x^2+7x-8 = 0$$
$$(x+8)(x-1) = 0$$
$$x+8 = 0 \quad \text{or} \quad x-1 = 0$$
$$x = -8 \qquad\qquad x = 1$$

The solutions are $x = 1$ and $x = -8$.

44.
$$\dfrac{5}{w}+3 = \dfrac{4}{w^2}$$

$$w^2\left(\dfrac{5}{w}+3\right) = w^2\dfrac{4}{w^2}$$

$$5w+3w^2 = 4$$
$$3w^2+5w-4 = 0$$

$$w = \dfrac{-5\pm\sqrt{5^2-4(3)(-4)}}{2(3)}$$

$$= \dfrac{-5\pm\sqrt{73}}{6}$$

The solutions are $w = \dfrac{-5\pm\sqrt{73}}{6}$.

45.
$$\dfrac{-3}{x+6}+\dfrac{2}{x+1} = \dfrac{x-2}{x+6}$$

We note that -6 and -1 are excluded values.

$$(x+6)(x+1)\cdot\left(\dfrac{-3}{x+6}+\dfrac{2}{x+1}\right) = (x+6)(x+1)\cdot\left(\dfrac{x-2}{x+6}\right)$$

$$(x+1)\cdot(-3)+(x+6)\cdot 2 = (x+1)(x-2)$$

$$-3x-3+2x+12 = x^2-2x+x-2$$

$$-x+9 = x^2-x-2$$

$$11 = x^2$$

$$\pm\sqrt{11} = x$$

Neither of these are excluded values, so we conclude that $\pm\sqrt{11}$ are the solutions of the equation.

46.

$$\frac{x-3}{2x^2-7x-4}-\frac{5}{2x^2+3x+1}=\frac{x-1}{x^2-3x-4}$$

$$\frac{x-3}{(2x+1)(x-4)}-\frac{5}{(2x+1)(x+1)}=\frac{x-1}{(x-4)(x+1)}$$

$$(2x+1)(x-4)(x+1)\left(\frac{x-3}{(2x+1)(x-4)}-\frac{5}{(2x+1)(x+1)}\right)$$

$$=(2x+1)(x-4)(x+1)\frac{x-1}{(x-4)(x+1)}$$

$$(x+1)(x-3)-5(x-4)=(2x+1)(x-1)$$

$$x^2-2x-3-5x+20=2x^2-x-1$$

$$x^2-7x+17=2x^2-x-1$$

$$-x^2-6x+18=0$$

$$x^2+6x-18=0$$

$$x=\frac{-6\pm\sqrt{6^2-4(1)(-18)}}{2}$$

$$=\frac{-6\pm\sqrt{36+72}}{2}$$

$$=\frac{-6\pm\sqrt{108}}{2}$$

$$=\frac{-6\pm\sqrt{36\cdot3}}{2}$$

$$=\frac{-6\pm6\sqrt{3}}{2}$$

$$=-3\pm3\sqrt{3}$$

The solutions are $x=-3\pm3\sqrt{3}$.

47.

$$\frac{2x}{x+6}-\frac{4}{x-3}=\frac{-37}{x^2+3x-18}$$

$$\frac{2x}{x+6}-\frac{4}{x-3}=\frac{-37}{(x+6)(x-3)}$$

$$\frac{2x(x-3)}{(x+6)(x-3)}-\frac{4(x+6)}{(x+6)(x-3)}=\frac{-37}{(x+6)(x-3)}$$

$$\frac{2x(x-3)-4(x+6)}{(x+6)(x-3)}=\frac{-37}{(x+6)(x-3)}$$

$$2x(x-3)-4(x+6)=-37$$

$$2x^2-6x-4x-24=-37$$

$$2x^2-10x=-13$$

$$2x^2-10x+13=0$$

$$x=\frac{10\pm\sqrt{(-10)^2-4(2)(13)}}{2(2)}$$

$$=\frac{10\pm\sqrt{100-104}}{4}$$

$$=\frac{10\pm\sqrt{-4}}{4}$$

$$=\frac{10\pm2i}{4}$$

$$=\frac{5\pm i}{2}$$

The complex solutions are $x=\dfrac{5\pm i}{2}$

48.

$$\frac{3}{2-x}-\frac{7}{x-2}-4=0$$

$$\left(\frac{-1}{-1}\right)\left(\frac{3}{2-x}\right)-\frac{7}{x-2}-4\left(\frac{x-2}{x-2}\right)=0$$

$$\frac{-3}{x-2}-\frac{7}{x-2}-\frac{4x-8}{x-2}=0$$

$$\frac{-3-7-4x+8}{x-2}=0$$

$$\frac{-4x-2}{x-2}=0$$

$$\frac{-2(2x+1)}{x-2}=0$$

$$2x+1=0$$

$$2x=-1$$

$$x=-\frac{1}{2}$$

49.

$$\frac{3}{x^2-25}+\frac{1}{x^2-x-30}$$

$$=\frac{3}{(x+5)(x-5)}+\frac{1}{(x-6)(x+5)}$$

$$=\frac{3(x-6)+1(x-5)}{(x+5)(x-5)(x-6)}$$

$$=\frac{3x-18+x-5}{(x+5)(x-5)(x-6)}$$

$$=\frac{4x-23}{(x+5)(x-5)(x-6)}$$

50.

$$\frac{3}{2-x} - \frac{7}{x-2} - 4$$

$$= \left(\frac{-1}{-1}\right)\left(\frac{3}{2-x}\right) - \frac{7}{x-2} - 4\left(\frac{x-2}{x-2}\right)$$

$$= \frac{-3}{x-2} - \frac{7}{x-2} - \frac{4x-8}{x-2}$$

$$= \frac{-3-7-4x+8}{x-2}$$

$$= \frac{-4x-2}{x-2}$$

$$= \frac{-2(2x+1)}{x-2}$$

51.

$$\frac{3}{x^2-25} + \frac{1}{x^2-x-30} = \frac{2}{x^2-11x+30}$$

$$\frac{3}{(x+5)(x-5)} + \frac{1}{(x-6)(x+5)} = \frac{2}{(x-5)(x-6)}$$

$$\frac{3(x-6)+1(x-5)}{(x+5)(x-5)(x-6)} = \frac{2}{(x-5)(x-6)}$$

$$\frac{3x-18+x-5}{(x+5)(x-5)(x-6)} = \frac{2}{(x-5)(x-6)}$$

$$\frac{4x-23}{(x+5)(x-5)(x-6)} = \frac{2}{(x-5)(x-6)}$$

$$\frac{4x-23}{(x+5)(x-5)(x-6)} = \frac{2}{(x-5)(x-6)}\left(\frac{x+5}{x+5}\right)$$

$$4x-23 = 2(x+5)$$

$$4x-23 = 2x+10$$

$$2x = 33$$

$$x = \frac{33}{2}$$

52.

$$0 = \frac{x-7}{x+1} - \frac{x+3}{x-4}$$

$$\frac{x-7}{x+1} = \frac{x+3}{x-4}$$

$$(x-4)(x-7) = (x+1)(x+3)$$

$$x^2-11x+28 = x^2+4x+3$$

$$25 = 15x$$

$$5 = 3x$$

$$x = \frac{5}{3}$$

The $x-$ intercept is $\left(\frac{5}{3}, 0\right)$.

53.

$$S = \frac{a}{1-r}$$

$$S(1-r) = a$$

$$S - Sr = a$$

$$-Sr = a - S$$

$$Sr = S - a$$

$$r = \frac{S-a}{S}$$

54. Let x be the number of ounces of diced tomatoes used to make 7 servings of chicken cacciatore.

$$\frac{4}{14} = \frac{7}{x}$$

$$14x\left(\frac{4}{14}\right) = 14x\left(\frac{7}{x}\right)$$

$$4x = 98$$

$$x = 24.5$$

So, 24.5 ounces of diced tomatoes should be used to make 7 servings of chicken cacciatore.

55.

$$\frac{x}{15} = \frac{11}{6}$$

$$\frac{x}{15} \cdot 15 = \frac{11}{6} \cdot 15$$

$$x = 27.5$$

The length is 27.5 yards.

56. H varies directly as the square of u.

57. w varies inversely as $\log(t)$.

58. $y = k\sqrt{x}$

Solve the following equation to find k.

$$2 = k\sqrt{49}$$

$$2 = 7k$$

$$\frac{2}{7} = k$$

The equation is $y = \frac{2}{7}\sqrt{x}$.

59. $B = \frac{k}{r^3}$

Solve the following equation find k.

$$9 = \frac{k}{2^3}$$

$$9 = \frac{k}{8}$$

$$72 = k$$

The equation is $B = \dfrac{72}{r^3}$.

60. Let w be the number of inches of water and s be the number of inches of snow.

$w = ks$

Solve the following equation to find k.

$2.24 = k(20)$

$0.112 = k$

Using the equation $w = 0.112s$ we get the following:

$w = 0.112(37)$

$w = 4.144$

If 37 inches of snow melts, there will be 4.144 inches of water.

61. a. $m = kr^3$

b. $k = \dfrac{m}{r^3}$

c.

r	m	$\dfrac{m}{r^3}$
1.0	17.1	17.1
1.2	29.4	17.01
1.4	46.7	17.02
1.6	69.6	16.99
1.8	99.1	16.99
2.0	135.9	16.99

A reasonable value for k would be the average of column $v3$, which is approximately 17.02.

d. $m = 17.02r^3$

e. The model fits the data very well.

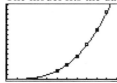

f. $m = 17.02(2.3)^3 \approx 207.1$ grams

62. a. $C(n) = 600 + 40n$

b. $M(n) = \dfrac{600 + 40n}{n}$

c. $M(270) = \dfrac{600 + 40(270)}{(270)} \approx 42.22$

The mean cost per person is \$42.22 if 270 people use the room.

d. $50 = \dfrac{600 + 40n}{n}$

$50 \cdot n = \dfrac{600 + 40n}{n} \cdot n$

$50n = 600 + 40n$

$10n = 600$

$n = 60$

In order for the mean cost per person to be \$50, 60 people must use the room.

63. a. $v(t) = -6.27t^2 + 129.7t - 576.2$

$d(t) = 4.83t^2 - 79.1t + 326.0$

$v + d = -6.27t^2 + 129.7t - 576.2 + 4.83t^2 - 79.$

$v + d = -1.44t^2 + 50.6t - 250.2$

t is the number of years since 1990. $v + d$ is the total number of videocassettes and DVDs sold as a function of this time.

b. $P(t) = 100\left(\dfrac{d}{v+d}\right)$

$= 100\left(\dfrac{4.83t^2 - 79.1t + 326.0}{-1.44t^2 + 50.6t - 250.2}\right)$

$P(t) = \dfrac{483t^2 - 7910t + 32600}{-1.44t^2 + 50.6t - 250.2}$

c. For 2000, $t = 10$, so

$P(10) = \dfrac{483(10)^2 - 7910(10) + 32600}{-1.44(10)^2 + 50.6(10) - 250.2}$

$\approx 16.1\%$

$P(10) = \dfrac{13.9}{13.9 + 99.4}(100)$

$\approx 12.3\%$

d. Using the graphing calculator, find the intersection point between the obtained function and $y = 100$. DVDs will dominate the market in two time locations – $t = 6.5$ (1990 + 6 = 1996) and again in $t = 14.2$ (1990 + 14 = 2004). The first value indicates a breakdown of the model, as DVD's were not the dominant format in 1996.

64. a.

$$T(a) = \frac{75}{a+50} + \frac{40}{a+65}$$

b.

$$T(5) = \frac{75}{(5)+50} + \frac{40}{(5)+65} \approx 1.94$$

When the student drives 5 mph above the speed limit, the driving time is 1.94 hours.

c.

$$2 = \frac{75}{a+50} + \frac{40}{a+65}$$

$$(a+50)(a+65) \cdot 2$$

$$= (a+50)(a+65)\left(\frac{75}{a+50} + \frac{40}{a+65}\right)$$

$$2(a^2 + 115a + 3250) = 75(a+65) + 40(a+5()$$

$$2a^2 + 230a + 6500 = 75a + 4875 + 40a + 20($$

$$2a^2 + 230a + 6500 = 115a + 6875$$

$$2a^2 + 115a - 375 = 0$$

$$a = \frac{-115 \pm \sqrt{115^2 - 4(2)(-375)}}{2(2)}$$

$$= \frac{-115 \pm \sqrt{13225 + 3000}}{4}$$

$$= \frac{-115 \pm \sqrt{16225}}{4}$$

The only answer that makes sense in this context is the positive value.

$$\frac{-115 + \sqrt{16225}}{4} \approx 3.1 \text{ mph above the}$$

speed limits.
The following graph shows the intersection of $y = 2$ and

$$y = \frac{75}{a+50} + \frac{40}{a+65}.$$

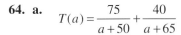

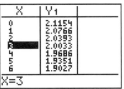

The table indicates that a value for a that is slightly in excess of 3 mph will make the driving time 2 hours.

Chapter 12 Test

1.
$$6x^2 + 11x - 10 = 0$$

$$x = \frac{-11 \pm \sqrt{11^2 - 4(6)(-10)}}{2(6)}$$

$$= \frac{-11 \pm \sqrt{121 + 240}}{12}$$

$$= \frac{-11 \pm \sqrt{361}}{12}$$

$$= \frac{-11 \pm 19}{12}$$

$$x = \frac{-11 + 19}{12} = \frac{2}{3} \quad \text{or} \quad x = \frac{-11 - 19}{12} = -\frac{5}{2}$$

The domain is the set of all real numbers except $\frac{2}{3}$ and $-\frac{5}{2}$.

2.
$$72 - 2x^2 = 0$$

$$36 - x^2 = 0$$

$$(6-x)(6+x) = 0$$

$$6 - x = 0 \quad \text{or} \quad 6 + x = 0$$

$$6 = x \qquad\qquad x = -6$$

The domain is the set of all real numbers except 6 and −6.

3. Since there is no value that will make the denominator 0, the domain is the set of all real numbers.

4. Answers may vary. Example:

$$f(x) = \frac{4}{(x+3)(x-7)}$$

5.
$$\frac{6-3x}{x^2 - 5x + 6} = \frac{-3(x-2)}{(x-2)(x-3)} = -\frac{3}{x-3}$$

6. $\dfrac{9x^2-1}{18x^3-12x^2+2x}=\dfrac{(3x+1)(3x-1)}{2x(9x^2-6x+1)}$

$=\dfrac{(3x+1)(3x-1)}{2x(3x-1)(3x-1)}=\dfrac{3x+1}{2x(3x-1)}$

7. $\dfrac{5x^4}{3x^2+6x+12}\cdot\dfrac{x^3-8}{15x^7}$

$=\dfrac{5x^4}{3(x^2+2x+4)}\cdot\dfrac{(x-2)(x^2+2x+4)}{3\cdot5\cdot x^4\cdot x^3}$

$=\dfrac{x-2}{9x^3}$

8. $\dfrac{p^2-4t^2}{p^2+6pt+9t^2}\div\dfrac{p^2-3pt+2t^2}{p^2+3pt}$

$=\dfrac{p^2-4t^2}{p^2+6pt+9t^2}\cdot\dfrac{p^2+3pt}{p^2-3pt+2t^2}$

$=\dfrac{(p-2t)(p+2t)}{(p+3t)(p+3t)}\cdot\dfrac{p(p+3t)}{(p-t)(p-2t)}$

$=\dfrac{(p-2t)(p+2t)p}{(p+3t)(p-t)(p-2t)}$

$=\dfrac{p(p+2t)}{(p+3t)(p-t)}$

9. $\dfrac{5x+12}{-2x^2-8x}-\dfrac{2x+1}{x^2+2x-8}$

$=\dfrac{5x+12}{-2x(x+4)}-\dfrac{2x+1}{(x-2)(x+4)}$

$=-\dfrac{\left(5x+12\right)}{2x(x+4)}\left(\dfrac{x-2}{x-2}\right)-\dfrac{(2x+1)}{(x-2)(x+4)}\left(\dfrac{2x}{2x}\right)$

$=\dfrac{-(5x+12)(x-2)}{2x(x+4)(x-2)}-\dfrac{2x(2x+1)}{2x(x+4)(x-2)}$

$=\dfrac{-(5x^2+2x-24)}{2x(x+4)(x-2)}-\dfrac{4x^2+2x}{2x(x+4)(x-2)}$

$=\dfrac{-5x^2-2x+24-4x^2-2x}{2x(x+4)(x-2)}$

$=\dfrac{-9x^2-4x+24}{2x(x+4)(x-2)}$

10. $\dfrac{x+2}{x^2-9}+\dfrac{3}{x^2+11x+24}$

$=\dfrac{x+2}{(x-3)(x+3)}+\dfrac{3}{(x+3)(x+8)}$

$=\dfrac{(x+2)(x+8)}{(x-3)(x+3)(x+8)}+\dfrac{3(x-3)}{(x-3)(x+3)(x+8)}$

$=\dfrac{x^2+10x+16+3x-9}{(x-3)(x+3)(x+8)}$

$=\dfrac{x^2+13x+7}{(x-3)(x+3)(x+8)}$

11. $\dfrac{3}{x^2-2x}\div\left(\dfrac{x}{5x-10}-\dfrac{x-1}{x^2-4}\right)$

$=\dfrac{3}{x^2-2x}\div\left(\dfrac{x}{5(x-2)}-\dfrac{x-1}{(x+2)(x-2)}\right)$

$=\dfrac{3}{x^2-2x}\div\left(\dfrac{x}{5(x-2)}\left(\dfrac{x+2}{x+2}\right)-\dfrac{(x-1)}{(x+2)(x-2)}\left(\dfrac{5}{5}\right)\right)$

$=\dfrac{3}{x^2-2x}\div\left(\dfrac{x^2+2x}{5(x-2)(x+2)}-\dfrac{5x-5}{5(x-2)(x+2)}\right)$

$=\dfrac{3}{x^2-2x}\div\left(\dfrac{x^2+2x-5x+5}{5(x-2)(x+2)}\right)$

$=\dfrac{3}{x^2-2x}\div\dfrac{x^2-3x+5}{5(x-2)(x+2)}$

$=\dfrac{3}{x(x-2)}\cdot\dfrac{5(x-2)(x+2)}{x^2-3x+5}$

$=\dfrac{15(x+2)}{x(x^2-3x+5)}$

12. $f(x)-g(x)=\dfrac{x+1}{x-5}-\dfrac{x-2}{x+4}$

$=\left(\dfrac{x+1}{x-5}\right)\left(\dfrac{x+4}{x+4}\right)-\left(\dfrac{x-2}{x+4}\right)\left(\dfrac{x-5}{x-5}\right)$

$=\dfrac{x^2+5x+4}{(x-5)(x+4)}-\dfrac{x^2-7x+10}{(x-5)(x+4)}$

$=\dfrac{x^2+5x+4-x^2+7x-10}{(x-5)(x+4)}$

$=\dfrac{12x-6}{(x-5)(x+4)}$

$=\dfrac{6(2x-1)}{(x-5)(x+4)}$

$(f-g)(0)=\dfrac{6(2(0)-1)}{(0-5)(0+4)}=\dfrac{-6}{(-5)(4)}=\dfrac{6}{20}=\dfrac{3}{10}$

13. $\dfrac{130 \text{ km}}{1 \text{ hour}} \cdot \dfrac{1 \text{ mile}}{1.61 \text{ km}} \approx 80.75 \dfrac{\text{miles}}{\text{hour}}$

So, the speed limit is 80.75 miles per hour.

14. $\dfrac{5+\frac{2}{x}}{3-\frac{4}{x-1}} = \left(\dfrac{5+\frac{2}{x}}{3-\frac{4}{x-1}}\right)\left(\dfrac{x(x-1)}{x(x-1)}\right)$

$= \dfrac{5x(x-1)+2(x-1)}{3x(x-1)-4x} = \dfrac{5x^2-5x+2x-2}{3x^2-3x-4x}$

$= \dfrac{5x^2-3x-2}{3x^2-7x} = \dfrac{(5x+2)(x-1)}{x(3x-7)}$

15. $\dfrac{2}{x-1} - \dfrac{5}{x+1} = \dfrac{4x}{x^2-1}$

$\dfrac{2(x+1)-5(x-1)}{(x+1)(x-1)} = \dfrac{4x}{(x+1)(x-1)}$

$2x+2-5x+5 = 4x$

$-3x+7 = 4x$

$7 = 7x$

$1 = x$

$x = 1$ makes the denominators $x-1$ and x^2-1 equal 0. This equation has no solution.

16. $\dfrac{5}{x-3} = \dfrac{x}{x-2} + \dfrac{x}{x^2-5x+6}$

$\dfrac{5}{x-3} = \dfrac{x}{x-2} + \dfrac{x}{(x-3)(x-2)}$

$\dfrac{5(x-2)}{(x-3)(x-2)} = \dfrac{x(x-3)}{(x-3)(x-2)} + \dfrac{x}{(x-3)(x-2)}$

$\dfrac{5(x-2)}{(x-3)(x-2)} = \dfrac{x(x-3)+x}{(x-3)(x-2)}$

$5(x-2) = x(x-3)+x$

$5x-10 = x^2-3x+x$

$5x-10 = x^2-2x$

$x^2-7x+10 = 0$

$(x-5)(x-2) = 0$

$x = 5$ and $x = 2$

$x = 2$ makes the denominators $x-2$ and x^2-5x+6 equal 0. The solution is $x = 5$.

17. $f(x) = \dfrac{2}{x-4} + \dfrac{3}{x+1}$

$5 = \dfrac{2}{x-4} + \dfrac{3}{x+1}$

$(x-4)(x+1) \cdot 5 = (x-4)(x+1)\left(\dfrac{2}{x-4} + \dfrac{3}{x+1}\right)$

$5(x^2-3x-4) = 2(x+1)+3(x-4)$

$5x^2-15x-20 = 2x+2+3x-12$

$5x^2-15x-20 = 5x-10$

$5x^2-20x-10 = 0$

$x^2-4x-2 = 0$

$x = \dfrac{4 \pm \sqrt{(-4)^2-4(1)(-2)}}{2(1)}$

$= \dfrac{4 \pm \sqrt{16+8}}{2}$

$= \dfrac{4 \pm \sqrt{24}}{2}$

$= \dfrac{4 \pm \sqrt{4 \cdot 6}}{2}$

$= \dfrac{4 \pm 2\sqrt{6}}{2}$

$= 2 \pm \sqrt{6}$

The solutions are $x = 2 \pm \sqrt{6}$.

18. $f(x) = \dfrac{(x-5)(x+2)}{(x-1)(x+3)}$

$f(-2) = \dfrac{((-2)-5)((-2)+2)}{((-2)-1)((-2)+3)}$

$= \dfrac{(-5)(0)}{(-3)(1)}$

$= 0$

19. $f(x) = \dfrac{(x-5)(x+2)}{(x-1)(x+3)}$

$f(1) = \dfrac{(1-5)(1+2)}{(1-1)(1+3)}$

$= \dfrac{(-4)(3)}{(0)(4)}$

$= \dfrac{-3}{0}$

The solution is undefined.

20.
$$f(x) = \frac{(x-5)(x+2)}{(x-1)(x+3)}$$

$$0 = \frac{(x-5)(x+2)}{(x-1)(x+3)}$$

$$(x-1)(x+3) \cdot 0$$

$$= (x-1)(x+3)\frac{(x-5)(x+2)}{(x-1)(x+3)}$$

$$0 = (x-5)(x+2)$$

$$x-5 = 0 \quad \text{or} \quad x+2 = 0$$

$$x = 5 \qquad\qquad x = -2$$

The solutions are $x = 5$ and $x = -2$.

21. Let x be the amount of gasoline required to travel 400 miles on highways.

$$\frac{153}{3} = \frac{400}{x}$$

$$3x\left(\frac{153}{3}\right) = 3x\left(\frac{400}{x}\right)$$

$$153x = 1200$$

$$x \approx 7.84$$

Approximately 7.84 gallons of gasoline are required to travel 400 miles on highways.

22.
$$\frac{x}{9} = \frac{14}{8}$$

$$\frac{x}{9} \cdot 9 = \frac{14}{8} \cdot 9$$

$$x = 15.75$$

The length is 15.75 meters.

23. $W = kt^2$

To find k solve the following equation:

$$3 = k(7)^2$$

$$3 = 49k$$

$$\frac{3}{49} = k$$

The equation is $W = \frac{3}{49}t^2$.

24.
$$y = \frac{k}{\sqrt{x}}$$

To find k solve the following equation:

$$8 = \frac{k}{\sqrt{25}}$$

$$8 = \frac{k}{5}$$

$$40 = k$$

The equation is $y = \frac{40}{\sqrt{x}}$.

25. a. $C(n) = 200n + 10000$

b.
$$B(n) = \frac{200n + 10000}{n}$$

c.
$$P(n) = \frac{200n + 10000}{n} + 150$$

$$= \frac{200n + 10000}{n} + 150 \cdot \frac{n}{n}$$

$$= \frac{200n + 10000}{n} + \frac{150n}{n}$$

$$= \frac{350n + 10000}{n}$$

d.
$$P(100) = \frac{350(100) + 10000}{100} = 450$$

If the bike manufacturer makes and sells 100 bikes in a month, the price of each bike should be \$450 to insure that the manufacturer makes a profit of \$150 per bike.

26. a.
$$T(a) = \frac{400}{a+70} + \frac{920}{a+75}$$

b.
$$T(5) = \frac{400}{(5)+70} + \frac{920}{(5)+75} \approx 16.83$$

When the student drives 5 mph above the speed limit, the trip takes about 16.8 hours.

c.
$$17 = \frac{400}{a+70} + \frac{920}{a+75}$$

$$(a+70)(a+75) \cdot 17$$

$$= (a+70)(a+75)\left(\frac{400}{a+70} + \frac{920}{a+75}\right)$$

$$17(a^2 + 145a + 5250)$$

$$= 400(a+75) + 920(a+70)$$

$$17a^2 + 2465a + 89250$$

$$= 400a + 30000 + 920a + 64400$$

$17a^2 + 2465a + 89250 = 1320a + 94400$

$17a^2 + 1145a - 5150 = 0$

$$a = \frac{-1145 \pm \sqrt{1145^2 - 4(17)(-5150)}}{2(17)}$$

$$= \frac{-1145 \pm \sqrt{1311025 + 350200}}{34}$$

$$= \frac{-1145 \pm \sqrt{1661225}}{34}$$

The only solution that makes sense in this context is the positive solution.

$$\frac{-1145 + \sqrt{1661225}}{34} \approx 4.23$$

This means the student must drive 4.23 mph above the speed limits for the driving time to be 17 hours.

27. a.

$$F = \frac{k}{L^2}$$

To find k solve the following equation:

$$50 = \frac{k}{8^2}$$

$$50 = \frac{k}{64}$$

$$3200 = k$$

The equation is $g(L) = F = \dfrac{3200}{L^2}$

b.

$$g(L) = F = \frac{3200}{6^2} \approx 88.9 \text{ hertz}$$

c.

$$200 = \frac{3200}{L^2}$$

$$200L^2 = 3200$$

$$L^2 = 16$$

$$L = 4 \text{ cm}$$

d. The graph is decreasing for $L > 0$.

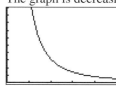

The longer the length of the prongs, the lower the frequency.

28. a. By using the quadratic regression feature of a graphing calculator, we get the equation:

$$r(t) = -0.28t^2 + 26.94t + 151.22$$

b. By using the linear regression feature of a graphing calculator, we get the equation:

$$n(t) = 50.84t + 275.13$$

c.

$$P(t) = \frac{r(t)}{n(t)} \cdot 100$$

$$= \left(\frac{-0.28t^2 + 26.94t + 151.22}{50.84t + 275.13} \right) \cdot 100$$

$$= \frac{-28t^2 + 2694t + 15122}{50.84t + 275.13}$$

d. For 2013, $t = 33$.

$$P(33) = \frac{-28(33)^2 + 2694(33) + 15122}{50.84(33) + 275.13} \backslash$$

$$\approx 37.65$$

In 2013, about 37.7% of prisoners will be released.

e.

$$37 = \frac{-28t^2 + 2694t + 1512}{50.84t + 275.13}$$

$$37(50.84t + 275.13) = -28t^2 + 2694t + 1512$$

$$1881.08t + 10179.81 = -28t^2 + 2694t + 1512$$

$$0 = -28t^2 + 812.92t + 494$$

$$t = \frac{-812.92 \pm \sqrt{812.92^2 - 4(-28)(4942.19)}}{2(\ 28)}$$

$$= \frac{-812.92 \pm \sqrt{1214364.21}}{2(-28)}$$

$$t \approx \frac{-812.92 \pm 1101.98}{-56}$$

$t \approx 34.19$ and $t \approx -5.16$

Considering the negative value to indicate model breakdown, in 1980 + 34 = 2014, about 37% of prisoners will be released.

Chapter 13
Radical Functions

Homework 13.1

1. $x^{2/5} = \sqrt[5]{x^2}$

3. $\sqrt[4]{x^3} = x^{3/4}$

5. $\sqrt{w} = w^{1/2}$

7. $(2x+9)^{3/7} = \sqrt[7]{(2x+9)^3}$

9. $\sqrt[7]{(3k+2)^4} = (3k+2)^{4/7}$

11. $\sqrt{50} = \sqrt{25 \cdot 2} = \sqrt{25}\sqrt{2} = 5\sqrt{2}$

13. $\sqrt{x^8} = x^{8/2} = x^4$

15. $\sqrt{36x^6} = \sqrt{36} \cdot \sqrt{x^6} = 6x^3$

17. $\sqrt{5a^2b^{12}} = \sqrt{5} \cdot \sqrt{a^2b^{12}} = ab^6\sqrt{5}$

19. $\sqrt{x^9} = \sqrt{x^8 \cdot x} = \sqrt{x^8} \cdot \sqrt{x} = x^4\sqrt{x}$

21. $\sqrt{24x^5} = \sqrt{4 \cdot 6 \cdot x^4 \cdot x}$
$= \sqrt{4} \cdot \sqrt{6} \cdot \sqrt{x^4} \cdot \sqrt{x}$
$= 2x^2\sqrt{6x}$

23. $\sqrt{80x^3y^8} = \sqrt{16 \cdot 5 \cdot x^2 \cdot x \cdot y^8}$
$= \sqrt{16} \cdot \sqrt{5} \cdot \sqrt{x^2} \cdot \sqrt{x} \cdot \sqrt{y^8}$
$= 4xy^4\sqrt{5x}$

25. $\sqrt{200a^3b^5} = \sqrt{100 \cdot 2 \cdot a^2 \cdot a \cdot b^4 \cdot b}$
$= \sqrt{100} \cdot \sqrt{2} \cdot \sqrt{a^2} \cdot \sqrt{a} \cdot \sqrt{b^4} \cdot \sqrt{b}$
$= 10ab^2\sqrt{2ab}$

27. $\sqrt{(2x+5)^8} = (2x+5)^{8/2} = (2x+5)^4$

29. $\sqrt{(6t+3)^5} = \sqrt{(6t+3)^4(6t+3)}$
$= \sqrt{(6t+3)^4} \cdot \sqrt{6t+3}$
$= (6t+3)^2\sqrt{6t+3}$

31. $\sqrt[3]{27} = 3$

33. $\sqrt[6]{x^6} = x^{6/6} = x^1 = x$

35. $\sqrt[3]{8x^3} = \sqrt[3]{8} \cdot \sqrt[3]{x^3} = 2x$

37. $\sqrt[5]{-32x^{20}} = \sqrt[5]{-32} \cdot \sqrt[5]{x^{20}} = -2x^4$

39. $\sqrt[4]{81a^{12}b^{28}} = \sqrt[4]{81} \cdot \sqrt[4]{a^{12}} \cdot \sqrt[4]{b^{28}} = 3a^3b^7$

41. $\sqrt[6]{x^{17}} = \sqrt[6]{x^{12} \cdot x^5} = \sqrt[6]{x^{12}} \cdot \sqrt[6]{x^5} = x^2\sqrt[6]{x^5}$

43. $\sqrt[3]{-125a^{17}b^{12}} = \sqrt[3]{-125 \cdot a^{15} \cdot a^2 \cdot b^{12}}$
$= \sqrt[3]{-125} \cdot \sqrt[3]{a^{15}} \cdot \sqrt[3]{a^2} \cdot \sqrt[3]{b^{12}}$
$= -5a^5b^4\sqrt[3]{a^2}$

45. $\sqrt[5]{64x^{39}y^7} = \sqrt[5]{32 \cdot 2 \cdot x^{35} \cdot x^4 \cdot y^5 \cdot y^2}$
$= \sqrt[5]{32} \cdot \sqrt[5]{2} \cdot \sqrt[5]{x^{35}} \cdot \sqrt[5]{x^4} \cdot \sqrt[5]{y^5} \cdot \sqrt[5]{y^2}$
$= 2x^7y\sqrt[5]{2x^4y^2}$

47. $\sqrt[5]{(6xy)^5} = (6xy)^{5/5} = (6xy)^1 = 6xy$

49. $\sqrt[4]{(3x+6)^4} = (3x+6)^{4/4} = (3x+6)^1 = 3x+6$

51. $\sqrt[5]{(4p+7)^{20}} = (4p+7)^{20/5} = (4p+7)^4$

53. $\sqrt[6]{(2x+9)^{31}} = \sqrt[6]{(2x+9)^{30}(2x+9)}$
$= \sqrt[6]{(2x+9)^{30}} \cdot \sqrt[6]{2x+9}$
$= (2x+9)^5\sqrt[6]{2x+9}$

55. $\sqrt[8]{x^6} = x^{6/8} = x^{3/4} = \sqrt[4]{x^3}$

57. $\sqrt[6]{x^4} = x^{4/6} = x^{2/3} = \sqrt[3]{x^2}$

59. $\sqrt[12]{(2m+7)^{10}} = (2m+7)^{10/12}$

$\qquad\qquad = (2m+7)^{5/6}$

$\qquad\qquad = \sqrt[6]{(2m+7)^5}$

61. $\sqrt[6]{x^{14}} = x^{14/6}$

$\qquad\quad = x^{7/3}$

$\qquad\quad = \sqrt[3]{x^7}$

$\qquad\quad = \sqrt[3]{x^6 \cdot x}$

$\qquad\quad = \sqrt[3]{x^6} \cdot \sqrt[3]{x}$

$\qquad\quad = x^2\sqrt[3]{x}$

63. $\sqrt[6]{27} = \sqrt[6]{3^3} = 3^{3/6} = 3^{1/2} = \sqrt{3}$

65. $\sqrt[4]{\sqrt[3]{p}} = \sqrt[4]{p^{1/3}} = p^{\frac{1}{3}\frac{1}{4}} = p^{1/12} = \sqrt[12]{p}$

67. $\sqrt[10]{16x^8} = \sqrt[10]{16} \cdot \sqrt[10]{x^8}$

$\qquad\qquad = \sqrt[10]{4^2} \cdot \sqrt[10]{x^8}$

$\qquad\qquad = 4^{2/10} \cdot x^{8/10}$

$\qquad\qquad = 4^{1/5} \cdot x^{4/5}$

$\qquad\qquad = \sqrt[5]{4} \cdot \sqrt[5]{x^4}$

$\qquad\qquad = \sqrt[5]{4x^4}$

69. $\sqrt[4]{\sqrt{ab}} = \sqrt[4]{ab^{1/2}} = ab^{\frac{1}{2}\frac{1}{4}} = ab^{1/8} = \sqrt[8]{ab}$

71. $f(-32) = \sqrt[5]{-32} = -2$

73. $g(2) = \sqrt[3]{3(2)+2} = \sqrt[3]{8} = 2$

75. $g(7) = \sqrt[3]{3(7)+2} = \sqrt[3]{23}$

77. $h(49) = 2\sqrt{49} - 5 = 2(7) - 5 = 14 - 5 = 9$

79.

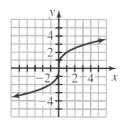

81. a.

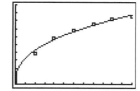

The model fits the data well.

b. $f(24) = 8.5\sqrt[5]{24^2} \approx 30.3$

The average temperature rise is about 30 degrees Fahrenheit.

c. $f(45) = 8.5\sqrt[5]{45^2} \approx 38.97$

$90 + 39 = 129$

The temperature in the car is about 129 degrees Fahrenheit.

d. $107 - 80 = 27$

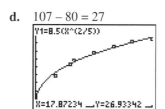

It would take about 18 minutes.

83. a. $f(3890) = \sqrt{9.8(3890)} \approx 195.25$

The speed of tsunami is about 195 meters per second.

b. $f(1000) = \sqrt{9.8(1000)} \approx 98.99$

$f(2000) = \sqrt{9.8(2000)} = 140$

$f(3000) = \sqrt{9.8(3000)} \approx 171.46$

f is an increasing function. This means that the speed of the tsunami increases as the depth of the ocean increases.

c. As a tsunami approaches the shore, the depth of the water decreases, which decreases the speed of the tsunami. At the same time, the height of the tsunami increases.

d. $195 \times 60 \times 60 = 702,000$ meters per hour
$702,000 \div 1609 \approx 436.3$ miles per hour
The tsunami travels at about 436 mph.

85. Answers may vary.
$$\sqrt{x^{16}} = \left(x^{16}\right)^{1/2} = x^{16 \cdot \frac{1}{2}} = x^8$$

87. $\sqrt[n]{\sqrt[n]{x}} = \sqrt[n]{x^{1/n}}$
$$= \left(x^{1/n}\right)^{1/n}$$
$$= x^{(1/n) \cdot (1/n)}$$
$$= x^{1/n^2}$$
$$= \sqrt[n^2]{x}$$

89. a. $\left(\sqrt{x}\right)^2 = \left(x^{1/2}\right)^2 = x^{2/2} = x^1 = x$

b. $\left(\sqrt[3]{x}\right)^3 = \left(x^{1/3}\right)^3 = x^{3/3} = x^1 = x$

c. $\left(\sqrt[n]{x}\right)^n = \left(x^{1/n}\right)^n = x^{n/n} = x^1 = x$

91. a. $\sqrt{16x^4 y^6} = \sqrt{16} \cdot \sqrt{x^4} \cdot \sqrt{y^6}$
$$= 4x^2 y^3$$

b. $\sqrt{16x^4 y^6} = \left(16x^4 y^6\right)^{1/2}$
$$= 16^{\frac{1}{2}} x^{4 \cdot \frac{1}{2}} y^{6 \cdot \frac{1}{2}}$$
$$= 4x^2 y^3$$

c. The answers are the same.

93. $\dfrac{2x}{x^2 + x - 6} - \dfrac{3x - 1}{x^2 + 6x + 9} = \dfrac{-3}{x + 3}$
$$\frac{2x}{(x+3)(x-2)} - \frac{3x-1}{(x+3)(x+3)} = \frac{-3}{x+3}$$
$$2x(x+3) - (3x-1)(x-2) = -3(x+3)(x-2)$$
$$2x^2 + 6x - 3x^2 + 7x - 2 = -3x^2 - 3x + 18$$
$$2x^2 + 6x - 3x^2 + 7x - 2 + 3x^2 + 3x - 18 = 0$$
$$2x^2 + 16x - 20 = 0$$
$$2(x^2 + 8x - 10) = 0$$

$$\frac{-b \pm \sqrt{b^2 - 4ac}}{2a} = \frac{-8 \pm \sqrt{8^2 - 4(1)(-10)}}{2(1)}$$
$$= \frac{-8 \pm \sqrt{104}}{2}$$
$$= -4 \pm \sqrt{26}$$

$\dfrac{2x}{x^2 + x - 6} - \dfrac{3x - 1}{x^2 + 6x + 9} = \dfrac{-3}{x + 3}$ is a rational equation in one variable.

95. $\dfrac{2x}{x^2 + x - 6} - \dfrac{3x - 1}{x^2 + 6x + 9}$
$$= \frac{2x}{(x+3)(x-2)} - \frac{3x-1}{(x+3)(x+3)}$$
$$= \frac{2x(x+3) - (3x-1)(x-2)}{(x+3)(x+3)(x-2)}$$
$$= \frac{2x^2 + 6x - 3x^2 + 7x - 2}{(x+3)(x+3)(x-2)}$$
$$= \frac{-x^2 + 13x - 2}{(x+3)(x+3)(x-2)}$$

$\dfrac{2x}{x^2 + x - 6} - \dfrac{3x - 1}{x^2 + 6x + 9}$ is a rational expression in one variable.

97. $f(x) = \dfrac{2x}{x^2 + x - 6} = \dfrac{2x}{(x+3)(x-2)}$

The domain of $f(x)$ is all real numbers except $x = -3$ and $x = 2$.

$f(x) = \dfrac{2x}{x^2 + x - 6}$ is a rational function.

Homework 13.2

1. $4\sqrt{3} + 5\sqrt{3} = (4 + 5)\sqrt{3} = 9\sqrt{3}$

3. $-3\sqrt{5} + 9\sqrt{5} = (-3 + 9)\sqrt{5} = 6\sqrt{5}$

5. $2\sqrt[3]{5x^2 y} - 6\sqrt[3]{5x^2 y} = (2 - 6)\sqrt[3]{5x^2 y}$
$$= -4\sqrt[3]{5x^2 y}$$

7. $3\sqrt{5a} + 2\sqrt{3b} - 6\sqrt{3b} + 7\sqrt{5a}$
$$= \left(3\sqrt{5a} + 7\sqrt{5a}\right) + \left(2\sqrt{3b} - 6\sqrt{3b}\right)$$
$$= (3 + 7)\sqrt{5a} + (2 - 6)\sqrt{3b}$$
$$= 10\sqrt{5a} - 4\sqrt{3b}$$

9.

$$2\sqrt{x}+5-7\sqrt[3]{x}-9+5\sqrt[3]{x}$$
$$=2\sqrt{x}+(5-9)+(-7+5)\sqrt[3]{x}$$
$$=2\sqrt{x}-4-2\sqrt[3]{x}$$

11.

$$6\sqrt[3]{x-1}-3\sqrt[3]{x-1}-2\sqrt{x-1}$$
$$=(6-3)\sqrt[3]{x-1}-2\sqrt{x-1}$$
$$=3\sqrt[3]{x-1}-2\sqrt{x-1}$$

13.

$$3.7\sqrt[4]{x}-1.1\sqrt[4]{x}-4.2\sqrt[6]{x}+4.2\sqrt[6]{x}$$
$$=(3.7-1.1)\sqrt[4]{x}+(-4.2+4.2)\sqrt[6]{x}$$
$$=2.6\sqrt[4]{x}$$

15.

$$3\left(7-\sqrt{x}+2\right)-\left(\sqrt{x}+2\right)$$
$$=3\cdot7-3\cdot\sqrt{x}+3\cdot2-\sqrt{x}-2$$
$$=21-3\sqrt{x}+6-\sqrt{x}-2$$
$$=-3\sqrt{x}-\sqrt{x}+21+6-2$$
$$=(-3-1)\sqrt{x}+(21+6-2)$$
$$=-4\sqrt{x}+25$$

17.

$$7\left(\sqrt[3]{x}+1\right)-7\left(\sqrt[3]{x}-1\right)$$
$$=7\cdot\sqrt[3]{x}+7\cdot1-7\cdot\sqrt[3]{x}-7(-1)$$
$$=7\sqrt[3]{x}+7-7\sqrt[3]{x}+7$$
$$=7\sqrt[3]{x}-7\sqrt[3]{x}+7+7$$
$$=14$$

19.

$$5\sqrt{6}-\sqrt{24}=5\sqrt{6}-\sqrt{4\cdot6}$$
$$=5\sqrt{6}-\sqrt{4}\sqrt{6}$$
$$=5\sqrt{6}-2\sqrt{6}$$
$$=3\sqrt{6}$$

21.

$$\sqrt{12b}+\sqrt{75b}=\sqrt{4\cdot3b}+\sqrt{25\cdot3b}$$
$$=2\sqrt{3b}+5\sqrt{3b}$$
$$=(2+5)\sqrt{3b}$$
$$=7\sqrt{3b}$$

23.

$$5\sqrt{12}+4\sqrt{75}-2\sqrt{3}=5\sqrt{4\cdot3}+4\sqrt{25\cdot3}-2\sqrt{3}$$
$$=5\sqrt{4}\sqrt{3}+4\sqrt{25}\sqrt{3}-2\sqrt{3}$$
$$=5\cdot2\sqrt{3}+4\cdot5\sqrt{3}-2\sqrt{3}$$
$$=10\sqrt{3}+20\sqrt{3}-2\sqrt{3}$$
$$=28\sqrt{3}$$

25.

$$\sqrt{18x^5}+2x\sqrt{50x^3}$$
$$=\sqrt{9\cdot2\cdot x^4\cdot x}+2x\sqrt{25\cdot2\cdot x^2\cdot x}$$
$$=\sqrt{9}\sqrt{x^4}\sqrt{2x}+2x\sqrt{25}\sqrt{x^2}\sqrt{2x}$$
$$=3x^2\sqrt{2x}+2x(5x)\sqrt{2x}$$
$$=3x^2\sqrt{2x}+10x^2\sqrt{2x}$$
$$=\left(3x^2+10x^2\right)\sqrt{2x}$$
$$=13x^2\sqrt{2x}$$

27.

$$5\sqrt{4x^3}-x\sqrt{36x}=5\sqrt{4\cdot x^2\cdot x}-x\sqrt{36\cdot x}$$
$$=5\sqrt{4}\sqrt{x^2}\sqrt{x}-x\sqrt{36}\sqrt{x}$$
$$=5(2)x\sqrt{x}-6x\sqrt{x}$$
$$=10x\sqrt{x}-6x\sqrt{x}$$
$$=(10-6)x\sqrt{x}$$
$$=4x\sqrt{x}$$

29.

$$3\sqrt{81x^2}-2\sqrt{100x^2}=3\cdot9x-2\cdot10x$$
$$=27x-20x$$
$$=7x$$

31.

$$a\sqrt{12b^3}+b\sqrt{75ba^2}$$
$$=a\sqrt{4b^2\cdot3b}+b\sqrt{25a^2\cdot3b}$$
$$=a\sqrt{4b^2}\sqrt{3b}+b\sqrt{25a^2}\sqrt{3b}$$
$$=2ab\sqrt{3b}+5ab\sqrt{3b}$$
$$=(2+5)ab\sqrt{3b}$$
$$=7ab\sqrt{3b}$$

33.

$$\sqrt[3]{27x^5}-x\sqrt[3]{8x^2}=\sqrt[3]{27x^3\cdot x^2}-x\sqrt[3]{8\cdot x^2}$$
$$=\sqrt[3]{27x^3}\sqrt[3]{x^2}-x\sqrt[3]{8}\sqrt[3]{x^2}$$
$$=3x\sqrt[3]{x^2}-2x\sqrt[3]{x^2}$$
$$=(3-2)x\sqrt[3]{x^2}$$
$$=x\sqrt[3]{x^2}$$

35.
$$y\sqrt[4]{16x^{11}y^4} - 3x\sqrt[4]{x^7 y^8}$$
$$= y\sqrt[4]{16 \cdot x^8 \cdot x^3 \cdot y^4} - 3x\sqrt[4]{x^4 \cdot x^3 \cdot y^8}$$
$$= y\sqrt[4]{16x^8 y^4}\,\sqrt[4]{x^3} - 3x\sqrt[4]{x^4 y^8}\,\sqrt[4]{x^3}$$
$$= y\left(2x^2 y\right)\sqrt[4]{x^3} - 3x(xy^2)\sqrt[4]{x^3}$$
$$= 2x^2 y^2 \sqrt[4]{x^3} - 3x^2 y^2 \sqrt[4]{x^3}$$
$$= \left(2x^2 y^2 - 3x^2 y^2\right)\sqrt[4]{x^3}$$
$$= -x^2 y^2 \sqrt[4]{x^3}$$

37.
$$\sqrt{2} \cdot \sqrt{5} = \sqrt{2 \cdot 5} = \sqrt{10}$$

39.
$$3\sqrt{x} \cdot 2\sqrt{x} = 3 \cdot 2 \cdot \sqrt{x} \cdot \sqrt{x}$$
$$= 6\sqrt{x \cdot x}$$
$$= 6\sqrt{x^2}$$
$$= 6x$$

41.
$$2\sqrt{5} \cdot \sqrt{10} = 2\sqrt{5 \cdot 10} = 2\sqrt{50}$$
$$= 2\sqrt{25 \cdot 2} = 2\sqrt{25}\sqrt{2}$$
$$= 2 \cdot 5\sqrt{2}$$
$$= 10\sqrt{2}$$

43.
$$-2\sqrt{5x} \cdot 4\sqrt{3x} = -2 \cdot 4 \cdot \sqrt{5x} \cdot \sqrt{3x}$$
$$= -8\sqrt{5x \cdot 3x}$$
$$= -8\sqrt{15x^2}$$
$$= -8\sqrt{15}\sqrt{x^2}$$
$$= -8x\sqrt{15}$$

45.
$$\sqrt{5}\left(1 + \sqrt{7}\right) = \sqrt{5} \cdot 1 + \sqrt{5} \cdot \sqrt{7}$$
$$= \sqrt{5} + \sqrt{35}$$

47.
$$2\sqrt{7t}\left(\sqrt{7t} - \sqrt{2t}\right) = 2\sqrt{7t} \cdot \sqrt{7t} - 2\sqrt{7t} \cdot \sqrt{2t}$$
$$= 2\sqrt{7t \cdot 7t} - 2\sqrt{7t \cdot 2t}$$
$$= 2\sqrt{49t^2} - 2\sqrt{14t^2}$$
$$= 2\sqrt{49}\sqrt{t^2} - 2\sqrt{14}\sqrt{t^2}$$
$$= 2 \cdot 7t - 2t\sqrt{14}$$
$$= 14t - 2t\sqrt{14}$$

49.
$$\left(4 + \sqrt{5}\right)\left(2 - \sqrt{5}\right) = 4 \cdot 2 - 4\sqrt{5} + 2\sqrt{5} - \sqrt{5}\sqrt{5}$$
$$= 8 - 4\sqrt{5} + 2\sqrt{5} - 5$$
$$= 8 - 2\sqrt{5} - 5$$
$$= 3 - 2\sqrt{5}$$

51.
$$\left(2\sqrt{x} + 6\right)\left(5\sqrt{x} + 4\right)$$
$$= 2\sqrt{x} \cdot 5\sqrt{x} + 6 \cdot 5\sqrt{x} + 2\sqrt{x} \cdot 4 + 6 \cdot 4$$
$$= 10\sqrt{x^2} + 30\sqrt{x} + 8\sqrt{x} + 24$$
$$= 10x + (30 + 8)\sqrt{x} + 24$$
$$= 10x + 38\sqrt{x} + 24$$

53.
$$\left(4\sqrt{x} + \sqrt{3}\right)\left(2\sqrt{x} - \sqrt{5}\right)$$
$$= 4\sqrt{x} \cdot 2\sqrt{x} + \sqrt{3} \cdot 2\sqrt{x} - 4\sqrt{x} \cdot \sqrt{5} - \sqrt{3}\sqrt{5}$$
$$= 8\sqrt{x^2} + 2\sqrt{3x} - 4\sqrt{5x} - \sqrt{15}$$
$$= 8x + 2\sqrt{3x} - 4\sqrt{5x} - \sqrt{15}$$

55.
$$\left(5\sqrt{a} + \sqrt{b}\right)\left(\sqrt{a} - 2\sqrt{b}\right)$$
$$= 5\sqrt{a} \cdot \sqrt{a} + \sqrt{b} \cdot \sqrt{a} - 5\sqrt{a} \cdot 2\sqrt{b} - \sqrt{b} \cdot 2\sqrt{b}$$
$$= 5\sqrt{a^2} + \sqrt{ab} - 10\sqrt{ab} - 2\sqrt{b^2}$$
$$= 5a + (1 - 10)\sqrt{ab} - 2b$$
$$= 5a - 2b - 9\sqrt{ab}$$

57.
$$\left(1 - \sqrt{w}\right)\left(1 + \sqrt{w}\right) = 1^2 - \left(\sqrt{w}\right)^2 = 1 - w$$

59.
$$\left(7x + \sqrt{5}\right)\left(7x - \sqrt{5}\right) = \left(7x\right)^2 - \left(\sqrt{5}\right)^2$$
$$= 49x^2 - 5$$

61.
$$\left(2\sqrt{a} - \sqrt{b}\right)\left(2\sqrt{a} + \sqrt{b}\right) = \left(2\sqrt{a}\right)^2 - \left(\sqrt{b}\right)^2$$
$$= 2^2 \left(\sqrt{a}\right)^2 - \left(\sqrt{b}\right)^2$$
$$= 4a - b$$

63.
$$\left(4 + \sqrt{7}\right)^2 = 4^2 + 2 \cdot 4 \cdot \sqrt{7} + \left(\sqrt{7}\right)^2$$
$$= 16 + 8\sqrt{7} + 7$$
$$= 23 + 8\sqrt{7}$$

65.
$$\left(5+6\sqrt{x}\right)^2 = 5^2 + 2(5)\left(6\sqrt{x}\right) + \left(6\sqrt{x}\right)^2$$
$$= 25 + 60\sqrt{x} + 6^2\left(\sqrt{x}\right)^2$$
$$= 25 + 60\sqrt{x} + 36x$$
$$= 36x + 60\sqrt{x} + 25$$

67.
$$\left(4\sqrt{x}-\sqrt{5}\right)^2 = \left(4\sqrt{x}\right)^2 - 2\left(4\sqrt{x}\right)\left(\sqrt{5}\right) + \left(\sqrt{5}\right)^2$$
$$= 4^2\left(\sqrt{x}\right)^2 - 8\sqrt{5x} + 5$$
$$= 16x - 8\sqrt{5x} + 5$$

69.
$$\left(\sqrt{a}+2\sqrt{b}\right)^2 = \left(\sqrt{a}\right)^2 + 2\left(\sqrt{a}\right)\left(2\sqrt{b}\right) + \left(2\sqrt{b}\right)^2$$
$$= a + 4\sqrt{ab} + 2^2\left(\sqrt{b}\right)^2$$
$$= a + 4\sqrt{ab} + 4b$$

71.
$$\left(\sqrt{2x-5}+3\right)^2$$
$$= \left(\sqrt{2x-5}\right)^2 + 2\left(\sqrt{2x-5}\right)(3) + (3)^2$$
$$= 2x - 5 + 6\sqrt{2x-5} + 9$$
$$= 2x + 6\sqrt{2x-5} + 4$$

73.
$$\sqrt{x}\sqrt[5]{x} = x^{1/2}\cdot x^{1/5} = x^{\frac{1}{2}+\frac{1}{5}}$$
$$= x^{\frac{5}{10}+\frac{2}{10}} = x^{7/10}$$
$$= \sqrt[10]{x^7}$$

75.
$$\sqrt[5]{x^4}\sqrt[5]{x^3} = \sqrt[5]{x^4\cdot x^3}$$
$$= \sqrt[5]{x^7}$$
$$= \sqrt[5]{x^5\cdot x^2}$$
$$= \sqrt[5]{x^5}\sqrt[5]{x^2}$$
$$= x\sqrt[5]{x^2}$$

77.
$$-5\sqrt{m}\left(\sqrt[4]{2m}-4\right) = -5\sqrt{m}\sqrt[4]{2m} - 5\sqrt{m}\left(-4\right)$$
$$= -5\sqrt{m}\sqrt[4]{2}\sqrt[4]{m} + 20\sqrt{m}$$
$$= -5\sqrt[4]{2}\;m^{1/2}\cdot m^{1/4} + 20\sqrt{m}$$
$$= -5\sqrt[4]{2}\;m^{\frac{1}{2}+\frac{1}{4}} + 20\sqrt{m}$$
$$= -5\sqrt[4]{2}m^{3/4} + 20\sqrt{m}$$
$$= -5\sqrt[4]{2}\sqrt[4]{m^3} + 20\sqrt{m}$$
$$= -5\sqrt[4]{2m^3} + 20\sqrt{m}$$

79.
$$\left(\sqrt[3]{x}+1\right)^2 = \left(\sqrt[3]{x}\right)^2 + 2\left(\sqrt[3]{x}\right)(1) + (1)^2$$
$$= \sqrt[3]{x^2} + 2\sqrt[3]{x} + 1$$

81.
$$\left(\sqrt[4]{k}-\sqrt[3]{k}\right)^2 = \left(\sqrt[4]{k}\right)^2 - 2\left(\sqrt[4]{k}\right)\left(\sqrt[3]{k}\right) + \left(\sqrt[3]{k}\right)^2$$
$$= \sqrt[4]{k^2} - 2k^{1/4}\cdot k^{1/3} + \sqrt[3]{k^2}$$
$$= k^{2/4} - 2k^{\frac{1}{4}+\frac{1}{3}} + \sqrt[3]{k^2}$$
$$= k^{1/2} - 2k^{7/12} + \sqrt[3]{k^2}$$
$$= \sqrt{k} - 2\sqrt[12]{k^7} + \sqrt[3]{k^2}$$

83.
$$\left(2\sqrt{x}-6\right)\left(3\sqrt[3]{x}+1\right)$$
$$= 2\sqrt{x}\cdot 3\sqrt[3]{x} - 6\cdot 3\sqrt[3]{x} + 2\sqrt{x}\cdot 1 - 6\cdot 1$$
$$= 6x^{1/2}\cdot x^{1/3} - 18\sqrt[3]{x} + 2\sqrt{x} - 6$$
$$= 6x^{\frac{1}{2}+\frac{1}{3}} - 18\sqrt[3]{x} + 2\sqrt{x} - 6$$
$$= 6x^{5/6} - 18\sqrt[3]{x} + 2\sqrt{x} - 6$$
$$= 6\sqrt[6]{x^5} - 18\sqrt[3]{x} + 2\sqrt{x} - 6$$

85.
$$\left(3\sqrt[4]{x}+5\right)\left(3\sqrt[4]{x}-5\right) = \left(3\sqrt[4]{x}\right)^2 - (5)^2$$
$$= 3^2\left(\sqrt[4]{x}\right)^2 - 25$$
$$= 9\sqrt{x} - 25$$

87. a. $n = 308\sqrt{t} + 1050$

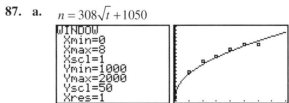

The model appears to fit the data pretty well.

b. For 2014, we have $t = 2014 - 1998 = 16$. Substitute 16 for t in the equation and solve for n.

$n = 308\sqrt{16} + 1050 = 2282$

The model predicts that there will be 2282 agents in Tucson in 2014.

c.

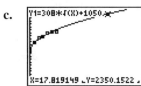

The model predicts that there will be 2350 agents in Tucson in 2016 (about 18 years after 1998).

89. a. The flow rate, r, increases much more quickly as the value of d is increased. From the table, when the diameter doubles from 0.5 to 1.0, the flow rate quadruples. In the equation, $r = 30d^2\sqrt{P}$, the value of d is squared, so as d increases, the value of r increases by the squared value of d. If you consider the situation, the flow rate r should increase at a greater rate as you increase the nozzle diameter d because more water is able to leave through the nozzle.

b. i.

$r = 30(0.5)^2\sqrt{100} = 75$ gallons/minute

$r = 30(1)^2\sqrt{100} = 300$ gallons/minute

$r = 30(1.5)^2\sqrt{100} = 675$ gallons/minute

$r = 30(2)^2\sqrt{100} = 1200$ gallons/minute

$r = 30(2.5)^2\sqrt{100} = 1875$ gallons/minute

ii. $d = 0.5$, error $= 75 - 74 = 1$
$d = 1$, error $= 300 - 297 = 3$
$d = 1.5$, error $= 675 - 668 = 7$
$d = 2$, error $= 1200 - 1188 = 12$
$d = 2.5$, error $= 1875 - 1857 = 18$
The estimate for $d = 2.5$ inches has the largest error at 18 gallons per minute.

iii. $d = 0.5$, % error $= \dfrac{1}{74} \times 100 = 1.35\%$

$d = 1$, % error $= \dfrac{3}{297} \times 100 = 1.01\%$

$d = 1.5$, % error $= \dfrac{7}{668} \times 100 = 1.05\%$

$d = 2$, % error $= \dfrac{12}{1188} \times 100 = 1.01\%$

$d = 2.5$, % error $= \dfrac{18}{1857} \times 100 = 0.97\%$

The estimate for $d = 0.5$ inches has the largest percentage error at 1.35%.

c. $r = 30(1.75)^2\sqrt{45} \approx 616.3$

The estimated flow rate is 616 gallons per minute. The minimum requirement of 500 gallons per minutes is met and exceeded.

91. The student squared each term individually instead of using FOIL.

$$\left(x + \sqrt{7}\right)^2 = \left(x + \sqrt{7}\right)\left(x + \sqrt{7}\right)$$
$$= (x)^2 + 2(x)\left(\sqrt{7}\right) + \left(\sqrt{7}\right)^2$$
$$= x^2 + 2x\sqrt{7} + 7$$

93. The student multiplied a number by a radical as if they were both radicals.

$$7\left(2\sqrt{3}\right) = 14\sqrt{3}$$

95. $\dfrac{\sqrt{x}}{\sqrt[3]{x}} = \dfrac{x^{1/2}}{x^{1/3}} = x^{\frac{1}{2} - \frac{1}{3}} = x^{\frac{3}{6} - \frac{2}{6}} = x^{\frac{1}{6}} = \sqrt[6]{x}$

97. a. $\sqrt[3]{x}\sqrt[4]{x} = x^{1/3} \cdot x^{1/4}$

$$= x^{\frac{1}{3} + \frac{1}{4}}$$
$$= x^{\frac{4}{12} + \frac{3}{12}}$$
$$= x^{7/12}$$
$$= \sqrt[12]{x^7}$$

b. $\sqrt[k]{x}\sqrt[n]{x} = x^{1/k} \cdot x^{1/n}$

$$= x^{\frac{1}{k} + \frac{1}{n}}$$
$$= x^{\frac{n}{n \cdot k} + \frac{k}{n \cdot k}}$$
$$= x^{\frac{n+k}{n \cdot k}}$$
$$= \sqrt[kn]{x^{k+n}}$$

c. $\sqrt[3]{x}\sqrt[4]{x} \rightarrow \quad k = 3, n = 4$

$\sqrt[3]{x}\sqrt[4]{x} = \sqrt[3 \cdot 4]{x^{3+4}} = \sqrt[12]{x^7}$

The results are the same.

d. $\sqrt[5]{x}\sqrt[7]{x} = \sqrt[5\cdot7]{x^{5+7}} = \sqrt[35]{x^{12}}$

99. Answers will vary. If the indexes are the same, use the Product Property. If the indexes are different, change the radicals to exponents, then use the properties of exponents to solve. Finally, change the exponential expression back into a radical.

101. $3\sqrt{x} - 5\sqrt{x} = (3-5)\sqrt{x} = -2\sqrt{x}$

103. $\left(3\sqrt{x}\right)\left(-5\sqrt{x}\right) = -15\sqrt{x^2} = -15x$

105.
$$\log_b\left(x^2 + 3x - 40\right) - \log_b\left(x^2 - 64\right)$$
$$= \log_b(x+8)(x-5) - \log_b(x+8)(x-8)$$
$$= \log_b \frac{(x+8)(x-5)}{(x+8)(x-8)}$$
$$= \log_b \frac{x-5}{x-8}$$
$\log_b\left(x^2 + 3x - 40\right) - \log_b\left(x^2 - 64\right)$ is a logarithmic expression in one variable.

107.
$$\log_2(3x-4) - \log_2(2x-3) = 3$$
$$\log_2\left(\frac{3x-4}{2x-3}\right) = 3$$
$$2^3 = \frac{3x-4}{2x-3}$$
$$8 = \frac{3x-4}{2x-3}$$
$$8(2x-3) = 3x-4$$
$$16x - 24 = 3x - 4$$
$$13x = 20$$
$$x = \frac{20}{13}$$
$\log_2(3x-4) - \log_2(2x-3) = 3$ is a logarithmic equation in one variable.

109.
$$2(3)^{5x-1} = 35$$
$$3^{5x-1} = 17.5$$
$$(5x-1)\ln 3 = \ln 17.5$$
$$5x - 1 = \frac{\ln 17.5}{\ln 3}$$
$$5x - 1 \approx 2.6053$$
$$5x \approx 3.6053$$
$$x \approx 0.7211$$
$2(3)^{5x-1} = 35$ is an exponential equation in one variable.

Homework 13.3

1.
$$\frac{8}{\sqrt{x}} = \frac{8}{\sqrt{x}} \cdot \frac{\sqrt{x}}{\sqrt{x}}$$
$$= \frac{8\sqrt{x}}{\left(\sqrt{x}\right)^2}$$
$$= \frac{8\sqrt{x}}{x}$$

3.
$$\frac{3}{\sqrt{5p}} = \frac{3}{\sqrt{5p}} \cdot \frac{\sqrt{5p}}{\sqrt{5p}}$$
$$= \frac{3\sqrt{5p}}{\left(\sqrt{5p}\right)^2}$$
$$= \frac{3\sqrt{5p}}{5p}$$

5.
$$\frac{4}{3\sqrt{2x}} = \frac{4}{3\sqrt{2x}} \cdot \frac{\sqrt{2x}}{\sqrt{2x}}$$
$$= \frac{4\sqrt{2x}}{3\left(\sqrt{2x}\right)^2}$$
$$= \frac{4\sqrt{2x}}{3\cdot 2x}$$
$$= \frac{2\sqrt{2x}}{3x}$$

7.
$$\frac{10}{\sqrt{8k}} = \frac{10}{\sqrt{8k}} \cdot \frac{\sqrt{8k}}{\sqrt{8k}}$$
$$= \frac{10\sqrt{8k}}{\left(\sqrt{8k}\right)^2}$$
$$= \frac{10\sqrt{4 \cdot 2k}}{8k}$$
$$= \frac{10(2)\sqrt{2k}}{8k}$$
$$= \frac{20\sqrt{2k}}{8k}$$
$$= \frac{5\sqrt{2k}}{2k}$$

9.
$$\sqrt{\frac{4}{x}} = \frac{\sqrt{4}}{\sqrt{x}}$$
$$= \frac{2}{\sqrt{x}} \cdot \frac{\sqrt{x}}{\sqrt{x}}$$
$$= \frac{2\sqrt{x}}{\left(\sqrt{x}\right)^2}$$
$$= \frac{2\sqrt{x}}{x}$$

11.
$$\sqrt{\frac{7}{2}} = \frac{\sqrt{7}}{\sqrt{2}}$$
$$= \frac{\sqrt{7}}{\sqrt{2}} \cdot \frac{\sqrt{2}}{\sqrt{2}}$$
$$= \frac{\sqrt{7 \cdot 2}}{\left(\sqrt{2}\right)^2}$$
$$= \frac{\sqrt{14}}{2}$$

13.
$$\sqrt{\frac{2y}{x}} = \frac{\sqrt{2y}}{\sqrt{x}}$$
$$= \frac{\sqrt{2y}}{\sqrt{x}} \cdot \frac{\sqrt{x}}{\sqrt{x}}$$
$$= \frac{\sqrt{2y \cdot x}}{\left(\sqrt{x}\right)^2}$$
$$= \frac{\sqrt{2xy}}{x}$$

15.
$$\sqrt{\frac{x}{12y}} = \frac{\sqrt{x}}{\sqrt{12y}}$$
$$= \frac{\sqrt{x}}{\sqrt{12y}} \cdot \frac{\sqrt{12y}}{\sqrt{12y}}$$
$$= \frac{\sqrt{x \cdot 12y}}{\left(\sqrt{12y}\right)^2}$$
$$= \frac{\sqrt{x \cdot 4 \cdot 3y}}{12y}$$
$$= \frac{2\sqrt{3xy}}{12y}$$
$$= \frac{\sqrt{3xy}}{6y}$$

17.
$$\frac{3}{\sqrt{x-4}} = \frac{3}{\sqrt{x-4}} \cdot \frac{\sqrt{x-4}}{\sqrt{x-4}}$$
$$= \frac{3\sqrt{x-4}}{\left(\sqrt{x-4}\right)^2}$$
$$= \frac{3\sqrt{x-4}}{x-4}$$

19.
$$\frac{\sqrt{2a^3}}{\sqrt{3b}} = \frac{\sqrt{2a^3}}{\sqrt{3b}} \cdot \frac{\sqrt{3b}}{\sqrt{3b}}$$
$$= \frac{\sqrt{6a^3b}}{\left(\sqrt{3b}\right)^2}$$
$$= \frac{\sqrt{6 \cdot a^2 \cdot a \cdot b}}{3b}$$
$$= \frac{a\sqrt{6ab}}{3b}$$

21.
$$\frac{2}{\sqrt[3]{5}} = \frac{2}{\sqrt[3]{5}} \cdot \frac{\sqrt[3]{25}}{\sqrt[3]{25}}$$
$$= \frac{2\sqrt[3]{25}}{\sqrt[3]{5 \cdot 25}}$$
$$= \frac{2\sqrt[3]{25}}{\sqrt[3]{125}}$$
$$= \frac{2\sqrt[3]{25}}{5}$$

23.

$$\frac{5}{\sqrt[3]{4}} = \frac{5}{\sqrt[3]{4}} \cdot \frac{\sqrt[3]{2}}{\sqrt[3]{2}}$$

$$= \frac{5\sqrt[3]{2}}{\sqrt[3]{4 \cdot 2}}$$

$$= \frac{5\sqrt[3]{2}}{\sqrt[3]{8}}$$

$$= \frac{5\sqrt[3]{2}}{2}$$

25.

$$\frac{4}{5\sqrt[3]{x}} = \frac{4}{5\sqrt[3]{x}} \cdot \frac{\sqrt[3]{x^2}}{\sqrt[3]{x^2}}$$

$$= \frac{4\sqrt[3]{x^2}}{5\sqrt[3]{x \cdot x^2}}$$

$$= \frac{4\sqrt[3]{x^2}}{5\sqrt[3]{x^3}}$$

$$= \frac{4\sqrt[3]{x^2}}{5x}$$

27.

$$\frac{6}{\sqrt[3]{2x^2}} = \frac{6}{\sqrt[3]{2x^2}} \cdot \frac{\sqrt[3]{4x}}{\sqrt[3]{4x}}$$

$$= \frac{6\sqrt[3]{4x}}{\sqrt[3]{2x^2 \cdot 4x}}$$

$$= \frac{6\sqrt[3]{4x}}{\sqrt[3]{8x^3}}$$

$$= \frac{6\sqrt[3]{4x}}{\sqrt[3]{8}\sqrt[3]{x^3}}$$

$$= \frac{6\sqrt[3]{4x}}{2x}$$

$$= \frac{3\sqrt[3]{4x}}{x}$$

29.

$$\frac{7t}{\sqrt[4]{4t^3}} = \frac{7t}{\sqrt[4]{4t^3}} \cdot \frac{\sqrt[4]{4t}}{\sqrt[4]{4t}}$$

$$= \frac{7t\sqrt[4]{4t}}{\sqrt[4]{4t^3 \cdot 4t}}$$

$$= \frac{7t\sqrt[4]{4t}}{\sqrt[4]{16t^4}}$$

$$= \frac{7t\sqrt[4]{4t}}{\sqrt[4]{16}\sqrt[4]{t^4}}$$

$$= \frac{7t\sqrt[4]{4t}}{2t}$$

$$= \frac{7\sqrt[4]{4t}}{2}$$

31.

$$\frac{\sqrt[3]{x}}{\sqrt{x}} = \frac{\sqrt[3]{x}}{\sqrt{x}} \cdot \frac{\sqrt{x}}{\sqrt{x}}$$

$$= \frac{x^{1/3} \cdot x^{1/2}}{\left(\sqrt{x}\right)^2}$$

$$= \frac{x^{\frac{1}{3} + \frac{1}{2}}}{x}$$

$$= \frac{x^{\frac{2}{6} + \frac{3}{6}}}{x}$$

$$= \frac{x^{5/6}}{x}$$

$$= \frac{\sqrt[6]{x^5}}{x}$$

33.

$$\sqrt[5]{\frac{2}{x^3}} = \frac{\sqrt[5]{2}}{\sqrt[5]{x^3}}$$

$$= \frac{\sqrt[5]{2}}{\sqrt[5]{x^3}} \cdot \frac{\sqrt[5]{x^2}}{\sqrt[5]{x^2}}$$

$$= \frac{\sqrt[5]{2 \cdot x^2}}{\sqrt[5]{x^3 \cdot x^2}}$$

$$= \frac{\sqrt[5]{2x^2}}{\sqrt[5]{x^5}}$$

$$= \frac{\sqrt[5]{2x^2}}{x}$$

35.

$$\sqrt[4]{\frac{4}{9x^2}} = \frac{\sqrt[4]{4}}{\sqrt[4]{9x^2}}$$

$$= \frac{\sqrt[4]{4}}{\sqrt[4]{9x^2}} \cdot \frac{\sqrt[4]{9x^2}}{\sqrt[4]{9x^2}}$$

$$= \frac{\sqrt[4]{4 \cdot 9x^2}}{\sqrt[4]{9x^2 \cdot 9x^2}}$$

$$= \frac{\sqrt[4]{36x^2}}{\sqrt[4]{81x^4}}$$

$$= \frac{\sqrt[4]{6^2 x^2}}{3x}$$

$$= \frac{6^{2/4} x^{2/4}}{3x}$$

$$= \frac{6^{1/2} x^{1/2}}{3x}$$

$$= \frac{\sqrt{6x}}{3x}$$

37.

$$\sqrt[5]{\frac{3w}{4x^4 y^2}} = \frac{\sqrt[5]{3w}}{\sqrt[5]{4x^4 y^2}}$$

$$= \frac{\sqrt[5]{3w}}{\sqrt[5]{4x^4 y^2}} \cdot \frac{\sqrt[5]{8xy^3}}{\sqrt[5]{8xy^3}}$$

$$= \frac{\sqrt[5]{3w}\sqrt[5]{8xy^3}}{\sqrt[5]{4x^4 y^2 \cdot 8xy^3}}$$

$$= \frac{\sqrt[5]{3w}\sqrt[5]{8xy^3}}{\sqrt[5]{32x^5 y^5}}$$

$$= \frac{\sqrt[5]{24wxy^3}}{2xy}$$

39.

$$\frac{1}{5+\sqrt{3}} = \frac{1}{5+\sqrt{3}} \cdot \frac{5-\sqrt{3}}{5-\sqrt{3}}$$

$$= \frac{1 \cdot 5 - 1 \cdot \sqrt{3}}{(5)^2 - (\sqrt{3})^2}$$

$$= \frac{5-\sqrt{3}}{25-3}$$

$$= \frac{5-\sqrt{3}}{22}$$

41.

$$\frac{2}{\sqrt{3}+\sqrt{7}} = \frac{2}{\sqrt{3}+\sqrt{7}} \cdot \frac{\sqrt{3}-\sqrt{7}}{\sqrt{3}-\sqrt{7}}$$

$$= \frac{2 \cdot \sqrt{3} - 2 \cdot \sqrt{7}}{(\sqrt{3})^2 - (\sqrt{7})^2}$$

$$= \frac{2\sqrt{3} - 2\sqrt{7}}{3-7}$$

$$= \frac{2\sqrt{3} - 2\sqrt{7}}{-4}$$

$$= \frac{\sqrt{7} - \sqrt{3}}{2}$$

43.

$$\frac{1}{3\sqrt{r}-7} = \frac{1}{3\sqrt{r}-7} \cdot \frac{3\sqrt{r}+7}{3\sqrt{r}+7}$$

$$= \frac{1 \cdot 3\sqrt{r} + 1 \cdot 7}{(3\sqrt{r})^2 - (7)^2}$$

$$= \frac{3\sqrt{r}+7}{9r-49}$$

45.

$$\frac{\sqrt{x}}{\sqrt{x}-1} = \frac{\sqrt{x}}{\sqrt{x}-1} \cdot \frac{\sqrt{x}+1}{\sqrt{x}+1}$$

$$= \frac{\sqrt{x} \cdot \sqrt{x} + \sqrt{x} \cdot 1}{(\sqrt{x})^2 - (1)^2}$$

$$= \frac{x+\sqrt{x}}{x-1}$$

47.

$$\frac{3\sqrt{x}}{4\sqrt{x}-\sqrt{5}} = \frac{3\sqrt{x}}{4\sqrt{x}-\sqrt{5}} \cdot \frac{4\sqrt{x}+\sqrt{5}}{4\sqrt{x}+\sqrt{5}}$$

$$= \frac{3\sqrt{x} \cdot 4\sqrt{x} + 3\sqrt{x} \cdot \sqrt{5}}{(4\sqrt{x})^2 - (\sqrt{5})^2}$$

$$= \frac{12(\sqrt{x})^2 + 3\sqrt{5x}}{4^2 (\sqrt{x})^2 - 5}$$

$$= \frac{12x + 3\sqrt{5x}}{16x-5}$$

49.
$$\frac{\sqrt{x}}{\sqrt{x}-y} = \frac{\sqrt{x}}{\sqrt{x}-y} \cdot \frac{\sqrt{x}+y}{\sqrt{x}+y}$$
$$= \frac{\sqrt{x}\cdot\sqrt{x}+\sqrt{x}\cdot y}{\left(\sqrt{x}\right)^2-\left(y\right)^2}$$
$$= \frac{x+y\sqrt{x}}{x-y^2}$$

51.
$$\frac{\sqrt{x}-5}{\sqrt{x}+5} = \frac{\sqrt{x}-5}{\sqrt{x}+5} \cdot \frac{\sqrt{x}-5}{\sqrt{x}-5}$$
$$= \frac{\left(\sqrt{x}\right)^2-2\left(\sqrt{x}\right)(5)+(5)^2}{\left(\sqrt{x}\right)^2-(5)^2}$$
$$= \frac{x-10\sqrt{x}+25}{x-25}$$

53.
$$\frac{2\sqrt{x}+5}{3\sqrt{x}+1} = \frac{2\sqrt{x}+5}{3\sqrt{x}+1} \cdot \frac{3\sqrt{x}-1}{3\sqrt{x}-1}$$
$$= \frac{2\sqrt{x}\cdot3\sqrt{x}-2\sqrt{x}\cdot1+5\cdot3\sqrt{x}-5\cdot1}{\left(3\sqrt{x}\right)^2-(1)^2}$$
$$= \frac{6\left(\sqrt{x}\right)^2-2\sqrt{x}+15\sqrt{x}-5}{3^2\left(\sqrt{x}\right)^2-1}$$
$$= \frac{6x+13\sqrt{x}-5}{9x-1}$$

55.
$$\frac{6\sqrt{x}+\sqrt{5}}{3\sqrt{x}-\sqrt{7}} = \frac{6\sqrt{x}+\sqrt{5}}{3\sqrt{x}-\sqrt{7}} \cdot \frac{3\sqrt{x}+\sqrt{7}}{3\sqrt{x}+\sqrt{7}}$$
$$= \frac{6\sqrt{x}\cdot3\sqrt{x}+6\sqrt{x}\cdot\sqrt{7}+\sqrt{5}\cdot3\sqrt{x}+\sqrt{5}\cdot\sqrt{7}}{\left(3\sqrt{x}\right)^2-\left(\sqrt{7}\right)^2}$$
$$= \frac{18\left(\sqrt{x}\right)^2+6\sqrt{7\cdot x}+3\sqrt{5\cdot x}+\sqrt{5\cdot7}}{3^2\left(\sqrt{x}\right)^2-7}$$
$$= \frac{18x+6\sqrt{7x}+3\sqrt{5x}+\sqrt{35}}{9x-7}$$

57.
$$\frac{\sqrt{x}-\sqrt{y}}{\sqrt{x}+\sqrt{y}} = \frac{\sqrt{x}-\sqrt{y}}{\sqrt{x}+\sqrt{y}} \cdot \frac{\sqrt{x}-\sqrt{y}}{\sqrt{x}-\sqrt{y}}$$
$$= \frac{\left(\sqrt{x}\right)^2-2\left(\sqrt{x}\right)\left(\sqrt{y}\right)+\left(\sqrt{y}\right)^2}{\left(\sqrt{x}\right)^2-\left(\sqrt{y}\right)^2}$$
$$= \frac{x-2\sqrt{xy}+y}{x-y}$$

59.
$$\frac{1}{\sqrt{x+1}-\sqrt{x}} = \frac{1}{\sqrt{x+1}-\sqrt{x}} \cdot \frac{\sqrt{x+1}+\sqrt{x}}{\sqrt{x+1}+\sqrt{x}}$$
$$= \frac{\sqrt{x+1}+\sqrt{x}}{\left(\sqrt{x+1}\right)^2-\left(\sqrt{x}\right)^2}$$
$$= \frac{\sqrt{x+1}+\sqrt{x}}{x+1-x}$$
$$= \sqrt{x+1}+\sqrt{x}$$

61. a.
$$\sqrt{\frac{3h}{2}} = \frac{\sqrt{3h}}{\sqrt{2}} = \frac{\sqrt{3h}}{\sqrt{2}} \cdot \frac{\sqrt{2}}{\sqrt{2}} = \frac{\sqrt{6h}}{\left(\sqrt{2}\right)^2} = \frac{\sqrt{6h}}{2}$$

b.
$$f(1450) = \frac{\sqrt{6(1450)}}{2} = \frac{\sqrt{8700}}{2} \approx 46.64$$
The horizon is about 47 miles from the top of the skyscraper.

c.
$$\frac{\sqrt{6(30,000)}}{2} = \frac{\sqrt{180,000}}{2}$$
$$\approx 212.13$$
The airplane is about 212 miles from the horizon.

63. a. Cut the paper in half so that the dimensions are $\frac{x\sqrt{2}}{2}$ by x.
$$\frac{x}{\frac{x\sqrt{2}}{2}} = \frac{x}{1} \cdot \frac{2}{x\sqrt{2}} = \frac{2x}{x\sqrt{2}} = \frac{2}{\sqrt{2}}$$
$$= \frac{2}{\sqrt{2}} \cdot \frac{\sqrt{2}}{\sqrt{2}} = \frac{2\sqrt{2}}{\left(\sqrt{2}\right)^2} = \frac{2\sqrt{2}}{2} = \frac{\sqrt{2}}{1}$$

b.

$$1 = x \cdot x\sqrt{2}$$

$$1 = x^2\sqrt{2}$$

$$x^2 = \frac{1}{\sqrt{2}}$$

$$x^2 = \frac{\sqrt{2}}{2}$$

$$x = \sqrt{\frac{\sqrt{2}}{2}}$$

$$x = \frac{\sqrt[4]{2}}{\sqrt{2}} \cdot \frac{\sqrt{2}}{\sqrt{2}}$$

$$x = \frac{2^{1/4} \cdot 2^{1/2}}{2}$$

$$x = \frac{\sqrt[4]{2^3}}{2}$$

$$x = \frac{\sqrt[4]{8}}{2}$$

$$x \approx 0.841$$

The page has a width of about 0.841 meters.

65. Student 1 did the work correctly. Student 2's error was to square the entire expression. This changes the value of the expression. To simplify the expression, you need to multiply by something equivalent to 1.

67. Answers may vary. The student did not rationalize the denominator correctly. For the radicand in the denominator to be a perfect cube, $\sqrt[3]{x}$ needs to be multiplied by $\sqrt[3]{x^2}$ to yield

$$\sqrt[3]{x} \cdot \sqrt[3]{x^2} = \sqrt[3]{x^3} \; .$$

$$\frac{5}{\sqrt[3]{x}} = \frac{5}{\sqrt[3]{x}} \cdot \frac{\sqrt[3]{x^2}}{\sqrt[3]{x^2}}$$

$$= \frac{5\sqrt[3]{x^2}}{\sqrt[3]{x \cdot x^2}}$$

$$= \frac{5\sqrt[3]{x^2}}{\sqrt[3]{x^3}}$$

$$= \frac{5\sqrt[3]{x^2}}{x}$$

69.

$$\frac{\sqrt{x}}{3} = \frac{\sqrt{x}}{3} \cdot \frac{\sqrt{x}}{\sqrt{x}} = \frac{\sqrt{x^2}}{3\sqrt{x}} = \frac{x}{3\sqrt{x}}$$

71.

$$\frac{\sqrt{x+2} - \sqrt{x}}{2} = \frac{\sqrt{x+2} - \sqrt{x}}{2} \cdot \frac{\sqrt{x+2} + \sqrt{x}}{\sqrt{x+2} + \sqrt{x}}$$

$$= \frac{\left(\sqrt{x+2}\right)^2 - \left(\sqrt{x}\right)^2}{2\left(\sqrt{x+2} + \sqrt{x}\right)}$$

$$= \frac{x+2-x}{2\left(\sqrt{x+2} + \sqrt{x}\right)}$$

$$= \frac{2}{2\left(\sqrt{x+2} + \sqrt{x}\right)}$$

$$= \frac{1}{\sqrt{x+2} + \sqrt{x}}$$

73.

$$\frac{\dfrac{1}{\sqrt{x}} - \dfrac{3}{x}}{\dfrac{2}{\sqrt{x}} + \dfrac{1}{x}} = \frac{\dfrac{1}{\sqrt{x}} \cdot \dfrac{\sqrt{x}}{\sqrt{x}} - \dfrac{3}{x}}{\dfrac{2}{\sqrt{x}} \cdot \dfrac{\sqrt{x}}{\sqrt{x}} + \dfrac{1}{x}}$$

$$= \frac{\dfrac{\sqrt{x}}{x} - \dfrac{3}{x}}{\dfrac{2\sqrt{x}}{x} + \dfrac{1}{x}}$$

$$= \frac{\dfrac{\sqrt{x} - 3}{x}}{\dfrac{2\sqrt{x} + 1}{x}}$$

$$= \frac{\sqrt{x} - 3}{x} \div \frac{2\sqrt{x} + 1}{x}$$

$$= \frac{\sqrt{x} - 3}{x} \cdot \frac{x}{2\sqrt{x} + 1}$$

$$= \frac{\sqrt{x} - 3}{2\sqrt{x} + 1}$$

$$= \frac{\sqrt{x} - 3}{2\sqrt{x} + 1} \cdot \frac{2\sqrt{x} - 1}{2\sqrt{x} - 1}$$

$$= \frac{\sqrt{x} \cdot 2\sqrt{x} - \sqrt{x} \cdot 1 - 3 \cdot 2\sqrt{x} - 3(-1)}{\left(2\sqrt{x}\right)^2 - (1)^2}$$

$$= \frac{2x - \sqrt{x} - 6\sqrt{x} + 3}{4x - 1}$$

$$= \frac{2x - 7\sqrt{x} + 3}{4x - 1}$$

75.
$$x\sqrt{2} + 3\sqrt{5} = 9\sqrt{5}$$
$$x\sqrt{2} = 9\sqrt{5} - 3\sqrt{5}$$
$$x\sqrt{2} = 6\sqrt{5}$$
$$x = \frac{6\sqrt{5}}{\sqrt{2}}$$
$$x = \frac{6\sqrt{5}}{\sqrt{2}} \cdot \frac{\sqrt{2}}{\sqrt{2}}$$
$$x = \frac{6\sqrt{10}}{2}$$
$$x = 3\sqrt{10}$$

77. Answers may vary.

1. Determine the conjugate of the denominator.

2. Multiply the original fraction by the fraction

$$\frac{\text{conjugate}}{\text{conjugate}}$$

3. Find the product of the fractions and simplify.

79. a. $A^3 + B^3 = (A+B)(A^2 - AB + B^2)$

b. $(A+B)(A^2 - AB + B^2)$
$$= A^3 - A^2B + AB^2 + A^2B - AB^2 + B^3$$
$$= A^3 + B^3$$
$(A+B)(A^2 - AB + B^2)$ is the factored form of $A^3 + B^3$.

c. $(x+2)(x^2 - 2x + 4)$
$$= x(x^2) + 2(x^2) - x(2x) - 2(2x) + x(4) + 2(4)$$
$$= x^3 + 2x^2 - 2x^2 - 4x + 4x + 8$$
$$= x^3 + 8$$
It follows the equation
$(A+B)(A^2 - AB + B^2) = A^3 + B^3$, where A
$= x$ and $B = 2$.

d. $\left(\sqrt[3]{x} + \sqrt[3]{2}\right)\left(\sqrt[3]{x^2} - \sqrt[3]{2x} + \sqrt[3]{4}\right)$

$$= \left(\sqrt[3]{x}\right)\left(\sqrt[3]{x^2}\right) + \left(\sqrt[3]{2}\right)\left(\sqrt[3]{x^2}\right) - \left(\sqrt[3]{x}\right)\left(\sqrt[3]{2x}\right)$$

$$- \left(\sqrt[3]{2}\right)\left(\sqrt[3]{2x}\right) + \left(\sqrt[3]{x}\right)\left(\sqrt[3]{4}\right) + \left(\sqrt[3]{2}\right)\left(\sqrt[3]{4}\right)$$

$$= \sqrt[3]{x^3} + \sqrt[3]{2x^2} - \sqrt[3]{2x^2} - \sqrt[3]{4x} + \sqrt[3]{4x} + \sqrt[3]{8}$$

$$= x + 2$$

It follows the equation
$(A+B)(A^2 - AB + B^2) = A^3 + B^3$, where A
$= \sqrt[3]{x}$ and $B = \sqrt[3]{2}$.

e.
$$\frac{1}{\sqrt[3]{x} + \sqrt[3]{2}}$$

$$= \frac{1}{\sqrt[3]{x} + \sqrt[3]{2}} \cdot \frac{\sqrt[3]{x^2} - \sqrt[3]{2x} + \sqrt[3]{4}}{\sqrt[3]{x^2} - \sqrt[3]{2x} + \sqrt[3]{4}}$$

$$= \frac{\sqrt[3]{x^2} - \sqrt[3]{2x} + \sqrt[3]{4}}{\sqrt[3]{x^3} + \sqrt[3]{2x^2} - \sqrt[3]{2x^2} - \sqrt[3]{4x} + \sqrt[3]{4x} + \sqrt[3]{8}}$$

$$= \frac{\sqrt[3]{x^2} - \sqrt[3]{2x} + \sqrt[3]{4}}{x + 2}$$

81.
$$(5x - 4)(3x^2 - 2x - 1)$$
$$= 5x \cdot 3x^2 - 4 \cdot 3x^2 - 5x \cdot 2x + 4 \cdot 2x - 5x \cdot 1 + 4 \cdot 1$$
$$= 15x^3 - 12x^2 - 10x^2 + 8x - 5x + 4$$
$$= 15x^3 - 22x^2 + 3x + 4$$
$(5x - 4)(3x^2 - 2x - 1)$ is a cubic polynomial in one variable.

83.
$$24x^3 - 3000 = 24(x^3 - 125)$$
$$= 24(x - 5)(x^2 + 5x + 25)$$
$24x^3 - 3000$ is a cubic polynomial in one variable.

85.
$$5x^2 - 3 = 4x - 1$$
$$5x^2 - 3 - 4x + 1 = 0$$
$$5x^2 - 4x - 2 = 0$$
$$a = 5, b = -4, c = -2$$
$$x = \frac{4 \pm \sqrt{(-4)^2 - 4(5)(-2)}}{2(5)}$$
$$= \frac{4 \pm \sqrt{56}}{10} = \frac{2 \pm \sqrt{14}}{5}$$

$5x^2 - 3 = 4x - 1$ is a quadratic equation in one variable.

Homework 13.4

1. $y = 2\sqrt{x}$

x	y
0	0
1	2
4	4
9	6
16	8

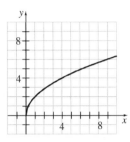

3. $y = -\sqrt{x}$

x	y
0	0
1	−1
4	−2
9	−3
16	−4

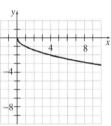

5. $y = \sqrt{x} + 3$

x	y
0	3
1	4
4	5
9	6
16	7

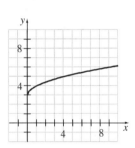

7. $y = 2\sqrt{x} - 5$

x	y
0	−5
1	−3
4	−1
9	1
16	3

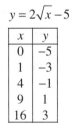

9. $y = -3\sqrt{x} + 4$

x	y
0	4
1	1
4	−2
9	−5
16	−8

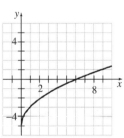

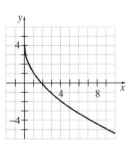

11. $y = \sqrt{x} - 2$

x	y
2	0
3	1
6	2
11	3
18	4

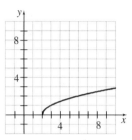

13. $y = -\sqrt{x} + 2$

x	y
−2	0
−1	−1
2	−2
7	−3
14	−4

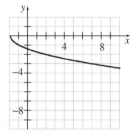

15. $y = \dfrac{1}{2}\sqrt{x} - 4$

x	y
4	0
5	$\frac{1}{2}$
8	1
13	$\frac{3}{2}$
20	2

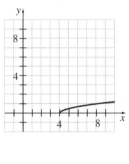

17. $y = \sqrt{x+3} + 2$

x	y
−3	2
−2	3
1	4
6	5
13	6

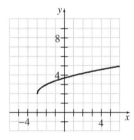

19. $y = -2\sqrt{x+3} - 4$

x	y
−3	−4
−2	−6
1	−8
6	−10
13	−12

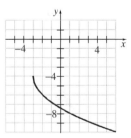

21. $y = 4\sqrt{x-1} - 3$

x	y
1	-3
2	1
5	5
10	9
17	13

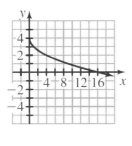

23. $\sqrt{x} + y = 4$

$y = -\sqrt{x} + 4$

x	y
0	4
1	3
4	2
9	1
16	0

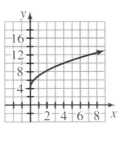

25. $2y - 6\sqrt{x} = 8$

$2y = 6\sqrt{x} + 8$

$y = 3\sqrt{x} + 4$

x	y
0	4
1	7
4	10
9	13
16	16

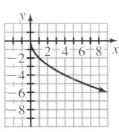

27. $y = -2\sqrt{x}$

x	y
0	0
1	-2
4	-4
9	-6
16	-8

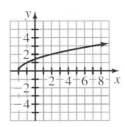

Domain: $x \geq 0$
Range: $y \leq 0$

29. $y = \sqrt{x+2}$

x	y
-2	0
-1	1
2	2
7	3
14	4

Domain: $x \geq -2$
Range: $y \geq 0$

31. $y = \sqrt{x} + 2$

x	y
0	2
1	3
4	4
9	5
16	6

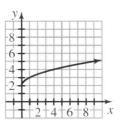

Domain: $x \geq 0$
Range: $y \geq 2$

33. $y = \sqrt{x-5} - 3$

x	y
5	-3
6	-2
9	-1
14	0
21	1

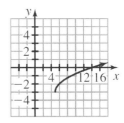

Domain: $x \geq 5$
Range: $y \geq -3$

35. $y = 2\sqrt{x+5} + 1$

x	y
-5	1
-4	3
-1	5
4	7
11	9

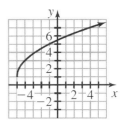

Domain: $x \geq -5$
Range: $y \geq 1$

37. $y = -\sqrt{x-2} + 4$

x	y
2	4
3	3
6	2
11	1
18	0

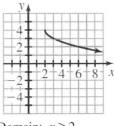

Domain: $x \geq 2$
Range: $y \leq 4$

39. a. $f(x) = 2\sqrt{x-3}$

x	$f(x)$
3	0
4	2
7	4
12	6
19	8

b.

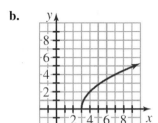

c. For each input-output pair, the output variable is equal to 2 times the square root of 3 less than the input variable.

41. a. $a < 0, h = 0,$ and $k > 0$

b. $a > 0, h < 0,$ and $k < 0$

c. $a > 0, h < 0,$ and $k > 0$

d. $a < 0, h > 0,$ and $k = 0$

43. Answers may vary. For the family of curves $y = a\sqrt{x - h} + k$, $k = 2$, and $h = 0$.

Let $a = -4, -3, -2, -1, -\dfrac{1}{2}, \dfrac{1}{2}, 1, 2, 3,$ and 4.

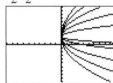

45. If $a < 0$, f has a maximum point at (h, k). If $a > 0$, f has a minimum point at (h, k).

47.
$$f(4) = 7\sqrt{4} - 3$$
$$= 7 \cdot 2 - 3$$
$$= 11$$

49.
$$f(9c) = 7\sqrt{9c} - 3$$
$$= 7 \cdot 3\sqrt{c} - 3$$
$$= 21\sqrt{c} - 3$$

51.
$$f + g = \left(5\sqrt{x} - 9\right) + \left(4\sqrt{x} + 1\right)$$
$$= 5\sqrt{x} - 9 + 4\sqrt{x} + 1$$
$$= 9\sqrt{x} - 8$$

53.
$$f \cdot g = \left(5\sqrt{x} - 9\right)\left(4\sqrt{x} + 1\right)$$
$$= 5\sqrt{x} \cdot 4\sqrt{x} - 9 \cdot 4\sqrt{x} + 5\sqrt{x} \cdot 1 - 9 \cdot 1$$
$$= 20x - 36\sqrt{x} + 5\sqrt{x} - 9$$
$$= 20x - 31\sqrt{x} - 9$$

55.
$$f - g = \left(2\sqrt{x} - 3\sqrt{5}\right) - \left(2\sqrt{x} + 3\sqrt{5}\right)$$
$$= 2\sqrt{x} - 3\sqrt{5} - 2\sqrt{x} - 3\sqrt{5}$$
$$= -6\sqrt{5}$$

57.
$$\frac{f}{g} = \frac{2\sqrt{x} - 3\sqrt{5}}{2\sqrt{x} + 3\sqrt{5}}$$
$$= \frac{2\sqrt{x} - 3\sqrt{5}}{2\sqrt{x} + 3\sqrt{5}} \cdot \frac{2\sqrt{x} - 3\sqrt{5}}{2\sqrt{x} - 3\sqrt{5}}$$
$$= \frac{\left(2\sqrt{x}\right)^2 - 2\left(2\sqrt{x}\right)\left(3\sqrt{5}\right) + \left(3\sqrt{5}\right)^2}{\left(2\sqrt{x}\right)^2 - \left(3\sqrt{5}\right)^2}$$
$$= \frac{4x - 12\sqrt{5x} + 45}{4x - 45}$$

59.
$$f + g = \left(\sqrt{x+1} - 2\right) + \left(\sqrt{x+1} + 2\right)$$
$$= \sqrt{x+1} - 2 + \sqrt{x+1} + 2$$
$$= 2\sqrt{x+1}$$

61.
$$f \cdot g = \left(\sqrt{x+1} - 2\right)\left(\sqrt{x+1} + 2\right)$$
$$= \left(\sqrt{x+1}\right)^2 - (2)^2$$
$$= x + 1 - 4$$
$$= x - 3$$

63. a.

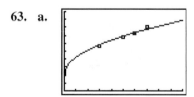

The model fits the data well.

b. $t = 2003 - 1999 = 4$
$$f(4) = 21.4\sqrt{4} + 21 = 63.8$$
In 2003, about 64% of e-mails were spam. This estimate involves interpolation, as it involves determining a value within existing data values.

c. $t = 2012 - 1999 = 13$

$f(13) = 21.4\sqrt{13} + 21 \approx 98.16$

In 2012, about 98% of e-mails will be spam. This estimate involves extrapolation, as it involves determining a value beyond existing values.

65. $f(-6) = 0$

67. $f(0) \approx 2.4$

69. $x = -6$

71. $x = 3$

73. $f(x) = 2\sqrt{x+3} + 2; \; g(x) = -2\sqrt{x+3} + 2$

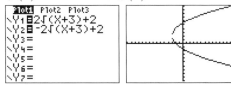

The graph looks like a parabola that opens to the right. The relation is not a function because it would fail the vertical line test.

75. Answers may vary. The graph of f can be found by translating the graph of $f(x) = \sqrt{x}$ horizontally by $|h|$ units (left if $h < 0$ and right if $h > 0$), and vertically by $|k|$ units (up if $k > 0$ and down if $k < 0$). Also, if $a > 0$, the graph is increasing and if $a < 0$, the graph is decreasing. The greater the absolute value of a, the steeper the slope of the graph.

77. $2x - 5y = 20$

$-5y = 20 - 2x$

$y = \dfrac{2}{5}x - 4$

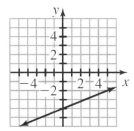

79. $y = 2\sqrt{x+3} - 4$

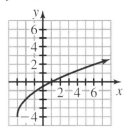

81. $y = 8\left(\dfrac{1}{2}\right)^x$

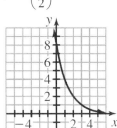

83. $6x^2 - 5x - 6 = (3x+2)(2x-3)$

$6x^2 - 5x - 6$ is a quadratic polynomial in one variable.

85.

$$f(x) = 3x^2 - 2x + 4$$

$$6 = 3x^2 - 2x + 4$$

$$0 = 3x^2 - 2x - 2$$

$$\frac{-b \pm \sqrt{b^2 - 4ac}}{2a} = \frac{2 \pm \sqrt{(-2)^2 - 4(3)(-2)}}{2(3)}$$

$$= \frac{2 \pm \sqrt{28}}{6}$$

$$= \frac{1 \pm \sqrt{7}}{3}$$

$f(x) = 3x^2 - 2x + 4$ is a quadratic function.

87.
$$f(x) = ax^2 + bx + c$$
$$14 = 9a + 3b + c$$
$$4 = a + b + c$$
$$10 = 8a + 2b$$
$$5 = 4a + b$$
$$b = 5 - 4a$$
$$25 = 16a + 4b + c$$
$$25 = 16a + 4(5 - 4a) + c$$
$$= 16a + 20 - 16a + c$$
$$c = 5$$
$$4 = a + 5 - 4a + 5$$
$$3a = 6$$
$$a = 2$$
$$b = 5 - 4(2) = -3$$
$$f(x) = 2x^2 - 3x + 5$$
$$f(x) = 2x^2 - 3x + 5 \text{ is a quadratic function.}$$

Homework 13.5

1.
$$\sqrt{x} = 5$$
$$\left(\sqrt{x}\right)^2 = 5^2$$
$$x = 25$$
Check: $x = 25$
$$\sqrt{(25)} \overset{?}{=} 5$$
$$5 = 5 \text{ true}$$
The solution is $x = 25$.

3.
$$\sqrt{x} = -2$$
$$\left(\sqrt{x}\right)^2 = (-2)^2$$
$$x = 4$$
Check $x = 4$
$$\sqrt{(4)} \overset{?}{=} -2$$
$$2 \overset{?}{=} -2 \text{ false}$$
There are no real solutions.

5.
$$\sqrt[3]{t} = -2$$
$$\left(\sqrt[3]{t}\right)^3 = (-2)^3$$
$$t = -8$$
Check: $t = -8$
$$\sqrt{(-8)} \overset{?}{=} -2$$
$$-2 \overset{?}{=} -2 \text{ true}$$
The solution is $t = -8$.

7.
$$\sqrt{x-1} = 2$$
$$\left(\sqrt{x-1}\right)^2 = 2^2$$
$$x - 1 = 4$$
$$x = 5$$
Check: $x = 5$
$$\sqrt{(5)-1} \overset{?}{=} 2$$
$$2 = 2 \text{ true}$$
The solution is $x = 5$.

9.
$$\sqrt[4]{r+2} = 2$$
$$\left(\sqrt[4]{r+2}\right)^4 = (2)^4$$
$$r + 2 = 16$$
$$r = 14$$
Check: $r = 14$
$$\sqrt[4]{14+2} \overset{?}{=} 2$$
$$2 \overset{?}{=} 2 \text{ true}$$
The solution is $r = 14$.

11.
$$3\sqrt{x} - 1 = 5$$
$$3\sqrt{x} = 6$$
$$\sqrt{x} = 2$$
$$\left(\sqrt{x}\right)^2 = 2^2$$
$$x = 4$$
Check: $x = 4$
$$3\sqrt{(4)} - 1 \overset{?}{=} 5$$
$$5 = 5 \text{ true}$$
The solution is $x = 4$.

13.

$$\sqrt{5x-7}+7=3$$
$$\sqrt{5x-7}=-4$$
$$\left(\sqrt{5x-7}\right)^2=(-4)^2$$
$$5x-7=16$$
$$5x=23$$
$$x=\frac{23}{5}$$

Check: $x=\frac{23}{5}$

$$\sqrt{5\left(\frac{23}{5}\right)-7}+7\overset{?}{=}3$$
$$11\overset{?}{=}3 \text{ false}$$

There are no real solutions.

15.

$$\sqrt[3]{2x-5}+3=7$$
$$\sqrt[3]{2x-5}=4$$
$$\left(\sqrt[3]{2x-5}\right)^3=(4)^3$$
$$2x-5=64$$
$$2x=69$$
$$x=\frac{69}{2}$$

Check: $x=\frac{69}{2}$

$$\sqrt[3]{2\left(\frac{69}{2}\right)-5}+3\overset{?}{=}7$$
$$7\overset{?}{=}7 \text{ true}$$

The solution is $x=\frac{69}{2}$.

17.

$$2-10\sqrt{6x+3}=-98$$
$$-10\sqrt{6x+3}=-100$$
$$\sqrt{6x+3}=10$$
$$\left(\sqrt{6x+3}\right)^2=(10)^2$$
$$6x+3=100$$
$$6x=97$$
$$x=\frac{97}{6}$$

Check: $x=\frac{97}{6}$

$$2-10\sqrt{6\left(\frac{97}{6}\right)+3}\overset{?}{=}-98$$
$$-98\overset{?}{=}-98 \text{ true}$$

The solution is $x=\frac{97}{6}$.

19.

$$\sqrt{3k+1}=\sqrt{2k+6}$$
$$\left(\sqrt{3k+1}\right)^2=\left(\sqrt{2k+6}\right)^2$$
$$3k+1=2k+6$$
$$k=5$$

Check: $k=5$

$$\sqrt{3(5)+1}\overset{?}{=}\sqrt{2(5+6}$$
$$4\overset{?}{=}4 \text{ true}$$

The solution is $k=5$.

21.

$$\sqrt[4]{6x-3}=\sqrt[4]{2x+17}$$
$$\left(\sqrt[4]{6x-3}\right)^4=\left(\sqrt[4]{2x+17}\right)^4$$
$$6x-3=2x+17$$
$$4x=20$$
$$x=5$$

Check: $x=5$

$$\sqrt[4]{6(5)-3}\overset{?}{=}\sqrt[4]{2(5)+17}$$
$$\sqrt[4]{27}\overset{?}{=}\sqrt[4]{27} \text{ true}$$

The solution is $x=5$.

23.

$$2\sqrt{1-x}-\sqrt{2x+5}=0$$
$$2\sqrt{1-x}=\sqrt{2x+5}$$
$$\left(2\sqrt{1-x}\right)^2=\left(\sqrt{2x+5}\right)^2$$
$$4(1-x)=2x+5$$
$$4-4x=2x+5$$
$$-6x=1$$
$$x=-\frac{1}{6}$$

Check: $x = -\dfrac{1}{6}$

$2\sqrt{1-\left(-\dfrac{1}{6}\right)} - \sqrt{2\left(-\dfrac{1}{6}\right)+5} \overset{?}{=} 0$

$2\sqrt{\dfrac{7}{6}} - \sqrt{\dfrac{28}{6}} \overset{?}{=} 0$

$\sqrt{\dfrac{28}{6}} - \sqrt{\dfrac{28}{6}} \overset{?}{=} 0$

$0 \overset{?}{=} 0$ true

The solution is $x = -\dfrac{1}{6}$.

25.
$$\sqrt{3w+3} = w-5$$
$$\left(\sqrt{3w+3}\right)^2 = (w-5)^2$$
$$3w+3 = w^2 - 10w + 25$$
$$w^2 - 13w + 22 = 0$$
$$(w-11)(w-2) = 0$$
$$w - 11 = 0 \ \text{or} \ w - 2 = 0$$
$$w = 11 \ \text{or} \ w = 2$$

Check: $w = 11$

$\sqrt{3(11)+3} \overset{?}{=} (11)-5$

$6 = 6$ true

Check: $w = 2$

$\sqrt{3(2)+3} \overset{?}{=} (2)-5$

$3 \overset{?}{=} -3$ false

The solution is $w = 11$.

27.
$$\sqrt{12x+13} + 2 = 3x$$
$$\sqrt{12x+13} = 3x - 2$$
$$\left(\sqrt{12x+13}\right)^2 = (3x-2)^2$$
$$12x + 13 = 9x^2 - 12x + 4$$
$$9x^2 - 24x - 9 = 0$$
$$3\left(3x^2 - 8x - 3\right) = 0$$
$$3(3x+1)(x-3) = 0$$
$$3x+1 = 0 \ \text{or} \ x-3 = 0$$
$$x = -\dfrac{1}{3} \ \text{or} \ x = 3$$

Check: $x = -\dfrac{1}{3}$

$\sqrt{12\left(-\dfrac{1}{3}\right)+13} + 2 \overset{?}{=} 3\left(-\dfrac{1}{3}\right)$

$5 \overset{?}{=} -1$ false

Check: $x = 3$

$\sqrt{12(3)+13} + 2 \overset{?}{=} 3(3)$

$9 = 9$ true

The solution is $x = 3$.

29.
$$\sqrt{3x-4} - x = 3$$
$$\sqrt{3x-4} = x + 3$$
$$\left(\sqrt{3x-4}\right)^2 = (x+3)^2$$
$$3x - 4 = x^2 + 6x + 9$$
$$x^2 + 3x + 13 = 0$$
$$x = \dfrac{-3 \pm \sqrt{(3)^2 - 4(1)(13)}}{2(1)}$$
$$= \dfrac{-3 \pm \sqrt{-43}}{2}$$

There are no real solutions.

31.
$$\sqrt{r^2 - 5r + 1} = r - 3$$
$$\left(\sqrt{r^2 - 5r + 1}\right)^2 = (r-3)^2$$
$$r^2 - 5r + 1 = r^2 - 6r + 9$$
$$r = 8$$

Check: $r = 8$

$\sqrt{(8)^2 - 5(8) + 1} \overset{?}{=} (8) - 3$

$5 = 5$ true

The solution is $r = 8$.

33.
$$\sqrt{x} - 1 = \sqrt{5-x}$$
$$\left(\sqrt{x} - 1\right)^2 = \left(\sqrt{5-x}\right)^2$$
$$x - 2\sqrt{x} + 1 = 5 - x$$
$$2x - 4 = 2\sqrt{x}$$
$$x - 2 = \sqrt{x}$$
$$(x-2)^2 = \left(\sqrt{x}\right)^2$$
$$x^2 - 4x + 4 = x$$
$$x^2 - 5x + 4 = 0$$
$$(x-4)(x-1) = 0$$

$x - 4 = 0 \ \text{ or } \ x - 1 = 0$

$x = 4 \ \text{ or } \ x = 1$

Check: $x = 4$

$$\sqrt{(4)} - 1 \overset{?}{=} \sqrt{5 - (4)}$$

$1 = 1$ true

Check: $x = 1$

$$\sqrt{(1)} - 1 \overset{?}{=} \sqrt{5 - (1)}$$

$0 \overset{?}{=} 2$ false

The solution is $x = 4$.

35.

$$\sqrt{x} - \sqrt{2x} = -1$$

$$\sqrt{2x} = \sqrt{x} + 1$$

$$\left(\sqrt{2x}\right)^2 = \left(\sqrt{x} + 1\right)^2$$

$$2x = x + 2\sqrt{x} + 1$$

$$x - 1 = 2\sqrt{x}$$

$$(x - 1)^2 = \left(2\sqrt{x}\right)^2$$

$$x^2 - 2x + 1 = 4x$$

$$x^2 - 6x + 1 = 0$$

$$x = \frac{-(-6) \pm \sqrt{(-6)^2 - 4(1)(1)}}{2(1)}$$

$$= \frac{6 \pm \sqrt{32}}{2}$$

$$= 3 \pm 2\sqrt{2}$$

Check: $3 + 2\sqrt{2} \ \ (x \approx 5.83)$

$$\sqrt{(5.83)} - \sqrt{2(5.83)} \overset{?}{=} -1$$

$$-1.00 \overset{?}{=} -1 \ \text{true}$$

Check: $3 - 2\sqrt{2} \ \ (x \approx 0.172)$

$$\sqrt{(0.172)} - \sqrt{2(0.172)} \overset{?}{=} -1$$

$$-0.172 \overset{?}{=} -1 \ \text{false}$$

The solution is $x = 3 + 2\sqrt{2}$.

37.

$$\sqrt{x - 3} + \sqrt{x + 5} = 4$$

$$\sqrt{x - 3} = 4 - \sqrt{x + 5}$$

$$\left(\sqrt{x - 3}\right)^2 = \left(4 - \sqrt{x + 5}\right)^2$$

$$x - 3 = 16 - 8\sqrt{x + 5} + x + 5$$

$$8\sqrt{x + 5} = 24$$

$$\sqrt{x + 5} = 3$$

$$\left(\sqrt{x + 5}\right)^2 = 3^2$$

$$x + 5 = 9$$

$$x = 4$$

Check: $x = 4$

$$\sqrt{(4) - 3} + \sqrt{(4) + 5} \overset{?}{=} 4$$

$$4 = 4 \ \text{true}$$

The solution is $x = 4$.

39.

$$\sqrt{2p - 1} + \sqrt{3p - 2} = 2$$

$$\sqrt{2p - 1} = 2 - \sqrt{3p - 2}$$

$$\left(\sqrt{2p - 1}\right)^2 = \left(2 - \sqrt{3p - 2}\right)^2$$

$$2p - 1 = 4 - 4\sqrt{3p - 2} + 3p - 2$$

$$4\sqrt{3p - 2} = p + 3$$

$$\left(4\sqrt{3p - 2}\right)^2 = (p + 3)^2$$

$$16(3p - 2) = p^2 + 6p + 9$$

$$48p - 32 = p^2 + 6p + 9$$

$$p^2 - 42p + 41 = 0$$

$$(p - 41)(p - 1) = 0$$

$$p - 41 = 0 \ \text{ or } \ p - 1 = 0$$

$$p = 41 \ \text{ or } \ p = 1$$

Check: $p = 41$

$$\sqrt{2(41) - 1} + \sqrt{3(41) - 2} \overset{?}{=} 2$$

$$20 \overset{?}{=} 2 \ \text{false}$$

Check: $p = 1$

$$\sqrt{2(1) - 1} + \sqrt{3(1) - 2} \overset{?}{=} 2$$

$$2 = 2 \ \text{true}$$

The solution is $p = 1$.

41.
$$\sqrt{\sqrt{x}-2}=3$$
$$\left(\sqrt{\sqrt{x}-2}\right)^2=3^2$$
$$\sqrt{x}-2=9$$
$$\sqrt{x}=11$$
$$\left(\sqrt{x}\right)^2=11^2$$
$$x=121$$
Check: $x=121$
$$\sqrt{\sqrt{(121)}-2}\overset{?}{=}3$$
$$3=3 \text{ true}$$
The solution is $x=121$.

43.
$$\frac{1}{\sqrt{x+2}}=3-\sqrt{x+2}$$
$$\sqrt{x+2}\cdot\frac{1}{\sqrt{x+2}}=\sqrt{x+2}\left(3-\sqrt{x+2}\right)$$
$$1=3\sqrt{x+2}-x-2$$
$$3\sqrt{x+2}=x+3$$
$$\left(3\sqrt{x+2}\right)^2=(x+3)^2$$
$$9(x+2)=x^2+6x+9$$
$$9x+18=x^2+6x+9$$
$$x^2-3x-9=0$$
$$x=\frac{-(-3)\pm\sqrt{(-3)^2-4(1)(-9)}}{2(1)}$$
$$=\frac{3\pm3\sqrt{5}}{2}$$
Check: $\dfrac{3+3\sqrt{5}}{2}$ $(x\approx 4.8541)$
$$\frac{1}{\sqrt{(4.8541)+2}}\overset{?}{=}3-\sqrt{(4.8541)+2}$$
$$0.382=0.382 \text{ true}$$
Check: $\dfrac{3-3\sqrt{5}}{2}$ $(x\approx -1.8541)$
$$\frac{1}{\sqrt{(-1.8541)+2}}\overset{?}{=}3-\sqrt{(-1.8541)+2}$$
$$2.62=2.62 \text{ true}$$
The solutions are $x=\dfrac{3+3\sqrt{5}}{2}$ and
$x=\dfrac{3-3\sqrt{5}}{2}$.

45.
$$5.2\sqrt{x}-2.8=13.9$$
$$5.2\sqrt{x}=16.7$$
$$\sqrt{x}=\frac{16.7}{5.2}$$
$$\left(\sqrt{x}\right)^2=\left(\frac{16.7}{5.2}\right)^2$$
$$x\approx 10.31$$

47.
$$1.52-4.91\sqrt{3.18x-7.14}=-0.69$$
$$-4.91\sqrt{3.18x-7.14}=-2.21$$
$$\sqrt{3.18x-7.14}\approx 0.45$$
$$\left(\sqrt{3.18x-7.14}\right)^2\approx(0.45)^2$$
$$3.18x-7.14\approx 0.20$$
$$3.18x\approx 7.34$$
$$x\approx 2.31$$

49.
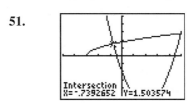
The solution is $x\approx 2.06$.

51.
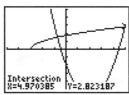
The solutions are $x\approx -0.74$ and $x\approx 4.97$.

53. The solutions are $x\approx -1.6$ and $x\approx 3.8$.

55. The solution is $x=-4$.

57. The solution is $(-3.2, 1.4)$.

59.

$$h(x) = 3\sqrt{-3x+4} - 15$$

$$3\sqrt{-3x+4} - 15 = 0$$

$$3\sqrt{-3x+4} = 15$$

$$\sqrt{-3x+4} = 5$$

$$\left(\sqrt{-3x+4}\right)^2 = 5^2$$

$$-3x + 4 = 25$$

$$-3x = 21$$

$$x = -7$$

Check: $x = -7$

$$3\sqrt{-3(-7)+4} - 15 \overset{?}{=} 0$$

$$0 = 0 \text{ true}$$

The x-intercept is $(-7, 0)$.

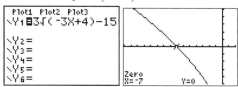

61.

$$f(x) = \sqrt{3x-2} - \sqrt{x+8}$$

$$\sqrt{3x-2} - \sqrt{x+8} = 0$$

$$\sqrt{3x-2} = \sqrt{x+8}$$

$$\left(\sqrt{3x-2}\right)^2 = \left(\sqrt{x+8}\right)^2$$

$$3x - 2 = x + 8$$

$$2x = 10$$

$$x = 5$$

Check: $x = 5$

$$\sqrt{3(5)-2} - \sqrt{(5)+8} \overset{?}{=} 0$$

$$0 = 0 \text{ true}$$

The x-intercept is $(5, 0)$.

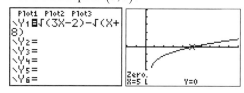

63.

$$h(x) = 2\sqrt{x+4} + 3\sqrt{x-5}$$

$$2\sqrt{x+4} + 3\sqrt{x-5} = 0$$

$$2\sqrt{x+4} = -3\sqrt{x-5}$$

$$\left(2\sqrt{x+4}\right)^2 = \left(-3\sqrt{x-5}\right)^2$$

$$4(x+4) = 9(x-5)$$

$$4x + 16 = 9x - 45$$

$$-5x = -61$$

$$x = \frac{61}{5}$$

Check: $x = \frac{61}{5}$

$$2\sqrt{\left(\frac{61}{5}\right)+4} + 3\sqrt{\left(\frac{61}{5}\right)-5} \overset{?}{=} 0$$

$$2\sqrt{\left(\frac{81}{5}\right)} + 3\sqrt{\left(\frac{36}{5}\right)} \overset{?}{=} 0$$

$$\frac{36}{\sqrt{5}} \overset{?}{=} 0 \text{ false}$$

No real number solution. There are no x-intercepts.

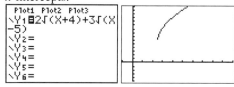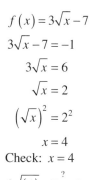

65.

$$f(x) = 3\sqrt{x} - 7$$

$$3\sqrt{x} - 7 = -1$$

$$3\sqrt{x} = 6$$

$$\sqrt{x} = 2$$

$$\left(\sqrt{x}\right)^2 = 2^2$$

$$x = 4$$

Check: $x = 4$

$$3\sqrt{(4)} - 7 \overset{?}{=} -1$$

$$-1 = -1 \text{ true}$$

When $x = 4$, $f(x) = -1$.

67.
$$f(x) = -2\sqrt{x-4} + 5$$
$$-2\sqrt{x-4} + 5 = 7$$
$$-2\sqrt{x-4} = 2$$
$$\sqrt{x-4} = -1$$
$$\left(\sqrt{x-4}\right)^2 = (-1)^2$$
$$x - 4 = 1$$
$$x = 5$$
Check: $x = 5$
$$-2\sqrt{(5)-4} - 5 \overset{?}{=} 7$$
$$-7 \overset{?}{=} 7 \text{ false}$$
No real number solutions. There is no value of x that would make $f(x) = 7$.

69. a.
$$f(t) = 21.4\sqrt{t} + 21$$
$$f(10) = 21.4\sqrt{10} + 21$$
$$f(10) \approx 88.7$$
In $1999 + 10 = 2009$, about 89% of e-mails will be spam.

b.
$$f(t) = 21.4\sqrt{t} + 21$$
$$95 = 21.4\sqrt{t} + 21$$
$$74 = 21.4\sqrt{t}$$
$$\frac{74}{21.4} = \sqrt{t}$$
$$11.96 \approx t$$
In $1999 + 12 = 2011$, 95% of e-mails will be spam.

c.
$$f(t) = 21.4\sqrt{t} + 21$$
$$100 = 21.4\sqrt{t} + 21$$
$$79 = 21.4\sqrt{t}$$
$$\frac{79}{21.4} = \sqrt{t}$$
$$13.63 \approx t$$
In $1999 + 14 = 2013$, 100% of e-mails will be spam. Model breakdown has likely occurred.

71. a.

The model fits the data well.

b. $f(2) = 257\sqrt[4]{2+1} \approx 338.23$
The estimated charge is about $338. It is an underestimate.

c.
$$385 = 257\sqrt[4]{n+1}$$
$$\frac{385}{257} = \sqrt[4]{n+1}$$
$$5.03 \approx n + 1$$
$$n \approx 4.03$$
Grade 4 students will pay this charge.

d. This charge is higher than what all other students pay, including those in higher grades. The table suggests that the function is increasing, and therefore the expected per-student charge would be between $365 and $410.

73. In the third line, the student did not properly square $(x+3)$.
$$\sqrt{x^2 + 4x + 5} = x + 3$$
$$\left(\sqrt{x^2 + 4x + 5}\right)^2 = (x+3)^2$$
$$x^2 + 4x + 5 = x^2 + 6x + 9$$
$$-2x = 4$$
$$x = -2$$

75.
$$S = \sqrt{gd}$$
$$(S)^2 = \left(\sqrt{gd}\right)^2$$
$$S^2 = gd$$
$$\frac{S^2}{g} = d$$

77.
$$d = \sqrt{\frac{3h}{2}}$$
$$(d)^2 = \left(\sqrt{\frac{3h}{2}}\right)^2$$
$$d^2 = \frac{3h}{2}$$
$$2d^2 = 3h$$
$$\frac{2d^2}{3} = h$$

79.

$$v = \sqrt{\frac{2GM}{R}}$$

$$(v)^2 = \left(\sqrt{\frac{2GM}{R}}\right)^2$$

$$v^2 = \frac{2GM}{R}$$

$$Rv^2 = 2GM$$

$$R = \frac{2GM}{v^2}$$

81.

$$y = 3\sqrt{x} - 4$$

$$y = -2\sqrt{x} + 6$$

Since the left hand sides are equal, set the right hand sides equal to each other and solve the resulting equation.

$$3\sqrt{x} - 4 = -2\sqrt{x} + 6$$

$$5\sqrt{x} = 10$$

$$\sqrt{x} = 2$$

$$\left(\sqrt{x}\right)^2 = 2^2$$

$$x = 4$$

Substitute this value into either original equation and solve for y.

$$y = 3\sqrt{(4)} - 4 = 2$$

The solution is $(4, 2)$.

 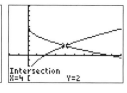

83. The left hand side was not squared properly in the second line. It should be:

$$(2x)^2 - 2(2x)(x) + (-x)^2$$

85.

$$3\sqrt{x} + 4 - 7\sqrt{x} + 1 = (3-7)\sqrt{x} + 5$$

$$= -4\sqrt{x} + 5$$

87.

$$3\sqrt{x} + 4 - 7\sqrt{x} + 1 = -7$$

$$(3-7)\sqrt{x} + 5 = -7$$

$$-4\sqrt{x} + 5 = -7$$

$$-4\sqrt{x} = -12$$

$$\sqrt{x} = 3$$

$$\left(\sqrt{x}\right)^2 = (3)^2$$

$$x = 9$$

89.

$$\left(\sqrt{p} + 3\right)\left(\sqrt{p} + 1\right) = 3$$

$$\sqrt{p} \cdot \sqrt{p} + 3 \cdot \sqrt{p} + \sqrt{p} \cdot 1 + 3 \cdot 1 = 3$$

$$p + 4\sqrt{p} + 3 = 3$$

$$p + 4\sqrt{p} = 0$$

$$p = 0$$

91.

$$\left(\sqrt{p} + 3\right)\left(\sqrt{p} + 1\right)$$

$$= \sqrt{p} \cdot \sqrt{p} + 3 \cdot \sqrt{p} + \sqrt{p} \cdot 1 + 3 \cdot 1$$

$$= p + 4\sqrt{p} + 3$$

93.

$$50 - 4(2)^x = -83$$

$$-4(2)^x = -133$$

$$2^x = 33.25$$

$$x \approx 5.0553$$

95.

$$\sqrt{x+3} - \sqrt{x-2} = 1$$

$$\sqrt{x+3} = 1 + \sqrt{x-2}$$

$$\left(\sqrt{x+3}\right)^2 = \left(1 + \sqrt{x-2}\right)^2$$

$$x + 3 = 1 + 2\sqrt{x-2} + x - 2$$

$$x + 3 = -1 + 2\sqrt{x-2} + x$$

$$4 = 2\sqrt{x-2}$$

$$2 = \sqrt{x-2}$$

$$(2)^2 = \left(\sqrt{x-2}\right)^2$$

$$4 = x - 2$$

$$6 = x$$

97.
$$-3(2k-5)+1=2(4k+3)$$
$$-6k+15+1=8k+6$$
$$-6k+16=8k+6$$
$$-14k=-10$$
$$k=\frac{5}{7}$$

99.
$$\log_2(5t-1)=5$$
$$5t-1=2^5$$
$$5t-1=32$$
$$5t=33$$
$$t=\frac{33}{5}$$

101.
$$\frac{3x^2-x-10}{x^3-x^2-x+1}\div\frac{3x^2-12}{2x^2+x-3}$$
$$=\frac{(3x+5)(x-2)}{(x-1)(x-1)(x+1)}\div\frac{3(x-2)(x+2)}{(2x+3)(x-1)}$$
$$=\frac{(3x+5)(x-2)}{(x-1)(x-1)(x+1)}\cdot\frac{(2x+3)(x-1)}{3(x-2)(x+2)}$$
$$=\frac{(3x+5)(2x+3)}{3(x+1)(x-1)(x+2)}$$

$\dfrac{3x^2-x-10}{x^3-x^2-x+1}\div\dfrac{3x^2-12}{2x^2+x-3}$ is a rational expression in one variable.

103.
$$\frac{6}{b-2}+\frac{3b}{b^2-7b+10}$$
$$=\frac{6(b-5)}{(b-2)(b-5)}+\frac{3b}{(b-2)(b-5)}$$
$$=\frac{3(3b-10)}{(b-2)(b-5)}$$

$\dfrac{6}{b-2}+\dfrac{3b}{b^2-7b+10}$ is a rational expression in one variable.

105.
$$\frac{6}{x-2}+\frac{3x}{x^2-7x+10}=\frac{x}{x-5}$$
$$\frac{6}{x-2}\cdot\frac{x-5}{x-5}+\frac{3x}{(x-2)(x-5)}=\frac{x}{x-5}\cdot\frac{x-2}{x-2}$$
$$6x-30+3x=x^2-2x$$
$$x^2-11x+30=0$$
$$(x-5)(x-6)=0$$

$x=5$ is not in the domain of the equation, so the only solution is $x=6$.

$\dfrac{6}{x-2}+\dfrac{3x}{x^2-7x+10}=\dfrac{x}{x-5}$ is a rational equation in one variable.

Homework 13.6

1. $(0,3)$ and $(4,5)$

Substitute the point $(0,3)$ into the equation $y=a\sqrt{x}+b$.
$$3=a\sqrt{0}+b$$
$$b=3$$
Substitute the point $(4,5)$ into the equation $y=a\sqrt{x}+3$ and solve for a.
$$5=a\sqrt{4}+3$$
$$2a=2$$
$$a=1$$
The equation is $y=\sqrt{x}+3$.

3. $(0,2)$ and $(9,6)$

Substitute the point $(0,2)$ into the equation $y=a\sqrt{x}+b$.
$$2=a\sqrt{0}+b$$
$$b=2$$
Substitute the point $(9,6)$ into the equation $y=a\sqrt{x}+2$ and solve for a.
$$6=a\sqrt{9}+2$$
$$3a=4$$
$$a=\frac{4}{3}$$
The equation is $y=\frac{4}{3}\sqrt{x}+2$.

5. (0, 4) and (5, 7)

Substitute the point (0, 4) into the equation
$y = a\sqrt{x} + b$.

$4 = a\sqrt{0} + b$

$b = 4$

Substitute the point (5, 7) into the equation
$y = a\sqrt{x} + 4$ and solve for a.

$7 = a\sqrt{5} + 4$

$3 = a\sqrt{5}$

$a \approx 1.34$

The equation is $y = 1.34\sqrt{x} + 4$.

7. (0, 9) and (3, 2)

Substitute the point (0, 9) into the equation
$y = a\sqrt{x} + b$.

$9 = a\sqrt{0} + b$

$b = 9$

Substitute the point (3, 2) into the equation
$y = a\sqrt{x} + 9$ and solve for a.

$2 = a\sqrt{3} + 9$

$-7 = a\sqrt{3}$

$a \approx -4.04$

The equation is $y = -4.04\sqrt{x} + 9$.

9. (1, 2) and (4, 3)

Substitute the points into the equation
$y = a\sqrt{x} + b$.

$2 = a\sqrt{1} + b$

$3 = a\sqrt{4} + b$

Rewrite as:

$a + b = 2$

$2a + b = 3$

Substitute $b = 2 - a$ into the second equation.

$2a + (2 - a) = 3$

$a = 1$

Solve for b.

$b = 2 - 1 = 1$

The equation is $y = \sqrt{x} + 1$.

11. $(2, 4)$ and $(3, 5)$

Substitute the points into the equation
$y = a\sqrt{x} + b$.

$4 = a\sqrt{2} + b$

$5 = a\sqrt{3} + b$

Rewrite as:

$1.4142a + b = 4$

$1.7321a + b = 5$

Solve the resulting system. Multiply the
first equation by -1 and add to the second
equation.

$-1.4142a - b = -4$

$\underline{1.7321a + b = 5}$

$0.3179a = 1$

$a \approx 3.15$

Substitute the point $(2, 4)$ into the equation

$y = 3.15\sqrt{x} + b$ and solve for b.

$4 = 3.15\sqrt{2} + b$

$b \approx -0.45$

The equation is roughly $y = 3.15\sqrt{x} - 0.45$.

13. $(2, 6)$ and $(5, 4)$

Substitute the points into the equation
$y = a\sqrt{x} + b$.

$6 = a\sqrt{2} + b$

$4 = a\sqrt{5} + b$

Rewrite as:

$1.4142a + b = 6$

$2.2361a + b = 4$

Solve the resulting system. Multiply the
first equation by -1 and add to the second
equation.

$-1.4142a - b = -6$

$\underline{2.2361a + b = 4}$

$0.8219a = -2$

$a \approx -2.43$

Substitute the point $(2, 6)$ into the equation

$y = -2.43\sqrt{x} + b$ and solve for b.

$6 = -2.43\sqrt{2} + b$

$b \approx 9.44$

The equation is roughly
$y = -2.43\sqrt{x} + 9.44$.

15. (5, 7) and (13, 21)

Substitute the points into the equation

$y = a\sqrt{x} + b$.

$7 = a\sqrt{5} + b$

$21 = a\sqrt{13} + b$

Rewrite as:

$2.2361a + b = 7$

$3.6056a + b = 21$

Solve the resulting system. Multiply the first equation by -1 and add to the second equation.

$-2.2361a - b = -7$

$\underline{3.6056a + b = 21}$

$1.3695a = 14$

$a \approx 10.22$

Substitute the point (5, 7) into the equation

$y = 10.22\sqrt{x} + b$ and solve for b.

$7 = 10.22\sqrt{5} + b$

$b \approx -15.85$

The equation is roughly

$y = 10.22\sqrt{x} - 15.85$.

17. (7, 31) and (10, 6)

Substitute the points into the equation

$y = a\sqrt{x} + b$.

$31 = a\sqrt{7} + b$

$6 = a\sqrt{10} + b$

Rewrite as:

$2.6458a + b = 31$

$3.1623a + b = 6$

Solve the resulting system. Multiply the first equation by -1 and add to the second equation.

$-2.6458a - b = -31$

$\underline{3.1623a + b = 6}$

$0.5165a = 25$

$a \approx -48.40$

Substitute the point (7, 31) into the equation

$y = -48.40\sqrt{x} + b$ and solve for b.

$31 = -48.40\sqrt{7} + b$

$b \approx 159.05$

The equation is roughly $y = -48.40\sqrt{x} + 159.05$.

19. (15, 3) and (35, 18)

Substitute the points into the equation

$y = a\sqrt{x} + b$.

$3 = a\sqrt{15} + b$

$18 = a\sqrt{35} + b$

Rewrite as:

$3.873a + b = 3$

$5.9161a + b = 18$

Solve the resulting system. Multiply the first equation by -1 and add to the second equation.

$-3.873a - b = -3$

$\underline{5.9161a + b = 18}$

$2.0431a = 15$

$a \approx 7.34$

Substitute the point (15, 3) into the equation

$y = 7.34\sqrt{x} + b$ and solve for b.

$3 = 7.34\sqrt{15} + b$

$b \approx -25.43$

The equation is roughly

$y = 7.34\sqrt{x} - 25.43$.

21. Increase the value of b to shift the graph up.

23. a. Start by plotting the data.

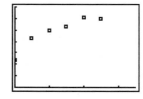

Answers may vary. Use the points (0, 12) and (4, 30.3).

Substitute the point (0, 12) into the equation

$y = a\sqrt{x} + b$.

$12 = a\sqrt{0} + b$

$b = 12$

Substitute the point (4, 30.3) into the equation $y = a\sqrt{x} + 12$ and solve for a.

$30.3 = a\sqrt{4} + 12$

$a = \dfrac{18.3}{2} = 9.15$

$f(t) = 9.15\sqrt{t} + 12$

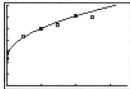

Your function may differ according to the points you chose.

b. The *n*-intercept is 12, which means that in 2002 *American Idol* was watched by an average of 12 million viewers per episode.

c. $39 = 9.15\sqrt{t} + 12$

$t \approx 8.71$

In about 2002 + 9 = 2011, the average number of viewers per episode will reach 39 million people.

d. $t = 2014 - 2002 = 12$

$f(12) = 9.15\sqrt{12} + 12 \approx 43.70$

In 2014, the average number of viewers will be about 43.70 million.

25. a. Start by plotting the data.

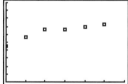

Answers may vary according to the points selected. Use the points (0, 9.1) and (5, 14.4).
Substitute the point (0, 9.1) into the equation $y = a\sqrt{x} + b$.

$9.1 = a\sqrt{0} + b$

$b = 9.1$

Substitute the point (5, 14.4) into the equation $y = a\sqrt{x} + 9.1$ and solve for a.

$14.4 = a\sqrt{5} + 9.1$

$a = \dfrac{5.3}{2.236} \approx 2.37$

$f(t) = 2.37\sqrt{t} + 9.1$

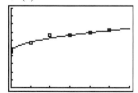

Your equation may differ according to the points you chose.

b. The *n*-intercept is 9.1, which means that 9.1 million households had webcams in 2000.

c. $f(14) = 2.37\sqrt{14} + 9.1 \approx 17.97$

In 2014, about 18 million households will have webcams.

d. $18 = 2.37\sqrt{t} + 9.1$

$t \approx 14.1$

In 2000 + 14 = 2014, 18 million households will have webcams.

27. a. $f(18000) = \sqrt{9.8(18000)} = 420$

The average speed would be 420 meters per second.

b. No, this would suggest that the depth is much less because the speed is half of what it should be.

c. $203 = \sqrt{9.8t}$

$t = 4205$

$210 = \sqrt{9.8t}$

$t = 4500$

The average depth would be 4205 to 4500 meters.

d. Yes.

29. a. Start by plotting the data.

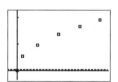

Answers may vary. A square root model seems to be appropriate. Use the points $(0,0)$ and $(52.5, 1.94)$.

Substitute the point $(0,0)$ into the equation $y = a\sqrt{x} + b$.

$0 = a\sqrt{0} + b$

$b = 0$

Substitute the point $(52.5, 1.94)$ into the equation $y = a\sqrt{x}$ and solve for a.

$$1.94 = a\sqrt{52.5}$$
$$a \approx 0.27$$
$$S(h) = 0.27\sqrt{h}$$

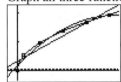

Your equation may differ according to the points you chose.

b. i. Graph all three functions.

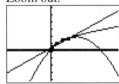

The model $S(h)$ appears to fit the best.

ii. $S(0) = 0; L(0) = 0.327; Q(0) = 0.165$

S models the situation best near 0 since it is the only model that passes through the origin.

iii. Zoom out.

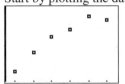

Q is not possible since it indicates that the falling time will reach 0 for larger drop heights.

iv. S models the situation the best and has no problems with larger h.

v.
$$T = \sqrt{\frac{2h}{32.2}}$$
$$= \sqrt{\frac{2}{32.2}}\sqrt{h}$$
$$\approx 0.249\sqrt{h}$$

This is close to the model
$$S(h) = 0.27\sqrt{h}.$$

c. $0.27\sqrt{h} = 3$
$$\sqrt{h} = \frac{3}{0.27}$$
$$\left(\sqrt{h}\right)^2 = \left(\frac{3}{0.27}\right)^2$$
$$h \approx 123.46$$

According to the model, the height of the cliff is roughly 123.46 feet.

d. $S(1250) = 0.27\sqrt{1250} \approx 9.55$

It would take about 9.55 seconds for the baseball to reach the ground if it were dropped from the top of New York City's Empire State Building.

31. a. Start by plotting the data.

A square root model may fit reasonably well.

Use the points $(2, 54.3)$ and $(4, 73)$.

Substitute the points into the equation $y = a\sqrt{x} + b$.

$$54.3 = a\sqrt{2} + b$$
$$73 = a\sqrt{4} + b$$

Rewrite as:
$$1.4142a + b = 54.3$$
$$2a + b = 73$$

Solve the system of equations. Multiply the first equation by -1 and add to the second equation.

$$-1.4142a - b = -54.3$$
$$\underline{2a + b = 73}$$
$$0.5858a = 18.7$$
$$a \approx 31.92$$

Substitute the point $(2, 54.3)$ into the equation $y = 31.92\sqrt{x} + b$ and solve for b.

$$54.3 = 31.92\sqrt{2} + b$$
$$b = 54.3 - 31.92\sqrt{2}$$
$$b \approx 9.16$$
$$f(n) = 31.92\sqrt{n} + 9.16$$

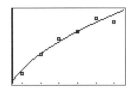

b. $f(7) = 31.92\sqrt{(7)} + 9.16 \approx 93.61$

About 93.6% of 7th births occurred despite the use of contraception.

c.
$$100 = 31.92\sqrt{n} + 9.16$$
$$31.92\sqrt{n} = 90.84$$
$$\sqrt{n} = \frac{90.84}{31.92}$$
$$\left(\sqrt{n}\right)^2 = \left(\frac{90.84}{31.92}\right)^2$$
$$n \approx 8.1$$

All 8th births occurred despite the use of contraception. Model breakdown has likely occurred.

d. The higher the birth order, the higher the percent of births that happened despite the use of contraception. Answers may vary. Perhaps couples without children are more careful in their use of contraception.

33. a. Start by plotting the data.

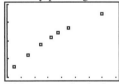

Either a quadratic function or a square root function may fit the data well.

b. Use the regression feature.
Quadratic.

$f(I) = -0.0037I^2 + 0.72I + 52.36$

Square root: Answers may vary. Use the points (5, 55.9) and (45, 77.2).
Substitute the points into the equation $y = a\sqrt{x} + b$.

$55.9 = a\sqrt{5} + b$

$77.2 = a\sqrt{45} + b$

Rewrite as:

$2.24a + b = 55.9$

$6.71a + b = 77.2$

Solve the system of equations. Multiply the first equation by -1 and add to the second equation.

$-2.24a - b = -55.9$

$\underline{6.71a + b = 77.2}$

$4.47a = 21.3$

$a \approx 4.77$

Substitute the point (5, 55.9) into the equation $y = 4.77\sqrt{x} + b$ and solve for b.

$55.9 = 4.77\sqrt{5} + b$

$b = 55.9 - 4.77\sqrt{5}$

$b \approx 45.23$

$f(I) = 4.77\sqrt{I} + 45.23$

c.

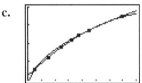

Both models fit the data well. The quadratic model fits the data a bit better than the square root model.

d.

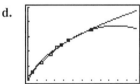

The quadratic model is decreasing for $I > 100$. This means that the percentage of adults who watch cable television decreases as incomes increase over $100 thousand. Model breakdown has occurred.
The square root model is increasing for $I > 100$. This means that the percentage of adults who watch cable television increase as incomes increase over $100 thousand.

e. Quadratic:

$f(130) = -0.0037(130)^2 + 0.72(130) + 52.36$
$= 83.43$

According to the quadratic model, about 83.4% of adults with an income of $130 thousand watch cable.
Square root:

$f(130) = 4.77\sqrt{130} + 45.23$
≈ 99.62

According to the square root model, about 99.6% of adults with an income of $130 thousand watch cable. The results are different because the quadratic model decreases for $I > 100$ and the square root model continue to increase for $I > 100$.

35. a. Answers may vary. Use the points $(0, 11)$ and $(8, 67)$.

Substitute the point $(0, 11)$ into the equation $y = a\sqrt{x} + b$.

$$11 = a\sqrt{0} + b$$
$$b = 11$$

Substitute the point $(8, 67)$ into the equation $y = a\sqrt{x} + 11$ and solve for a.

$$67 = a\sqrt{8} + 11$$
$$56 = a\sqrt{8}$$
$$a \approx 19.8$$
$$f(t) = 20\sqrt{t} + 11$$

b. The p-intercept is 11, which means that 11% of tires were reused or recycled in 1990.

c. Substitute 50 for p and solve for t.

$$50 = 20\sqrt{t} + 11$$
$$39 = 20\sqrt{t}$$
$$\frac{39}{20} = \sqrt{t}$$
$$\left(\frac{39}{20}\right)^2 = t \quad \text{or} \quad t \approx 3.8$$

The model predicts that half the tires will be reused or recycled in 1994.

d. Substitute 100 for p and solve for t.

$$100 = 20\sqrt{t} + 11$$
$$89 = 20\sqrt{t}$$
$$\frac{89}{20} = \sqrt{t}$$
$$\left(\frac{89}{20}\right)^2 = t \quad \text{or} \quad t \approx 19.8$$

The model predicts that all tires will be reused or recycled in 2010.

37. a.

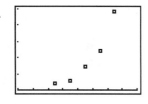

Answers may vary.
Either an exponential or quadratic function may fit the data well.

b. Use the regression feature.

Exponential: $f(t) = 0.92(1.39)^t$

Quadratic: $g(t) = 4.07t^2 - 78.86t + 401.3$

c.

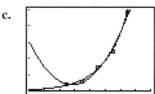

Both functions fit the data well.

d. The exponential function fits the data better before 1999.

e.
$$1200 = 0.92(1.39)^t$$
$$1304.35 \approx (1.39)^t$$
$$t \approx 21.78$$
$$1200 = 4.07t^2 - 78.86t + 401.3$$
$$0 = 4.07t^2 - 78.86t - 798.7$$
$$4.07t^2 - 78.86t - 798.7$$
$$t = \frac{78.86 \pm \sqrt{(-78.86)^2 - 4(4.07)(-798.7)}}{2(4.07)}$$
$$= \frac{78.86 \pm \sqrt{19221.74}}{8.14}$$
$$t \approx 26.72 \quad \text{or} \quad t \approx -7.34$$

According to the exponential model, there will be 1200 U.S. communities with red-light cameras in $1990 + 22 = 2012$. According to the quadratic model (using just the positive root), this will occur in $1990 + 27 = 2017$. The exponential model increases at a much faster rate than the quadratic model.

f. Answers may vary. Using the exponential model, Redflex will reach $260 million in revenue in 2012. Using the quadratic model, Redflex will reach $260 million in revenue in 2017.

39. Answers may vary.

$$\frac{4x-1}{2} = \frac{5x+3}{3}$$
$$12x - 3 = 10x + 6$$
$$2x = 9$$
$$x = \frac{9}{2}$$

41. Answers may vary.
$$\frac{4x-1}{2} - \frac{5x+3}{3} = \frac{12x-3}{6} - \frac{10x+6}{6}$$
$$= \frac{2x-9}{6}$$

43. Answers may vary.
$$2\sqrt{x} - 5 = 4$$
$$2\sqrt{x} = 9$$
$$\sqrt{x} = \frac{9}{2}$$
$$x = \frac{81}{4}$$

45. Answers may vary.
$$f(x) = 2(3)^x - 2.5$$

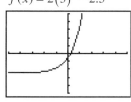

Chapter 13 Review Exercises

1. $x^{3/7} = \sqrt[7]{x^3}$

2. $\sqrt[5]{(3x+4)^7} = (3x+4)^{7/5}$

3.
$$\sqrt{8x^6} = \sqrt{4x^6 \cdot 2}$$
$$= \sqrt{4x^6}\sqrt{2}$$
$$= 2x^3\sqrt{2}$$

4.
$$\sqrt{18x^7 y^{10}} = \sqrt{9x^6 y^{10} \cdot 2x}$$
$$= \sqrt{9x^6 y^{10}}\sqrt{2x}$$
$$= 3x^3 y^5 \sqrt{2x}$$

5.
$$\sqrt[8]{x^6} = x^{6/8}$$
$$= x^{3/4}$$
$$= \sqrt[4]{x^3}$$

6.
$$\sqrt[3]{24x^{10} y^{24}} = \sqrt[3]{8x^9 y^{24} \cdot 3x}$$
$$= \sqrt[3]{8x^9 y^{24}} \sqrt[3]{3x}$$
$$= 2x^3 y^8 \sqrt[3]{3x}$$

7.
$$\sqrt[5]{(6x+11)^{27}} = \sqrt[5]{(6x+11)^{25} \cdot (6x+11)^2}$$
$$= \sqrt[5]{(6x+11)^{25}} \sqrt[5]{(6x+11)^2}$$
$$= (6x+11)^5 \sqrt[5]{(6x+11)^2}$$

8.
$$2\sqrt{5} - 3\sqrt{7} - 8\sqrt{5} = 2\sqrt{5} - 8\sqrt{5} - 3\sqrt{7}$$
$$= (2-8)\sqrt{5} - 3\sqrt{7}$$
$$= -6\sqrt{5} - 3\sqrt{7}$$

9.
$$5\sqrt{20x} - 2\sqrt{45x} + 7\sqrt{5x}$$
$$= 5\sqrt{4 \cdot 5x} - 2\sqrt{9 \cdot 5x} + 7\sqrt{5x}$$
$$= 5\sqrt{4}\sqrt{5x} - 2\sqrt{9}\sqrt{5x} + 7\sqrt{5x}$$
$$= 10\sqrt{5x} - 6\sqrt{5x} + 7\sqrt{5x}$$
$$= 11\sqrt{5x}$$

10.
$$5\sqrt{3x^2} - 3x\sqrt{48} = 5\sqrt{x^2 \cdot 3} - 3x\sqrt{16 \cdot 3}$$
$$= 5\sqrt{x^2}\sqrt{3} - 3x\sqrt{16}\sqrt{3}$$
$$= 5x\sqrt{3} - 3x \cdot 4\sqrt{3}$$
$$= 5x\sqrt{3} - 12x\sqrt{3}$$
$$= -7x\sqrt{3}$$

11.
$$b\sqrt[3]{16a^5 b} + a\sqrt[3]{2a^2 b^4}$$
$$= b\sqrt[3]{8a^3 \cdot 2a^2 b} + a\sqrt[3]{b^3 \cdot 2a^2 b}$$
$$= b\sqrt[3]{8a^3}\sqrt[3]{2a^2 b} + a\sqrt[3]{b^3}\sqrt[3]{2a^2 b}$$
$$= 2ab\sqrt[3]{2a^2 b} + ab\sqrt[3]{2a^2 b}$$
$$= 3ab\sqrt[3]{2a^2 b}$$

12.
$$5(4\sqrt{x} - \sqrt[3]{x}) - 2\sqrt[3]{x} + 8\sqrt{x}$$
$$= 20\sqrt{x} - 5\sqrt[3]{x} - 2\sqrt[3]{x} + 8\sqrt{x}$$
$$= (-5 - 2)\sqrt[3]{x} + (20 + 8)\sqrt{x}$$
$$= -7\sqrt[3]{x} + 28\sqrt{x}$$

13.
$$3\sqrt{x}(\sqrt{x} - 7) = 3\sqrt{x} \cdot \sqrt{x} - 3\sqrt{x} \cdot 7$$
$$= 3\sqrt{x \cdot x} - 21\sqrt{x}$$
$$= 3\sqrt{x^2} - 21\sqrt{x}$$
$$= 3x - 21\sqrt{x}$$

14.
$$2\sqrt{7}(5\sqrt{3} + \sqrt{7}) = 2\sqrt{7}(5\sqrt{3}) + 2\sqrt{7}(\sqrt{7})$$
$$= 10\sqrt{7 \cdot 3} + 2\sqrt{7 \cdot 7}$$
$$= 10\sqrt{21} + 2 \cdot 7$$
$$= 10\sqrt{21} + 14$$

15.
$$(t + \sqrt{3})(t + \sqrt{5})$$
$$= t^2 + t\sqrt{5} + \sqrt{3} \cdot t + \sqrt{3}\sqrt{5}$$
$$= t^2 + t\sqrt{5} + t\sqrt{3} + \sqrt{15}$$

16.
$$(4\sqrt{x} - 3)(2\sqrt{x} + 1)$$
$$= 4\sqrt{x} \cdot 2\sqrt{x} - 3 \cdot 2\sqrt{x} + 4\sqrt{x} \cdot 1 - 3 \cdot 1$$
$$= 8\sqrt{x \cdot x} - 6\sqrt{x} + 4\sqrt{x} - 3$$
$$= 8\sqrt{x^2} - 2\sqrt{x} - 3$$
$$= 8x - 2\sqrt{x} - 3$$

17.
$$(2\sqrt{a} - \sqrt{b})(5\sqrt{a} + \sqrt{b})$$
$$= 2\sqrt{a} \cdot 5\sqrt{a} - \sqrt{b} \cdot 5\sqrt{a} + 2\sqrt{a} \cdot \sqrt{b} - \sqrt{b} \cdot \sqrt{b}$$
$$= 10\sqrt{a \cdot a} - 5\sqrt{a \cdot b} + 2\sqrt{a \cdot b} - \sqrt{b \cdot b}$$
$$= 10\sqrt{a^2} - 3\sqrt{ab} - \sqrt{b^2}$$
$$= 10a - 3\sqrt{ab} - b$$

18.
$$(b - \sqrt{3})(b + \sqrt{3}) = b^2 - (\sqrt{3})^2$$
$$= b^2 - 3$$

19.
$$(5\sqrt{a} - 7\sqrt{b})(5\sqrt{a} + 7\sqrt{b})$$
$$= 5\sqrt{a} \cdot 5\sqrt{a} - 7\sqrt{b} \cdot 5\sqrt{a} + 5\sqrt{a} \cdot 7\sqrt{b} - 7\sqrt{b} \cdot 7\sqrt{b}$$
$$= 25\sqrt{a \cdot a} - 35\sqrt{a \cdot b} + 35\sqrt{a \cdot b} - 49\sqrt{b \cdot b}$$
$$= 25\sqrt{a^2} - 35\sqrt{ab} + 35\sqrt{ab} - 49\sqrt{b^2}$$
$$= 25a - 49b$$

20.
$$(4\sqrt{x} + 3)^2 = (4\sqrt{x})^2 + 2(4\sqrt{x})(3) + (3)^2$$
$$= 16x + 24\sqrt{x} + 9$$

21.
$$(3\sqrt{5} - 4\sqrt{2})^2 = (3\sqrt{5})^2 - 2(3\sqrt{5})(4\sqrt{2}) + (4\sqrt{2})^2$$
$$= 3^2(\sqrt{5})^2 - 2 \cdot 3 \cdot 4\sqrt{5 \cdot 2} + 4^2(\sqrt{2})^2$$
$$= 9 \cdot 5 - 24\sqrt{10} + 16 \cdot 2$$
$$= 45 - 24\sqrt{10} + 32$$
$$= 77 - 24\sqrt{10}$$

22.
$$(2\sqrt[3]{x} - 5)^2 = (2\sqrt[3]{x})^2 - 2(2\sqrt[3]{x})(5) + (5)^2$$
$$= 4\sqrt[3]{x^2} - 20\sqrt[3]{x} + 25$$

23.
$$\sqrt[4]{x}\sqrt[5]{x} = x^{1/4} \cdot x^{1/5}$$
$$= x^{\frac{1}{4} + \frac{1}{5}}$$
$$= x^{\frac{5}{20} + \frac{4}{20}}$$
$$= x^{9/20}$$
$$= \sqrt[20]{x^9}$$

24.
$$\sqrt[3]{\sqrt[6]{x}} = (x^{1/6})^{1/3}$$
$$= x^{\frac{1}{6} \cdot \frac{1}{3}}$$
$$= x^{\frac{1}{18}}$$
$$= \sqrt[18]{x}$$

25.

$$\frac{\sqrt[4]{x}}{\sqrt[6]{x}} = \frac{x^{1/4}}{x^{1/6}}$$

$$= x^{\frac{1}{4} - \frac{1}{6}}$$

$$= x^{\frac{3}{12} - \frac{2}{12}}$$

$$= x^{1/12}$$

$$= \sqrt[12]{x}$$

26.

$$\sqrt{\frac{3}{x}} = \frac{\sqrt{3}}{\sqrt{x}}$$

$$= \frac{\sqrt{3}}{\sqrt{x}} \cdot \frac{\sqrt{x}}{\sqrt{x}}$$

$$= \frac{\sqrt{3 \cdot x}}{\sqrt{x \cdot x}}$$

$$= \frac{\sqrt{3x}}{x}$$

27.

$$\frac{5t}{\sqrt[3]{t}} = \frac{5t}{\sqrt[3]{t}} \cdot \frac{\sqrt[3]{t^2}}{\sqrt[3]{t^2}}$$

$$= \frac{5t\sqrt[3]{t^2}}{\sqrt[3]{t \cdot t^2}}$$

$$= \frac{5t\sqrt[3]{t^2}}{\sqrt[3]{t^3}}$$

$$= \frac{5t\sqrt[3]{t^2}}{t}$$

$$= 5\sqrt[3]{t^2}$$

28.

$$\sqrt[5]{\frac{7y}{27x^2}} = \frac{\sqrt[5]{7y}}{\sqrt[5]{27x^2}}$$

$$= \frac{\sqrt[5]{7y}}{\sqrt[5]{27x^2}} \cdot \frac{\sqrt[5]{9x^3}}{\sqrt[5]{9x^3}}$$

$$= \frac{\sqrt[5]{7y \cdot 9x^3}}{\sqrt[5]{27x^2 \cdot 9x^3}}$$

$$= \frac{\sqrt[5]{63x^3 y}}{\sqrt[5]{243x^5}}$$

$$= \frac{\sqrt[5]{63x^3 y}}{3x}$$

29.

$$\frac{5}{3+\sqrt{x}} = \frac{5}{3+\sqrt{x}} \cdot \frac{3-\sqrt{x}}{3-\sqrt{x}}$$

$$= \frac{5\left(3-\sqrt{x}\right)}{\left(3\right)^2 - \left(\sqrt{x}\right)^2}$$

$$= \frac{15 - 5\sqrt{x}}{9 - x}$$

30.

$$\frac{\sqrt{a}}{\sqrt{a}-2\sqrt{b}} = \frac{\sqrt{a}}{\sqrt{a}-2\sqrt{b}} \cdot \frac{\sqrt{a}+2\sqrt{b}}{\sqrt{a}+2\sqrt{b}}$$

$$= \frac{\sqrt{a}\left(\sqrt{a}+2\sqrt{b}\right)}{\left(\sqrt{a}\right)^2 - \left(2\sqrt{b}\right)^2}$$

$$= \frac{a + 2\sqrt{ab}}{a - 4b}$$

31.

$$\frac{5\sqrt{x}-4}{2\sqrt{x}+3} = \frac{5\sqrt{x}-4}{2\sqrt{x}+3} \cdot \frac{2\sqrt{x}-3}{2\sqrt{x}-3}$$

$$= \frac{5\sqrt{x}\cdot 2\sqrt{x} - 4\cdot 2\sqrt{x} - 5\sqrt{x}\cdot 3 + 4\cdot 3}{\left(2\sqrt{x}\right)^2 - \left(3\right)^2}$$

$$= \frac{10\sqrt{x\cdot x} - 8\sqrt{x} - 15\sqrt{x} + 12}{4x - 9}$$

$$= \frac{10x - 23\sqrt{x} + 12}{4x - 9}$$

32. $y = -2\sqrt{x}$

x	y
0	0
1	-2
4	-4
9	-6
16	-8

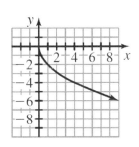

33. $y = 3\sqrt{x} + 1$

x	y
0	1
1	4
4	7
9	10
16	13

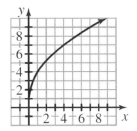

599

34. $y = -\sqrt{x-5} + 3$

x	y
5	3
6	2
9	1
14	0
21	-1

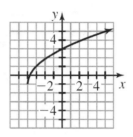

35. $y = 2\sqrt{x+4} - 1$

x	y
-4	-1
-3	1
0	3
5	5
12	7

36. $f + g = \left(3\sqrt{x} + 5\right) + \left(2 - 4\sqrt{x}\right)$

$\qquad = 3\sqrt{x} + 5 + 2 - 4\sqrt{x}$

$\qquad = -\sqrt{x} + 7$

37. $f - g = \left(3\sqrt{x} + 5\right) - \left(2 - 4\sqrt{x}\right)$

$\qquad = 3\sqrt{x} + 5 - 2 + 4\sqrt{x}$

$\qquad = 7\sqrt{x} + 3$

38. $f \cdot g = \left(3\sqrt{x} + 5\right)\left(2 - 4\sqrt{x}\right)$

$\qquad = 3\sqrt{x} \cdot 2 + 5 \cdot 2 - 3\sqrt{x} \cdot 4\sqrt{x} - 5 \cdot 4\sqrt{x}$

$\qquad = 6\sqrt{x} + 10 - 12x - 20\sqrt{x}$

$\qquad = -12x - 14\sqrt{x} + 10$

39. $\dfrac{f}{g} = \dfrac{3\sqrt{x} + 5}{2 - 4\sqrt{x}}$

$\qquad = \dfrac{3\sqrt{x} + 5}{2 - 4\sqrt{x}} \cdot \dfrac{2 + 4\sqrt{x}}{2 + 4\sqrt{x}}$

$\qquad = \dfrac{3\sqrt{x} \cdot 2 + 5 \cdot 2 + 3\sqrt{x} \cdot 4\sqrt{x} + 5 \cdot 4\sqrt{x}}{(2)^2 - \left(4\sqrt{x}\right)^2}$

$\qquad = \dfrac{6\sqrt{x} + 10 + 12x + 20\sqrt{x}}{4 - 16x}$

$\qquad = \dfrac{12x + 26\sqrt{x} + 10}{4 - 16x}$

$\qquad = \dfrac{2\left(6x + 13\sqrt{x} + 5\right)}{2(2 - 8x)}$

$\qquad = \dfrac{6x + 13\sqrt{x} + 5}{2 - 8x}$

40. $\sqrt{3r + 8} = -7$

Since the principle square root must be nonnegative, the equation has no solution.

41. $2\sqrt{x} - 5 = 11$

$\qquad 2\sqrt{x} = 16$

$\qquad \sqrt{x} = 8$

$\qquad \left(\sqrt{x}\right)^2 = 8^2$

$\qquad x = 64$

Check: $2\sqrt{64} - 5 \overset{?}{=} 11$

$\qquad 2(8) - 5 \overset{?}{=} 11$

$\qquad 11 \overset{?}{=} 11$ true

The solution is 64.

42. $\sqrt{2x + 1} + 4 = 7$

$\qquad \sqrt{2x + 1} = 3$

$\qquad \left(\sqrt{2x + 1}\right)^2 = 3^2$

$\qquad 2x + 1 = 9$

$\qquad 2x = 8$

$\qquad x = 4$

Check $x = 4$

$$\sqrt{2(4)+1}+4\overset{?}{=}7$$
$$7=7 \text{ true}$$

The solution is $x=4$.

43.
$$\sqrt{2x-4}-x=-2$$
$$\sqrt{2x-4}=x-2$$
$$\left(\sqrt{2x-4}\right)^2=(x-2)^2$$
$$2x-4=x^2-4x+4$$
$$x^2-6x+8=0$$
$$(x-4)(x-2)=0$$
$$x-4=0 \text{ or } x-2=0$$
$$x=4 \text{ or } x=2$$

Check $x=4$
$$\sqrt{2(4)-4}-4\overset{?}{=}-2$$
$$-2=-2 \text{ true}$$

Check $x=2$
$$\sqrt{2(2)-4}-2\overset{?}{=}-2$$
$$-2=-2 \text{ true}$$
The solutions are $x=4$ and $x=2$.

44.
$$\sqrt{x}+6=x$$
$$\sqrt{x}=x-6$$
$$\left(\sqrt{x}\right)^2=(x-6)^2$$
$$x=x^2-12x+36$$
$$x^2-13x+36=0$$
$$(x-9)(x-4)=0$$
$$x-9=0 \text{ or } x-4=0$$
$$x=9 \text{ or } x=4$$

Check $x=9$
$$\sqrt{9}+6\overset{?}{=}9$$
$$9=9 \text{ true}$$

Check $x=4$
$$\sqrt{4}+6\overset{?}{=}4$$
$$8=4 \text{ false}$$

The solution is $x=9$.

45.
$$\sqrt{13x+4}=\sqrt{5x+20}$$
$$\left(\sqrt{13x+4}\right)^2=\left(\sqrt{5x+20}\right)^2$$
$$13x+4=5x+20$$
$$8x=16$$
$$x=2$$
Check $x=2$
$$\sqrt{13(2)+4}\overset{?}{=}\sqrt{5(2)+20}$$
$$\sqrt{30}=\sqrt{30} \text{ true}$$
The solution is $x=2$.

46.
$$\sqrt{2x-1}=1+\sqrt{x+3}$$
$$\left(\sqrt{2x-1}\right)^2=\left(1+\sqrt{x+3}\right)^2$$
$$2x-1=1+2\sqrt{x+3}+x+3$$
$$2x-1=x+4+2\sqrt{x+3}$$
$$x-5=2\sqrt{x+3}$$
$$(x-5)^2=\left(2\sqrt{x+3}\right)^2$$
$$x^2-10x+25=4(x+3)$$
$$x^2-10x+25=4x+12$$
$$x^2-14x+13=0$$
$$(x-13)(x-1)=0$$
$$x=13 \text{ or } x=1$$
Check $x=1$
$$\sqrt{2(1)-1}\overset{?}{=}1+\sqrt{1+3}$$
$$\sqrt{1}=1+\sqrt{4} \text{ false}$$
Check $x=13$
$$\sqrt{2(13)-1}\overset{?}{=}1+\sqrt{13+3}$$
$$\sqrt{25}=1+\sqrt{16} \text{ true}$$
The solution is $x=13$.

47.
$$\sqrt{x+2}+\sqrt{x+9}=7$$
$$\sqrt{x+2}=7-\sqrt{x+9}$$
$$\left(\sqrt{x+2}\right)^2=\left(7-\sqrt{x+9}\right)^2$$
$$x+2=49-14\sqrt{x+9}+x+9$$
$$14\sqrt{x+9}=56$$

$$\sqrt{x+9} = 4$$

$$\left(\sqrt{x+9}\right)^2 = 4^2$$

$$x+9 = 16$$

$$x = 7$$

Check $x = 7$

$$\sqrt{(7)+2} + \sqrt{(7)+9} \overset{?}{=} 7$$

$$7 = 7 \quad \text{true}$$

The solution is $x = 7$.

48.

$$3.57 + 2.99\sqrt{8.06x - 6.83} = 14.55$$

$$2.99\sqrt{8.06x - 6.83} = 10.98$$

$$\sqrt{8.06x - 6.83} \approx 3.67$$

$$8.06x - 6.83 \approx 13.47$$

$$8.06x \approx 20.3$$

$$x \approx 2.52$$

49.

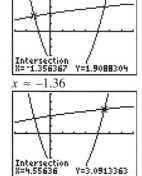

$x \approx -1.36$

$x \approx 4.56$

50. $f(x) = \sqrt{4x-7} - \sqrt{2x+1}$

$$\sqrt{4x-7} - \sqrt{2x+1} = 0$$

$$\sqrt{4x-7} = \sqrt{2x+1}$$

$$\left(\sqrt{4x-7}\right)^2 = \left(\sqrt{2x+1}\right)^2$$

$$4x-7 = 2x+1$$

$$2x = 8$$

$$x = 4$$

Check $x = 4$

$$\sqrt{4(4)-7} - \sqrt{2(4)+1} \overset{?}{=} 0$$

$$0 = 0 \quad \text{true}$$

The *x*-intercept is $(4,0)$.

 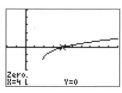

51. $g(x) = -3\sqrt{x+2} + 9$

$$-3\sqrt{x+2} + 9 = 0$$

$$-3\sqrt{x+2} = -9$$

$$\sqrt{x+2} = 3$$

$$\left(\sqrt{x+2}\right)^2 = (3)^2$$

$$x+2 = 9$$

$$x = 7$$

Check $x = 7$

$$-3\sqrt{7+2} + 9 \overset{?}{=} 0$$

$$-9 + 9 = 0 \quad \text{true}$$

The *x*-intercept is $(7,0)$.

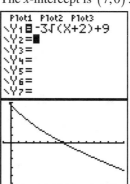

52. Increase b to raise the *y*-intercept and decrease a to lower the rate of increase. Sketches may vary.

53. The equation is of the form $y = a\sqrt{x} + b$.

The *y*-intercept is $(0,3)$ so $b = 3$.

Substitute the point $(4,8)$ into the equation

$y = a\sqrt{x} + 3$ and solve for a.

$$8 = a\sqrt{4} + 3$$

$$2a = 5$$

$$a = \frac{5}{2}$$

The equation is $y = \frac{5}{2}\sqrt{x} + 3$.

54. The equation is of the form $y = a\sqrt{x} + b$.

The y-intercept is $(0,7)$ so $b = 7$.

Substitute the point $(9,3)$ into the equation

$y = a\sqrt{x} + 7$ and solve for a.

$3 = a\sqrt{9} + 7$

$3a = -4$

$a = -\dfrac{4}{3}$

The equation is $y = -\dfrac{4}{3}\sqrt{x} + 7$.

55. $(3,7)$ and $(5,4)$

Substitute the points into the equation

$y = a\sqrt{x} + b$.

$7 = a\sqrt{3} + b$

$4 = a\sqrt{5} + b$

Rewrite as:

$1.7321a + b = 7$

$2.2361a + b = 4$

Solve the system of equations. Multiply the first equation by -1 and add to the second equation.

$-1.7321a - b = -7$

$\underline{2.2361a + b = 4}$

$0.504a = -3$

$a \approx -5.95$

Substitute the point $(3,7)$ into the equation

$y = -5.95\sqrt{x} + b$ and solve for b.

$7 = -5.95\sqrt{3} + b$

$b = 7 + 5.95\sqrt{3}$

$b \approx 17.31$

The equation is roughly $y = -5.95\sqrt{x} + 17.31$.

56. $(2, 5)$ and $(3, 6)$

Substitute the points into the equation

$y = a\sqrt{x} + b$.

$5 = a\sqrt{2} + b$

$6 = a\sqrt{3} + b$

Rewrite as:

$1.4142a + b = 5$

$1.732a + b = 6$

Solve the system of equations. Multiply the first equation by -1 and add to the second equation.

$-1.4142a - b = -5$

$\underline{1.732a + b = 6}$

$0.3178a = 1$

$a \approx 3.15$

Substitute the point $(3,6)$ into the equation

$y = 3.15\sqrt{x} + b$ and solve for b.

$6 = 3.15\sqrt{3} + b$

$b = 6 - 3.15\sqrt{3}$

$b \approx 0.54$

The equation is roughly $y = 3.15\sqrt{x} + 0.54$.

57. **a.** Start by plotting the data.

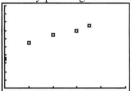

A square root model of the form

$y = a\sqrt{x} + b$ seems reasonable.

Use the points $(0,0.7)$ and $(7,1.5)$.

The y-intercept is $(0,0.7)$ so $b = 0.7$.

Substitute the point $(7,1.5)$ into the equation

$y = a\sqrt{x} + 0.7$ and solve for b.

$1.5 = a\sqrt{7} + 0.7$

$0.8 = a\sqrt{7}$

$a \approx 0.30$

$f(t) = 0.3\sqrt{t} + 0.7$

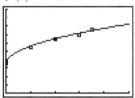

Models may vary according to the points selected.

b. n-intercept: $(0,0.7)$; In 1998, 700 single men adopted children from foster care.

c. $f(16) = 0.3\sqrt{16} + 0.7 = 1.9$

This means that, in $1998 + 16 = 2014$, 1900 single men will adopt children from foster care.

d.

$$2 = 0.3\sqrt{t} + 0.7$$

$$1.3 = 0.3\sqrt{t}$$

$$4.33 \approx \sqrt{t}$$

$$18.7 \approx t$$

In about 1998 + 19 = 2017, 2000 single men will adopt children from foster care.

Chapter 13 Test

1.
$$\sqrt{32x^9 y^{12}} = \sqrt{16x^8 y^{12} \cdot 2x}$$
$$= \sqrt{16x^8 y^{12}}\sqrt{2x}$$
$$= 4x^4 y^6 \sqrt{2x}$$

2.
$$\sqrt[3]{64x^{22} y^{14}} = \sqrt[3]{64x^{21} y^{12} \cdot xy^2}$$
$$= \sqrt[3]{64x^{21} y^{12}} \sqrt[3]{xy^2}$$
$$= 4x^7 y^4 \sqrt[3]{xy^2}$$

3.
$$\sqrt[4]{(2x+8)^{27}} = \sqrt[4]{(2x+8)^{24} \cdot (2x+8)^3}$$
$$= \sqrt[4]{(2x+8)^{24}} \sqrt[4]{(2x+8)^3}$$
$$= (2x+8)^6 \sqrt[4]{(2x+8)^3}$$

4.
$$\frac{4\sqrt[3]{x}}{6\sqrt[5]{x}} = \frac{2x^{1/3}}{3x^{1/5}}$$
$$= \frac{2}{3} x^{\frac{1}{3} - \frac{1}{5}}$$
$$= \frac{2}{3} x^{\frac{5}{15} - \frac{3}{15}}$$
$$= \frac{2}{3} x^{2/15}$$
$$= \frac{2\sqrt[15]{x^2}}{3}$$

5.
$$\frac{\sqrt{x}+1}{2\sqrt{x}-3} = \frac{\sqrt{x}+1}{2\sqrt{x}-3} \cdot \frac{2\sqrt{x}+3}{2\sqrt{x}+3}$$
$$= \frac{\sqrt{x} \cdot 2\sqrt{x} + 1 \cdot 2\sqrt{x} + \sqrt{x} \cdot 3 + 1 \cdot 3}{\left(2\sqrt{x}\right)^2 - (3)^2}$$
$$= \frac{2x + 2\sqrt{x} + 3\sqrt{x} + 3}{4x - 9}$$
$$= \frac{2x + 5\sqrt{x} + 3}{4x - 9}$$

6.
$$4\sqrt{12x^3} - 2x\sqrt{75x} + \sqrt{3x^3}$$
$$= 4\sqrt{4x^2 \cdot 3x} - 2x\sqrt{25 \cdot 3x} + \sqrt{x^2 \cdot 3x}$$
$$= 4 \cdot 2x\sqrt{3x} - 2x \cdot 5\sqrt{3x} + x\sqrt{3x}$$
$$= 8x\sqrt{3x} - 10x\sqrt{3x} + x\sqrt{3x}$$
$$= -x\sqrt{3x}$$

7.
$$3\sqrt{x}\left(6\sqrt{x} - 5\right) = 3\sqrt{x} \cdot 6\sqrt{x} - 3\sqrt{x} \cdot 5$$
$$= 18\sqrt{x^2} - 15\sqrt{x}$$
$$= 18x - 15\sqrt{x}$$

8.
$$\left(2 + 4\sqrt{x}\right)\left(3 - 5\sqrt{x}\right)$$
$$= 2 \cdot 3 + 4\sqrt{x} \cdot 3 - 2 \cdot 5\sqrt{x} - 4\sqrt{x} \cdot 5\sqrt{x}$$
$$= 6 + 12\sqrt{x} - 10\sqrt{x} - 20\sqrt{x^2}$$
$$= -20x + 2\sqrt{x} + 6$$

9.
$$\left(3\sqrt{a} - 5\sqrt{b}\right)\left(3\sqrt{a} + 5\sqrt{b}\right) = \left(3\sqrt{a}\right)^2 - \left(5\sqrt{b}\right)^2$$
$$= 9a - 25b$$

10.
$$\left(4\sqrt[5]{x} - 3\right)^2 = \left(4\sqrt[5]{x}\right)^2 - 2\left(4\sqrt[5]{x}\right)(3) + (3)^2$$
$$= 16\sqrt[5]{x^2} - 24\sqrt[5]{x} + 9$$

11.
$$\frac{\sqrt[n]{x}}{\sqrt[k]{x}} = \frac{x^{1/n}}{x^{1/k}}$$
$$= x^{\frac{1}{n} - \frac{1}{k}}$$
$$= x^{\frac{k}{kn} - \frac{n}{kn}}$$
$$= x^{\frac{k-n}{kn}}$$
$$= \sqrt[kn]{x^{k-n}}$$

12. $y = -2\sqrt{x+3} + 1$

x	y
-3	1
-2	-1
1	-3
6	-5
13	-7

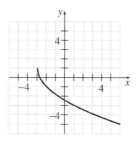

13. **a.** We need $a < 0$ and $k \geq 0$, or we need $a > 0$ and $k \leq 0$. In either case, h can be any real number.

b. $f(x) = a\sqrt{x-h} + k$

$$a\sqrt{x-h} + k = 0$$
$$a\sqrt{x-h} = -k$$
$$\sqrt{x-h} = -\frac{k}{a}$$
$$\left(\sqrt{x-h}\right)^2 = \left(-\frac{k}{a}\right)^2$$
$$x - h = \frac{k^2}{a^2}$$
$$x = h + \frac{k^2}{a^2}$$

The x-intercept is $\left(h + \dfrac{k^2}{a^2}, 0\right)$.

14. $f + g = \left(7 - 3\sqrt{x}\right) + \left(4 + 5\sqrt{x}\right)$
$$= 7 - 3\sqrt{x} + 4 + 5\sqrt{x}$$
$$= 2\sqrt{x} + 11$$

15. $f - g = \left(7 - 3\sqrt{x}\right) - \left(4 + 5\sqrt{x}\right)$
$$= 7 - 3\sqrt{x} - 4 - 5\sqrt{x}$$
$$= 3 - 8\sqrt{x}$$

16. $f \cdot g = \left(7 - 3\sqrt{x}\right)\left(4 + 5\sqrt{x}\right)$
$$= 7 \cdot 4 - 3\sqrt{x} \cdot 4 + 7 \cdot 5\sqrt{x} - 3\sqrt{x} \cdot 5\sqrt{x}$$
$$= 28 - 12\sqrt{x} + 35\sqrt{x} - 15x$$
$$= -15x + 23\sqrt{x} + 28$$

17. $\dfrac{f}{g} = \dfrac{7 - 3\sqrt{x}}{4 + 5\sqrt{x}}$

$$= \frac{7 - 3\sqrt{x}}{4 + 5\sqrt{x}} \cdot \frac{4 - 5\sqrt{x}}{4 - 5\sqrt{x}}$$

$$= \frac{7 \cdot 4 - 3\sqrt{x} \cdot 4 - 7 \cdot 5\sqrt{x} + 3\sqrt{x} \cdot 5\sqrt{x}}{(4)^2 - \left(5\sqrt{x}\right)^2}$$

$$= \frac{28 - 12\sqrt{x} - 35\sqrt{x} + 15x}{16 - 25x}$$

$$= \frac{15x - 47\sqrt{x} + 28}{16 - 25x}$$

18. $2\sqrt{x} + 3 = 13$
$$2\sqrt{x} = 10$$
$$\sqrt{x} = 5$$
$$\left(\sqrt{x}\right)^2 = 5^2$$
$$x = 25$$
Check $x = 25$
$$2\sqrt{(25)} + 3 \overset{?}{=} 13$$
$$13 = 13 \quad \text{true}$$
The solution is $x = 25$.

19. $3\sqrt{5b-4} = 27$
$$\sqrt{5b-4} = 9$$
$$\left(\sqrt{5b-4}\right)^2 = 9^2$$
$$5b - 4 = 81$$
$$5b = 85$$
$$b = 17$$
Check $b = 17$
$$3\sqrt{5(17)-4} \overset{?}{=} 27$$
$$27 = 27 \quad \text{true}$$
The solution is $b = 17$.

20.
$$3 - 2\sqrt{x} + \sqrt{9-x} = 0$$
$$\sqrt{9-x} = 2\sqrt{x} - 3$$
$$\left(\sqrt{9-x}\right)^2 = \left(2\sqrt{x}-3\right)^2$$
$$9 - x = 4x - 12\sqrt{x} + 9$$
$$12\sqrt{x} = 5x$$
$$\left(12\sqrt{x}\right)^2 = \left(5x\right)^2$$
$$144x = 25x^2$$
$$25x^2 - 144x = 0$$
$$x\left(25x - 144\right) = 0$$
$$x = 0 \text{ or } 25x - 144 = 0$$
$$x = 0 \text{ or } x = \frac{144}{25}$$

Check $x = 0$
$$3 - 2\sqrt{(0)} + \sqrt{9-(0)} \overset{?}{=} 0$$
$$6 \overset{?}{=} 0 \quad \text{false}$$

Check $x = \dfrac{144}{25}$
$$3 - 2\sqrt{\left(\frac{144}{25}\right)} + \sqrt{9 - \left(\frac{144}{25}\right)} \overset{?}{=} 0$$
$$0 = 0 \quad \text{true}$$

The solution is $x = \dfrac{144}{25}$.

21.
$$f(8) = 6 - 4\sqrt{(8)+1}$$
$$= 6 - 4\sqrt{9}$$
$$= 6 - 4(3)$$
$$= 6 - 12$$
$$= -6$$

22.
$$-2 = 6 - 4\sqrt{x+1}$$
$$-8 = -4\sqrt{x+1}$$
$$2 = \sqrt{x+1}$$
$$4 = x+1$$
$$3 = x$$

23.
$$f(x) = 3\sqrt{2x-4} - 2\sqrt{2x+1}$$
$$3\sqrt{2x-4} - 2\sqrt{2x+1} = 0$$
$$3\sqrt{2x-4} = 2\sqrt{2x+1}$$
$$\left(3\sqrt{2x-4}\right)^2 = \left(2\sqrt{2x+1}\right)^2$$
$$9(2x-4) = 4(2x+1)$$
$$18x - 36 = 8x + 4$$
$$10x = 40$$
$$x = 4$$

Check $x = 4$
$$3\sqrt{2(4)-4} - 2\sqrt{2(4)+1} \overset{?}{=} 0$$
$$0 = 0 \quad \text{true}$$

The x-intercept is $(4,0)$.

24.
$$\sqrt{x+4} = x^2 - 4x + 5$$
$$x \approx 0.9 \text{ and } x \approx 3.3$$

25.
$$\sqrt{x+4} = 1$$
$$x = -3$$

26. Decrease b to lower the y-intercept and increase a to increase the rate of increase. Graphs may vary.

27. Substitute the points $(2,4)$ and $(5,6)$ into the equation $y = a\sqrt{x} + b$.
$$4 = a\sqrt{2} + b$$
$$6 = a\sqrt{5} + b$$
Rewrite as:
$$1.4142a + b = 4$$
$$2.2361a + b = 6$$
Solve the system of equations. Multiply the first equation by -1 and add to the second equation.
$$-1.4142a - b = -4$$
$$\underline{2.2361a + b = 6}$$
$$0.8219a = 2$$
$$a \approx 2.43$$
Substitute the point $(2,4)$ into the equation $y = 2.43\sqrt{x} + b$ and solve for b.
$$4 = 2.43\sqrt{2} + b$$
$$b = 4 - 2.43\sqrt{2}$$
$$b \approx 0.56$$
The equation is roughly $y = 2.43\sqrt{x} + 0.56$.

28.   **a.**   Start by plotting the data.

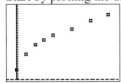

Answers may vary according to the points selected. Use the points $(0, 20.5)$ and $(60, 43.4)$.

The *y*-intercept is $(0, 20.5)$ so $b = 20.5$.

Substitute the point $(60, 43.4)$ into the equation $y = a\sqrt{x} + 20.5$ and solve for *a*.

$$43.4 = a\sqrt{60} + 20.5$$
$$a\sqrt{60} = 22.9$$
$$a \approx 2.96$$
$$f(t) = 2.96\sqrt{t} + 20.5$$

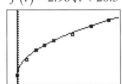

b. $t = 6$ years $= 6 \times 12$ months $= 72$ months
$$f(72) = 2.96\sqrt{72} + 20.5$$
$$\approx 45.6$$
According to the model, the median height of 6-year-old boys is about 45.6 inches.

c. $f(t) = 3$ feet $= 3 \times 12$ inches $= 36$ inches
$$36 = 2.96\sqrt{t} + 20.5$$
$$2.96\sqrt{t} = 15.5$$
$$\sqrt{t} = \frac{15.5}{2.96}$$
$$\left(\sqrt{t}\right)^2 = \left(\frac{15.5}{2.96}\right)^2$$
$$t \approx 27.42$$
The median height of 27-month-old boys is 3 feet.

d.   The *h*-intercept is $(0, 20.5)$. The median height of boys at birth is 20.5 inches.

Chapter 14
Sequences and Series

1. $11-3=8, 19-11=8, 27-19=8,$
$35-27=8$
The sequence has a common difference of 8.
It is arithmetic.

3. $5-1=4, 7-5=2$
The sequence does not have a common
difference. It is not arithmetic.

5. $-13-(-20)=7, -6-(-13)=7,$
$1-(-6)=7, 8-1=7$
The sequence has a common difference of 7.
It is arithmetic.

7. $44-4=40, 444-44=400$
The sequence does not have a common
difference. It is not arithmetic.

9. The sequence has a common difference of 6.
$$a_n = 5+(n-1)\cdot 6$$
$$= 5+6n-6$$
$$a_n = 6n-1$$

11. The sequence has a common difference of
-11.
$$a_n = -4+(n-1)\cdot(-11)$$
$$= -4+(-11n)+11$$
$$a_n = -11n+7$$

13. The sequence has a common difference of
-6.
$$a_n = 100+(n-1)\cdot(-6)$$
$$= 100-6n+6$$
$$a_n = -6n+106$$

15. The sequence has a common difference of 2.
$$a_n = 1+(n-1)\cdot 2$$
$$= 1+2n-2$$
$$a_n = 2n-1$$

17. The sequence has a common difference of 3.
$$a_{37} = 5+(37-1)\cdot 3$$
$$= 5+36\cdot 3$$
$$= 5+108$$
$$= 113$$

19. The sequence has a common difference of
-9.
$$a_{45} = 200+(45-1)\cdot(-9)$$
$$= 200+44\cdot(-9)$$
$$= 200+(-396)$$
$$= -196$$

21. The sequence has a common difference of
1.6.
$$a_{96} = 4.1+(96-1)\cdot 1.6$$
$$= 4.1+95\cdot 1.6$$
$$= 4.1+152$$
$$= 156.1$$

23. The sequence has a common difference of 1.
$$a_{400} = 1+(400-1)\cdot 1$$
$$= 400$$

25. The sequence has a common difference of 5.
$$533 = 3+(n-1)\cdot 5$$
$$533 = 3+5n-5$$
$$533 = 5n-2$$
$$535 = 5n$$
$$107 = n$$
533 is the 107th term.

27. The sequence has a common difference of 8.
$$695 = 7+(n-1)\cdot 8$$
$$695 = 7+8n-8$$
$$695 = 8n-1$$
$$696 = 8n$$
$$87 = n$$
695 is the 87th term.

29. The sequence has a common difference of 8.

$2469 = -27 + (n-1) \cdot 8$

$2469 = -27 + 8n - 8$

$2469 = 8n - 35$

$2504 = 8n$

$313 = n$

2469 is the 313th term.

31. The sequence has a common difference of -4.

$-14251 = 29 + (n-1) \cdot (-4)$

$-14251 = 29 - 4n + 4$

$-14251 = 33 - 4n$

$-14284 = -4n$

$3571 = n$

-14251 is the 3571st term.

33. **EQ 1**

$24 = a_1 + (7-1)d$

$24 = a_1 + 6d$

$24 - 6d = a_1$

EQ 2

$66 = a_1 + (13-1)d$

$66 = a_1 + 12d$

$66 - 12d = a_1$

Solve the system of linear equations by setting the left side of each equation equal to each other.

$24 - 6d = 66 - 12d$

$6d = 42$

$d = 7$

Use EQ 1 and $d = 7$ to find a_1.

$24 - 6(7) = a_1$

$-18 = a_1$

$a_{40} = -18 + (40-1) \cdot 7$

$= -18 + 39 \cdot 7$

$= 255$

35.

EQ 1	**EQ 2**
$500 = a_1 + (41-1)d$	$500 = a_1 + (81-1)d$
$500 = a_1 + 40d$	$500 = a_1 + 80d$
$500 - 40d = a_1$	$500 - 80d = a_1$

$500 = a_1 + (81-1)d$

$500 = a_1 + 80d$

$500 - 80d = a_1$

Solve the system of linear equations by setting the left side of each equation equal to each other.

$500 - 40d = 500 - 80d$

$40d = 0$

$d = 0$

Use EQ 1 and $d = 0$ to find a_1.

$500 - 40 \cdot 0 = a_1$

$500 = a_1$

$a_{990} = 500 + (990-1) \cdot 0$

$= 500$

37.

$f(1) = 4(1) - 2 = 2$

$f(2) = 4(2) - 2 = 6$

$f(3) = 4(3) - 2 = 10$

Yes, this sequence is arithmetic with a common difference equal to the slope, 4.

39.

$f(1) = 1^2 = 1$

$f(2) = 2^2 = 4$

$f(3) = 3^2 = 9$

No, this sequence is not arithmetic. There is no common difference.

41. The student's work is not correct. The sequence is not arithmetic because there is no common difference.

43. $15 - 8 = 7, 22 - 15 = 7, 29 - 22 = 7,$

$36 - 29 = 7$

The sequence has a common difference of 7. It is arithmetic.

$2537 = 8 + (n-1) \cdot 7$

$2537 = 8 + 7n - 7$

$2537 = 7n + 1$

$2536 = 7n$

$n \approx 362.3$

Since n is not a counting number, 2537 is not a term in the sequence.

45. Since $d = 9$ and $a_1 = 8$,

$$f(n) = 8 + (n-1) \cdot 9$$
$$= 8 + 9n - 9$$
$$= 9n - 1$$

47. a. $a_n = 27,500 + (n-1) \cdot 800$
$$= 27,500 + 800n - 800$$
$$a_n = 26,700 + 800n$$

b. $a_{22} = 26,700 + 800 \cdot 22$
$$= \$44,300$$
The salary for the 22nd year will be \$44,300.

c. $50,000 = 26,700 + 800n$
$$23,300 = 800n$$
$$29.125 = n$$
The salary will first be above \$50,000 in the 30th year.

49. a. $a_n = 35 + \dfrac{1}{6}n$

b.
$$a_1 = 35 + \frac{1}{6} \cdot 1 \approx 35.17$$
$$a_2 = 35 + \frac{1}{6} \cdot 2 \approx 35.33$$
$$a_3 = 35 + \frac{1}{6} \cdot 3 = 35.5$$
$$a_4 = 35 + \frac{1}{6} \cdot 4 \approx 35.67$$

These values represent the number of hours the instructor would work if she had 1, 2, 3, or 4 students, respectively.

c.
$$a_{130} = 35 + \frac{1}{6} \cdot 130$$
$$\approx 56.67$$

56.7 hours per week

d.
$$60 = 35 + \frac{1}{6}n$$
$$25 = \frac{1}{6}n$$
$$150 = n$$
The greatest number is 150 students.

51. a. The band collects $0.3(6) = \$1.80$ per cover charge, so the common difference is 1.8.

$$a_n = -50 + 0.3(6)n$$
$$= -50 + 1.8n$$

b. $256 = -50 + 1.8n$
$$306 = 1.8n$$
$$170 = n$$
170 people paid the cover charge.

c. Total number of people who pay is
$200 - 18 - 11 - 6 = 165$.
$$a_{165} = -50 + 1.8(165)$$
$$= 247$$
Their maximum profit is \$247.00.

d. $0 = -50 + 0.3(6)n$
$$0 = -50 + 1.8n$$
$$50 = 1.8n$$
$$n \approx 27.8$$
Little Muddy will lose money for values of n less than or equal to 27.

53. a.

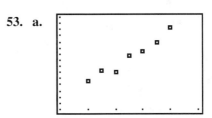

b. $f(t) = 13.61t + 39.04$

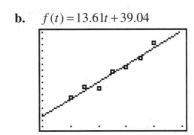

c. $f(6) \approx 121$
$$f(7) \approx 134$$
$$f(8) \approx 148$$
$$f(9) \approx 162$$
$$f(10) \approx 175$$

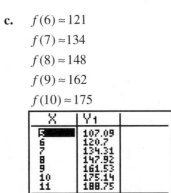

These values represent the pharmaceutical

industry's spending on government and politics (in millions of dollars) in 2001, 2002, 2003, 2004, and 2005 respectively.

d. $f(19) = 13.61(19) + 39.04 \approx 297.6$

The predicted pharmaceutical industry's spending in 2014 is about $298 million.

55. a. $a_n = 0.83 + (n-1) \cdot 0.17$
$\quad = 0.83 + 0.17n - 0.17$
$a_n = 0.66 + 0.17n$

b. $a_{13} = 0.66 + 0.17(13)$
$\quad = 2.87$
a_{13} is equal to $2.87.

c. $a_{16} = 0.66 + 0.17(16)$
$\quad = 3.38$
No, $3.38 is a better deal.

d. 5 pounds is equivalent to 80 ounces.
$a_{80} = 0.66 + 0.17(80)$
$\quad = 14.26$
a_{80} is equal to $14.26.

57. a. $7 - 5 = 2, 9 - 7 = 2, 11 - 9 = 2,$
$13 - 11 = 2$
The arithmetic sequence has a common difference of 2.

b. $m = \dfrac{7-5}{2-1} = \dfrac{2}{1} = 2$

$m = \dfrac{9-7}{3-2} = \dfrac{2}{1} = 2$

$m = \dfrac{11-9}{4-3} = \dfrac{2}{1} = 2$

$m = \dfrac{13-11}{5-4} = \dfrac{2}{1} = 2$

The slope of the line containing the points given is $m = 2$.

c. The common difference of the arithmetic sequence is equal to the slope of the function. Answers may vary. The form of the equation of an arithmetic sequence is the same as the form of a line in slope-intercept form, where m takes the place of d.

59.
$$2\sqrt{x+3} - 1 = 5$$
$$2\sqrt{x+3} = 6$$
$$\sqrt{x+3} = 3$$
$$x + 3 = 9$$
$$x = 6$$
$$check:$$
$$2\sqrt{(6)+3} - 1 = 5$$
$$2\sqrt{9} - 1 = 5$$
$$2(3) - 1 = 5$$
$$6 - 1 = 5$$
$$5 = 5$$

$2\sqrt{x+3} - 1 = 5$ is a radical equation in one variable.

61.

$f(x) = 2\sqrt{x+3} - 1$ is a radical function.

63.
$$\left(4\sqrt{x} - 5\right)\left(3\sqrt{x} - 2\right)$$
$$= 12 \cdot x - 8\sqrt{x} - 15\sqrt{x} + 10$$
$$= 12x - 23\sqrt{x} + 10$$

It is a radical expression in one variable.

Homework 14.2

1. $\dfrac{28}{4} = 7, \dfrac{196}{28} = 7, \dfrac{1372}{196} = 7, \dfrac{9604}{1372} = 7...$

The sequence has a common ratio of 7. It is geometric.

3. $6 - 13 = -7, -1 - 6 = -7, -8 - (-1) = -7,$
$-15 - (-8) = -7...$

The sequence has a common difference of -7. It is arithmetic.

5. $\dfrac{4}{3} \approx 1.33, \dfrac{6}{4} = 1.5$

The sequence has no common ratio.

$4 - 3 = 1, 6 - 4 = 2$

The sequence has no common difference.
The sequence is neither arithmetic nor geometric.

7. $\dfrac{40}{200} = \dfrac{1}{5}, \dfrac{8}{40} = \dfrac{1}{5}, \dfrac{\frac{8}{5}}{8} = \dfrac{1}{5}, \dfrac{\frac{8}{25}}{\frac{8}{5}} = \dfrac{1}{5}$

The sequence has a common ratio of $\dfrac{1}{5}$. It is geometric.

9. The sequence has a common ratio of 2.

$a_n = 3(2)^{n-1}$

$ = 3(2)^n(2)^{-1}$

$a_n = \dfrac{3(2)^n}{2} = \dfrac{3}{2}(2)^n$

Solution: $a_n = 3(2)^{n-1}$ or $a_n = \dfrac{3}{2}(2)^n$

11. The sequence has a common ratio of $\dfrac{1}{4}$.

$a_n = 800\left(\dfrac{1}{4}\right)^{n-1}$

$ = 800\left(\dfrac{1}{4}\right)^n\left(\dfrac{1}{4}\right)^{-1}$

$ = 800\left(\dfrac{1}{4}\right)^n(4)$

$a_n = 3200\left(\dfrac{1}{4}\right)^n$

Solution: $a_n = 800\left(\dfrac{1}{4}\right)^{n-1}$ or $a_n = 3200\left(\dfrac{1}{4}\right)^n$

13. The sequence has a common ratio of $\dfrac{1}{2}$.

$a_n = 100\left(\dfrac{1}{2}\right)^{n-1}$

$ = 100\left(\dfrac{1}{2}\right)^n\left(\dfrac{1}{2}\right)^{-1}$

$ = 100\left(\dfrac{1}{2}\right)^n(2)$

$a_n = 200\left(\dfrac{1}{2}\right)^n$

Solution: $a_n = 100\left(\dfrac{1}{2}\right)^{n-1}$ or $a_n = 200\left(\dfrac{1}{2}\right)^n$

15. The sequence has a common ratio of 4.

$a_n = 1(4)^{n-1}$

$ = 4^n(4)^{-1}$

$ = 4^n\left(\dfrac{1}{4}\right)$

$a_n = \dfrac{1}{4}(4)^n$

Solution: $a_n = 1(4)^{n-1}$ or $a_n = \dfrac{1}{4}(4)^n$

17. The sequence has a common ratio of 5.

$a_{34} = 4(5)^{34-1}$

$\phantom{a_{34}} = 4(5)^{33}$

$\phantom{a_{34}} \approx 4.6566 \times 10^{23}$

19. The sequence has a common ratio of $\dfrac{1}{2}$.

$a_{27} = 80\left(\dfrac{1}{2}\right)^{27-1}$

$\phantom{a_{27}} = 80\left(\dfrac{1}{2}\right)^{26}$

$\phantom{a_{27}} \approx 1.1921 \times 10^{-6}$

21. The sequence has a common ratio of 2.

$a_{23} = 8(2)^{23-1}$

$\phantom{a_{23}} = 8(2)^{22}$

$\phantom{a_{23}} = 33,554,432$

$\phantom{a_{23}} \approx 3.3554 \times 10^7$

23. The sequence has a common ratio of $\frac{1}{2}$.

$$0.46875 = 240\left(\frac{1}{2}\right)^{n-1}$$

$$0.001953125 = \left(\frac{1}{2}\right)^{n-1}$$

$$\log(0.001953125) = \log\left(\frac{1}{2}\right)^{n-1}$$

$$\log(0.001953125) = (n-1)\log\left(\frac{1}{2}\right)$$

$$\frac{\log(0.001953125)}{\log\left(\frac{1}{2}\right)} = n-1$$

$$\frac{\log(0.001953125)}{\log\left(\frac{1}{2}\right)} + 1 = n$$

$$10 = n$$

25. Use the sequence 0.00224, 0.0112, 0.056, 0.28, 1.4,…,109,375. This sequence has a common ratio of 5.

$$109,375 = 0.00224(5)^{n-1}$$

$$48,828,125 = 5^{n-1}$$

$$\log(48,828,125) = \log(5^{n-1})$$

$$\log(48,828,125) = (n-1)\log 5$$

$$\frac{\log(48,828,125)}{\log 5} = n-1$$

$$\frac{\log(48,828,125)}{\log 5} + 1 = n$$

$$12 = n$$

27. The sequence has a common ratio of 2.

$$3,407,872 = 13(2^{n-1})$$

$$262,144 = 2^{n-1}$$

$$\log(262,144) = \log(2^{n-1})$$

$$\log(262,144) = (n-1)\log 2$$

$$\frac{\log(262,144)}{\log 2} = n-1$$

$$\frac{\log(262,144)}{\log 2} + 1 = n$$

$$19 = n$$

29. The sequence has a common ratio of 3.

$$28,697,814 = 2(3)^{n-1}$$

$$14,348,907 = 3^{n-1}$$

$$\log(14,348,907) = \log(3^{n-1})$$

$$\log(14,348,907) = (n-1)\log 3$$

$$\frac{\log(14,348,907)}{\log 3} = n-1$$

$$\frac{\log(14,348,907)}{\log 3} + 1 = n$$

$$16 = n$$

31. The sequence is geometric. The common ratio is 5.

33. The sequence is arithmetic. The common difference is the slope which is 7.

35. The sequence has a common ratio of 3.
$$f(n) = 8(3)^{n-1}$$

37. Answers may vary. The sequence is geometric with a common ratio of 2 and $a_1 = 13$. Therefore, all terms must be divisible by 13. 9,238,946 is not divisible by 13, so it is not a term in the geometric sequence.

39. The student's work is not correct. The student is using the formula for a geometric sequence but the sequence is arithmetic. The arithmetic sequence has a common difference of 4.
$$a_{17} = 2 + (17-1) \cdot 4$$
$$= 66$$

41. a. $a_n = 27,000(1.04)^{n-1}$

b. $a_{10} = 27,000(1.04)^{10-1}$
$$= 27,000(1.04)^9$$
$$\approx \$38,429.42$$

The person's salary will be \$38,429.42 for the 10th year.

c.
$$50{,}000 = 27{,}000(1.04)^{n-1}$$

$$\frac{50}{27} = 1.04^{n-1}$$

$$\log\left(\frac{50}{27}\right) = \log\left(1.04^{n-1}\right)$$

$$\log\left(\frac{50}{27}\right) = (n-1)\log 1.04$$

$$\frac{\log\left(\dfrac{50}{27}\right)}{\log 1.04} = n-1$$

$$\frac{\log\left(\dfrac{50}{27}\right)}{\log 1.04} + 1 = n$$

$$16.7 \approx n$$

The salary will first exceed \$50,000 in the 17th year.

43. a. $2, 4, 8, 16, 32$

b. The sequence has a common ratio of 2.
$$a_n = 2(2)^{n-1}$$
$$= 2^1 \cdot 2^{n-1}$$
$$= 2^{1+n-1}$$
$$= 2^n$$

c. $a_8 = 2^8 = 256$ ancestors

d. $a_{35} = 2^{35}$
$$\approx 3.436 \times 10^{10}$$
$$\approx 34.36 \text{ billion ancestors}$$
Model breakdown has occurred. Answers may vary. The number of ancestors is much higher than the world's current population. One assumption is that no ancestor is related to any other ancestor, and this assumption is likely false.

45. a.

b.
```
ExpReg
 y=a*b^x
 a=865.4700996
 b=1.385797706
```

$$f(t) = 865.47(1.39)^t$$

c. $f(1) = 865.47(1.39)^1$
$$\approx 1203$$
$$f(2) = 865.47(1.39)^2$$
$$\approx 1672$$
$$f(3) = 865.47(1.39)^3$$
$$\approx 2324$$
$$f(4) = 865.47(1.39)^4 \quad f(5) = 865.47(1.39)^5$$
$$\approx 3231 \qquad\qquad \approx 4491$$
According to the exponential model, in 2001, 1203 girls named Nevaeh were born; in 2002, 1672 girls named Nevaeh were born; in 2003, 2324 girls named Nevaeh were born; in 2004, 3231 girls named Nevaeh were born; in 2005, 4491 girls named Nevaeh were born.

d. $f(t) = 865.47(1.39)^t$
$$f(14) = 865.47(1.39)^{14}$$
$$\approx 86987.98$$
86,988 is about 4.35% of 2,000,000. 1.25% of 2,000,000 indicates 25,000 girls will be named Emily. Nevaeh will be a more popular name than Emily.

47. a. $a_n = 5(3)^{n-1}$

b. $a_5 = 5(3)^{5-1}$
$$= 5(3)^4$$
$$= 405$$
a_5 is equal to 405 students.

c. $a_{11} = 5(3)^{11-1}$
$$= 5(3)^{10}$$
$$= 295{,}245$$
Answers may vary. Model breakdown has occurred. No campus has 295,245 students.

d. Answers may vary. One of the assumptions

was that a student would tell the rumor to 3 other students who have not heard the rumor yet. This assumption is reasonable for the first several days. However, as the number of students who heard the rumor grows larger, it is unlikely that those students would each know 3 other students who had not heard the rumor yet.

49. a. $\dfrac{14}{7} = 2, \dfrac{28}{14} = 2, \dfrac{56}{28} = 2, \dfrac{112}{56} = 2$

The series is geometric with a common ratio of 2.

b.
$$y = ab^x$$
$$7 = a \cdot b^1$$
$$7 = ab$$
$$a = \frac{7}{b}$$

Substituting $a = \dfrac{7}{b}$ into $14 = ab^2$

$$14 = \left(\frac{7}{b}\right)b^2$$
$$14 = 7b$$
$$2 = b$$

So the base is 2.

c. The common ratio for the sequence and the base of the function are the same. Answers may vary. The form of the equation of an geometric sequence is the same as the form of an exponential function, where the common ratio of the sequence is the base of the function.

51. The sequence has a common difference of 5.
$$a_n = 14 + (n-1) \cdot 5$$
$$= 14 + 5n - 5$$
$$= 5n + 9$$

53. The sequence has a common ratio of $\dfrac{1}{2}$.

$$a_n = 448\left(\frac{1}{2}\right)^{n-1}$$
$$= 448\left(\frac{1}{2}\right)^n \left(\frac{1}{2}\right)^{-1}$$
$$= 448\left(\frac{1}{2}\right)^n (2)$$
$$a_n = 896\left(\frac{1}{2}\right)^n$$

Solution: $a_n = 448\left(\dfrac{1}{2}\right)^{n-1}$ or $a_n = 896\left(\dfrac{1}{2}\right)^n$

55. The sequence has a common ratio of 5.
$$a_9 = 2(5)^{9-1}$$
$$= 2(5)^8$$
$$= 781,250$$

57. The sequence has a common difference of -5.
$$a_{99} = 17 + (99 - 1) \cdot (-5)$$
$$= -473$$

59. The sequence has a common difference of 3.
$$367 = 4 + (n-1) \cdot 3$$
$$367 = 4 + 3n - 3$$
$$367 = 1 + 3n$$
$$366 = 3n$$
$$122 = n$$

61. The sequence is geometric with a common ratio of $\dfrac{1}{4}$ and $a_1 = 8192$.

$$0.0078125 = 8192\left(\frac{1}{4}\right)^{n-1}$$
$$9.536743164 \times 10^{-7} = \left(\frac{1}{4}\right)^{n-1}$$
$$\log 9.536743164 \times 10^{-7} = \log\left(\frac{1}{4}\right)^{n-1}$$
$$\log 9.536743164 \times 10^{-7} = (n-1)\log\left(\frac{1}{4}\right)$$
$$\frac{\log 9.536743164 \times 10^{-7}}{\log\left(\frac{1}{4}\right)} = n - 1$$

$$n = \frac{\log 9.536743164 \times 10^{-7}}{\log\left(\frac{1}{4}\right)} + 1 = 11$$

0.0078125 is the 11th term of the geometric sequence.

63.

$$-3(4)^x = -44$$

$$4^x = \frac{44}{3}$$

$$\log 4^x = \log\left(\frac{44}{3}\right)$$

$$x\log 4 = \log\left(\frac{44}{3}\right)$$

$$x = \frac{\log\left(\frac{44}{3}\right)}{\log 4} \approx 1.9372$$

Check:

$$-3(4)^{1.937234559} = -44$$

$$-3\left(\frac{44}{3}\right) = -44$$

$$-44 = -44 \text{ True}$$

$-3(4)^x = -44$ is an exponential equation in one variable

65.

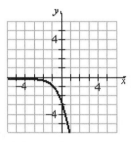

$f(x) = -3(4)^x$ is an exponential function.

67.

$$2\log_b\left(5x^3\right) - 3\log_b\left(2x^7\right)$$

$$= \log_b\left(5x^3\right)^2 - \log_b\left(2x^7\right)^3$$

$$= \log_b\left(25x^6\right) - \log_b\left(8x^{21}\right)$$

$$= \log_b\left(\frac{25x^6}{8x^{21}}\right)$$

$$= \log_b\left(\frac{25}{8x^{15}}\right)$$

It is a logarithmic expression in two variables.

Homework 14.3

1.

$$S_{90} = \frac{90(2 + 447)}{2}$$

$$= 20,205$$

3.

$$S_{108} = \frac{108(13 + 548)}{2}$$

$$= 30,294$$

5.

$$S_{72} = \frac{72\left(37 + (-1099)\right)}{2}$$

$$= -38,232$$

7. The series is arithmetic with a common difference of 8.

$$S_{74} = \frac{74(5 + 589)}{2}$$

$$= 21,978$$

9. The series is arithmetic with a common difference of –4.

$$S_{101} = \frac{101\left(93 + (-307)\right)}{2}$$

$$= -10,807$$

11. The series is arithmetic with a common difference of 0.

$$S_{117} = \frac{117(4 + 4)}{2}$$

$$= 468$$

13. The series is arithmetic with a common difference of 10.

$$a_{125} = 3 + (125 - 1)\cdot 10$$

$$= 3 + 124\cdot 10$$

$$= 1243$$

$$S_{125} = \frac{125(3 + 1243)}{2}$$

$$= 77,875$$

15. The series is arithmetic with a common difference of 11.

$$a_{81} = 8 + (81-1) \cdot 11$$
$$= 8 + 80 \cdot 11$$
$$= 888$$
$$S_{81} = \frac{81(8+888)}{2}$$
$$= 36,288$$

17. The series is arithmetic with a common difference of -13.
$$a_{152} = -15 + (152-1) \cdot (-13)$$
$$= -1978$$
$$S_{152} = \frac{152(-15 + (-1978))}{2}$$
$$= -151,468$$

19. The series is arithmetic with a common difference of 3.
$$a_{137} = -40 + (137-1) \cdot 3$$
$$= 368$$
$$S_{137} = \frac{137(-40 + 368)}{2}$$
$$= 22,468$$

21. The series is arithmetic with a common difference of 6.
$$247 = 19 + (n-1) \cdot 6$$
$$247 = 19 + 6n - 6$$
$$247 = 13 + 6n$$
$$234 = 6n$$
$$39 = n$$
So $247 = a_{39}$
$$S_{39} = \frac{39(19+247)}{2}$$
$$= 5187$$

23. The series is arithmetic with a common difference of -8.
$$-900 = 900 + (n-1) \cdot (-8)$$
$$-900 = 900 - 8n + 8$$
$$-900 = 908 - 8n$$
$$-1808 = -8n$$
$$226 = n$$

So $-900 = a_{226}$
$$S_{226} = \frac{226(900 + (-900))}{2}$$
$$= 0$$

25. The series is arithmetic with a common difference of 3.
$$340 = 4 + (n-1) \cdot 3$$
$$340 = 4 + 3n - 3$$
$$340 = 3n + 1$$
$$339 = 3n$$
$$113 = n$$
So $340 = a_{113}$
$$S_{113} = \frac{113(4+340)}{2}$$
$$= 19,436$$

27. The series is arithmetic with a common difference of 1.
$$10,000 = 1 + (n-1) \cdot 1$$
$$10,000 = 1 + n - 1$$
$$10,000 = n$$
So $10,000 = a_{10000}$
$$S_{10,000} = \frac{10,000(1+10,000)}{2}$$
$$= 50,005,000$$

29. S_n is positive it will be the sum of n positive numbers.

31. S_n is positive because it will be the sum of three relatively small negative numbers and many larger positive numbers.

33. Yes, the series is arithmetic. The common difference is the slope, 7.

35. a.
$$a_{28} = 28,500 + (28-1) \cdot 1100$$
$$= 28,500 + 27 \cdot 1100$$
$$= \$58,200$$

b.
$$S_{28} = \frac{28(28,500 + 58,200)}{2}$$
$$= \$1,213,800$$

37.

Company A

$$a_{20} = 35,000 + (20-1) \cdot 700$$
$$= \$48,300$$
$$S_{20} = \frac{20(35,000 + 48,300)}{2}$$
$$= \$833,000$$

Company B

$$a_{20} = 27,000 + (20-1) \cdot 1500$$
$$= \$55,500$$
$$S_{20} = \frac{20(27,000 + 55,500)}{2}$$
$$= \$825,000$$

Your total earnings for 20 years would be greater at Company A by $8000.

39. a.

$$a_{30} = 20 + (30-1) \cdot 4$$
$$= 136$$

There are 136 seats in the 30th row, the back row.

b.

$$S_{30} = \frac{30(20+136)}{2}$$
$$= 2340$$

There are 2340 seats in the auditorium.

41. a. Since $t = 4$ corresponds to the year 1999, according to the model,

$$f(4) = 13.61(4) + 39.04 = 93.48$$

The model estimates that the pharmaceutical industry spent approximately $93 million on government and politics in 1999.

b. Since $t = 18$ corresponds to the year 2013, according to the model,

$$f(18) = 13.61(18) + 39.04 = 284.02$$

In 2013, the pharmaceutical industry will spend approximately $284 million on government and politics.

c.

$$S_{15} = \frac{15(93 + 284)}{2}$$
$$= 2827.5$$

From 1999 through 2013 (including both 2009 and 2013), the pharmaceutical industry will spend a total of approximately $2828 million, or $2.828 billion, on government and politics.

43. a.

$$a_{26} = 24,800 + (26-1) \cdot 1200$$
$$= \$54,800$$
$$S_{26} = \frac{26(24,800 + 54,800)}{2}$$
$$= \$1,034,800$$

b.

$$a_1 = 0$$
$$a_{26} = 54,800 - 24,800$$
$$= 30,000$$
$$n = 26$$
$$S_{26} = \frac{26(0 + 30,000)}{2}$$
$$= 390,000$$

Alternatively, subtract the total with no raises, or $24,800(26) = $644,800, from the total with raises.
$1,034,800 - $644,800 = $390,000
The total amount of money earned from raises in 26 years is $390,000.

c.

$$\text{mean} = \frac{1,034,800}{26}$$
$$= \$39,800$$

The mean salary over the 26 years is $39,800. For the first 13 years this mean will be greater than the yearly salary. For the last 13 years, the mean will be less than the yearly salary.

d. The taxable income for the first 5 years is $20,550, $21,750, $22,950, $24,150, and $25,350. The taxable income does not exceed $25,000 until the 5th year. Therefore, the total income taxed at the lower rate will be

$$20,550 + 21,750 + 22,950 + 24,150$$
$$+ 22(25,000)$$
$$= \$639,400.$$

The taxable income at the higher rate is an arithmetic sequence whose first term is $350 ($25,350 - 25,000$) and whose common difference is $1200. The number of terms in this sequence is 22 because taxable income did not exceed $25,000 until the 5th year.

$$a_{22} = 350 + (22-1) \cdot 1200$$
$$= \$25,550$$
$$S_{22} = \frac{22(350 + 25,550)}{2}$$
$$= \$284,900$$

The estimated income tax will be
$$\$639,400(0.15016) + \$284,900(0.1704)$$
$$\approx \$144,559.26$$

45. The arithmetic sequence has a common difference of 16.
$$a_{15} = 8 + (15-1)\cdot 16$$
$$= 232$$

47. The arithmetic series has a common difference of 16.
$$a_{15} = 8 + (15-1)\cdot 16$$
$$= 232$$
$$S_{15} = \frac{15(8+232)}{2}$$
$$= 1800$$

49.
$$\frac{x-5}{x^2-9} + \frac{x+3}{x^2-8x+15}$$
$$= \frac{x-5}{(x-3)(x+3)} + \frac{x+3}{(x-3)(x-5)}$$
$$= \frac{(x-5)}{(x-3)(x+3)}\cdot\frac{(x-5)}{(x-5)} + \frac{(x+3)}{(x-3)(x-5)}\cdot\frac{(x+3)}{(x+3)}$$
$$= \frac{(x-5)(x-5)}{(x-3)(x+3)(x-5)} + \frac{(x+3)(x+3)}{(x-3)(x-5)(x+3)}$$
$$= \frac{(x-5)(x-5)+(x+3)(x+3)}{(x-3)(x+3)(x-5)}$$
$$= \frac{x^2-5x-5x+25+x^2+3x+3x+9}{(x-3)(x+3)(x-5)}$$
$$= \frac{2x^2-4x+34}{(x-3)(x+3)(x-5)}$$
$$= \frac{2\left(x^2-2x+17\right)}{(x-3)(x+3)(x-5)}$$

It is a rational expression in one variable.

51.
$$\frac{x-5}{x^2-9}\cdot\frac{x+3}{x^2-8x+15}$$
$$= \frac{x-5}{(x-3)(x+3)}\cdot\frac{x+3}{(x-3)(x-5)}$$
$$= \frac{(x-5)}{(x-3)\,(x+3)}\cdot\frac{(x+3)}{(x-3)(x-5)}$$
$$= \frac{(x-5)}{(x-3)}\cdot\frac{1}{(x-3)(x-5)}$$
$$= \frac{1}{(x-3)^2}$$

It is a rational expression in one variable.

53.
$$\frac{x-5}{x^2-9} + \frac{x+3}{x^2-8x+15} = \frac{2}{x-5}$$
$$\frac{x-5}{(x-3)(x+3)} + \frac{x+3}{(x-3)(x-5)} = \frac{2}{x-5}$$
$$(x-5)(x-5)+(x+3)(x+3) = 2(x-3)(x+3)$$
$$x^2-10x+25+x^2+6x+9 = 2x^2-18$$
$$2x^2-4x+34 = 2x^2-18$$
$$-4x+34 = -18$$
$$-4x = -52$$
$$x = 13$$

Check:
$$\frac{(13)-5}{(13)^2-9} + \frac{(13)+3}{(13)^2-8(13)+15} = \frac{2}{(13)-5}$$
$$0.25 = 0.25 \quad \text{True}$$

It is a rational equation in one variable.

Homework 14.4

1.
$$S_{13} = \frac{5(1-2^{13})}{1-2}$$
$$= 40,955$$

3.
$$S_{12} = \frac{6(1-1.3^{12})}{1-1.3}$$
$$\approx 445.9617$$

5.
$$S_{13} = \frac{13(1-0.8^{13})}{1-0.8}$$
$$\approx 61.4266$$

7.
$$S_{10} = \frac{2.3(1-0.9^{10})}{1-0.9}$$
$$\approx 14.9804$$

9. The series is geometric with a common ratio of 5.
$$S_{13} = \frac{2(1-5^{13})}{1-5}$$
$$= 610,351,562$$

11. The series is geometric with a common ratio of 0.3.
$$S_{11} = \frac{600(1-0.3^{11})}{1-0.3}$$
$$\approx 857.1413$$

13. The series is geometric with a common ratio of $\frac{2}{3}$.
$$S_{10} = \frac{3\left(1-\left(\frac{2}{3}\right)^{10}\right)}{1-\frac{2}{3}}$$
$$\approx 8.8439$$

15. The series is geometric with a common ratio of 4.
$$67,108,864 = 1(4)^{n-1}$$
$$\log 67,108,864 = \log 4^{n-1}$$
$$\log 67,108,864 = (n-1)\log 4$$
$$\frac{\log 67,108,864}{\log 4} = n-1$$
$$\frac{\log 67,108,864}{\log 4}+1 = n$$
$$14 = n$$
$$S_{14} = \frac{1(1-4^{14})}{1-4}$$
$$= 89,478,485$$

17. The series is geometric with a common ratio of 1.2.

$$21.4990848 = 5(1.2)^{n-1}$$
$$4.29981696 = 1.2^{n-1}$$
$$\log 4.29981696 = \log 1.2^{n-1}$$
$$\log 4.29981696 = (n-1)\log 1.2$$
$$\frac{\log 4.29981696}{\log 1.2} = n-1$$
$$\frac{\log 4.29981696}{\log 1.2}+1 = n$$
$$9 = n$$
$$S_9 = \frac{5(1-1.2^9)}{1-1.2}$$
$$\approx 103.9945$$

19. The series is geometric with common ratio of $\frac{1}{2}$.
$$4.8828125 = 10,000\left(\frac{1}{2}\right)^{n-1}$$
$$0.00048828125 = \left(\frac{1}{2}\right)^{n-1}$$
$$\log 0.00048828125 = \log\left(\frac{1}{2}\right)^{n-1}$$
$$\log 0.00048828125 = (n-1)\log\left(\frac{1}{2}\right)$$
$$\frac{\log 0.00048828125}{\log\left(\frac{1}{2}\right)} = n-1$$
$$\frac{\log 0.00048828125}{\log\left(\frac{1}{2}\right)}+1 = n$$
$$12 = n$$
$$S_{12} = \frac{10,000\left(1-\left(\frac{1}{2}\right)^{12}\right)}{1-\frac{1}{2}}$$
$$\approx 19,995.1172$$

21. The series is arithmetic with a common difference of 0.
$$S_{100} = \frac{100(1+1)}{2}$$
$$= 100$$

23. The series is geometric with a common ratio of $\frac{1}{3}$.

$$\frac{4}{729} = 324\left(\frac{1}{3}\right)^{n-1}$$

$$\frac{4}{729} = 324\left(\frac{1}{3}\right)^{n-1}$$

$$1.693508781 \times 10^{-5} = \left(\frac{1}{3}\right)^{n-1}$$

$$\log\left(1.693508781 \times 10^{-5}\right) = \log\left(\frac{1}{3}\right)^{n-1}$$

$$\log\left(1.693508781 \times 10^{-5}\right) = (n-1)\log\left(\frac{1}{3}\right)$$

$$\frac{\log\left(1.693508781 \times 10^{-5}\right)}{\log\left(\frac{1}{3}\right)} = n-1$$

$$\frac{\log\left(1.693508781 \times 10^{-5}\right)}{\log\left(\frac{1}{3}\right)} + 1 = n$$

$$11 = n$$

$$S_{11} = \frac{324\left(1 - \left(\frac{1}{3}\right)^{11}\right)}{1 - \left(\frac{1}{3}\right)}$$

$$\approx 485.9973$$

25. S_n must be positive because it is the sum of all positive values.

27. The series is arithmetic because $f(x)$ is linear. The common difference of the series is the slope of $f(x)$ which is -1.

29.

$$S_{20} = \frac{23500(1 - 1.04^{20})}{1 - 1.04}$$
$$\approx \$699,784.85$$

The person's total earnings after 20 years of work will be $699,784.85.

31. **Company A**

$$S_{30} = \frac{26000(1 - 1.05^{30})}{1 - 1.05} \approx \$1,727,410.04$$

Company B

$$S_{30} = \frac{31000(1 - 1.03^{30})}{1 - 1.03} \approx \$1,474,837.89$$

The earnings at Company A after 30 years will be $252,572.15 more than Company B.

33. Recall, the number of ancestors n generations back is a geometric series with a common ratio of 2.

$$S_n = \frac{2(1 - 2^{10})}{1 - 2} \text{ ancestors}$$
$$= 2046$$

35. a. The entrepreneur's name would be taken off the list in the 11th round. The amount of money sent to the entrepreneur each round is a geometric series with common ratio 8.

$$S_{10} = \frac{40(1 - 8^{10})}{1 - 8}$$
$$= 6,135,667,560$$

The entrepreneur could receive as much as approximately $6.14 billion.

b.

$$6,500,000,000 = \frac{8(1 - 8^n)}{1 - 8}$$

$$6,500,000,000 = -\frac{8}{7}(1 - 8^n)$$

$$5,687,500,000 = 8^n - 1$$

$$8^n = 5,687,500,001$$

$$\log 8^n = \log 5,687,500,001$$

$$n\log 8 = \log 5,687,500,001$$

$$n = \frac{\log 5,687,500,001}{\log 8}$$

$$n \approx 10.80$$

There will be ten full rounds and part of an 11th round.

c. The money from the first 10 rounds will go to the entrepreneur. The chain letter runs out of people (and money!) to complete the 11th round. All the money from the 11th round would go to the first 8 people besides the entrepreneur. This amount is (in billions):

$$\frac{32.5 - 6.136}{8} \approx 3.3$$

So, 9 people will receive money from the chain letters. The entrepreneur will receive approximately $6.14 billion. The 8 people besides the entrepreneur will receive an average of $3.30 billion.

37. a. $f(t) = 865.47(1.39)^t$

$f(1) = 865.47(1.39)^1$

≈ 1203.00

This means that in 2001, approximately 1203 girls named Nevaeh were born.

b. $f(14) = 865.47(1.39)^{14}$

$\approx 86,988$

This means that in 2014, approximately 86,988 girls named Nevaeh will be born.

c. Find the sum of

$f(1), f(2), \cdots, f(13), f(14)$

$S_{14} = \dfrac{1203(1 - 1.39^{14})}{1 - 1.39}$

$\approx 306,948.6$

This means that from 2001 through 2014 (including 2014), a total of about 306,949 girls named Nevaeh will be born.

39. a. The series is geometric with a common ratio of 2.

$2560 = 5(2)^{n-1}$

$512 = (2)^{n-1}$

$\log 512 = \log(2)^{n-1}$

$\log 512 = (n-1)\log(2)$

$\dfrac{\log 512}{\log 2} = n - 1$

$\dfrac{\log 512}{\log 2} + 1 = n$

$10 = n$

$S_{10} = \dfrac{5(1 - 2^{10})}{1 - 2}$

$= 5115$

b.

$a_n = a_1 r^{n-1}$

$\dfrac{a_n}{a_1} = r^{n-1}$

$\log \dfrac{a_n}{a_1} = \log r^{n-1}$

$\log \dfrac{a_n}{a_1} = (n-1)\log r$

$\dfrac{\log\left(\dfrac{a_n}{a_1}\right)}{\log r} = (n-1)$

$n = \dfrac{\log\left(\dfrac{a_n}{a_1}\right)}{\log r} + 1$

$n = \dfrac{\log\left(\dfrac{a_n}{a_1}\right)}{\log r} + \dfrac{\log r}{\log r}$

$n = \dfrac{\log\left(\dfrac{a_n}{a_1}\right) + \log r}{\log r}$

$n = \dfrac{\log\left(\dfrac{a_n r}{a_1}\right)}{\log r}$

c.

$S_n = \dfrac{a_1\left(1 - r^n\right)}{1 - r}$

$S_n = \dfrac{a_1\left(1 - r^{\log(a_n r/a_1)/\log r}\right)}{1 - r}$

d.

$S_{10} = \dfrac{5\left(1 - 2^{\log(2560 \cdot 2/5)/\log 2}\right)}{1 - 2}$

$S_{10} = \dfrac{5\left(1 - 2^{10}\right)}{1 - 2}$

$S_{10} = 5115$

e. Answers may vary.

41. The series is arithmetic with a common difference of 6.

$$351 = 3 + (n-1)\cdot 6$$
$$351 = 3 + 6n - 6$$
$$351 = 6n - 3$$
$$354 = 6n$$
$$59 = n$$
$$S_{59} = \frac{59(3+351)}{2}$$
$$= 10,443$$

43. The series is geometric with a common ratio of 0.9.

$$3.486784401 = 10(0.9)^{n-1}$$
$$0.3486784401 = (0.9)^{n-1}$$
$$\log 0.3486784401 = \log(0.9)^{n-1}$$
$$\log 0.3486784401 = (n-1)\log 0.9$$
$$\frac{\log 0.3486784401}{\log 0.9} = n - 1$$
$$\frac{\log 0.3486784401}{\log 0.9} + 1 = n$$
$$11 = n$$
$$S_{11} = \frac{10(1-0.9^{11})}{1-0.9}$$
$$\approx 68.6189$$

45. Answers may vary.

$$y = 4x^2 - 8x + 6$$

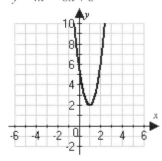

47. Answers may vary.

$$\frac{x^2-6x+9}{x^2+7x+10} \div \frac{x-3}{x+2} = \frac{(x-3)(x-3)}{(x+5)(x+2)} \cdot \frac{x+2}{x-3}$$
$$= \frac{x-3}{x+5}$$

49. Answers may vary.

$$x^2 - 9x + 14 = 0$$
$$(x-2)(x-7) = 0$$
$$x - 2 = 0 \quad \text{or} \quad x - 7 = 0$$
$$x = 2 \qquad\qquad x = 7$$

51. Answers may vary.

$$y = 3(2)^x$$

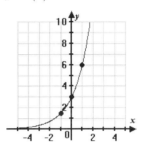

53. Answers may vary.

$$y = x + 3$$
$$4x + 2y = 15$$

Solve by substitution:

$$4x + 2(x+3) = 15$$
$$4x + 2x + 6 = 15$$
$$6x = 9$$
$$x = \frac{3}{2}$$

Substitute $x = \frac{3}{2}$ into $y = x + 3$:

$$y = x + 3$$
$$y = \frac{3}{2} + 3$$
$$y = \frac{9}{2}$$

The solution is $\left(\frac{3}{2}, \frac{9}{2}\right)$.

53. Answers may vary.

Chapter 14 Review Exercises

1. $\dfrac{40}{160} = \dfrac{1}{4}, \dfrac{10}{40} = \dfrac{1}{4}, \dfrac{2.5}{10} = \dfrac{1}{4}, \dfrac{0.625}{2.5} = \dfrac{1}{4}$

The sequence is geometric with a common ratio of $\dfrac{1}{4}$.

2. $24 - 13 = 11, 35 - 24 = 11, 46 - 35 = 11,$
$57 - 46 = 11$

The series is arithmetic with a common difference of 11.

3. $95 - 101 = -6, 89 - 95 = -6,$
$83 - 89 = -6, 77 - 83 = -6$

The sequence is arithmetic with a common difference of -6.

4. $\dfrac{18}{9} = 2, \dfrac{36}{18} = 2, \dfrac{72}{36} = 2, \dfrac{144}{72} = 2$

The series is geometric with a common ratio of 2.

5. $\dfrac{\frac{7}{5}}{7} = \dfrac{1}{5}, \dfrac{\frac{7}{25}}{\frac{7}{5}} = \dfrac{1}{5}, \dfrac{\frac{7}{125}}{\frac{7}{25}} = \dfrac{1}{5}, \dfrac{\frac{7}{625}}{\frac{7}{125}} = \dfrac{1}{5}$

The series is geometric with a common ratio of $\dfrac{1}{5}$.

6. $4 - 3 = 1, 6 - 4 = 2, 9 - 6 = 3, 13 - 9 = 4$
The series is increasing, so it is neither arithmetic nor geometric.

7. The sequence is geometric with a common ratio of 3.
$$a_n = 2(3)^{n-1}$$
$$= 2(3)^n (3)^{-1}$$
$$= 2(3)^n \left(\frac{1}{3}\right)$$
$$a_n = \frac{2}{3}(3)^n$$

Solution: $a_n = 2(3)^{n-1}$ or $a_n = \dfrac{2}{3}(3)^n$

8. The sequence is arithmetic with a common difference of 3.
$$a_n = 25 + (n-1) \cdot (3)$$
$$= 25 + 3n - 3$$
$$a_n = 22 + 3n$$

9. The sequence is arithmetic with a common difference of -5.
$$a_n = 9 + (n-1) \cdot (-5)$$
$$= 9 - 5n + 5$$
$$a_n = 14 - 5n$$

10. The sequence is geometric with a common ratio of $\dfrac{1}{2}$.
$$a_n = 200\left(\frac{1}{2}\right)^{n-1}$$
$$= 200\left(\frac{1}{2}\right)^n \left(\frac{1}{2}\right)^{-1}$$
$$= 200\left(\frac{1}{2}\right)^n (2)$$
$$a_n = 400\left(\frac{1}{2}\right)^n$$

Solution: $a_n = 200\left(\dfrac{1}{2}\right)^{n-1}$ or $a_n = 400\left(\dfrac{1}{2}\right)^n$

11. The sequence is arithmetic with a common difference of 2.7.
$$a_n = 3.2 + (n-1) \cdot 2.7$$
$$= 3.2 + 2.7n - 2.7$$
$$a_n = 2.7n + 0.5$$

12. The sequence is geometric with a common ratio 0.7.
$$a_n = 800\left(\frac{7}{10}\right)^{n-1}$$
$$= 800\left(\frac{7}{10}\right)^n \left(\frac{7}{10}\right)^{-1}$$
$$= 800(0.7)^n \left(\frac{10}{7}\right)$$
$$a_n = \frac{8000}{7}(0.7)^n$$

Solution: $a_n = 800(0.7)^{n-1}$ or $a_n = \dfrac{8000}{7}(0.7)^n$

13. The sequence is geometric with a common ratio 2.
$$a_{47} = 6(2)^{47-1}$$
$$= 6(2)^{46}$$
$$\approx 4.2221 \times 10^{14}$$

14. The sequence is geometric with a common ratio $\frac{1}{4}$.

$$a_9 = 768\left(\frac{1}{4}\right)^{9-1}$$
$$= 768\left(\frac{1}{4}\right)^{8}$$
$$\approx 1.1719 \times 10^{-2}$$

15. The sequence is arithmetic with a common difference of -3.

$$a_{98} = 87 + (98-1)\cdot(-3)$$
$$= -204$$

16. The sequence is arithmetic with a common difference of 2.6.

$$a_{87} = 2.3 + (87-1)\cdot 2.6$$
$$= 225.9$$

17. The sequence is arithmetic with a common difference 4.

$$2023 = 7 + (n-1)\cdot 4$$
$$2023 = 7 + 4n - 4$$
$$2023 = 3 + 4n$$
$$2020 = 4n$$
$$505 = n$$

2023 is the 505th term.

18. The sequence is arithmetic with a common difference -8.

$$-107 = 501 + (n-1)\cdot(-8)$$
$$-107 = 501 - 8n + 8$$
$$-107 = 509 - 8n$$
$$-616 = -8n$$
$$77 = n$$

-107 is the 77th term.

19. The sequence is geometric with a common ratio 3.

$$470,715,894,135 = 5(3)^{n-1}$$
$$94,143,178,827 = 3^{n-1}$$
$$\log 94,143,178,827 = \log 3^{n-1}$$
$$\log 94,143,178,827 = (n-1)\log 3$$
$$\frac{\log 94,143,178,827}{\log 3} = n-1$$
$$n = \frac{\log 94,143,178,827}{\log 3} + 1$$
$$= 24$$

$470,715,894,135$ is the 24th term.

20. **EQ 1**
$$52 = a_1 + (5-1)d$$
$$52 = a_1 + 4d$$
$$52 - 4d = a_1$$

EQ 2
$$36 = a_1 + (9-1)d$$
$$36 = a_1 + 8d$$
$$36 - 8d = a_1$$

Solve the system of linear equations by setting the left side of each equation equal to each other.
$$52 - 4d = 36 - 8d$$
$$4d = -16$$
$$d = -4$$

Use EQ 1 and $d = -4$ to find a_1.
$$52 - 4\cdot(-4) = a_1$$
$$68 = a_1$$
$$a_{69} = 68 + (69-1)\cdot(-4)$$
$$= -204$$

21.
$$S_{43} = \frac{43(52 + -200)}{2}$$
$$= -3182$$

22.
$$S_{22} = \frac{4(1 - 1.7^{22})}{1 - 1.7}$$
$$\approx 671,173.0723$$

23. The series is geometric with a common ratio of 2.

$$1,610,612,736 = 3(2)^{n-1}$$
$$536,870,912 = 2^{n-1}$$
$$\log 536,870,912 = \log 2^{n-1}$$
$$\log 536,870,912 = (n-1)\log 2$$
$$\frac{\log 536,870,912}{\log 2} = n-1$$
$$n = \frac{\log 536,870,912}{\log 2} + 1$$
$$= 30$$
$$S_{30} = \frac{3(1-2^{30})}{1-2}$$
$$= 3,221,225,469$$

24. The series is arithmetic with a common difference of 6.

$$1200 = 30 + (n-1)\cdot 6$$
$$1200 = 30 + 6n - 6$$
$$1200 = 24 + 6n$$
$$1176 = 6n$$
$$196 = n$$
$$S_{196} = \frac{196(30+1200)}{2}$$
$$= 120,540$$

25. The series is arithmetic with a common difference of -4.

$$a_{33} = 11 + (33-1)\cdot(-4)$$
$$= -117$$
$$S_{33} = \frac{33(11+(-117))}{2} = -1749$$

26. The series is geometric with a common ratio of $\frac{1}{3}$.

$$a_n = a_1 r^{n-1}$$
$$a_{13} = 531,441\left(\frac{1}{3}\right)^{13-1}$$
$$= 1$$
$$S_{13} = \frac{531,441\left(1-\left(\frac{1}{3}\right)^{13}\right)}{1-\frac{1}{3}}$$
$$= 797,161$$

27. A geometric series with a common ratio of 5, since the ratio of any two consecutive terms is 5.

$$\frac{4(5)^x}{4(5)^{x-1}} = \frac{4(5)^x}{4(5)^x(5)^{-1}}$$
$$= \frac{1}{(5)^{-1}}$$
$$= 5.$$

28. An arithmetic sequence with a common difference of -9, since the difference between two consecutive terms is -9.

$$(-9(x)+40) - (-9(x-1)+40) =$$
$$(-9x+40) - (-9x+9+40) =$$
$$(-9x+40) - (-9x+49) =$$
$$-9x+40+9x-49 = -9$$

29. a. **Company A**
$$a_{25} = 28,000(1.04)^{25-1}$$
$$\approx \$71,772.52$$
Company B
$$a_{25} = 34,000 + (24-1)\cdot 1500$$
$$= \$70,000$$

b. **Company A**
$$S_{25} = \frac{28,000(1-1.04^{25})}{1-1.04}$$
$$\approx \$1,166,085.43$$
Company B
$$S_{25} = \frac{25(34000+70000)}{2}$$
$$= \$1,300,000$$

c. You could earn more money in the early years at Company A, but receive smaller raises. Answers may vary.

30. a. Using linear regression, we get
$$f(t) = 2.09t + 26.03$$

b. The slope of the graph of $f(t) = 2.09t + 26.03$ is 2.09. The slope indicates that the spending on pets increases each year by \$2.09 billion.

c. $f(14) = 2.09(14) + 26.03 = 55.29$
The spending on pets in 2014 is predicted to be \$55.29 billion.

d. Since f is linear we can treat the sum of all the terms as an arithmetic series with a common difference of 2.09. Since $f(0) = 2.09(0) + 26.03 = 26.03$,

$a_0 = 26.03$. Since there are 15 terms, we find S_{15}.

$$S_{15} = \frac{15(26.03 + 55.29)}{2} = 609.9$$

The total spending on pets from 2000 through 2014 is estimated to be \$609.9 billion.

Chapter 14 Test

1. $\dfrac{6}{3} = 2, \dfrac{12}{6} = 2, \dfrac{24}{12} = 2, \dfrac{48}{24} = 2$

It is a geometric sequence with a common ratio of 2.

2. $19 - 20 = -1, 17 - 19 = -2$

$\dfrac{19}{20} = 0.95, \dfrac{17}{19} \approx 0.89$

The sequence has neither a common difference nor a common ratio, so it is none of these.

3. $\dfrac{35}{7} = 5, \dfrac{175}{35} = 5, \dfrac{875}{175} = 5, = \dfrac{4375}{875} = 5$

It is a geometric series with a common ratio of 5.

4. It is an arithmetic series with a common difference of -8.

5. The sequence is arithmetic with a common difference of -6.

$a_n = 31 + (n-1) \cdot (-6)$

$\quad = 31 - 6n + 6$

$a_n = 37 - 6n$

6. The sequence is geometric with a common ratio of 6.

$a_n = 6(4)^{n-1}$

$\quad = 6(4)^n (4)^{-1}$

$\quad = 6(4)^n \left(\dfrac{1}{4}\right)$

$a_n = \dfrac{3}{2}(4)^n$

Solution: $a_n = 6(4)^{n-1}$ or $a_n = \dfrac{3}{2}(4)^n$

7. The sequence is arithmetic with a common difference of 3.

$a_{87} = 4 + (87 - 1) \cdot 3$

$\quad = 262$

8. The sequence is geometric with a common ratio of $\dfrac{1}{2}$.

$a_{16} = 6144 \left(\dfrac{1}{2}\right)^{16-1}$

$\quad = \dfrac{3}{16}$ or 0.1875

9. The sequence is arithmetic with a common difference of 4.

$1789 = -27 + (n-1) \cdot 4$

$1789 = -27 + 4n - 4$

$1789 = -31 + 4n$

$1820 = 4n$

$455 = n$

1789 is the 455th term in the sequence.

10. The sequence is geometric with a common ratio of 1.1.

$428.717762 = 200(1.1)^{n-1}$

$2.14358881 = (1.1)^{n-1}$

$\log 2.14358881 = \log 1.1^{n-1}$

$\log 2.14358881 = (n-1) \log 1.1$

$\dfrac{\log 2.14358881}{\log 1.1} = n - 1$

$n = \dfrac{\log 2.14358881}{\log 1.1} + 1$

$\quad = 9$

428.717762 is the 9th term in the sequence.

11. The series is geometric with a common ratio of $\dfrac{1}{3}$.

$$S_{20} = \frac{27\left(1 - \left(\frac{1}{3}\right)^{20}\right)}{1 - \frac{1}{3}}$$

$\quad \approx 40.5000$

12. The series is geometric with a common ratio of 2.

$$2{,}147{,}483{,}648 = 4(2)^{n-1}$$

$$536{,}870{,}912 = 2^{n-1}$$

$$\log 536{,}870{,}912 = \log 2^{n-1}$$

$$\log 536{,}870{,}912 = (n-1)\log 2$$

$$\frac{\log 536{,}870{,}912}{\log 2} = n-1$$

$$n = \frac{\log 536{,}870{,}912}{\log 2} + 1$$

$$= 30$$

$$S_{30} = \frac{4(1-2^{30})}{1-2}$$

$$= 4{,}294{,}967{,}292$$

$$\approx 4.295 \times 10^9$$

13. The series is arithmetic with a common difference of −4.

$$-78 = 50 + (n-1)\cdot(-4)$$

$$-78 = 50 - 4n + 4$$

$$-78 = 54 - 4n$$

$$-132 = -4n$$

$$33 = n$$

$$S_{33} = \frac{33(50+(-78))}{2}$$

$$= -462$$

14. The series is arithmetic with a common difference of 14.

$$a_{400} = 19 + (400-1)\cdot 14$$

$$= 5605$$

$$S_{400} = \frac{400(19+5605)}{2} = 1{,}124{,}800$$

$$= 1.1248 \times 10^6$$

15.
$$(7+2)+(7\cdot 2+2^2)+(7\cdot 3+2^3)+(7\cdot 4+2^4)$$

$$+(7\cdot 5+2^5)+\ldots+(7\cdot 20+2^{20})$$

$$=(7+7\cdot 2+7\cdot 3+7\cdot 4+7\cdot 5+\ldots+7\cdot 20)$$

$$+(2+2^2+2^3+2^4+2^5+\ldots+2^{20})$$

$$=\frac{20(7+140)}{2}+\frac{2(1-2^{20})}{1-2}$$

$$=1470+2{,}097{,}150$$

$$=2{,}098{,}620$$

16.
$$f(1)=3(1)^2+1=4$$

$$f(2)=3(2)^2+1=13$$

$$f(3)=3(3)^2+1=28$$

The series has neither a common difference nor a common ratio, so it is neither geometric nor arithmetic.

17. S_n is negative because most of the terms of the series will be negative. The sum of negative numbers is negative.

18. a.

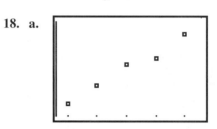

b. Use a linear regression to find $f(t)$.
$$f(t)=35t+7.2$$

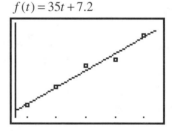

c. $f(1)=35(1)+7.2=42.2$

This value estimates the dollars of retail sales (in billions) in 2001.

d. $f(15)=35(15)+7.2\approx 532.2$

This value estimates the dollars of retail sales (in billions) in 2015.

e. Since f is linear we can treat the sum of all the terms as an arithmetic series with a common difference of 35 and $a_1=42.2$.

$$S_{15}=\frac{15(42.2+532.2)}{2}$$

$$\approx 4308$$

From 2001 through 2015 (including 2015) there will be about 4308 billion dollars of retail sales, or about 4.3 trillion dollars ($4,308,000,000,000).

19. a. $a_n=32(1.03)^{n-1}$

b.

$$40 = 32(1.03)^{n-1}$$

$$1.25 = 1.03^{n-1}$$

$$\log 1.25 = \log 1.03^{n-1}$$

$$\log 1.25 = (n-1)\log 1.03$$

$$\frac{\log 1.25}{\log 1.03} = n-1$$

$$n = \frac{\log 1.25}{\log 1.03} + 1$$

$$\approx 8.5$$

The salary will first be above $40,000 in the 9th year.

c. $a_{25} = 32(1.03)^{24} \approx 65.04941$ (in thousands)

The salary in the 25th year will be $65,049.41.

d. $S_{25} = \dfrac{32(1-1.03^{25})}{1-1.03}$

$$\approx 1,166.69646$$

(in thousands) The salary for the sum of the 1st through 25th years will be $1,166,696.46.

Cumulative Review of Chapters 1 - 14

1.

$$4x^2 - 49 = 0$$

$$(2x-7)(2x+7) = 0$$

$$2x-7 = 0 \quad \text{or} \quad 2x+7 = 0$$

$$x = \frac{7}{2} \quad \text{or} \quad x = -\frac{7}{2}$$

2.

$$6x^2 + 13x = 5$$

$$6x^2 + 13x - 5 = 0$$

$$(3x-1)(2x+5) = 0$$

$$3x-1 = 0 \quad \text{or} \quad 2x+5 = 0$$

$$x = \frac{1}{3} \quad \text{or} \quad x = -\frac{5}{2}$$

3. $\log_3(4x-7) = 4$

$$4x-7 = 3^4$$

$$4x-7 = 81$$

$$4x = 88$$

$$x = 22$$

4.

$$(t+3)(t-4) = 5$$

$$t^2 + 3t - 4t - 12 = 5$$

$$t^2 - t - 17 = 0$$

$$t = \frac{-(-1) \pm \sqrt{(-1)^2 - 4(1)(-17)}}{2(1)}$$

$$= \frac{1 \pm \sqrt{69}}{2}$$

5.

$$\frac{1}{w^2 - w - 6} - \frac{w}{w+2} = \frac{w-2}{w-3}$$

$$\frac{1}{(w-3)(w+2)} - \frac{w}{w+2} = \frac{w-2}{w-3}$$

$$\frac{1}{(w-3)(w+2)} - \frac{w(w-3)}{(w-3)(w+2)} = \frac{(w-2)(w+2)}{(w-3)(w+2)}$$

$$\frac{1 - w^2 + 3w}{(w-3)(w+2)} = \frac{w^2 - 4}{(w-3)(w+2)}$$

$$\frac{w^2 - 4 - 1 + w^2 - 3w}{(w-3)(w+2)} = 0$$

$$\frac{2w^2 - 3w - 5}{(w-3)(w+2)} = 0$$

$$2w^2 - 3w - 5 = 0 \quad w \neq 3, -2$$

$$(2w-5)(w+1) = 0$$

$$2w-5 = 0 \quad \text{or} \quad w+1 = 0$$

$$w = \frac{5}{2} \quad \text{or} \quad w = -1$$

6. $5(3x-2)^2 + 7 = 17$

$$5(3x-2)^2 = 10$$

$$(3x-2)^2 = 2$$

$$3x-2 = \pm\sqrt{2}$$

$$3x = 2 \pm \sqrt{2}$$

$$x = \frac{2 \pm \sqrt{2}}{3}$$

7. $\log_6(3x)+\log_6(x-1)=1$

$\quad\quad \log_6(3x(x-1))=1$

$\quad\quad \log_6(3x^2-3x)=1$

$\quad\quad\quad\quad\quad\quad 6^1=3x^2-3x$

$\quad\quad\quad\quad\quad\quad 6=3x^2-3x$

$\quad\quad\quad\quad\quad\quad 0=3x^2-3x-6$

$\quad\quad\quad\quad\quad\quad 0=3(x^2-x-2)$

$\quad\quad\quad\quad\quad\quad 0=3(x-2)(x+1)$

$\quad\quad\quad\quad\quad\quad 0=(x-2)(x+1)$

$\quad\quad\quad\quad\quad\quad 0=x-2 \text{ or } 0=x+1$

$\quad\quad\quad\quad\quad\quad x=2 \quad\text{ or }\quad \cancel{x=-1}$

Check:

$\log_6(3(2))+\log_6((2)-1)=1$

$\quad\quad \log_6 6+\log_6 1=1$

$\quad\quad\quad\quad 1+0=1$

$\quad\quad\quad\quad\quad\quad 1=1\,\text{TRUE}$

$\log_6(3(-1))+\log_6((-1)-1)=1$

$\quad\quad \log_6(-3)+\log_6(-2)=1\,\text{FALSE}$

Cannot take the logarithm of a negative number.
Solution: *x = 2.*

8. $20-4x=7(2x+9)$

$20-4x=14x+63$

$-4x=14x+43$

$-18x=43$

$x=-\dfrac{43}{18}$

$\quad=-2\dfrac{7}{18}$

9. $\sqrt{x+1}-\sqrt{2x-5}=1$

$\quad\quad \sqrt{x+1}=1+\sqrt{2x-5}$

Square both sides.

$\left(\sqrt{x+1}\right)^2=\left(1+\sqrt{2x-5}\right)^2$

$x+1=1+\sqrt{2x-5}+\sqrt{2x-5}+(2x-5)$

$x+1=1+2\sqrt{2x-5}+2x-5$

$x+1=2\sqrt{2x-5}+2x-4$

$-x+5=2\sqrt{2x-5}$

$\dfrac{-x+5}{2}=\sqrt{2x-5}$

Square both sides again.

$\left(\dfrac{-x+5}{2}\right)^2=\left(\sqrt{2x-5}\right)^2$

$\dfrac{x^2-5x-5x+25}{4}=2x-5$

$\dfrac{x^2-10x+25}{4}=2x-5$

$x^2-10x+25=8x-20$

$x^2-18x+45=0$

$(x-3)(x-15)=0$

$\quad\quad (x-3)=0\,\text{or}\,(x-15)=0$

$\quad\quad\quad\quad x=3\,\text{or}\,\cancel{x=15}$

$\quad\quad\quad\quad\quad check:$

$\sqrt{(3)+1}-\sqrt{2(3)-5}=1$

$\quad\quad \sqrt{4}-\sqrt{1}=1$

$\quad\quad\quad\quad 2-1=1$

$\quad\quad\quad\quad\quad 1=1\,\text{TRUE}$

$\sqrt{(15)+1}-\sqrt{2(15)-5}=1$

$\quad\quad \sqrt{16}-\sqrt{25}=1$

$\quad\quad\quad\quad 4-5=1$

$\quad\quad\quad\quad\quad -1=1\,\text{FALSE}$

10. $\quad 3(2x-5)+4=(x-3)^2$

$\quad\quad 6x-15+4=x^2-6x+9$

$\quad\quad\quad 6x-11=x^2-6x+9$

$\quad\quad x^2-12x+20=0$

$\quad\quad (x-10)(x-2)=0$

$\quad\quad x-10=0 \text{ or } x-2=0$

$\quad\quad\quad x=10 \text{ or } \quad x=2$

11. $\log_b 81=4$

$\quad\quad b^4=81$

$\quad\quad b=81^{1/4}$

$\quad\quad b=3 \text{ or } \cancel{b=-3}$

Check:

$\log_3 81 = 4 \,\text{TRUE}$

$\log_{-3} 81 = 4 \,\text{FALSE}$

Cannot take the logarithm of a negative number.
Solution: $b = 3$.

12. $2b^7 - 3 = 51$

$2b^7 = 54$

$b^7 = 27$

$b = 27^{1/7}$

$b = \sqrt[7]{27} \approx 1.6013$

13. $6(3)^x - 5 = 52$

$6(3)^x = 57$

$3^x = \dfrac{19}{2}$

$x = \log_3 \dfrac{19}{2}$

$\quad = \dfrac{\ln(19/2)}{\ln 3}$

$\quad \approx 2.0492$

14. $5e^x = 98$

$e^x = \dfrac{98}{5}$

$\ln(e^x) = \ln\left(\dfrac{98}{5}\right)$

$x = \ln\left(\dfrac{98}{5}\right) \approx 2.9755$

15. $4\ln(2x^3) - \ln(8x^6) = 9$

$\ln(2x^3)^4 - \ln(8x^6) = 9$

$\ln(16x^{12}) - \ln(8x^6) = 9$

$\ln\left(\dfrac{16x^{12}}{8x^6}\right) = 9$

$\ln(2x^6) = 9$

$2x^6 = e^9$

$x^6 = \dfrac{e^9}{2}$

$x = \left(\dfrac{e^9}{2}\right)^{1/6} \approx 3.9927$

16. $3x^2 - 5x + 1 = 0$

$3x^2 - 5x = -1$

$3\left(x^2 - \dfrac{5}{3}x\right) = -1$

$3\left(x^2 - \dfrac{5}{3}x + \dfrac{25}{36}\right) = -1 + 3 \cdot \dfrac{25}{36}$

$3\left(x - \dfrac{5}{6}\right)^2 = -1 + \dfrac{75}{36}$

$3\left(x - \dfrac{5}{6}\right)^2 = \dfrac{39}{36}$

$\left(x - \dfrac{5}{6}\right)^2 = \dfrac{13}{36}$

$x - \dfrac{5}{6} = \pm\sqrt{\dfrac{13}{36}}$

$x = \dfrac{5}{6} \pm \dfrac{\sqrt{13}}{6}$

$x = \dfrac{5 \pm \sqrt{13}}{6}$

17. $2x^2 = 4x - 3$

$2x^2 - 4x + 3 = 0$

$x = \dfrac{-(-4) \pm \sqrt{(-4)^2 - 4(2)(3)}}{2(2)}$

$\quad = \dfrac{4 \pm \sqrt{-8}}{4}$

$\quad = \dfrac{4 \pm i\sqrt{8}}{4}$

$\quad = \dfrac{4 \pm 2i\sqrt{2}}{4}$

$\quad = \dfrac{2 \pm i\sqrt{2}}{2}$

18. $\dfrac{x}{a} + \dfrac{y}{b} = 1$

$\dfrac{y}{b} = 1 - \dfrac{x}{a}$

$\dfrac{y}{b} = \dfrac{a - x}{a}$

$y = \dfrac{b(a - x)}{a}$

$y = \dfrac{ab - bx}{a}$

19. $2x + 4y = 0$

$5x + 3y = 7$

Multiply the first equation by –3 and the second equation by 4.

$-6x - 12y = 0$

$20x + 12y = 28$

Add the two equations and solve the result for *x*.

$14x = 28$

$x = 2$

Substitute this result for *x* in the first equation.

$2(2) + 4y = 0$

$4 + 4y = 0$

$4y = -4$

$y = -1$

The solution to the system is $(2, -1)$.

20. $y = 3x + 9$

$4x + 2y = -2$

Substitute the first equation for *y* in the second equation.

$4x + 2(3x + 9) = -2$

$4x + 6x + 18 = -2$

$10x = -20$

$x = -2$

Substitute this value for *x* into the first equation.

$y = 3x + 9$

$= 3(-2) + 9$

$= -6 + 9$

$= 3$

The solution to the system is $(-2, 3)$.

21. $2x - 3y + 4z = 19$

$5x + y - 5z = -6$

$3x - y + 2z = 13$

Multiply the second equation by 3 and add to first equation.

$2x - 3y + 4z = 19$

$15x + 3y - 15z = -18$

$17x - 11z = 1$

Add the second and third equations.

$5x + y - 5z = -6$

$3x - y + 2z = 13$

$8x - 3z = 7$

$8x - 3z = 7 \quad \rightarrow \quad -88x + 33z = -77$

$17x - 11z = 1 \quad \rightarrow \quad 51x - 33z = 3$

$-37x = -74$

$x = 2$

S̲ubstitute $x = 2$ into $8x - 3z = 7$ and solve for *z*.

$8(2) - 3z = 7$

$16 - 3z = 7$

$-3z = -9$

$z = 3$

Substitute $x = 2$ and $z = 3$ into

$2x - 3y + 4z = 19$ and solve for *y*.

$2(2) - 3y + 4(3) = 19$

$4 - 3y + 12 = 19$

$-3y + 16 = 19$

$-3y = 3$

$y = -1$

The solution is $(2, -1, 3)$.

22. $5 - 2(3x - 5) + 1 \geq 2 - 4x$

$5 - 6x + 10 + 1 \geq 2 - 4x$

$16 - 6x \geq 2 - 4x$

$-2x \geq -14$

$x \leq 7$

Interval: $(-\infty, 7]$

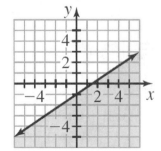

23. $4x - 6y - 6 \geq 0$

$-6y \geq -4x + 6$

$\dfrac{-6y}{-6} \leq \dfrac{-4x + 6}{-6}$

$y \leq \dfrac{2}{3}x - 1$

24. $2x - 4y \le 8$

$\qquad -4y \le -2x + 8$

$\qquad \dfrac{-4y}{-4} \ge \dfrac{-2x + 8}{-4}$

$\qquad y \ge \dfrac{1}{2}x - 2$

$\quad 3x + 5y \le 10$

$\qquad 5y \le -3x + 10$

$\qquad \dfrac{5y}{5} \le \dfrac{-3x + 10}{5}$

$\qquad y \le -\dfrac{3}{5}x + 2$

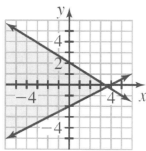

25. $\left(3b^{-2}c^{-3}\right)^4\left(6b^{-5}c^2\right)^2 = 81b^{-8}c^{-12} \cdot 36b^{-10}c^4$

$\qquad\qquad = 2916b^{-8+(-10)}c^{-12+4}$

$\qquad\qquad = 2916b^{-18}c^{-8}$

$\qquad\qquad = \dfrac{2916}{b^{18}c^8}$

26. $\left(\dfrac{14b^3c^5}{21b^{\,9}c^{\,4}}\right)^2 = \dfrac{14^2 b^6 c^{10}}{21^2 b^{-18} c^{-8}}$

$\qquad\qquad = \dfrac{196}{441}b^{6-(-18)}c^{10-(-8)}$

$\qquad\qquad = \dfrac{4}{9}b^{24}c^{18}$

$\qquad\qquad = \dfrac{4b^{24}c^{18}}{9}$

27. $\dfrac{8b^{1/2}c^{-4/3}}{10b^{3/4}c^{-7/3}} = \dfrac{4}{5}b^{1/2-3/4}c^{-4/3-(-7/3)}$

$\qquad\qquad = \dfrac{4}{5}b^{2/4-3/4}c^{-4/3+7/3}$

$\qquad\qquad = \dfrac{4}{5}b^{-1/4}c^{3/3}$

$\qquad\qquad = \dfrac{4c}{5b^{1/4}}$

28. $3y\sqrt{8x^3} - 2x\sqrt{18xy^2}$

$\quad = 3y\sqrt{4x^2 \cdot 2x} - 2x\sqrt{9 \cdot 2x \cdot y^2}$

$\quad = 3y\sqrt{4x^2}\sqrt{2x} - 2x\sqrt{9}\sqrt{2x}\sqrt{y^2}$

$\quad = 3y \cdot 2x\sqrt{2x} - 2x \cdot 3y\sqrt{2x}$

$\quad = 6xy\sqrt{2x} - 6xy\sqrt{2x}$

$\quad = 0$

29. $\sqrt[4]{(5x-7)^{21}} = (5x-7)^{21/4}$

$\qquad\qquad = (5x-7)^5(5x-7)^{1/4}$

$\qquad\qquad = (5x-7)^5\sqrt[4]{5x-7}$

30. $\sqrt{12x^7y^{14}} = \sqrt{4x^6 \cdot 3x \cdot y^{14}}$

$\qquad\qquad = \sqrt{4x^6}\sqrt{3x}\sqrt{y^{14}}$

$\qquad\qquad = 2x^3y^7\sqrt{3x}$

31. $\sqrt[3]{\dfrac{4}{x}} = \dfrac{\sqrt[3]{4}}{\sqrt[3]{x}}$

$\qquad\quad = \dfrac{\sqrt[3]{4}}{\sqrt[3]{x}} \cdot \dfrac{\sqrt[3]{x^2}}{\sqrt[3]{x^2}}$

$\qquad\quad = \dfrac{\sqrt[3]{4 \cdot x^2}}{\sqrt[3]{x \cdot x^2}}$

$\qquad\quad = \dfrac{\sqrt[3]{4x^2}}{x}$

32.
$$\frac{3\sqrt{x}-\sqrt{y}}{2\sqrt{x}+\sqrt{y}}$$

$$=\frac{3\sqrt{x}-\sqrt{y}}{2\sqrt{x}+\sqrt{y}}\cdot\frac{2\sqrt{x}-\sqrt{y}}{2\sqrt{x}-\sqrt{y}}$$

$$=\frac{3\sqrt{x}\cdot2\sqrt{x}-3\sqrt{x}\cdot\sqrt{y}-2\sqrt{x}\cdot\sqrt{y}+\sqrt{y}\cdot\sqrt{y}}{\left(2\sqrt{x}\right)^2-\left(\sqrt{y}\right)^2}$$

$$=\frac{6x-3\sqrt{xy}-2\sqrt{xy}+y}{4x-y}$$

$$=\frac{6x-5\sqrt{xy}+y}{4x-y}$$

33.
$$2\ln\left(x^4\right)+3\ln\left(x^9\right)=\ln\left(x^4\right)^2+\ln\left(x^9\right)^3$$
$$=\ln\left(x^8\right)+\ln\left(x^{27}\right)$$
$$=\ln\left(x^8x^{27}\right)$$
$$=\ln\left(x^{8+27}\right)$$
$$=\ln\left(x^{35}\right)$$

34.
$$4\log_b\left(x^5\right)-5\log_b\left(2x\right)$$
$$=\log_b\left(x^5\right)^4-\log_b\left(2x\right)^5$$
$$=\log_b\left(x^{20}\right)-\log_b\left(32x^5\right)$$
$$=\log_b\left(\frac{x^{20}}{32x^5}\right)$$
$$=\log_b\left(\frac{x^{20-5}}{32}\right)$$
$$=\log_b\left(\frac{x^{15}}{32}\right)$$

35.
$$\left(3a-5b\right)^2=\left(3a\right)^2-2\left(3a\right)\left(5b\right)+\left(5b\right)^2$$
$$=9a^2-30ab+25b^2$$

36.
$$\left(3\sqrt{k}-4\right)\left(2\sqrt{k}+7\right)$$
$$=3\sqrt{k}\cdot2\sqrt{k}-4\cdot2\sqrt{k}+3\sqrt{k}\cdot7-4\cdot7$$
$$=6k-8\sqrt{k}+21\sqrt{k}-28$$
$$=6k+13\sqrt{k}-28$$

37.
$$\left(2x^2-x+3\right)\left(x^2+2x-1\right)$$
$$=2x^2\left(x^2+2x-1\right)-x\left(x^2+2x-1\right)$$
$$\qquad+3\left(x^2+2x-1\right)$$
$$=2x^4+4x^3-2x^2-x^3-2x^2+x+3x^2+6x-3$$
$$=2x^4+3x^3-x^2+7x-3$$

38.
$$-2x\left(x^2+1\right)\left(x^3+5\right)$$
$$=-2x\left(x^2\cdot x^3+x^2\cdot5+1\cdot x^3+1\cdot5\right)$$
$$=-2x\left(x^5+5x^2+x^3+5\right)$$
$$=-2x^6-2x^4-10x^3-10x^2$$

39.
$$\frac{x^3-27}{2x^2-3x+1}\div\frac{2x^3+6x^2+18x}{4x^2-1}$$
$$=\frac{x^3-27}{2x^2-3x+1}\cdot\frac{4x^2-1}{2x^3+6x^2+18x}$$
$$=\frac{(x-3)\left(x^2+3x+9\right)}{(2x-1)(x-1)}\cdot\frac{(2x-1)(2x+1)}{2x\left(x^2+3x+9\right)}$$
$$=\frac{(x-3)\left(\cancel{x^2+3x+9}\right)}{\cancel{(2x-1)}(x-1)}\cdot\frac{\cancel{(2x-1)}(2x+1)}{2x\left(\cancel{x^2+3x+9}\right)}$$
$$=\frac{(x-3)(2x+1)}{2x(x-1)}$$

40.
$$\frac{3x}{x^2-10x+25}-\frac{x+2}{x^2-7x+10}$$
$$=\frac{3x}{(x-5)(x-5)}-\frac{x+2}{(x-5)(x-2)}$$
$$=\frac{3x(x-2)}{(x-5)(x-5)(x-2)}-\frac{(x+2)(x-5)}{(x-5)(x-5)(x-2)}$$
$$=\frac{3x^2-6x}{(x-5)^2(x-2)}-\frac{x^2-3x-10}{(x-5)^2(x-2)}$$
$$=\frac{3x^2-6x-x^2+3x+10}{(x-5)^2(x-2)}$$
$$=\frac{2x^2-3x+10}{(x-5)^2(x-2)}$$

41. $\dfrac{4x - x^2}{6x^2 + 10x - 4} \cdot \dfrac{7 - 21x}{x^2 - 8x + 16}$

$= \dfrac{-x(x-4)}{2(3x-1)(x+2)} \cdot \dfrac{-7(3x-1)}{(x-4)(x-4)}$

$= \dfrac{-x\cancel{(x-4)}}{2\cancel{(3x-1)}(x+2)} \cdot \dfrac{-7\cancel{(3x-1)}}{(x-4)\cancel{(x-4)}}$

$= \dfrac{7x}{2(x+2)(x-4)}$

42. $\dfrac{1}{x^2 + 12x + 27} + \dfrac{x+2}{x^3 + x^2 - 9x - 9}$

$= \dfrac{1}{(x+9)(x+3)} + \dfrac{x+2}{x^2(x+1) - 9(x+1)}$

$= \dfrac{1}{(x+9)(x+3)} + \dfrac{x+2}{(x+1)(x^2-9)}$

$= \dfrac{1}{(x+9)(x+3)} + \dfrac{x+2}{(x+1)(x+3)(x-3)}$

$= \dfrac{(x-3)(x+1)}{(x+9)(x+3)(x-3)(x+1)}$

$\quad + \dfrac{(x+2)(x+9)}{(x+1)(x+9)(x-3)(x+9)}$

$= \dfrac{x^2 - 3x + x - 3 + x^2 + 2x + 9x + 18}{(x+9)(x+3)(x-3)(x+1)}$

$= \dfrac{2x^2 + 9x + 15}{(x+9)(x+3)(x-3)(x+1)}$

43. $\dfrac{\dfrac{x+2}{x^2 - 64}}{\dfrac{x^2 + 4x + 4}{3x + 24}} = \dfrac{x+2}{x^2 - 64} \cdot \dfrac{3x + 24}{x^2 + 4x + 4}$

$\quad = \dfrac{(x+2)}{(x-8)(x+8)} \cdot \dfrac{3(x+8)}{(x+2)(x+2)}$

$\quad = \dfrac{\cancel{(x+2)}}{(x-8)(x+8)} \cdot \dfrac{3(x+8)}{(x+2)\cancel{(x+2)}}$

$\quad = \dfrac{1}{(x-8)\cancel{(x+8)}} \cdot \dfrac{3\cancel{(x+8)}}{(x+2)}$

$\quad = \dfrac{3}{(x-8)(x+2)}$

44. $f(x) = -3(x+3)^2 - 7$

$\quad = -3(x^2 + 6x + 9) - 7$

$\quad = -3x^2 - 18x - 27 - 7$

$\quad = -3x^2 - 18x - 34$

$f(x) = -3x^2 - 18x - 34$

45. $4x^3 - 8x^2 - 25x + 50 = 4x^2(x-2) - 25(x-2)$

$= (x-2)(4x^2 - 25)$

$= (x-2)(2x-5)(2x+5)$

46. $2x^3 - 4x^2 - 30x = 2x(x^2 - 2x - 15)$

$= 2x(x-5)(x+3)$

47. $6w^2 + 2wy - 20y^2 = 2(3w^2 + wy - 10y^2)$

$= 2(3w - 5y)(w + 2y)$

48. $100p^2 - 1 = (10p - 1)(10p + 1)$

49. $f(2) = 3$

50. When $f(x) = 3$, $x = 0$ or $x = 2$.

51. The graph is quadratic so the function is of the form $f(x) = a(x-h)^2 + k$. The vertex is $(h, k) = (1, 4)$ so we have

$f(x) = a(x-1)^2 + 4$.

Choosing another point on the graph, $(0, 3)$, we can find the value of a.

$3 = a(0-1)^2 + 4$

$3 = a + 4$

$-1 = a$

Thus, the function is

$f(x) = -(x-1)^2 + 4$

$\quad = -x^2 + 2x + 3$

52. Domain of *f*:
the set of all real numbers or $(-\infty, \infty)$

53. Range of *f*: $\{y \mid y \le 4\}$ or $(-\infty, 4]$

54. $y = 5(2)^x$

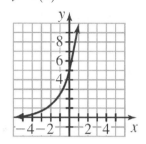

55. $y = -3(x-4)^2 + 3$

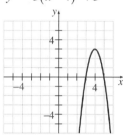

56. $y = 2\sqrt{x+5} - 4$

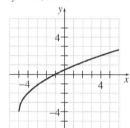

57. $y = 15\left(\dfrac{1}{3}\right)^x$

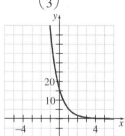

58. $y = 2x^2 + 5x - 1$

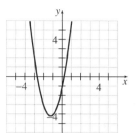

59. $y = -\dfrac{3}{5}x + 4$

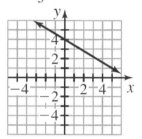

60. $2x(x-3) + y = 5(x+1)$

$$2x^2 - 6x + y = 5x + 5$$

$$y = -2x^2 + 11x + 5$$

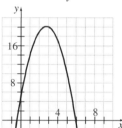

61. $(-3, 2)$ and $(2, -5)$

$$m = \frac{-5-2}{2-(-3)} = -\frac{7}{5}$$

Using the slope m and the point $(-3, 2)$, we get:

$$y = mx + b$$

$$2 = -\frac{7}{5}(-3) + b$$

$$b = -\frac{11}{5}$$

The equation of the line is $y = -\dfrac{7}{5}x - \dfrac{11}{5}$ or $7x + 5y = -11$.

62. $(3,95)$ and $(6,12)$

We want to fit the model $y = a(b)^x$. Plug both points into the equation.

$$95 = a(b)^3$$
$$12 = a(b)^6$$

Divide the second equation by the first.

$$\frac{12}{95} = \frac{ab^6}{ab^3}$$
$$\frac{12}{95} = b^3$$
$$b = \sqrt[3]{\frac{12}{95}}$$
$$b \approx 0.50$$

Substitute the point $(3,95)$ into the equation $y = a(0.50)^x$.

$$95 = a(0.50)^3$$
$$a = \frac{95}{0.50^3} \approx 752$$

The equation is $y = 752(0.50)^x$.

63. $(2,1), (3,6),$ and $(4,15)$

Substitute the points into the equation $y = ax^2 + bx + c$.

$$1 = a(2)^2 + b(2) + c$$
$$6 = a(3)^2 + b(3) + c$$
$$15 = a(4)^2 + b(4) + c$$

Rewrite as:
$$4a + 2b + c = 1$$
$$9a + 3b + c = 6$$
$$16a + 4b + c = 15$$

Multiply the first equation by -1 and add to both the second and third equations.

$$4a + 2b + c = 1$$
$$5a + b = 5$$
$$12a + 2b = 14$$

Multiply the second equation by -2 and add to the third equation.

$$4a + 2b + c = 1$$
$$5a + b = 5$$
$$2a = 4$$

Solve the third equation for a.

$$2a = 4$$
$$a = 2$$

Substitute this value into the second equation and solve for b.

$$5(2) + b = 5$$
$$10 + b = 5$$
$$b = -5$$

Substitute the values for a and b into the first equation and solve for c.

$$4(2) + 2(-5) + c = 1$$
$$8 - 10 + c = 1$$
$$c = 3$$

The equation is $y = 2x^2 - 5x + 3$.

64. $(2,5)$ and $(6,17)$

Substitute the points into the equation $y = a\sqrt{x} + b$.

$$5 = a\sqrt{2} + b$$
$$17 = a\sqrt{6} + b$$

Rewrite as:
$$1.4142a + b = 5$$
$$2.4495a + b = 17$$

Multiply the first equation by -1 and add to the second equation.

$$1.4142a + b = 5$$
$$1.0353a = 12$$

Solve the second equation for a.

$$1.0353a = 12$$
$$a \approx 11.59$$

Substitute this value into the first equation and solve for b.

$$1.4142(11.59) + b = 5$$
$$b \approx -11.39$$

The equation is roughly $y = 11.59\sqrt{x} - 11.39$.

65. a. <u>Linear:</u> $f(x) = mx + b$

The y-intercept is $(0,2)$ so $b = 2$.

$$m = \frac{4-2}{1-0} = 2$$
$$f(x) = 2x + 2$$

Exponential:

$g(x) = a \cdot b^x$

The y-intercept is $(0,2)$ so $a = 2$.

Now plug in the point $(1,4)$.

$4 = 2(b)^1$

$4 = 2b$

$2 = b$

$g(x) = 2(2)^x$

Quadratic:

$h(x) = ax^2 + bx + c$

Answers may vary. One possibility:

Let $a = 2$ so we have $h(x) = 2x^2 + bx + c$.

Plug in the point $(0,2)$.

$2 = 2(0)^2 + b(0) + c$

$2 = c$

$h(x) = 2x^2 + bx + 2$

Plug in the point $(1,4)$.

$4 = 2(1)^2 + b(1) + 2$

$4 = 2 + b + 2$

$4 = b + 4$

$0 = b$

$h(x) = 2x^2 + 2$

b.

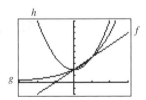

66. $\log_3(81) = \log_3(3^4)$

$= 4\log_3 3$

$= 4 \cdot 1$

$= 4$

67. $\log_b(\sqrt{b}) = \log_b(b^{1/2})$

$= \frac{1}{2}\log_b b$

$= \frac{1}{2} \cdot 1$

$= \frac{1}{2}$

68. $\log(0.001) = \log(10^{-4})$

$= -4\log(10)$

$= -4 \cdot 1$

$= -4$

69. $y = g(x) = \log_2 x$

Switch x and y, and solve for y.

$x = \log_2 y$

$y = 2^x$

$g^{-1}(x) = 2^x$

70. $y = f(x) = -4x - 7$

Switch x and y, and solve for y.

$x = -4y - 7$

$4y = -x - 7$

$y = -\frac{1}{4}x - \frac{7}{4}$

$f^{-1}(x) = -\frac{1}{4}x - \frac{7}{4}$

71. $f(x) = \frac{x-3}{x^2 - 2x - 35} = \frac{x-3}{(x-7)(x+5)}$

The domain is the set of all real numbers except 7 and -5 since these values make the denominator equal zero.

72. The sequence is geometric with a common ratio of 4.

$a_n = a_1 r^{n-1}$

$a_{10} = 2(4)^{10-1}$

$= 524,288$

73. This is an arithmetic sequence with a common difference of $d = 4$. Since $a_1 = -86$ and $a_n = 170$, we have

$$a_n = a_1 + d(n-1)$$
$$170 = -86 + 4(n-1)$$
$$256 = 4(n-1)$$
$$64 = n-1$$
$$65 = n$$

The last term in the sequence is term 65.

74. This is a geometric series with $r = \dfrac{1}{2}$ and $a_1 = 98,304$.

$$a_n = a_1 r^{n-1}$$
$$3 = 98304 \left(\frac{1}{2}\right)^{n-1}$$
$$\frac{3}{98304} = \left(\frac{1}{2}\right)^{n-1}$$
$$\ln\left(\frac{3}{98304}\right) = (n-1)\ln\left(\frac{1}{2}\right)$$
$$\frac{\ln\left(\dfrac{3}{98304}\right)}{\ln\left(\dfrac{1}{2}\right)} = n-1$$
$$15 = n-1$$
$$16 = n$$

There are 16 terms in the series.

$$S_{16} = \frac{a_1\left(1-r^{16}\right)}{1-r}$$
$$= \frac{98304\left(1-\left(\dfrac{1}{2}\right)^{16}\right)}{1-\dfrac{1}{2}}$$
$$= 196,605$$

The sum of the series is 196,605.

75. This is an arithmetic series with $d = 3$ and $a_1 = 11$.

$$a_n = a_1 + (n-1)d$$
$$182 = 11 + (n-1)3$$
$$171 = 3(n-1)$$
$$57 = n-1$$
$$58 = n$$

There are 58 terms in the series.

$$S_n = \frac{n(a_1 + a_n)}{2}$$
$$S_{58} = \frac{58(11+182)}{2}$$
$$= 29(11+182)$$
$$= 29(193)$$
$$= 5597$$

76. Let x = number of liters of 15% acid solution
Let y = number of liters of 30% acid solution

EQ 1: $x + y = 6$

EQ 2: $0.15x + 0.30y = (0.25)6$

Multiply both sides of equation 2 by 100.
$$15x + 30y = 150$$

To use elimination, multiply both sides of equation 1 by -15 to eliminate x when added to equation 2.

$$x + y = 6 \;\rightarrow\; -15x - 15y = -90$$
$$15x + 30y = 150$$

$$\begin{array}{r} 15x + 30y = 150 \\ -15x - 15y = -90 \\ \hline 15y = 60 \\ y = 4 \end{array}$$

Plug $y = 4$ into $x + y = 6$ to find x.
$$x + 4 = 6$$
$$x = 2$$

The chemist needs to mix 2 liters of the 15% acid solution with 4 liters of the 30% acid solution to create 6 liters of the 25% acid solution.

77. a. $f(t) = 29.38t + 532.59$

b. $n = f(t) = 29.38t + 532.59$
Solve for t.
$$n = 29.38t + 532.59$$
$$n - 532.59 = 29.38t$$
$$t = \frac{n - 532.59}{29.38}$$
$$t = 0.034n - 18.13$$
$$f^{-1}(n) = 0.034n - 18.13$$

c. $f(13) = 29.38(13) + 532.59 = 914.53$
In 2013, there will be about 914,530 slot machines and video poker machines.

d. $f^{-1}(1000) = 0.034(1000) - 18.13 = 15.87$

There will be about 1,000,000 (or 1 million) slot machines and video poker machines in about 2000 + 16 = 2016.

e. The slope of $f(t) = 29.38t + 532.59$ is 29.38. The slope means that the number of slot machines and video poker machines increases by about 29.38 thousand, or 29,380, machines each year.

78. a. We are given two data points for India's population: $(0, 0.687)$ and $(25, 1.003)$

The y-intercept is $(0, 0.687)$ so $b = 0.687$.
The slope of the line can be found by using the two given points.
$$m = \frac{1.003 - 0.687}{25 - 0} = 0.0126$$
The linear model is $L(t) = 0.0126t + 0.687$.

b. We now fit the model $y = a(b)^x$. Since the y-intercept is $(0, 0.687)$, we have $a = 0.687$.
Substitute the point $(25, 1.003)$ into the equation $y = 0.687(b)^x$ and solve for b.
$$1.003 = 0.687(b)^{25}$$
$$b^{25} = \frac{1.003}{0.687}$$
$$b = \sqrt[25]{\frac{1.003}{0.687}}$$
$$\approx 1.0153$$
The model is $E(t) = 0.687(1.0153)^t$.

c. $L(70) = 0.0126(70) + 0.687 = 1.569$

$E(70) = 0.687(1.0153)^{70} = 1.989$

According to the linear model, India's population will be 1.569 billion in 2050. According to the exponential model, India's population will be 1.989 billion in 2050.

d. $(E - L)(70) = 1.989 - 1.569 = 0.42$

The exponential model's predicted population exceeds that of the linear model by 420 million. This is equal to the size of the predicted U.S. population for 2050.

e. $L(t) = 0.0126t + 0.687$
$$1.424 = 0.0126t + 0.687$$
$$0.737 = 0.0126t$$
$$t \approx 58$$
$$E(t) = 0.687(1.0153)^t$$
$$1.424 = 0.687(1.0153)^t$$
$$2.07 = (1.0153)^t$$
$$\log 2.07 = \log(1.0153)^t$$
$$\log 2.07 = t \log 1.0153$$
$$t = \frac{\log 2.07}{\log 1.0153}$$
$$\approx 48$$

According to the linear model, India's population will reach 1.424 billion about 58 years after 1980 in 2038.
According to the exponential model, India's population will reach 1.424 billion about 48 years after 1980 in 2028.

79. a.

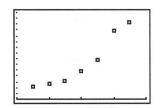

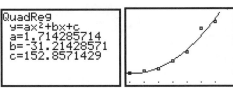

$Q(t) = 1.71t^2 - 31.21t + 152.86$

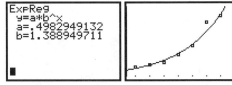

$E(t) = 0.50(1.39)^t$

Each fits most of the data well.
Answers may vary.

b. The exponential model. Answers may vary.

c.

$$E(t) = 0.50(1.39)^t$$

$$400 = 0.50(1.39)^t$$

$$800 = (1.39)^t$$

$$\log 800 = \log(1.39)^t$$

$$\log 800 = t \log 1.39$$

$$t = \frac{\log 800}{\log 1.39}$$

$$\approx 20.3$$

Solution: 20.3, or about 20.3 years after 1990.
According to the exponential model, by 2010 there will be 400 thousand complaints about consumer debt collection.

d.

$$Q(t) = 1.71t^2 - 31.21t + 152.86$$

$$400 = 1.71t^2 - 31.21t + 152.86$$

Graph $\backslash Y_1 = 1.71t^2 - 31.21t + 152.86$

$\backslash Y_2 = 400$

Use the intersection function (on the Calculate menu).

Window shown: x: [10,30] y: [250,500]
Solution: $x = 24.218951$, or about 24 years after 1990. The other solution is −5.98, or 6 years before 1990. The negative solution is discarded as nonsensical in this situation. According to the quadratic model, by 2014 there will be 400 thousand complaints about consumer debt collection.

e. Exponential growth functions tend to grow much more rapidly than quadratic ones. Answers may vary.

80. a. Start by plotting the data.

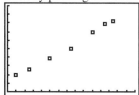

Use a linear regression to find $B(t)$.

$$B(t) = y = 1.41t + 5.75$$

b. Start by plotting the data.

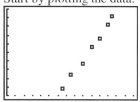

Use a linear regression to find $R(t)$.

$$R(t) = y = 33.76t - 99.59$$

c.

$$P(t) = \frac{B(t)}{R(t)} \cdot 100$$

$$= \frac{1.41t + 5.75}{33.76t - 99.59} \cdot 100$$

$$= \frac{141t + 575}{33.76t - 99.59}$$

d.

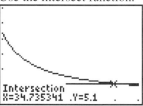

P is decreasing for t-values between 10 and 40. This means that the percentage of total recreational expenditures that consist of book sales is expected to be decreasing from 1990 through 2020.

e.

$$5.1 = \frac{141t + 575}{33.76t - 99.59}$$

Set

$$\backslash Y_1 = \frac{141t + 575}{33.76t - 99.59}$$

$\backslash Y_2 = 5.1$

Use the intersect function.

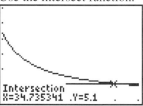

5.1% of recreational expenditures will consist of book sales in approximately 1980 + 35 = 2015.

Chapter 15
Additional Topics

Homework 15.1

1. $|x| = 7$

$x = 7 \ \text{ or } \ x = -7$

3. $|x| = -3$

Since $|x|$ is always nonnegative, the solution set for $|x| = -3$ is the empty set.

5. $5|p| - 3 = 15$

$5|p| = 18$

$|p| = \dfrac{18}{5}$

$p = -\dfrac{18}{5} \ \text{ or } \ p = \dfrac{18}{5}$

7. $|x + 2| = 5$

$x + 2 = -5 \ \text{ or } \ x + 2 = 5$

$x = -7 \ \text{ or } \ x = 3$

9. $|x - 5| = 0$

$x - 5 = 0$

$x = 5$

11. $|3t - 1| = 11$

$3t - 1 = -11 \ \text{ or } \ 3t - 1 = 11$

$3t = -10 \ \text{ or } \ 3t = 12$

$t = -\dfrac{10}{3} \ \text{ or } \ t = 4$

13. $|2x + 9| = -6$

Since $|2x + 9|$ is always nonnegative, the solution set for $|2x + 9| = -6$ is the empty set.

15. $|4x| + 1 = 9$

$|4x| = 8$

$4x = -8 \ \text{ or } \ 4x = 8$

$x = -2 \ \text{ or } \ x = 2$

17. $2|a + 5| = 8$

$|a + 5| = 4$

$a + 5 = -4 \ \text{ or } \ a + 5 = 4$

$a = -9 \ \text{ or } \ a = -1$

19. $|2x - 5| - 4 = -3$

$|2x - 5| = 1$

$2x - 5 = -1 \ \text{ or } \ 2x - 5 = 1$

$2x = 4 \ \text{ or } \ 2x = 6$

$x = 2 \ \text{ or } \ x = 3$

21. $|4x - 5| = |3x + 2|$

$4x - 5 = -(3x + 2) \ \text{ or } \ 4x - 5 = 3x + 2$

$4x - 5 = -3x - 2 \ \text{ or } \ 4x = 3x + 7$

$7x = 3 \qquad\qquad \text{ or } \ x = 7$

$x = \dfrac{3}{7} \qquad\qquad \text{ or } \ x = 7$

23. $|5w + 1| = |3 - w|$

$5w + 1 = -(3 - w) \ \text{ or } \ 5w + 1 = 3 - w$

$5w + 1 = -3 + w \ \text{ or } \ 5w = 2 - w$

$4w = -4 \qquad\quad \text{ or } \ 6w = 2$

$w = -1 \qquad\qquad \text{ or } \ w = \dfrac{1}{3}$

25. $\left|\dfrac{4x + 3}{2}\right| = 5$

$\dfrac{4x + 3}{2} = -5 \ \text{ or } \ \dfrac{4x + 3}{2} = 5$

$4x + 3 = -10 \ \text{ or } \ 4x + 3 = 10$

$4x = -13 \ \text{ or } \ 4x = 7$

$x = -\dfrac{13}{4} \ \text{ or } \ x = \dfrac{7}{4}$

27. $\left|\dfrac{1}{2}x - \dfrac{5}{3}\right| = \dfrac{7}{6}$

$\dfrac{1}{2}x - \dfrac{5}{3} = -\dfrac{7}{6}$ or $\dfrac{1}{2}x - \dfrac{5}{3} = \dfrac{7}{6}$

$\dfrac{1}{2}x = -\dfrac{7}{6} + \dfrac{5}{3}$ or $\dfrac{1}{2}x = \dfrac{7}{6} + \dfrac{5}{3}$

$\dfrac{1}{2}x = \dfrac{1}{2}$ or $\dfrac{1}{2}x = \dfrac{17}{6}$

$x = 1$ or $x = \dfrac{17}{3}$

29. $\left|\dfrac{2}{3}k + \dfrac{4}{9}\right| = \left|\dfrac{5}{6}k - \dfrac{1}{3}\right|$

$\dfrac{2}{3}k + \dfrac{4}{9} = -\left(\dfrac{5}{6}k - \dfrac{1}{3}\right)$ or $\dfrac{2}{3}k + \dfrac{4}{9} = \dfrac{5}{6}k - \dfrac{1}{3}$

$\dfrac{2}{3}k + \dfrac{5}{6}k = \dfrac{1}{3} - \dfrac{4}{9}$ or $\dfrac{2}{3}k - \dfrac{5}{6}k = -\dfrac{1}{3} - \dfrac{4}{9}$

$\dfrac{3}{2}k = -\dfrac{1}{9}$ or $-\dfrac{1}{6}k = -\dfrac{7}{9}$

$k = -\dfrac{2}{27}$ or $k = \dfrac{14}{3}$

31. $4.7|x| - 3.9 = 8.8$

$4.7|x| = 12.7$

$|x| \approx 2.70$

$x \approx -2.70$ or $x \approx 2.70$

33. $|2.1x + 5.8| - 9.7 = 10.2$

$|2.1x + 5.8| = 19.9$

$2.1x + 5.8 = -19.9$ or $2.1x + 5.8 = 19.9$

$2.1x = -25.7$ or $2.1x = 14.1$

$x \approx -12.24$ or $x \approx 6.71$

35.

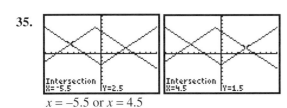

$x = -5.5$ or $x = 4.5$

37.

$x \approx -6.67$ or $x \approx -2.67$

39. $x = \pm 4$

41. $x = 2$ or $x = -3$

43. $f(x) = 2|x| - 11$

$f(-5) = 2|-5| - 11$

$f(-5) = 2(5) - 11$

$f(-5) = -1$

45. $f(x) = 2|x| - 11$

$-5 = 2|x| - 11$

$6 = 2|x|$

$3 = |x|$

$x = -3$ or $x = 3$

47. $f(x) = |4x + 7| - 9$

$f(-3) = |4(-3) + 7| - 9$

$f(-3) = |-12 + 7| - 9$

$f(-3) = |-5| - 9$

$f(-3) = 5 - 9$

$f(-3) = -4$

49. $f(x) = |4x + 7| - 9$

$-3 = |4x + 7| - 9$

$6 = |4x + 7|$

$4x + 7 = -6$ or $4x + 7 = 6$

$4x = -13$ or $4x = -1$

$x = -\dfrac{13}{4}$ or $x - -\dfrac{1}{4}$

51. $|x| < 4$

$-4 < x < 4$

Interval: $(-4, 4)$

53. $|x| \geq 3$

$x \leq -3$ or $x \geq 3$

Interval: $(-\infty, -3] \cup [3, \infty)$

55. $|r| < -3$

Since $|r|$ is nonnegative, the inequality $|r| < -3$ has an empty set solution.

57. $|x| > 0$

$x < 0$ or $x > 0$

Interval: $(-\infty, 0) \cup (0, \infty)$

59. $|7x + 15| > -4$

Since $|7x + 15|$ is always nonnegative, the solution set for the inequality $|7x + 15| > -4$ is the set of all real numbers.

Interval: $(-\infty, \infty)$

61. $|0.25t - 1.3| \geq 1.1$

$0.25t - 1.3 \leq -1.1$ or $0.25t - 1.3 \geq 1.1$

$0.25t \leq 0.2$ or $0.25t \geq 2.4$

$t \leq 0.8$ or $t \geq 9.6$

Interval: $(-\infty, 0.8] \cup [9.6, \infty)$

63. $2|x| - 5 > 3$

$2|x| > 8$

$|x| > 4$

$x < -4$ or $x > 4$

Interval: $(-\infty, -4) \cup (4, \infty)$

65. $2 - 5|p| \leq -8$

$-5|p| \leq -10$

$|p| \geq 2$

$p \leq -2$ or $p \geq 2$

Interval: $(-\infty, -2] \cup [2, \infty)$

67. $|x - 6| \geq 7$

$x - 6 \leq -7$ or $x - 6 \geq 7$

$x \leq -1$ or $x \geq 13$

Interval: $(-\infty, -1] \cup [13, \infty)$

69. $|2x + 5| < 15$

$-15 < 2x + 5 < 15$

$-20 < 2x < 10$

$-10 < x < 5$

Interval: $(-10, 5)$

71. $7 - |x + 3| \leq 2$

$-|x + 3| \leq -5$

$|x + 3| \geq 5$

$x + 3 \leq -5$ or $x + 3 \geq 5$

$x \leq -8$ or $x \geq 2$

Interval: $(-\infty, -8] \cup [2, \infty)$

73. $\left| \dfrac{x + 4}{3} \right| \geq 2$

$\dfrac{x + 4}{3} \leq -2$ or $\dfrac{x + 4}{3} \geq 2$

$x + 4 \leq -6$ or $x + 4 \geq 6$

$x \leq -10$ or $x \geq 2$

Interval: $(-\infty, -10] \cup [2, \infty)$

75. $\left| \dfrac{2x}{5} + \dfrac{3}{2} \right| \leq \dfrac{9}{20}$

$-\dfrac{9}{20} \leq \dfrac{2x}{5} + \dfrac{3}{2} \leq \dfrac{9}{20}$

$-\dfrac{39}{20} \leq \dfrac{2x}{5} \leq -\dfrac{21}{20}$

$-\dfrac{39}{4} \leq 2x \leq -\dfrac{21}{4}$

$-\dfrac{39}{8} \leq x \leq -\dfrac{21}{8}$

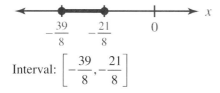

Interval: $\left[-\dfrac{39}{8}, -\dfrac{21}{8}\right]$

77. $|mx+b|+c=k$

$|mx+b|=k-c$

$mx+b=-(k-c)$ or $mx+b=k-c$

$mx=-b-(k-c)$ or $mx=-b+(k-c)$

$x=\dfrac{-b\pm(k-c)}{m}$

79. Answers may vary. The student failed to use the Absolute Value Property for Equations. Instead, the student tried to take the absolute value of $x-5$ directly, but this leads to the wrong answer. Also, the student incorrectly interchanges $x-5$ with $x+5$ in line two.

$|x-5|=7$

$x-5=-7$ or $x-5=7$

$x=-2$ or $x=12$

81. Answers may vary. The student attempted to use the Absolute Value Property for Equations, but he or she should have used the Absolute Value Property for Inequalities.

$|x+3|<10$

$-10<x+3<10$

$-13<x<7$

83. a. $|2x+3|-13$

$2x+3=-13$ or $2x+3=13$

$2x=-16$ or $2x=10$

$x=-8$ or $x=5$

b. $|2x+3|<13$

$-13<2x+3<13$

$-16<2x<10$

$-8<x<5$

c. $|2x+3|>13$

$2x+3<-13$ or $2x+3>13$

$2x<-16$ or $2x>10$

$x<-8$ or $x>5$

d.

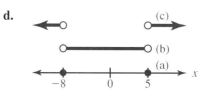

Answers may vary. The three different graphs each use –8 and 5, either as included points or as non-included endpoints. Between the three graphs, every part of the number line is covered.

85. Answers may vary. The statement "$|a+b|=|a|+|b|$ for all real numbers a and b" is false. For a counterexample, let $a=-1$ and $b=3$.

$|-1+3|\neq|-1|+|3|$

$|2|\neq 1+3$

$2\neq 4$

87. $|x-5|=4$

$x-5=-4$ or $x-5=4$

$x=1$ or $x=9$

89. $|2^y-5|=4$

$2^y-5=-4$ or $2^y-5=4$

$2^y=1$ or $2^y=9$

$y=0$ or $y\approx 3.1699$

91. $\left|\dfrac{2x+3}{x-2}-5\right|=4$

$\dfrac{2x+3}{x-2}-5=-4$ or $\dfrac{2x+3}{x-2}-5=4$

$\dfrac{2x+3}{x-2}=1$ or $\dfrac{2x+3}{x-2}=9$

$2x+3=x-2$ or $2x+3=9x-18$

$x=-5$ or $-7x=-21$

$x=-5$ or $x=3$

93. $3(2x)-5\leq 7$

$6x\leq 12$

$x\leq 2$

Interval: $(-\infty, 2]$

95.
$$3|2x| - 5 \le 7$$
$$3|2x| \le 12$$
$$|2x| \le 4$$
$$-4 \le 2x \le 4$$
$$-2 \le x \le 2$$

Interval: $[-2, 2]$

97.

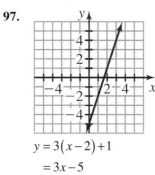

$$y = 3(x-2)+1$$
$$= 3x - 5$$

This is a linear function.

99.
$$3|x-2| + 1 = 7$$
$$3|x-2| = 6$$
$$|x-2| = 2$$
$$x - 2 = -2 \text{ or } x - 2 = 2$$
$$x = 0 \text{ or } x = 4$$

$3|x-2|+1 = 7$ is an absolute value equation in one variable.

101. If the line contains the points $(-4, 2)$ and $(5, -3)$, the slope is $\dfrac{-3-2}{5-(-4)} = -\dfrac{5}{9}$.

$$y = mx + b$$
$$2 = -\frac{5}{9}(-4) + b$$
$$2 = \frac{20}{9} + b$$
$$-\frac{2}{9} = b$$

The equation is $y = -\dfrac{5}{9}x - \dfrac{2}{9}$, which is a linear equation in two variables.

Quiz 15.1

1.
$$3|t| - 4 = 11$$
$$3|t| = 15$$
$$|t| = 5$$
$$t = 5 \text{ or } t = -5$$

2.
$$5|6r - 5| = 15$$
$$|6r - 5| = 3$$
$$6r - 5 = -3 \text{ or } 6r - 5 = 3$$
$$6r = 2 \quad \text{ or } 6r = 8$$
$$r = \frac{1}{3} \quad \text{ or } r = \frac{4}{3}$$

3. $|7x + 1| = -3$

Since $|7x + 1|$ is always nonnegative, the solution set for $|7x + 1| = -3$ is the empty set.

4.
$$|5x - 2| = |3x + 6|$$
$$5x - 2 = -(3x + 6) \text{ or } 5x - 2 = 3x + 6$$
$$5x = -3x - 4 \quad \text{ or } 5x = 3x + 8$$
$$8x = -4 \qquad \text{ or } 2x = 8$$
$$x = -\frac{1}{2} \qquad \text{ or } x = 4$$

5.
$$\left|\frac{3}{4}x - \frac{1}{2}\right| = \frac{7}{8}$$
$$\frac{3}{4}x - \frac{1}{2} = -\frac{7}{8} \text{ or } \frac{3}{4}x - \frac{1}{2} = \frac{7}{8}$$
$$\frac{3}{4}x = -\frac{3}{8} \text{ or } \frac{3}{4}x = \frac{11}{8}$$
$$x = -\frac{1}{2} \text{ or } x = \frac{11}{6}$$

6. Answers may vary. The statement "$|a - b| = |a| - |b|$ for all real numbers a and b" is false. For a counterexample, let $a = -1$ and $b = 3$.
$$|-1 - 3| \ne |-1| - |3|$$
$$|-4| \ne 1 - 3$$
$$4 \ne -2$$

7. $3|k| - 4 \geq 2$

$3|k| \geq 6$

$|k| \geq 2$

$k \leq -2$ or $k \geq 2$

Interval: $(-\infty, -2] \cup [2, \infty)$

8. $|4c - 8| > 12$

$4c - 8 < -12$ or $4c - 8 > 12$

$4c < -4$ or $4c > 20$

$c < -1$ or $c > 5$

Interval: $(-\infty, -1) \cup (5, \infty)$

9. $7|3x - 2| \leq 42$

$|3x - 2| \leq 6$

$-6 \leq 3x - 2 \leq 6$

$-4 \leq 3x \leq 8$

$-\dfrac{4}{3} \leq x \leq \dfrac{8}{3}$

Interval: $\left[-\dfrac{4}{3}, \dfrac{8}{3}\right]$

10. $|x - 5| < -7$

Since $|x - 5|$ is always nonnegative, the solution set for $|x - 5| < -7$ is the empty set.

Homework 15.2

1. $(4 - 7i) + (3 + 10i) = 4 - 7i + 3 + 10i$

$= 4 + 3 - 7i + 10i$

$= 7 + 3i$

3. $(5 - \sqrt{-9}) + (2 - \sqrt{-25}) = 5 - 3i + 2 - 5i$

$= 5 + 2 - 3i - 5i$

$= 7 - 8i$

5. $(6 - 5i) - (2 - 13i) = 6 - 5i - 2 + 13i$

$= 6 - 2 - 5i + 13i$

$= 4 + 8i$

7. $(6 - \sqrt{-49}) - (1 + \sqrt{-81}) = 6 - 7i - 1 - 9i$

$= 6 - 1 - 7i - 9i$

$= 5 - 16i$

9. $2i \cdot 9i = 18i^2$

$= 18(-1)$

$= -18$

11. $-10i(-5i) = 50i^2$

$= 50(-1)$

$= -50$

13. $\sqrt{-4}\sqrt{-25} = 2i \cdot 5i$

$= 10i^2$

$= 10(-1)$

$= -10$

15. $\sqrt{-3}\sqrt{-5} = i\sqrt{3} \cdot i\sqrt{5}$

$= i^2\sqrt{15}$

$= (-1)\sqrt{15}$

$= -\sqrt{15}$

17. $(8i)^2 = 64i^2$

$= 64(-1)$

$= -64$

19. $5i(3 - 2i) = 5i \cdot 3 - 5i \cdot 2i$

$= 15i - 10i^2$

$= 15i - 10(-1)$

$= 15i + 10$

$= 10 + 15i$

21. $20 - 3i(2 - 7i) = 20 - 3i \cdot 2 + 3i \cdot 7i$

$= 20 - 6i + 21i^2$

$= 20 - 6i + 21(-1)$

$= 20 - 6i - 21$

$= -1 - 6i$

23. $(2 + 5i)(3 + 4i) = 2 \cdot 3 + 2 \cdot 4i + 5i \cdot 3 + 5i \cdot 4i$

$= 6 + 8i + 15i + 20i^2$

$= 6 + 23i + 20(-1)$

$= 6 + 23i - 20$

$= -14 + 23i$

25. $(3-6i)(5+2i) = 3\cdot 5 + 3\cdot 2i - 6i\cdot 5 - 6i\cdot 2i$
$$= 15 + 6i - 30i - 12i^2$$
$$= 15 - 24i - 12(-1)$$
$$= 15 - 24i + 12$$
$$= 27 - 24i$$

27. $(-6+4i)(-2+7i) = 12 - 42i - 8i + 28i^2$
$$= 12 - 28 - 42i - 8i$$
$$= -16 - 50i$$

29. $(5+4i)(5-4i) = 5^2 - (4i)^2$
$$= 25 - 16i^2$$
$$= 25 - 16(-1)$$
$$= 25 + 16$$
$$= 41$$

31. $(2-9i)(2+9i) = 2^2 - (9i)^2$
$$= 4 - 81i^2$$
$$= 4 - 81(-1)$$
$$= 4 + 81$$
$$= 85$$

33. $(1+i)(1-i) = 1^2 - i^2$
$$= 1 - (-1)$$
$$= 1 + 1$$
$$= 2$$

35. $(2+7i)^2 = 2^2 + 2(2)(7i) + (7i)^2$
$$= 4 + 28i + 49i^2$$
$$= 4 - 49 + 28i$$
$$= -45 + 28i$$

37. $(4-5i)^2 = 4^2 - 2(4)(5i) + (5i)^2$
$$= 16 - 40i + 25i^2$$
$$= 16 - 25 - 40i$$
$$= -9 - 40i$$

39. $(-4+3i)^2 = (-4)^2 + 2(-4)(3i) + (3i)^2$
$$= 16 - 24i + 9i^2$$
$$= 16 - 9 - 24i$$
$$= 7 - 24i$$

41. $\dfrac{3}{2+5i} = \dfrac{3}{2+5i}\cdot\dfrac{2-5i}{2-5i}$
$$= \dfrac{6-15i}{4-25i^2}$$
$$= \dfrac{6-15i}{4-25(-1)}$$
$$= \dfrac{6-15i}{4+25}$$
$$= \dfrac{6-15i}{29}$$
$$= \dfrac{6}{29} - \dfrac{15}{29}i$$

43. $\dfrac{3i}{7-2i} = \dfrac{3i}{7-2i}\cdot\dfrac{7+2i}{7+2i}$
$$= \dfrac{21i+6i^2}{49-4i^2}$$
$$= \dfrac{-6+21i}{53}$$
$$= -\dfrac{6}{53} + \dfrac{21}{53}i$$

45. $\dfrac{2+3i}{7+i} = \dfrac{2+3i}{7+i}\cdot\dfrac{7-i}{7-i}$
$$= \dfrac{14+21i-2i-3i^2}{49-i^2}$$
$$= \dfrac{17+19i}{50}$$
$$= \dfrac{17}{50} + \dfrac{19}{50}i$$

47. $\dfrac{3+4i}{3-4i} = \dfrac{3+4i}{3-4i}\cdot\dfrac{3+4i}{3+4i}$
$$= \dfrac{9+12i+12i+16i^2}{9-16i^2}$$
$$= \dfrac{9+24i+16(-1)}{9-16(-1)}$$
$$= \dfrac{-7+24i}{25}$$
$$= -\dfrac{7}{25} + \dfrac{24}{25}i$$

49. $\dfrac{3-5i}{2-9i} = \dfrac{3-5i}{2-9i} \cdot \dfrac{2+9i}{2+9i}$

$\qquad = \dfrac{6+27i-10i-45i^2}{4-81i^2}$

$\qquad = \dfrac{51+17i}{85}$

$\qquad = \dfrac{51}{85} + \dfrac{17}{85}i$

$\qquad = \dfrac{3}{5} + \dfrac{1}{5}i$

51. $\dfrac{5+7i}{4i} = \dfrac{5+7i}{4i} \cdot \dfrac{i}{i}$

$\qquad = \dfrac{5i+7i^2}{4i^2}$

$\qquad = \dfrac{-7+5i}{-4}$

$\qquad = \dfrac{7}{4} - \dfrac{5}{4}i$

53. $\dfrac{7}{5i} = \dfrac{7}{5i} \cdot \dfrac{i}{i}$

$\qquad = \dfrac{7i}{5i^2}$

$\qquad = -\dfrac{7}{5}i$

55. Answers may vary. Student 2's work is correct, and Student 1's work is incorrect. If a radical has a negative radicand, you must rewrite the radical using i before performing any operations. Student 1 did not perform this step, and therefore got the wrong answer.

57. **a.** Answers may vary. A possible answer is $a = 3$, $b = -2$, $c = -8$, and $d = 5$.
$(a+bi)+(c+di) = (3-2i)+(-8+5i)$
$\qquad\qquad\qquad = 3-8-2i+5i$
$\qquad\qquad\qquad = -5+3i$

b. Answers may vary. A possible answer is $a = -2$, $b = 5$, $c = -3$, and $d = -5$.
$(a+bi)+(c+di) = (-2+5i)+(-3-5i)$
$\qquad\qquad\qquad = -2-3+5i-5i$
$\qquad\qquad\qquad = -5$

c. Answers may vary. A possible answer is $a = 7$, $b = -4$, $c = -7$, and $d = -2$.
$(a+bi)+(c+di) = (7-4i)+(-7-2i)$
$\qquad\qquad\qquad = 7-7-4i-2i$
$\qquad\qquad\qquad = -6i$

59. The square of a pure imaginary number will always be a negative real number. A pure imaginary number has two parts: the coefficient and i. When the coefficient is squared, it always becomes a positive real number. When i is squared, it always becomes -1. Multiplying a positive real number by -1 always gives a negative real product.

61. $\dfrac{4}{3+2\sqrt{x}} = \dfrac{4}{3+2\sqrt{x}} \cdot \dfrac{3-2\sqrt{x}}{3-2\sqrt{x}}$

$\qquad = \dfrac{12-8\sqrt{x}}{9-\left(2\sqrt{x}\right)^2}$

$\qquad = \dfrac{12-8\sqrt{x}}{9-4x}$

63. $\dfrac{4}{3+2i} = \dfrac{4}{3+2i} \cdot \dfrac{3-2i}{3-2i}$

$\qquad = \dfrac{12-8i}{9-4i^2}$

$\qquad = \dfrac{12-8i}{13}$

$\qquad = \dfrac{12}{13} - \dfrac{8}{13}i$

65. $3x^2 - 2x + 3 = 0$

$\dfrac{-b \pm \sqrt{b^2-4ac}}{2a} = \dfrac{2 \pm \sqrt{(-2)^2 - 4(3)(3)}}{2(3)}$

$\qquad\qquad = \dfrac{2 \pm \sqrt{-32}}{6}$

$\qquad\qquad = \dfrac{2 \pm 4i\sqrt{2}}{6}$

$\qquad\qquad = \dfrac{1 \pm 2i\sqrt{2}}{3}$

67. $5x^2 - 4x = -1$

$5x^2 - 4x + 1 = 0$

$\dfrac{-b \pm \sqrt{b^2 - 4ac}}{2a} = \dfrac{4 \pm \sqrt{(-4)^2 - 4(5)(1)}}{2(5)}$

$\phantom{\dfrac{-b \pm \sqrt{b^2 - 4ac}}{2a}} = \dfrac{4 \pm \sqrt{-4}}{10}$

$\phantom{\dfrac{-b \pm \sqrt{b^2 - 4ac}}{2a}} = \dfrac{4 \pm 2i}{10}$

$\phantom{\dfrac{-b \pm \sqrt{b^2 - 4ac}}{2a}} = \dfrac{2 \pm i}{5}$

69. $(x-3)(2x+1) = -10$

$x \cdot 2x + x \cdot 1 - 3 \cdot 2x - 3 \cdot 1 = -10$

$2x^2 + x - 6x - 3 + 10 = 0$

$2x^2 - 5x + 7 = 0$

$\dfrac{-b \pm \sqrt{b^2 - 4ac}}{2a} = \dfrac{5 \pm \sqrt{(-5)^2 - 4(2)(7)}}{2(2)}$

$\phantom{\dfrac{-b \pm \sqrt{b^2 - 4ac}}{2a}} = \dfrac{5 \pm \sqrt{-31}}{4}$

$\phantom{\dfrac{-b \pm \sqrt{b^2 - 4ac}}{2a}} = \dfrac{5 \pm i\sqrt{31}}{4}$

71. $x(3x-2) = 2 + 2(x-3)$

$3x^2 - 2x = 2 + 2x - 6$

$3x^2 - 2x - 2x - 2 + 6 = 0$

$3x^2 - 4x + 4 = 0$

$\dfrac{-b \pm \sqrt{b^2 - 4ac}}{2a} = \dfrac{4 \pm \sqrt{(-4)^2 - 4(3)(4)}}{2(3)}$

$\phantom{\dfrac{-b \pm \sqrt{b^2 - 4ac}}{2a}} = \dfrac{4 \pm \sqrt{-32}}{6}$

$\phantom{\dfrac{-b \pm \sqrt{b^2 - 4ac}}{2a}} = \dfrac{4 \pm 4i\sqrt{2}}{6}$

$\phantom{\dfrac{-b \pm \sqrt{b^2 - 4ac}}{2a}} = \dfrac{2 \pm 2i\sqrt{2}}{3}$

73. $(5x+3)^2 = -20$

$25x^2 + 2(5x)(3) + 9 + 20 = 0$

$25x^2 + 30x + 29 = 0$

$\dfrac{-b \pm \sqrt{b^2 - 4ac}}{2a} = \dfrac{-30 \pm \sqrt{30^2 - 4(25)(29)}}{2(25)}$

$\phantom{\dfrac{-b \pm \sqrt{b^2 - 4ac}}{2a}} = \dfrac{-30 \pm \sqrt{900 - 2900}}{50}$

$\phantom{\dfrac{-b \pm \sqrt{b^2 - 4ac}}{2a}} = \dfrac{-30 \pm \sqrt{-2000}}{50}$

$\phantom{\dfrac{-b \pm \sqrt{b^2 - 4ac}}{2a}} = \dfrac{-30 \pm 20i\sqrt{5}}{50}$

$\phantom{\dfrac{-b \pm \sqrt{b^2 - 4ac}}{2a}} = \dfrac{-3 \pm 2i\sqrt{5}}{5}$

75. $4x^2 - 2x + 3 = 0$

$\dfrac{-b \pm \sqrt{b^2 - 4ac}}{2a} = \dfrac{2 \pm \sqrt{(-2)^2 - 4(4)(3)}}{2(4)}$

$\phantom{\dfrac{-b \pm \sqrt{b^2 - 4ac}}{2a}} = \dfrac{2 \pm \sqrt{-44}}{8}$

$\phantom{\dfrac{-b \pm \sqrt{b^2 - 4ac}}{2a}} = \dfrac{2 \pm 2i\sqrt{11}}{8}$

$\phantom{\dfrac{-b \pm \sqrt{b^2 - 4ac}}{2a}} = \dfrac{1 \pm i\sqrt{11}}{4}$

$4x^2 - 2x + 3 = 0$ is a quadratic equation in one variable.

77. $10x^2 - 19x + 6$

$= (5x - 2)(2x - 3)$

$10x^2 - 19x + 6$ is a quadratic polynomial in one variable.

79. $(3i - 7)(4i + 6) = 12i^2 + 18i - 28i - 42$

$ = -12 - 42 + 18i - 28i$

$ = -54 - 10i$

$(3i - 7)(4i + 6)$ is an imaginary number.

Quiz 15.2

1. $(6 - 2i) + (3 - 4i) = 6 - 2i + 3 - 4i$

$ = 6 + 3 - 2i - 4i$

$ = 9 - 6i$

2. $(3 + 7i) - (8 - 2i) = 3 + 7i - 8 + 2i$

$ = 3 - 8 + 7i + 2i$

$ = -5 + 9i$

3. $-4i \cdot 3i = -12i^2$
$$= -12(-1)$$
$$= 12$$

4. $\sqrt{-2}\sqrt{-7} = i\sqrt{2} \cdot i\sqrt{7}$
$$= i^2\sqrt{14}$$
$$= -\sqrt{14}$$

5. $(5-3i)(7+i) = 5 \cdot 7 + 5 \cdot i - 3i \cdot 7 - 3i \cdot i$
$$= 35 + 5i - 21i - 3i^2$$
$$= 35 - 16i - 3(-1)$$
$$= 35 - 16i + 3$$
$$= 38 - 16i$$

6. $(4-3i)^2 = (4)^2 - 2(4)(3i) + (3i)^2$
$$= 16 - 24i + 9i^2$$
$$= 16 - 24i + 9(-1)$$
$$= 16 - 24i - 9$$
$$= 7 - 24i$$

7. $(8+5i)(8-5i) = (8)^2 - (5i)^2$
$$= 64 - 25i^2$$
$$= 64 - 25(-1)$$
$$= 64 + 25$$
$$= 89$$

8. $\dfrac{3+2i}{5-4i} = \dfrac{3+2i}{5-4i} \cdot \dfrac{5+4i}{5+4i}$
$$= \frac{15 + 12i + 10i + 8i^2}{25 - 16i^2}$$
$$= \frac{15 + 22i + 8(-1)}{25 - 16(-1)}$$
$$= \frac{7 + 22i}{41}$$
$$= \frac{7}{41} + \frac{22}{41}i$$

9. $\dfrac{5-7i}{6i} = \dfrac{5-7i}{6i} \cdot \dfrac{i}{i}$
$$= \frac{5i - 7i^2}{6i^2}$$
$$= \frac{7 + 5i}{-6}$$
$$= -\frac{7}{6} - \frac{5}{6}i$$

10. False. Answers may vary.
The number $3i$ (or $0 + 3i$) is a complex number and i is a pure imaginary number. Then $(i)(3i) = 3i^2 = -3$. Since -3 is not an imaginary number, the statement is false.

Homework 15.3

1. Since the lengths of the legs are given, we find the length of the hypotenuse. Substitute $a = 4$ and $b = 5$ into $a^2 + b^2 = c^2$ and solve for c.
$$4^2 + 5^2 = c^2$$
$$16 + 25 = c^2$$
$$41 = c^2$$
$$c = \sqrt{41} \quad \text{(disregard the negative)}$$
The length of the hypotenuse is $\sqrt{41}$ units (about 6.40 units).

3. The length of the hypotenuse is 9 and the length of one of the legs is 4. We substitute $a = 4$ and $c = 9$ into $a^2 + b^2 = c^2$ and solve for b.
$$4^2 + b^2 = 9^2$$
$$16 + b^2 = 81$$
$$b^2 = 65$$
$$b = \sqrt{65} \quad \text{(disregard the negative)}$$
The length of the other leg is $\sqrt{65}$ units (about 8.06 units).

5. The length of the hypotenuse is 12 and the length of one of the legs is 10. We substitute $a = 10$ and $c = 12$ into $a^2 + b^2 = c^2$ and solve for b.

$$10^2 + b^2 = 12^2$$
$$100 + b^2 = 144$$
$$b^2 = 44$$
$$b = \sqrt{44}$$
$$b = 2\sqrt{11} \quad \text{(disregard the negative)}$$

The length of the other side is $2\sqrt{11}$ units (about 6.63 units).

7.
$$c^2 = a^2 + b^2$$
$$c^2 = 5^2 + 12^2$$
$$c^2 = 25 + 144$$
$$c^2 = 169$$
$$c = 13$$

9.
$$c^2 = a^2 + b^2$$
$$c^2 = 6^2 + 7^2$$
$$c^2 = 36 + 49$$
$$c^2 = 85$$
$$c = \sqrt{85}$$

11.
$$a^2 + b^2 = c^2$$
$$3^2 + b^2 = 8^2$$
$$9 + b^2 = 64$$
$$b^2 = 55$$
$$b = \sqrt{55}$$

13.
$$a^2 + b^2 = c^2$$
$$a^2 + 5^2 = 7^2$$
$$a^2 + 25 = 49$$
$$a^2 = 24$$
$$a = \sqrt{24}$$
$$a = 2\sqrt{6}$$

15.
$$c^2 = a^2 + b^2$$
$$c^2 = \left(\sqrt{2}\right)^2 + \left(\sqrt{5}\right)^2$$
$$c^2 = 2 + 5$$
$$c^2 = 7$$
$$c = \sqrt{7}$$

17. First we define c to be the straight line distance (in miles) between the student's home and school. Then we draw a diagram that describes the situation.

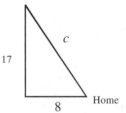

The triangle is a right triangle with legs of length 8 miles and 17 miles.

$$a^2 + b^2 = c^2$$
$$8^2 + 17^2 = c^2$$
$$64 + 289 = c^2$$
$$353 = c^2$$
$$c = \sqrt{353} \approx 18.8 \text{ miles}$$

The length of the trip would be about 18.8 miles.

19. First we define h to be the height (in feet) that the 12-foot ladder can reach. Then we draw a diagram that describes the situation.

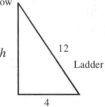

The triangle is a right triangle with one leg measuring 4 feet and a hypotenuse of 12 feet.

$$a^2 + b^2 = c^2$$
$$4^2 + b^2 = 12^2$$
$$16 + b^2 = 144$$
$$b^2 = 128$$
$$L = \sqrt{128} = 8\sqrt{2} \approx 11.3$$

The 12-foot ladder is long enough to reach the bottom of the window.

21.
$$a^2 + b^2 = c^2$$
$$13^2 + b^2 = 20^2$$
$$169 + b^2 = 400$$
$$b^2 = 231$$
$$b = \sqrt{231} \approx 15.2$$
The width of the screen is about 15.2 inches.

23.
$$a^2 + b^2 = c^2$$
$$24^2 + b^2 = 37^2$$
$$576 + b^2 = 1369$$
$$b^2 = 793$$
$$b = \sqrt{793} \approx 28.2$$
The length of the painting is about 28.2 inches.

25. $a = 2.8, \ b = $ distance across lake, $c = 3.4$
$$a^2 + b^2 = c^2$$
$$2.8^2 + b^2 = 3.4^2$$
$$7.84 + b^2 = 11.56$$
$$b^2 = 3.72$$
$$b = \sqrt{3.72}$$
$$b \approx 1.9$$
The distance across the lake must be approximately 1.9 miles.

27. 100 yards = 300 feet
53 yards 1 foot = 160 feet.
Let d be the distance the player runs (in feet).
$$a^2 + b^2 = c^2$$
$$160^2 + 300^2 = d^2$$
$$25,600 + 90,000 = d^2$$
$$115,600 = d^2$$
$$d = \sqrt{115,600} = 340$$
The player would run 340 feet (113 yards 1 foot).

29. $a = 465, c = 964, b = $ distance

$$a^2 + b^2 = c^2$$
$$465^2 + b^2 = 964^2$$
$$b^2 = 713071$$
$$b = \sqrt{713071}$$
$$b \approx 844.4$$
$$a + b + c = 465 + 844.4 + 964$$
$$= 2273.4$$
The total distance of the road trip would be approximately 2273.4 miles.

31. $(2, 9)$ and $(8, 1)$
$$d = \sqrt{(8-2)^2 + (1-9)^2}$$
$$= \sqrt{6^2 + (-8)^2}$$
$$= \sqrt{36 + 64}$$
$$= \sqrt{100}$$
$$= 10$$

33. $(-3, 5)$ and $(4, 2)$
$$d = \sqrt{(4-(-3))^2 + (2-5)^2}$$
$$= \sqrt{7^2 + (-3)^2}$$
$$= \sqrt{49 + 9}$$
$$= \sqrt{58}$$

35. $(-6, -3)$ and $(-4, 1)$

$$d = \sqrt{(-4-(-6))^2 + (1-(-3))^2}$$
$$= \sqrt{2^2 + 4^2}$$
$$= \sqrt{4 + 16}$$
$$= \sqrt{20}$$
$$= 2\sqrt{5}$$

37. $(-4, -5)$ and $(-8, -9)$
$$d = \sqrt{(-8-(-4))^2 + (-9-(-5))^2}$$
$$= \sqrt{(-4)^2 + (-4)^2}$$
$$= \sqrt{16 + 16}$$
$$= \sqrt{32}$$
$$= 4\sqrt{2}$$

39. $(2.1, 8.9)$ and $(5.6, 1.7)$

$$d = \sqrt{(5.6 - 2.1)^2 + (1.7 - 8.9)^2}$$
$$= \sqrt{3.5^2 + (-7.2)^2}$$
$$= \sqrt{12.25 + 51.84}$$
$$= \sqrt{64.09}$$
$$\approx 8.01$$

41. $(-2.18, -5.74)$ and $(3.44, 6.29)$

$$d = \sqrt{(3.44 - (-2.18))^2 + (6.29 - (-5.74))^2}$$
$$= \sqrt{5.62^2 + 12.03^2}$$
$$= \sqrt{31.5844 + 144.7209}$$
$$= \sqrt{176.3053}$$
$$\approx 13.28$$

43. $C(0,0)$ and $r = 7$

$$(x - h)^2 + (y - k)^2 = r^2$$
$$(x - 0)^2 + (y - 0)^2 = 7^2$$
$$x^2 + y^2 = 49$$

45. $C(0,0)$ and $r = 6.7$

$$(x - h)^2 + (y - k)^2 = r^2$$
$$(x - 0)^2 + (y - 0)^2 = 6.7^2$$
$$x^2 + y^2 = 44.89$$

47. $C(5,3)$ and $r = 2$

$$(x - h)^2 + (y - k)^2 = r^2$$
$$(x - 5)^2 + (y - 3)^2 = 2^2$$
$$(x - 5)^2 + (y - 3)^2 = 4$$

49. $C(-2,1)$ and $r = 4$

$$(x - h)^2 + (y - k)^2 = r^2$$
$$(x - (-2))^2 + (y - 1)^2 = 4^2$$
$$(x + 2)^2 + (y - 1)^2 = 16$$

51. $C(-7, -3)$ and $r = \sqrt{3}$

$$(x - h)^2 + (y - k)^2 = r^2$$
$$(x - (-7))^2 + (y - (-3))^2 = (\sqrt{3})^2$$
$$(x + 7)^2 + (y + 3)^2 = 3$$

53. $x^2 + y^2 = 25$

The equation has the form $x^2 + y^2 = r^2$.

Therefore, $C = (0,0)$ and

$$r^2 = 25$$
$$r = \sqrt{25}$$
$$r = 5$$

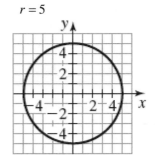

55. $x^2 + y^2 = 8$

The equation has the form $x^2 + y^2 = r^2$.

Therefore, $C = (0,0)$ and

$$r^2 = 8$$
$$r = \sqrt{8}$$
$$r = 2\sqrt{2}$$

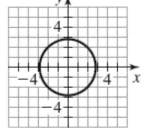

57. $(x-3)^2 + (y-5)^2 = 16$

The equation is in the form
$(x-h)^2 + (y-k)^2 = r^2$.

The center is (h,k) or $C(3,5)$ and

$r^2 = 16$

$r = \sqrt{16}$

$r = 4$

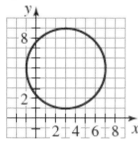

59. $(x+6)^2 + (y-1)^2 = 7$

$(x-(-6))^2 + (y-1)^2 = (\sqrt{7})^2$

The equation is in the form
$(x-h)^2 + (y-k)^2 = r^2$. The center is

$C(-6,1)$ and the radius is $r = \sqrt{7}$.

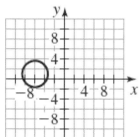

61. $(x+3)^2 + (y+2)^2 = 1$

$(x-(-3))^2 + (y-(-2))^2 = 1^2$

The equation is in the form
$(x-h)^2 + (y-k)^2 = r^2$. The center is

$C(-3,-2)$ and the radius is $r = 1$.

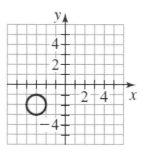

63. $C(0,0)$ and $r = 3$.

$(x-h)^2 + (y-k)^2 = r^2$

$(x-0)^2 + (y-0)^2 = 3^2$

$x^2 + y^2 = 9$

65. $C(-3,2)$ and $r = 2$.

$(x-h)^2 + (y-k)^2 = r^2$

$(x-(-3))^2 + (y-2)^2 = 2^2$

$(x+3)^2 + (y-2)^2 = 4$

67. The radius is the distance from the center to
any point on the circle. The distance between
$C(3,2)$ and $(5,6)$ is given by:

$d = \sqrt{(5-3)^2 + (6-2)^2}$

$\quad = \sqrt{2^2 + 4^2}$

$\quad = \sqrt{4+16}$

$\quad = \sqrt{20}$

The radius is $r = \sqrt{20}$.
The equation of the circle is

$(x-h)^2 + (y-k)^2 = r^2$

$(x-3)^2 + (y-2)^2 = (\sqrt{20})^2$

$(x-3)^2 + (y-2)^2 = 20$

69. Answers may vary. One possible answer:

$$(x-2)^2 + (y-3)^2 = 9$$

$$(x-5)^2 + (y-6)^2 = 9$$

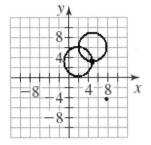

71. a. $x^2 + y^2 = 16$

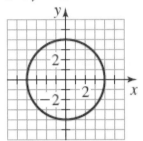

b. Answers may vary.

x	y
−4	0
−2	$2\sqrt{3} \approx 3.46$
−2	$-2\sqrt{3} \approx -3.46$
0	4
0	−4
2	$2\sqrt{3} \approx 3.46$
2	$-2\sqrt{3} \approx -3.46$
4	0

c. For each input-output pair, the sum of the square of the input and the square of the output is 16.

73. Find the equation of the circle that has center $C(3,2)$ and $r = 4$.

$$(x-h)^2 + (y-k)^2 = r^2$$

$$(x-3)^2 + (y-2)^2 = 4^2$$

$$(x-3)^2 + (y-2)^2 = 16$$

Find the coordinates of five points, (x, y), that satisfy this equation. Answers will vary. Five possible answers are: $(3,6)$, $(3,-2)$,

$(7,2)$, $(-1,2)$, and $\left(5, 2+\sqrt{12}\right)$.

75. No. Answers may vary. The graph of the relation is a circle with radius 7 and centered at the origin. The graph fails the vertical line test.

77. a. The square root of a nonnegative number is a nonnegative real number and the square root of a negative number is an imaginary number. Therefore, $y \geq 0$ for real number values of y.

b.

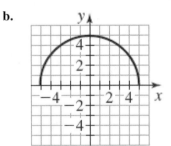

79. a. Sketches may vary. One example:

b. $a = k, b = k$

$$c^2 = a^2 + b^2$$

$$c^2 = k^2 + k^2$$

$$c^2 = 2k^2$$

$$c = \sqrt{2k^2}$$

$$c = \sqrt{2}\sqrt{k^2}$$

$$c = k\sqrt{2}$$

c. $c = k\sqrt{2}$

$$= 3\sqrt{2}$$

d.
$$c = k\sqrt{2}$$
$$5 = k\sqrt{2}$$
$$k = \frac{5}{\sqrt{2}}$$
$$k = \frac{5}{\sqrt{2}} \cdot \frac{\sqrt{2}}{\sqrt{2}}$$
$$k = \frac{5\sqrt{2}}{2}$$

81. $x + y = 4$

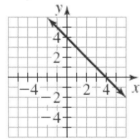

83. $x^2 + y^2 = 4$

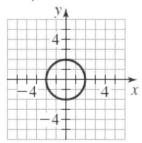

85. $2^x + y = 0$

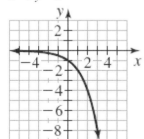

87. $f(x) = 2(x-4)^2 - 3$

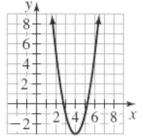

$f(x) = 2(x-4)^2 - 3$ is a quadratic function.

89.
$$6x^2 - 16x + 8 = 2\left(3x^2 - 8x + 4\right)$$
$$= 2(3x-2)(x-2)$$

$6x^2 - 16x + 8$ is a quadratic polynomial in one variable.

91.
$$x(5x-3) = 3(x+1)$$
$$5x^2 - 3x = 3x + 3$$
$$5x^2 - 6x - 3 = 0$$
$$\frac{-b \pm \sqrt{b^2 - 4ac}}{2a} = \frac{6 \pm \sqrt{(-6)^2 - 4(5)(-3)}}{2(5)}$$
$$= \frac{6 \pm \sqrt{36 + 60}}{10}$$
$$= \frac{6 \pm 4\sqrt{6}}{10}$$
$$= \frac{3 \pm 2\sqrt{6}}{5}$$

$x(5x-3) = 3(x+1)$ is a quadratic equation in one variable.

Quiz 15.3

1. $a = 4, c = 8$
$$a^2 + b^2 = c^2$$
$$4^2 + b^2 = 8^2$$
$$16 + b^2 = 64$$
$$b^2 = 48$$
$$b = \sqrt{48}$$
$$b = 4\sqrt{3} \approx 6.9$$

The other leg is $4\sqrt{3}$ inches.

2. $b = 16, c = 19$

$$a^2 + b^2 = c^2$$
$$a^2 + 16^2 = 19^2$$
$$a^2 + 256 = 361$$
$$a^2 = 105$$
$$a = \sqrt{105}$$
$$a \approx 10.2$$

The height of the screen is about 10.2 inches.

3. $(-2, -5)$ and $(3, -1)$

$$d = \sqrt{(3 - (-2))^2 + (-1 - (-5))^2}$$
$$= \sqrt{5^2 + 4^2}$$
$$= \sqrt{25 + 16}$$
$$= \sqrt{41}$$

4. $(-3, 2)$ and $(-7, -2)$

$$d = \sqrt{(-7 - (-3))^2 + (-2 - 2)^2}$$
$$= \sqrt{(-4)^2 + (-4)^2}$$
$$= \sqrt{16 + 16}$$
$$= \sqrt{32}$$
$$= 4\sqrt{2}$$

5. $C(-3, 2)$ and $r = 6$

$$(x - h)^2 + (y - k)^2 = r^2$$
$$(x - (-3))^2 + (y - 2)^2 = 6^2$$
$$(x + 3)^2 + (y - 2)^2 = 36$$

6. $C(0, 0)$ and $r = 2.8$

$$(x - h)^2 + (y - k)^2 = r^2$$
$$(x - 0)^2 + (y - 0)^2 = 2.8^2$$
$$x^2 + y^2 = 7.84$$

7. $x^2 + y^2 = 12$

The equation is in the form $x^2 + y^2 = r^2$. The center is $C(0, 0)$ and

$$r^2 = 12$$
$$r = \sqrt{12}$$
$$r = 2\sqrt{3}$$

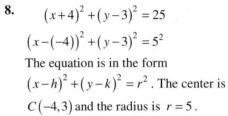

8.
$$(x + 4)^2 + (y - 3)^2 = 25$$
$$(x - (-4))^2 + (y - 3)^2 = 5^2$$

The equation is in the form $(x - h)^2 + (y - k)^2 = r^2$. The center is $C(-4, 3)$ and the radius is $r = 5$.

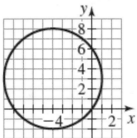

9. $C(2, -1)$

The radius is the distance from the center, $C(2, -1)$, to the point $(4, 7)$ that lies on the circle.

$$d = \sqrt{(4 - 2)^2 + (7 - (-1))^2}$$
$$= \sqrt{2^2 + 8^2}$$
$$= \sqrt{4 + 64}$$
$$= \sqrt{68}$$

The equation of the circle is

$$(x - h)^2 + (y - k)^2 = r^2$$
$$(x - 2)^2 + (y - (-1))^2 = (\sqrt{68})^2$$
$$(x - 2)^2 + (y + 1)^2 = 68$$

10. Answers may vary. One possible answer:

$(x+2)^2 + y^2 = 4$

$(x-3)^2 + y^2 = 9$

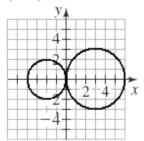

Homework 15.4

1. $\dfrac{x^2}{36} + \dfrac{y^2}{9} = 1$

$a^2 = 36, a = 6$

x-intercepts: $(-6,0),(6,0)$

$b^2 = 9, b = 3$

y-intercepts: $(0,-3),(0,3)$

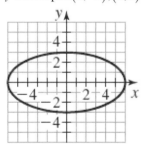

3. $\dfrac{x^2}{4} + \dfrac{y^2}{36} = 1$

$a^2 = 4, a = 2$

x-intercepts: $(-2,0),(2,0)$

$b^2 = 36, b = 6$

y-intercepts: $(0,-6),(0,6)$

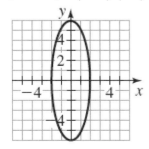

5. $\dfrac{x^2}{100} + \dfrac{y^2}{16} = 1$

$a^2 = 100, a = 10$

x-intercepts: $(-10,0),(10,0)$

$b^2 = 16, b = 4$

y-intercepts: $(0,-4),(0,4)$

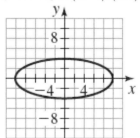

7. $25x^2 + 4y^2 = 100$

$\dfrac{25x^2}{100} + \dfrac{4y^2}{100} = \dfrac{100}{100}$

$\dfrac{x^2}{4} + \dfrac{y^2}{25} = 1$

$a^2 = 4, a = 2$

x-intercepts: $(-2,0),(2,0)$

$b^2 = 25, b = 5$

y-intercepts: $(0,-5),(0,5)$

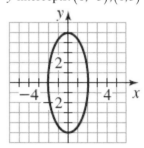

9. $9x^2 + 100y^2 = 900$

$$\frac{9x^2}{900} + \frac{100y^2}{900} = \frac{900}{900}$$

$$\frac{x^2}{100} + \frac{y^2}{9} = 1$$

$a^2 = 100, a = 10$

x-intercepts: $(-10, 0), (10, 0)$

$b^2 = 9, b = 3$

y-intercepts: $(0, -3), (0, 3)$

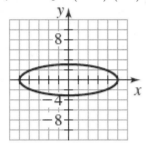

11. $x^2 + y^2 = 36$

$$\frac{x^2}{36} + \frac{y^2}{36} = \frac{36}{36}$$

$$\frac{x^2}{36} + \frac{y^2}{36} = 1$$

$a^2 = 36, a = 6$

x-intercepts: $(-6, 0), (6, 0)$

$b^2 = 36, b = 6$

y-intercepts: $(0, -6), (0, 6)$

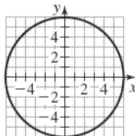

13. $x^2 + 25y^2 = 25$

$$\frac{x^2}{25} + \frac{25y^2}{25} = \frac{25}{25}$$

$$\frac{x^2}{25} + \frac{y^2}{1} = 1$$

$a^2 = 25, a = 5$

x-intercepts: $(-5, 0), (5, 0)$

$b^2 = 1, b = 1$

y-intercepts: $(0, -1), (0, 1)$

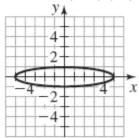

15. $5x^2 + 16y^2 = 80$

$$\frac{5x^2}{80} + \frac{16y^2}{80} = \frac{80}{80}$$

$$\frac{x^2}{16} + \frac{y^2}{5} = 1$$

$a^2 = 16, a = 4$

x-intercepts: $(-4, 0), (4, 0)$

$b^2 = 5, b = \sqrt{5}$

y-intercepts: $\left(0, -\sqrt{5}\right), \left(0, \sqrt{5}\right)$

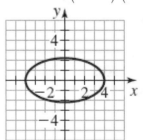

17. The x-intercepts are $(5, 0)$ and $(-5, 0)$, so $a = 5$. The y-intercepts are $(3, 0)$ and $(-3, 0)$, so $b = 3$. Therefore:

$$\frac{x^2}{5^2} + \frac{y^2}{3^2} = 1$$

$$\frac{x^2}{25} + \frac{y^2}{9} = 1$$

19. $\dfrac{x^2}{16} - \dfrac{y^2}{4} = 1$

$a^2 = 16, a = 4$

x-intercepts: $(-4,0),(4,0)$

$b^2 = 4, b = 2$

Sketch a dashed rectangle that contains the points $(-4,0),(4,0),(0,-2),$ and $(0,2),$ and then sketch the inclined asymptotes.

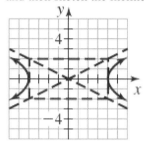

21. $\dfrac{y^2}{16} - \dfrac{x^2}{25} = 1$

$b^2 = 16, b = 4$

y-intercepts: $(0,-4),(0,4)$

$a^2 = 25, a = 5$

Sketch a dashed rectangle that contains the points $(-5,0),(5,0),(0,-4),$ and $(0,4),$ and then sketch the inclined asymptotes.

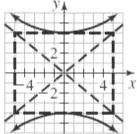

23. $\dfrac{x^2}{25} - \dfrac{y^2}{81} = 1$

$a^2 = 25, b = 5$

x-intercepts: $(5,0),(-5,0)$

$b^2 = 81, b = 9$

Sketch a dashed rectangle that contains the points $(-5,0),(5,0),(0,-9),$ and $(0,9),$ and then sketch the inclined asymptotes.

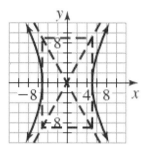

25. $16x^2 - 4y^2 = 64$

$\dfrac{16x^2}{64} - \dfrac{4y^2}{64} = \dfrac{64}{64}$

$\dfrac{x^2}{4} - \dfrac{y^2}{16} = 1$

$a^2 = 4, a = 2$

x-intercepts: $(-2,0),(2,0)$

$b^2 = 16, b = 4$

Sketch a dashed rectangle that contains the points $(-2,0),(2,0),(0,-4),$ and $(0,4),$ and then sketch the inclined asymptotes.

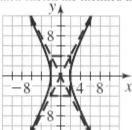

27. $x^2 - 9y^2 = 9$

$\dfrac{x^2}{9} - \dfrac{9y^2}{9} = \dfrac{9}{9}$

$\dfrac{x^2}{9} - \dfrac{y^2}{1} = 1$

$a^2 = 9, a = 3$

x-intercepts: $(-3,0),(3,0)$

$b^2 = 1, b = 1$

Sketch a dashed rectangle that contains the points $(-3,0),(3,0),(0,-1),$ and $(0,1),$ and then sketch the inclined asymptotes.

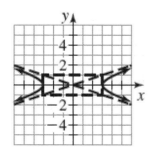

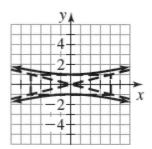

29. $y^2 - x^2 = 4$

$$\frac{y^2}{4} - \frac{x^2}{4} = \frac{4}{4}$$

$$\frac{y^2}{4} - \frac{x^2}{4} = 1$$

$b^2 = 4, b = 2$

y-intercepts: $(0, -2), (0, 2)$

$a^2 = 4, a = 2$

Sketch a dashed rectangle that contains the points $(-2, 0), (2, 0), (0, -2)$, and $(0, 2)$, and then sketch the inclined asymptotes.

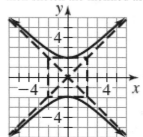

31. $16y^2 - x^2 = 16$

$$\frac{16y^2}{16} - \frac{x^2}{16} = \frac{16}{16}$$

$$\frac{y^2}{1} - \frac{x^2}{16} = 1$$

$b^2 = 1, b = 1$

y-intercepts: $(0, -1), (0, 1)$

$a^2 = 16, a = 4$

Sketch a dashed rectangle that contains the points $(-4, 0), (4, 0), (0, -1)$, and $(0, 1)$, and then sketch the inclined asymptotes.

33. $25x^2 - 7y^2 = 175$

$$\frac{25x^2}{175} - \frac{7y^2}{175} = \frac{175}{175}$$

$$\frac{x^2}{7} - \frac{y^2}{25} = 1$$

$a^2 = 7, a = \sqrt{7}$

x-intercepts: $\left(-\sqrt{7}, 0\right), \left(\sqrt{7}, 0\right)$

$b^2 = 25, b = 5$

Sketch a dashed rectangle that contains the points $\left(-\sqrt{7}, 0\right), \left(\sqrt{7}, 0\right), (0, -5)$, and $(0, 5)$, and then sketch the inclined asymptotes.

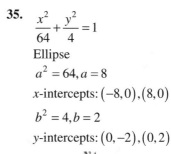

35. $\dfrac{x^2}{64} + \dfrac{y^2}{4} = 1$

Ellipse

$a^2 = 64, a = 8$

x-intercepts: $(-8, 0), (8, 0)$

$b^2 = 4, b = 2$

y-intercepts: $(0, -2), (0, 2)$

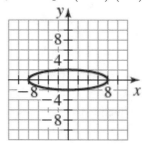

37. $x^2 - y^2 = 1$

$\dfrac{x^2}{1} - \dfrac{y^2}{1} = 1$

Hyperbola

$a^2 = 1, a = 1$

x-intercepts: $(-1,0),(1,0)$

$b^2 = 1, b = 1$

Sketch a dashed rectangle that contains the points $(-1,0),(1,0),(0,-1)$, and $(0,1)$, and then sketch the inclined asymptotes.

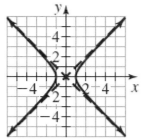

39. $81x^2 + 49y^2 = 3969$

$\dfrac{81x^2}{3969} + \dfrac{49y^2}{3969} = \dfrac{3969}{3969}$

$\dfrac{x^2}{49} + \dfrac{y^2}{81} = 1$

Ellipse

$a^2 = 49, a = 7$

x-intercepts: $(-7,0),(7,0)$

$b^2 = 81, b = 9$

y-intercepts: $(0,-9),(0,9)$

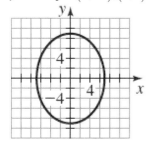

41. $x^2 + y^2 = 1$

$\dfrac{x^2}{1} + \dfrac{y^2}{1} = 1$

Circle

$a^2 = 1, a = 1$

x-intercepts: $(-1,0),(1,0)$

$b^2 = 1, b = 1$

y-intercepts: $(0,-1),(0,1)$

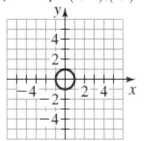

43. $9y^2 - 4x^2 = 144$

$\dfrac{9y^2}{144} - \dfrac{4x^2}{144} = \dfrac{144}{144}$

$\dfrac{y^2}{16} - \dfrac{x^2}{36} = 1$

Hyperbola

$b^2 = 16, b = 4$

y-intercepts: $(0,-4),(0,4)$

$a^2 = 36, a = 6$

Sketch a dashed rectangle that contains the points $(-6,0),(6,0),(0,-4)$, and $(0,4)$, and then sketch the inclined asymptotes.

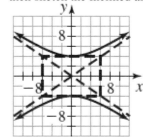

45. $\dfrac{x^2}{25} - \dfrac{y^2}{25} = 1$

Hyperbola

$a^2 = 25, a = 5$

x-intercepts: $(-5,0),(5,0)$

$b^2 = 25, b = 5$

Sketch a dashed rectangle that contains the points $(-5,0),(5,0),(0,-5),$ and $(0,5)$, and then sketch the inclined asymptotes.

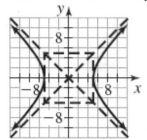

47. $x^2 + y^2 = 16$

$\dfrac{x^2}{16} + \dfrac{y^2}{16} = 1$

Circle

$a^2 = 16, a = 4$

x-intercepts: $(-4,0),(4,0)$

$b^2 = 16, b = 4$

y-intercepts: $(0,-4),(0,4)$

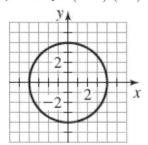

49. $9x^2 + 16y^2 = 144$

$\dfrac{9x^2}{144} + \dfrac{16y^2}{144} = 1$

$\dfrac{x^2}{16} + \dfrac{y^2}{9} = 1$

Ellipse

$a^2 = 16, a = 4$

x-intercepts: $(-4,0),(4,0)$

$b^2 = 9, b = 3$

y-intercepts: $(0,-3),(0,3)$

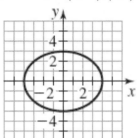

51. $\dfrac{x^2}{16} + \dfrac{y^2}{16} = 1$

Circle

$a^2 = 16, a = 4$

x-intercepts: $(-4,0),(4,0)$

$b^2 = 16, b = 4$

y-intercepts: $(0,-4),(0,4)$

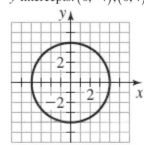

53. a.

i. $\dfrac{x^2}{c}+\dfrac{y^2}{d}=1$

$\dfrac{x^2}{4}+\dfrac{y^2}{16}=1$

Ellipse

$a^2=4, a=2$

x-intercepts: $(-2,0),(2,0)$

$b^2=16, b=4$

y-intercepts: $(0,-4),(0,4)$

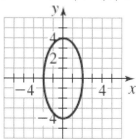

ii. $\dfrac{x^2}{c}+\dfrac{y^2}{d}=1$

$\dfrac{x^2}{4}-\dfrac{y^2}{16}=1$

Hyperbola

$a^2=4, a=2$

x-intercepts: $(-2,0),(2,0)$

$b^2=16, b=4$

Sketch a dashed rectangle that contains the points $(-2,0),(2,0),(0,-4),$ and $(0,4)$, and then sketch the inclined asymptotes.

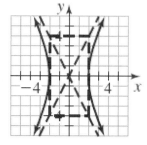

iii. $\dfrac{x^2}{c}+\dfrac{y^2}{d}=1$

$\dfrac{y^2}{16}-\dfrac{x^2}{4}=1$

Hyperbola

$b^2=16, b=4$

y-intercepts: $(0,-4),(0,4)$

$a^2=4, a=2$

Sketch a dashed rectangle that contains the points $(-2,0),(2,0),(0,-4),$ and $(0,4)$, and then sketch the asymptotes.

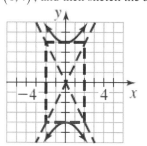

iv. $\dfrac{x^2}{c}+\dfrac{y^2}{d}=1$

$\dfrac{x^2}{4}+\dfrac{y^2}{4}=1$

Circle

$a^2=4, a=2$

x-intercepts: $(-2,0),(2,0)$

$b^2=4, b=2$

y-intercepts: $(0,-2),(0,2)$

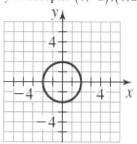

b. If $c>0$ and $d>0$ and $c\neq d$, then the graph is an ellipse.
If $c>0$ and $d<0$, then the graph is a hyperbola with x-intercepts.
If $c<0$ and $d>0$, then the graph is a hyperbola with y-intercepts.
If $c=d$ and $c>0$, then the graph is a circle.

665

55. a.

$$4x^2 + 25y^2 = 100$$

$$\frac{4x^2}{100} + \frac{25y^2}{100} = 1$$

$$\frac{x^2}{25} + \frac{y^2}{4} = 1$$

Ellipse

$$a^2 = 25, a = 5$$

x-intercepts: $(-5,0),(5,0)$

$$b^2 = 4, b = 2$$

y-intercepts: $(0,-2),(0,2)$

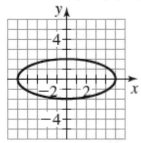

b. Answers may vary.

x	y
-5	0
-2	$\sqrt{3.36} \approx 1.83$
-2	$-\sqrt{3.36} \approx -1.83$
0	2
0	-2
2	$\sqrt{3.36} \approx 1.83$
2	$-\sqrt{3.36} \approx -1.83$
5	0

c. For each input-output pair, the sum of the square of the input divided by 25 and the square of the output divided by 4 is 1.

57. a.

$$y = \frac{5}{2}\sqrt{4 - x^2}$$

Answers may vary. The square root of a nonnegative number is a nonnegative real number and the square root of a negative number is an imaginary number. Since $\frac{5}{2}$ is positive, $\frac{5}{2}\sqrt{4 - x^2}$ is nonnegative for real values of y. Thus, $y \geq 0$ for real number values of y.

b.

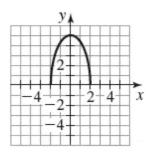

59. Answers may vary. Possible answer:

$$\frac{x^2}{a^2} + \frac{y^2}{b^2} = 1$$

To keep the ellipses from intersecting, we increase the value of a and b for each equation. Some possible equations:

$$\frac{x^2}{1} + \frac{y^2}{4} = 1, \frac{x^2}{4} + \frac{y^2}{9} = 1,$$

$$\frac{x^2}{9} + \frac{y^2}{16} = 1, \frac{x^2}{16} + \frac{y^2}{25} = 1,$$

$$\frac{x^2}{25} + \frac{y^2}{36} = 1$$

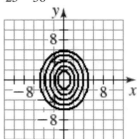

61.

$$x^2 + y^2 = r^2$$

$$\frac{x^2}{r^2} + \frac{y^2}{r^2} = \frac{r^2}{r^2}$$

$$\frac{x^2}{r^2} + \frac{y^2}{r^2} = 1$$

Ellipse

Since $a^2 = b^2 = r^2$, it is also a circle. (Note that all circles are ellipses just as all squares are rectangles.)

63. a.

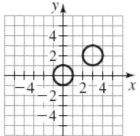

To get the graph of $(x-3)^2+(y-2)^2=1$, translate the graph of $x^2+y^2=1$ rightward by 3 units and upward by 2 units.

b.

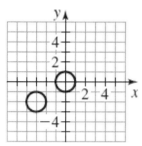

To get the graph of $(x+3)^2+(y+2)^2=1$, translate the graph of $x^2+y^2=1$ leftward by 3 units and downward by 2 units.

c. Translate the graph of $x^2+y^2=r^2$ by h units to the right if $h>0$ or by $|h|$ units to the left if $h<0$, then by k units up if $k>0$ or by $|k|$ units down if $k<0$.

d.

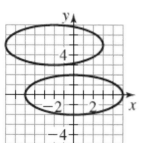

e.

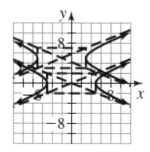

65. $y=\log_2(x)$

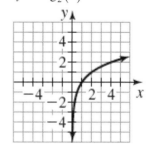

67. $y=3\sqrt{x+5}-4$

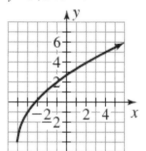

69. No, the relation is not a function. Answers may vary. The graph of $\dfrac{x^2}{4}+\dfrac{y^2}{81}=1$ is an ellipse, which does not pass the vertical line test.

71.
$$y=2x^2-8x+3$$
$$y=2(x^2-4x)+3$$
$$y=2(x^2-4x+4)+3-8$$
$$y=2(x-2)^2-5$$

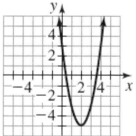

$y=2x^2-8x+3$ is a quadratic function.

73. $2x^2 - 8x + 3 = 0$

$$\frac{-b \pm \sqrt{b^2 - 4ac}}{2a} = \frac{8 \pm \sqrt{(-8)^2 - 4(2)(3)}}{2(2)}$$

$$= \frac{8 \pm \sqrt{64 - 24}}{4}$$

$$= \frac{8 \pm 2\sqrt{10}}{4}$$

$$= \frac{4 \pm \sqrt{10}}{2}$$

$2x^2 - 8x + 3 = 0$ is a quadratic equation in one variable.

75. $-5x(2x-1)(3x-1)$

$-5x(2x \cdot 3x - 1(2x) - 1(3x) - 1(-1))$

$-5x(6x^2 - 5x + 1)$

$-30x^3 + 25x^2 - 5x$

$-5x(2x-1)(3x-1)$ is a cubic polynomial in one variable.

Quiz 15.4

1. $\dfrac{x^2}{9} + \dfrac{y^2}{25} = 1$

$a^2 = 9, a = 3$

x-intercepts: $(-3,0),(3,0)$

$b^2 = 25, b = 5$

y-intercepts: $(0,-5),(0,5)$

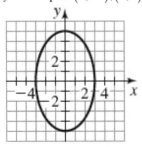

2. $\dfrac{y^2}{49} - \dfrac{x^2}{9} = 1$

$b^2 = 49, b = 7$

y-intercepts: $(0,-7),(0,7)$

$a^2 = 9, a = 3$

Sketch a dashed rectangle that contains the points $(-3,0),(3,0),(0,-7)$, and $(0,7)$, and then sketch the inclined asymptotes.

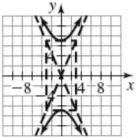

3. $4x^2 - y^2 = 16$

$$\frac{4x^2}{16} - \frac{y^2}{16} = \frac{16}{16}$$

$$\frac{x^2}{4} - \frac{y^2}{16} = 1$$

$a^2 = 4, a = 2$

x-intercepts: $(-2,0),(2,0)$

$b^2 = 16, b = 4$

Sketch a dashed rectangle that contains the points $(-2,0),(2,0),(0,-4)$, and $(0,4)$, and then sketch the inclined asymptotes.

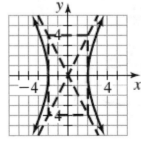

4. $16x^2 + 3y^2 = 48$

$$\frac{16x^2}{48} + \frac{3y^2}{48} = \frac{48}{48}$$

$$\frac{x^2}{3} + \frac{y^2}{16} = 1$$

$a^2 = 3, a = \sqrt{3}$

x-intercepts: $\left(-\sqrt{3}, 0\right), \left(\sqrt{3}, 0\right)$

$b^2 = 16, b = 4$

y-intercepts: $(0, -4), (0, 4)$

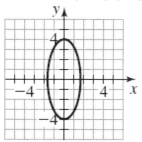

5. $x^2 - 9y^2 = 81$

$$\frac{x^2}{81} - \frac{9y^2}{81} = 1$$

$$\frac{x^2}{81} - \frac{y^2}{9} = 1$$

$a^2 = 81, a = 9$

x-intercepts: $(-9, 0), (9, 0)$

$b^2 = 9, b = 3$

Sketch a dashed rectangle that contains the points $(-9, 0), (9, 0), (0, -3)$, and $(0, 3)$, and then sketch the inclined asymptotes.

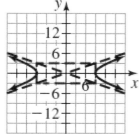

6. $4y^2 - 4x^2 = 16$

$$\frac{4y^2}{16} - \frac{4x^2}{16} = \frac{16}{16}$$

$$\frac{y^2}{4} - \frac{x^2}{4} = 1$$

$b^2 = 4, b = 2$

y-intercepts: $(0, -2), (0, 2)$

$a^2 = 4, a = 2$

Sketch a dashed rectangle that contains the points $(-2, 0), (2, 0), (0, -2)$, and $(0, 2)$, and then sketch the inclined asymptotes.

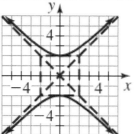

7. $\dfrac{x^2}{5} + \dfrac{y^2}{14} = 1$

$a^2 = 5, a = \sqrt{5}$

x-intercepts: $\left(-\sqrt{5}, 0\right), \left(\sqrt{5}, 0\right)$

$b^2 = 14, b = \sqrt{14}$

y-intercepts: $\left(0, -\sqrt{14}\right), \left(0, \sqrt{14}\right)$

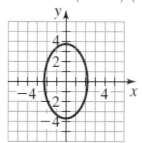

8.
$$\frac{x^2}{8} + \frac{y^2}{3} = 1$$
$$a^2 = 8, a = 2\sqrt{2}$$
x-intercepts: $\left(-2\sqrt{2}, 0\right), \left(2\sqrt{2}, 0\right)$
$$b^2 = 3, b = \sqrt{3}$$
y-intercepts: $\left(0, -\sqrt{3}\right), \left(0, \sqrt{3}\right)$

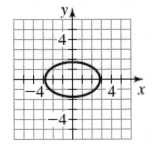

9. No. The graph of $\dfrac{x^2}{9} - \dfrac{y^2}{4} = 1$ is a hyperbola. The graph fails the vertical line test.

10. Answers will vary. The points $(0,3)$ and $(0,-3)$ are y-intercepts. An ellipse with these y-intercepts has the form $\dfrac{x^2}{a^2} + \dfrac{y^2}{9} = 1$. Three possibilities: let $a = 1, 2,$ and 4.
$$\frac{x^2}{1} + \frac{y^2}{9} = 1$$
$$\frac{x^2}{4} + \frac{y^2}{9} = 1$$
$$\frac{x^2}{16} + \frac{y^2}{9} = 1$$

Homework 15.5

1. $x^2 + y^2 = 25$
$$4x^2 + 25y^2 = 100$$
The two intersection points $(-5, 0)$ and $(5, 0)$ are the solutions to the system.
Solve using elimination:

$$-4x^2 - 4y^2 = -100$$
$$\underline{4x^2 + 25y^2 = 100}$$
$$21y^2 = 0$$
$$y^2 = 0$$
$$y = 0$$
Let $y = 0$ in $x^2 + y^2 = 25$ and solve for x.
$$x^2 + 0^2 = 25$$
$$x^2 = 25$$
$$x = \pm 5$$
The solutions are $(-5, 0)$ and $(5, 0)$.

3. $y = x^2 + 1$
$y = -x + 3$

The two intersection points $(-2, 5)$ and $(1, 2)$ are solutions of the system.
Solve using substitution.
Substitute $x^2 + 1$ for y in the second equation.
$$y = -x + 3$$
$$x^2 + 1 = -x + 3$$
$$x^2 + x - 2 = 0$$
$$(x+2)(x-1) = 0$$
$$x + 2 = 0 \quad \text{or} \quad x - 1 = 0$$
$$x = -2 \quad \text{or} \quad x = 1$$
Let $x = -2$ and $x = 1$ in $y = -x + 3$ and solve for y.
$$y = -(-2) + 3 \qquad y = -(1) + 3$$
$$= 2 + 3 \qquad\qquad = -1 + 3$$
$$= 5 \qquad\qquad\quad = 2$$
The solutions are $(-2, 5)$ and $(1, 2)$.

5. $y = x^2 - 2$

$y = -x^2 + 6$

The two intersection points $(2, 2)$ and $(-2, 2)$ are solutions of the system.

Solve using substitution.

Substitute $x^2 - 2$ for y in the second equation.

$$y = -x^2 + 6$$
$$x^2 - 2 = -x^2 + 6$$
$$2x^2 = 8$$
$$x^2 = 4$$
$$x = \pm 2$$

Let $x = -2$ and $x = 2$ in $y = x^2 - 2$ and solve for y.

$$y = (-2)^2 - 2 \quad y = (2)^2 - 2$$
$$= 4 - 2 \qquad\quad = 4 - 2$$
$$= 2 \qquad\qquad = 2$$

The solutions are $(-2, 2)$ and $(2, 2)$.

7. $x^2 + y^2 = 49$

$x^2 + y^2 = 16$

The graphs do not intersect. The solution set is the empty set.

Solve using elimination.

$$x^2 + y^2 = 49$$
$$\underline{-x^2 - y^2 = -16}$$
$$ 0 = 33 \quad \text{False}$$

There is no solution.

9. $x^2 + y^2 = 25$

$y = -x - 1$

The two intersection points $(-4, 3)$ and $(3, -4)$ are solutions of the system.

Solve using substitution.

Substitute $-x - 1$ for y in the first equation.

$$x^2 + y^2 = 25$$
$$x^2 + (-x - 1)^2 = 25$$
$$x^2 + x^2 + 2x + 1 = 25$$
$$2x^2 + 2x - 24 = 0$$
$$x^2 + x - 12 = 0$$
$$(x + 4)(x - 3) = 0$$
$$x + 4 = 0 \quad \text{or} \quad x - 3 = 0$$
$$x = -4 \quad \text{or} \quad x = 3$$

Let $x = -4$ and $x = 3$ in $y = -x - 1$ and solve for y.

$$y = -(-4) - 1 \qquad y = -(3) - 1$$
$$= 4 - 1 \qquad\qquad = -3 - 1$$
$$= 3 \qquad\qquad\quad = -4$$

The solutions are $(-4, 3)$ and $(3, -4)$.

11. $y^2 - x^2 = 16$

$y + x^2 = 4$

The three intersection points $(-3, -5)$, $(0, 4)$, and $(3, -5)$ are the solutions to the system.

Solve using elimination.

$$y^2 - x^2 = 16$$
$$\underline{y + x^2 = 4}$$
$$y^2 + y = 20$$
$$y^2 + y - 20 = 0$$
$$(y + 5)(y - 4) = 0$$
$$y + 5 = 0 \quad \text{or} \quad y - 4 = 0$$
$$y = -5 \quad \text{or} \quad y = 4$$

Let $y = -5$ and $y = 4$ in $y + x^2 = 4$ and solve for x.

$$-5 + x^2 = 4 \qquad 4 + x^2 = 4$$
$$x^2 = 9 \qquad\qquad x^2 = 0$$
$$x = \pm 3 \qquad\qquad x = 0$$

The solutions are $(-3, -5)$, $(3, -5)$, and $(0, 4)$.

671

13. $25x^2 - 9y^2 = 225$

$4x^2 + 9y^2 = 36$

The two intersection points $(-3,0)$ and

$(3,0)$ are solutions of the system.

Solve using elimination.

$25x^2 - 9y^2 = 225$

$\underline{4x^2 + 9y^2 = 36}$

$29x^2 = 261$

$x^2 = 9$

$x = \pm 3$

Let $x = -3$ and $x = 3$ in $4x^2 + 9y^2 = 36$

and solve for y.

$\begin{array}{ll} 4(-3)^2 + 9y^2 = 36 & 4(3)^2 + 9y^2 = 36 \\ 36 + 9y^2 = 36 & 36 + 9y^2 = 36 \\ 9y^2 = 0 & 9y^2 = 0 \\ y^2 = 0 & y^2 = 0 \\ y = 0 & y = 0 \end{array}$

The solutions are $(-3,0)$ and $(3,0)$.

15. $9x^2 + y^2 = 9$

$y = 3x + 3$

The two intersection points $(-1,0)$ and

$(0,3)$ are solutions of the system.

Solve using substitution.

Substitute $3x + 3$ for y in the first equation.

$9x^2 + y^2 = 9$

$9x^2 + (3x + 3)^2 = 9$

$9x^2 + 9x^2 + 18x + 9 = 9$

$18x^2 + 18x = 0$

$18x(x + 1) = 0$

$18x = 0$ or $x + 1 = 0$

$x = 0$ or $x = -1$

Let $x = 0$ and $x = -1$ in $y = 3x + 3$ and

solve for y.

$\begin{array}{ll} y = 3(0) + 3 & y = 3(-1) + 3 \\ = 0 + 3 & = -3 + 3 \\ = 3 & = 0 \end{array}$

The solutions are $(0,3)$ and $(-1,0)$.

17. $4x^2 + 9y^2 = 36$

$16x^2 + 25y^2 = 225$

The graphs do not intersect. The solution set is the empty set.

Solve using elimination.

$-16x^2 - 36y^2 = -144$

$\underline{16x^2 + 25y^2 = 225}$

$-11y^2 = 81$

$y^2 = -\dfrac{81}{11}$

Since y^2 cannot be negative (in the real number system), there is no solution.

19. $y = \sqrt{x} - 3$

$y = -x - 1$

The intersection point $(1,-2)$ is the solution to the system.

Solve using substitution.

Substitute $\sqrt{x} - 3$ for y in the second equation.

$y = -x - 1$

$\sqrt{x} - 3 = -x - 1$

$\sqrt{x} = -x + 2$

$\left(\sqrt{x}\right)^2 = (-x + 2)^2$

$x = x^2 - 4x + 4$

$x^2 - 5x + 4 = 0$

$(x - 4)(x - 1) = 0$

$x - 4 = 0$ or $x - 1 = 0$

$x = 4$ or $x = 1$

Let $x = 4$ and $x = 1$ in $y = \sqrt{x} - 3$ and solve

for y.

$\begin{array}{ll} y = \sqrt{4} - 3 & y = \sqrt{1} - 3 \\ = 2 - 3 & = 1 - 3 \\ = -1 & = -2 \end{array}$

Check each result in $y = -x - 1$.

$\begin{array}{ll} -1 = -(4) - 1 & -2 = -1 - 1 \\ -1 = -5 \text{ False} & -2 = -2 \text{ True} \end{array}$

The only solution is $(1,-2)$.

21. $y = 2x^2 - 5$

$y = x^2 - 2$

The two intersection points $\left(-\sqrt{3}, 1\right)$ and

$\left(\sqrt{3}, 1\right)$ are solutions of the system.

Solve using substitution.

Substitute $2x^2 - 5$ for y in the second equation.

$y = x^2 - 2$

$2x^2 - 5 = x^2 - 2$

$x^2 = 3$

$x = \pm\sqrt{3}$

Let $x = -\sqrt{3}$ and $x = \sqrt{3}$ in $y = x^2 - 2$ and solve for y.

$y = \left(-\sqrt{3}\right)^2 - 2 \qquad y = \left(\sqrt{3}\right)^2 - 2$

$\quad = 3 - 2 \qquad\qquad = 3 - 2$

$\quad = 1 \qquad\qquad\quad = 1$

The solutions are $\left(-\sqrt{3}, 1\right)$ and $\left(\sqrt{3}, 1\right)$.

23. $25y^2 - 4x^2 = 100$

$9x^2 + y^2 = 9$

The four intersection points $\left(-0.74, -2.02\right)$,

$\left(-0.74, 2.02\right)$, $\left(0.74, -2.02\right)$, and

$\left(0.74, 2.02\right)$ are solutions of the system.

Solve using substitution.

$9x^2 + y^2 = 9$

$y^2 = 9 - 9x^2$

Substitute $9 - 9x^2$ for y^2 in the first equation.

$25y^2 - 4x^2 = 100$

$25\left(9 - 9x^2\right) - 4x^2 = 100$

$225 - 225x^2 - 4x^2 = 100$

$-229x^2 = -125$

$x^2 = \dfrac{125}{229}$

$x = \pm\sqrt{\dfrac{125}{229}} \approx \pm 0.74$

Let $x = -0.74$ and $x = 0.74$ in $9x^2 + y^2 = 9$ and solve for y.

$9(-0.74)^2 + y^2 = 9$

$y^2 = 4.07$

$y = \pm\sqrt{4.07} \approx \pm 2.02$

$9(0.74)^2 + y^2 = 9$

$y^2 = 4.07$

$y = \pm\sqrt{4.07} \approx \pm 2.02$

The solutions are $\left(-0.74, -2.02\right)$,

$\left(-0.74, 2.02\right)$, $\left(0.74, -2.02\right)$, and

$\left(0.74, 2.02\right)$.

25. $25x^2 + 9y^2 = 225$

$x^2 + y^2 = 16$

The four intersection points $\left(-2.25, -3.31\right)$,

$\left(-2.25, 3.31\right)$, $\left(2.25, -3.31\right)$, and

$\left(2.25, 3.31\right)$ are solutions of the system.

Solve using elimination.

$25x^2 + 9y^2 = 225$

$\underline{-9x^2 - 9y^2 = -144}$

$16x^2 = 81$

$x^2 = \dfrac{81}{16}$

$x = \pm\dfrac{9}{4}$

$x = \pm 2.25$

Let $x = -2.25$ and $x = 2.25$ in $x^2 + y^2 = 16$ and solve for y.

$(-2.25)^2 + y^2 = 16$

$y^2 = 10.9375$

$y = \pm 3.31$

$(2.25)^2 + y^2 = 16$

$y^2 = 10.9375$

$y = \pm 3.31$

The solutions are $\left(-2.25, -3.31\right)$,

$\left(-2.25, 3.31\right)$, $\left(2.25, -3.31\right)$, and

$\left(2.25, 3.31\right)$.

27. $9x^2 + y^2 = 85$

$2x^2 - 3y^2 = 6$

Solve using elimination.

$27x^2 + 3y^2 = 255$

$\underline{2x^2 - 3y^2 = 6}$

$29x^2 = 261$

$x^2 = 9$

$x = \pm 3$

Let $x = -3$ and $x = 3$ in $9x^2 + y^2 = 85$ and solve for y.

$9(-3)^2 + y^2 = 85 \qquad 9(3)^2 + y^2 = 85$

$81 + y^2 = 85 \qquad\quad 81 + y^2 = 85$

$y^2 = 4 \qquad\qquad\quad y^2 = 4$

$y = \pm 2 \qquad\qquad\quad y = \pm 2$

The four solutions are $(-3, -2)$, $(-3, 2)$, $(3, -2)$, and $(3, 2)$. Each result satisfies both equations.

29. $4y^2 + x^2 = 25$

$y = -x + 5$

Solve using substitution.

Substitute $-x + 5$ for y in the first equation.

$4y^2 + x^2 = 25$

$4(-x + 5)^2 + x^2 = 25$

$4(x^2 - 10x + 25) + x^2 = 25$

$4x^2 - 40x + 100 + x^2 = 25$

$5x^2 - 40x + 75 = 0$

$x^2 - 8x + 15 = 0$

$(x - 5)(x - 3) = 0$

$x - 5 = 0 \ \text{ or } \ x - 3 = 0$

$x = 5 \ \text{ or } \ x = 3$

Let $x = 5$ and $x = 3$ in $y = -x + 5$ and solve for y.

$y = -(5) + 5 \qquad y = -(3) + 5$

$= -5 + 5 \qquad\qquad = -3 + 5$

$= 0 \qquad\qquad\qquad = 2$

The solutions are $(3, 2)$ and $(5, 0)$. Each result satisfies both equations.

31. $y = x^2 - 3x + 2$

$y = 2x - 4$

Solve using substitution.

Substitute $2x - 4$ for y in the first equation.

$y = x^2 - 3x + 2$

$2x - 4 = x^2 - 3x + 2$

$x^2 - 5x + 6 = 0$

$(x - 3)(x - 2) = 0$

$x - 3 = 0 \ \text{ or } \ x - 2 = 0$

$x = 3 \ \text{ or } \ x = 2$

Let $x = 3$ and $x = 2$ in $y = 2x - 4$ and solve for y.

$y = 2(3) - 4 \qquad y = 2(2) - 4$

$= 6 - 4 \qquad\qquad = 4 - 4$

$= 2 \qquad\qquad\quad = 0$

The solutions are $(3, 2)$ and $(2, 0)$. Each result satisfies both equations.

33. $x^2 + y^2 = 25$

$4x^2 - 25y^2 = 100$

$4x^2 + 25y^2 = 100$

The two intersection points for all three graphs are $(-5, 0)$ and $(5, 0)$. These are the solutions to the system. Each result satisfies all three equations.

35. Answers may vary. One possible answer:

$x^2 + y^2 = 16$

$x^2 - y^2 = 16$

37. $2x^2 + cy^2 = 82$

$y = x^2 + dx + 5$

Substitute $(1, 4)$ into each equation.

$2(1)^2 + c(4)^2 = 82 \qquad 4 = (1)^2 + d(1) + 5$

$2 + 16c = 82 \qquad\qquad 4 = 1 + d + 5$

$16c = 80 \qquad\qquad\quad d = -2$

$c = 5$

39. Answers may vary. Graph each of the equations on the same coordinate plane, then find the points of intersection. These points are the solutions to the system.

41.

$y = 2^x$

$y = 4\left(\dfrac{1}{2}\right)^x$

Solve by substitution.

Substitute 2^x for y in the second equation.

$2^x = 4\left(\dfrac{1}{2}\right)^x$

$2^x = 2^2\left(2^{-1}\right)^x$

$2^x = 2^2\left(2^{-x}\right)$

$2^x = 2^{2-x}$

$x = 2 - x$

$x = 1$

Let $x = 1$ in $y = 2^x$ and solve for y.

$y = 2^1$

$y = 2$

The solution is $(1, 2)$

43. Answers may vary.

$y = -2x + 9$

45. Answers may vary.

$\dfrac{5x - 7}{2x + 2} = 4$

$5x - 7 = 4(2x + 2)$

$5x - 7 = 8x + 8$

$-3x = 15$

$x = -5$

47. Answers may vary.

$y = 3^x$

49. Answers may vary.

$y = x^2 - 6x + 7$

51. Answers may vary.

$2x^2 + 8x - 10 = 0$

$2\left(x^2 + 4x - 5\right) = 0$

$2(x + 5)(x - 1) = 0$

$x + 5 = 0$

$x = -5$

$x - 1 = 0$

$x = 1$

The solutions are –5 and 1.

Quiz 15.5

1.

$9x^2 + y^2 = 81$

$x^2 + y^2 = 9$

The two intersection points $(-3, 0)$ and $(3, 0)$ are the solutions to the system.

Solve using elimination.

$9x^2 + y^2 = 81$

$\underline{-9x^2 - 9y^2 = -81}$

$-8y^2 = 0$

$y^2 = 0$

$y = 0$

Let $y = 0$ in $x^2 + y^2 = 9$ and solve for x.

$x^2 + y^2 = 9$

$x^2 + 0^2 = 9$

$x^2 = 9$

$x = \pm 3$

The solutions are $(-3, 0)$ and $(3, 0)$.

2.

$y = x^2 - 2$

$y = -2x + 1$

The two intersection points $(1, -1)$ and $(-3, 7)$ are the solutions to the system.

Solve using substitution.

Substitute $x^2 - 2$ for y in the second equation.

$y = -2x + 1$

$x^2 - 2 = -2x + 1$

$x^2 + 2x - 3 = 0$

$(x + 3)(x - 1) = 0$

$x + 3 = 0$ or $x - 1 = 0$

$x = -3$ or $x = 1$

Let $x = -3$ and $x = 1$ in $y = -2x + 1$ and solve for y.

$y = -2(-3) + 1 \qquad y = -2(1) + 1$

$\quad = 6 + 1 \qquad\qquad = -2 + 1$

$\quad = 7 \qquad\qquad\quad = -1$

The solutions are $(-3, 7)$ and $(1, -1)$.

3. $y = x^2 + 3$

$y = x^2 - 6x + 9$

The intersection point $(1, 4)$ is the solution to the system.

Solve using substitution.

Substitute $x^2 + 3$ for y in the second equation.

$$y = x^2 - 6x + 9$$

$$x^2 + 3 = x^2 - 6x + 9$$

$$6x - 6 = 0$$

$$x - 1 = 0$$

$$x = 1$$

Let $x = 1$ in $y = x^2 + 3$ and solve for y.

$$y = (1)^2 + 3$$

$$= 1 + 3$$

$$= 4$$

The solution is $(1, 4)$.

4. $25x^2 - 4y^2 = 100$

$9x^2 + y^2 = 9$

The graphs do not intersect. There are no solutions to the system.

Solve using elimination.

$$225x^2 - 36y^2 = 900$$

$$\underline{-225x^2 - 25y^2 = -225}$$

$$-61y^2 = 675$$

$$y^2 = -\frac{675}{61}$$

Since y^2 must be nonnegative (in the real number system), there are no solutions to the system. The solution set is the empty set.

5. $x^2 - y^2 = 16$

$x^2 + y^2 = 16$

$y = (x + 4)^2$

The intersection point of all three graphs is $(-4, 0)$. This is the solution of the system.

6. Answers may vary. One possible answer:

$x^2 + y^2 = 25$

$y = x^2 + 5$